Web Sites

- How-to videos help students understand and solve homework problems
- Hundreds of character-building and parenting articles and videos
- Sites for everyone from preschool through parenthood

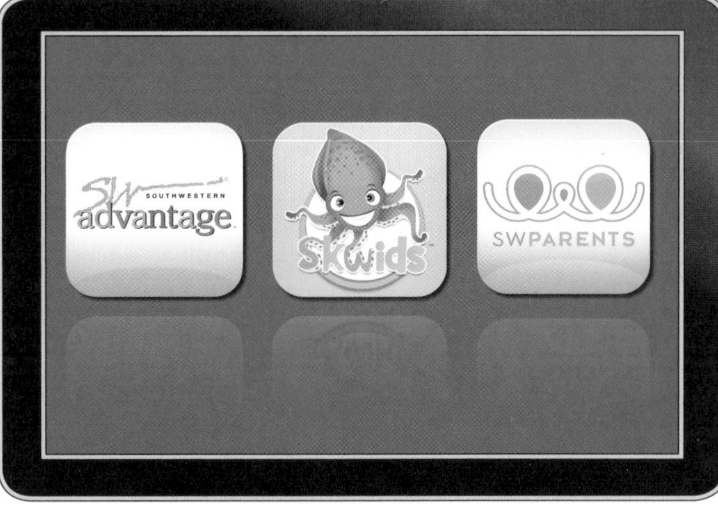

SW SOUTHWESTERN advantage
Learning System

Software

- Younger education packages introduce children to computers and give them games to encourage learning
- Older students can use the software to edit and research reports, practice revision techniques, and write practice papers
- The College Prep Pack is specially designed to help college-bound students

www.SWadvantage.com

Books

- Essential tools to help students excel in school as well as prepare for life
- Easily accessible, yet authoritative for the most important academic subjects
- Designed to teach children through exciting activity-based learning

Sharing the Advantage

Southwestern Advantage is an effective learning system and an important key to a better education and achieving success in life. Our mission is to share education and learning skills with every child and every family, regardless of their circumstances, through qualified nonprofit partnerships and local community involvement with organizations focused on helping young people. Southwestern Advantage will also donate one SWadvantage.com membership for each one purchased.

Thank you for helping us Share the Advantage!

MATH I

Southwestern Advantage

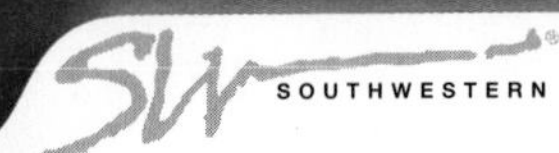

Nashville, Tennessee
ISBN 978-0-87197-558-4
Reprinted 2012

Henry Bedford
Chief Executive Officer, Southwestern/Great American, Inc.

Dan Moore
President, Southwestern

Dave Kempf
President, Southwestern Publishing Group, Inc.

Chris Adams
Dave Causer
Lester Crafton
Grant Greder
Kevin Johnson
Robin Mukherjee
Mark Rau
Tim Ritzer
Chris Samuels
Nate Vogel

Sales Directors

Printed in the United States of America by
R. R. Donnelley

Front cover "monogram" art and back cover "Southwestern Advantage logo" are both proprietary trademarks of Southwestern/Great American, Inc., dba The Southwestern Company
Front cover art created by Travis Rader

Editorial

Executive Editor and President
Dan Moore

Editorial Director
Mary Cummings

Managing Editor
Judy Jackson

Senior Editor
Barbara J. Reed

Editor
Alison Nash

Section Editors
Julee Hicks
Cathy Ropp
Tanis Westbrook

Design

Senior Art Directors
Steve Newman
Starletta Polster

Senior Designer
Travis Rader

Composition and Production Design
Jessie Anglin
Sara Anglin

Production

Production Manager
Powell Ropp

Production Coordinator
Wanda Sawyer

Preface

Welcome to *Southwestern Advantage Math*. We are pleased to bring you these unique, user-friendly reference books. Designed in such a way that students can spend "more time learning, less time looking," the pages are open and inviting, and critical information is summarized in boxes, lists, and other easily usable and understandable pieces.

Problems are shown worked out step-by-step. Where a problem can be worked by more than one method, those methods are also shown. Additionally, simply by keying in the page number, you can access step-by-step videos of each problem from that page at **SWadvantage.com**.

Got to Know boxes summarize the most essential information; cross-references in the **Need More Help** boxes direct you to pages where you can find additional information or review material. **Try It This Way** suggests alternative ways people with various learning styles can use to more effectively approach, work, or visualize problems and concepts. **Watch Out** boxes alert students to things that might be easily confused or that might give students difficulty.

We hope you will find these books both useful and enjoyable. Every effort has been made to ensure that the information in these books is as accurate as possible. If errors should be found, however, we would appreciate hearing from you. Please send your comments or suggestions to editor@southwestern.com or to Editor, The Southwestern Company, P.O. Box 305142, Nashville, TN 37230.

How to Use Southwestern Advantage

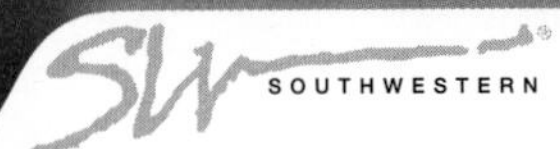

How to Use These Books

Designed in such a way that students can spend "more time learning, less time looking," these books are divided into nine "strands": Foundations of Mathematics; Numbers and Operations; Measurement; Geometry; Trigonometry; Statistics and Probability; Algebra; Advanced Algebra; and Calculus. Each strand is then divided into smaller units.

The first navigational tool is the detailed, color-coded table of contents. Each book contains a detailed listing of its own contents, plus a list of the strands covered in the other book. The contents pages also indicate separately where the special features of the book can be found, such as tables, charts, and glossaries.

FOUNDATIONS OF MATHEMATICS

NUMBERS AND OPERATIONS

MEASUREMENT

GEOMETRY

TRIGONOMETRY

Next, color bars above the heading on the right-hand text pages tell you exactly where you are in the book. The bar that extends all the way to the edge of the page is the unit color; the other bar denotes the strand. The strand color is repeated in a tab at the bottom of the page. When the book is closed, you can tell at a glance where each strand and unit begins and ends.

When the book is open, headings on the pages also help to tell you exactly where you are in the book, for example, the Infinite Limits section of Limits and Continuity in the Calculus strand.

Strand color bar

SEARCH

To see step-by-step videos of these problems, enter the page number into the SWadvantage.com Search Bar.

Ways to REMEMBER

Think of the weights of items that are familiar to you. For example, a bird weighs a few ounces, flour comes in 1-, 5-, and 10-pound bags, and a truck weighs several tons. This will help you remember when to use the different units of weight.

How to Use Southwestern Advantage Online (www.SWadvantage.com)

An integral part of Southwestern Advantage is the accompanying Web site. Organized by subject areas, it is a comprehensive suite of online study helps, additional in-depth subject matter, tips for parents, and coaching for students on how to get better at life.

STATISTICS AND PROBABILITY

ALGEBRA

ADVANCED ALGEBRA

CALCULUS

SPECIAL ADVANTAGES

Limits and Continuity **CALCULUS**

Unit within Calculus

Name of strand Calculus strand

Unit color bar

Try It This Way

You can visualize and then use mental math to solve Example 4(b).

Add each measure mentally.

3 yd 2 ft
+ 5 yd 2 ft
8 yd 4 ft

Think: 3 ft = 1 yd

Think: 4 ft is 3 ft + 1 ft

8 yd + 4 ft

8 yd + 1 yd + 1 ft

9 yd 1 ft

Got to KNOW!

Bias

Bias can occur in different stages of the surveying process. The identified population, the sample chosen, or a survey question is biased if it in any way influences the results of the survey.

Need More HELP

When you write a unit in a different form, you rename the unit. The directions below mean the same thing.

Rename 5 feet as inches.

Express 5 feet as inches.

Convert 5 feet to inches.

Watch Out!

To make a general statement based on information from a sample, the sample must be *random*.
To learn more, see *Random Sampling* on page 1224.

Strand color tab

Contents

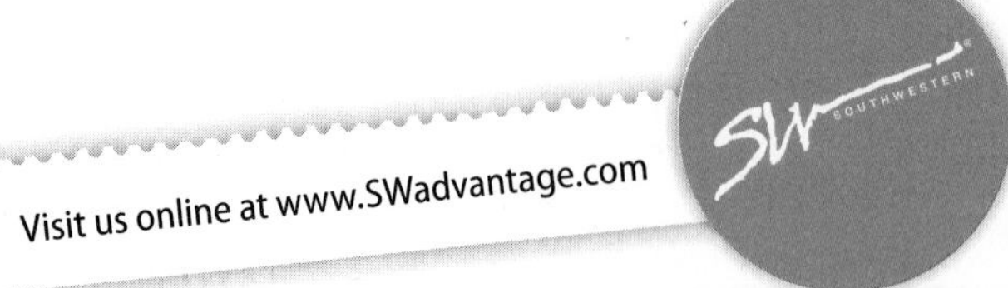

Visit us online at www.SWadvantage.com

Foundations of Mathematics........36

Contents

Contents

Geometry ... 608

Contents

Special Features

In the Other Book

Math Curricula and Programs

TODAY'S INSTRUCTIONAL APPROACHES In today's math class, it may not be so much what you know, but rather *how* you know it. While many students still learn math the same way their parents were taught, more and more are learning the basic operations of addition, subtraction, multiplication, and division through nontraditional methods. These methods have been introduced in a number of new math curricula and programs developed over the last 25 years. Three such programs are *Saxon Math*, *Everyday Mathematics*, and the Singapore Math curriculum.

Saxon Math

The *Saxon Math* program was developed by math educator John Saxon (1923–1996). Its emphasis is on incremental learning of math concepts. This incremental approach differs significantly from other math programs. In many traditional math programs, a concept is introduced, practiced, and assessed in a specified block of time. Once students are tested on the concept, the block is finished and students move on to a new concept.

Saxon felt that big math concepts were easier to learn and master when broken down into smaller concepts that are introduced separately and reviewed continually. Following this approach, the *Saxon Math* program introduces a new concept every day. The concept is practiced and reviewed continually throughout the year, and it is expanded on in subsequent lessons, enabling students to build on what they know.

Need More HELP

An *algorithm* is a step-by-step procedure for performing a math computation.

An example is Saxon's approach to multiplication.

- Students are introduced to multiplication as repeated addition and then by making a multiplication table.
- Two days later, they learn how to multiply by one-digit numbers. The multiplication concept reappears a few lessons later with an explanation on how to multiply by multiples of 10 and 100.
- In the next appearance of the concept, students learn how to multiply by two-digit numbers and then three-digit numbers.
- When the concept appears again, students learn how to multiply fractions.
- By the end of the year, students are learning how to multiply decimals and mixed numbers. All along the way, students are continually reviewing and practicing the multiplication concepts they've already learned.

In contrast to many of the newer instructional approaches, *Saxon Math* relies heavily on the traditional, or standard, *algorithms* for teaching the basic operations of addition, subtraction, multiplication, and division.

Everyday Mathematics

Everyday Mathematics (also called Everyday Math or Chicago Math) is a preK–6 math curriculum that was developed in the 1980's by the University of Chicago School Mathematics Project. The program is designed to encourage students to explore a variety of methods for working math problems. For example, to solve an addition problem, they might use a parts-and-total diagram, or they might work a multiplication problem by shading in the squares of an array.

As with traditional math programs, students of *Everyday Mathematics* commonly use algorithms to work arithmetic problems. But these algorithms are not the standard algorithms you may be accustomed to seeing. As a parent, it is important for you to understand these "non-standard" algorithms and to be able to support your child in applying them. The following pages present a brief overview of some of these procedures.

Singapore Math

The term "Singapore math" refers to a math program developed in the early 1980's by the Ministry of Education in Singapore. This program has since been revised and expanded. In its present form, Singapore math aligns with the National Council of Teachers of Mathematics (NCTM) principles and standards. *Math in Focus: The Singapore Approach* is the U.S. edition of Singapore math.

A distinguishing characteristic of Singapore math is its use of graphic representations and modeling strategies to solve all types of problems, from simple to complex. The models, often called box models or bar models, enable students to represent a word problem visually so they can see the number relationships in the problem.

The box model below shows the relationship of two given numbers, 12 and 45, to an unknown number. It is clear from the model that you would subtract to find the unknown value.

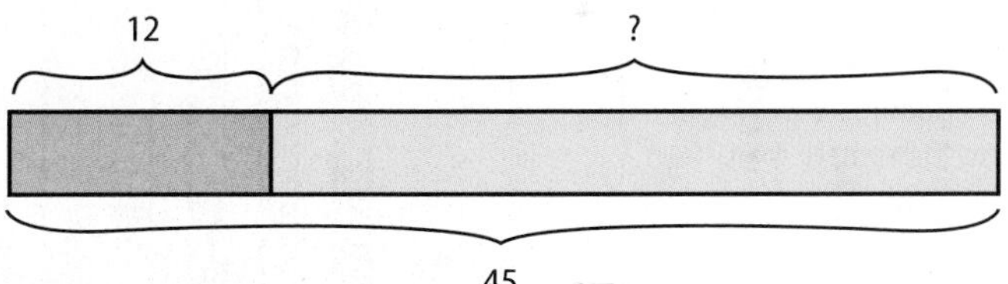

The word problem section on pages 34–35 shows the use of box models to solve word problems.

Partial Sums

When using the **partial-sums addition method**, first add the largest place value, then the next place value, and the next, and so on until the ones are added. Then add the partial sums. This process allows for more mental math than paper-and-pencil computation does. It also reduces the need to regroup.

The "partial sums" method is sometimes called the **left-to-right addition method** because you work from the largest to the smallest place value.

EXAMPLE 1

Add 25 + 47.

STEP 1 Use base ten blocks to model the addition.

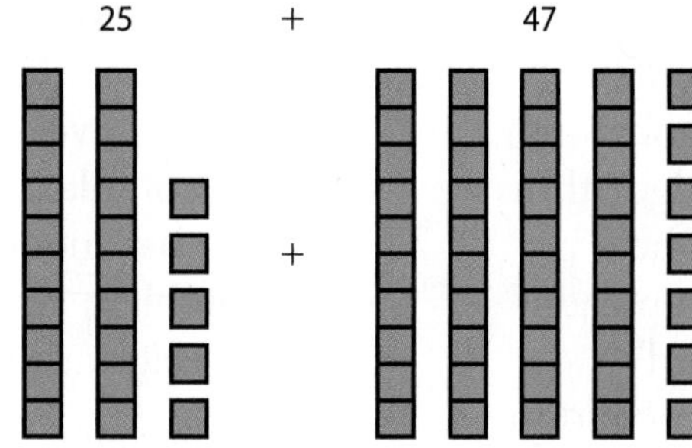

STEP 2 Add the tens.

2 tens + 4 tens = 6 tens, or 60

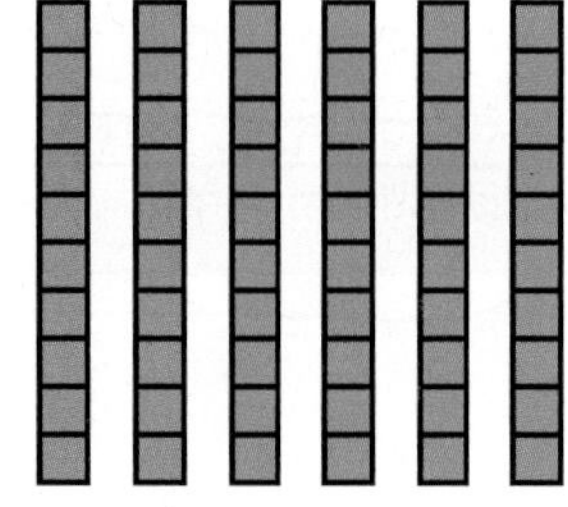

STEP 3 Add the ones.

5 ones + 7 ones = 12 ones, or 12

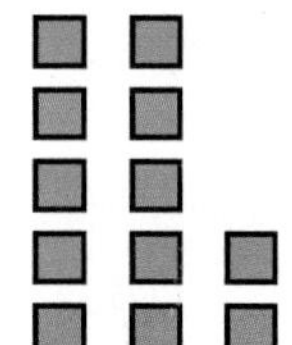

STEP 4 Add the partial sums.

$$\begin{array}{r} 25 \\ +\ 47 \\ \hline 60 \\ 12 \\ \hline 72 \end{array}$$

The sum of 25 and 47 is 72.

To see another method for adding 25 + 47, go to Example 4 on page 18.

Once you understand the method, you can use it without the models.

EXAMPLE 2

Add 347 + 236.

METHOD 1

Add horizontally.

	347 + 236
Add the hundreds.	300 + 200 = 500
Add the tens.	40 + 30 = 70
Add the ones.	7 + 6 = 13
Add the partial sums.	500 + 70 + 13 = 583

The sum of 347 and 236 is 583.

METHOD 2

Use a vertical format.

	347
	+ 236
Add the hundreds: 300 + 200	500
Add the tens: 40 + 30	70
Add the ones: 7 + 6	+ 13
Add the partial sums.	583

The sum of 347 and 236 is 583.

SEARCH

To see step-by-step videos of these problems, enter the page number into the SWadvantage.com Search Bar.

To review basic addition facts, go to *Addition Facts* in *Foundations of Mathematics* (p. 56).

EXAMPLE 3

Add 173 + 458.

	173
	+ 458
Add the hundreds: 100 + 400	500
Add the tens: 70 + 50	120
Add the ones: 3 + 8	+ 11
Add the partial sums.	631

The sum of 173 and 458 is 631.

Try It This Way

To see two other methods for adding 173 + 458, go to Example 5 on page 18 and Example 7 on page 19.

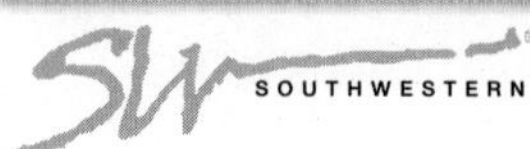

Column Addition

When using the **column addition method**, draw lines to separate each place value. Add the digits in each place. Then, if there are 2 digits in the sum of a place, trade 10 in for 1 in the next column to the left.

Try It This Way

You may see this method shown with a horizontal line between each of the steps.

	Tens	Ones
	2	5
+	4	7
	6	12
	7	2

EXAMPLE 4

Add 25 + 47.

Write the addition problem in a vertical format.

		Tens	Ones
		2	5
	+	4	7
Add the digits in each place.		6	12
Adjust the sum by trading 10 ones for 1 ten in the next column.		7	2

The sum of 25 and 47 is 72.

Try It This Way

To see two other methods for adding 173 + 458, go to Example 3 on page 17 and Example 7 on page 19.

EXAMPLE 5

Add 173 + 458.

Write the addition problem in a vertical format.

		Hundreds	Tens	Ones
		1	7	3
	+	4	5	8
Add the digits in each place.		5	12	11
Trade 10 ones for 1 ten.		5	13	1
Trade 10 tens for 1 hundred.		6	3	1

The sum of 173 and 458 is 631.

EXAMPLE 6

Add 536 + 289.

Write the addition problem in a vertical format.

	Hundreds	Tens	Ones
	5	3	6
	+ 2	8	9
Add the digits in each place.	7	11	15
Trade 10 ones for 1 ten.	7	12	5
Trade 10 tens for 1 hundred.	8	2	5

The sum of 536 and 289 is 825.

SEARCH

To see step-by-step videos of these problems, enter the page number into the SWadvantage.com Search Bar.

Opposite-Change Addition

When using the **opposite-change addition method**, change one addend to a number that ends in zero (or a series of zeros) by adding or subtracting a number. Next, change the other addend using the same number but the opposite operation. Then add the resulting addends. The idea is to simplify a problem to reduce the number of times you need to regroup.

EXAMPLE 7

Add 173 + 458.

METHOD 1

Think: What number can I add or subtract to 173 to get a 0 in the ones place?

Subtract 3 from 173 to get a 0 as the last digit.	173	− 3 =	170
Do the opposite: Add 3 to 458.	+ 458	+ 3 =	+ 461
Add the new addends.			631

The sum of 173 and 458 is 631.

METHOD 2

Think: What number can I add or subtract to 458 to get a 0 in the ones place?

Add 2 to 458 to get 460.	173	− 2 =	171
Do the opposite: Subtract 2 from 173.	+ 458	+ 2 =	+ 460
Add the new addends.			631

The sum of 173 and 458 is 631.

Try It This Way

To see two other methods for adding 173 + 458, go to Example 3 on page 17 and Example 5 on page 18.

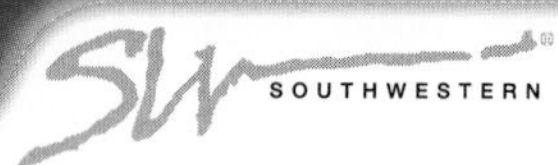

Trade-First Subtraction

When using the **trade-first subtraction method**, you must regroup (trade) when the digit in the minuend (top number) has a lesser value than the digit in the subtrahend (bottom number). You can use a model or the algorithm shown in Examples 2 and 3.

A subtraction problem consists of these three parts:

$$\begin{array}{rl} 85 & \text{minuend} \\ -\ \underline{12} & \text{subtrahend} \\ 73 & \text{difference} \end{array}$$

EXAMPLE 1

Subtract 57 − 28.

STEP 1 Use base ten blocks to model the minuend, 57.

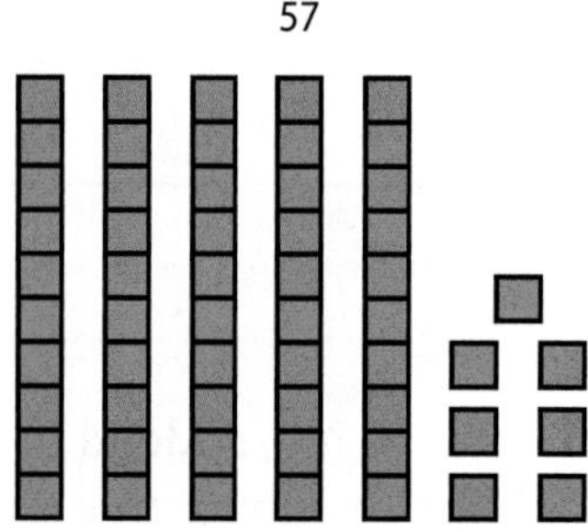

STEP 2 Since 8 ones > 7 ones, you cannot subtract 28 until you regroup 57.

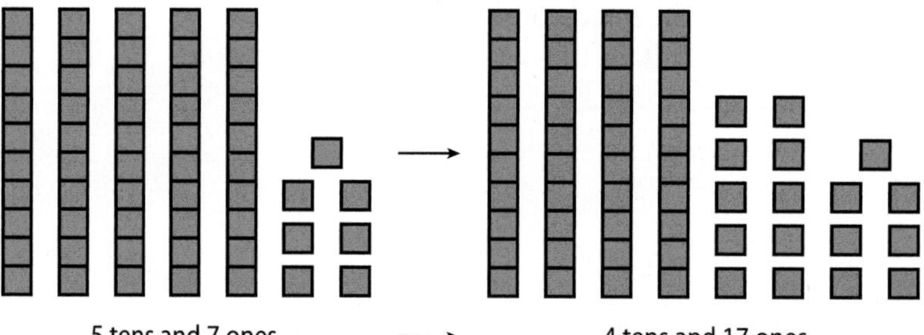

STEP 3 Subtract the ones by removing 8 ones. Subtract the tens by removing 2 tens.

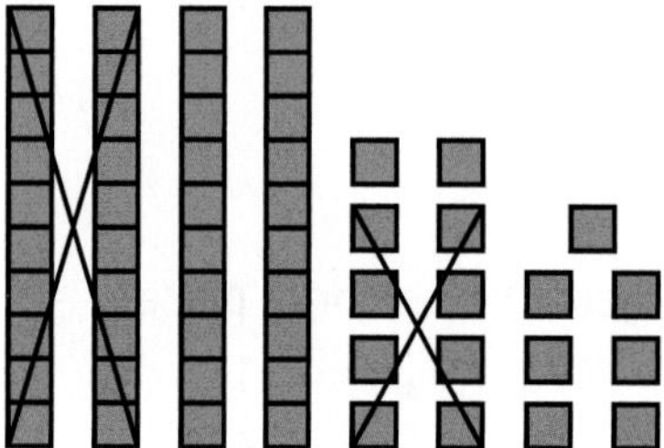

STEP 4 Count the remaining bars and squares to find the difference.

4 tens − 2 tens = 2 tens, or 20
17 ones − 8 ones = 9 ones, or 9

$$\begin{array}{r} 20 \\ \underline{9} \\ 29 \end{array}$$

The difference between 57 and 28 is 29.

To use the Trade First method without a model, first write the problem numbers with plenty of space between the columns and space above the columns. Then do all of the trading, from right to left. When you have completed the trading, then subtract.

EXAMPLE 2

Subtract 5,482 − 1,393.

STEP 1 Trade from right to left.

- Ones column: You cannot subtract 2 − 3. Trade 1 ten for 10 ones. Now you have 7 tens and 12 ones.

		7	12
5	4	~~8~~	~~2~~
− 1	3	9	3

- Tens column: You cannot subtract 7 − 9. Trade 1 hundred for 10 tens. Now you have 3 hundreds and 17 tens.
- Hundreds column: You can subtract 3 − 3.
- Thousands column: You can subtract 5 − 1.

		17	
	3	~~7~~	12
5	~~4~~	~~8~~	~~2~~
− 1	3	9	3

STEP 2 Subtract.

Because you have already done the trading, you can subtract from right to left or from left to right.

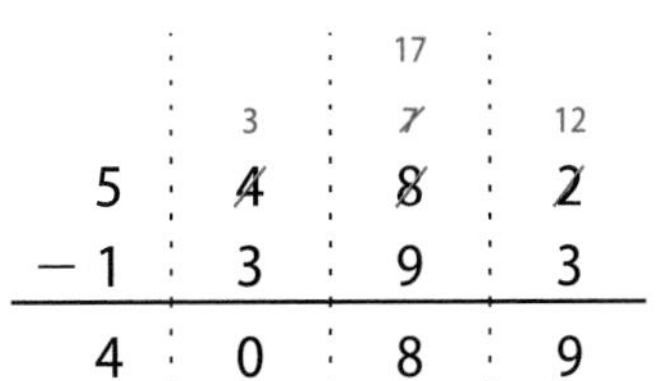

		17	
	3	~~7~~	12
5	~~4~~	~~8~~	~~2~~
− 1	3	9	3
4	0	8	9

12 − 3 = 9 17 − 9 = 8
3 − 3 = 0 5 − 1 = 4

The difference between 5,482 and 1,393 is 4,089.

Need More HELP

To review basic subtraction facts, go to *Subtraction Facts* in *Foundations of Mathematics* (p. 62).

Try It This Way

To see other methods for subtracting 5,482 − 1,393, go to Example 7 on page 23 and Example 11 on page 25.

EXAMPLE 3

Subtract 503 − 129.

STEP 1 Trade from right to left.

You cannot subtract 3 − 9 but there are no tens to trade.
First trade 1 hundred for 10 tens.
Then trade 1 ten for 10 ones.
Now you have 4 hundreds, 9 tens, and 13 ones.

	9	
4	~~10~~	13
~~5~~	~~0~~	~~3~~
− 1	2	9
3	7	4

STEP 2 Subtract.

13 − 9 = 4 9 − 2 = 7 4 − 1 = 3

The difference between 503 and 129 is 374.

SEARCH

To see step-by-step videos of these problems, enter the page number into the SWadvantage.com Search Bar.

Counting-Up Subtraction

When using the **counting-up subtraction method**, first write the subtrahend, the number being subtracted. Then, count up to get the next place value. Circle each number used to count up. Then add the circled numbers to find the difference.

Need More HELP

To review basic addition facts, go to *Addition Facts* in *Foundations of Mathematics* (p. 56).

EXAMPLE 4

Subtract 93 − 38.

Write the subtrahend.	38
Count up to the nearest ten.	+ (2) = 40
Count up to the tens place (9) in the minuend, 93.	+ (50) = 90
Count up to the minuend.	+ (3) = 93

Add the circled numbers. $2 + 50 + 3 = 55$

The difference between 93 and 38 is 55.

EXAMPLE 5

Subtract 741 − 57.

Write the subtrahend.	57
Count up to the nearest ten.	+ (3) = 60
Count up to one hundred.	+ (40) = 100
Count up to the hundreds place (7) in the minuend, 741.	+ (600) = 700
Count up to the minuend.	+ (41) = 741

Add the circled numbers. $3 + 40 + 600 + 41 = 684$

The difference between 741 and 57 is 684.

Left-to-Right Subtraction

When using the **left-to-right subtraction method**, first subtract the leftmost digits (the digits with the greatest place value). Continue subtracting working toward the right until the ones have been subtracted. You can work horizontally or vertically.

Subtract 842 − 197.

The subtrahend 197 is the same as 100 + 90 + 7.

METHOD 1

Subtract the hundreds.	842 − 100 = 742
Subtract the tens.	742 − 90 = 652
Subtract the ones.	652 − 7 = 645

The difference between 842 and 197 is 645.

METHOD 2

$$\begin{array}{lr} & 842 \\ \text{Subtract the hundreds.} & -\,100 \\ \hline & 742 \\ \text{Subtract the tens.} & -\,90 \\ \hline & 652 \\ \text{Subtract the ones.} & -\,7 \\ \hline & 645 \end{array}$$

The difference between 842 and 197 is 645.

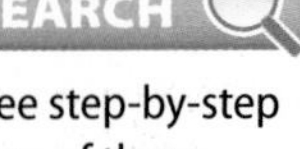

To see step-by-step videos of these problems, enter the page number into the SWadvantage.com Search Bar.

Subtract 5,482 − 1,393.

The subtrahend 1,393 is the same as 1,000 + 300 + 90 + 3.

Subtract the thousands.	5,482 − 1,000 = 4,482
Subtract the hundreds.	4,482 − 300 = 4,182
Subtract the tens.	4,182 − 90 = 4,092
Subtract the ones.	4,092 − 3 = 4,089

The difference between 5,482 and 1,393 is 4,089.

Try It This Way

To see other methods for subtracting 5,482 − 1,393, go to Example 2 on page 21 and Example 11 on page 25.

Partial Differences

The **partial-differences subtraction method** is similar to the partial-sums method for addition. Starting on the left, with the greatest place value, subtract from left to right until you have subtracted the ones. Then combine the partial differences to find the total difference.

SEARCH

To see step-by-step videos of these problems, enter the page number into the SWadvantage.com Search Bar.

EXAMPLE 8

Subtract 493 − 361.

$$\begin{array}{r} 493 \\ -\ 361 \\ \hline \end{array}$$

Subtract the hundreds: 400 − 300	100
Subtract the tens: 90 − 60	30
Subtract the ones: 3 − 1	2
Add the partial differences.	100 + 30 + 2 = 132

493 − 361 = 132

EXAMPLE 9

Subtract 6,378 − 1,243.

$$\begin{array}{r} 6{,}378 \\ -\ 1{,}243 \\ \hline \end{array}$$

Subtract the thousands: 6,000 − 1,000	5,000
Subtract the hundreds: 300 − 200	100
Subtract the tens: 70 − 40	30
Subtract the ones: 8 − 3	5
Add the partial differences.	5,000 + 100 + 30 + 5 = 5,135

6,378 − 1,243 = 5,135

Same-Change Subtraction

When using the **same-change subtraction method**, the same number is added to or subtracted from *both* the minuend and the subtrahend. Then the resulting numbers are subtracted. The idea is to change the numbers so the subtrahend ends in zero or in a series of zeros. If you choose the number added or subtracted carefully, you may be able to get two zeros in one step, as shown in Example 11.

EXAMPLE 10

Subtract 352 − 171.

Think: How can I get the subtrahend 171 to end in zeros?

STEP 1 Subtract 1 to change the right-most 1 in 171 to 0.

Subtract 1 from both numbers. $(352 - 1) - (171 - 1)$

$351 - 170$

STEP 2 Add 30 to change the 7 in 170 to 0.

Add 30 to both numbers. $(351 + 30) - (170 + 30)$

$381 - 200$

Subtract the resulting numbers.

$$\begin{array}{r} 381 \\ -\ 200 \\ \hline 181 \end{array}$$

$352 - 171 = 181$

EXAMPLE 11

Subtract 5,482 − 1,393.

Think: 1,393 is almost 1,400.

STEP 1 Add 7 to 1,393 to get 1,400.

Add 7 to both numbers. $(5{,}482 + 7) - (1{,}393 + 7)$

$5{,}489 - 1{,}400$

STEP 2 Subtract the resulting numbers.

$$\begin{array}{r} 5{,}489 \\ -\ 1{,}400 \\ \hline 4{,}089 \end{array}$$

$5{,}482 - 1{,}393 = 4{,}089$

Try It This Way

To see other methods for subtracting 5,482 − 1,393, go to Example 2 on page 21 and Example 7 on page 23.

To review basic multiplication facts, go to *Multiplication Facts* in *Foundations of Mathematics* (p. 68).

Partial Products

When using the **partial-products multiplication method**, first break down each factor to show the value of its digits. Then multiply each part of one factor by each part of the other factor to get the partial product. Finally, add all of the partial products.

EXAMPLE 1

Multiply 73 × 18.

Think: (70 + 3) × (10 + 8)

Multiply 7 tens and 1 ten.	$70 \times 10 = 700$
Multiply 7 tens and 8 ones.	$70 \times 8 = 560$
Multiply 3 ones and 1 ten.	$3 \times 10 = 30$
Multiply 3 ones and 8 ones.	$3 \times 8 = 24$
Add the partial products.	$700 + 560 + 30 + 24 = 1{,}314$

The product of 73 and 18 is 1,314.

EXAMPLE 2

Multiply 132 × 46.

Think: (100 + 30 + 2) × (40 + 6)

Multiply 1 hundred and 4 tens.	$100 \times 40 = 4{,}000$
Multiply 1 hundred and 6 ones.	$100 \times 6 = 600$
Multiply 3 tens and 4 tens.	$30 \times 40 = 1{,}200$
Multiply 3 tens and 6 ones.	$30 \times 6 = 180$
Multiply 2 ones and 4 tens.	$2 \times 40 = 80$
Multiply 2 ones and 6 ones.	$2 \times 6 = 12$
Add the partial products.	$4{,}000 + 600 + 1{,}200 + 180 + 80 + 12 = 6{,}072$

The product of 132 and 46 is 6,072.

You can also use a vertical format for the partial products method, as shown in Example 3 and Example 4 below.

EXAMPLE 3

Multiply 62 × 37.

STEP 1 Think: $(60 + 2) \times (30 + 7)$

STEP 2 Write the problem in vertical format. Then multiply each part of one factor by each part of the other factor.

$$\begin{array}{lcr} & & 62 \\ & & \times\ 37 \\ \hline 60 \times 30 = 1800 & \rightarrow & 1800 \\ 60 \times 7 = 420 & \rightarrow & 420 \\ 2 \times 30 = 60 & \rightarrow & 60 \\ 2 \times 7 = 14 & \rightarrow & 14 \end{array}$$

STEP 3 Add the partial products.

$1{,}800 + 420 + 60 + 14 = 2{,}294$

The product of 62 and 37 is 2,294.

SEARCH

To see step-by-step videos of these problems, enter the page number into the SWadvantage.com Search Bar.

EXAMPLE 4

Multiply 235 × 74.

STEP 1 Think: $(200 + 30 + 5) \times (70 + 4)$

STEP 2 Write the problem in vertical format. Then multiply each part of one factor by each part of the other factor.

$$\begin{array}{lcr} & & 235 \\ & & \times\ 74 \\ \hline 200 \times 70 = 14{,}000 & \rightarrow & 14000 \\ 200 \times 4 = 800 & \rightarrow & 800 \\ 30 \times 70 = 2100 & \rightarrow & 2100 \\ 30 \times 4 = 120 & \rightarrow & 120 \\ 5 \times 70 = 350 & \rightarrow & 350 \\ 5 \times 4 = 20 & \rightarrow & 20 \end{array}$$

STEP 3 Add the partial products.

$14{,}000 + 800 + 2{,}100 + 120 + 350 + 20 = 17{,}390$

The product of 235 and 74 is 17,390.

To see another method for multiplying 235 × 74, go to Example 6 on page 29.

Egyptian Multiplication

When using the **Egyptian multiplication method**, write the problem horizontally with a column of numbers below each factor.

- The left column *always* shows powers of 2 (the number 1 is doubled). Double until you reach a number that is greater than the factor above the column.
- The right column starts with the factor above it. Double this factor until there are the same number of entries as in the column on the left.

Find two or more numbers in the left column that equal the factor on the left. Then add the corresponding numbers in the right column to find the product.

Need More HELP

Egyptian Multiplication was developed by the ancient Egyptians although they used hieroglyphs rather than numerals. It is very similar to another method called Russian Peasant Multiplication.

You can write the factors in any order. In Example 5, you could write the problem as 52 × 36 and double 36.

For any problem, look at the factors carefully and decide which will be easiest to double. Place that factor on the right.

EXAMPLE 5

Multiply 36 × 52.

STEP 1 Write the multiplication horizontally. Below the factor on the left, double the number 1 until you reach a number that is greater than the factor, 36. Since 64 > 36, stop with 32.

For this multiplication, there are six entries in the left column.

36	×	52
1		
2		
4		
8		
16		
32		
~~64~~		

STEP 2 Below the factor on the right, write the factor. Then double the factor until there are six entries in the column on the right.

36	×	52
1		52
2		104
4		208
8		416
16		832
32		1,664

STEP 3 Find two numbers in the column on the left whose sum is 36.

$4 + 32 = 36$

Find the corresponding numbers in the column on the right: 208 and 1,664.

36	×	52
1		52
2		104
4	→	**208**
8		416
16		832
32	→	**1,664**

STEP 4 Add the two numbers in the column on the right.

$208 + 1{,}664 = 1{,}872$

The product of 36 and 52 is 1,872.

Lattice Multiplication

The **lattice multiplication method** uses a grid of squares with each square divided by a diagonal. The factors are placed as follows.

- One factor is written along the top, left to right, with a digit above each square.
- The other factor is written along the right side of the grid, from top to bottom, with a digit to the right of each square.

Multiply each digit in one factor by each digit in the other factor. For each product, place the tens digit above the diagonal and the ones digit below it.

Then add the digits along each diagonal, starting at the bottom right corner. Place the sum at the bottom of each diagonal *outside* of the grid. If necessary, carry the tens digit to the next diagonal. Read the answer down the left side and then from left to right across the bottom.

EXAMPLE 6

Multiply 235 × 74.

STEP 1 Place the multiplication on a grid.

First multiply $7 \times 5 = 35$. Place the 3 above the diagonal and the 5 below the diagonal. Continue multiplying, each time writing the partial product on the grid.

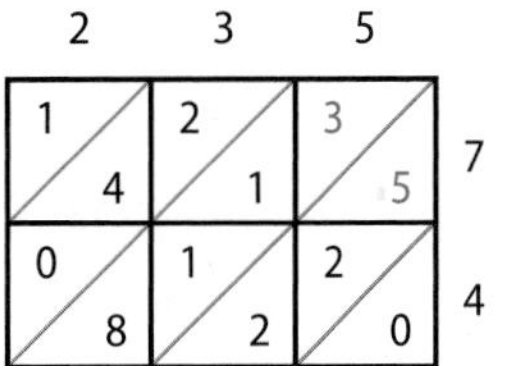

$7 \times 3 = 21$ $\quad$ $7 \times 2 = 14$

$4 \times 5 = 20$ $\quad$ $4 \times 3 = 12$

$4 \times 2 = 8$

STEP 2 Add the partial products starting at the bottom right corner and moving left. If you extend the diagonal lines, you can see the diagonals better.

1st diagonal: 0

2nd diagonal: $5 + 2 + 2 = 9$

3rd diagonal: $3 + 1 + 1 + 8 = 13$
Write 3 in the diagonal and place the 1 ten in the next diagonal.

4th diagonal: $1 + 2 + 4 + 0 = 7$

5th diagonal: 1

STEP 3 Find the product. Start with the top left digit outside of the grid, 1. Move down and then across the bottom of the grid. Write the digits in order: 1 7 3 9 0

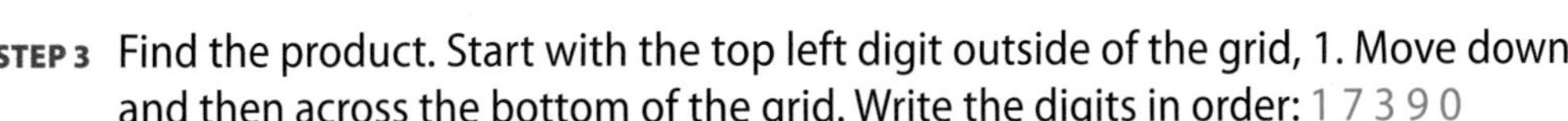

The product of 235 and 74 is 17,390.

Try It This Way

To see another method for multiplying 235×74, go to Example 4 on page 27.

SEARCH

To see step-by-step videos of these problems, enter the page number into the SWadvantage.com Search Bar.

Lattice Method and Grids

Sometimes lattice multiplication is shown using a grid for all of the numbers, as shown in Example 7 and Example 8. The cells on the grid that show the products may have a heavier border, or they may be tinted. Although lattice styles may differ somewhat, the steps for finding the product remain the same.

EXAMPLE 7

Multiply 432 × 36.

STEP 1 Place the multiplication on a grid.

First multiply $3 \times 2 = 6$. There are no tens, so place a 0 above the diagonal and the 6 below the diagonal.

Continue multiplying, each time writing the partial product on the grid.

$3 \times 3 = 9$ $\quad$ $3 \times 4 = 12$

$6 \times 2 = 12$ $\quad$ $6 \times 3 = 18$

$6 \times 4 = 24$

	4	3	2	
	1/2	0/9	0/6	3
	2/4	1/8	1/2	6

STEP 2 Add the partial products starting at the bottom right corner and moving left.

1st diagonal: 2

2nd diagonal: $6 + 1 + 8 = 15$
Write 5 in the box and place the 1 ten in the next diagonal.

3rd diagonal: $1 + 9 + 1 + 4 = 15$
Write 5 in the box and place the 1 ten in the next diagonal.

4th diagonal: $1 + 0 + 2 + 2 = 5$

5th diagonal: 1

	4	3	2	
1	1/2	0 [1] /9	0 [1] /6	3
5	2/4	1/8	1/2	6
	5	5	2	

STEP 3 Find the product.

Start with the top left digit outside of the grid, 1. Move down and then across the bottom of the grid. Write the digits in order: 1 5 5 5 2

The product of 432 and 36 is 15,552.

EXAMPLE 8

Multiply 6,387 × 209.

STEP 1 Place the multiplication on a grid.

Then multiply. Remember to place the tens digit above the diagonal and the ones digit below it.

First multiply each digit in the factor 6,387 by 2.

Next, multiply each digit by 0.

Finally, multiply each digit by 9.

	6	3	8	7	
	1 / 2	0 / 6	1 / 6	1 / 4	2
	0 / 0	0 / 0	0 / 0	0 / 0	0
	5 / 4	2 / 7	7 / 2	6 / 3	9

STEP 2 Add the partial products starting at the bottom right corner and moving left.

1st diagonal: 3

2nd diagonal: $0 + 6 + 2 = 8$

3rd diagonal: $4 + 7 + 7 = 18$
Write 5 in the box and place the 1 ten in the next diagonal.

4th diagonal: $1 + 1 + 6 + 2 + 4 = 14$
Write 4 in the box and place the 1 ten in the next diagonal.

5th diagonal: $1 + 1 + 6 + 5 = 13$
Write 3 in the box and place the 1 ten in the next diagonal.

6th diagonal: $1 + 0 + 2 + 0 = 3$

7th diagonal: 1

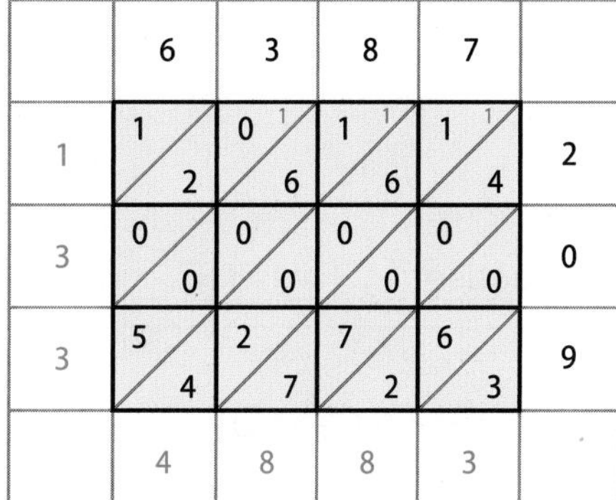

STEP 3 Find the product.

Start with the top left digit outside of the grid, 1. Move down and then across the bottom of the grid. Write the digits in order: 1 3 3 4 8 8 3

The product of 6,387 and 209 is 1,334,883.

SEARCH

To see step-by-step videos of these problems, enter the page number into the SWadvantage.com Search Bar.

Partial Quotients

A division problem consists of these three parts:

```
        quotient
divisor)dividend
```

The **partial-quotients division method** involves making a series of estimates by multiplying the divisor by a small number and subtracting. Continue until no more divisions are possible. Add the partial quotients. Include any remainder in the final quotient.

EXAMPLE 1

Divide 14 ÷ 4.

Think: The divisor is 4. Since $4 \times 2 = 8$, there are at least two 4's in 14.

Write 4×2.
Then subtract $14 - 8 = 6$

```
4)14   4 × 2
  −8
   6
```

There is a remainder of 6, so there is another 4 in 6.

Write 4×1.
Then subtract $6 - 4 = 2$.

```
4)14   4 × 2
  −8
   6   4 × 1
  −4
   2
```

In the number 14, there are 3 groups of 4 with a remainder of 2.

Write the quotient: 3 R2.

```
     3 R2
4)14   4 × 2
  −8
   6   4 × 1
  −4   _____
   2       3
```

The quotient 14 ÷ 4 is 3 R2.

EXAMPLE 2

Divide 137 ÷ 9.

Estimate the number of times the divisor 9 will go into the dividend 137.

Think: Since $9 \times 10 = 90$, it will go at least 10 times. Write 9×10.

Subtract $137 - 90 = 47$. There is a remainder of 47. Estimate again.

```
       15 R2
9)137      9 × 10
  −90
   47      9 ×  5
  −45      ______
    2          15
```

Think: Since $9 \times 5 = 45$, it will go 5 times. Write $9 \times 5 = 45$.

Subtract $47 - 45 = 2$. There are no more groups of 9 so 2 is the remainder.

There are 15 groups of 9 with 2 left over, so the quotient 137 ÷ 9 is 15 R2.

Try It This Way

To see another method for dividing 137 ÷ 9, go to Example 3 on page 33.

Column Division

The **column division method** is a variation of the standard long division algorithm. Vertical lines, which form columns, are inserted to separate the digits in the dividend. Remainders are always repositioned before performing the next division. Example 4 shows a variation of the algorithm for this method.

Need More **HELP**

To review basic division facts, go to *Division Facts* in *Foundations of Mathematics* (p. 74).

EXAMPLE 3

Divide 137 ÷ 9.

```
   0¦ 1¦ 5  R2
9)1¦ 3¦ 7
 −0¦  ¦
  1¦  ¦
   ¦13¦
  −¦ 9¦
   ¦ 4¦
   ¦  ¦47
   ¦−¦45
   ¦  ¦ 2
```

STEP 1 First Division

- Determine how many times 9 will go into 1. Since $9 > 0$, it will not go.
- Write 0 above the 1 in the dividend. Then subtract $1 - 0 = 1$.
- Bring down the 3. Reposition the remainder 1 to the left of the 3 to show 13.

STEP 2 Second Division

- Determine how many times 9 will go into 13. Since $2 \times 9 = 18$, it will go 1 time.
- Write 1 above the 3 in the dividend. Then subtract $13 - 9 = 4$.
- Bring down the 7. Reposition the remainder 4 to the left of the 7 to show 47.

STEP 3 Third Division

- Determine how many times 9 will go into 47. Since $5 \times 9 = 45$, it will go 5 times.
- Write 5 above the 7 in the dividend. There are no more digits in the dividend to bring down. Subtract $47 - 45 = 2$.

The quotient 137 ÷ 9 is 15 R2.

Try It This Way

To see another method for dividing 137 ÷ 9, go to Example 2 on page 32.

EXAMPLE 4

Divide 925 ÷ 17.

```
     0 ¦  5 ¦  4   R7
17)9 ¦ 92 ¦ 75
  −0 ¦ 85 ¦ 68
   9 ¦  7 ¦  7
```

Determine how many times 17 will go into 9.

- Since $17 > 9$, write 0 in the dividend. Then subtract $9 - 0 = 9$.
- Place a 9 next to the next number in the dividend, 2, to get 92.
- Continue dividing in this way, as shown on the right.

The quotient 925 ÷ 17 is 54 R7.

SEARCH

To see step-by-step videos of these problems, enter the page number into the SWadvantage.com Search Bar.

Box Models

For more word problems involving whole numbers, go to *Word Problems* in *Foundations of Mathematics* (p. 104).

In a **box model**, the "box" is a rectangular bar that shows the relationship between a known and an unknown quantity. This type of model can help you visualize what operation is needed to solve a problem. For more complex problems, two or more bars may be used to represent the situation.

EXAMPLE 1

Hector has 4 fish in his fish tank. He buys 5 more at the pet store. How many fish does he have now?

Draw a bar and divide it into two parts. Let one part represent 4 fish. Let the other part represent 5 more fish.

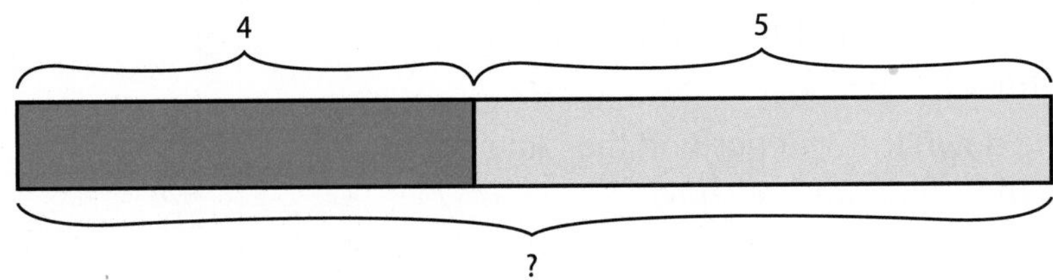

Add the two known parts to find the whole, or unknown, part: $4 + 5 = 9$.

Hector has 9 fish now.

EXAMPLE 2

Daniel collected 38 rocks. Sonya found 17 fewer rocks than Daniel. How many rocks does Sonya have?

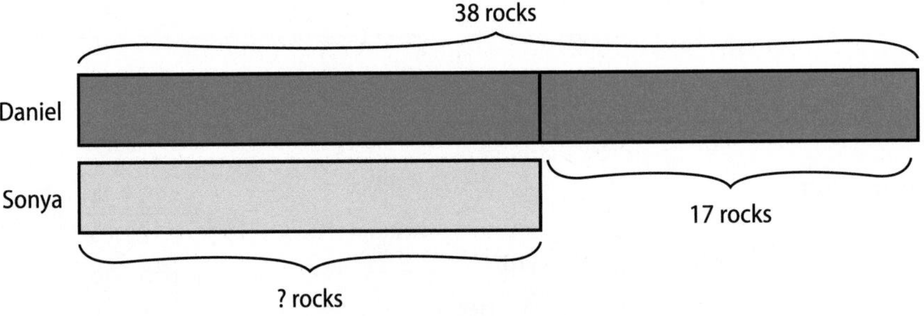

The whole is 38 rocks, the number Daniel collected.
A known part is 17 rocks.
Subtract to find the unknown part: $38 - 17 = 21$

Sonya has 21 rocks.

EXAMPLE 3

The sum of two numbers is 96. One of the numbers is three times greater than the other number. What are the two numbers?

Represent the two numbers as rectangles. The rectangle for the larger number is three times the length of the rectangle for the smaller number.

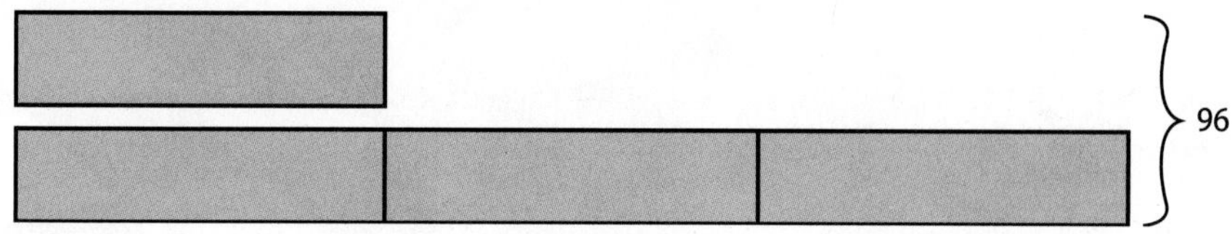

There are 4 equal sections, so the smaller number is $96 \div 4 = 24$. The larger number is $24 \times 3 = 72$. Since $24 + 72 = 96$, these values must be correct.

The numbers are 24 and 72.

SEARCH

To see step-by-step videos of these problems, enter the page number into the SWadvantage.com Search Bar.

EXAMPLE 4

Lee had 185 trading cards. Debora had 100 fewer trading cards. Lee gives Debora some of his cards. Now he has 2 times as many cards as Debora.

a. At first, how many trading cards did Debora have?

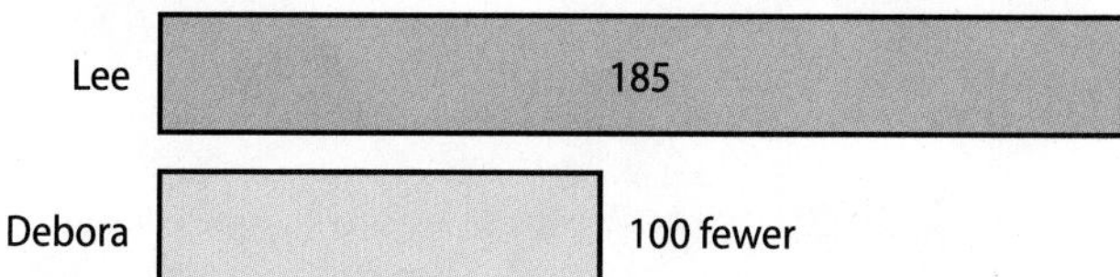

Debora: $185 - 100 = 85$

At first, Debora had 85 trading cards.

b. How many trading cards do they both have now?

The total number of cards is $185 + 85 = 270$. The 270 cards are shared between Lee and Debora. After giving Debora some cards, Lee has $2 \times$ as many cards as she has.

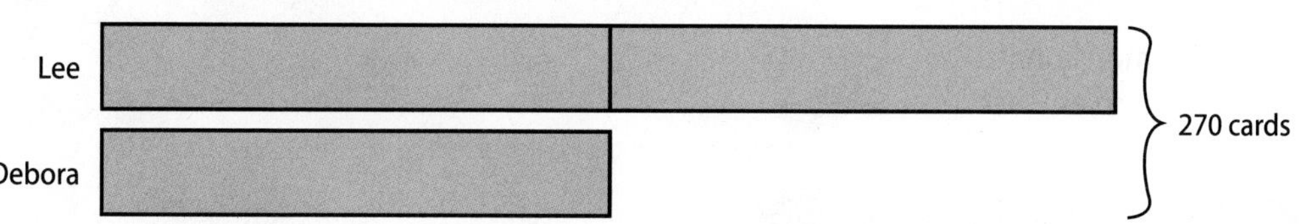

Debora: $270 \div 3 = 90$ Lee $= 90 \times 2 = 180$ Total: $90 + 180 = 270$

Now, Lee has 180 cards and Debora has 90 cards.

Foundations of Mathematics

A tile setter needs to understand two-dimensional geometric shapes to follow a design pattern and set the tiles correctly.

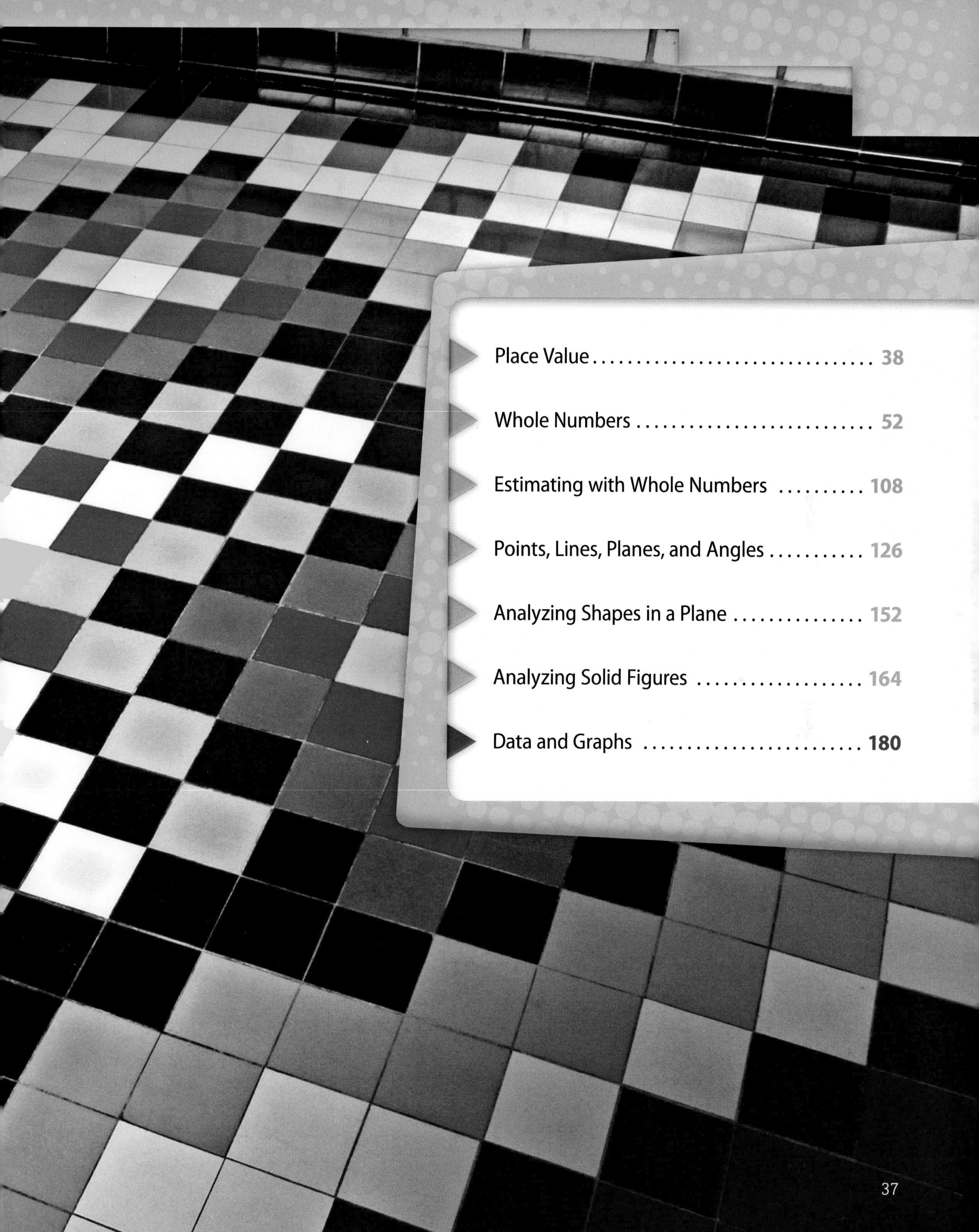

Place Value

What Came Before?

- Adding and subtracting 1-digit counting numbers
- Multiplying and dividing 1-digit counting numbers

What's This About?

- Using place value to read and write whole numbers
- Comparing and ordering whole numbers
- Rounding whole numbers

Practical Apps

- An office manager uses place value to compare the prices of office supplies.
- A payroll clerk must be careful not to make a place value error on a paycheck.

Just for FUN!

Q: If you can guess the 3 consecutive numbers I'm thinking of, I'll trade you three of these for five of those.

A: The numbers are: three, four, five!

CONTENTS UPLOAD DOWNLOAD

Foundations of Mathematics

You can find more practice problems online by visiting:
www.SWadvantage.com

Place Value to Billions

Using a Place-Value Chart

The *periods* on a place-value chart are sometimes called *families.* For example, the Thousands Family contains one thousands, ten thousands, and hundred thousands.

All whole numbers are formed by arranging the digits 0, 1, 2, 3, 4, 5, 6, 7, 8, and 9 in different orders. The value of each digit depends on its place in a number. A *place-value chart* can help you find the value of the digits. Each group of three places on the chart is called a **period**. Commas separate each period into hundreds, tens, and ones.

EXAMPLE 1

The planet Mercury is 57,909,175 kilometers (km) from the sun. Use the place-value chart to help you find the value of this number.

Billions			Millions			Thousands			Ones		
hundred billions	ten billions	billions	hundred millions	ten millions	millions	hundred thousands	ten thousands	thousands	hundreds	tens	ones
				5	7,	9	0	9,	1	7	5

Start with the period farthest to the left.

STEP 1 The digits in the *millions period* are 5 and 7. Say: 57 million.

STEP 2 The digits in the *thousands period* are 9, 0, and 9. Say: 909 thousand.

STEP 3 The digits in the *ones period* are 1, 7, and 5. Say: 175 as one hundred seventy-five. Do not say the name of the period.

Mercury is 57 million, 909 thousand, 175 kilometers from the sun.

Values of Each Place

The value of each place on a place-value chart is 10 times greater than the place to its right. The value of a digit in a number is the product of that digit and the value of its place.

In 57,909,175, from left to right:

The first 5 has a value of 5 × 10,000,000, or 50,000,000.

The first 7 has a value of 7 × 1,000,000, or 7,000,000.

The first 9 has a value of 9 × 100,000, or 900,000.

The second 5 has a value of 5 × 1, or 5.

The second 7 has a value 7 × 10, or 70.

The second 9 has a value of 9 × 1,000, or 9,000.

Using Place Value

The same digit may appear in more than one place in a number. A place-value chart can help you compare the values of these digits.

EXAMPLE 2

a. The table shows gasoline sales over a three-month period. In which month was the least amount of gasoline sold?

Month	Gallons Sold
January	18,088,688
February	18,866,000
March	18,860,086

STEP 1 For each month, the digit in the *ten millions* place is 1, and the digit in the *millions* place is 8.

STEP 2 For January, the digit in the *hundred thousands* place is 0. For February and March, the digit in the *hundred thousands* place is 8.

This means that the number for January contains no hundred thousands, and the numbers for February and March contain 8 hundred thousands.

The least amount of gas was sold in January.

b. Look at the digit pairs in the number for January: 18,088,688. How do the values differ?

The red digit on the left has a value that is 10 × the value of the red digit to its right. 80,000 vs. 8,000

The green digit on the left has a value that is 10 × the value of the green digit to its right. 80 vs. 8

SEARCH

To see step-by-step videos of these problems, enter the page number into the SWadvantage.com Search Bar.

EXAMPLE 3

A mystery number has: 1 in the *billions* and the *thousands* places; 0 in the *hundred millions, ten millions,* and *tens* places; 3 in the *ten billions* and *hundred thousands* places; 5 in the *millions* place; 4 in the *ones* place; 8 in the *ten thousands* place; and 7 in the *hundreds* place. Use a place-value chart to write the mystery number.

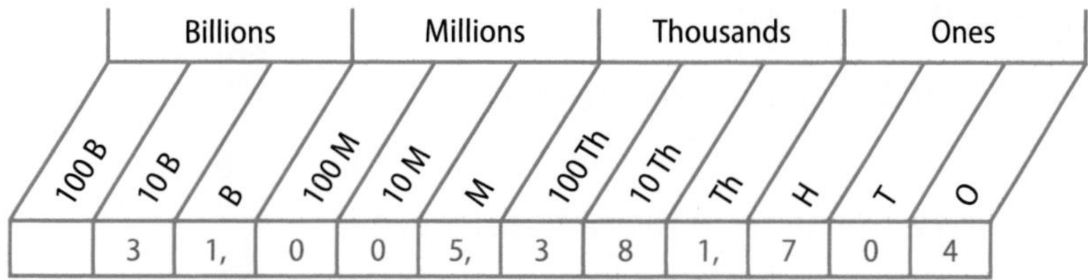

Billions
Millions
Thousands
Ones
100 B
10 B
B
100 M
10 M
M
100 Th
10 Th
Th
H
T
O
3
1,
0
0
5,
3
8
1,
7
0
4

Using Words to Express Numbers

You already know that you can write a number with digits alone or with both digits and words. For example, you can arrange the digits 8, 4, 0, 3, 0, and 4 to form the number 384,400. Another way is to write this number as 384 thousand, 400. Still another way is to write the **word form** of the number using only words.

EXAMPLE 1

The average distance from Earth to the moon is about 384,400 km. Use the place-value chart to help you read the words that name this number.

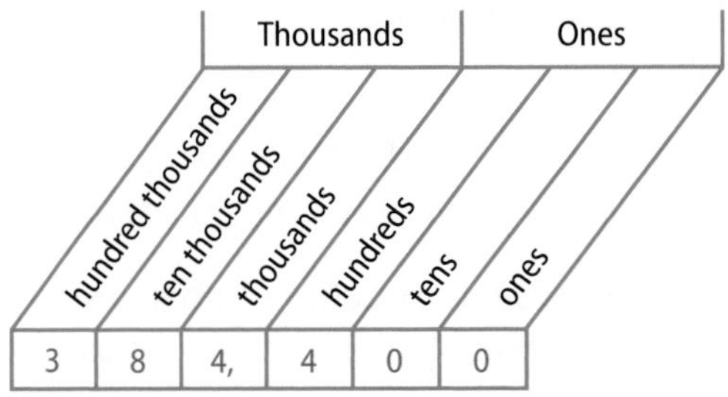

Start with the period farthest to the left.

STEP 1 The digits 3, 8, and 4 are in the *thousands* period.
Say: three hundred eighty-four *thousand*

STEP 2 The digits 4, 0, and 0 are in the *ones* period.
Say: four hundred. For *ones*, do not say the name of the period.

The distance from Earth to the moon is three hundred eighty-four thousand, four hundred km.

SEARCH

To see step-by-step videos of these problems, enter the page number into the SWadvantage.com Search Bar.

Periods

Each group of three digits makes up a period. The period's name is the name of the place in the period that has the *least* value.

425,027,614 The millions period contains the digits 4, 2, and 5.

From left to right the value of these places are: 100 millions, 10 millions, and 1 millions.

The place with the least value is millions, which is the name of the period. Notice that you do not say the 1.

Reading Larger Numbers

Remember, the commas separate the numbers in the periods. Use the commas to read each number. Start on the left, with the numbers in the greatest period. Refer to a place-value chart if you need to.

Need More HELP

In some countries, a space is used between the periods instead of a comma. So the number 561,082,850 would be written as 561 082 850.

EXAMPLE 2

a. 561,082,850

Read the millions, then the thousands, and then the ones:

five hundred sixty-one *million*, eighty-two *thousand*, eight hundred fifty

b. 703,005,866,038

Read the billions, then the millions, then the thousands, and then the ones:

seven hundred three *billion*, five *million*, eight hundred sixty-six *thousand*, thirty-eight

c. 19,429,000,109

Read the billions, then the millions, then the thousands, and then the ones:

nineteen *billion*, four hundred twenty-nine *million*, one hundred nine

Notice that all the digits in the thousands period are zeros. Since this family has no values, you do not say its name.

EXAMPLE 3

The planet Neptune's average distance from the sun is 4,498,252,900 km. Dhara is not sure how to read this number. How should she read the values of the two 4s that begin this number?

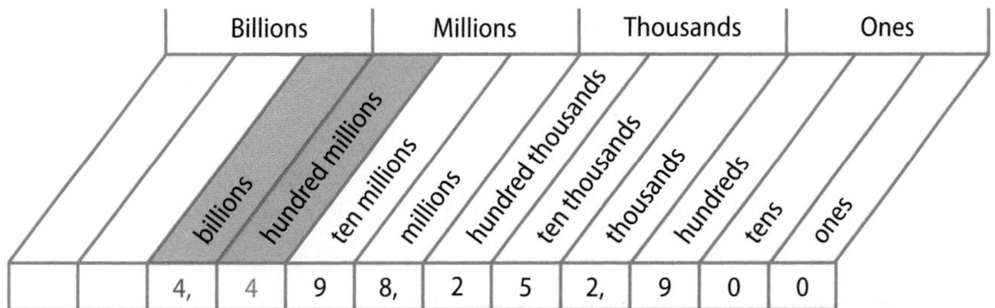

The first 4 is in the *billions* place. The next 4 is in the *hundred millions* place.

Begin reading the number by saying, "four billion, four hundred ninety-eight million."

Writing Whole Numbers

Standard Form

The **standard form** of a number expresses the number with digits. The example below shows a number written in word form and in standard form.

Word form: three hundred fifteen million, six hundred fifty-two thousand, twelve
Standard form: 315,652,012

SEARCH

To see step-by-step videos of these problems, enter the page number into the SWadvantage.com Search Bar.

EXAMPLE 1

The total land area of the state of Texas is two hundred sixty-one thousand, nine hundred fourteen square miles. What is the area in standard form?

Start with the greatest period, in this case the thousands period.

STEP 1 Write the digits for the thousands—two hundred sixty-one. Place a comma after the digits in the period.
261,

STEP 2 Write the digits for the ones—nine hundred fourteen.
261,914

The standard form of the area is 261,914 square miles.

Expanded Form

The **expanded form** of a number expresses the number as the sum of the values of its digits. Expanded form is a way of breaking a number down into the sum of its place values.

Need More HELP

Expanded form is sometimes called *expanded notation.*

EXAMPLE 2

Write 5,067 in expanded form.

STEP 1 Find the value of the digit in each place in the number.

thousands place, 5	$5 \times 1{,}000 = 5{,}000$
hundreds place, 0	$0 \times 100 = 0$
tens place, 6	$6 \times 10 = 60$
ones place, 7	$7 \times 1 = 7$

STEP 2 Write the number as the sum of the values. Omit any values of zero.
$5{,}000 + 60 + 7$

The expanded form of 5,067 is $5{,}000 + 60 + 7$.

Expressing a Number in a Different Form

EXAMPLE 3

Kiri wrote the area of the state of Alaska in this way:

(5 × 100,000) + (7 × 10,000) + (3 × 100) + (7 × 10) + (4 × 1) square miles

Express the area in standard form.

Multiply the numbers in parentheses. Then add to find the sum.

500,000 + 70,000 + 300 + 70 + 4 = 570,374

In standard form, the area is 570,374 square miles.

Try It This Way

Use a place-value chart for Example 3. Find the place for hundred thousands and write 5. Continue until you have placed all the digits on the place-value chart.

No value is given for thousands, so its value is zero. Write a zero in the thousands place.

EXAMPLE 4

Josie tried to write the expanded form of 633,700,412, as shown below. She made several errors. Identify and correct Josie's errors.

600,000 + 700 + 400 + 12

There should be seven values, one for each non-zero digit.

Digit	Value
6	6 × 100,000,000 = 600,000,000
3	3 × 10,000,000 = 30,000,000
3	3 × 1,000,000 = 3,000,000
7	7 × 100,000 = 700,000
4	4 × 100 = 400 (Josie wrote this value correctly.)
1	1 × 10 = 10
2	2 × 1 = 2

The correct form is: 600,000,000 + 30,000,000 + 3,000,000 + 700,000 + 400 + 10 + 2.

WatchOut!

Expanded form includes an addend for only non-zero digits. Do not include an addend for any value of zero.

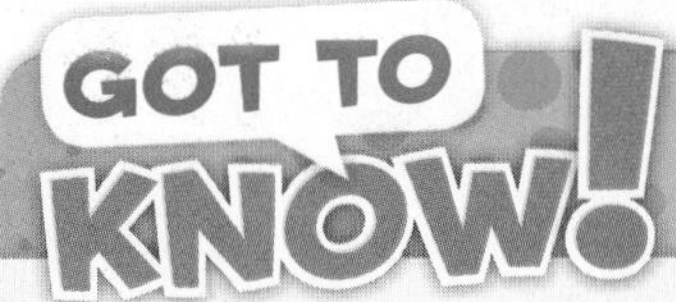

Forms of a Number

Standard form	82,401
Expanded form	80,000 + 2,000 + 400 + 1
Word form	eighty-two thousand, four hundred one
Short word form	82 thousand, 401

Comparing Whole Numbers

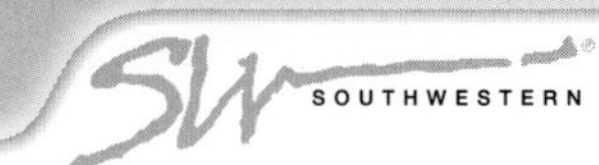

Using Symbols to Compare

To compare two numbers, decide if their values are greater than, equal to, or less than each other. Use the comparison symbols to compare numbers.

Read $>$ as "is greater than." $5 > 4$

Read $=$ as "is equal to." $3 = 3$

Read $<$ as "is less than." $8 < 12$

Ways to REMEMBER

On a sheet of paper, write a 6 and a 3 several inches apart. Use the thumb and forefinger of your *right* hand to model the greater-than symbol, $>$. Now, place your hand between the number pair. Notice how the larger number could "swallow" the smaller number.

$6 > 3$

Next, write a 2 and a 7. Repeat the process using the thumb and forefinger of your *left* hand to form the less-than symbol, $<$.

EXAMPLE 1

Compare 271,879 and 273,435. Use $>$, $<$, or $=$.

STEP 1 Write the numbers one below the other on a place-value chart.

Millions			Thousands			Ones		
hundred millions	ten millions	millions	hundred thousands	ten thousands	thousands	hundreds	tens	ones
			2	7	3,	4	3	5
			2	7	1,	8	7	9

STEP 2 Start at the greatest place-value position. Compare the digits on the place-value chart from left to right until you reach two digits that have a different value.

Compare the hundred thousands place: $2 = 2$
Compare the ten thousands place: $7 = 7$
Compare the thousands place: $3 > 1$

STEP 3 The digits in the thousands place are different.

271,879 contains 1 thousand.
273,435 contains 3 thousands.

$273{,}435 > 271{,}879$

Comparing Two Whole Numbers

Different number of digits:

- The number with the greater number of digits has the greater value.

Same number of digits:

- Compare the digits from left to right.
- Look for the first place in which the digits differ. The number with the greater digit in that place is the greater number.

Comparing Data in Tables

EXAMPLE 2

Use the population data in the table below.

City	Population
Calgary	1,230,248
Dallas	1,299,543
Philadelphia	1,547,297
Phoenix	1,601,587
San Diego	1,306,301

a. Which is greater, the population of Dallas or the population of Calgary?

STEP 1 Line up the numbers.

Calgary: 1,230,248
Dallas: 1,299,543

STEP 2 Start at the left. Compare digits.

The digits in the millions place are the same: 1 = 1
The digits in the hundred thousands place are the same: 2 = 2
The digits in the ten thousands place are different: 9 > 3
1,299,543 > 1,230,248

The population of Dallas is greater than the population of Calgary.

b. Which is less, the population of San Diego or the population of Philadelphia?

STEP 1 Line up the numbers.

San Diego: 1,306,301
Philadelphia: 1,547,297

STEP 2 Start at the left. Compare digits.

The digits in the millions place are the same: 1 = 1
The digits in the hundred thousands place are different: 3 < 5
1,306,301 < 1,547,297

The population of San Diego is less than the population of Philadelphia.

c. Which city has the greatest population? How do you know?

All the digits in the millions place are 1. Look at the digits in the hundred thousands place. The greatest digit is 6, so Phoenix's population is the greatest.

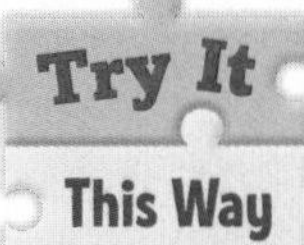

This Way

Use a sheet of paper to cover all the digits to the right of the column of digits you are comparing. This will help you compare only the digits in the same place-value position.

It's easier to compare the digits in the hundred thousands place when the rest are covered.

1,230,248
1,299,543
1,547,297
1,601,587
1,306,301

SEARCH

To see step-by-step videos of these problems, enter the page number into the SWadvantage.com Search Bar.

Using Place Value to Order Numbers

Use what you know about comparing numbers to place a set of numbers in order. Numbers can be ordered from least to greatest or from greatest to least.

Need More HELP

For help with comparing whole numbers, go to *Comparing Whole Numbers* on pages 46–47.

EXAMPLE 1

Order these numbers from greatest to least: 228,917 24,062 243,529

STEP 1 Write the numbers according to place value, one below the other.

228,917
 24,062
243,529

STEP 2 The number 24,062 has fewer digits than the other two numbers. It has the least value. Place it last.

__________ > __________ > 24,062

STEP 3 Compare the digits in the other numbers from left to right.

- 228,917 / 243,529 — The digits in the hundred thousands place are the same.
- 228,917 / 243,529 — The digits in the ten thousands place are different. 4 > 2, so 243,529 > 228,917.

The order from greatest to least is 243,529 > 228,917 > 24,062.

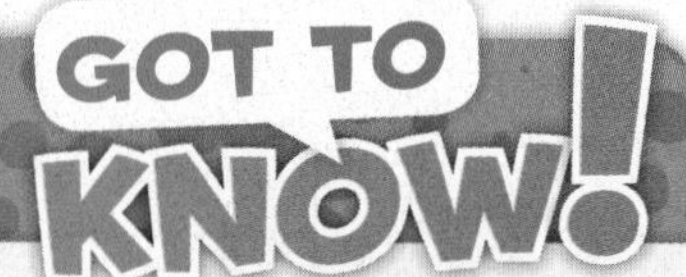

GOT TO KNOW!

Ordering Whole Numbers

To order numbers, first line them up according to place value.

If the numbers have a *different* amount of digits:

- The number with the most digits is the greatest number.
- The number with the fewest digits is the least number.

If the numbers have *the same* amount of digits:

- Compare the digits in each place-value position, from left to right.
- Look for the first place in which the digits differ. The number with the greatest digit in that place is the greatest number.

Write the numbers in order using the symbols > or <.

Using a Number Line to Order Numbers

A number line can show the order of a set of numbers visually. The number farthest to the left on a number line is the least number. The number farthest to the right is the greatest number.

EXAMPLE 2

Order these numbers from least to greatest: 37,118 32,973 35,067

Plot each number on a number line. Use an arrow and a label to show each number's approximate position.

STEP 1 Look at the scale on the number line. It goes from 30,000 to 40,000. Unlabeled tick marks show the halfway points between the numbered tick marks. You will need to estimate the position of each number.

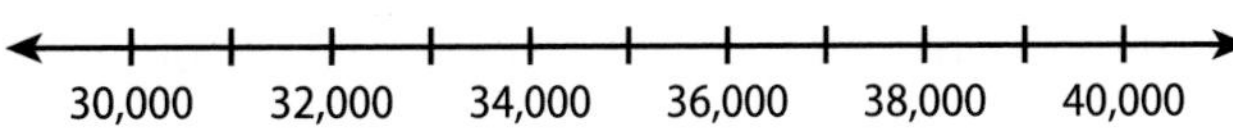

STEP 2 On the number line, plot and label a point for each number.

37,118 is about halfway between 36,000 and 38,000.
32,973 is about halfway between 32,000 and 34,000.
35,067 is about halfway between 34,000 and 36,000.

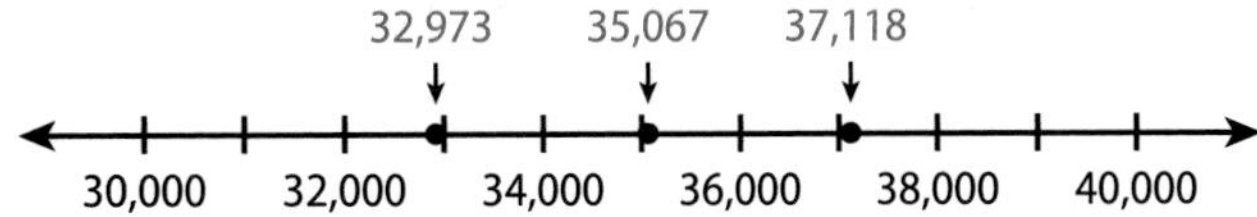

The order from least to greatest is 32,973 < 35,067 < 37,118.

EXAMPLE 3

Order these numbers from greatest to least: 117,062 187,002 145,908

Plot each number on a number line. Use an arrow and a label to show each number's approximate position.

117,062 is between 100,000 and 120,000, but closer to 120,000.
187,002 is about halfway between 180,000 and 200,000.
145,908 is between 140,000 and 160,000, but closer to 140,000.

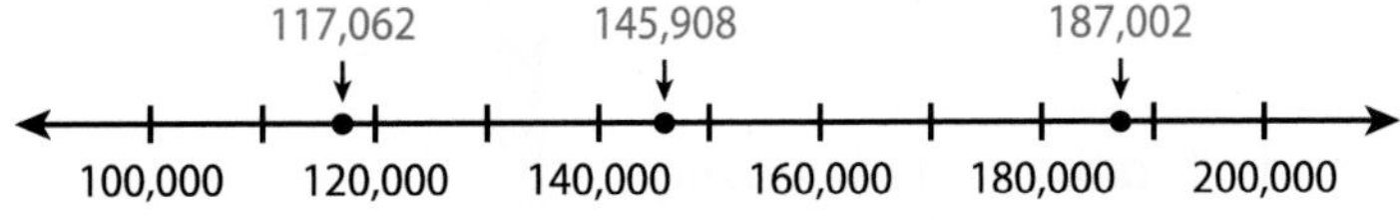

The order from greatest to least is 187,002 > 145,908 > 117,062.

GOT TO KNOW!

Using Symbols to Order Numbers

When you are ordering numbers from *least to greatest,* use this format:

___ < ___ < ___

When you are ordering numbers from *greatest to least,* use this format:

SEARCH

To see step-by-step videos of these problems, enter the page number into the SWadvantage.com Search Bar.

Rounding Whole Numbers

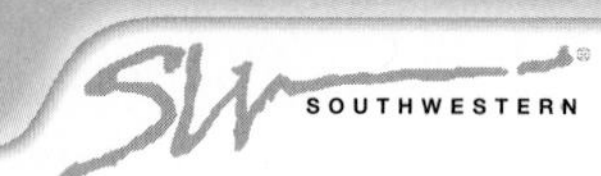

Round Using Place Value

Sometimes it is helpful to know an approximate value instead of an exact value. You can find the approximate value of a number by **rounding** the exact value to a given place. A rounded number tells *about* how much or *about* how many.

This Way

To better see the place to which you will round, write the number with extra space between the digits.

Then circle the digit in that place.

Then underline the digit to its right.

3 ⑥ 8, 4 9 0

EXAMPLE 1

Round 368,490 to the nearest ten thousand.

STEP 1 Identify the digit in the ten thousands place, 6. 368,490

STEP 2 Look at the digit in the place to its right, 8. 368,490

STEP 3 If this digit is greater than or equal to 5, increase the 6 ten thousands by 1.
If this digit is less than 5, leave the 6 in the ten thousands place.
Since $8 > 5$, increase the 6 by 1: $6 + 1 = 7$
Change all the digits to the right of 7 to zeros. 370,000

368,490 rounded to the nearest ten thousand is 370,000.

EXAMPLE 2

Round 14,359,808 to the nearest million.

STEP 1 Identify the digit in the millions place, 4. 14,359,808

STEP 2 Look at the digit in the place to its right, 3. 14,359,808

STEP 3 If this digit is greater than or equal to 5, increase the 4 millions by 1.
If this digit is less than 5, leave the 4 in the millions place.
Since $3 < 5$, leave the 4 in the millions place.
Change all the digits to the right of 4 to zeros. 14,000,000

14,359,808 rounded to the nearest million is 14,000,000.

Rounding Rules

1. Underline the digit in the place you are rounding to.
2. Look at the digit to its right.
   - If the digit is greater than or equal to 5, add 1 to the underlined digit.
   - If the digit is less than 5, do not change the underlined digit.
3. Drop the digits to the right of the underlined digit and add zeros in their place.

Round Using a Number Line or Place-Value Chart

EXAMPLE 3

Use the number line to round 289,692 and 515,749 to the nearest hundred thousand.

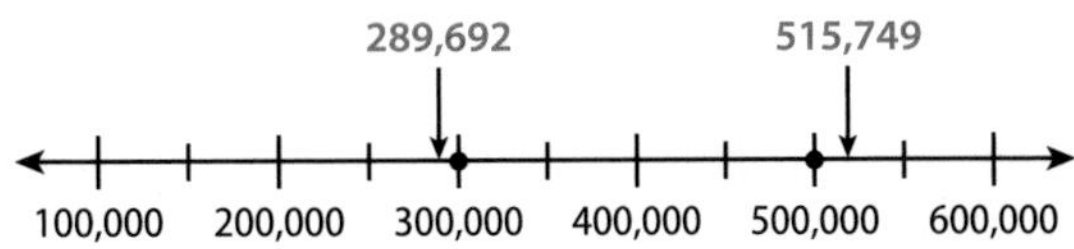

STEP 1 Look at the labels below the number line. The scale goes from 100,000 to 600,000 in increments of 100,000. The unlabeled tick marks show the halfway points between the labeled whole numbers.

STEP 2 Look at the locations of the points and decide how to round each number.

Think: 289,692 is between 250,000 and 300,000, but closer to 300,000.

Think: 515,749 is between 500,000 and 550,000, but closer to 500,000.

289,692 rounds to 300,000.
515,749 rounds to 500,000.

SEARCH

To see step-by-step videos of these problems, enter the page number into the SWadvantage.com Search Bar.

EXAMPLE 4

Ben has a collection of pennies. He writes the number of pennies on a place-value chart. Then he rounds the number to the greatest possible place value. What is Ben's rounded number?

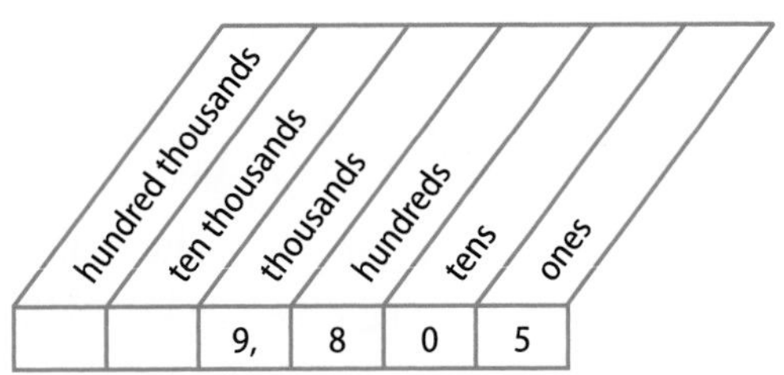

- The greatest place in the number is the thousands place.
- There is a 9 in the thousands place.
- There is an 8 to its right in the hundreds place.
- Since 8 > 5, Ben must have rounded 9 to the next higher digit, 10.
- The digits to the left of the 10 become zeros.

Ben's rounded number is 10,000.

Watch Out !

The 805 in the number becomes 000. The zero in the thousands place is not one of the digits that were changed to zero.

Whole Numbers

What Came Before?

- Using place value to read and write whole numbers
- Comparing, ordering, and rounding whole numbers

What's This About?

- Adding and subtracting whole numbers
- Multiplying and dividing whole numbers
- Solving word problems by using one or more operations

Practical Apps

- Stock clerks use whole numbers to check inventory and to count packages in shipments.
- Caterers multiply and divide whole numbers to find the number of meals to prepare.

just for FUN!

Q: How many wings are there on 2 chickens?

A: Before or after dinner?

CONTENTS | UPLOAD | DOWNLOAD

Foundations of Mathematics

You can find more practice problems online by visiting:
www.SWadvantage.com

Odd and Even Numbers

What Are Odd and Even Numbers?

If a whole number is divisible by 2, it is an **even number**. An even number of things can be put into pairs.

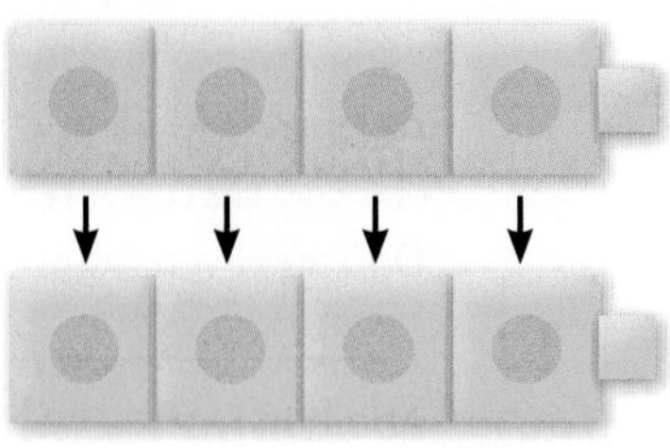

Odd numbers are *not* divisible by 2. When you try to put an odd number of things into pairs, there is always 1 thing left over.

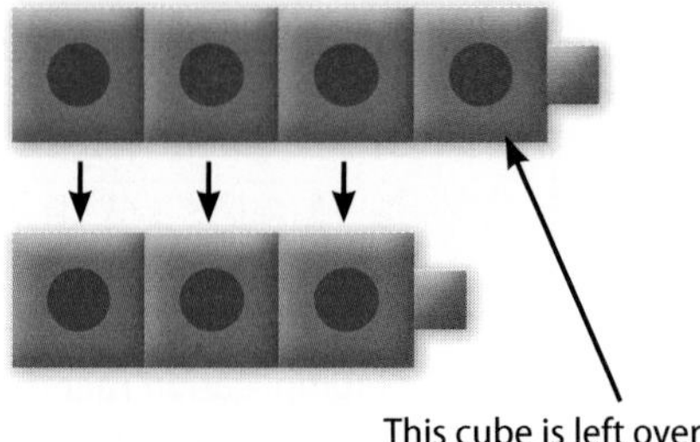

This cube is left over.

Ways to REMEMBER

You may have heard the phrase, "an odd sock." This means a sock without the sock that matches it. The term *odd* means "without a matching item."

EXAMPLE 1

Does the diagram at the right show an even or an odd number of dots?

6 dots

METHOD 1

Check to see if the dots can be put into pairs with none left over.

The dots are in pairs with none left over.

METHOD 2

Count the number of dots. Is the number divisible by 2?

There are 6 dots, and 6 is divisible by 2.

There is an even number of dots.

EXAMPLE 2

Does the diagram at the right show an even or an odd number of dots?

13 dots

METHOD 1

Check to see if the dots can be put into pairs with none left over.

The dots are in pairs with one left over.

METHOD 2

Count the number of dots. Is the number divisible by 2?

13 ends with 3, which is not divisible by 2.

There is an odd number of dots.

EXAMPLE 3

Classify each number as even or odd. Explain your choice.

a. 23 Odd. It ends in 3, which is not divisible by 2.

b. 48 Even. It ends in 8, which is divisible by 2.

c. 580 Even. It ends in 0, which is divisible by 2.

d. 329 Odd. It ends in 9, which is not divisible by 2.

SEARCH

To see step-by-step videos of these problems, enter the page number into the SWadvantage.com Search Bar.

EXAMPLE 4

Decide if each group contains an even or an odd number of objects. Explain your choice.

a.

Even. The squares form 8 pairs with no squares left over.

b.

Odd. There is a triangle left over.

c.

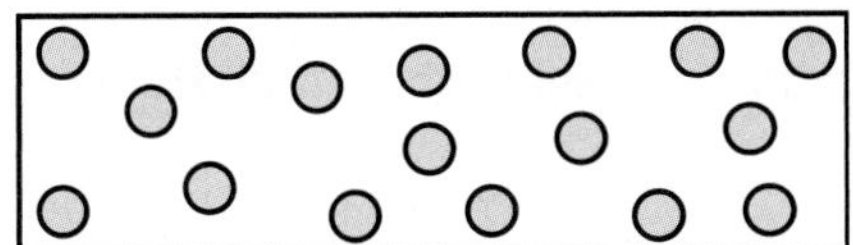

Odd. There are 17 circles. 17 ends with 7, which is not divisible by 2.

d.

Even. There are 8 stars, and 8 is divisible by 2.

Even Numbers	Odd Numbers
Even numbers are divisible by 2. They always end with 0, 2, 4, 6, or 8.	Odd numbers are not divisible by 2. They always end with 1, 3, 5, 7, or 9.
Since zero is divisible by 2, zero is an even number.	Odd numbers of items cannot be placed in pairs. There will always be one item left over.
Even numbers of items can be placed into pairs with none left over.	

What Is Addition?

Addition is a mathematic operation in which you find the total of two or more numbers. The total is called the **sum**.

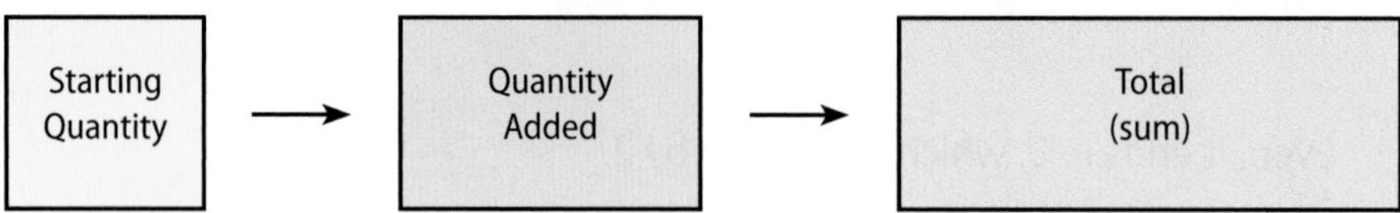

EXAMPLE 1

How many is 3 plus 1 more?

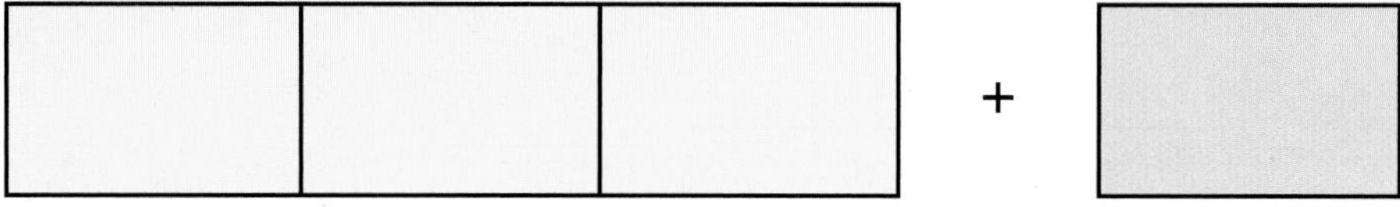

One way to find the answer is to count from left to right: 1, 2, 3, 4.
This method works fine for small numbers. It may not work well for large numbers.

$3 + 1 = 4$

SEARCH

To see step-by-step videos of these problems, enter the page number into the SWadvantage.com Search Bar.

EXAMPLE 2

Solve the problem.

There are 4 beads in a bowl. Then, 2 more beads are placed in the bowl. How many beads are there in all?

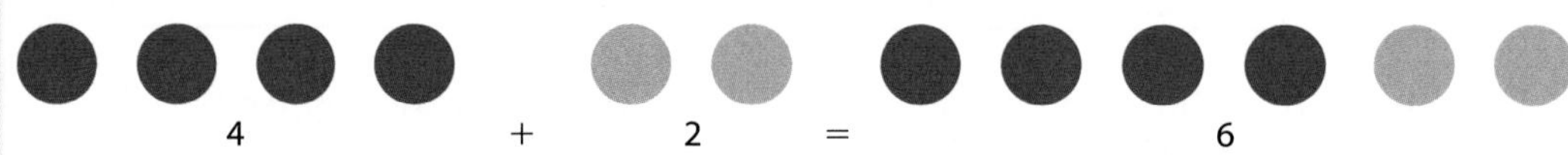

There are 6 beads in all.

Addition Is . . .

a mathematic operation.

Use addition to find the sum (total) of two or more quantities.

The addition sign is the plus symbol, +.

Addition as Part-Part-Whole

Sometimes addition describes two parts and the total is the whole.

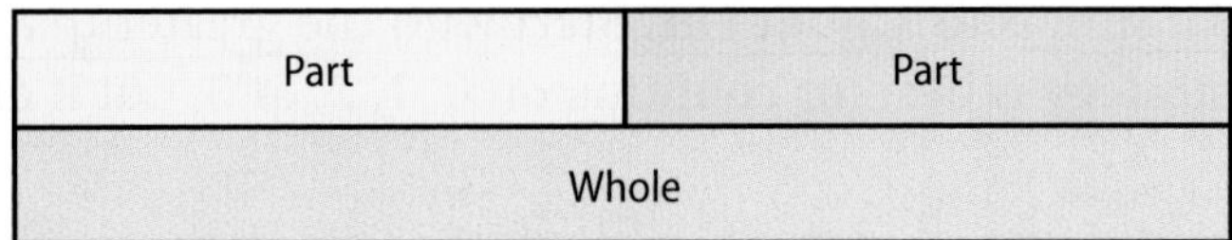

Solve the problem.

There are 3 purple circles. There are 2 blue circles. How many circles are there in all?

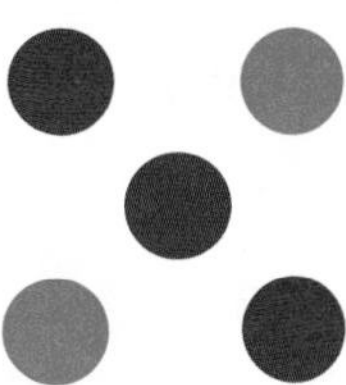

$3 + 2 = 5$

There are 5 circles in all.

Models for Addition

There are many ways to model addition. You can use a ten frame or a number line. Both of the models below show $8 + 2 = 10$.

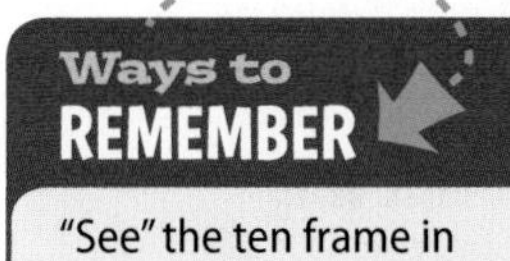

ten frame

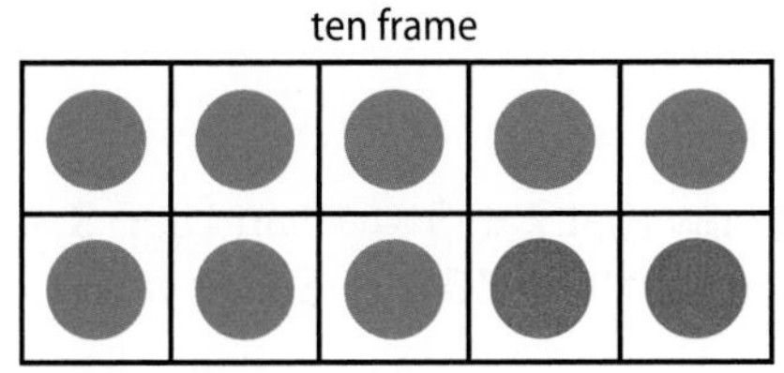

number line

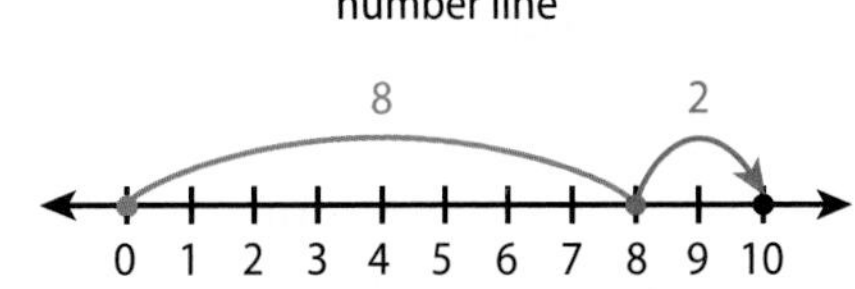

$8 + 2 = 10$

Use a model to solve the problem.

Kent painted for 3 hours. Then he painted for 4 more hours. How many hours did he paint in all?

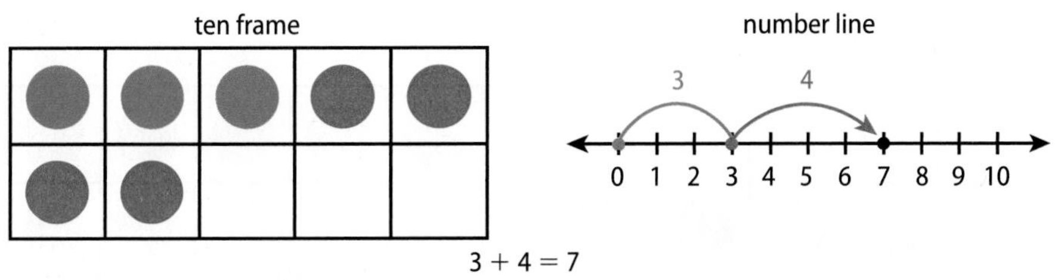

$3 + 4 = 7$

Kent painted 7 hours in all.

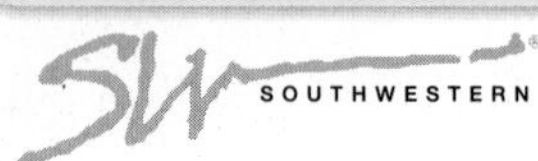

Strategies for Finding Sums

There are many strategies to help find the sum for addition problems.

One way to find a sum is to **Count On**. Start with the greater quantity and then count on. This strategy is best for counting on 0, 1, 2, or 3, but it can work for any numbers.

EXAMPLE 5

Laura had 5 T-shirts. She got 3 more T-shirts. How many T-shirts in all?

Start with the greater number of T-shirts, 5.

Then count on 3 more: 5, 6, 7, 8.
(6, 7, 8: 3 more)

$5 + 3 = 8$, so, Laura has 8 T-shirts.

Another way to find a sum is to **Memorize the Addition Facts**. See pages 60 and 61 for ways to make this task easier.

Try It This Way

Use the number line on page 57.

Or, look up the fact using the addition chart on page 61.

EXAMPLE 6

Find the missing numbers.
$7 + 3 = ?$ $? + 3 = 11$

If you have memorized the addition facts, you know that $7 + 3 = 10$ and $8 + 3 = 11$. If you only know that $7 + 3 = 10$, you can reason that 11 is $10 + 1$. So the missing number is one more than 7, or $7 + 1 = 8$.

Another strategy is the **Switch the Order** of the numbers. You can add two numbers starting with either number. If you remember the fact in one order, you can use it to add in the other order.

EXAMPLE 7

Find the missing number. $4 + 6 = ?$

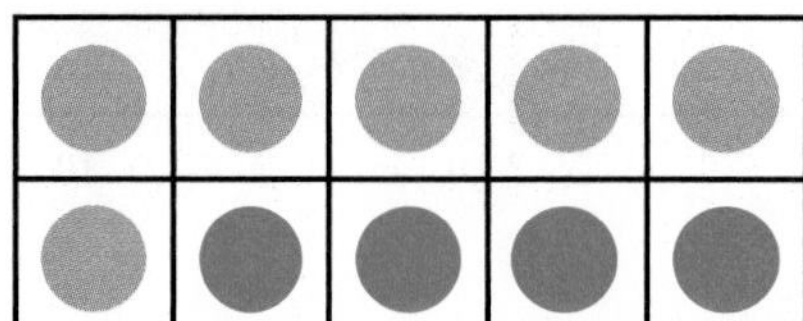

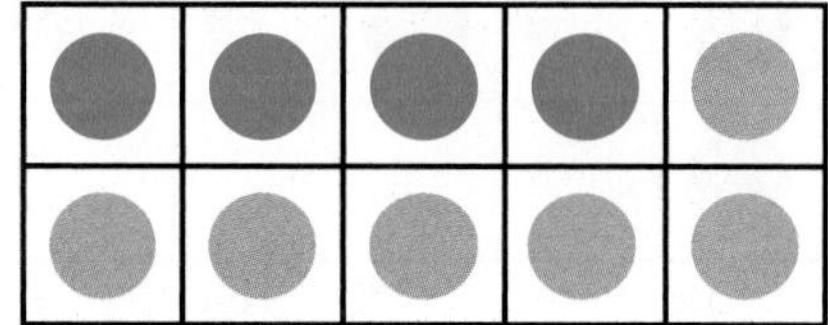

If you know $6 + 4 = 10$, you can use that to know that $4 + 6 = 10$.

Another strategy is **Doubles and Near Doubles**. Facts such as $2 + 2 = 4$ or $8 + 8 = 16$ are easy to remember. Because the number is added to itself, these facts are known as *doubles*.

Some facts are called *near doubles.* These are facts in which the sum is one more or one less than doubles.

Double: $2 + 2 = 4$
Near Double: $2 + 3 = 5$
The sum is 1 more than the double.

Double: $8 + 8 = 16$
Near Double: $8 + 7 = 15$
The sum is 1 less than the double.

EXAMPLE 8

5 + 6 = ?

5 + 6 is a near doubles fact. Here are two ways to find the sum.

Double: 5 + 5 = 10
Near Double: 5 + 6 = 11

Double: 6 + 6 = 12
Near Double: 6 + 5 = 11

5 + 6 = 11

SEARCH

To see step-by-step videos of these problems, enter the page number into the SWadvantage.com Search Bar.

When you know the facts that make ten, you can use the **Make Ten** strategy. In this strategy, you break apart numbers to make a ten. Then you add on the rest.

EXAMPLE 9

8 + 6 = ?

Rearrange the numbers in the ten frames. You have a group of 10 and 4 more.

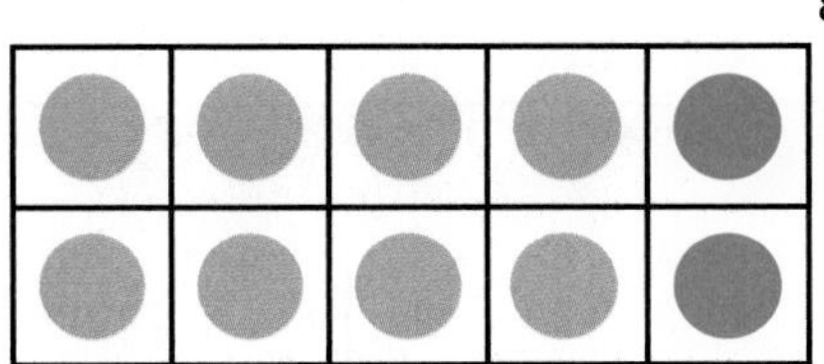

8 + 6 = 14

GOT TO KNOW!

Powerful Addition Strategies

If you can use these strategies, you can add any two numbers that have a sum up to 20.

Memorize the Addition Facts (facts with sums up to 10)

Make Ten

Switch the Order

Memorizing Addition Facts

Although you can use strategies to figure out the sum of addition problems, you will be more powerful mathematically if you memorize the basic facts.

There are 121 basic addition facts. They are listed in the two charts below.

This chart organizes the numbers in columns and rows.

SEARCH

To see step-by-step videos of these problems, enter the page number into the SWadvantage.com Search Bar.

Basic Addition Facts											
+	**0**	**1**	**2**	**3**	**4**	**5**	**6**	**7**	**8**	**9**	**10**
0	0	1	2	3	4	5	6	7	8	9	10
1	1	2	3	4	5	6	7	8	9	10	11
2	2	3	4	5	6	7	8	9	10	11	12
3	3	4	5	6	7	8	9	10	11	12	13
4	4	5	6	7	8	9	10	11	12	13	14
5	5	6	7	8	9	10	11	12	13	14	15
6	6	7	8	9	10	11	12	13	14	15	16
7	7	8	9	10	11	12	13	14	15	16	17
8	8	9	10	11	12	13	14	15	16	17	18
9	9	10	11	12	13	14	15	16	17	18	19
10	10	11	12	13	14	15	16	17	18	19	20

Use these steps to find a sum on the chart above.

- Find the first number (addend) in the column on the left. For example, 5.
- Find the second addend in the row along the top. For example, 3.
- Find the sum where the row and the column meet. The chart shows how to find $5 + 3 = 8$.

This chart shows every fact as an equation.

Basic Addition Facts										
0 + 0 = 0	1 + 0 = 1	2 + 0 = 2	3 + 0 = 3	4 + 0 = 4	5 + 0 = 5	6 + 0 = 6	7 + 0 = 7	8 + 0 = 8	9 + 0 = 0	10 + 0 = 10
0 + 1 = 1	1 + 1 = 2	2 + 1 = 3	3 + 1 = 4	4 + 1 = 5	5 + 1 = 6	6 + 1 = 7	7 + 1 = 8	8 + 1 = 9	9 + 1 = 10	10 + 1 = 11
0 + 2 = 2	1 + 2 = 3	2 + 2 = 4	3 + 2 = 5	4 + 2 = 6	5 + 2 = 7	6 + 2 = 8	7 + 2 = 9	8 + 2 = 10	9 + 2 = 11	10 + 2 = 12
0 + 3 = 3	1 + 3 = 4	2 + 3 = 5	3 + 3 = 6	4 + 3 = 7	5 + 3 = 8	6 + 3 = 9	7 + 3 = 10	8 + 3 = 11	9 + 3 = 12	10 + 3 = 13
0 + 4 = 4	1 + 4 = 5	2 + 4 = 6	3 + 4 = 7	4 + 4 = 8	5 + 4 = 9	6 + 4 = 10	7 + 4 = 11	8 + 4 = 12	9 + 4 = 13	10 + 4 = 14
0 + 5 = 5	1 + 5 = 6	2 + 5 = 7	3 + 5 = 8	4 + 5 = 9	5 + 5 = 10	6 + 5 = 11	7 + 5 = 12	8 + 5 = 13	9 + 5 = 14	10 + 5 = 15
0 + 6 = 6	1 + 6 = 7	2 + 6 = 8	3 + 6 = 9	4 + 6 = 10	5 + 6 = 11	6 + 6 = 12	7 + 6 = 13	8 + 6 = 14	9 + 6 = 15	10 + 6 = 16
0 + 7 = 7	1 + 7 = 8	2 + 7 = 9	3 + 7 = 10	4 + 7 = 11	5 + 7 = 12	6 + 7 = 13	7 + 7 = 14	8 + 7 = 15	9 + 7 = 16	10 + 7 = 17
0 + 8 = 8	1 + 8 = 9	2 + 8 = 10	3 + 8 = 11	4 + 8 = 12	5 + 8 = 13	6 + 8 = 14	7 + 8 = 15	8 + 8 = 16	9 + 8 = 17	10 + 8 = 18
0 + 9 = 9	1 + 9 = 10	2 + 9 = 11	3 + 9 = 12	4 + 9 = 13	5 + 9 = 14	6 + 9 = 15	7 + 9 = 16	8 + 9 = 17	9 + 9 = 18	10 + 9 = 19
0 + 10 = 10	1 + 10 = 11	2 + 10 = 12	3 + 10 = 13	4 + 10 = 14	5 + 10 = 15	6 + 10 = 16	7 + 10 = 17	8 + 10 = 18	9 + 10 = 19	10 + 10 = 20

Memorize Fewer than 121

There are 121 basic facts, but here are some ways to cut down the task. Use math knowledge to make memorizing some facts very easy.

- 0 plus any number is that number.
- 1 plus any number is the next number when you count.
- 2 plus any even number is the next even number.
- 2 plus any odd number is the next odd number.
- 10 plus any one-digit number is a teen number with the 1 in the tens place and the one-digit number in the ones place.
- If you know 2 + 3, you know 3 + 2. This takes care of half of the 121 facts.
- Once you memorize the doubles, the near doubles are easy to remember.
- Any number plus 9 is one less than that number plus ten.
- This leaves the ten most difficult facts to memorize.

+	0	1	2	3	4	5	6	7	8	9	10
0	0	1	2	3	4	5	6	7	8	9	10
1	1	2	3	4	5	6	7	8	9	10	11
2	2	3	4	5	6	7	8	9	10	11	12
3	3	4	5	6	7	8	9	10	11	12	13
4	4	5	6	7	8	9	10	11	12	13	14
5	5	6	7	8	9	10	11	12	13	14	15
6	6	7	8	9	10	11	12	13	14	15	16
7	7	8	9	10	11	12	13	14	15	16	17
8	8	9	10	11	12	13	14	15	16	17	18
9	9	10	11	12	13	14	15	16	17	18	19
10	10	11	12	13	14	15	16	17	18	19	20

Hints on Memorizing Addition Facts

1. Memorize the facts by saying the facts aloud. When you see 3 + 8, say "Three plus eight equals eleven."
2. Memorize a few facts at a time, 2 or 3 facts per day. Start with easier facts.
3. Practice saying the facts in reverse order, so you don't have to memorize so may facts: 8 + 5 = 13, 5 + 8 = 13.
4. Play addition fact games. For example, toss two dice and add the dots that come up. Make or buy addition facts bingo to play with a friend.
5. Make flash cards and use them by yourself or with friends and family.
6. Every day, review the facts you know or usually know.

Try It This Way

Practice your facts using a calculator.

For example, as you push the matching keys, say "3 + 5". Think of the answer and say "equals 8" as you press ENTER.

The display will show whether you were right!

Subtraction Facts

What Is Subtraction?

Subtraction is a mathematical operation in which you take a certain quantity away from another quantity. The amount left is called the **difference**.

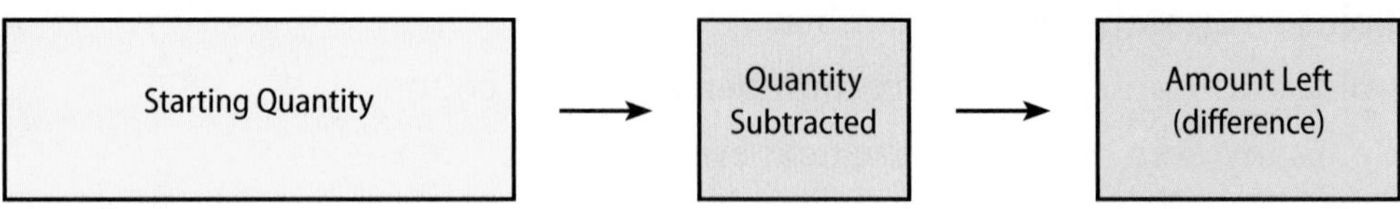

SEARCH

To see step-by-step videos of these problems, enter the page number into the SWadvantage.com Search Bar.

EXAMPLE 1

How many is 5 take away 3?

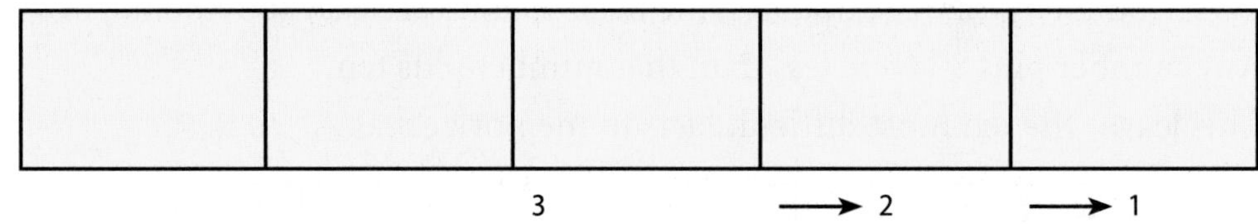

One way to find the answer is to count from right to left three places: 1, 2, 3. There are two rectangles left.

This method works fine for small numbers. It may not work well for large numbers.

$5 - 3 = 2$

EXAMPLE 2

Amaya had 7 apples. She ate 2 of the apples. How many are left?

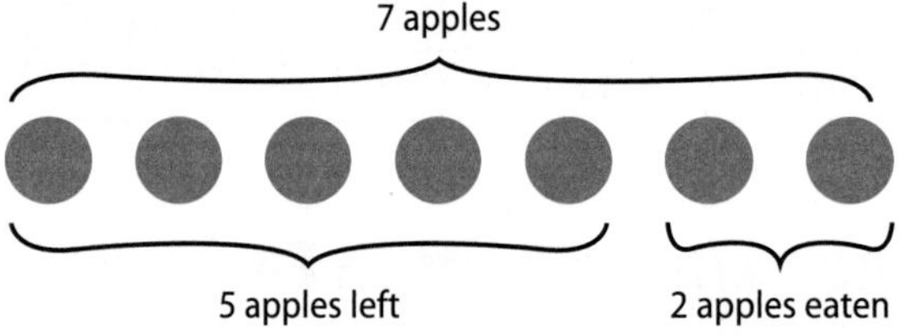

$7 - 2 = 5$

There are 5 apples left.

GOT TO KNOW!

Subtraction is . . .

a mathematical operation.

Use subtraction to find the amount left (difference) when you take one quantity from another quantity.

The subtraction sign is the minus symbol, –.

Subtract to Compare

When you compare quantities to find the amount left, or difference, you subtract. When a problem asks, "How many more?" you subtract.

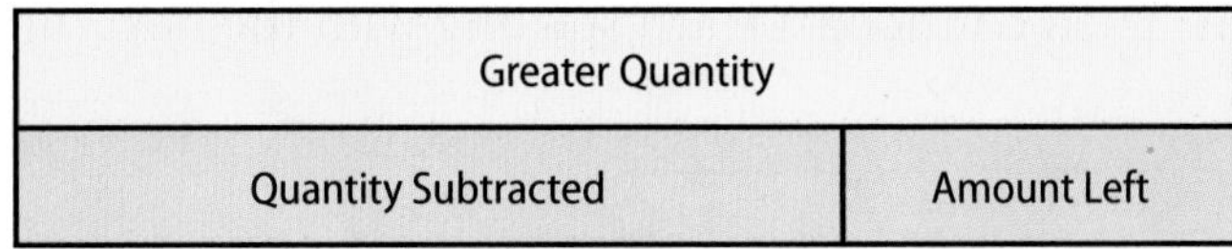

Tre has 7 cans to recycle. Jill has 4 cans. How many more does Tre have?

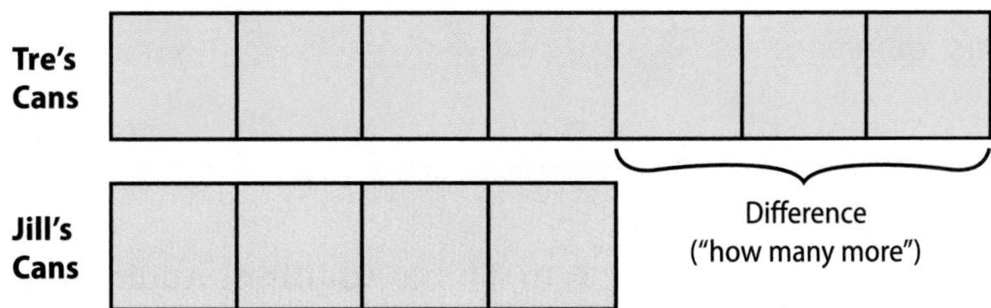

$7 - 4 = 3$ (or $7 = 4 + \underline{3}$)

Tre has 3 more cans than Jill.

Watch Out !

When a problem is about parts of a whole, it can be either addition or subtraction. Carefully identify what is missing. If it is a missing part, use subtraction. If it is a missing whole, use addition.

Subtract to Find the Missing Part

Subtract when you know the whole and a part, and you want to find the missing part.

Whole (known) –	
Part (known) =	Part (unknown)

Dhara has 10 sticky-note pads. Six of the pads are blue. The rest are yellow. How many pads are yellow?

$10 - 6 = 4$

Dhara has 4 yellow sticky-note pads.

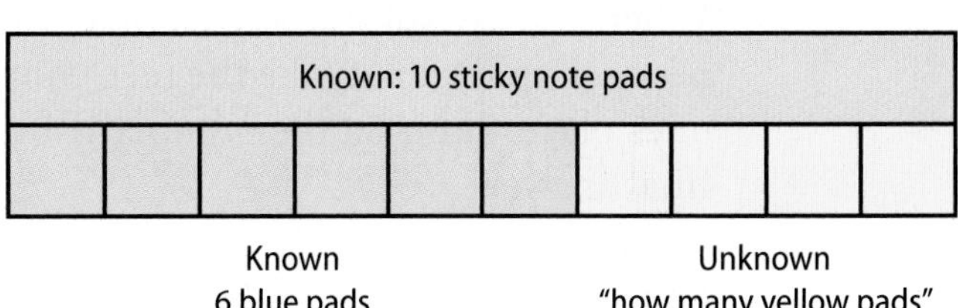

Strategies for Finding Differences

There are many strategies to help you figure the difference for subtraction.

One way to find a difference is to **Count Back**. Start with the quantity you are subtracting from. Then count backward starting with the next number.

Watch Out !

When you count back, start at the number you are subtracting from. Do not count that number, but the number one less as "one."

For example, to count back to solve $9 - 2$, you think "8 (one), 7 (two). So $9 - 2 = 7$.

EXAMPLE 5

Count Back **to solve $11 - 3$.**

Count back 3 numbers starting with 10 ⟶ 10, 9, 8.

11, 10, 9, 8, 7, 6, 5, 4, 3, 2, 1

three numbers difference

$11 - 3 = 8$

Another way to find the difference is to **Think Addition**. Addition is putting together, and subtraction is taking apart. If you want to find $12 - 9 = ?$, you can think $9 + 3 = 12$. So the missing number is 3, and $12 - 9 = 3$.

EXAMPLE 6

Use *Think Addition* to find $13 - 5 = ?$

$13 - 5 = ?$ and $5 + 8 = 13$

$13 - 5 = 8$

There are a number of ways you can **Use Tens** to subtract. Examples 7 and 8 show two of the ways.

When you are subtracting from a number in the teens, Use Tens to take the number apart. First take the teen number apart into 10 and the number in the ones place. Subtract the number from the 10. Then add what's left to get the final answer.

EXAMPLE 7

Use Tens **to find $15 - 8 = ?$**

Think: $15 = 10 + 5$	$10 + 5$
Subtract 8 from the 10.	$-\ 8$
Add the result to the 5.	$2 + 5 = 7$

$15 - 8 = 7$

When you are subtracting a number from 9 or 11, Use Tens and the One More or One Less method.

EXAMPLE 

a. *Use Tens* to find 11 − 6 = ?

Think: Eleven is 1 more than 10.

Subtract: 10 − 6 = 4

Add the 1 more: 4 + 1 = 5

11 − 6 = 5

b. *Use Tens* to find 9 − 7 = ?

Think: Nine is 1 less than 10.

Subtract: 10 − 7 = 3

Subtract the 1 less: 3 − 1 = 2

9 − 7 = 2

SEARCH

To see step-by-step videos of these problems, enter the page number into the SWadvantage.com Search Bar.

You can also **Use a Model**, such as a number line or ten frame, to subtract.

EXAMPLE 9

***Use a Model* to find 10 − 2.**

When you remove 2 counters from the ten frame, there are 8 counters left. When you count back 2 places on the number line, you end up at 8.

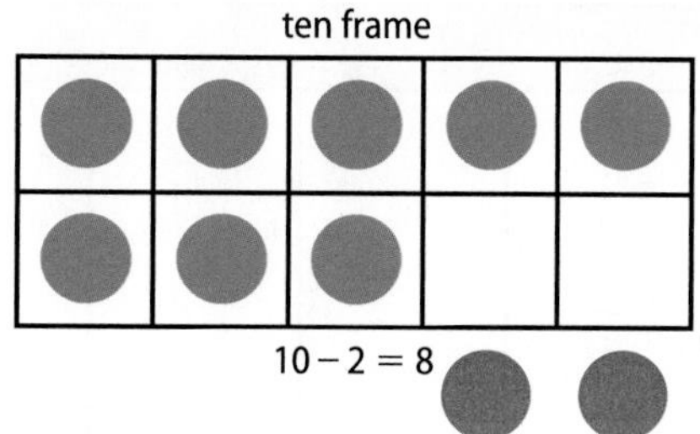

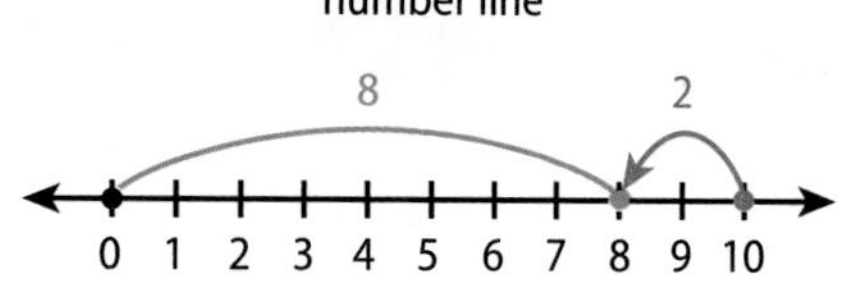

10 − 2 = 8

GOT TO KNOW!

Powerful Subtraction Strategies

If you can use these strategies, you will be quick and accurate in subtraction.

Think Addition
Use Tens

Memorizing Subtraction Facts

Although you can use strategies to figure out the difference in subtraction problems, you will be more powerful mathematically if you memorize the basic facts.

There are 121 basic subtraction facts. They are listed in the two charts below.

This chart organizes the numbers in columns and rows.

SEARCH

To see step-by-step videos of these problems, enter the page number into the SWadvantage.com Search Bar.

Basic Subtraction Facts

−	0	1	2	3	4	5	6	7	8	9	10
0	0										
1	1	0									
2	2	1	0								
3	3	2	1	0							
4	4	3	2	1	0						
5	5	4	3	2	1	0					
6	6	5	4	3	2	1	0				
7	7	6	5	4	3	2	1	0			
8	8	7	6	5	4	3	2	1	0		
9	9	8	7	6	5	4	3	2	1	0	
10	10	9	8	7	6	5	4	3	2	1	0

Use these steps to find a difference on the chart above.

- Find the first number (the whole) in the column on the left. For example, 8.
- Find the number subtracted in the row along the top. For example, 5.
- Find the difference where the row and the column meet. The chart shows how to find 8 − 5 = 3.

This chart shows the basic subtraction facts as equations.

Basic Subtraction Facts										
0−0=0										
1−0=1	1−1=0									
2−0=2	2−1=1	2−2=0								
3−0=3	3−1=2	3−2=1	3−3=0							
4−0=4	4−1=3	4−2=2	4−3=1	4−4=0						
5−0=5	5−1=4	5−2=3	5−3=2	5−4=1	5−5=0					
6−0=6	6−1=5	6−2=4	6−3=3	6−4=2	6−5=1	6−6=0				
7−0=7	7−1=6	7−2=5	7−3=4	7−4=3	7−5=2	7−6=1	7−7=0			
8−0=8	8−1=7	8−2=6	8−3=5	8−4=4	8−5=3	8−6=2	8−7=1	8−8=0		
9−0=9	9−1=8	9−2=7	9−3=6	9−4=5	9−5=4	9−6=3	9−7=2	9−8=1	9−9=0	
10−0=10	10−1=9	10−2=8	10−3=7	10−4=6	10−5=5	10−6=4	10−7=3	10−8=2	10−9=1	10−10=0

Memorize Fewer than 121

There are 121 basic facts, but here are some ways to cut down the task. Use math knowledge to make memorizing subtraction facts very easy.

- Any number minus 0 is itself.
- Any number minus itself is 0.
- Any number minus 1 is the previous counting number.
- Any even number minus 2 is the previous even number.
- Any odd number minus 2 is the previous odd number.
- Any teen number minus 10 is the digit in the ones place of the teen number.
- If you know $8 - 3 = 5$, you also know $8 - 5 = 3$. This takes care of half of the subtraction facts.
- Nine minus any number is one less than 10 minus the same number.

Practice your facts using a calculator.

For example, as you push the matching keys, say "13 minus 7." Think of the answer and say "equals 6" as you press ENTER.

The display will show whether you were right!

Hints on Memorizing Subtraction Facts

1. Memorize the facts by saying the whole fact aloud. When you see $8 - 3$, say "Eight minus three equals five."
2. Memorize a few facts at a time. Work on 2 or 3 facts per day. Start with the easier facts.
3. Practice saying the facts in reverse order, so you don't have to memorize so many facts: $9 - 4 = 5$, $9 - 5 = 4$.
4. Play subtraction fact games. For example, toss two dice and add the dots that come up. Then have a friend toss two dice and add the dots. Then subtract the smaller sum from the larger sum.

5. Make flash cards and use them by yourself or with friends and family.

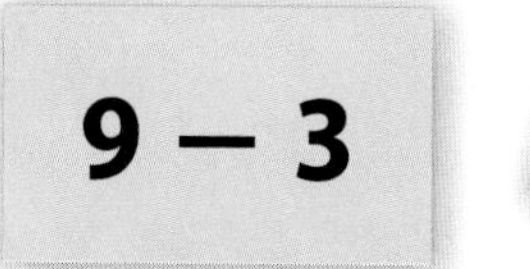

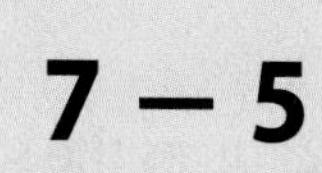

6. Every day, review the facts you know or usually know. Work on two new facts and play games to practice them.

Multiplication Facts

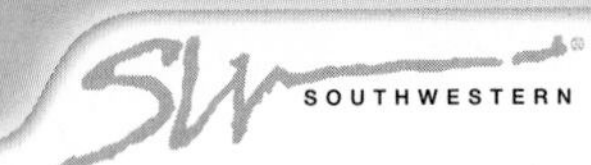

Watch Out!

Unlike addition and subtraction, the numbers in a multiplication problem do not mean two different amounts of the same category.

One number tells the number of equal groups. The other number tells the size of each equal group.

What Is Multiplication?

Multiplication is a mathematical operation in which a particular number of equal-sized groups are combined. The result is called the *product*. In the multiplication below, there are 3 groups of 4 rectangles. When the groups are combined, there are 12 rectangles.

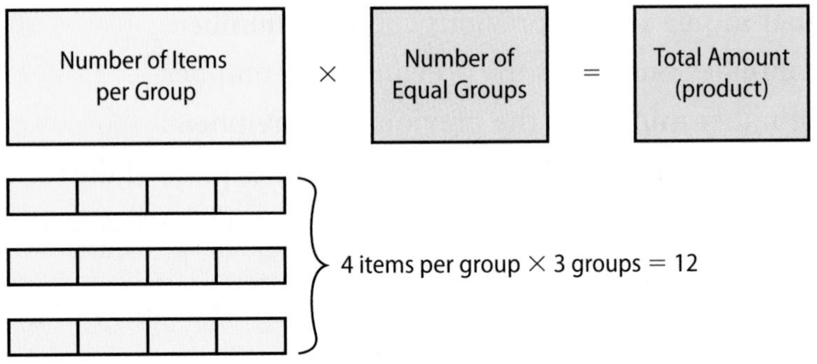

3×4 means the same thing as: $4 + 4 + 4 = 12$.

EXAMPLE 1

Kimi, Joe, and Bob each have two books. How many books do they have in all?

2 books per person	×	3 people	=	6 books

$2 \times 3 = 6$

There are 6 books in all.

To see step-by-step videos of these problems, enter the page number into the SWadvantage.com Search Bar.

GOT TO KNOW!

Multiplication is . . .

a mathematical operation. The product gives the same result as the sum of adding the number of items in each group. You can change any multiplication problem into an addition problem.

Multiplication	Addition
$5 \times 3 = 15$	$5 + 5 + 5 = 15$
5 items per group × 3 groups = 15	5 items per group + 5 items per group + 5 items per group = 15

Models for Multiplication

Three ways to model multiplication are: use counters, make an *array*, and skip count on a number line. An **array** is an arrangement of objects in rows and columns. Each row has the same number of objects.

3 groups of 2 counters

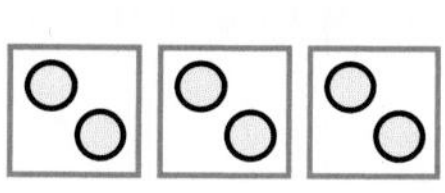

3 rows of 2

$3 \times 2 = 6$

3 jumps of 2 spaces

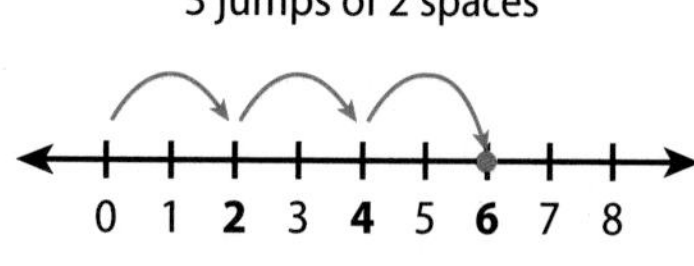

Watch Out !

In multiplication, all of the groups must be the same size.

$7 + 7 + 7 + 7 + 7 = 5 \times 7$

$7 + 7 + 7 + 7 + 8 = 4 \times 7$, plus 8

EXAMPLE 2

Javier's classroom has 4 rows of desks. There are 6 desks in each row. How many desks in all?

There are the same number of desks in each row. This is an equal groups problem, so you can multiply. Model the problem using an array.

$6 \times 4 = 24$

There are 24 desks in all.

EXAMPLE 3

Use a number line to find $3 \times 6 = ?$

3 jumps of 6 spaces

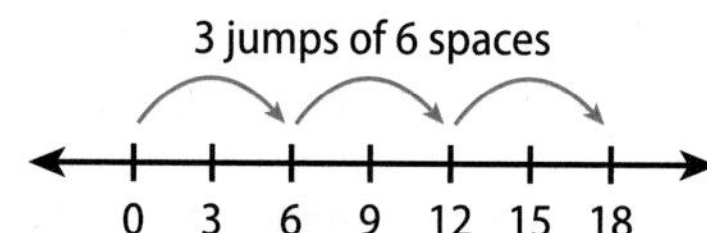

$3 \times 6 = 18$

Strategies for Finding Products

There are several strategies to help you find the product for multiplication problems.

One way to find a product is to use **Repeated Addition**. Because multiplication is a short way to do repeated addition (where you add the same number a certain number of times), you can always convert a multiplication problem to an addition problem and add.

So 4×8 can be rewritten as $8 + 8 + 8 + 8$.

SEARCH

To see step-by-step videos of these problems, enter the page number into the SWadvantage.com Search Bar.

EXAMPLE 4

Use repeated addition to find 3 × 7.

$$3 \times 7 = \underbrace{\underbrace{7 + 7}_{14} + 7}_{21}$$

$3 \times 7 = 21$

You can **Add or Subtract from a Known Fact** to find a product. Use the closest fact you know.

EXAMPLE 5

Add or subtract from a known fact to find 4 × 7.

Suppose you know one of these facts: $3 \times 7 = 21$ or $5 \times 7 = 35$.

METHOD 1

$3 \times 7 = 21$

Think: Since 3 is 1 less than 4, I need one more group of 7.

Add 7.

$21 + 7 = 28$

$4 \times 7 = 28$

METHOD 2

$5 \times 7 = 35$

Think: Since 5 is 1 more than 4, I need one less group of 7.

Subtract 7.

$35 - 7 = 28$

$4 \times 7 = 28$

Either method will work, but you may find it easier to add $21 + 7$.

You can use the **Take Apart** strategy when you know two simpler facts. Separate the multiplication into two smaller problems and add the results together.

EXAMPLE 6

Use the Take Apart strategy to find the product of 7×8.

Draw an array. Then shade the array so it shows 8×5 and 8×2. Find each product. Then add them together.

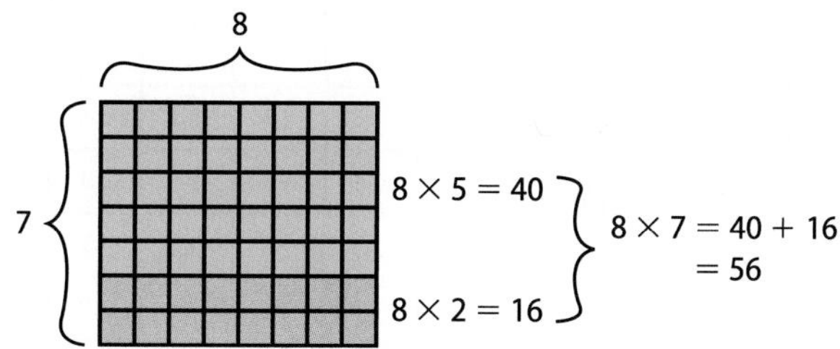

$7 \times 8 = 56$

You can **Switch Factors** in a multiplication problem and the product will not change. If you know that $6 \times 7 = 42$, you also know that $7 \times 6 = 42$.

EXAMPLE 7

Use Switch Factors to find 9×4.

The figure below shows that if you rotate (turn) an array you can describe it using a related multiplication fact.

$9 \times 4 = 36$

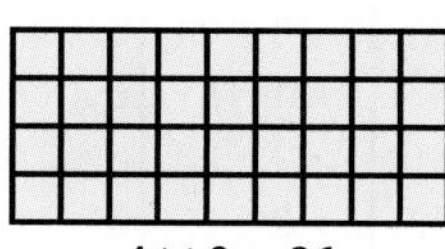

$4 \times 9 = 36$

9 rows of 4 is the same as 4 rows of 9.

$9 \times 4 = 36$

GOT TO KNOW!

Powerful Multiplication Strategies

If you can use these strategies, you'll not only be able to solve many basic facts, but it will help you solve more difficult multiplication problems.

Repeated Addition
Switch Factors
Take Apart

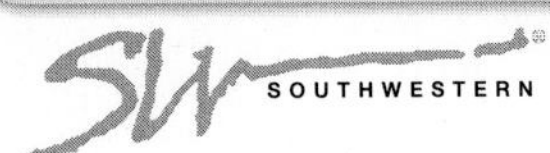

Memorizing Multiplication Facts

Although you can always add to find the answer to a multiplication problem, it is much quicker to simply recall a fact you have memorized.

There are 121 basic facts. They are listed in the two charts below.

The chart below organizes the numbers in columns and rows.

SEARCH

To see step-by-step videos of these problems, enter the page number into the SWadvantage.com Search Bar.

Basic Multiplication Facts

×	0	1	2	3	4	5	6	7	8	9	10
0	0	0	0	0	0	0	0	0	0	0	0
1	0	1	2	3	4	5	6	7	8	9	10
2	0	2	4	6	8	10	12	14	16	18	20
3	0	3	6	9	12	15	18	21	24	27	30
4	0	4	8	12	16	20	24	28	32	36	40
5	0	5	10	15	20	25	30	35	40	45	50
6	0	6	12	18	24	30	36	42	48	54	60
7	0	7	14	21	28	35	42	49	56	63	70
8	0	8	16	24	32	40	48	56	64	72	80
9	0	9	18	27	36	45	54	63	72	81	90
10	0	10	20	30	40	50	60	70	80	90	100

Use these steps to find a product on the chart above.

- Find the first number in the column on the left. For example, 4.
- Find the second number in the row along the top. For example, 3.
- Find the product where the row and the column meet. The chart shows how to find $4 \times 3 = 12$.

The chart below shows every fact as an equation.

Basic Multiplication Facts

zeros	$0 \times 0 = 0$	$1 \times 0 = 0$	$2 \times 0 = 0$	$3 \times 0 = 0$	$4 \times 0 = 0$	$5 \times 0 = 0$	$6 \times 0 = 0$	$7 \times 0 = 0$	$8 \times 0 = 0$	$9 \times 0 = 0$	$10 \times 0 = 0$
ones	$0 \times 1 = 0$	$1 \times 1 = 1$	$2 \times 1 = 2$	$3 \times 1 = 3$	$4 \times 1 = 4$	$5 \times 1 = 5$	$6 \times 1 = 6$	$7 \times 1 = 7$	$8 \times 1 = 8$	$9 \times 1 = 9$	$10 \times 1 = 10$
twos	$0 \times 2 = 0$	$1 \times 2 = 2$	$2 \times 2 = 4$	$3 \times 2 = 6$	$4 \times 2 = 8$	$5 \times 2 = 10$	$6 \times 2 = 12$	$7 \times 2 = 14$	$8 \times 2 = 16$	$9 \times 2 = 18$	$10 \times 2 = 20$
threes	$0 \times 3 = 0$	$1 \times 3 = 3$	$2 \times 3 = 6$	$3 \times 3 = 9$	$4 \times 3 = 12$	$5 \times 3 = 15$	$6 \times 3 = 18$	$7 \times 3 = 21$	$8 \times 3 = 24$	$9 \times 3 = 27$	$10 \times 3 = 30$
fours	$0 \times 4 = 0$	$1 \times 4 = 4$	$2 \times 4 = 8$	$3 \times 4 = 12$	$4 \times 4 = 16$	$5 \times 4 = 20$	$6 \times 4 = 24$	$7 \times 4 = 28$	$8 \times 4 = 32$	$9 \times 4 = 36$	$10 \times 4 = 40$
fives	$0 \times 5 = 0$	$1 \times 5 = 5$	$2 \times 5 = 10$	$3 \times 5 = 15$	$4 \times 5 = 20$	$5 \times 5 = 25$	$6 \times 5 = 30$	$7 \times 5 = 35$	$8 \times 5 = 40$	$9 \times 5 = 45$	$10 \times 5 = 50$
sixes	$0 \times 6 = 0$	$1 \times 6 = 6$	$2 \times 6 = 12$	$3 \times 6 = 18$	$4 \times 6 = 24$	$5 \times 6 = 30$	$6 \times 6 = 36$	$7 \times 6 = 42$	$8 \times 6 = 48$	$9 \times 6 = 54$	$10 \times 6 = 60$
sevens	$0 \times 7 = 0$	$1 \times 7 = 7$	$2 \times 7 = 14$	$3 \times 7 = 21$	$4 \times 7 = 28$	$5 \times 7 = 35$	$6 \times 7 = 42$	$7 \times 7 = 49$	$8 \times 7 = 56$	$9 \times 7 = 63$	$10 \times 7 = 70$
eights	$0 \times 8 = 0$	$1 \times 8 = 8$	$2 \times 8 = 16$	$3 \times 8 = 24$	$4 \times 8 = 32$	$5 \times 8 = 40$	$6 \times 8 = 48$	$7 \times 8 = 56$	$8 \times 8 = 64$	$9 \times 8 = 72$	$10 \times 8 = 80$
nines	$0 \times 9 = 0$	$1 \times 9 = 9$	$2 \times 9 = 18$	$3 \times 9 = 27$	$4 \times 9 = 36$	$5 \times 9 = 45$	$6 \times 9 = 54$	$7 \times 9 = 63$	$8 \times 9 = 72$	$9 \times 9 = 81$	$10 \times 9 = 90$
tens	$0 \times 10 = 0$	$1 \times 10 = 10$	$2 \times 10 = 20$	$3 \times 10 = 30$	$4 \times 10 = 40$	$5 \times 10 = 50$	$6 \times 10 = 60$	$7 \times 10 = 70$	$8 \times 10 = 80$	$9 \times 10 = 90$	$10 \times 10 = 100$

Memorize Fewer Than 121

There are 121 basic facts, but here are some ways to cut down the task.

- Any number times 0 is 0.
- Any number times 1 is itself.
- Any number times 10 is that number with a zero to its right.
- Any number times 2 is the double of that number.
  For example $2 \times 3 = 3 + 3$, or 6.
- The product of any number times 5 will always have 0 or 5 in the ones place.
- Four times a number is its double times 2.

$$\begin{aligned} 4 \times 3 &= 2(2 \times 3) \\ &= 2\,(6) \\ &= 12 \end{aligned}$$

- Flip the numbers. If you know $3 \times 7 = 21$, you also know that $7 \times 3 = 21$.
- Think "one group more" or "one group less." If you know that $3 \times 4 = 12$, you know that $4 \times 4 = 12 + 4 = 16$.

Try It This Way

Practice your facts using a calculator. For example, as you enter 9×6, think of the answer. Say "equals 54" as you push the = key. The display will show whether you were right.

Hints for Memorizing Multiplication Facts

1. Focus on the ways to memorize fewer than 121 facts.
2. Memorize a few facts at a time. Work on 2 or 3 facts per day. Start with the easier facts.
3. Memorize one set of times tables at a time. Work on the set until you have mastered it. Then move to another set.
4. Memorize the facts by saying the whole fact aloud. When you see 8×7, say "Eight times seven equals fifty-six."
5. Every day, review the facts you know or usually know. Practice them until they become automatic and always accurate.
6. Play multiplication fact games. For example, play multiplication facts bingo with some friends.
7. Make flash cards and use them on your own or with friends and family.

Division Facts

For help with long division and division with a remainder, go to *Dividing Whole Numbers* (p. 100).

What Is Division?

Division is a mathematical operation in which you arrange a larger quantity into smaller equal-sized groups. The number of equal-sized groups you can make is called the quotient.

Larger Quantity	÷	Size of Smaller Groups	=	Total Number of Smaller Groups (quotient)

EXAMPLE 1

Kelsey has 14 slices of bread to use for sandwiches. She uses 2 slices of bread for each sandwich. How many sandwiches can she make?

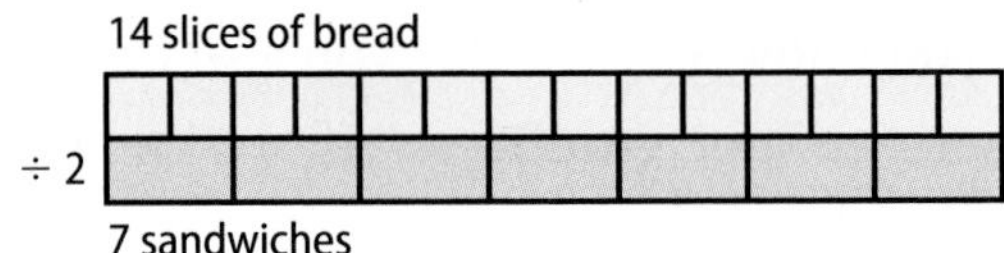

There are 7 groups of 2.

Kelsey can make 7 sandwiches.

Division Is . . .

a mathematical operation. Use division when you need to separate a larger amount into smaller, equal-size groups. The quotient gives the same result as repeated subtraction.

Division

$8 \div 4 = 2$

8 items divided into 4 equal-sized groups equals 2 groups of 4 items.

Subtraction

$8 - 4 = 4 - 4 = 0$

2 groups of 4

8 items minus 2 groups of 4 items

Relating Division to Multiplication

An important strategy for figuring the quotient for a division fact is **Think Multiplication**. Multiplication is combining equal groups. Division is separating into equal groups. So, division is the opposite, or inverse of, multiplication.

If you know $3 \times 5 = 15$, you also know $15 \div 5 = 3$ and $15 \div 3 = 5$.

EXAMPLE 2

Use multiplication to find the missing quotient: $21 \div 7 = ?$

Use a related multiplication fact. $3 \times \underline{7} = \underline{21}$

Use logical reasoning. Then $21 \div 7$ must be 3.

$21 \div 7 = 3$

SEARCH

To see step-by-step videos of these problems, enter the page number into the SWadvantage.com Search Bar.

Models for Division

Three ways to model division are: use counters, make an *array*, and skip count on a number line. An **array** is an arrangement of objects in rows and columns. Each row has the same number of objects.

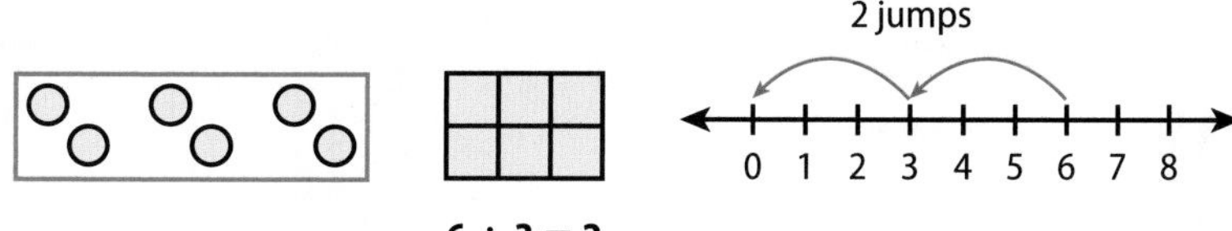

$6 \div 3 = 2$

EXAMPLE 3

Victor has 8 cookies to give to 4 friends. How many cookies does each friend get?

Use counters.

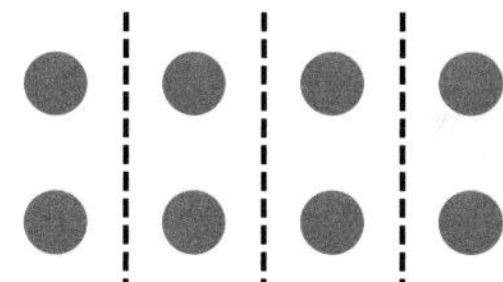

$8 \div 4 = 2$

Each friend gets 2 cookies.

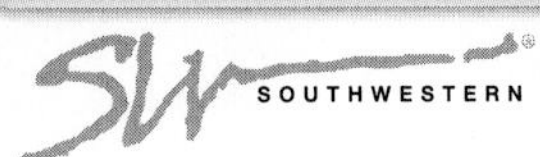

Models for Division

EXAMPLE 4

Use an array to find the missing quotient: 28 ÷ 7 = ?

Draw rows of 7 until you have 28. Then count the number of rows.

There are four rows, so 28 ÷ 7 = 4.

EXAMPLE 5

Divide 84 ÷ 2.

STEP 1 Use models to show 84.

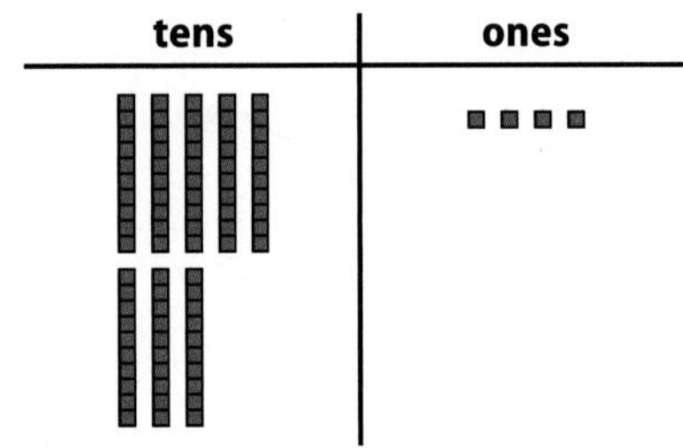

STEP 2 Group into 2 equal groups.

tens ones

There are 4 tens and 2 ones in each group, so 84 ÷ 2 = 42.

EXAMPLE 6

Divide $2\overline{)64}$.

Take the problem apart by writing it as shown below.

	Divide the tens.	Divide the ones.
	3 tens	3 tens 2 ones
$2\overline{)6 \text{ tens } 4 \text{ ones}}$	$2\overline{)6 \text{ tens } 4 \text{ ones}}$	$2\overline{)6 \text{ tens } 4 \text{ ones}}$

Express the quotient in standard form:

64 ÷ 2 = 32

GOT TO KNOW!

Division Statements

Read $2\overline{)64}$ as, "64 divided by 2." This means the same thing as "How many 2's are in 64?" You may see it expressed as, "2 goes into 64 how many times?"

Two other ways to write this statement are: 64 ÷ 2 and $\frac{64}{2}$.

Dividing by a 1-Digit Divisor

Another way to divide is to use the standard short division algorithm. An *algorithm* is a step-by-step plan for finding an answer.

EXAMPLE 7

Divide 96 ÷ 3.

STEP 1 Divide the tens.
Think: $3 \times 3 = 9$, so $9 \div 3 = 3$

$$3\overline{)96}\ \text{quotient } 3$$

STEP 2 Divide the ones.
Think: $3 \times 2 = 6$, so $6 \div 3 = 2$

$$3\overline{)96}\ \text{quotient } 32$$

$96 \div 3 = 32$

SEARCH

To see step-by-step videos of these problems, enter the page number into the SWadvantage.com Search Bar.

EXAMPLE 8

Divide 248 ÷ 4.

STEP 1 Think: $4 \times 6 = 24$, so $24 \div 4 = 6$

$$4\overline{)248}\ \text{quotient } 6$$

STEP 2 Think: $8 \div 4 = 2$

$$4\overline{)248}\ \text{quotient } 62$$

$248 \div 4 = 62$

EXAMPLE 9

Divide 1,015 ÷ 5.

STEP 1 $10 \div 5 = 2$

$$5\overline{)1{,}015}\ \text{quotient } 2$$

STEP 2 5 goes into 1 zero times.

$$5\overline{)1{,}015}\ \text{quotient } 20$$

STEP 3 $15 \div 5 = 3$

$$5\overline{)1{,}015}\ \text{quotient } 203$$

$1{,}015 \div 5 = 203$

Watch Out!

In Step 2, you cannot divide 5 into 1 and get a whole number answer. Write the zero and then divide 15 by 5.

GOT TO KNOW!

Check Division by Multiplying

Remember, division is the inverse, or opposite, of multiplication. Use multiplication to check:

$248 \div 4 = 62$

$$\begin{array}{r} 62 \\ \times\ 4 \\ \hline 248 \end{array}$$

$4 \times 2 = 8$

$4 \times 6 = 24$

Dividing by Zero

You cannot divide by zero.

12 ÷ 12 = 1

12 ÷ 2 = 6

12 ÷ 4 = 3

12 ÷ 3 = 4

12 ÷ 2 = 6

12 ÷ 12 = 1

12 ÷ 0 =

Oops, you cannot divide 12 into zero groups. There will always be at least 1 group of 12.

Memorizing Division Facts

Although you can always subtract to find the answer to a division problem, it is much quicker to simply recall a fact you have memorized.

There are 100 basic facts. They are listed in the two charts below.

The chart just below organizes the numbers in columns and rows.

Basic Division Facts

÷	1	2	3	4	5	6	7	8	9	10
1	1	2	3	4	5	6	7	8	9	10
2	2	4	6	8	10	12	14	16	18	20
3	3	6	9	12	15	18	21	24	27	30
4	4	8	12	16	20	24	28	32	36	40
5	5	10	15	20	25	30	35	40	45	50
6	6	12	18	24	30	36	42	48	54	60
7	7	14	21	28	35	42	49	56	63	70
8	8	16	24	32	40	48	56	64	72	80
9	9	18	27	36	45	54	63	72	81	90
10	10	20	30	40	50	60	70	80	90	100

Use these steps to find a quotient on the chart above. Suppose you want to know the quotient of 56 ÷ 8.

- Find the number you are dividing by, 8, in the top row.
- Move straight down to 56.
- Move left along the row to find the quotient, 7. The chart shows 56 ÷ 8 = 7.

The chart below shows every fact as an equation.

Basic Division Facts

ones	0 ÷ 1 = 0	1 ÷ 1 = 1	2 ÷ 1 = 2	3 ÷ 1 = 3	4 ÷ 1 = 4	5 ÷ 1 = 5	6 ÷ 1 = 6	7 ÷ 1 = 7	8 ÷ 1 = 8	9 ÷ 1 = 9	10 ÷ 1 = 10
twos	0 ÷ 2 = 0	2 ÷ 2 = 1	4 ÷ 2 = 2	6 ÷ 2 = 3	8 ÷ 2 = 4	10 ÷ 2 = 5	12 ÷ 2 = 6	14 ÷ 2 = 7	16 ÷ 2 = 8	18 ÷ 2 = 9	20 ÷ 2 = 10
threes	0 ÷ 3 = 0	3 ÷ 3 = 1	6 ÷ 3 = 2	9 ÷ 3 = 3	12 ÷ 3 = 4	15 ÷ 3 = 5	18 ÷ 3 = 6	21 ÷ 3 = 7	24 ÷ 3 = 8	27 ÷ 3 = 9	30 ÷ 3 = 10
fours	0 ÷ 4 = 0	4 ÷ 4 = 1	8 ÷ 4 = 2	12 ÷ 4 = 3	16 ÷ 4 = 4	20 ÷ 4 = 5	24 ÷ 4 = 6	28 ÷ 4 = 7	32 ÷ 4 = 8	36 ÷ 4 = 9	40 ÷ 4 = 10
fives	0 ÷ 5 = 0	5 ÷ 5 = 1	10 ÷ 5 = 2	15 ÷ 5 = 3	20 ÷ 5 = 4	25 ÷ 5 = 5	30 ÷ 5 = 6	35 ÷ 5 = 7	40 ÷ 5 = 8	45 ÷ 5 = 9	50 ÷ 5 = 10
sixes	0 ÷ 6 = 0	6 ÷ 6 = 1	12 ÷ 6 = 2	18 ÷ 6 = 3	24 ÷ 6 = 4	30 ÷ 6 = 5	36 ÷ 6 = 6	42 ÷ 6 = 7	48 ÷ 6 = 8	54 ÷ 6 = 9	60 ÷ 6 = 10
sevens	0 ÷ 7 = 0	7 ÷ 7 = 1	14 ÷ 7 = 2	21 ÷ 7 = 3	28 ÷ 7 = 4	35 ÷ 7 = 5	42 ÷ 7 = 6	49 ÷ 7 = 7	56 ÷ 7 = 8	63 ÷ 7 = 9	70 ÷ 7 = 10
eights	0 ÷ 8 = 0	8 ÷ 8 = 1	16 ÷ 8 = 2	24 ÷ 8 = 3	32 ÷ 8 = 4	40 ÷ 8 = 5	48 ÷ 8 = 6	56 ÷ 8 = 7	64 ÷ 8 = 8	72 ÷ 8 = 9	80 ÷ 8 = 10
nines	0 ÷ 9 = 0	9 ÷ 9 = 1	18 ÷ 9 = 2	27 ÷ 9 = 3	36 ÷ 9 = 4	45 ÷ 9 = 5	54 ÷ 9 = 6	63 ÷ 9 = 7	72 ÷ 9 = 8	81 ÷ 9 = 9	90 ÷ 9 = 10
tens	0 ÷ 10 = 0	10 ÷ 10 = 1	20 ÷ 10 = 2	30 ÷ 10 = 3	40 ÷ 10 = 4	50 ÷ 10 = 5	60 ÷ 10 = 6	70 ÷ 10 = 7	80 ÷ 10 = 8	90 ÷ 10 = 9	100 ÷ 10 = 10

Memorize Fewer Than 100

If you memorize the division facts up to 100 ÷ 10, there are 100 facts to remember. Here are some ways to reduce the number of facts you need to memorize.

- Any number divided by 1 is the number itself.
- Any number divided by itself is 1.
- When a number that ends in zero is divided by 10, the quotient is the number without the zero. For example, 50 ÷ 10 = 5.
- Pairs of facts are related. If you know that 15 ÷ 3 = 5, then you know that 15 ÷ 5 = 3.

Hints for Memorizing Division Facts

1. Focus on the ways to memorize fewer than 100 facts.
2. Use the relationship of multiplication to division. To remember 10 ÷ 2 = 5, think 5 × 2 = 10.
3. After you have memorized the easy facts, such as 4 ÷ 2 = 2, memorize only 2 or 3 new facts per day.
4. Memorize the facts by saying the whole fact aloud. When you see 56 ÷ 8, say "Fifty-six divided by eight equals seven."
5. Every day, review the facts you know or usually know. Practice them until they become automatic and you are always accurate.
6. Make flash cards and use them on your own or with friends and family.
7. Play division fact games such as "Beat the Clock." Use your flash cards and time how long it takes you to say a set of facts. Try this again the next day and see if you can beat your previous time.
8. Use a calculator. Enter the fact, such as 45 ÷ 5. Before you press ENTER or =, say the product. Then press ENTER to see if you are correct.

To see step-by-step videos of these problems, enter the page number into the SWadvantage.com Search Bar.

Fact Families

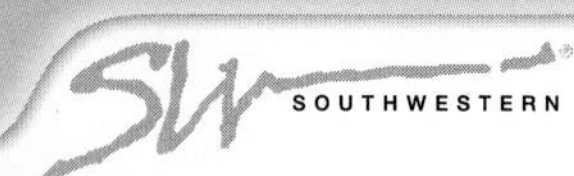

Addition and Subtraction Fact Families

Fact families are sets of related facts that use the same numbers. There are addition-subtraction fact families and multiplication-division fact families.

An addition-subtraction fact family usually contains four facts. For example, you can use the numbers in $4 + 3 = 7$ to form 2 addition facts and 2 subtraction facts.

$4 + 3 = 7$ $3 + 4 = 7$ $7 - 4 = 3$ $7 - 3 = 4$

When the same two numbers are added, there are only two facts in the fact family. For example, you can use the numbers in $2 + 2 = 4$ to form 1 addition fact and 1 subtraction fact.

$2 + 2 = 4$ $4 - 2 = 2$

SEARCH

To see step-by-step videos of these problems, enter the page number into the SWadvantage.com Search Bar.

EXAMPLE 1

Look at the figure below. List the four related facts for the figure's fact family.

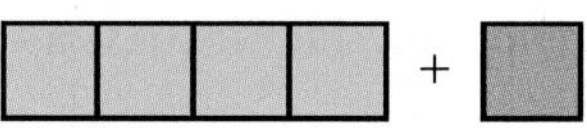

The figure shows 4 plus 1 more.

It belongs to the fact family:

$4 + 1 = 5$ $1 + 4 = 5$ $5 - 4 = 1$ $5 - 1 = 4$

Multiplication and Division Fact Families

A multiplication-division fact family usually contains four facts. Look at the fact family for $3 \times 2 = 6$. The same three numbers are used to form 2 multiplication facts and 2 division facts.

$3 \times 2 = 6$ $2 \times 3 = 6$ $6 \div 2 = 3$ $6 \div 3 = 2$

When the same two numbers are multiplied, there are only two facts in the fact family. Look at the fact family for $3 \times 3 = 9$.

$3 \times 3 = 9$ $9 \div 3 = 3$

Watch Out!

You cannot "flip" the division facts as you do the multiplication facts.

$2 \times 3 = 6$

$3 \times 2 = 6$

$6 \div 2 = 3$, but

$2 \div 6 \neq 3$.

The related division facts are $6 \div 2 = 3$ and $6 \div 3 = 2$.

EXAMPLE 2

Rearrange the numbers in this multiplication fact to make another multiplication fact and two division facts.

$2 \times 4 = 8$

$4 \times 2 = 8$ $8 \div 2 = 4$ $8 \div 4 = 2$

Inverse Operations

When operations perform opposite tasks, they are called **inverse operations**.

Addition combines and subtraction takes apart. They are inverse operations.

$2 + 1 = 3$ $3 - 1 = 2$

Multiplication combines equal groups, and division separates into equal groups. They are inverse operations.

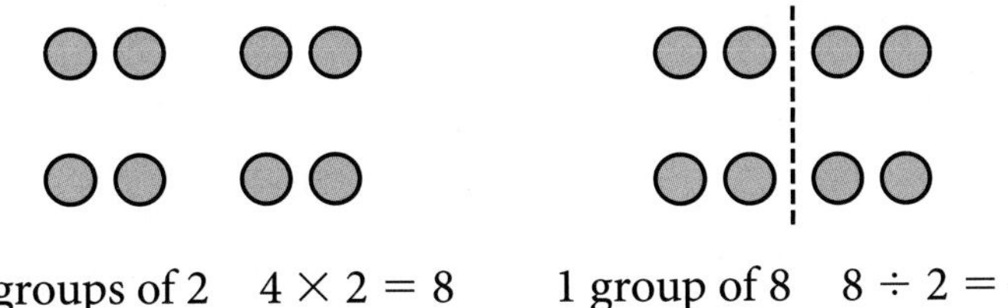

4 groups of 2 $4 \times 2 = 8$ 1 group of 8 $8 \div 2 = 4$

EXAMPLE 3

Use inverse operations to find each answer.

a. $\mathbf{8 - 2 = 6}$
$\mathbf{6 + 2 = ?}$

Addition undoes subtraction. The sum is 8.

b. $\mathbf{150 + 75 = 225}$
$\mathbf{225 - 75 = ?}$

Subtraction undoes addition. The difference is 150.

c. $\mathbf{12 \times 3 = 36}$
$\mathbf{36 \div 3 = ?}$

Division undoes multiplication. The quotient is 12.

Fact Families and Inverse Operations

A **fact family** is a group of related facts. As shown by the fact families below, **inverse operations** undo each other.

Addition and Subtraction	Multiplication and Division
$6 + 3 = 9 \longrightarrow 9 - 3 = 6$	$5 \times 4 = 20 \longrightarrow 20 \div 4 = 5$
$3 + 6 = 9 \longrightarrow 9 - 6 = 3$	$4 \times 5 = 20 \longrightarrow 20 \div 5 = 4$

Adding Numbers Greater Than 10

Addition is a mathematical operation in which the value of two or more numbers is calculated. The numbers added are called **addends**. The total of the addends is the **sum**.

32	addend
+ 25	addend
57	sum

You can use what you know about addition facts and strategies to combine addends greater than ten and to add three or more addends.

For example, in the *Make Ten* strategy, you break apart one addend to make tens, which are easy to add. Use a variation of the *Make Ten* strategy to add 17 + 18.

Think: 18 is 2 less than 20, which is 2 tens. I could make tens.

Regroup 17 as 10 + 5 + 2.	17 + 18
Add 2 + 18 first.	10 + 5 + 2 + 18
Add the tens: 10 + 20 = 30. Add 5 more: 35.	10 + 5 + 20

17 + 18 = 35

Need More HELP

For more about the *Make Ten* strategy and other addition strategies, go to *Addition Facts* (p. 56).

EXAMPLE 1

Add 47 + 24.

Think: 47 is close to 50. 50 is 5 tens, which would be easy to add.
Count On to make 50: 47–48–49–50, so 47 + 3 = 50.

Regroup 24 as 3 + 21.	47 + 24
Add 47 + 3 = 50.	47 + 3 + 21
Add. 50 + 20 = 70. Add 1 more: 71.	50 + 21

47 + 24 = 71

Make the Addition Easier

You can break addends apart into smaller numbers that are easy to add.

38 + 13 = 38 + 2 + 11 = 40 + 11 = 51

You can arrange the addends in any order.

98 + 43 + 2 = 98 + 2 + 43 = 98 + 2 + 43 = 100 + 43 = 143

EXAMPLE 2

Add 4 + 8 + 6 + 3 + 9 + 2.

The *Make Tens* strategy is good for adding several 1-digit numbers. Look for combinations of numbers with a sum of 10.

$4 + 8 + 6 + 3 + 9 + 2$

10 10 10 + 2 = 32

Think: 4 + 6 = 10

8 + 2 = 10

3 + 9 = 10 + 2

10 + 10 + 10 + 2 = 32

4 + 8 + 6 + 3 + 9 + 2 = 32

SEARCH

To see step-by-step videos of these problems, enter the page number into the SWadvantage.com Search Bar.

EXAMPLE 3

Add 124 + 351.

Use place value to think about the problem.

1 hundred	2 tens	4 ones
+ 3 hundreds	5 tens	1 one
4 hundreds	7 tens	5 ones

124 + 351 = 475

Watch Out !

Before you reorder the addends, count how many there are. Count again after you reorder to be certain you have the same number of addends.

EXAMPLE 4

Add 257 + 365.

Find the largest numbers within the problem that you can add easily. Then break the numbers apart into multiples of 5 and 10.

Think: It would be easy to add 250 + 350.

Regroup 257 as 250 + 5 + 2.	(250 + 5 + 2) + 365
Regroup 365 as 350 + 10 + 5.	(250 + 5 + 2) + (350 + 10 + 5)
Reorder the addends so you can add easily.	(250 + 350) + 10 + 5 + 5 + 2
Add 250 + 350.	600 + 10 + 5 + 5 + 2
Add 10 + 5 + 5.	600 + 20 + 2
Add 600 + 20 + 2.	622

257 + 365 = 622

Regrouping

Each place in the base-10 number system can contain only one digit (0 through 9). When the sum of two or more numbers is 10 or more, you need to *regroup*. When you **regroup**, you organize a value in a different way and rename it. The number's name changes, but its value remains the same.

For example, when you write the addition fact 6 + 6 = 12, the 12 ones are regrouped as 1 ten and 2 ones, or twelve.

$$\begin{array}{r} 6 \\ +\ 6 \\ \hline 12 \end{array}$$

12 ones = 1 ten and 2 ones

Need More HELP

In addition, *regrouping* is sometimes called *carrying* because part of a renamed value is "carried" to the next higher place value.

Modeling a problem using Base 10 Blocks can help you understand how to regroup larger numbers. Suppose you want to add 34 + 28.

Model 34 using 3 tens blocks and 4 ones blocks.

Model 28 using 2 tens blocks and 8 ones blocks.

Add the ones: 4 + 8 = 12 ones. Regroup 12 ones as 1 tens block and 2 ones blocks.

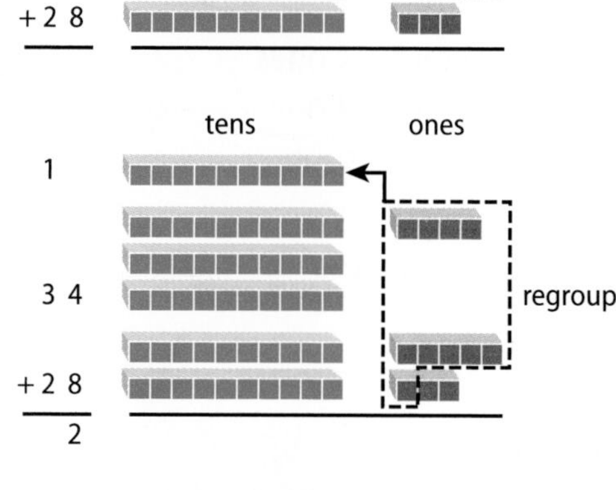

Add the tens. 1 + 3 + 2 = 6 tens. Now you have 6 tens blocks and 2 ones blocks.

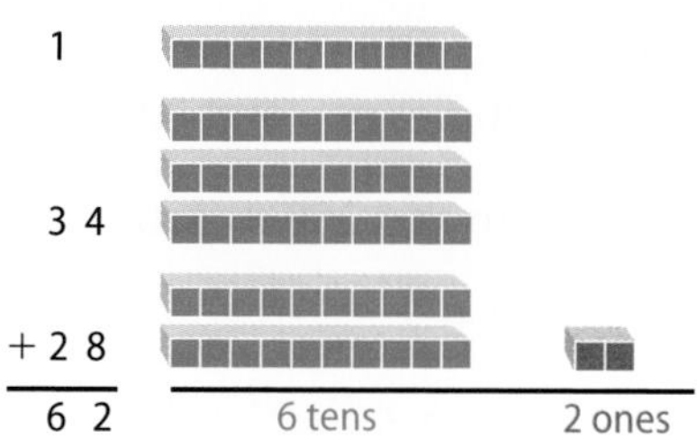

34 + 28 = 62

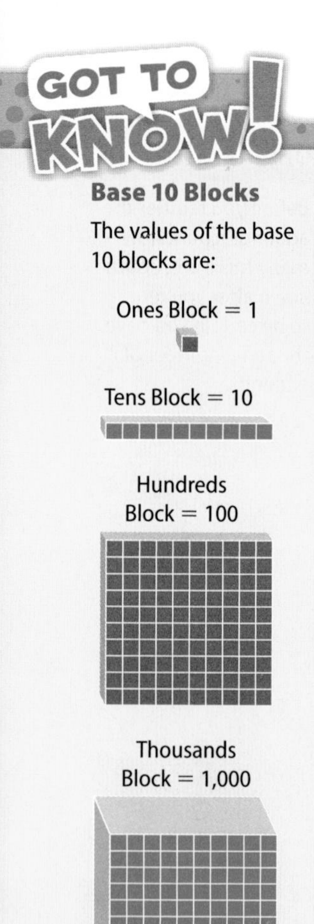

Once you understand how to regroup the ones, you can use the same method to regroup the tens or the hundreds. You can use a simpler model, like the one shown below.

EXAMPLE 5

Model adding 107 + 46.

$$\begin{array}{r} {\scriptstyle 1} \\ 107 \\ +\ 46 \\ \hline 153 \end{array}$$

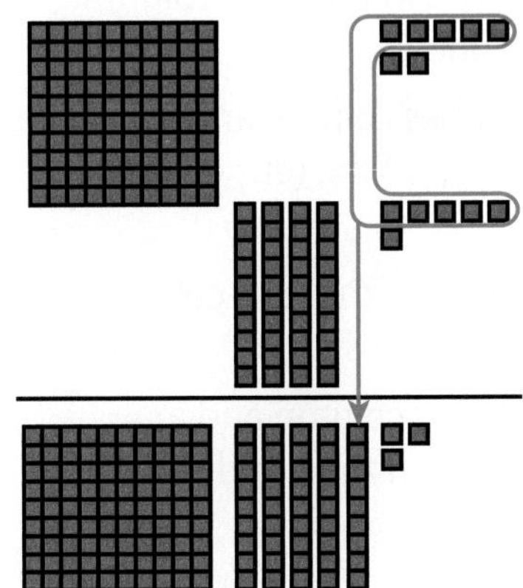

Regroup 10 ones as 1 ten.
Now you have 1 hundreds block, 5 tens blocks, and 3 ones blocks.

$107 + 46 = 153$

Need More HELP

In Example 5, when adding the tens column, you say $1 + 4 = 5$ but you are actually adding $10 + 40 = 50$.

SEARCH

To see step-by-step videos of these problems, enter the page number into the SWadvantage.com Search Bar.

EXAMPLE 6

a. In the problem below, 8 hundreds + 6 hundreds = 14 hundreds. How will you regroup?

$$\begin{array}{r} \mathbf{1{,}824} \\ +\ \ \mathbf{651} \\ \hline \mathbf{75} \end{array}$$

Regroup 14 hundreds as 1 thousand and 4 hundreds.

8 hundreds

6 hundreds

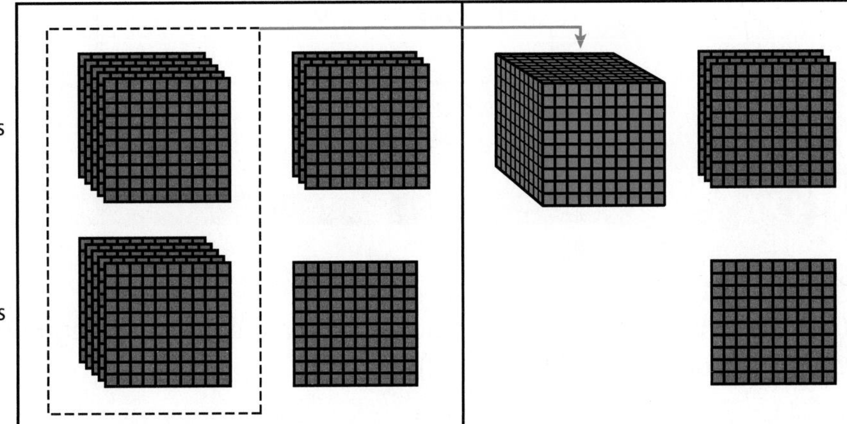

1 thousand
4 hundreds

b. What is the sum of the problem in part (a) above?

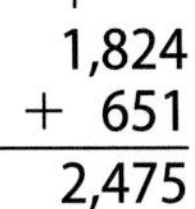

$$\begin{array}{r} {\scriptstyle 1} \\ 1{,}824 \\ +\ \ 651 \\ \hline 2{,}475 \end{array}$$

The sum is 2,475.

Using a Place-Value Chart

You may find it helpful to write the problem on a place-value chart. This can make it easier to keep the columns straight and see how to regroup.

Need More HELP

For more about the base ten system and place value, go to *Place Value* (pp. 40, 42, 44).

EXAMPLE 7

Use a place-value chart to find the sum 731 + 569.

STEP 1 Add the numbers in the ones column:
1 + 9 = 10 ones

Write 0 in the ones column and a small 1 at the top of the tens column.

	H	T	O
	7	$^{1}3$	1
+	5	6	9
			0

STEP 2 Add the numbers in the tens column:
1 + 3 + 6 = 10 tens

Write 0 in the tens column and a small 1 at the top of the hundreds column.

	H	T	O
	$^{1}7$	$^{1}3$	1
+	5	6	9
		0	0

STEP 3 Add the numbers in the hundreds column: 1 + 7 + 5 = 13 hundreds

Write 3 in the hundreds column and a small 1 at the top of the thousands column.

	T	H	T	O
	1	$^{1}7$	$^{1}3$	1
+		5	6	9
		3	0	0

STEP 4 Add the numbers in the thousands column.

731 + 569 = 1,300

	T	H	T	O
	1	$^{1}7$	$^{1}3$	1
+		5	6	9
	1	3	0	0

SEARCH

To see step-by-step videos of these problems, enter the page number into the SWadvantage.com Search Bar.

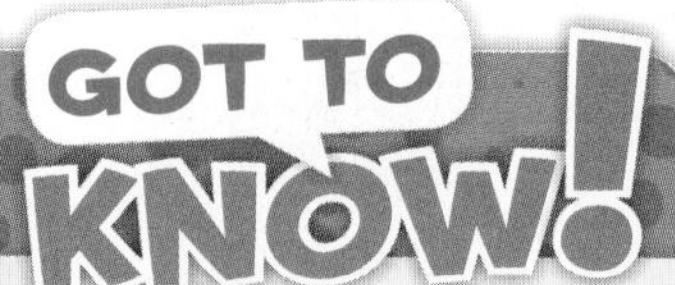

Regrouping

When the sum of two or more numbers is 10 or more, you must regroup. When you *regroup*, you organize a value in a different way and *rename* it.

```
   11
  238   8 + 3 = 11          Regroup 11 as 1 ten and 1 one.
+ 193   1 + 3 + 9 = 13      Regroup 13 as 1 hundred and 3 tens.
  431
```

Using the Standard Addition Algorithm

EXAMPLE 8

Use the standard algorithm to add 768 + 395 + 288.

- Line up the numbers so the digits with the same place value are in the same column.
- Add the ones: 8 + 5 + 8 = 21 ones. Regroup 21 ones as 2 tens and 1 one.
- Add the tens: 2 + 6 + 9 + 8 = 25 tens. Regroup 25 tens as 2 hundreds and 5 tens.
- Add the hundreds: 2 + 7 + 3 + 2 = 14 hundreds. Regroup 14 hundreds as 1 thousand and 4 hundreds.

$$\begin{array}{r} {\scriptstyle 1\,2\,2} \\ 768 \\ 395 \\ +\ 288 \\ \hline 1{,}451 \end{array}$$

768 + 395 + 288 = 1,451

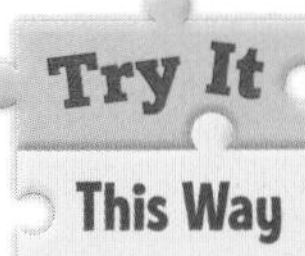

You may find it helpful to use graph paper when using the standard algorithm. Write each digit in one grid square. Work as neatly as you can. This will help you:

- align addends by their place value,
- add only numbers with the same place value, and
- insert the regroup number above the correct column.

EXAMPLE 9

294 fans of the home team and 135 fans of the visiting team attended the game. How many fans were at the game in all? Solve the problem and check your answer.

- Add to find the total number of fans. 294 + 135
- Line up the numbers so the digits with the same place value are in the same column.
- Add the ones. 4 + 5 = 9. Since 9 < 10, you do not need to regroup.
- Add the tens. 9 + 3 = 12. Regroup.
- Add the hundreds. 1 + 2 + 1 = 4. Since 4 < 10, you do not need to regroup.

$$\begin{array}{r} {\scriptstyle 1} \\ 294 \\ +\ 135 \\ \hline 429 \end{array}$$

CHECK Round the addends to the nearest 50 to see if the sum is reasonable.

294 rounds to 300 135 rounds to 150
300 + 150 = 450
The rounded answer of 450 is close to 429. The sum is reasonable. ✔

There were 429 fans at the game.

For help with rounding, go to *Rounding Whole Numbers* (p. 50).

Subtracting Whole Numbers

Subtracting from Numbers Greater Than 20

Subtraction is a mathematical operation in which the value of one number is taken away from the value of another number. In subtraction, a **subtrahend** is taken from a **minuend** to find a **difference**.

32	minuend
− 25	subtrahend
7	difference

You can use what you know about subtraction facts and strategies to subtract from numbers greater than 20.

Need More HELP

For help with the *Use Tens* strategy, go to *Subtraction Facts* (p. 62).

For example, in the *Use Tens* strategy you can break a number apart to make a ten, which is easy to subtract from. Use this variation of the *Make Ten* strategy to subtract 27 − 8.

Think: 8 is 2 less than 10, and 20 is 2 tens.

	27 − 8
Regroup 27 as 17 + 10.	(17 + 10) − 8
Change the grouping.	17 + (10 − 8)
Subtract 10 − 8.	17 + 2
Add 17 + 2.	19

27 − 8 = 19

EXAMPLE 1

Solve 34 − 16.

Think: It would be easy to subtract 20 − 16. I could regroup 34.

	34 − 16
Regroup 34 as 20 + 14.	20 + 14 − 16
Reorder the addends.	14 + (20 − 16)
Subtract.	14 + 4
Add.	18

34 − 16 = 18

Making Subtraction Easier

You can break subtrahends apart into smaller numbers that are easy to subtract.

42 − 16 = (20 + 22) − 16

Reorder the addends and subtract.

22 + (20 − 16)

22 + 4 = 26

42 − 16 = 26

EXAMPLE 2

Subtract 987 − 456.

Use place value to think about the problem.

9 hundreds	8 tens	7 ones
− 4 hundreds	5 tens	6 ones
5 hundreds	3 tens	1 one

987 − 456 = 531

SEARCH

To see step-by-step videos of these problems, enter the page number into the SWadvantage.com Search Bar.

EXAMPLE 3

Subtract 67 − 28.

Use the *Think Addition* strategy.

Think: 28 + ? = 67
28 + 2 = 30
30 + 37 = 67
Think: I added 2 to 28, so I need to add 2 to 37.
37 + 2 = 39
28 + 39 = 67
So: 67 − 28 = 39

67 − 28 = 39

Need More HELP

For help with the *Think Addition* or the *Count Back* strategy, go to *Subtraction Facts* (p. 62).

EXAMPLE 4

Solve 448 − 395.

Use the *Count Back* strategy.

Start with 448 and count back by tens.

Counted back 5 tens, or 50. 438, 428, 418, 408, 398

Start with 397 and count back by ones.

Counted back 3 ones, or 3. 397, 396, 395

50 + 3 = 53

448 − 395 = 53

CHECK Add.
$$\begin{array}{r} {}^{1}395 \\ +\ 53 \\ \hline 448 \end{array}$$ ✔

Regrouping

Need More HELP

In subtraction, regrouping is sometimes called "trading." This term means the same thing as *regrouping*.

When the subtrahend is greater than the minuend, you need to *regroup* the value in the next higher place so you can subtract. When you **regroup**, you organize a value in a different way and rename it. The number's name changes, but its value remains the same.

For example, suppose you want to subtract 14 − 8. You cannot subtract 8 from 4, so you regroup 14 as 14 ones. Now you can subtract.

14	1 ten	4 ones	14 ones
− 8		8 ones	8 ones
6			6 ones

Modeling a problem using Base 10 Blocks can help you understand how to regroup larger numbers. Suppose you want to subtract 92 − 47.

Model 92 using 9 tens blocks and 2 ones blocks.

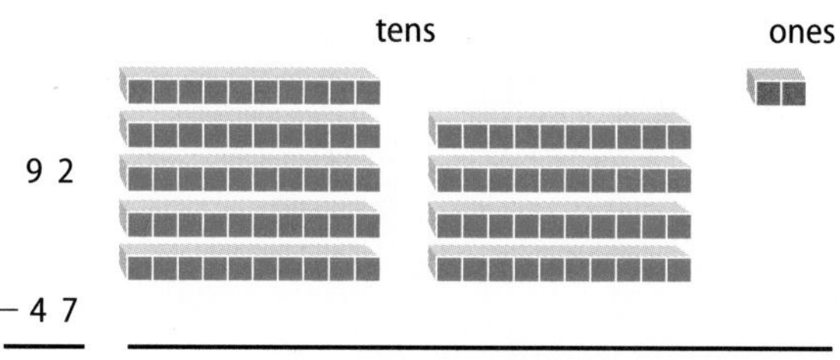

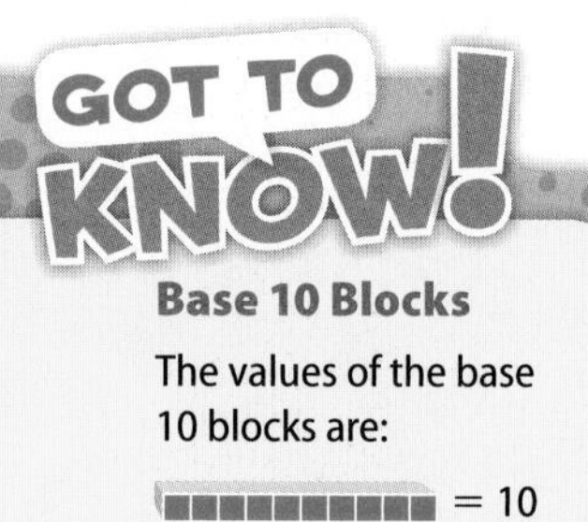

Base 10 Blocks

The values of the base 10 blocks are:

= 10

= 1

Model 47 using 4 tens blocks and 7 ones blocks.

Subtract the ones: 2 − 7. Since 2 < 7, regroup 1 tens block as 10 ones blocks. Now you have 8 tens and 12 ones. 12 − 7 = 5.

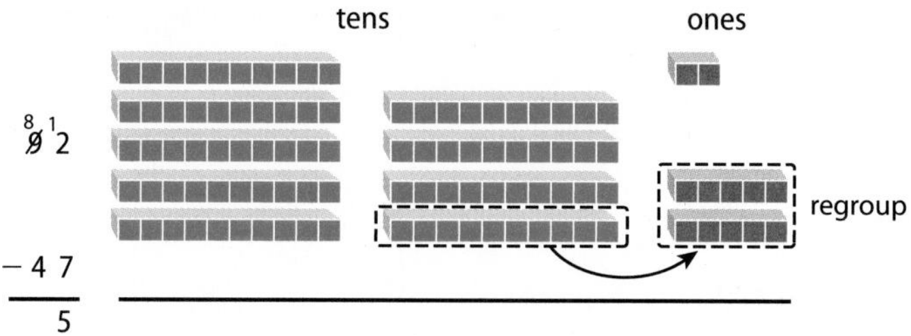

Subtract the tens. 8 tens − 4 tens = 4 tens

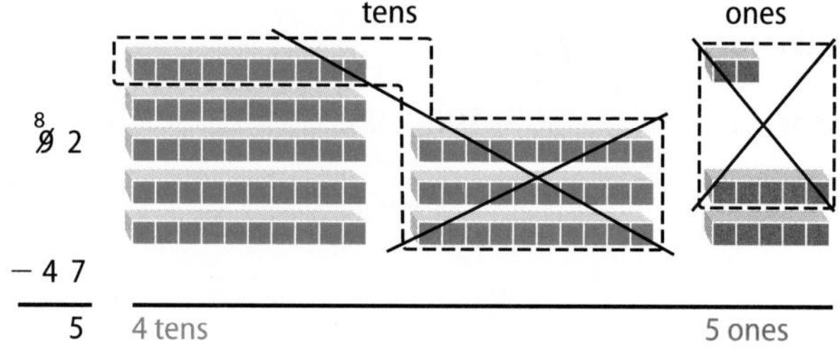

To see step-by-step videos of these problems, enter the page number into the SWadvantage.com Search Bar.

Now you have 4 tens and 5 ones.

92 − 47 = 45

Once you understand how to regroup tens so you can subtract ones, you can use the same method to regroup hundreds to subtract tens, thousands to subtract hundreds, and so on. You can use a simpler model, like the one shown below.

EXAMPLE 5

Model subtracting 72 − 58.

```
   1
  ⁶72
− 58
  14
```

STEP 1

8 > 2. Regroup 70 tens as 6 tens and 10 ones. You now have 10 ones + 2 ones = 12 ones, and you can subtract.

STEP 2

Subtract 8 ones.
Subtract 5 tens.

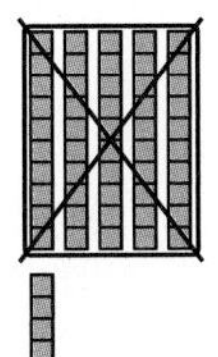

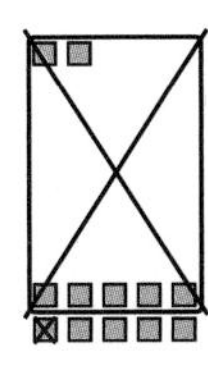

> **Watch Out!**
>
> When you regroup the 70 tens, completely remove one of the tens and replace it with 10 ones, which has exactly the same value.

EXAMPLE 6

Model subtracting 600 − 327.

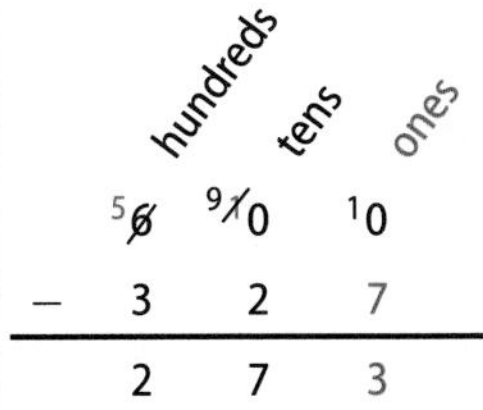

Regroup 6 hundreds as 5 hundreds and 10 tens. Regroup 10 tens as 9 tens and 10 ones. Now you have 5 hundreds, 9 tens, and 10 ones.

Subtract 7 ones, 2 tens, and 3 hundreds.

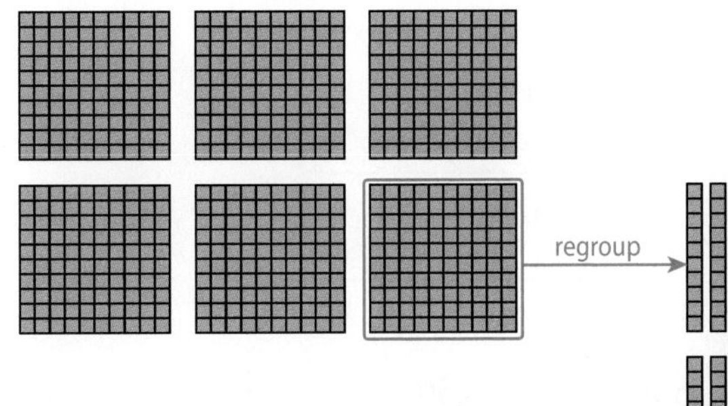

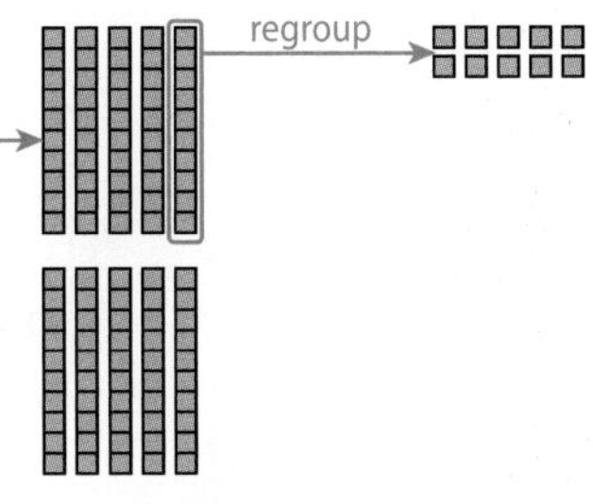

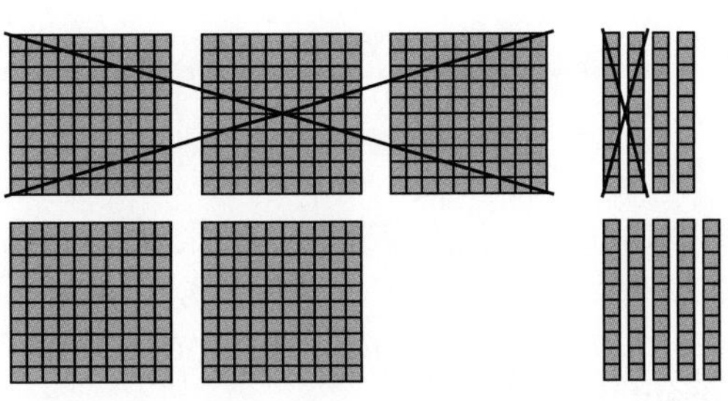

> **Watch Out!**
>
> The subtraction in Example 6 is called a "subtraction over zeros" problem. Since 7 > 0, you need to regroup some tens but there are no tens. You need to regroup 100 first, then regroup tens, and finally subtract the ones.

Using a Place-Value Chart

You may find it helpful to write the problem on a place-value chart. This can make it easier to keep the columns straight and see how to regroup.

Need More HELP

For help with place value, go to *Place Value* (pp. 40, 42, 44).

EXAMPLE 7

Use a place-value chart to find the difference 539 − 289.

STEP 1 Subtract the numbers in the ones column.

$9 - 9 = 0$

Write 0 in the ones column.

STEP 2 Subtract the numbers in the tens column.

$8 > 3$

You cannot subtract. Regroup the 5 hundreds as 4 hundreds and 10 tens.

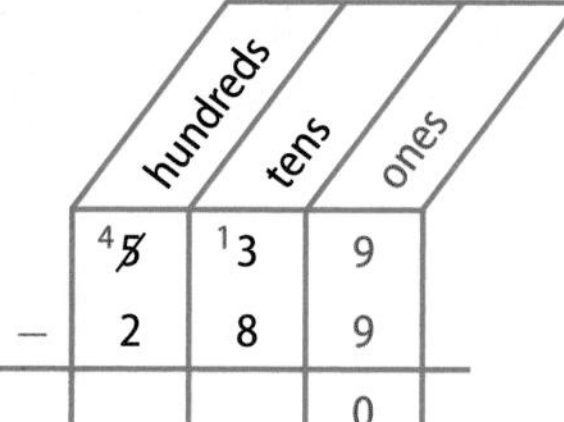

STEP 3 Now you have 13 tens. Subtract.

$13 - 8 = 5$

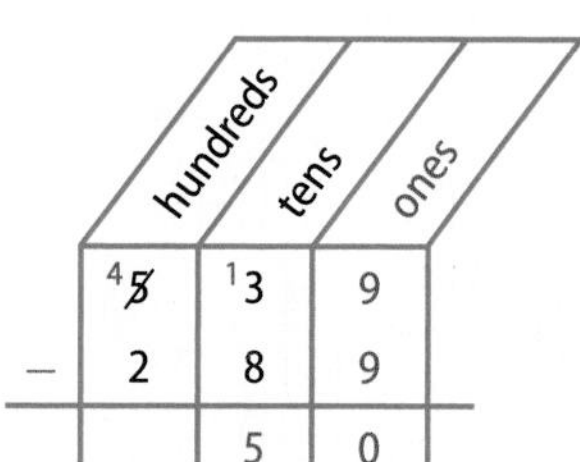

hundreds
tens
ones
4 5 1 3 9
− 2 8 9
5 0

STEP 4 Subtract the numbers in the hundreds column.

$4 - 2 = 2$

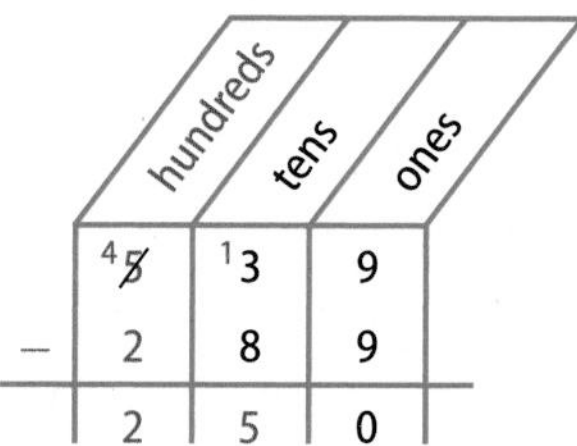

$539 - 289 = 250$

Regrouping in Subtraction

When the subtrahend is greater than the minuend, you must regroup *before* you can subtract. When you *regroup*, you organize a value in a different way and rename it. Regrouping is sometimes called *trading*.

$$\begin{array}{r} \overset{1}{\cancel{2}}\overset{1}{3}8 \\ -\ 193 \\ \hline 45 \end{array}$$

3 < 8, you can subtract.
9 > 3, regroup 2 hundreds as 1 hundred and 10 tens. Subtract.

Subtracting Using the Standard Algorithm

To subtract using the standard algorithm, you subtract numbers that have the same place value. When you do not have enough in a place to take away the number in the subtrahend, you regroup.

EXAMPLE 8

Use the standard algorithm to solve 3,501 − 1,367.

- Line up the numbers so that the digits with the same place value align.
- Subtract the ones. 7 > 1, so regroup the tens. Since there are 0 tens, regroup the 5 hundreds as 4 hundreds and 10 tens.
- Now, regroup the 10 tens as 9 tens and 10 ones.
- Now you have 3 thousands, 4 hundreds, 9 tens, and 11 ones.
- Subtract the ones: 11 − 7 = 4
  Subtract the tens: 9 − 6 = 3
  Subtract the hundreds. 4 − 3 = 1
  Subtract the thousands: 3 − 1 = 2

3,501 − 1,367 = 2,134

$$\begin{array}{r} 3,\overset{4}{\cancel{5}}\overset{\overset{9}{10}}{\cancel{0}}\overset{1}{}1 \\ -\ 1,367 \\ \hline 2,134 \end{array}$$

SEARCH

To see step-by-step videos of these problems, enter the page number into the SWadvantage.com Search Bar.

EXAMPLE 9

198 fans attended the second game of the season. The championship game had 323 fans. How many more fans attended the championship game?

Subtract 323 (fans at championship game) − 198 (fans at second game).

- Line up the numbers so that the digits with the same place value align.
- Subtract the ones. Regroup 2 tens as 1 ten and 10 ones. Now you have 13 ones. 13 − 8 = 5.
- Subtract the tens. Regroup 3 hundreds as 2 hundreds and 10 tens. Now you have 11 tens. 11 − 9 = 2.
- Subtract the hundreds. 2 − 1 = 1

$$\begin{array}{r} \overset{2}{\cancel{3}}\overset{\overset{11}{1}}{\cancel{2}}\overset{1}{}3 \\ -\ 198 \\ \hline 125 \end{array}$$

323 − 198 = 125
125 more fans attended the championship game.

For more about exponents, go to *Exponents* (p. 294).

Powers of 10

When you multiply the number 10 by itself any number of times, the product ends in zero and is called a **power of ten**. Another way to write the product is as an exponent. An **exponent** is a number that tells how many times the factor 10 is repeated. The table below shows the first four powers of ten.

Factors	Product	Exponent Form	10 is repeated
10×1	$= 10$	$= 10^1$	1 time
10×10	$= 100$	$= 10^2$	2 times
$10 \times 10 \times 10$	$= 1{,}000$	$= 10^3$	3 times
$10 \times 10 \times 10 \times 10$	$= 10{,}000$	$= 10^4$	4 times

When you multiply a number by a power of 10, the product always ends in zero.

$3 \times 10 = 30$
$3 \times 100 = 300$
$3 \times 1{,}000 = 3{,}000$
$3 \times 10{,}000 = 30{,}000$

$6 \times 10 = 60$
$6 \times 100 = 600$
$6 \times 1{,}000 = 6{,}000$
$6 \times 10{,}000 = 60{,}000$

$15 \times 10 = 150$
$15 \times 100 = 1{,}500$
$15 \times 1{,}000 = 15{,}000$
$15 \times 10{,}000 = 150{,}000$

Notice that the same pattern of zeros appears in each list of products. Once you understand the pattern, you can easily multiply (or divide) by a power of 10.

SEARCH

To see step-by-step videos of these problems, enter the page number into the SWadvantage.com Search Bar.

EXAMPLE 1

Use a model to find each product.

a. Multiply: 4 × 10

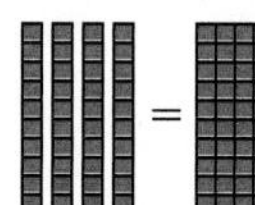

Four groups of ten is equal to 4 tens and 0 ones.

$4 \times 10 = 40$

b. Multiply: 13 × 100

=

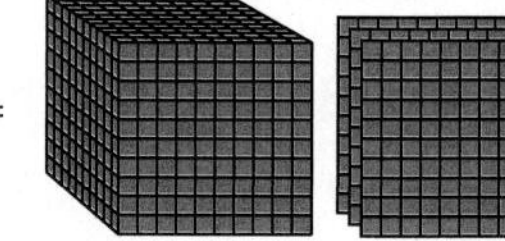

Regroup 10 hundreds as 1 thousand. You have 1 thousand and 3 hundreds.

$13 \times 100 = 1{,}300$

EXAMPLE 2

Multiply: 22 × 1,000

Think: There are 3 zeros in 1,000.
Add 3 zeros to the right of 22 ⟶ 22000

$22 \times 1{,}000 = 22{,}000$

Multiplying by Multiples of 10

A ***multiple*** is a number that is a product of a given number. When the factors in a multiplication problem are multiples of 10, you can use the number of zeros in the factors and multiplication facts to find the product.

Factors	Zeros	Product	Factors	Zeros	Product
3 × 40	1	120	8 × 20	1	160
30 × 40	2	1,200	80 × 20	2	1,600
300 × 40	3	12,000	800 × 200	4	160,000

Use a multiplication fact and the total number of zeros in the factors to find each product.

a. 3 × 200

Multiplication fact:
3 × 2 = 6
Number of zeros: 2

3 × 200 = 600

b. 70 × 500

Multiplication fact:
7 × 5 = 35
Number of zeros: 3

70 × 500 = 35,000

c. 4,000 × 80

Multiplication fact:
4 × 8 = 32
Number of zeros: 4

8,000 × 40 = 320,000

Dividing by Multiples of 10

Division is the inverse of multiplication. When you divide by a multiple of 10, you remove the same number of zeros from the dividend and the divisor. The number of zeros that remain is the number of zeros in the quotient.

Division	Remove Zeros	Division Fact	Quotient
4,800 ÷ 10	4,80~~0~~ ÷ 1~~0~~	48 ÷ 1 = 48	4,800 ÷ 10 = 480
1,500 ÷ 300	1,5~~00~~ ÷ 3~~00~~	15 ÷ 3 = 5	1,500 ÷ 300 = 5
36,000 ÷ 900	36,0~~00~~ ÷ 9~~00~~	36 ÷ 9 = 4	360 ÷ 9 = 40

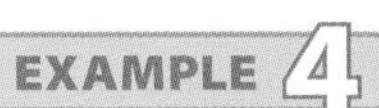

Find each quotient.

a. 600 ÷ 30

Remove zeros:
60~~0~~ ÷ 3~~0~~ = 60 ÷ 3
6 ÷ 3 = 2,
so 60 ÷ 3 = 20

b. 3,600 ÷ 900

Remove zeros:
3,6~~00~~ ÷ 9~~00~~ = 36 ÷ 9
36 ÷ 9 = 4

c. 210,000 ÷ 700

Remove zeros:
210,0~~00~~ ÷ 7~~00~~ = 2,100 ÷ 7
21 ÷ 7 = 3,
so 2,100 ÷ 7 = 300

GOT TO KNOW!

Multiplying and Dividing by Multiples of Ten

When you ***multiply***, count the number of zeros in the factors. Place the same number of zeros to the right of the last digit in the product.

When you ***divide***, remove the same number of zeros from the dividend and the divisor. Then divide to find the quotient.

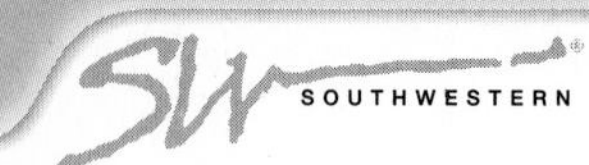

Multiplying Numbers Greater than 10

There are several ways to indicate multiplication.

3×4

$3 \cdot 4$

$3(4)$

Each expression means to multiply the factors 3 and 4.

Multiplication is a mathematical operation used to combine a number of sets that are of equal size. The number that tells the size of the set is the **multiplicand**, and number that tells how many sets is called the **multiplier**. The final quantity is the **product**. The two numbers multiplied are also called the **factors**.

6 multiplicand	6×3 means that 3 sets of 6 are combined.
$\times$ 3 multiplier	It is the same as adding: $6 + 6 + 6 = 18$.
18 product	

You can use what you know about multiplication facts and strategies to multiply when one or both factors are greater than 10.

In the *Take Apart* strategy, you can break apart numbers to multiply. For example, use two simpler facts to find the product of 8×12.

Think: $12 = 10 + 2$. I know the facts 8×10 and 8×2.

$$\begin{aligned} 8 \times 12 &= (8 \times 10) + (8 \times 2) \\ &= 80 + 16 \\ &= 96 \end{aligned}$$

One- and Two-Digit Multipliers

To multiply a number by a one-digit multiplier, multiply each digit in the multiplicand by the multiplier. Each product is called a **partial product**. You can add the partial products last, as shown in Example 1, or as you multiply, as shown in Example 2.

You can also use the *Take Apart* strategy with 2-digit multipliers. Another method is to use a place-value chart.

Watch Out!

In Example 1, remember that 5×3 tens is 150, **not** 15.

EXAMPLE 1

Multiply 36 × 5. Add the partial products last.

Multiply 5×6 ones $= 30$.
Write the partial product, 30.

Multiply 5×3 tens $= 150$.
Write the partial product, 150.

$$\begin{array}{r} 36 \\ \times \quad 5 \\ \hline 30 \\ +\ 150 \\ \hline 180 \end{array} \quad \begin{array}{l} \\ \\ 5 \times 6 = 30 \\ 5 \times 3 = 150 \\ \\ \end{array}$$
(partial products)

Add the partial products.

$5 \times 36 = 180$

EXAMPLE 2

Multiply 32 × 8. Add the partial products as you multiply.

Multiply 8 × 2 ones = 16 ones.
Regroup 16 as 6 ones and 1 ten.

Multiply 8 × 30 tens = 24 tens.
Add the 1 ten you regrouped.
24 tens + 1 ten = 25 tens.

$$\begin{array}{r} {}^{1} \\ 32 \\ \times\ 8 \\ \hline 256 \end{array}$$

8 × 2 = 16 ones
8 × 30 = 24 tens

24 tens + 1 ten = 25 tens

32 × 8 = 256

Watch Out !

In Example 2, although 25 tens = 250, you do **not** have to add a 0 to 25. The digit 6 fills the ones place.

EXAMPLE 3

Use an array to show 14 × 13.

Express the factors in expanded form. (10 + 4) × (10 + 3).

Multiply by 10: 10 × 10 = 100 10 × 3 = 30
Multiply by 4: 4 × 10 = 40 4 × 3 = 12

- Draw an array to represent the multiplication.
- Add to find the product: 100 + 30 + 40 + 12 = 182

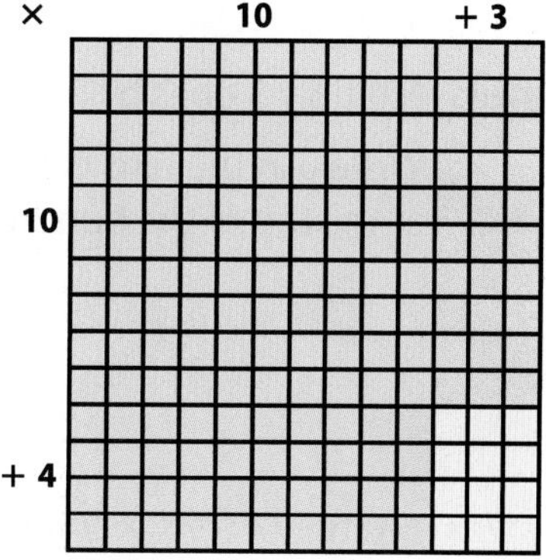

14 × 13 = 182

To see step-by-step videos of these problems, enter the page number into the SWadvantage.com Search Bar.

GOT TO KNOW!

Take Apart Numbers to Multiply

Here are two ways to use the *Take Apart* strategy. Both ways multiply the ones, tens, and hundreds separately, and then add the partial products to find the final product.

134 × 7
134 = 100 + 30 + 4
(7 × 100) + (7 × 30) + (7 × 4)
700 + 210 + 28 = 938

$$\begin{array}{r} 134 \\ \times\ 7 \\ \hline 28 \\ 210 \\ +700 \\ \hline 938 \end{array}$$

Using a Place-Value Chart

EXAMPLE 4

Use a place-value chart to multiply 45 × 23.

STEP 1 Multiply 5 ones × 3 ones = 1 ten and 5 ones.

Write the 5 in the ones column and a small 1 in the tens column.

	tens	ones
	[1]4	5
×	2	3
		5

STEP 2 Multiply 4 tens × 3 ones = 12 tens.

Add the regrouped 1 ten:
12 tens + 1 ten = 13 tens.

Write 3 in the tens column and 1 in the hundreds column.

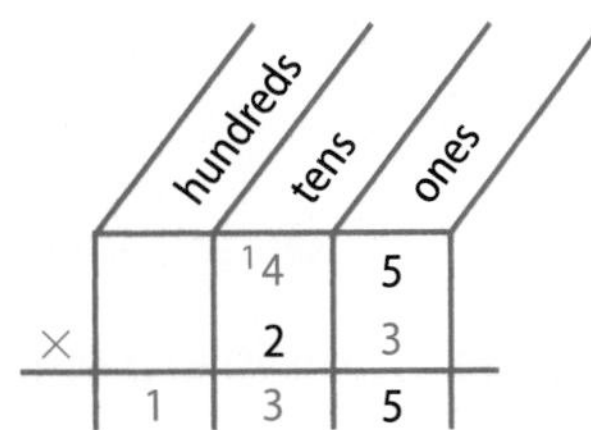

STEP 3 Multiply 5 ones by 2 tens = 10 tens.

Write 0 in the tens column and a small 1 at the top of the hundreds column.

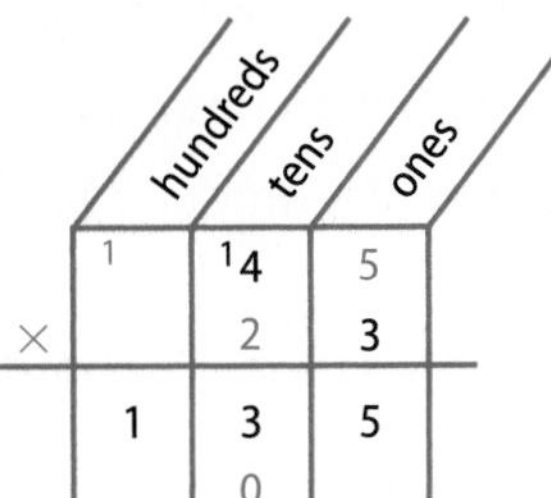

STEP 4 Multiply 4 tens × 2 tens = 8 hundreds.

Add the regrouped 1 hundred:
8 hundreds + 1 hundred = 9 hundreds.

Write the 9 in the hundreds column.

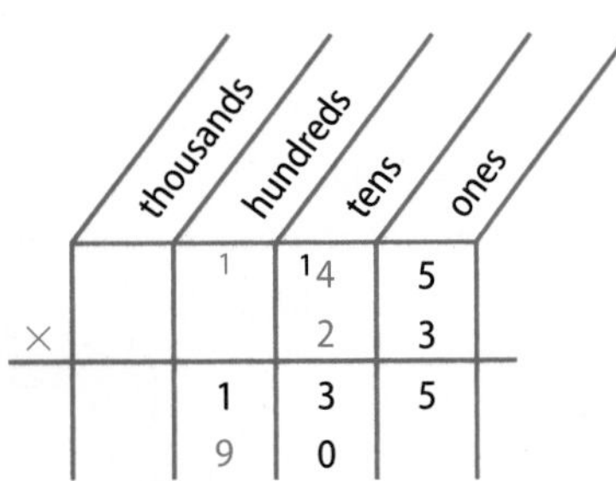

STEP 5 Add the partial products.

	thousands	hundreds	tens	ones
		1	[1]4	5
×			2	3
		1	3	5
		9	0	
	1	0	3	5

45 × 23 = 1,035

SEARCH

To see step-by-step videos of these problems, enter the page number into the SWadvantage.com Search Bar.

Watch Out!

In Step 3, 10 tens is actually 100. You can do one of two things:

1. Just write a 0 in the tens column, as shown, or
2. Write a zero in the tens and the ones column.

The zero in the ones column is often called a placeholder zero. It helps you remember that you are multiplying by tens, not ones, and that you should not start writing the second partial product in the ones column.

Multiplying Using the Standard Algorithm

Using the standard algorithm is similar to using a place-value chart.

EXAMPLE 5

Use the standard algorithm to solve 319 × 524.

STEP 1 Multiply ones, tens, and hundreds by ones. Regroup as necessary.

```
   3
  319
× 524
 1276
```

STEP 2 Multiply ones, tens, and hundreds by tens. Regroup as necessary.

```
   1
  319
× 524
 1276
 638
```

STEP 3 Multiply ones, tens, and hundreds by hundreds. Regroup as necessary.

```
   4
  319
× 524
 1276
 638
1595
```

STEP 4 Add the partial products.

```
    319
  × 524
   1276
   638
  1595
 167156
```

319 × 524 = 167,156

Use your calculator to check the final product. Enter 3 1 9, press ×, enter 5 2 4, press =. If the display shows the product you calculated, your answer is correct.

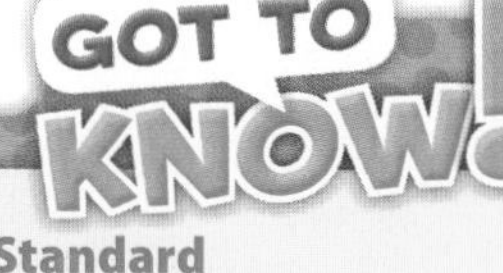

Standard Algorithm

The standard algorithm uses place value to multiply the multiplicand by the different place values in the multiplier.

```
 421
× 43
```

First, multiply 421 by 3 ones.

```
 421
× 43
1263 partial product
```

Then multiply 421 by 4 tens, and add the partial products.

```
  421
×  43
 1263 partial product
+1684  partial product
18,103 final product
```

EXAMPLE 6

Mr. Rose has 108 small jars of coins. He says that each jar contains 75 quarters. How many quarters is this in all?

This problem asks, if there are 75 quarters in a group, how many quarters are in 108 groups? Because the multiplicand has a zero in the tens place, you will not need to regroup.

```
   108
 ×  75
   540
+ 7560
 8,100
```

There are 8,100 quarters in the 108 jars.

Dividing Whole Numbers

Thinking About Division

When you divide, you are actually asking how many groups of a certain size are in a larger group. For example, 12 ÷ 3 means "how many groups of 3 are in a group of 12?"

quotient → 4
divisor → $3\overline{)12}$
dividend ↑

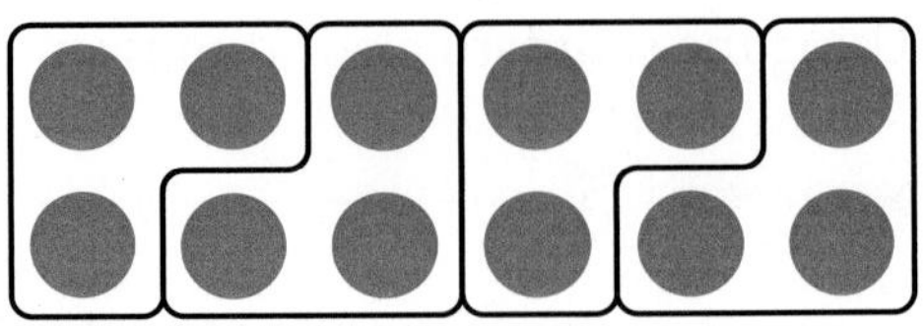

You can see that there are 4 groups of 3 in 12. In this example, the **dividend**, or the number being divided, is 12. The **divisor**, or number by which the dividend is divided, is 3. The **quotient**, or number of groups of three, is 4.

Sometimes, the divisor does not divide evenly into the dividend. The left-over quantity is called the **remainder**, as shown below.

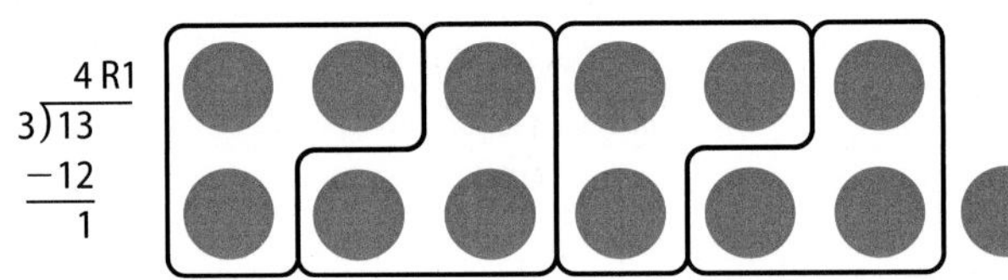

EXAMPLE 1

Find the quotient: 28 ÷ 9

Think: $9 \times 3 = 27$

$28 - 27 = 1$

$28 \div 3 = 9\text{ R}1$

$$\begin{array}{r} 3\text{ R}1 \\ 9\overline{)28} \\ -27 \\ \hline 1 \end{array}$$

Division Is About Equal Groups

Division is the *inverse* of multiplication. In multiplication, you take a number of equal groups and find their total. In division, you are given the total and the size of equal groups, and you need to find how many equal groups are in the total.

You can think of division as the repeated subtraction of equal-sized groups. For example, dividing 24 by 3 is the same as subtracting 3 from 24 eight times.

$24 \div 3 = 8$

$24 - 3 = 21 - 3 = 18 - 3 = 15 - 3 = 12 - 3 =$
$9 - 3 = 6 - 3 = 3 - 3 = 0$

Dividing Using the Standard Algorithm

The standard division algorithm is often called *long division*. This is one way to divide. It can be helpful to look first at the algorithm on a place-value chart. Here is how to find the quotient of 528 ÷ 3.

STEP 1 Divide the first digit: 5 ÷ 3 = 1

	H	T	O
	1	7	
3)	5	2	8
−	3		
	2	2	

Multiply 3 × 1 = 3
Subtract 5 − 3 = 2
Bring down the second digit, 2.
Now you have 22.

STEP 2 Divide 22 ÷ 3 = 7

	H	T	O
	1	7	
3)	5	2	8
−	3		
	2	2	
−	2	1	
		1	8

Multiply 3 × 7 = 21
Subtract 22 − 21 = 1
Bring down the third digit, 8.
Now you have 18.

STEP 3 Divide 18 ÷ 3 = 6

	H	T	O
	1	7	6
3)	5	2	8
−	3		
	2	2	
−	2	1	
		1	8
	−	1	8
			0

Multiply 3 × 6 = 18
Subtract 18 − 18 = 0
There are no more digits to bring down, and there is no remainder.

528 ÷ 3 = 176

Notice that long division starts at the left, and the steps—which each include divide, multiply, subtract, and bring down—repeat until there are no more digits to bring down.

EXAMPLE 2

Divide: 85 ÷ 6

STEP 1 Divide the first digit: 8 ÷ 6 = 1

```
   1
6)85
 -6
  25
```

Multiply 6 × 1 = 6
Subtract 8 − 6 = 2
Bring down the 5.
Now you have 25.

STEP 2 Divide 25 ÷ 6 = 4

```
  14
6)85
 -6
  25
 -24
   1
```

Multiply 6 × 4 = 24
Subtract 25 − 24 = 1
1 < 6, so it is the remainder.

CHECK Multiply the quotient by the divisor.

```
  ²
  14  quotient
× 6   divisor
  84
+ 1   Add the remainder.
  85
```

The product is the dividend. The answer checks. ✔

85 ÷ 6 = 14 R1

Need More HELP

For more about multiplication and division facts, go to *Memorizing Multiplication Facts* (p. 72) and *Memorizing Division Facts* (p. 76).

SEARCH

To see step-by-step videos of these problems, enter the page number into the SWadvantage.com Search Bar.

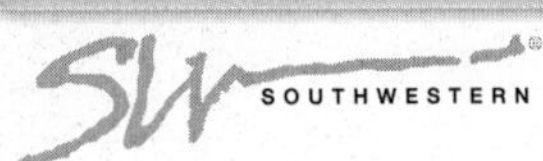

Zeros in Quotients and Dividends

Problems that have zeros or with multi-digit divisors may look harder but the process is the same. Treat the zero as you would any other digit.

EXAMPLE 3

Divide: 432 ÷ 4

STEP 1 Divide the first digit: $4 \div 4 = 1$

$$\begin{array}{r} 1 \\ 4\overline{)432} \\ -4 \\ \hline 03 \end{array}$$

Multiply $4 \times 1 = 4$
Subtract $4 - 4 = 0$
Bring down the second digit, 3.
Now you have 3.

STEP 2 Divide $3 \div 4 = 0$

$$\begin{array}{r} 10 \\ 4\overline{)432} \\ -4 \\ \hline 32 \end{array}$$

Since 4 goes into 3 zero times, *you must write a zero in the quotient*. You do not need to multiply 4×0. Bring down the third digit, 2. Now you have 32.

STEP 3 Divide $32 \div 4 = 8$

$$\begin{array}{r} 108 \\ 4\overline{)432} \\ -4 \\ \hline 32 \\ -32 \\ \hline 0 \end{array}$$

Multiply $4 \times 8 = 32$
Subtract $32 - 32 = 0$
There are no more digits to bring down, and there is no remainder.

$432 \div 4 = 108$

Try It This Way

In Example 3, Step 2, you can include the multiplication of 4×0 if you find it helpful.

$$\begin{array}{r} 10 \\ 4\overline{)432} \\ -4 \\ \hline 3 \\ -0 \\ \hline 32 \end{array}$$

Because subtracting zero from 3 does not change its value, this step is usually skipped.

EXAMPLE 4

Divide: 2,808 ÷ 26

STEP 1 Since 26 will not divide into 2, the first division is: $28 \div 26 = 1$

$$\begin{array}{r} 1 \\ 26\overline{)2,808} \\ -2\,6 \\ \hline 20 \end{array}$$

Multiply $26 \times 1 = 26$
Subtract $28 - 26 = 2$
Bring down the second digit, 0.
Now you have 20.

STEP 2 Divide $20 \div 26 = 0$

$$\begin{array}{r} 10 \\ 26\overline{)2,808} \\ -2\,6 \\ \hline 208 \end{array}$$

Since 26 goes into 20 zero times, *you must write a zero in the quotient*. You do not need to multiply 26×0. Simply bring down the fourth digit, 8. Now you have 208.

STEP 3 Divide $208 \div 26$
You can estimate.
Think: $200 \div 25 = 8$.
Try 8.

$$\begin{array}{r} 108 \\ 26\overline{)2,808} \\ -2\,6 \\ \hline 208 \\ -208 \\ \hline 0 \end{array}$$

Multiply
$26 \times 8 = 208$
Subtract
$208 - 208 = 0$

$2,808 \div 26 = 108$

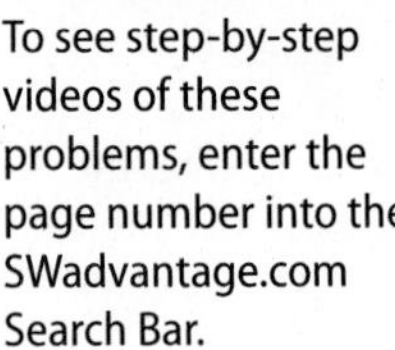

To see step-by-step videos of these problems, enter the page number into the SWadvantage.com Search Bar.

EXAMPLE 5

Divide: 11,004 ÷ 524

STEP 1 Since 524 will not divide into 1, 11, or 110, the first division is: 1,100 ÷ 524 Think: 1,000 ÷ 500 = 2. Try 2.

```
       2
524)11,004
   -10 48
      524
```

Multiply
524 × 2 = 1,048
Subtract
1,100 − 1,048 = 52
Bring down the 4.
Now you have 524.

STEP 2 Divide 524 ÷ 524 = 1

```
      21
524)11,004
   -10 48
      524
     -524
        0
```

Multiply
524 × 1 = 524
Subtract
524 − 524 = 0
There are no more digits to bring down, and there is no remainder.

CHECK *Estimate*:
10,000 ÷ 500 = 20, so a quotient of 21 is reasonable.

Calculator: Use your calculator to multiply 524 × 21. The display will show the product: 11,004. ✔

11,004 ÷ 524 = 21

Need More HELP

For more about multiplication and division facts, go to *Memorizing Multiplication Facts* (p. 72) and *Memorizing Division Facts* (p. 76).

Thinking About Remainders in Problems

In word problems, the remainder is treated differently depending on the context of the problem. You can *include the remainder in the answer, drop the remainder, round up,* or *use the remainder as the answer.*

EXAMPLE 6

Read each scenario, and decide what to do with the remainder.

a. 22 people, 5 people per car. How many cars are needed?

Think: 22 people ÷ 5 people per car = 4 cars R2 people. Since 2 people still need a ride, 4 cars are not enough. *Round up* to 5 cars.

b. 282 buttons, 50 buttons per bag. How many bags of 50 buttons can you make?

Think: 282 buttons ÷ 50 per bag = 5 R32 bags. You can make 5 bags of buttons with 50 buttons per bag. *Drop the remainder.*

c. 36 movie passes shared equally among 5 friends. How many passes are left?

Think: 36 passes ÷ 5 friends = 7 R1 passes. Since 5 × 7 = 35, there is 1 pass left and *the remainder is the answer.*

GOT TO KNOW!

Long Division

This method of division uses repeated steps—which each include Divide, Multiply, Subtract, and Bring Down.

```
  24
4)96
 -8↓
  16
 -16
   0
```

STEP 1

Divide: 9 ÷ 4 = 2

Multiply: 4 × 2 = 8

Subtract: 9 − 8 = 1

Bring down: 16

STEP 2

Divide: 16 ÷ 4 = 4

Multiply: 4 × 4 = 16

Subtract: 16 − 16 = 0

Thinking About Word Problems

Here are a few tips for solving word problems.

- Read the problem carefully.
- Understand what the question means, and write it in your own words.
- Look for information in the problem that will help you answer the question.
- Think: What operation should I use to answer the question?
- Estimate the answer first. Then compare your exact answer to the estimate.

For help determining what operation to use, go to

Addition Facts (p. 56),
Subtraction Facts (p. 62),
Multiplication Facts (p. 68), and
Division Facts (p. 74).

If you write your answer using the same words used in the problem, you can be certain you answer the correct question. For example,

Question: How many bottles will she need?

Answer: She will need 14 bottles.

EXAMPLE 1

Sue has 112 oz of carrot juice. She will pour the juice into 8-oz bottles. How many bottles will she need?

Know: 112 oz carrot juice 8-oz bottles

Question: How many bottles are needed to hold 112 oz of juice?

Think: You know that 112 oz of juice will be shared out into 8-oz bottles. Sharing out means that you use division to solve the problem.

Estimate first:

112 is close to 100, and
8 is close to 10.
$100 \div 10 = 10$, so the answer is about 10.

Divide:

$$\begin{array}{r} 14 \\ 8\overline{)112} \\ \underline{-8} \\ 32 \\ \underline{-32} \\ 0 \end{array}$$

14 is close to the estimate of 10.

Sue will need 14 bottles.

EXAMPLE 2

Carl has \$83 today. He had \$52 yesterday. How much more money does he have today than he had yesterday?

Know: Carl has \$83 today. He had \$52 yesterday.

Question: \$83 is how much more than \$52?

Think: The phrase "how much more" means subtraction.

Estimate first:

\$83 is about \$80,
and \$52 is about \$50.
$\$80 - \$50 = \$30$, so the answer is about 30.

Subtract:

$$\begin{array}{r} \$83 \\ \underline{-\ 52} \\ \$31 \end{array}$$

\$31, which is about \$30

Carl has \$31 more today than he had yesterday.

EXAMPLE 3

The Art Club members made 15 boxes of greeting cards. There are 12 cards in each box. How many cards did they make altogether?

Know: 15 boxes of cards 12 cards in each box

Question: How many greeting cards did the members of the Art Club make?

Think: You know that there are 15 boxes and 12 cards in each box. The word "altogether" means you need to find a total. You could add 12 fifteen times. However, since there are 15 *equal groups* you can use multiplication.

Estimate first:

12 is close to 10.

$15 \times 10 = 150$, so the answer is close to 150. Because you rounded 12 down to 10, the exact answer will be greater than 150.

Multiply:

$$\begin{array}{r} {}^{1}15 \\ \times\ 12 \\ \hline 30 \\ +\ 150 \\ \hline 180 \end{array}$$

The Art Club members made 180 greeting cards.

Need More HELP

For help with estimating, go to *Estimating Sums* (p. 110), *Estimating Differences* (p. 114), *Estimating Products* (p. 118), and *Estimating Quotients* (p. 122).

EXAMPLE 4

Janet collected 18 bottles for recycling on Monday, 24 on Tuesday, 53 on Wednesday, 11 on Thursday, and 15 on Friday. How many bottles did she collect in all?

Know: Janet collected these numbers of bottles: 18, 24, 53,11, 15.

Question: How many bottles did she collect from Monday through Friday?

Think: The phrase "in all" means you need to find a total. Use addition and add the number of bottles she collected each day.

Estimate first:

18 is about 20 24 is about 25
53 is about 50 11 is about 10
15 leave as 15

Add the tens: $20 + 20 + 50 + 10 + 10 = 110$
Add the ones: $5 + 5 = 10$
Estimate the total: $110 + 10 = 120$

Add:

$$\begin{array}{r} {}^{2}18 \\ 24 \\ 53 \\ 11 \\ +\ 15 \\ \hline 121 \end{array}$$

Janet collected 121 bottles in all.

SEARCH

To see step-by-step videos of these problems, enter the page number into the SWadvantage.com Search Bar.

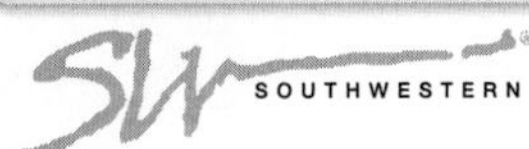

The Four-Step Problem Solving Process

You may find it helpful to use the four-step problem solving process shown in the *Got To Know!* box on the left.

Four-Step Problem Solving Process

READ Read the problem carefully. Identify the following:

Know: the information given in the problem, *Need to Find:* the question

PLAN Decide what operation you need to use to answer the question.

SOLVE Carry out your plan. State the answer in terms of the question.

CHECK Decide if your answer is reasonable. Use estimation, inverse operations, or number sense.

EXAMPLE 5

There are 368 crayons to share fairly between 24 students. How many crayons does each student get? Are there any crayons left over?

READ Read the problem carefully. Be sure you understand the question. Then look for information that will help you find the answer to the question.

Know: 368 crayons, 24 students

Need to Find: the number of crayons per student, the number of crayons left over

PLAN Think: The crayons are shared fairly, so each student will get the same number of crayons. When you share a quantity equally, you divide.

SOLVE

$$\begin{array}{r} 15\text{ R}8 \\ 24\overline{)368} \\ -24 \\ \hline 128 \\ -120 \\ \hline 8 \end{array}$$

CHECK

You can estimate to check. Compatible numbers are $350 \div 25 = 14$ or $400 \div 20 = 20$.

Since 15 is between 14 and 20, the answer is reasonable.

Each student gets 15 crayons, and there are 8 crayons left over.

EXAMPLE 6

Selena has 6 cartons of books to unpack. Each carton has 12 books inside. How many books will Selena have to unpack?

READ Read the problem carefully. Be sure you understand the question. Then look for information that will help you find the answer to the question.

Know: 6 cartons of books to unpack, 12 books in each carton

Need to Find: the number of books to unpack

PLAN Think: There are 6 *equal groups* of 12. Multiply to find the total.

SOLVE

$$\begin{array}{r} \overset{1}{1}2 \\ \times 6 \\ \hline 72 \end{array}$$

CHECK

You can estimate to check the answer.
12 is a little more than 10.
$10 \times 6 = 60$
The answer will be a little more than 60, so 72 is reasonable.

Selena will have to unpack 72 books.

Remember, *compatible numbers* are numbers that are easy to work with mentally.

EXAMPLE 7

Delmar has 142 comic books. He sells 35 on Tuesday and another 24 on Friday. How many comic books does he have left?

READ Know: 142 comic books to start. 35 are sold. Then 24 more are sold.

Need to Find: the number of comic books that are left

PLAN A "how many are left" question is almost always a subtraction problem.

SOLVE Think: There are two ways to solve this problem. You can subtract twice, or you can add the comic books sold and then subtract once.

METHOD 1

$$\begin{array}{r} 142 \\ -\ 35 \\ \hline 107 \end{array} \qquad \begin{array}{r} 107 \\ -\ 24 \\ \hline 83 \end{array}$$

METHOD 2

$$\begin{array}{r} 35 \\ +\ 24 \\ \hline 59 \end{array} \qquad \begin{array}{r} 142 \\ -\ 59 \\ \hline 83 \end{array}$$

CHECK

Estimate: Compatible numbers are $140 - 30 - 20 = 140 - (50) = 90$. The answer is reasonable.

Delmar has 83 comic books left.

SEARCH

To see step-by-step videos of these problems, enter the page number into the SWadvantage.com Search Bar.

EXAMPLE 8

On Friday, 423 people saw a popular movie at the local theater. On Saturday, 597 people saw the movie. On Sunday, 115 fewer saw the movie than saw it on Saturday. How many people saw the movie over the three-day period?

READ Know: These numbers of people saw the movie:

Friday: 423 Saturday: 597 Sunday: 115 fewer than Saturday

Need to Know: total number of people who saw the movie

PLAN Think: On Sunday, there were 115 less people than on Saturday, or $597 - 115$. Write and solve an addition number sentence that represents the problem.

SOLVE $423 + 597 + (597 - 115) =$ total number of people who saw the movie

Subtract first.

$$\begin{array}{r} 597 \\ -\ 115 \\ \hline 482 \end{array}$$

482 people saw the movie on Sunday.

Add.

$$\begin{array}{r} {}^{2\,1}\!423 \\ 597 \\ +\ 482 \\ \hline 1{,}502 \end{array}$$

CHECK Estimate:

$423 + 597 + (597 - 115) =$
$400 + 600 + (600 - 100) =$
$400 + 600 + 500 = 1{,}500$, so the answer 1,502 is reasonable.

A total of 1,502 people saw the movie over the three-day period.

Watch Out !

Examples 1 through 7 can be solved using one operation. Some problems, like Example 8, require more than one operation to find the answer.

Estimating with Whole Numbers

What Came Before?

- Adding, subtracting, multiplying, and dividing whole numbers
- Rounding and comparing whole numbers

What's This About?

- Estimating sums and differences
- Estimating products and quotients
- Using estimation to solve word problems

Practical Apps

- Apartment managers use estimation to decide if electricity usage is reasonable.
- Realtors study comparable house prices in an area to estimate the best selling or purchasing price for a home.

just for FUN!

Q: How much is 2×2?

A: Do you want the exact answer or an estimate?

CONTENTS UPLOAD DOWNLOAD

Foundations of Mathematics

You can find more practice problems online by visiting:
www.SWadvantage.com

Estimating Sums

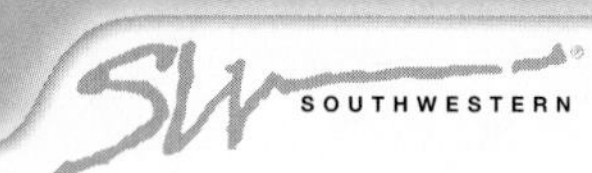

Watch Out !

When both addends are rounded up, the rounded sum will be *greater than* the actual sum. When both addends are rounded down, the rounded sum will be *less than* the actual sum.

Use Rounding

When you do not need to know an exact sum, you can *estimate*. An **estimate** tells you *about* how much or *about* how many. You can also estimate to decide whether an exact sum is reasonable. One way to estimate is by *rounding*.

EXAMPLE 1

Round to estimate the sum: 14,217 + 6,866

STEP 1 Round each number to the *thousands* place.

14,217	rounds to	14,000
+ 6,866	rounds to	+ 7,000

STEP 2 Add the rounded numbers.

$$\begin{array}{r} 14{,}000 \\ +\ 7{,}000 \\ \hline 21{,}000 \end{array}$$

14,217 + 6,866 is *about* 21,000.

EXAMPLE 2

Round to estimate the sum: \$54.87 + \$29.95

STEP 1 Round each number to the *nearest dollar* (ones place).

\$54.87	rounds to	\$55.00
+ 29.95	rounds to	+ 30.00

STEP 2 Add the rounded numbers.

$$\begin{array}{r} \$55.00 \\ +\ 30.00 \\ \hline \$85.00 \end{array}$$

The sum of \$54.87 + \$29.95 is *about* \$85.00.

Methods for Estimating a Sum

Round • Use Compatible Numbers • Use Front-End Estimation

Use Compatible Numbers

Another way to estimate a sum is by using *compatible numbers*. **Compatible numbers** are numbers that are easy to add mentally.

EXAMPLE 3

Suppose you found the sum of 651,973 and 49,200. Use compatible numbers to estimate the sum. If your estimate is close to your calculated sum, then your answer is reasonable.

Calculated Sum		Estimated Sum
651,973	651,973 is close to 650,000.	650,000
+ 49,200	49,200 is close to 50,000.	+ 50,000
701,173		700,000

700,000 is close to 701,173. So, your actual sum makes sense.

Notice that 49,200 was changed to 50,000 because this number is easy to add to 650,000.

SEARCH

To see step-by-step videos of these problems, enter the page number into the SWadvantage.com Search Bar.

EXAMPLE 4

Rajat used his calculator to add 77,099 and 24,056. He got this number on the calculator display:

31155

Use compatible numbers to decide if Rajat input the addends correctly.

Calculator Sum		Estimated Sum
31,155	77,099 is close to 75,000.	75,000
	24,056 is close to 25,000.	+ 25,000
		100,000

The estimate is 100,000, but the number in the calculator display is 31,155, which is less than the first addend.

Rajat must have input the addends incorrectly.

In fact, Rajat went too fast and entered 7,099 instead of 77,099.

When he reentered the numbers, he got the sum of 101,155, which is close to 100,000.

Watch Out !

When you use a calculator to add, estimate to make sure that the sum in the display makes sense. It's easy to enter digits incorrectly.

Use Front-End Estimation

Another way to estimate a sum is to use *front-end estimation.* With this method, you round and add only the digits on the far left (front end) of each number. If one of the numbers you are adding has fewer digits than the other numbers, round the place at the far left of the longer numbers.

Watch Out !

In Exercise 5, two of the numbers are in the hundreds, so you round them to the hundreds place. The number 29 must be rounded to the hundreds place also. So, 29 rounds to 0, not 30.

EXAMPLE 5

Use front-end estimation to estimate the sum: 409 + 29 + 879

The front-end digit is in the hundreds place in 409 and 879.
The front-end digit is in the tens place in 29, but you need to round to the hundreds place.

	Round.	Estimate
409	409 rounds to 400.	400
29	29 rounds to 0.	0
+ 879	879 rounds to 900.	+ 900
		1,300

The sum of 409 + 29 + 879 is *about* 1,300.

Sometimes, after rounding and adding the front-end digits, you need a closer estimate. Use *front-end estimation with adjustment.* Add the front-end digits *without* rounding them. Round to adjust any remaining digits, and then add them. Finally, add the two sums.

EXAMPLE 6

Brianna and Grace had lunch at a restaurant. They used *front-end estimation with adjustment* to decide if the total of $14.86 on their check was reasonable.

		Add the front-end digits.	Adjust the other digits.	
2 burgers	$7.96	$7	Round $.96 to $1.	$1
1 milk	1.25	1	Round $.25 to 0.	0
1 large cola	1.75	1	Round $.75 to $1.	1
2 desserts	3.90	+3	Round $.90 to $1.	+1
	$14.86	$12		$3

$12 + $3 = $15, which is close to $14.86.

The total on the check is reasonable.

Estimating to Solve Problems

Some word problems do not require an exact answer, and you can estimate the answer. But watch out. In problems where you must find out if a certain quantity is "enough," you must *overestimate* the quantity needed by rounding up. In other problems where you want to be certain you have reached a minimum amount, you can *underestimate* by rounding down.

EXAMPLE 7

The Super-Soft Ware Company recycles cans. In March, it recycled 3,198 cans. In April, it recycled 4,879 cans. About how many cans did the company recycle in total during March and April?

STEP 1

Round to the thousands place.

$$\begin{array}{r} 3{,}198 \rightarrow 3{,}000 \\ +\ 4{,}879 \rightarrow 5{,}000 \end{array}$$

STEP 2

Add.

$$\begin{array}{r} 3{,}000 \\ +\ 5{,}000 \\ \hline 8{,}000 \end{array}$$

The question asks "*about* how many." You do not need an exact answer. The Super-Soft Ware Company recycled *about* 8,000 cans in March and April.

SEARCH

To see step-by-step videos of these problems, enter the page number into the SWadvantage.com Search Bar.

EXAMPLE 8

An online store sells cell-phone apps. Trevor has $16 to spend. He wants to buy the following apps.

Sports app – $4.99 **Game app – $2.99** **Printer app – $6.99**

Does he have enough money?

Since Trevor has only a certain amount of money to spend, you need to *overestimate* by rounding up. Round to estimate the total cost of the apps. Then compare the rounded sum to the amount of money he has.

Sports app	$4.99 rounds to 5.00.
Game app	$2.99 rounds to 3.00.
Printer app	$6.99 rounds to 7.00.

$\$5 + \$3 + \$7 = \$15$, which is a slight overestimate. Since $15 < 16$, he has enough money.

Estimating Differences

For help with estimating, go to *Estimating to Predict or Check* in *Numbers and Operations* (p. 410).

Use Rounding

When you do not need to know an exact difference, you can estimate. An **estimate** tells you about how much or about how many. You can also estimate to decide whether an exact difference is reasonable. One way to estimate is by rounding both numbers in the calculation.

When both numbers in the subtraction are rounded up, the rounded difference will be *greater than* the actual difference. When both numbers are rounded down, the rounded difference will be *less than* the actual difference.

EXAMPLE 1

Round to estimate the difference: 161,219 − 89,405

STEP 1 Round each number to the *ten thousands* place.

161,219	rounds to	160,000
− 89,405	rounds to	− 90,000

STEP 2 Subtract the rounded numbers.

$$\begin{array}{r} 160{,}000 \\ -\ 90{,}000 \\ \hline 70{,}000 \end{array}$$

161,219 − 89,405 is *about* 70,000.

EXAMPLE 2

Round to estimate the difference: \$229.42 − \$48.31

STEP 1 Round each number to the *nearest ten dollars* (tens place).

\$229.42	rounds to	\$230.00
− 48.31	rounds to	− 50.00

STEP 2 Subtract the rounded numbers.

$$\begin{array}{r} \$230.00 \\ -\ 50.00 \\ \hline \$180.00 \end{array}$$

\$229.42 − \$48.31 is *about* \$180.00.

Use Compatible Numbers

Another way to estimate a difference is by using *compatible numbers.* **Compatible numbers** are numbers that are easy to subtract mentally.

EXAMPLE 3

Suppose you found the difference of 934,298 minus 535,084. Use compatible numbers to estimate the difference. If your estimation is close to your calculated difference, then your answer is reasonable.

Calculated Difference		Estimated Difference
934,298	934,298 is close to 950,000.	950,000
− 535,084	535,084 is close to 550,000.	− 550,000
399,214		400,000

400,000, is close to 399,214. So, your actual difference makes sense.

Notice that both numbers were rounded up so the estimated numbers would be easy to subtract.

SEARCH

To see step-by-step videos of these problems, enter the page number into the SWadvantage.com Search Bar.

EXAMPLE 4

Selena used a calculator to subtract 15,985 from 18,607. This number showed on the calculator display:

2622

Use compatible numbers to decide if Selena input the digits in both numbers correctly.

Calculator Difference		Estimated Difference
2,622	18,607 is close to 18,500.	18,500
	15,985 is close to 16,000.	− 16,000
		2,500

The estimate, 2,500, is close to the number on the calculator display. So, Selena most likely input the digits correctly.

Whenever you use a calculator to subtract, estimate to make sure that the difference on the display makes sense.

Methods for Estimating a Difference

Use these estimation methods to find an approximate difference or to check that your actual difference is reasonable.

Round to Estimate • Use Compatible Numbers • Use Front-End Estimation

Use Front-End Estimation

Another way to estimate a difference is to use **front-end estimation**. With this method, you round and subtract only the digits on the far left (front end) of each number.

EXAMPLE 5

Use front-end estimation to estimate the difference: 722 − 397

The front-end digit is in the hundreds place in both numbers.

	Round.	Estimate.
722	722 rounds to 700.	700
− 397	397 rounds to 400.	− 400
		300

The difference of 722 − 397 is *about* 300.

Front-End Estimation with Adjustment

Sometimes, after rounding and subtracting the front-end digits, you need a closer estimate. Use *front-end estimation with adjustment*. Subtract the front-end digits *without* rounding them. Round to adjust any remaining digits, and then subtract them. Finally, subtract the two differences.

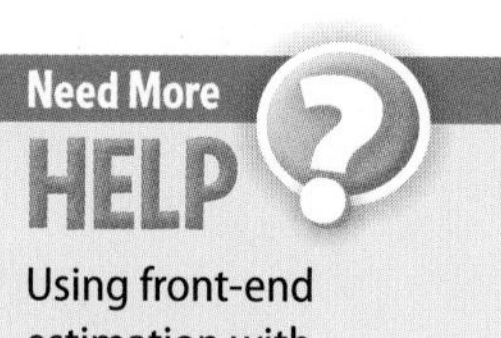

Using front-end estimation with adjustment makes sense whenever you need to estimate money amounts.

EXAMPLE 6

Parents raised $529.85 for the media center. The media specialist spent $304.63 of the money for software and would like to buy some new keyboards also. About how much money is left to buy keyboards?

	Subtract the front-end digits.	Adjust the other digits.	
$529.85	$ 500	Round $29.85 to $30.	$30
− 304.63	− 300	Round $4.63 to $5.	− 5
	$200		$25

$200 + $25 = $225. There is about $225 left to buy keyboards.

Estimating to Solve Problems

Some word problems do not require an exact answer, and you can estimate the answer. But watch out. In problems where you must find out if a certain quantity is "enough," you must *overestimate* the quantity needed by rounding up. In other problems where you want to be certain you have reached a minimum amount, you can *underestimate* by rounding down.

EXAMPLE 7

The school had a book sale. Mario bought a photography book for $11.95. He paid with a $20 bill. Does he have enough money left to buy a history book for $6.95?

You need to subtract $11.95 from $20.

Round $11.95 to the nearest dollar: $12.00

Use mental math to subtract: $20.00 − $12.00 = $8.00.

Mario should get *about* $8.00 in change. Since you rounded up to $12.00, $8.00 in change is a slight underestimate. He will have enough money to buy the history book.

SEARCH

To see step-by-step videos of these problems, enter the page number into the SWadvantage.com Search Bar.

EXAMPLE 8

Emma's family is driving to visit a national park. The distance from their house to the park is 2,365 miles. On the first day of the trip they drive 522 miles. About how much farther do they have left to drive?

METHOD 1

Round both numbers to the nearest hundred.
Total distance: 2,365 rounds to 2,400.
Distance driven: 522 rounds to 500.

Subtract to find the estimated difference.

$$\begin{array}{r} 2{,}400 \text{ miles} \\ -\ 500 \text{ miles} \\ \hline 1{,}900 \text{ miles} \end{array}$$

METHOD 2

Use compatible numbers to estimate the difference.
Total distance: 2,365 changes to 2,350.
Distance driven: 522 changes to 550.

Subtract to find the estimated difference.

$$\begin{array}{r} 2{,}350 \text{ miles} \\ -\ 550 \text{ miles} \\ \hline 1{,}800 \text{ miles} \end{array}$$

They have about 1,800 or about 1,900 miles left to drive.

The actual distance left to drive is 1,843 miles. Both estimates are acceptable.

Notice that Method 1 gives an overestimate while Method 2 gives an underestimate.

Estimating Products

Use Rounding

When you do not need to know an exact product, you can *estimate*. An **estimate** tells you *about* how much or *about* how many. You can also estimate to decide whether an exact product is reasonable. One way to estimate is by *rounding*.

You can round a factor to its greatest place-value position. But, rounding to a lesser position helps you find an estimate that is closer to the actual product.

EXAMPLE 1

a. Round to estimate the product: 3 × 407

METHOD 1

Round 407 to the hundreds place.

Round: 407 rounds to 400.

Multiply the rounded factor.

$$\begin{array}{r} 400 \\ \times \quad 3 \\ \hline 1{,}200 \end{array}$$

$3 \times 407 \approx 1{,}200$

METHOD 2

Round 407 to the tens place.

Round: 407 rounds to 410.

Multiply the rounded factor.

$$\begin{array}{r} 410 \\ \times \quad 3 \\ \hline 1{,}230 \end{array}$$

$3 \times 407 \approx 1{,}230$

b. Compare the two estimates.

The actual product of 3 × 407 is 1,221.

$1{,}200 + 21 = 1{,}221$
$1{,}230 - 9 = 1{,}221$

Since 21 > 9, rounding to the lesser place, tenths, gives the closer estimate.

SEARCH

To see step-by-step videos of these problems, enter the page number into the SWadvantage.com Search Bar.

EXAMPLE 2

Round to estimate the product: 9 × $14.85

Round both factors.

$14.85 rounds to $15.00
9 rounds to 10.

Multiply the rounded numbers.

$$\begin{array}{r} \$15.00 \\ \times \quad 10 \\ \hline \$150.00 \end{array}$$

9 × $14.85 is about $150.00.

Use Compatible Numbers

Another way to estimate a product is by using *compatible numbers.* **Compatible numbers** are numbers that are easy to multiply mentally.

EXAMPLE 3

Suppose you found this product: 847 × 19 = 16,093. Estimate to see if your actual product makes sense. Use compatible numbers.

Calculated Product		Estimated Product
847	847 is close to 800:	800
× 19	19 is close to 20:	× 20
16,093		16,000

The estimate, 16,000, is close to the actual product, 16,093. Your actual product makes sense.

EXAMPLE 4

Jarad used a calculator to multiply 7,890 by 7. The calculator display showed the product: 5,523. Use compatible numbers to estimate the product. Decide if Jarad input the digits correctly.

Calculator Product		Estimated Product
5,523	7,890 is close to 8,000.	8,000
		× 7
		56,000

The estimate, 56,000, has five digits, but the number in the calculator display has only four digits. So, Jarad must have input the factors incorrectly.

In fact, he went too fast and entered 789 instead of 7,890. When he reentered the numbers he got the product 55,230, which is close to 56,000.

Watch Out !

Whenever you use a calculator to multiply, always estimate to make sure that the product in the display makes sense. It's easy to enter digits incorrectly.

Estimating Products

Use estimation to find an approximate product or to check that an actual product is reasonable. Estimation methods include:

- Rounding
- Compatible Numbers
- Front-End Estimation

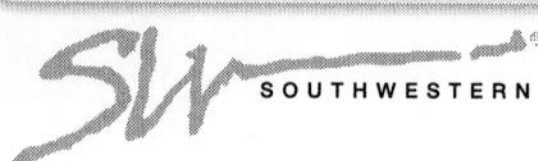

Use Front-End Estimation

Another way to estimate a product is to use *front-end estimation.* With this method, you multiply only the digits on the far left (front end) of each number.

EXAMPLE 5

Use front-end estimation to estimate the product: 53 × 75.

The front-end digit is in the tens place in both factors.

		Estimated Product
75	Change 75 to 70.	70
× 53	Change 53 to 50.	× 50
		3,500

The product of 53 × 75 is about 3,500.

The actual product of 53 × 75 is 3,975, almost 500 more than the estimate. You may find that for multiplication, other methods give a closer estimate.

Watch Out !

The estimate you get using front-end estimation may not be very close to the actual product.

Estimating to Solve Problems

Some word problems do not require an exact answer, and you can estimate the answer. But watch out. In problems where you must find out if a certain quantity is "enough," you must *overestimate* the quantity needed by rounding up. In other problems where you want to be certain you have reached a minimum amount, you can *underestimate* by rounding down.

EXAMPLE 6

Terrell and his father are birdwatchers. Terrell has seen 37 different kinds of birds. His father has seen 8 times as many different kinds of birds. About how many different kinds of birds has Terrell's father seen?

Think: I need to find 8 times 37.

Round the factor 37 to 40.

Mentally multiply: 40 × 8 = 320

Terrell's father has seen about 320 different kinds of birds.

This is an overestimate because you rounded 37 up to 40. However, in this problem an overestimate is okay.

Try It This Way

Use this example to help you visualize the difference between underestimating and overestimating.

3 × 10 = 30
3 × 16 = 48
3 × 20 = 60

30 < **48** < 60

under ← **48** → over
estimate estimate

EXAMPLE 7

Terrell's father wants to buy binoculars and a copy of *A Field Guide to Birds* for each of his 3 children. Binoculars cost $64.75, and a field guide costs $19.95. Is $250 enough to pay for these items?

Overestimate to be sure that $250 will be enough.

STEP 1 Estimate the prices of one of each item.

Binoculars: Round $64.75 up to $70.
Field Guide: Round $19.95 to $20.

STEP 2 Find the sum and multiply by 3.

$\$70 + \$20 = \$90$

$\$90 \times 3 = \$270$

$250 < 270$, so $250 is not enough to pay for the items.

Notice that if you had rounded $64.50 to $60, your estimate would be $(60 + 20) \times 3 = \$240$. Underestimating shows that $250 is enough money when that is not the case.

Need More HELP

When you *overestimate* money amounts and get an estimate that is less than the actual product, you know you have enough money to pay for something.

EXAMPLE 8

One morning, a muffin shop sold 31 bran muffins. It sold 3 times as many corn muffins as bran muffins. It also sold 2 times as many carrot muffins as corn muffins. About how many muffins were sold altogether?

STEP 1 Estimate the number of bran muffins sold.

Round 31 to 30.

STEP 2 Estimate the number of corn muffins sold.

3×30 bran muffins = about 90 corn muffins

STEP 3 Estimate the number of carrot muffins sold.

2×90 corn muffins = about 180 carrot muffins

STEP 4 Add all types of muffins.

$30 + 90 + 180 = 300$

About 300 muffins were sold altogether.

This is an underestimate because you rounded 31 to 30. In this problem, an underestimate is okay.

SEARCH

To see step-by-step videos of these problems, enter the page number into the SWadvantage.com Search Bar.

Estimating Quotients

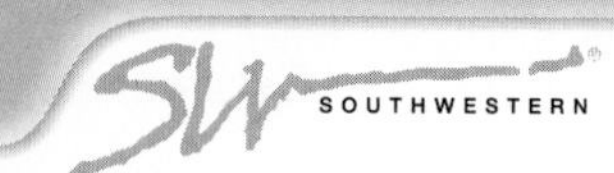

Rounding to Estimate Quotients

When you do not need an exact quotient, you can *estimate*. An **estimate** tells you *about* how much or *about* how many. You also can estimate to predict a quotient or to be sure that an exact quotient is reasonable. One way to estimate is by *rounding*.

SEARCH

To see step-by-step videos of these problems, enter the page number into the SWadvantage.com Search Bar.

EXAMPLE 1

Round to estimate the quotient: $8\overline{)592}$

STEP 1 Round the dividend 592 to the hundreds place.

$\overline{)592}$ rounds to $\overline{)600}$

STEP 2 Use mental math to divide the rounded dividend by 8.

$$\begin{array}{r} 75 \\ 8\overline{)600} \end{array}$$

The quotient is *about* 75. A calculator shows that the exact quotient is 74.

EXAMPLE 2

Round to estimate the quotient: \$23.76 ÷ 12

STEP 1 Round the dividend \$23.76 to the nearest ten dollars.

\$23.76 rounds to \$20.00

STEP 2 Round the divisor to the nearest 10.

12 rounds to 10.

STEP 3 Divide the rounded numbers.

\$20 ÷ 10 = \$2

The quotient is *about* \$2. A calculator shows that the exact quotient is \$1.98.

Estimating a Quotient

Use estimation to find an approximate quotient or to check that your actual quotient is reasonable. Estimation methods include:

- Rounding
- Compatible Numbers
- Front-End Estimation

Using Compatible Numbers

Another way to estimate a quotient is by using *compatible numbers.* **Compatible numbers** are numbers that are easy to divide mentally.

EXAMPLE 3

Suppose you calculate the quotient of 263 divided by 5. Use compatible numbers to estimate the quotient. If your estimate is close to your calculated quotient, then your answer is reasonable.

Choose a pair of compatible numbers that you can divide using mental math.

METHOD 1

Use the compatible numbers 5 and 30.

Calculated Quotient		Estimated Quotient
$5\overline{)263}$ = 52 R3	263 is close to 300. Divide 300 by 5.	$5\overline{)300}$ = 60

60 is close to 52R3.

METHOD 2

Use the compatible numbers 5 and 25.

Actual Quotient		Estimated Quotient
$5\overline{)263}$ = 52 R3	263 is close to 250. Divide 250 by 5.	$5\overline{)250}$ = 50

50 is close to 52R3.

Both estimates show that your calculated quotient is reasonable. Because 263 is closer to 250 than to 300, writing 263 as 250 gives a closer estimate.

Need More HELP

Sometimes, estimating two ways makes sense. In Example 3, the estimated quotient 60 is an *overestimate.* The estimated quotient 50 is an *underestimate.* You can be sure that the actual quotient is a number between these two numbers.

EXAMPLE 4

Kyra used a calculator to divide 35,298 by 6. She got this number on the calculator display: 5,883. Use compatible numbers to decide if Kyra input the calculation correctly.

35,298 is close to 36,000. Divide 36,000 by 6.

Estimate: $6\overline{)36{,}000}$ = 6,000

The estimated quotient, 6,000, is close to the number in the display. Kyra most likely input the digits correctly.

Watch Out!

If you use a calculator to divide, always estimate to make sure that the number in the display makes sense.

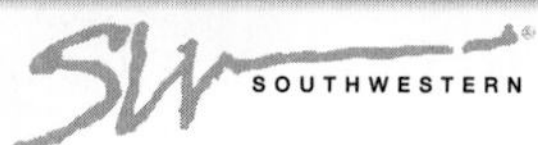

Using Front-End Estimation

Another way to estimate a quotient is to use *front-end estimation*. With this method, you use the digit at the front, or beginning, of the dividend, and you replace the other digits with zeros. Then divide to get an estimated quotient.

SEARCH

To see step-by-step videos of these problems, enter the page number into the SWadvantage.com Search Bar.

EXAMPLE 5

Use front-end estimation to estimate the quotient: 981 ÷ 3

STEP 1 The front-end digit, 9, is in the hundreds place. Change 981 to 900.

STEP 2 Divide to estimate the quotient.

Estimated Quotient

$$3\overline{)900}\quad 300$$

The quotient is *about* 300. A calculator shows that the actual quotient is 327.

Estimating to Solve Problems

Decide whether or not you need to find the exact answer to solve a division problem. Sometimes, all you need is an estimate. When an estimate will do, be careful. In problems where you must find out if a certain quantity is "enough," you must *overestimate* the quantity needed. In other problems where you want to be certain you have reached a minimum amount, you can *underestimate*.

EXAMPLE 6

A store had a 1-hour sale on cameras. The sales for this period totaled $657.92. Eight people bought cameras. About how much was the average price of the eight cameras sold?

The question asks *about* how much, so an estimated answer is all you need. Use compatible numbers to estimate the price.

Think: Eight people bought cameras, and $8 \times 8 = 64$.

$657.92 is close to $640.

Divide: $640 \div 8 = 80$

The average price of the eight cameras sold was about $80.

A calculator shows that the average price was $82.24 per camera. However, in this situation, it does not matter if the estimate is an underestimate or an overestimate.

EXAMPLE 7

A tour bus company has mini buses that can seat 10 passengers. A group of 55 students and teachers want to rent buses to go on a field trip. What is the fewest number of buses that they need to rent?

STEP 1 Use front-end estimation. Change 55 to 50.

STEP 2 Mentally divide:

50 passengers ÷ 10 passengers per bus = 5 buses

STEP 3 Think: 55 was rounded down to 50, so this is an underestimate. Ask yourself, are 5 buses really enough?

Multiply to find out: 5 buses × 10 passengers per bus = 50 passengers

There are 55 students and teachers, so they will need 6 buses. In this situation, an underestimate gives a number of buses that will not seat 55 people.

EXAMPLE 8

There are 23 students in Mr. Kemp's class. They kept a class tally of the number of hours and the types of programs they watched on TV during a 1-month period.

Type of Program	Total Hours
Nature	62
Movies	111
Dancing	135
Sports	163
Cartoons	63

a. Estimate the average number of hours per month that each student spent watching sports.

STEP 1 Find the number of hours spent watching sports.

163 hours

STEP 2 Divide 163 hours by 23 students. Use numbers compatible for the divisor and the dividend.

Change 163 to 160.

Change 23 to 20.

STEP 3 Use mental math to divide.

160 ÷ 20 = 8

The average number of hours a month that each student spent watching sports is 8 hours.

b. Does it matter if the answer is an overestimate or an underestimate?

No. You do not need to know if a certain number of hours are "enough" and you do not need to find a "minimum" number of hours.

Points, Lines, Planes, and Angles

What Came Before?

- Arithmetic operations
- Comparing, rounding, and estimating numbers

What's This About?

- Planes, points, and lines, including parallel and perpendicular lines
- Parts of lines—segments and rays
- Measuring and classifying angles

Practical Apps

- Crane operators must be able to judge the angle of the sling that holds the load they will move.
- Railroad engineers must make sure that train tracks are always parallel.

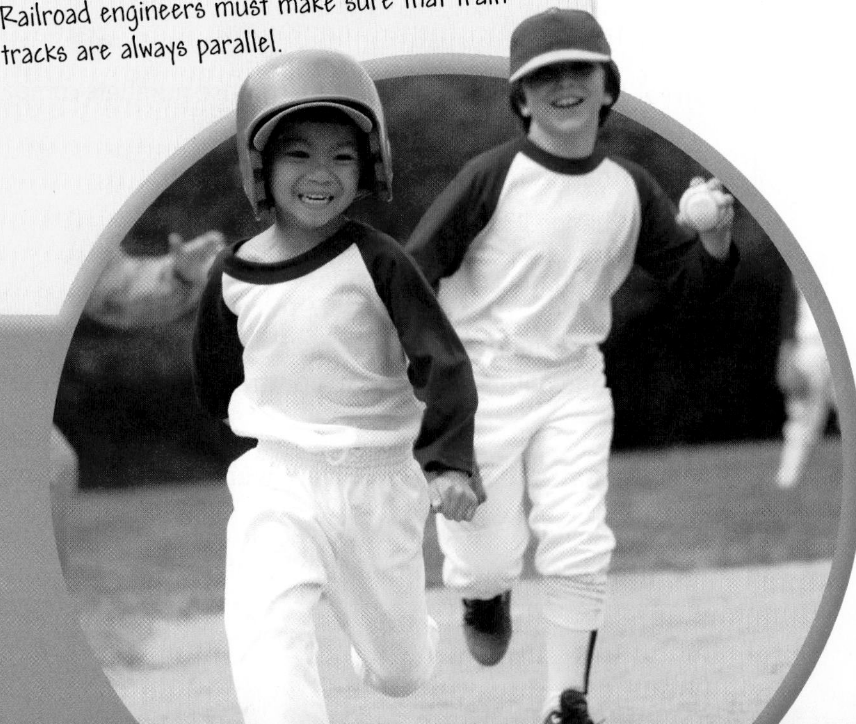

Q: What are the most geometric baseball teams?

A: The Tampa Bay Rays and the Anaheim Angles.

CONTENTS | UPLOAD | DOWNLOAD | *Foundations of Mathematics*

Topics	Vocabulary	Pages
Points and Lines in a Plane	*plane* *point* *line* *parallel lines* *intersecting lines* *perpendicular lines*	128–131
Segments, Rays, and Distance	*line segment* *ray*	132–135
Measuring Angles	*angle* *vertex* *protractor*	136–139
Classifying Angles	*right angle* *acute angle* *obtuse angle* *straight angle*	140–143
Skew Lines	*plane* *skew lines*	144–145
Special Pairs of Angles	*vertical angles* *congruent* *adjacent angles* *complementary angles* *supplementary angles* *transversal* *alternate interior angles* *alternate exterior angles*	146–151

You can find more practice problems online by visiting:
www.SWadvantage.com

Points and Lines in a Plane

What Is a Plane?

In geometry, a **plane** is a flat, or 2-dimensional, surface that goes on and on in each direction without ending. You may see a plane described as extending infinitely in all directions.

Need More HELP

The two arrowheads on the line mean that it goes on and on in both directions without ending.

A **point** is an exact location in space. Although points have no size, we use dots to show their locations and use letters to name them.

A **line** is a straight path in a plane that continues without end in two directions.

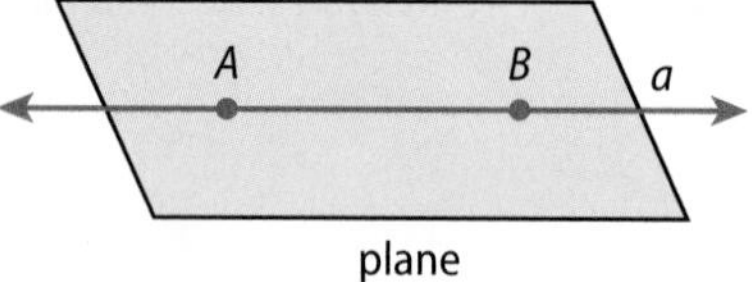

The flat surface of the plane continues without end. Points *A* and *B* are on line *a*.

a. Draw and label two points on the part of the plane shown. Label one point *P* and label the other point *R*.

You can place the points anywhere on the plane. One placement is shown.

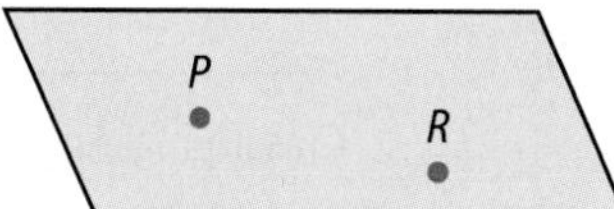

b. Draw a line through the two points and label it *m*.

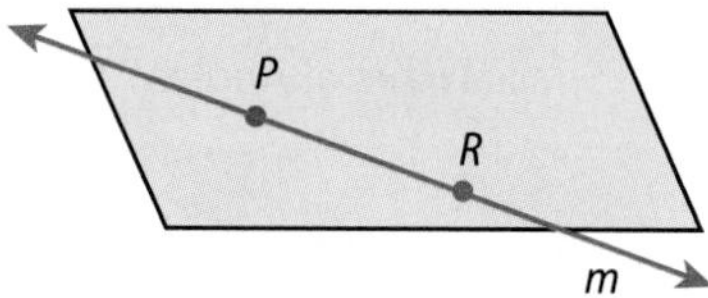

Another way to name line *m* is by writing the names of two points on the line and drawing a double arrow over them, $\overleftrightarrow{PR}$. Read this as, "line *PR*." You can also name the line $\overleftrightarrow{RP}$.

Points and Lines on a Plane

A **plane** is a flat surface that extends forever.

A **point** is an exact location in space.

A **line** is a straight path in a plane and goes on infinitely in both directions.

Parallel Lines

Parallel lines lie in the same plane and are exactly the same distance apart. No matter how far parallel lines are extended, the distance between them does not change.

The symbol || is used to show that lines are parallel. Read $\overleftrightarrow{AB} \parallel \overleftrightarrow{EF}$ as "line *AB* is parallel to line *EF*."

Ways to REMEMBER

The parallel symbol || shows lines that are the same distance apart. You may have heard of parallel parking, where the car is in line with the direction of the curb, or parallel to it.

EXAMPLE 2

Draw parallel lines *LM* and *OP*.

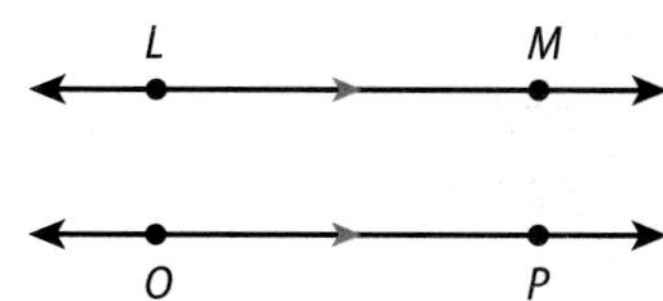

Here is one way to draw the parallel lines. The small arrowheads on the lines mean that the lines are parallel. You could also draw parallel vertical lines or parallel slanted lines.

Intersecting Lines

Intersecting lines are lines that share exactly one point. Some intersecting lines cross each other.

EXAMPLE 3

a. Draw intersecting lines *QR* and *ST* that cross at point *X*.

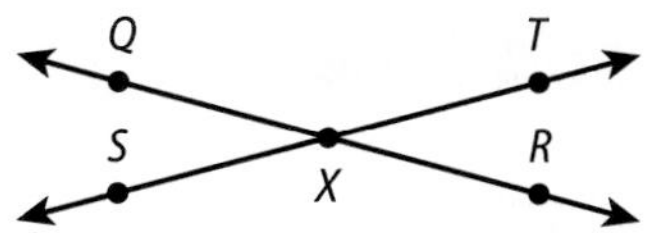

Here is one way to draw the lines. The only requirement is that the lines intersect.

b. Write two true statements about the lines.

Lines *QR* and *ST* intersect at point *X*.

$\overleftrightarrow{QR}$ and $\overleftrightarrow{ST}$ are not parallel.

SEARCH

To see step-by-step videos of these problems, enter the page number into the SWadvantage.com Search Bar.

SOUTHWESTERN

Perpendicular Lines

When two lines intersect, and the 4 angles on all sides of the intersection are exactly the same, the lines are called **perpendicular lines**. Those four angles are called *right angles*. (For more on right angles, go to p. 140.) Sometimes the symbol ⊥ is used to show that lines are perpendicular. Perpendicular lines intersect.

Ways to REMEMBER

The symbol ⊥ tells that two lines are perpendicular. When the symbol is used between the labels for line *HI* and line *JK*, you can say "*HI* is perpendicular to *JK*."

EXAMPLE 4

a. Draw perpendicular lines *HI* and *JK*. Use a right angle symbol to show that they are perpendicular.

Here is one way to draw the lines. The only requirement is that the lines intersect to form right angles.

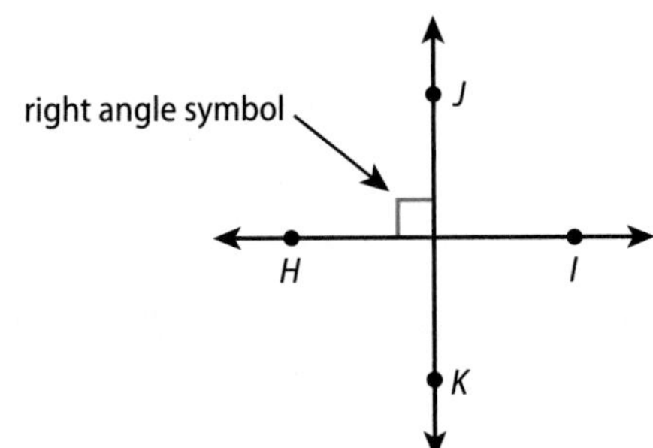

b. Use a symbol to write a statement that says the lines are perpendicular.

You can write the statement in any of the following ways.

line *HI* ⊥ line *JK* line *JK* ⊥ line *HI*

$\overleftrightarrow{HI} \perp \overleftrightarrow{JK}$ $\overleftrightarrow{JK} \perp \overleftrightarrow{HI}$

If you reverse the order of the points in the names, the statements are still true. For example, lines *IH* and *KJ* are perpendicular.

Identifying Points and Lines

EXAMPLE 5

Use the diagram to answer the questions.

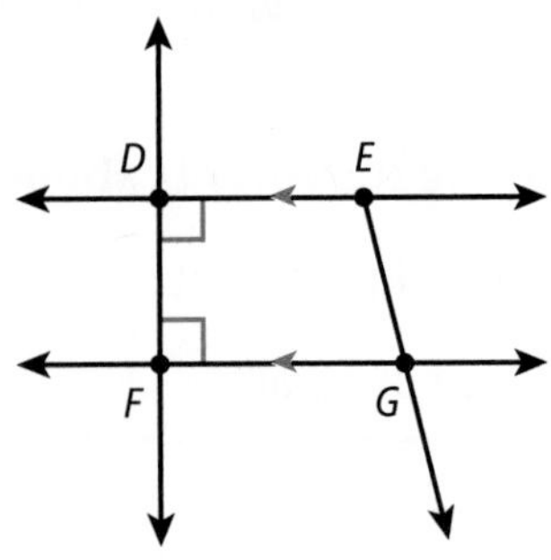

a. Name a pair of parallel lines.

Lines *DE* and *FG* are parallel.

b. Name a pair of perpendicular lines.

Lines *DF* and *DE* are perpendicular and lines *DF* and *FG* are perpendicular.

Watch Out !

EG is not a line because it extends in one direction only. *EG* is a ray. (See p. 133.) It intersects lines *DE* and *FG* but is not perpendicular to them.

Look around your environment. You can find parallel, intersecting, and perpendicular lines just about everywhere.

EXAMPLE 

Find examples of parallel, intersecting, and perpendicular lines in this picture. Identify at least two of each.

Parallel lines include:
- the boards on the fence
- the stripes on the boy's shirt

Intersecting lines include:
- the strings on the basketball net
- the label on the green book and the edge of the book

Perpendicular lines include:
- the side of the window and the bottom of the window
- the boards in the fence and the ground

SEARCH

To see step-by-step videos of these problems, enter the page number into the SWadvantage.com Search Bar.

Parallel, Perpendicular, and Intersecting Lines

Parallel lines lie in the same plane and are the same distance apart. They never intersect. The symbol || means that lines are parallel.

Perpendicular lines intersect to form right angles. The symbol $\perp$ means that lines are perpendicular.

Intersecting lines are lines that share exactly one point. Here are two ways lines might intersect: $\times$ and $\perp$.

Segments, Rays, and Distance

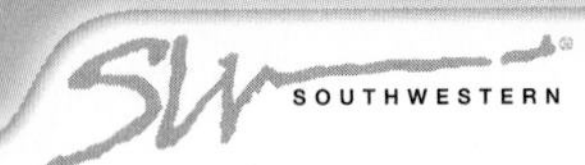

What Is a Line Segment?

Remember, a *line* is a straight path in a plane that continues without end in two directions.

A **line segment** is a part of a line between two endpoints. Use the endpoints to name the line segment

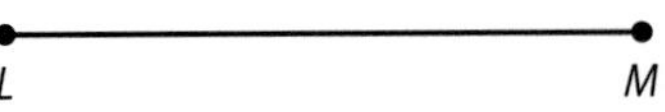

The figure above shows line segment *LM*. Another way to write this is with a small bar above the letters, $\overline{LM}$. Read it as, "line segment *LM*." You can also name the line segment in reverse order as line segment *ML* or $\overline{ML}$.

EXAMPLE 1

Write the name of the figure below in four ways.

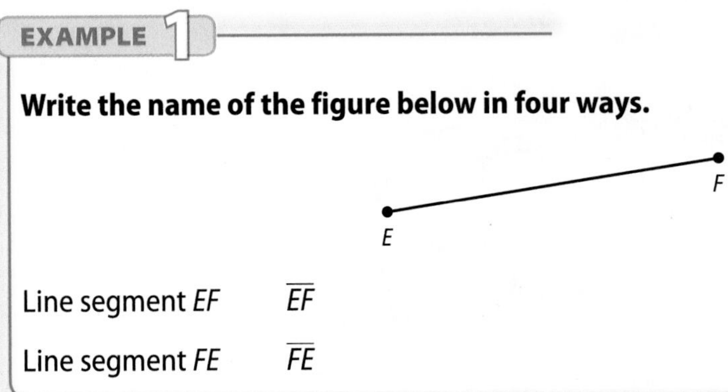

Line segment *EF* $\overline{EF}$

Line segment *FE* $\overline{FE}$

EXAMPLE 2

SEARCH

To see step-by-step videos of these problems, enter the page number into the SWadvantage.com Search Bar.

Look at the figures below.

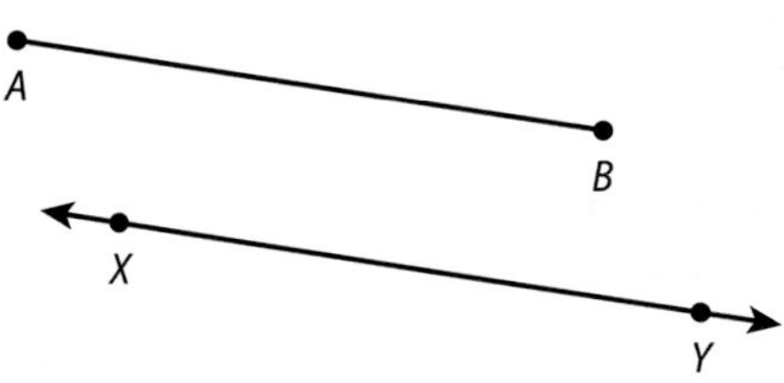

a. Which figure is a line segment? Explain your answer.

The top figure is a line segment because it has two endpoints, *A* and *B*.

b. Name each figure in words and by using a symbol.

Top figure:	line segment *AB*	$\overline{AB}$
Bottom figure:	line *XY*	$\overleftrightarrow{XY}$

Rays

A **ray** is part of a line that begins at a point and extends forever in one direction.

The figure above shows ray *VW*. Another way to write this is with a small arrow above the letters, $\overrightarrow{VW}$. Read this as, "ray *VW*."

When naming a ray, the endpoint of the ray comes first. You cannot name a ray in reverse order because it goes in one direction only.

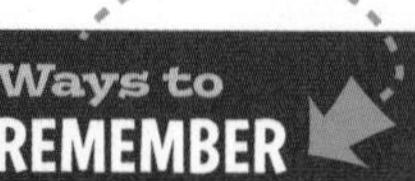

A *segment* is a portion of something. You may watch a segment of your favorite program on TV. A *ray* moves in one direction from a point, like a ray of light from a flashlight.

EXAMPLE 3

a. Draw and label ray *YZ*.

This is one way to draw ray *YZ*. The ray can extend from point *Y* in any direction.

b. Write the name of the ray, using a symbol instead of the word "ray."

$\overrightarrow{YZ}$

GOT TO KNOW!

Naming Line Segments and Rays

Use capital, italic letters to name line segments and rays.

A **line segment** is part of a line between *two* endpoints.

This is line segment *QR*, or $\overline{QR}$.

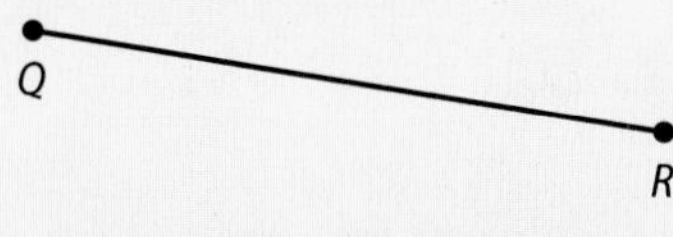

A **ray** is part of a line that begins at *one* endpoint. It extends forever in one direction.

This is ray *TU*, or $\overrightarrow{TU}$.

SOUTHWESTERN

Rays and Segments

EXAMPLE 4

The figure below shows line *AZ*. It contains several line segments and rays.

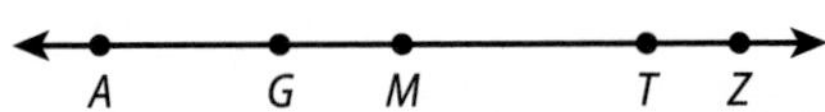

a. Can you use points *A* and *G* to name a line segment? Why or why not?

Yes. A line segment is a part of a line between two endpoints.

Line segment *AG* names the part of the line between point *A* and point *G*.

b. Which is a ray, *MT* or *MZ*? Explain your choice.

MZ

Ray *MZ* is a part of the line that starts at point *M* and extends through point *Z* forever. *MT* names a line segment that starts at point *M* and ends at point *T*.

Distance

When you know one distance along a line, you can often figure out other distances. The notation *AB* (without the bar) means the length of $\overline{AB}$. You read *AB* as "the length of line segment *AB*."

EXAMPLE 5

Look at the figure below. If *AB* = 5 units and *BC* = 2 units, what is the length of line segment *AC*?

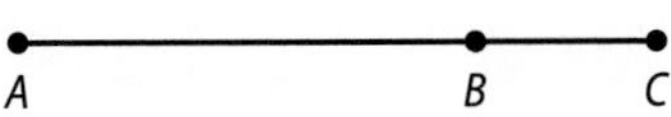

To find the length of line segment *AC*, add the lengths of line segments *AB* and *BC*.

$AB + BC = AC$

5 units + 2 units = 7 units

The length of $\overline{AC}$ is 7 units.

In Examples 5–7, the figures show line segments. In the questions and answers the line segments are simply called by their two points.

EXAMPLE 6

Look at the figure below. If $MN = 4$ units and $MO = 10$ units, what is the length of line segment NO?

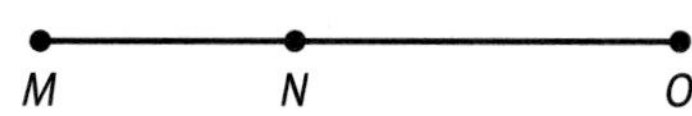

To find *NO*, subtract *MN* from *MO*.

10 units − 4 units = 6 units

The length of line segment *NO* is 6 units.

SEARCH

To see step-by-step videos of these problems, enter the page number into the SWadvantage.com Search Bar.

EXAMPLE 7

Look at the figure below. $AE = 16$ units and $BD = 10$ units. $\overline{AB}$ is twice as long as $\overline{DE}$. What are the lengths of segments AB and DE?

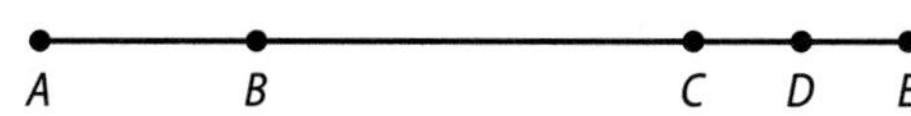

STEP 1 Find the total of *AB* and *DE*.

$AE - BD = AB + DE$

Subtract: $AE - BD$

$= 16 - 10$

$= 6$ units

The total of *AB* and *DE* is 6 units.

STEP 2 Find *AB* and then *DE*.

Think: You know that *AB* is twice *DE*.

You know that the total length of the two segments is 6 units.

Use logical reasoning: If *AB* were 2, then *DE* would be 1, for a total of 3 units.

Since $3 \times 2 = 6$, double the measures.

If *AB* were 4 units, then *DE* would be 2 units for a total of 6 units.

The length of $\overline{AB}$ is 4 units and the length of $\overline{DE}$ is 2 units.

CHECK You can add the lengths you found to the given *BD*. If your calculations are correct, the total should be $AE = 16$ units.

$AB + DE + BD = 16$ units

$4 + 2 + 10 = 16$ units ✔

Measuring Angles

SOUTHWESTERN

What Is an Angle?

An **angle** is a figure formed by two rays with a common endpoint. The endpoint of the angle is called the **vertex**.

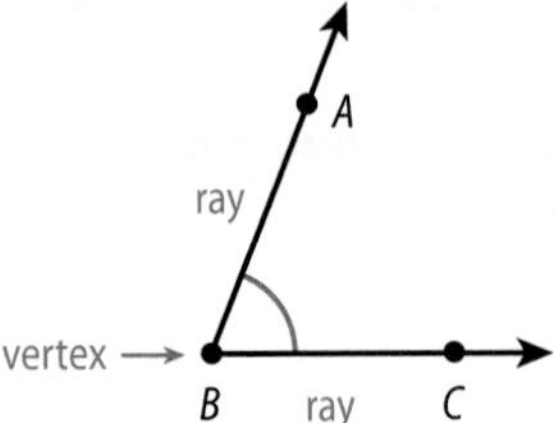

There is more than one way to name an angle. You can name the angle above in the following ways.

- Use three capital letters with the vertex as the middle letter: $\angle ABC$ or $\angle CBA$.
- Use the name of the vertex only: $\angle B$.

Sometimes there is a number in the vertex of an angle. In these cases, you can use the number to name the angle. For example, $\angle 1$.

SEARCH

To see step-by-step videos of these problems, enter the page number into the SWadvantage.com Search Bar.

EXAMPLE 1

Look at the angle below.

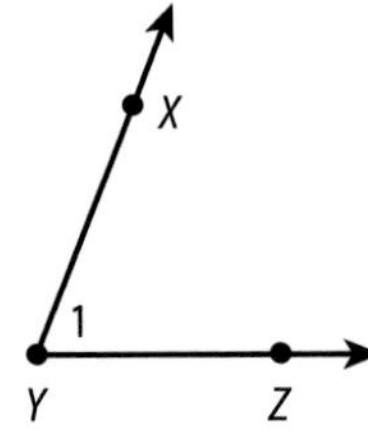

a. Name the rays that form the angle.

ray *YZ* and ray *YX*

b. Name the angle in four different ways.

$\angle Y$, $\angle 1$, $\angle XYZ$, $\angle ZYX$

EXAMPLE 2

Look at the figure below. Why would it be difficult to correctly identify $\angle N$?

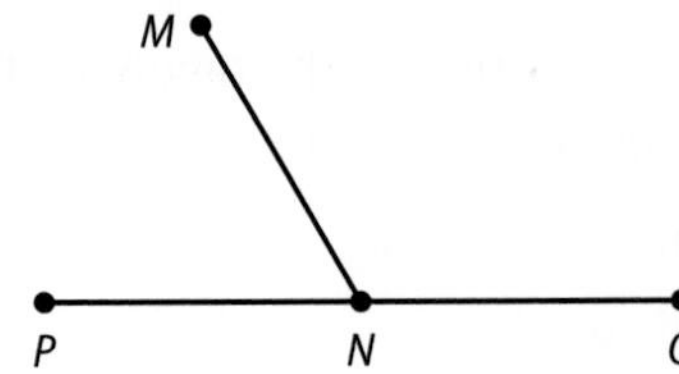

It would be difficult because $\angle N$ could mean either $\angle MNO$ or $\angle MNP$.

Measuring Angles

The size of an angle is measured in degrees (°). A **protractor** is a tool used to measure angles. It has an inner and an outer scale that go in opposite directions. Each scale goes from 0° to 180°.

To measure an angle by using a protractor, follow these steps.

Find the measure of $\angle XYZ$.

- Place the center point of the protractor over the vertex of the angle.
- Line up one ray of the angle with 0°.
- Look where the other ray crosses the scale of the protractor.

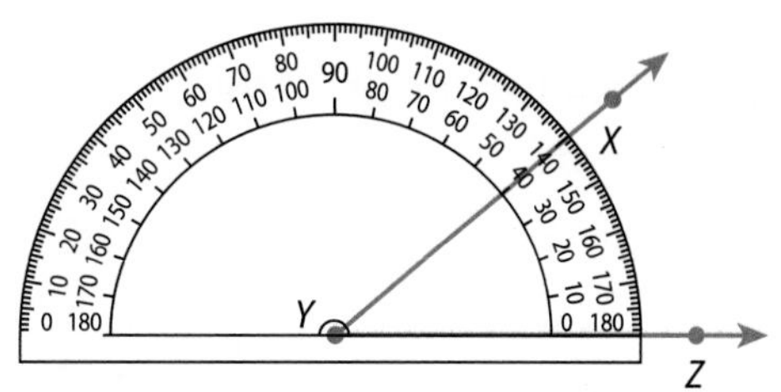

In $\angle XYZ$, the vertex of the angle is at point Y. Ray YZ is at 0° on the scale. Ray YX crosses the scale at the 140/40. Count up from 0° to 40°. $\angle XYZ$ measures 40°.

> **Watch Out !**
>
> Different types of protractors mark their "center point" differently. If you move straight down from 90 on the scale, you should find the center point.
>
> Be certain you use the correct scale. The inner and outer scales can vary. If the angle opens to the right, count up from the 0 on the right. If it opens to the left, count up from the 0 on the left.

EXAMPLE 3

Use the steps above to find the measure of $\angle EFG$.

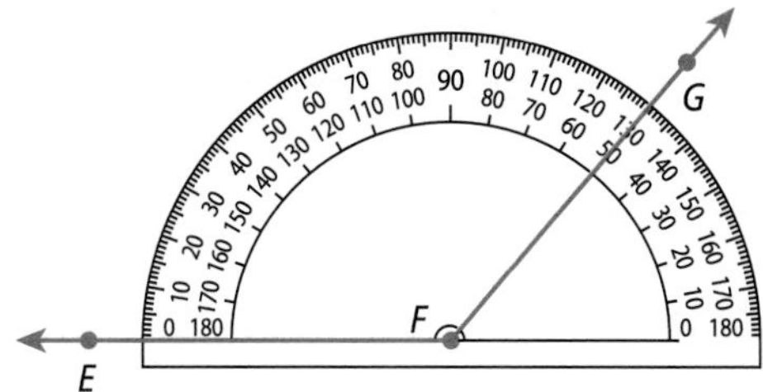

STEP 1 Place the center point of the protractor over the vertex of the angle, point F.

STEP 2 Line up ray FE with 0° on the protractor.

STEP 3 Look where ray FG crosses the scale. The scale reads 130/50. Count up from 0 to 130.

$\angle EFG$ measures 130°.

Measuring Angles

Some newer model protractors have a swing arm. With these protractors, place the vertex at the center point of the protractor and line up one ray with 0°. Then move the swing arm so it covers the other ray. This will help you see the measure on the scale. Exercises 4 and 5 show a swing arm protractor.

Watch Out !

On this protractor, the direction of the inner and outer scales is opposite that on the protractor on the previous pages. Be sure you understand the scales on your protractor.

EXAMPLE 4

What is the measure of ∠*TUV*?

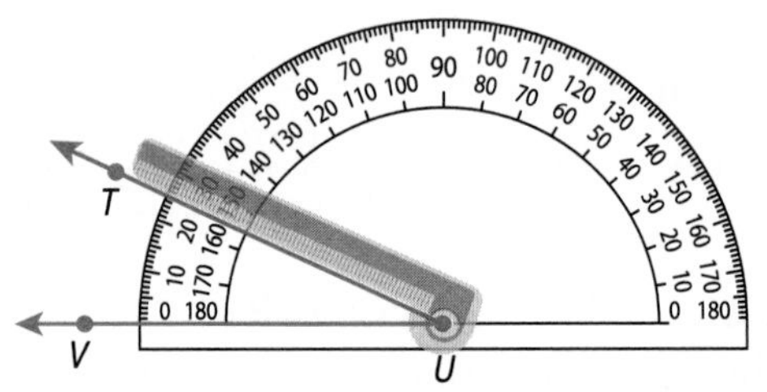

One ray is on 0°.

The swing arm on the other ray crosses the scale at halfway between 20 and 30.

Remember, you count up from 0° to 20°. Then count the tick marks: 21, 22, 23, 24, 25.

∠*TUV* measures 25°.

Need More HELP ?

You may see the measure of an angle written in this form: *m∠LMN*. Read this as, "the measure of angle *LMN*."

EXAMPLE 5

What is the measure of ∠*LMN*?

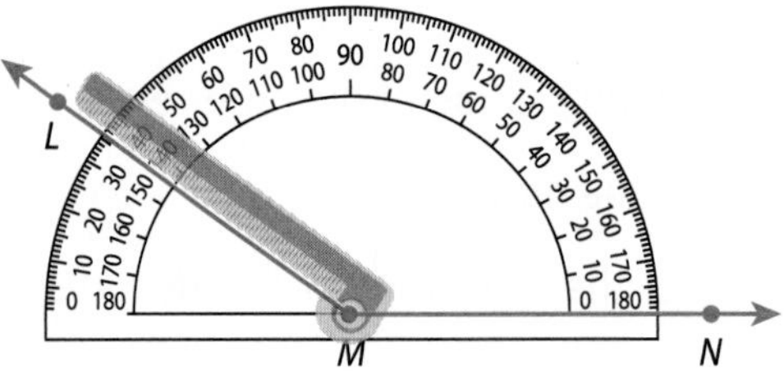

One ray is on 0°.

The swing arm on the other ray crosses the scale between 140 and 150.

Count up from 0° to 140°. Then count the tick marks: 141, 142, 143, 144.

∠*LMN* measures 144°.

Drawing Angles

You can use a protractor to draw an angle of a given size.

EXAMPLE 6

Draw an angle that measures 95°.

Suppose you choose to draw the angle opening to the right.

STEP 1 Draw a ray that points to the right.

STEP 2 Place the center point of the protractor over the endpoint of the ray. Line up the protractor with the ray so that the end of the ray is on the 0 mark on the scale.

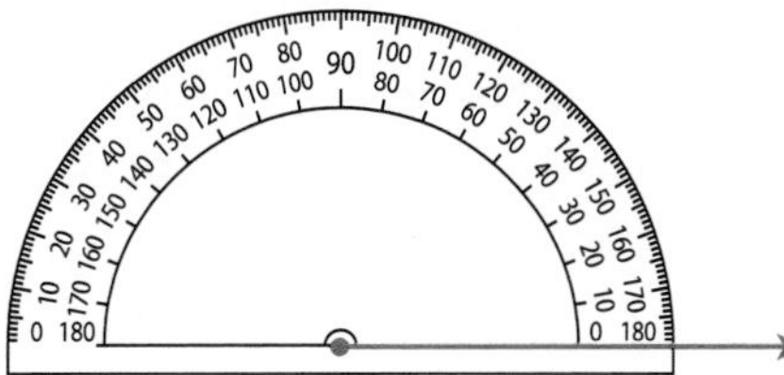

STEP 3 Draw a dot on your paper just above the 95 mark you reached after counting up from 0°.

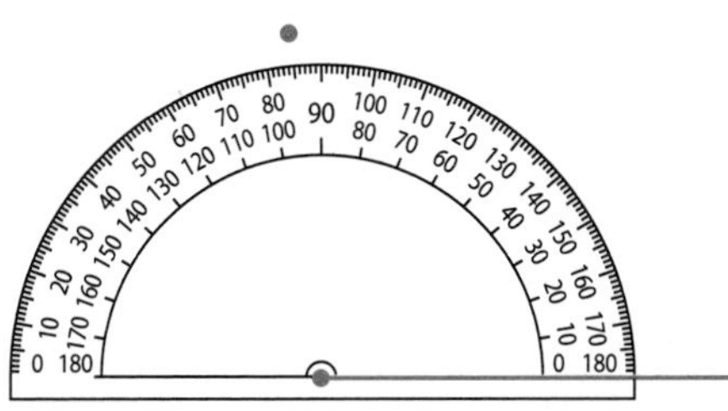

STEP 4 Remove the protractor. Use a ruler or straight edge to draw a line from the endpoint of the ray to the dot.

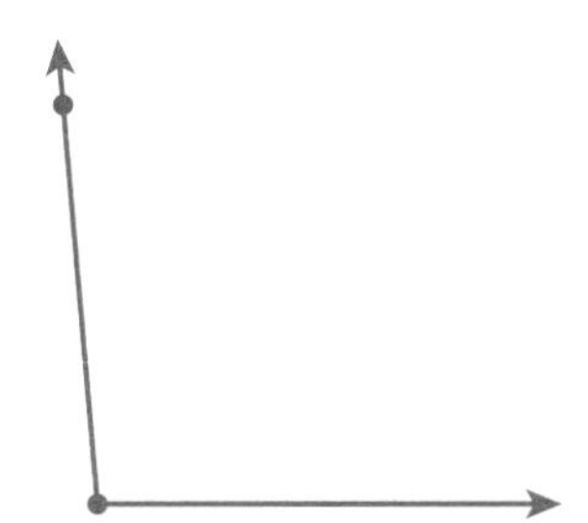

SEARCH

To see step-by-step videos of these problems, enter the page number into the SWadvantage.com Search Bar.

Naming and Measuring Angles

Name an angle in two ways.

- three capital letters with the vertex as the middle letter: $\angle ABC$ or $\angle CBA$
- the name of the vertex only, if no other angle could have this name: $\angle B$

An angle is measured in degrees (°) by using a tool called a protractor.

Classifying Angles

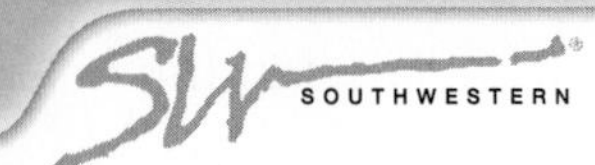

Using Measures to Classify Angles

The size of an angle is measured in degrees (°), and angles can be classified by their measures. A **right angle** measures exactly 90°. An **obtuse angle** measures between 90° and 180°. An **acute angle** measures between 0° and 90°. A **straight angle** measures exactly 180°.

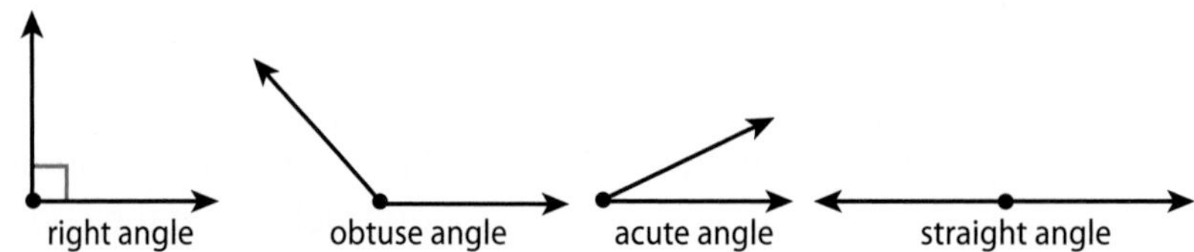

You can use right angles and straight angles as benchmarks. A *right angle* forms a square corner, so it is easy to recognize. A *straight angle* forms a straight line, so it is also easy to recognize.

- An angle that appears to be smaller than a right angle is an *acute angle*.
- An angle that appears to be greater than a right angle, but less than a straight angle, is an *obtuse angle*.

SEARCH

To see step-by-step videos of these problems, enter the page number into the SWadvantage.com Search Bar.

EXAMPLE 1

Classify each angle as *right, acute, obtuse,* or *straight*.

a.

This angle is greater than a right angle, but smaller than a straight angle. It is an obtuse angle.

b.

This angle is a straight line. It is a straight angle.

c.

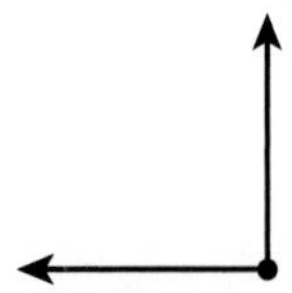

This angle forms a square corner. It is a right angle.

d.

This angle is smaller than a right angle. It is an acute angle.

EXAMPLE 2

Yasmine drew an acute angle. Could any of the angles below be the angle she drew? Explain your answer.

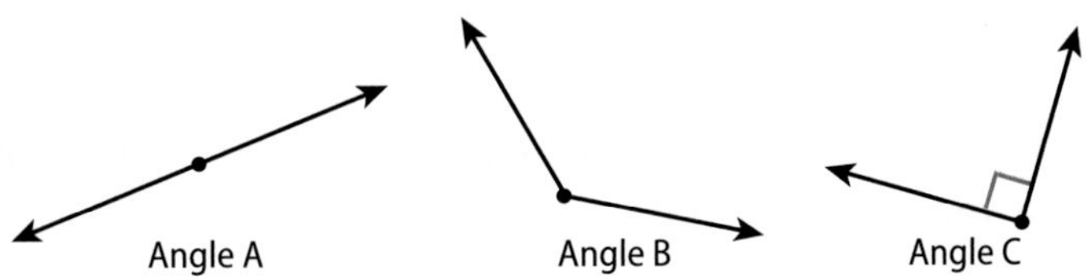

No. An acute angle is smaller than a right angle. Angle *C* is a right angle. Angles *A* and *B* are both greater than a right angle.

EXAMPLE 3

Find each given angle on the figure at the right. Then classify each angle as *right, acute, obtuse,* or *straight*. Explain your reasoning.

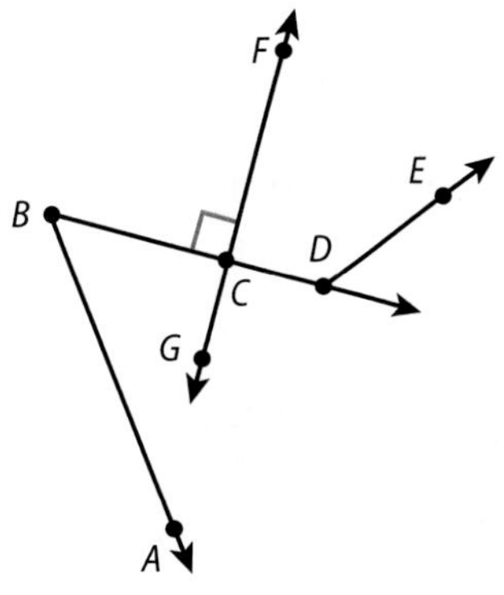

a. ∠*ABC* This is an acute angle because it is smaller than a square corner.

b. ∠*CDE* This is an obtuse angle because it is larger than a right angle.

c. ∠*FCG* This is a straight angle because it forms a straight line.

d. ∠*GCB* This is a right angle because *GC* and *BC* meet to form a square corner.

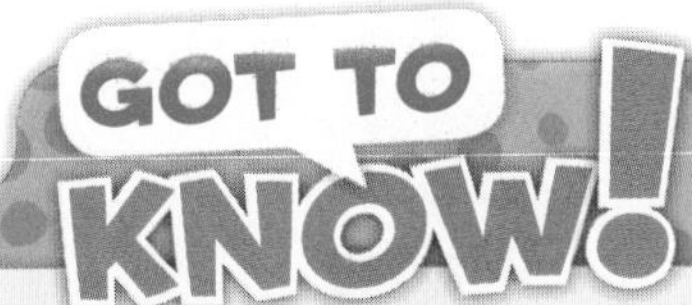

Remember that angles can be named starting with either ray, with the vertex in the middle. ∠*ABC* and ∠*CBA* are different ways to name the same angle.

GOT TO KNOW!

Classify Angles by Size

One way to classify an angle is by the size of the opening between the two rays that form the angle.

Angle Type	Measure	Example
Right angle	90°	
Acute angle	< 90°	
Obtuse angle	> 90° but < 180°	
Straight angle	180°	

Time to Classify Angles

The minute and the hour hand on a traditional clock meet to form an angle. You can classify these angles by their size.

EXAMPLE 4

Look at the angle formed by the hands on each clock. Classify each angle as *right*, *acute*, *obtuse*, or *straight*.

a. 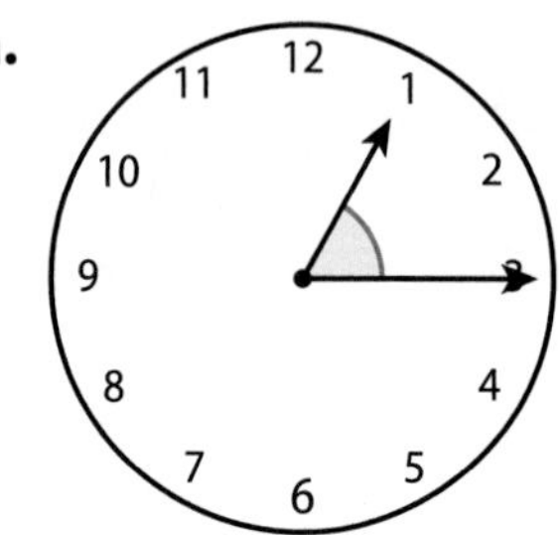

The hands form an acute angle.

b. 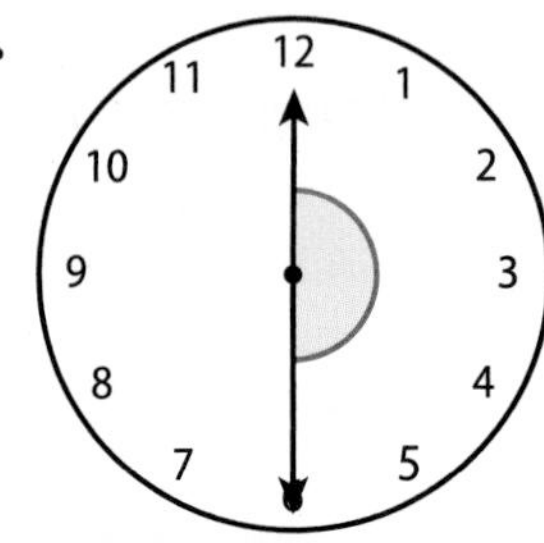

The hands form a straight angle.

c. 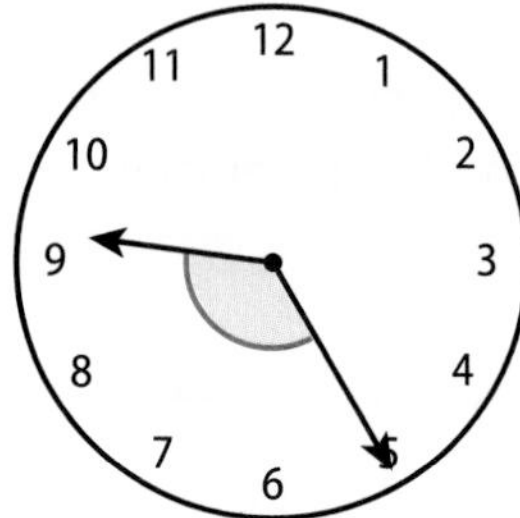

The hands form an obtuse angle.

Ways to REMEMBER

Use your hands to help you remember how right angles can look on a clock.

EXAMPLE 5

Tyler drew the hour hand on each clock. To which numbers could the minute hand point to form the given type of angle? Explain your answer.

a. right angle

The minute hand points to 3. A right angle forms a square corner. The hour hand could be at 12 or 6.

b. acute angle

The minute hand points to 2. An acute angle is smaller than a right angle. The hour hand could be at 12, 1, 3, or 4.

c. obtuse angle

The minute hand points to 7. An obtuse angle is $> 90°$ but $< 180°$. The hour hand could be at 11, 12, 2, or 3.

Try It This Way

For Exercise 5, use the side of a small sheet of paper to test each number. For (a), place the paper so it aligns with the vertex of the clock and the number 12. Decide if the angle is a right angle. Then test using the 1, the 2, and so on.

Identifying Angles All Around

You can find angles of every kind as you look around at home, at school—just about everywhere!

EXAMPLE 6

Look at the angles drawn on the picture. Then cover the right column of the table and read the descriptions in the left column of the table. Name the angles in the picture that match each description.

Angles that measure:	Names of Angles
exactly 180°	∠*ABC* and ∠*JKL*
between 0° and 90°	∠*MNO* and ∠*GHY*
exactly 90°	∠*DEF* and ∠*PQR*
more than 90°, but less than 180°	∠*GHI* and ∠*VWX*

Try It This Way

Use two pencils with erasers to help you see the angles. For example, place the eraser end of two pencils on point *W*, but face the pencils in opposite directions. One pencil will cross point *V* and the other will cross point *X*. Name the angle the pencils form, ∠*VWX*, and decide what type of angle it is (obtuse).

SEARCH

To see step-by-step videos of these problems, enter the page number into the SWadvantage.com Search Bar.

Skew Lines

For help with understanding planes, parallel lines, intersecting lines, and perpendicular lines, go to *Points and Lines in a Plane* on page 128.

What Is a Skew Line?

A **plane** is a flat, or 2-dimensional, surface that goes on and on in each direction without ending. Parallel lines, perpendicular lines, and lines that intersect lie in the same plane. Lines that do not intersect and are not parallel are called **skew lines**. Skew lines do not lie in the same plane.

Imagine a cube like the one below. Each side of the cube is in a different plane.

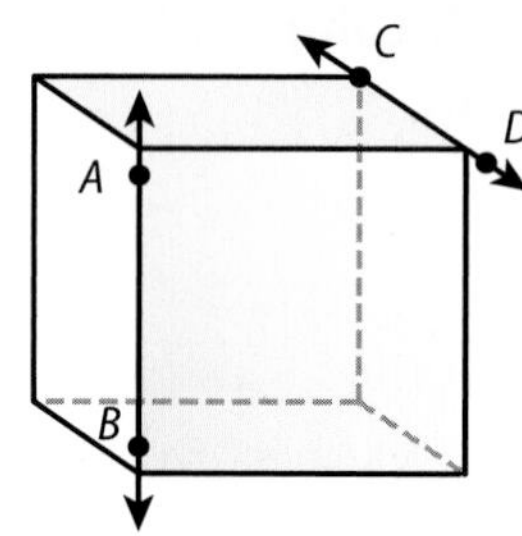

$\overleftrightarrow{AB}$ and $\overleftrightarrow{CD}$ are skew lines. They are not parallel. These lines will not intersect, no matter how far you extend them, because they lie in two different planes.

Watch Out!

Parallel lines must lie in the same plane.

Classify each pair of lines as *skew, perpendicular, parallel,* or *intersecting*.

a.

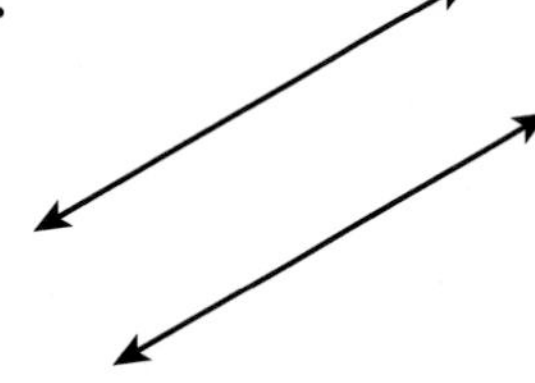

The lines appear to be on the same plane and equidistance apart. They are parallel lines.

b.

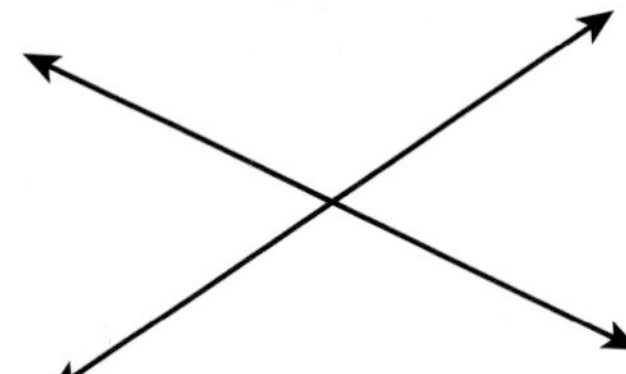

The lines cross each other. They are intersecting lines.

c.

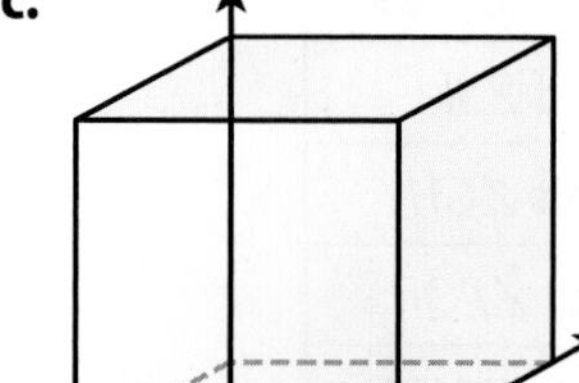

The lines are in two different planes. They are skew lines.

d.

The lines meet to form a right angle. They are perpendicular lines.

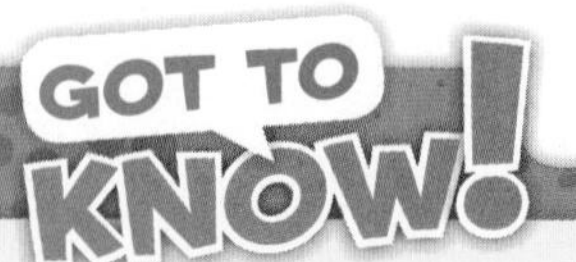

Skew Lines

Lines that lie in different planes are **skew lines.**

Skew lines are never parallel, and they never intersect.

EXAMPLE 2

Look at the cube at the right. Name the four lines that are skew to each given line.

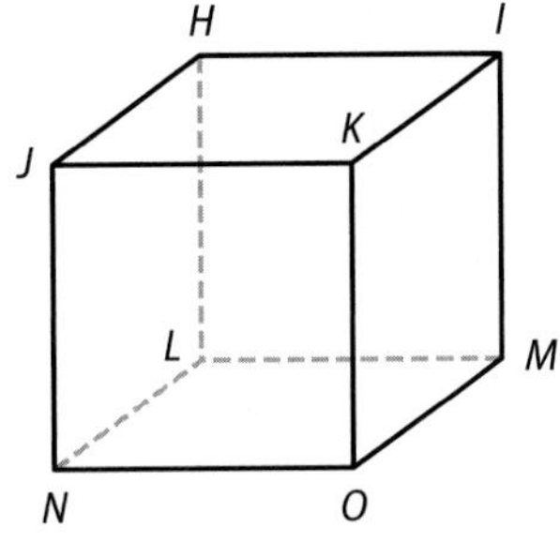

a. $\overline{HI}$

This is the top, back edge of the cube. The following lines are skew to it: $\overline{MO}$, $\overline{LN}$, $\overline{JN}$, and $\overline{KO}$.

b. $\overline{JN}$

This is the front, left edge of the cube. The following lines are skew to it: $\overline{LM}$, $\overline{HI}$, $\overline{IK}$, and $\overline{MO}$.

SEARCH

To see step-by-step videos of these problems, enter the page number into the SWadvantage.com Search Bar.

EXAMPLE 3

Read each statement. Decide whether it is: *always true, sometimes true,* or *never true.* Support your answer.

a. Skew lines can be parallel.

Never true. By definition, parallel lines are in the same plane and skew lines are in different planes.

b. Skew lines lie in more than one plane.

Always true. By definition, skew lines are in different planes.

c. Two lines in the same plane can be skew.

Never true. By definition, skew lines are in different planes.

d. The edges of a cube form skew lines.

Sometimes true. Edges that do not intersect form skew lines. For example the top left edge and the bottom right edge form skew lines. However, the top left edge and the top back edge intersect. They do not form skew lines.

EXAMPLE 4

Square *DCFG* makes up the right side of this cube. Square *EFGH* makes up the base of the cube. These two planes intersect at edge *GF*. Name a square on another plane that never intersects with square *DCFG*.

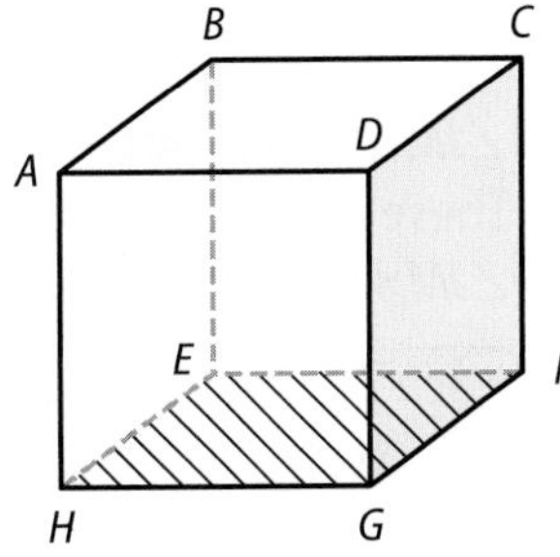

Square *ABEH* shares no sides with square *DCFG*. The planes in which these two squares lie will never intersect.

Special Pairs of Angles

Vertical and Adjacent Angles

Pairs of angles can be classified by their position and the sum of their measures. As shown in the figure below, **vertical angles** are the two opposite angles formed where two lines intersect. Vertical angles have exactly the same measure, so they are **congruent**. The figure below shows two pairs of vertical angles: $\angle QUT$ and $\angle SUR$, and $\angle QUS$ and $\angle TUR$.

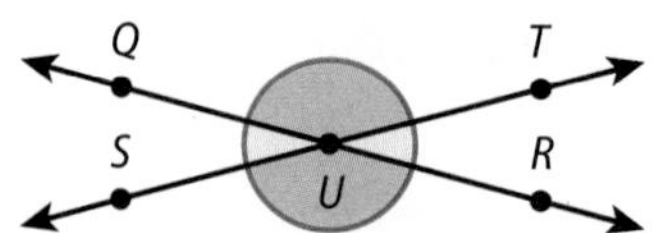

Angles that share an endpoint (vertex) and one side are **adjacent angles**. As shown on the figure below, adjacent angles may or may not be congruent.

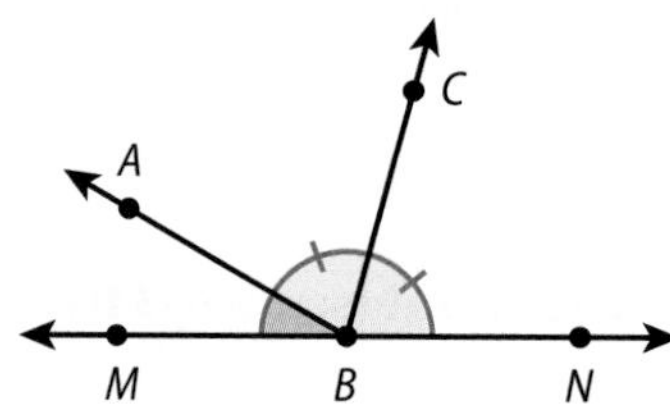

$\angle ABC$ is adjacent to both $\angle ABM$ and $\angle CBN$. $\angle ABC$ is congruent only to $\angle CBN$.

EXAMPLE 1

Identify the angle pairs at right as *vertical* or *adjacent*, and as *congruent* or *not congruent*. Support your answers.

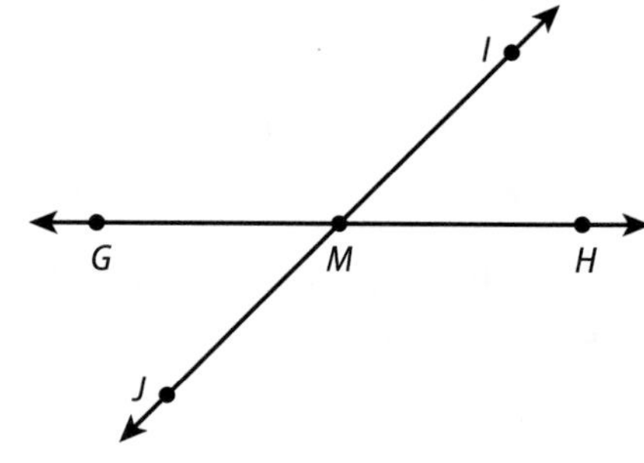

a. $\angle GMI$ and $\angle IMH$

These angles share the vertex M and side MI. They are adjacent angles.
$\angle GMI$ is greater than 90° and $\angle IMH$ is less than 90°, so the angles are not congruent.

b. $\angle HMI$ and $\angle GMJ$

These angles are opposite angles formed where two lines intersect. They are vertical angles. They are also congruent because vertical angles are equal in measure.

c. $\angle JMH$ and $\angle JMG$

These angles share the vertex M and side JM. They are adjacent angles.
$\angle JMH$ is greater than 90° and $\angle JMG$ is less than 90°, so the angles are not congruent.

SEARCH

To see step-by-step videos of these problems, enter the page number into the SWadvantage.com Search Bar.

EXAMPLE 2

In the figure, the angles are identified by the letters at their vertices.

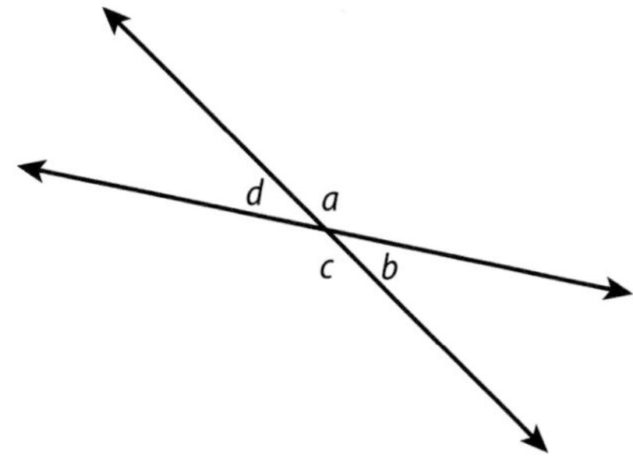

a. Name all the pairs of adjacent angles in the figure.

The adjacent angle pairs are: $\angle a$ and $\angle b$, $\angle b$ and $\angle c$, $\angle c$ and $\angle d$, $\angle d$ and $\angle a$.

b. Name all the pairs of vertical angles in the figure.

The vertical angle pairs are: $\angle a$ and $\angle c$ and $\angle d$ and $\angle b$.

Need More **HELP**

Vertices is the plural form of the word *vertex*.

For example, you can refer to the vertex of angle *a* or to the vertices of angles *a* and *c*.

EXAMPLE 3

In the figure at the right, angle *DEF* is a straight angle. Angle *b* measures 150°. Angles *a* and *c* are congruent. Find the measures of angles *a* and *c*.

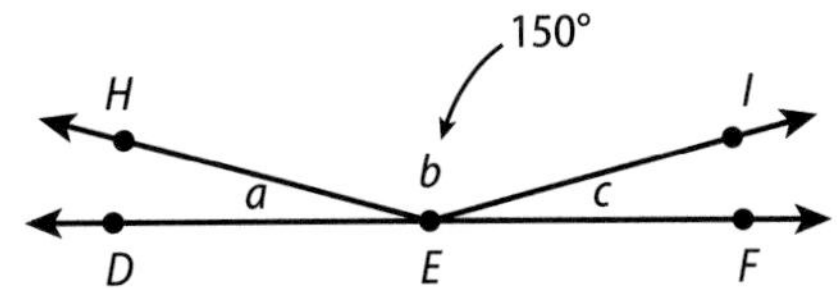

Need More **HELP**

Remember, a straight angle measures 180°.

THINK You know the following: a straight angle $= 180°$, $\angle b = 150°$, and $\angle a = \angle c$.
The sum of angle *a* and angle *c* must be: $\angle a + \angle c = 180° - \angle b$

Substitute and simplify. $\angle a + \angle c = 180° - 150°$

$\angle a + \angle c = 30°$

Since angle *a* and angle *c* are congruent, divide 30° by 2: $30° \div 2 = 15°$

Angle *a* and angle *c* each measure 15°.

Vertical and Adjacent Angles

Intersecting lines form two pairs of **vertical angles**. The angles in each pair are always **congruent**, or equal in measures.

- $\angle 1$ and $\angle 3$ are vertical angles.
- $\angle 2$ and $\angle 4$ are vertical angles.

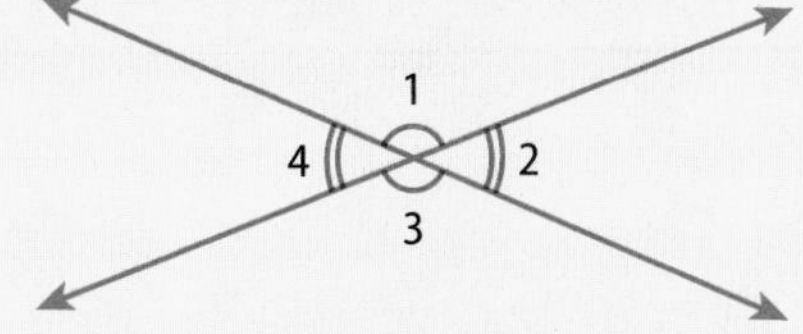

Adjacent angles have the same vertex and share one side. They may, or may not, be congruent.

- $\angle a$ and $\angle b$ are adjacent and congruent.
- $\angle b$ and $\angle c$ are adjacent but not congruent.

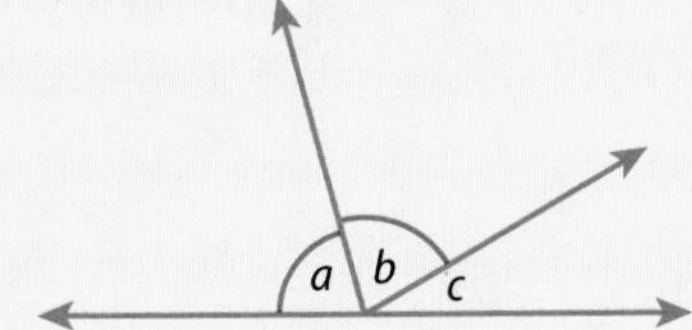

Ways to REMEMBER

The letter ***c*** comes before the letter ***s*** in the alphabet. The counting number **90** comes before **180**. So, ***c***omplementary angles total **90°**, and ***s***upplementary angles total **180°**.

Complementary and Supplementary Angles

Complementary angles are two angles whose measures total 90°.

Supplementary angles are two angles whose measures total 180°.

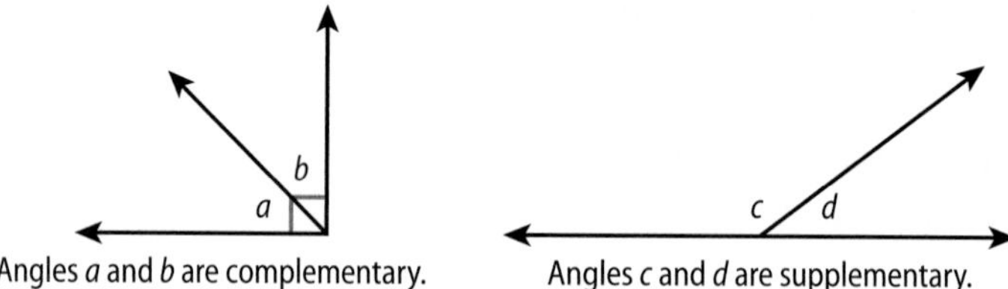

Angles *a* and *b* are complementary. Angles *c* and *d* are supplementary.

EXAMPLE 4

The figure shows a pair of complementary angles. Find the measure of angle *a*.

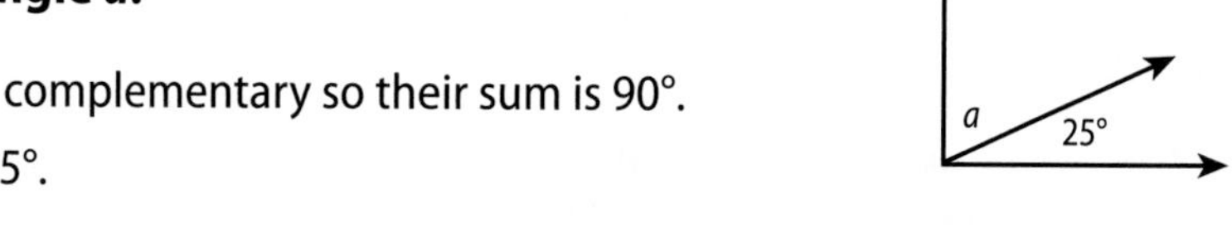

THINK The angles are complementary so their sum is 90°.

One angle = 25°.

PLAN AND SOLVE You can subtract to find the measure of $\angle a$.

$\angle a = 90° - 25°$

$= 65°$

The measure of $\angle a$ is 65°.

GOT TO KNOW!

Complementary Angles

The sum of the measures of complementary angles is 90°.

Supplementary Angles

The sum of the measures of supplementary angles is 180°.

EXAMPLE 5

The figure shows a pair of supplementary angles. Find the measure of angle *b*.

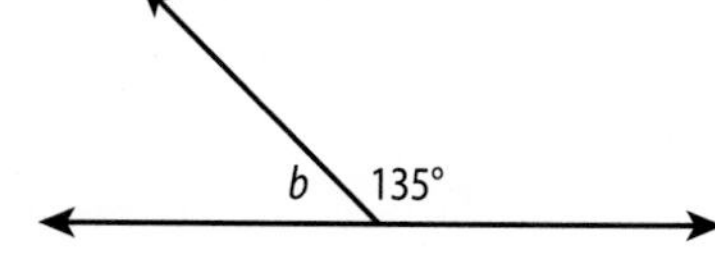

THINK The angles are supplementary so their sum is 180°.

One angle = 135°.

PLAN AND SOLVE You can subtract to find the measure of $\angle b$.

$\angle b = 180° - 135°$

$= 45°$

The measure of $\angle b$ is 45°.

EXAMPLE 6

In the figure shown, angles *a* and *c* are congruent. Find the measures of angles *a*, *b*, and *c*.

STEP 1 Angle a and the 75°-angle are supplementary.

$$\angle a + 75° = 180°$$

Subtract to find the measure of $\angle a$.

$$\angle a = 180° - 75°$$

$$\angle a = 105°$$

STEP 2 Angles a and b are supplementary, so their sum is 180°. Subtract the measure of $\angle a$ from 180° to find the measure of $\angle b$.

$$\angle b = 180° - 105°$$

$$\angle b = 75°$$

STEP 3 Angles a and c are vertical angles, so they have the same measure.

$$\angle a = \angle c, \text{ so } \angle c = 105°$$

Angle $a = 105°$, angle $b = 75°$, and angle $c = 105°$.

SEARCH

To see step-by-step videos of these problems, enter the page number into the SWadvantage.com Search Bar.

Other Angle Pairs

A line that intersects two or more lines is called a **transversal**. In the figure at the right, $\overleftrightarrow{XY}$ is a transversal that crosses $\overleftrightarrow{MN}$ and $\overleftrightarrow{OP}$. *Interior* and *exterior* angles are formed by the transversal crossing the lines. Angles a, d, f, and g are *interior* to the lines crossed by $\overleftrightarrow{XY}$. Angles b, c, h, and e are *exterior* to the lines crossed.

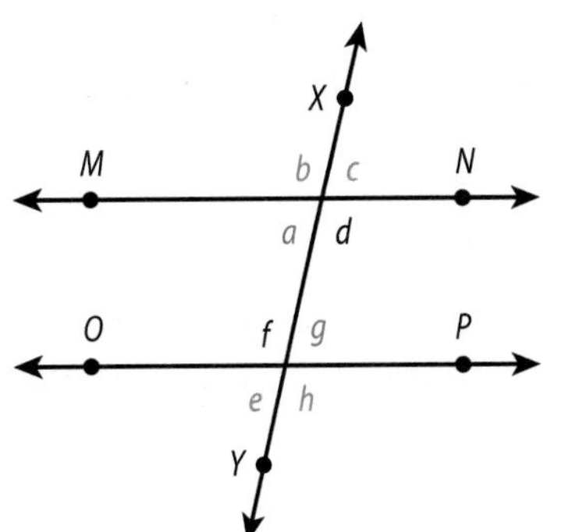

Need More HELP

Interior means *inside of*. Exterior means *outside of*. So wherever a transversal crosses two lines, interior angles form *inside* the lines. Exterior angles form *outside* the lines.

Interior and exterior angles can be identified in more detail.

Alternate interior angles are two *non-adjacent* interior angles on opposite sides of the transversal. The alternate interior angles in the figure are:

$\angle a$ and $\angle g$ $\qquad$ $\angle d$ and $\angle f$

Alternate exterior angles are two *non-adjacent* exterior angles on opposite sides of the transversal. The alternate exterior angles in the figure are:

$\angle b$ and $\angle h$ $\qquad$ $\angle c$ and $\angle e$

Other Angle Pairs

EXAMPLE 7

Use the figure below to answer each question.

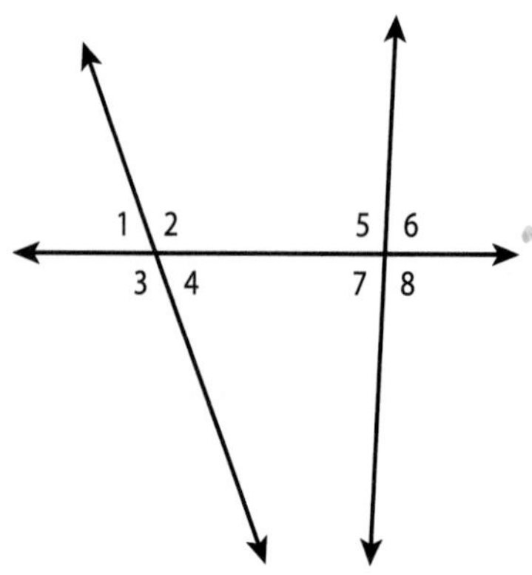

Try It This Way

To help see the difference between the interior and exterior angles, use a pencil to lightly shade all interior angles. Use a pencil of another color to lightly shade the exterior angles. Then decide which are alternate angles.

a. Name the pairs of *alternate interior* angles.

Angles 2, 4, 5, and 7 are *interior* angles. They are interior to (inside of) the lines crossed by the transversal.

The *alternate interior* angle pairs are: ∠2 and ∠7, ∠4 and ∠5.
These angle pairs are on alternate (opposite) sides of the transversal.

b. Name the pairs of *alternate exterior* angles.

Angles 1, 3, 6, and 8 are *exterior* angles. They are exterior to (outside of) the lines crossed by the transversal.

The *alternate exterior* angle pairs are: ∠1 and ∠8, ∠3 and ∠6.
These angle pairs are on alternate (opposite) sides of the transversal.

Alternate Angles

Alternate interior angles are angle pairs that lie inside the lines on opposite sides of a transversal.

Alternate exterior angles are angle pairs that lie outside the lines on opposite sides of a transversal.

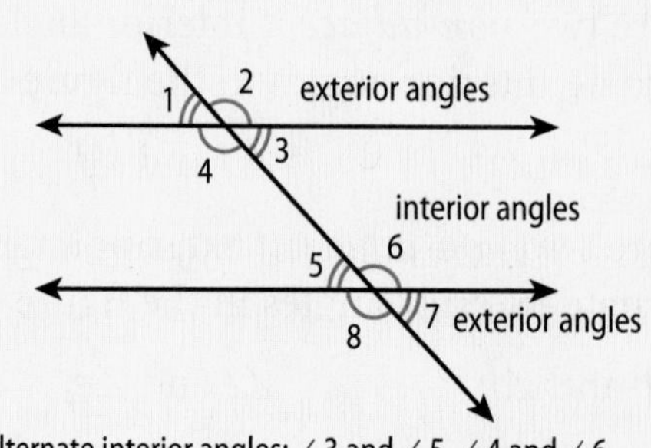

Alternate interior angles: ∠3 and ∠5, ∠4 and ∠6
Alternate exterior angles: ∠2 and ∠8, ∠1 and ∠7

Parallel Lines and Transversals

When a transversal crosses two parallel lines, several pairs of congruent angles are formed.

When the transversal is perpendicular to the lines, the lines form eight right angles.

When the transversal is not parallel to the lines, the lines form four equal acute angles and four equal obtuse angles.

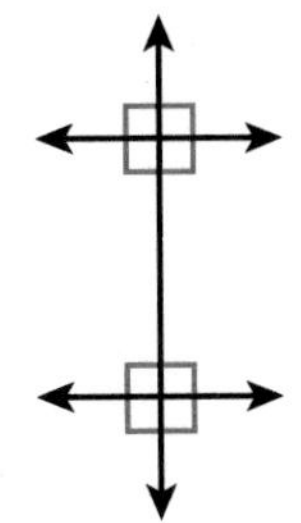

Transversal is parallel.
8 right angles

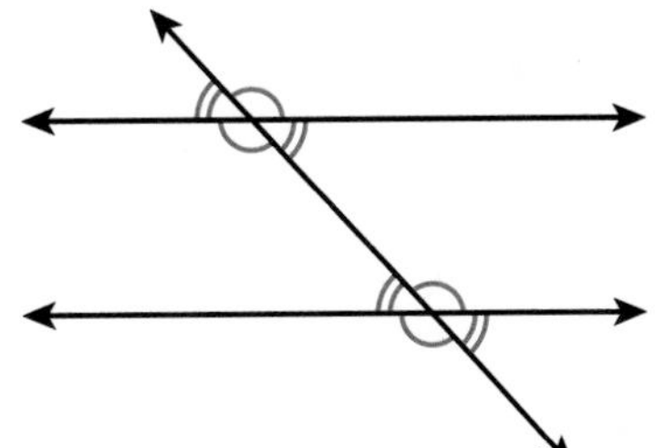

Transversal is not parallel.
4 acute and 4 obtuse angles

EXAMPLE 8

In the figure shown, two parallel lines are crossed by a transversal. The lines form angles 1 though 8.

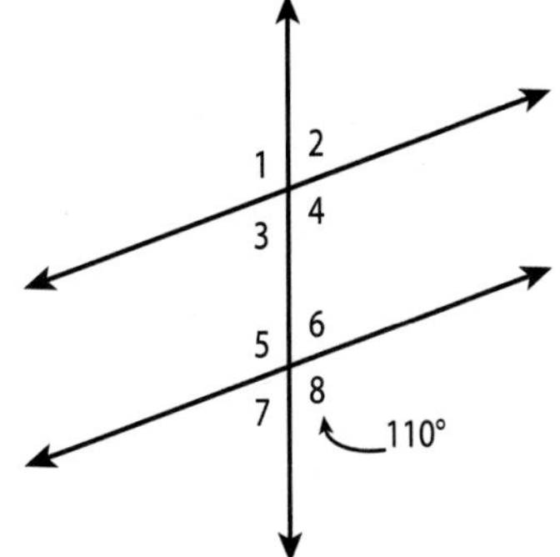

a. Name the pairs of vertical angles.
Vertical angles are the two opposite angles formed where two lines intersect.
The following angle pairs are vertical angles:
$\angle 1$ and $\angle 4$, $\angle 2$ and $\angle 3$, $\angle 5$ and $\angle 8$, $\angle 6$ and $\angle 7$

b. Explain how you can find the measures of angles 5, 6, and 7.
The measure of $\angle 8$ is given as 110°. Vertical angles are congruent.
So $\angle 5$ measures 110°.
$\angle 6$ and $\angle 8$ are supplementary angles, so $\angle 6 = 180° - 110° = 70°$.
$\angle 6$ and $\angle 7$ are vertical angles, so $\angle 7 = 70°$.

c. Now you know that $\angle 8 = 110°$, $\angle 6 = 70°$, $\angle 5 = 110°$, and $\angle 7 = 70°$. Use this information to find the measures of angles 1–4.
The transversal forms four equal acute angles and four equal obtuse angles.
Angles 2 and 3 are acute angles. They measure 70°, just as angles 6 and 7 do.
Angles 1 and 4 are obtuse angles. They measure 110°, just as angles 5 and 8 do.

SEARCH

To see step-by-step videos of these problems, enter the page number into the SWadvantage.com Search Bar.

Analyzing Shapes in a Plane

What Came Before?

- Points and lines on a plane
- Types of angles

What's This About?

- Classifying polygons
- Types of triangles and quadrilaterals
- Parts of a circle

Practical Apps

- A tile setter needs to understand two-dimensional geometric shapes to follow a design pattern and set the tiles correctly.
- Video game designers can make what appear to be solid figures by using polygons.

just for FUN!

Q: How did the quadrilateral get to school?

A: It took the rhombus.

CONTENTS UPLOAD DOWNLOAD

Foundations of Mathematics

You can find more practice problems online by visiting:
www.SWadvantage.com

Polygons

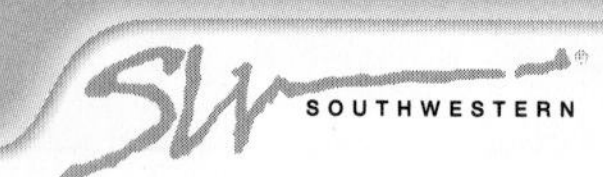

Classifying Polygons

A **polygon** is a closed flat figure with three or more straight sides. Polygons are named by the number of sides they have. The name begins with a prefix that tells how many sides the polygon has. For example, the prefix *tri-* means 3, so a triangle has 3 sides. Four other prefixes to remember are:

quad- means 4   *penta-* means 5   *hexa-* means 6   *octa-* means 8

The point at which two sides meet is called a **vertex** (vertices, plural).

The polygons below are *regular polygons.* A **regular polygon** has sides of equal length and angles of equal measure.

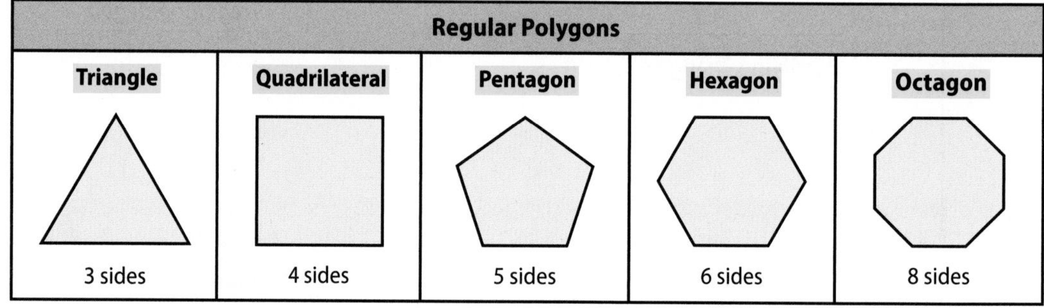

Regular Polygons				
Triangle	Quadrilateral	Pentagon	Hexagon	Octagon
3 sides	4 sides	5 sides	6 sides	8 sides

The table below shows three *irregular polygons.* An **irregular polygon** is any polygon that is not regular.

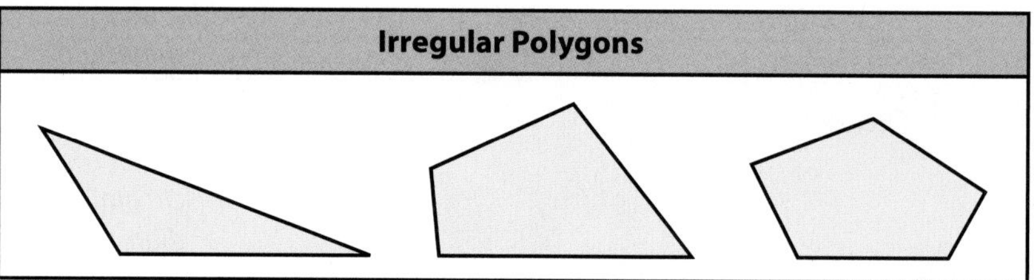

Look closely at the regular and irregular polygons. Notice that each polygon has the same number of sides, vertices, and angles.

Polygon Facts

- A polygon is a closed flat figure with three or more straight sides.
- A polygon has the same number of sides, angles, and vertices.
- A *regular* polygon has all sides equal and all angles equal.

Classify polygons according to the numbers of sides they have.

Triangle – 3 sides

Quadrilateral – 4 sides

Pentagon – 5 sides

Hexagon – 6 sides

Octagon – 8 sides

EXAMPLE 1

Classify each figure as a *polygon* or *not a polygon*. Explain your reasoning.

a. 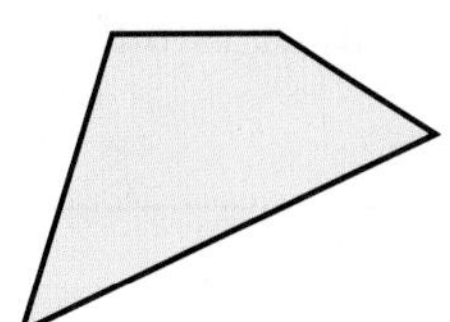

Polygon. The figure is closed and has straight sides.

b. 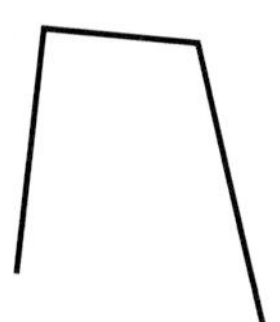

Not a polygon. The figure has straight sides but it is not closed.

c. 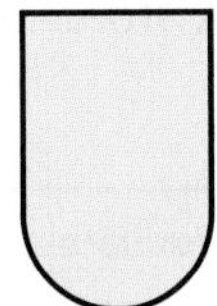

Not a polygon. The figure is closed but not all of its sides are straight.

> **Watch Out !**
>
> For a figure to be a polygon it must have both of these characteristics.
>
> - It is a flat, closed figure.
> - All of its sides are straight.

EXAMPLE 2

Name the polygon and classify it as *regular* or *irregular*. Explain your reasoning.

a. 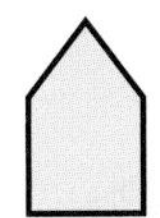

Irregular pentagon

The figure is closed. It has five sides that are not equal.

b. 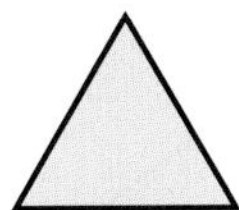

Regular triangle

The figure is a closed figure. It appears to have three equal sides and three equal angles.

c. 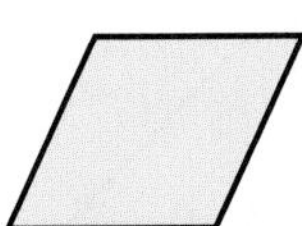

Irregular quadrilateral

The figure is closed. Its four sides appear to be equal but it does not have four equal angles.

> **Watch Out !**
>
> For a figure to be a regular polygon, it must have both equal sides and equal angles.

EXAMPLE 3

Travis says that this rectangle is a regular quadrilateral because it has 4 right angles. His friend Hae says it is not a regular quadrilateral. Who is correct? Explain your reasoning.

Hae is correct. The rectangle is a closed figure, and it has four equal angles. However, its sides are not equal in length, so it is an irregular polygon.

> **SEARCH**
>
> To see step-by-step videos of these problems, enter the page number into the SWadvantage.com Search Bar.

Classifying Triangles

Classifying Triangles

A triangle is a three-sided polygon. One way to classify triangles is by the length of their sides. When the sides of a triangle (or any polygon) have the same number of small tick marks, it means that the sides are congruent, or equal in length.

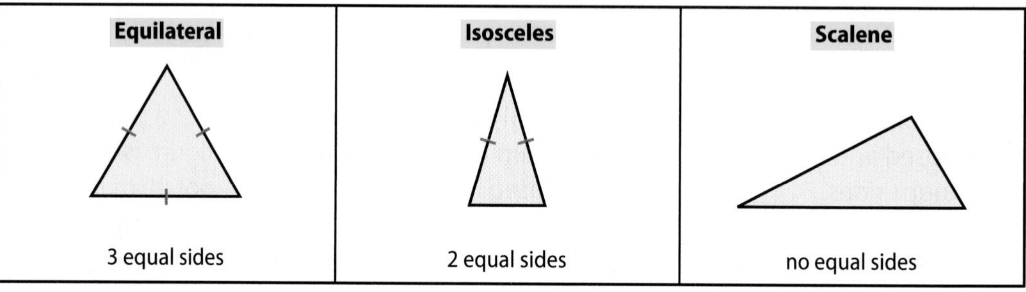

Another way to classify triangles is by the measure of their angles.

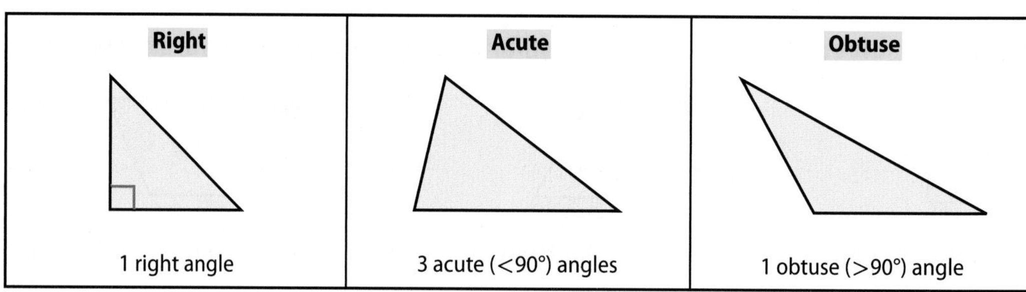

For more about types of angles, go to *Classifying Angles* in *Points, Lines, Planes, and Angles* (p. 140).

Classify each triangle in two ways.

Triangle *ABC*

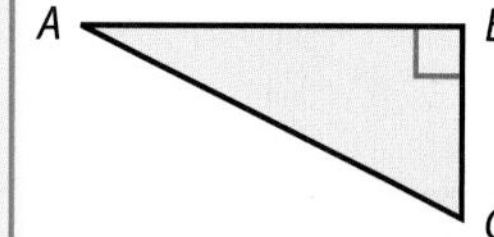

a. by the length of its sides

No sides appear equal in length. It is a scalene triangle.

b. by the measure of its angles

One angle is a right angle. It is a right triangle.

Triangle *ABC* is a scalene, right triangle.

Triangle *DEF*

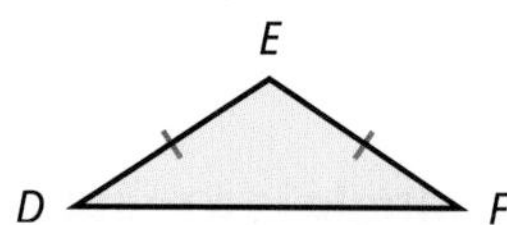

a. by the length of its sides

Two sides are equal in length. It is an isosceles triangle.

b. by the measure of its angles

Angle *E* is an obtuse angle. It is an obtuse triangle.

Triangle *DEF* is an isosceles, obtuse triangle.

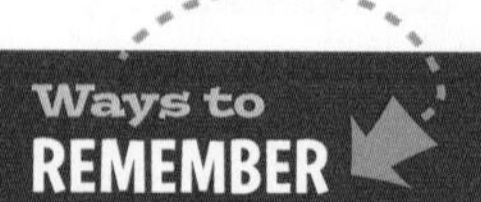

equilater**AL**
ALL sides equal

isosce**LES**
LESS **E**qual **S**ides

scale**NE**
No **E**qual sides

EXAMPLE 2

Use the color of the triangles to answer each question.

a. Which triangle(s) is an obtuse, scalene triangle?

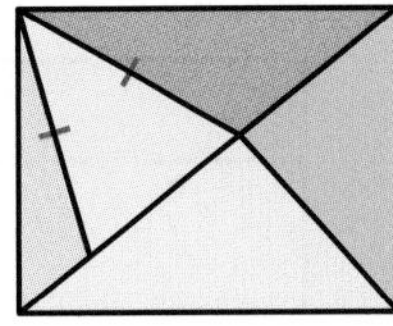

The pink triangle and the orange triangle, because they have one obtuse angle and their sides are different lengths.

b. Which triangle(s) is an isosceles acute triangle?

The blue triangle, because it has two equal sides and all its angles are acute.

c. Which triangle(s) appear to be a right scalene triangle?

The tan triangle and the green triangle, because they appear to have one right angle and no sides that are the same length.

To see step-by-step videos of these problems, enter the page number into the SWadvantage.com Search Bar.

EXAMPLE 3

An equilateral triangle is also *equiangular*. One side of this equilateral triangle measures 6 inches. Angle *a* measures 60°.

a. What is the measure of the other two sides?

The other two sides measure 6 inches because all the sides of an equilateral triangle have the same length.

b. What is the measure of angles *b* and *c*?

Angles *b* and *c* measure 60° because an equilateral triangle is also equiangular.

The prefix *equi-* means equal, so *equilateral* means equal lengths, and *equiangular* means equal angles.

EXAMPLE 4

Triangle *MNO* is an obtuse triangle. Angle *N* measures 75°. Angle *O* measures 45°. Classify angle *M*. Explain your thinking.

Angle *M* is an obtuse angle. Because triangle *MNO* is an obtuse triangle, it contains an obtuse angle. Angles *N* and *O* are acute angles, so angle *M* must be an obtuse angle.

Classifying Triangles

By Side Length

Equilateral: 3 equal sides

Isosceles: 2 equal sides

Scalene: 0 equal sides

By Angle Measure

Right: 1 right angle

Acute: 3 acute angles

Obtuse: 1 obtuse angle

Classifying Quadrilaterals

Classifying Quadrilaterals

A **quadrilateral** is a four-sided polygon. You can classify quadrilaterals according to the properties of their sides and angles.

Types of Quadrilaterals	
Trapezoid One pair of parallel sides	
Parallelogram Two pairs of parallel sides	
Rhombus Parallelogram with 4 congruent sides	
Rectangle Parallelogram with 4 right angles	
Square Rectangle with 4 congruent sides	

The term *trapezoid* usually refers to a quadrilateral with exactly 1 set of parallel sides. A quadrilateral with no parallel sides is sometimes called a *trapezium*.

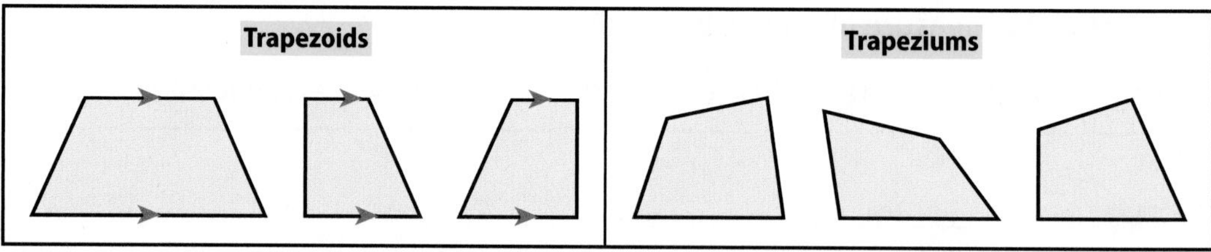

Quadrilaterals are named by capital letters located at each vertex (corner) in order around the figure, as shown on parallelogram *WXYZ* at right.

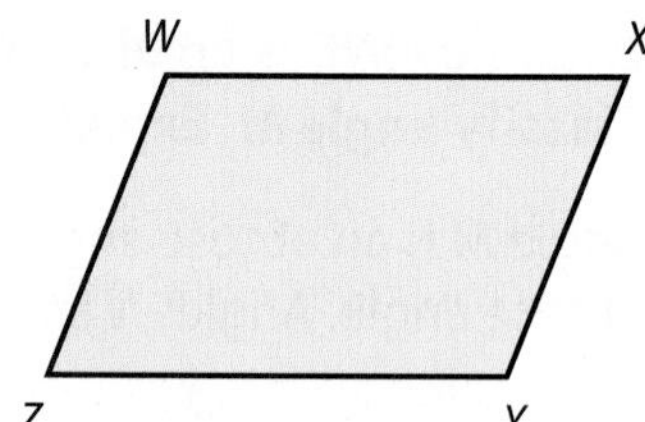

You can name the angles using one or three letters. For example, the upper right angle is $\angle X$ or $\angle WXY$.

The characteristic that defines a parallelogram is two pairs of parallel sides. Notice that *when both pairs of opposite sides are parallel, both pairs of opposite sides are also equal in length.*

Remember, a *polygon* is a closed, flat figure. Some polygons have congruent sides and angles. *Congruent sides* have the same length, and *congruent angles* have the same measure.

Watch Out!

Some books use the term *trapezoid* to describe a quadrilateral with no parallel sides. In British English, the term *trapezium* refers to what Americans call a *trapezoid*.

EXAMPLE 1

Elena drew a quadrilateral *ABCD* with 1 pair of parallel sides.

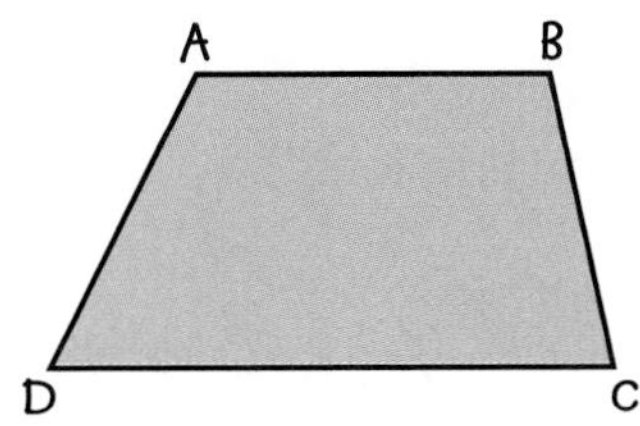

a. Name the parallel sides.

Sides *AB* and *CD* are parallel.

b. Classify the quadrilateral. Explain your reasoning.

The quadrilateral is a trapezoid. It has exactly 1 pair of parallel sides.

To see step-by-step videos of these problems, enter the page number into the SWadvantage.com Search Bar.

Special Types of Parallelograms

Rectangles, rhombuses, and squares are types of parallelograms. You can see their relationship more easily on the figure below.

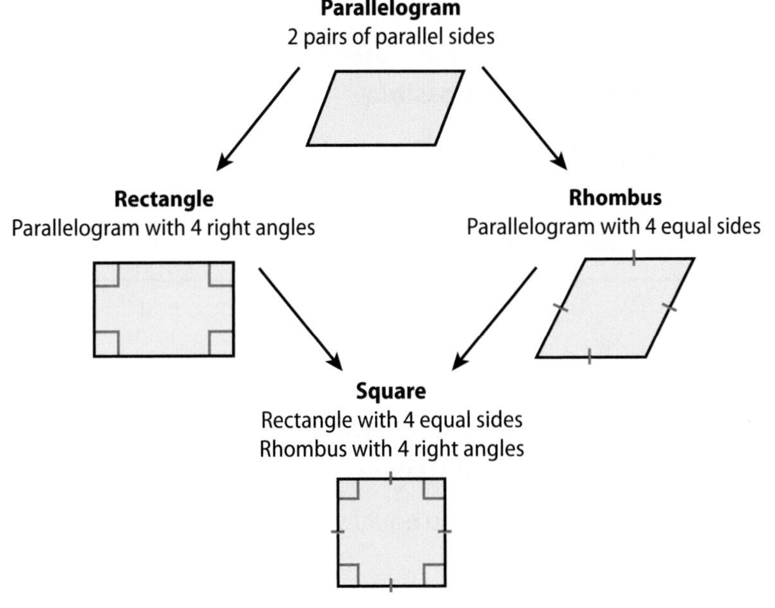

To find out more about special types of parallelograms, go to *Properties of Special Parallelograms* in *Geometry* (p. 650).

EXAMPLE 2

Marcel drew quadrilateral *STUV*. Classify his quadrilateral in four different ways.

S T V U

Quadrilateral *STUV* has the following characteristics:
2 pairs of parallel sides, so it is a parallelogram
4 right angles, so it is a rectangle
4 equal sides, so it is a square

Quadrilateral *STUV* is a *parallelogram*, a *rectangle*, and a *square*.

Equality Symbols on Figures

In geometry, symbols are placed on figures to show relationships.

Tick marks show that sides are equal in length.

Small arrowheads show that sides are parallel.

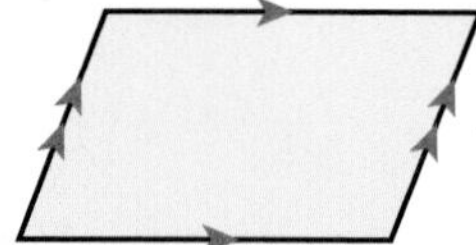

Arcs show that angles are equal.

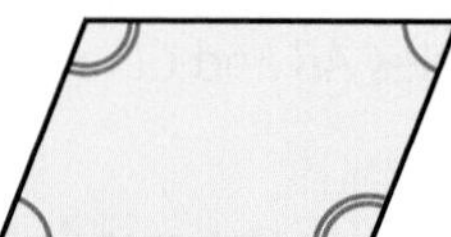

Identifying Quadrilaterals

For Examples 3 through 7, use the characteristics of quadrilaterals to identify each figure. Use this definition for a *trapezoid*: a quadrilateral with exactly 1 set of parallel sides.

SEARCH

To see step-by-step videos of these problems, enter the page number into the SWadvantage.com Search Bar.

EXAMPLE 3

Identify the characteristics of the quadrilateral at right. Then classify it in as many ways as possible.

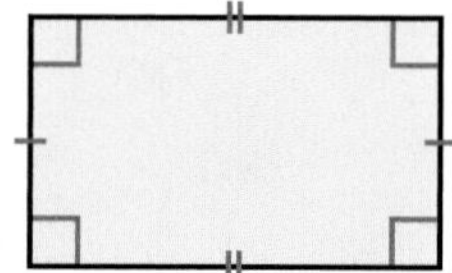

The quadrilateral has opposite sides equal. It also has 4 right angles.

The quadrilateral is a *parallelogram* and a *rectangle*.

EXAMPLE 4

Identify the characteristics of the quadrilateral at right. Then classify it in as many ways as possible.

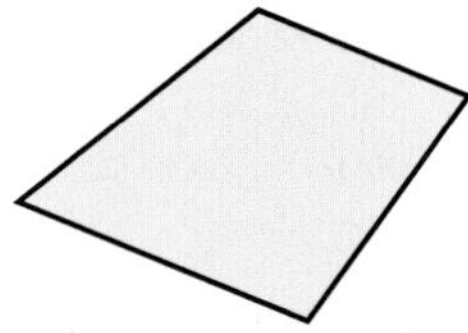

The quadrilateral has no parallel sides, no equal sides, and no equal angles.

The figure is a *quadrilateral*.

EXAMPLE 5

Identify the characteristics of the quadrilateral at right. Then classify it in as many ways as possible.

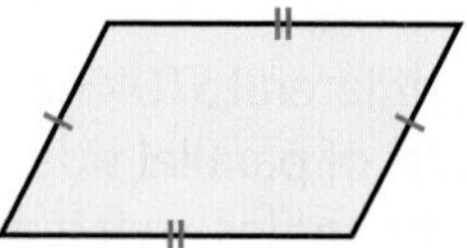

The quadrilateral has opposite sides equal.
It has no right angles.

The quadrilateral is a *parallelogram*.

EXAMPLE 6

Identify the characteristics of the quadrilateral at right. Then classify it in as many ways as possible.

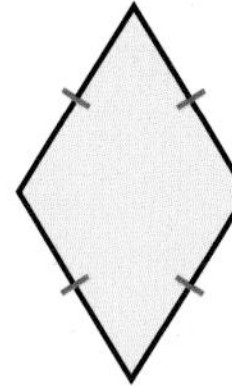

The quadrilateral has 4 equal sides but no right angles.

The quadrilateral is a *parallelogram* and a *rhombus*.

EXAMPLE 7

Identify the characteristics of the quadrilateral at right. Then classify it in as many ways as possible.

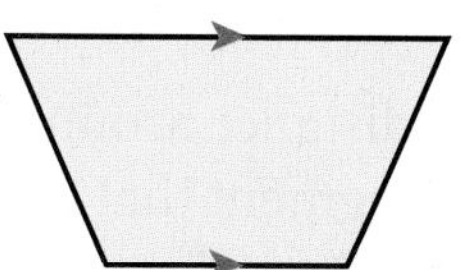

The quadrilateral has 1 pair of parallel sides.

The quadrilateral is a *trapezoid*.

GOT TO KNOW!

Classifying Quadrilaterals

Trapezoid		1 pair of parallel sides
Parallelogram		2 pairs of parallel sides Opposite sides equal Opposite angles equal
Rhombus		2 pairs of parallel sides All sides equal Opposite angles equal
Rectangle		2 pairs of parallel sides Opposite sides equal 4 right angles
Square		2 pairs of parallel sides All sides equal 4 right angles

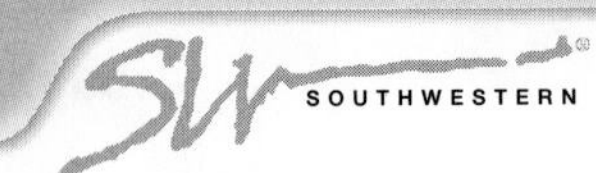

Identifying Parts of a Circle

A **circle** is a closed, flat figure in which every point is the same distance from a given point within the circle. The given point within the circle is called the **center** of the circle.

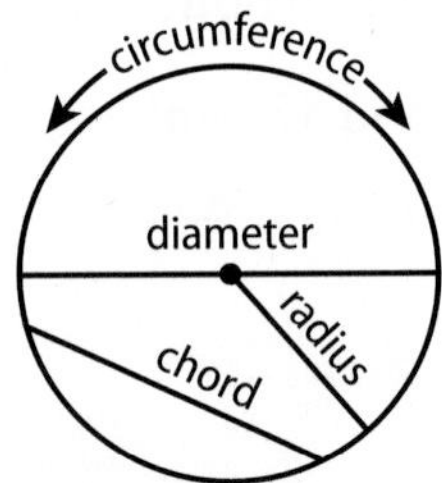

The distance around a circle is its **circumference**. A **diameter** of a circle is a line segment that contains the center of a circle and has both endpoints on the circle. A **radius** is a line segment that has one endpoint at the center and the other endpoint on the circle. A **chord** is a line segment within a circle whose endpoints are on the circle. A chord that passes though the center of a circle is called a diameter.

SEARCH

To see step-by-step videos of these problems, enter the page number into the SWadvantage.com Search Bar.

EXAMPLE 1

Use the circle at right to answer each question.

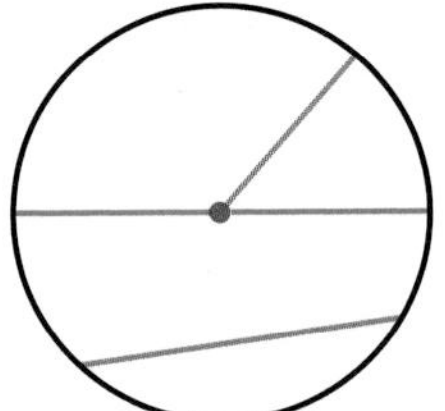

a. Name the part of the circle that is red.

The point is the *center* of the circle.

b. Name the part of the circle that is green.

The green line segment has both endpoints on the circle, so it is a *chord.*

c. Name the part of the circle that is purple.

The purple line segment goes from the center to a point on the circle, so it is a *radius.*

d. Name the part of the circle that is blue.

The blue line segment goes across the circle through its center, so it is a *diameter.*

It is important to understand the relationship between the lengths of the diameter and the radius of a circle. The length of the diameter is twice the length of the radius. The length of the radius of the circle is half the length of the diameter.

Need More HELP

You may see the relationship between the diameter and the radius of a circle written as a formula, where d = diameter and r = radius.

$$r = \frac{1}{2}d$$

$$d = 2r$$

EXAMPLE 2

a. If the radius of a circle is 3 cm long, what is the length of the diameter?

The diameter is twice the length of the radius: 2×3 cm $= 6$ cm
The length of the diameter is 6 cm.

b. If the diameter is 8 in. long, what is the length of the radius?

The radius is one-half the length of the diameter: 8 in. $\div 2 = 4$ in.
The length of the radius is 4 in.

EXAMPLE 3

Use the name of the line segments to identify the parts of Circle *D*.

a. Which line segment is the diameter?

line segment *FG*

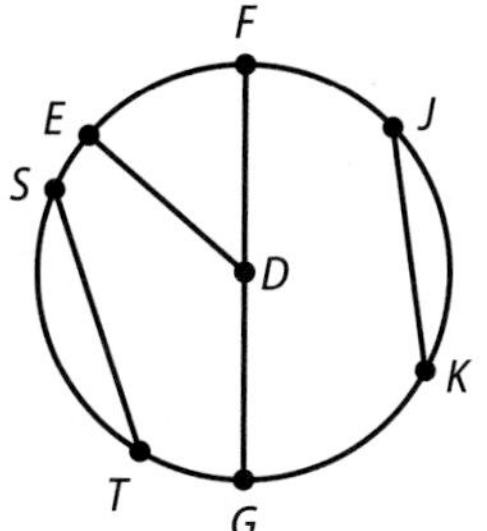

b. Which line segments are chords but not diameters?

line segments *ST* and *JK*

c. Name three line segments that are radii.

line segments *DF*, *DG*, and *DE*

Need More HELP

For help with naming line segments, go to *Segments, Rays, and Distance* in *Points, Lines, Planes, and Angles* (p. 132).

Parts of a Circle

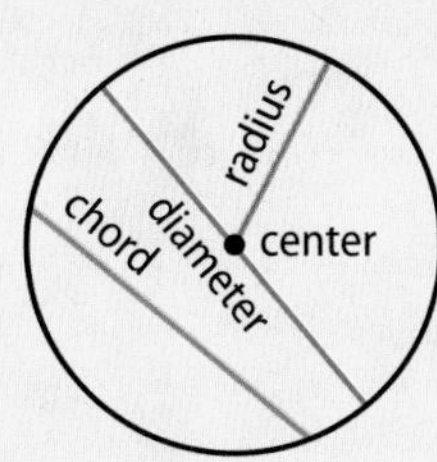

circumference = distance around a circle

diameter = radius $\times$ 2

radius = diameter $\div$ 2

Analyzing Solid Figures

What Came Before?

- Plane figures—polygons and circles
- Identifying and classifying polygons

What's This About?

- Identifying and classifying solid figures—figures with three dimensions
- Describing a solid figure by its bases, faces, vertices, and edges
- Using nets of solid figures

Practical Apps

- Set designers make three-dimensional models before designing a set for a play.
- Marketing experts know that the shape of a product's packaging can affect how well it sells.

Just for FUN!

DIZZY: Can we go to the ice cream parlor?

TIZZY: Why?

DIZZY: I need to study cones!

CONTENTS UPLOAD DOWNLOAD *Foundations of Mathematics*

You can find more practice problems online by visiting:
www.SWadvantage.com

Geometric Solids

Geometric **solids** are 3-dimensional figures that have length, width, and height. A **prism** is a type of geometric solid with two congruent, parallel faces that are polygons, and are called **bases**. The other faces of a prism are rectangles.

Remember, the term *congruent* means "having exactly the same size and shape."

You can describe a prism by its number of *faces, edges,* and *vertices*. A **face** is a flat surface on a geometric solid. An **edge** is a line segment formed where two faces meet. A **vertex** is a point where two or more edges meet.

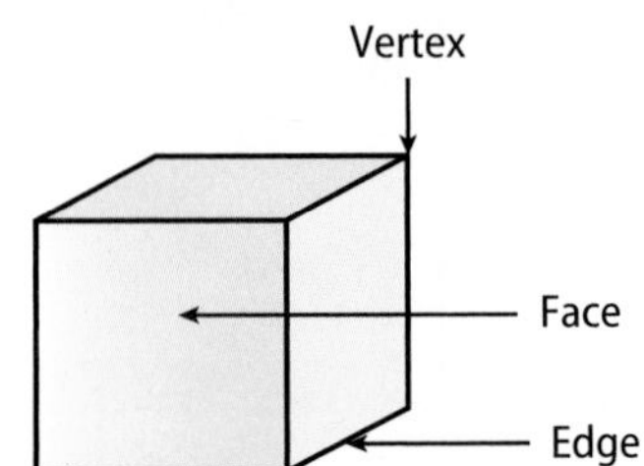

A **rectangular prism** has 2 congruent rectangular bases. Its 4 other faces are also rectangles.

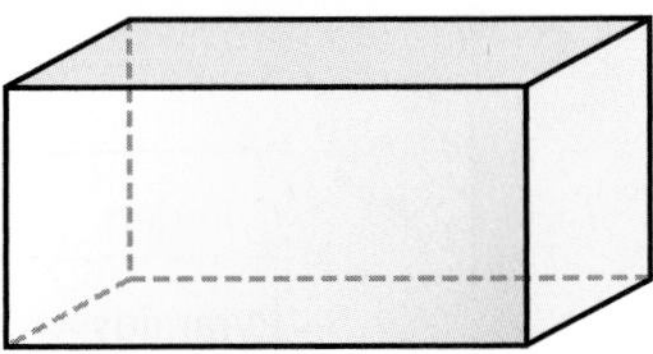

A **cube** is a rectangular prism with bases and faces that are congruent squares.

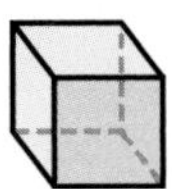

EXAMPLE 1

Look at the cube above. How many faces, edges, and vertices does the cube have?

There are the top and bottom faces and four sides. The cube has 6 faces.

It has 12 edges. It has 8 vertices.

SEARCH

To see step-by-step videos of these problems, enter the page number into the SWadvantage.com Search Bar.

EXAMPLE 2

Look at the geometric solid at right. Name the solid. Then tell how many faces, edges, and vertices it has.

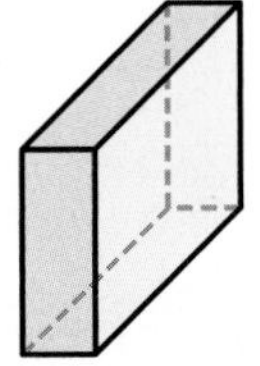

The figure has 2 congruent rectangular bases and 4 faces that are rectangles. It is a *rectangular prism*.

It has 6 faces, 12 edges, and 8 vertices.

Most prisms are named by using the name of the polygon that forms the bases of the prism.

A **triangular prism** has 2 bases that are congruent triangles and 3 faces that are rectangles.

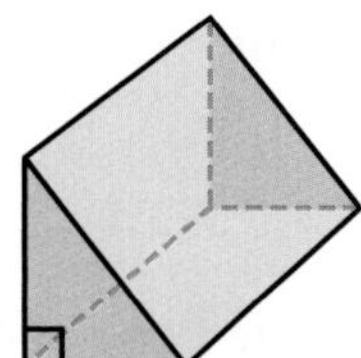

A **hexagonal prism** has 2 bases that are congruent hexagons and 6 faces that are rectangles.

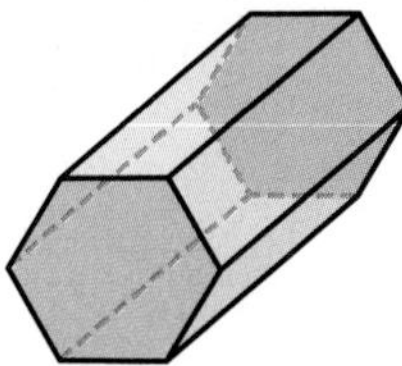

An **octagonal prism** has 2 bases that are congruent octagons and 8 faces that are rectangles.

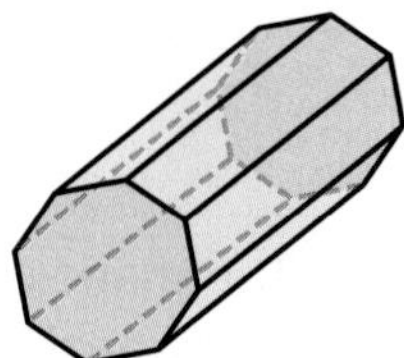

Ways to REMEMBER

The number of faces is always equal to the number of sides in the base plus 2. For example, the base of a triangular prism has 3 sides. The prism has 2 bases. A triangular prism has $3 + 2 = 5$ faces.

EXAMPLE 3

Use the figures above to describe each prism below. First, name the polygon that forms the base. Then tell the number of faces, edges, and vertices on the prism.

a. triangular prism

The 2 bases are triangles.
There are 3 rectangular faces for a total of 5 faces.
The prism has 9 edges and 6 vertices.

b. hexagonal prism

The 2 bases are hexagons.
There are 6 rectangular faces for a total of 8 faces.
The prism has 18 edges and 12 vertices.

c. octagonal prism

The 2 bases are octagons.
There are 8 rectangular faces for a total of 10 faces.
The prism has 24 edges and 16 vertices.

Watch Out!

The bases of a prism are also faces. If a question asks, "How many faces?" be sure to include the bases in your count.

Sometimes a question will ask about *bases* and *faces* separately.

Classifying Prisms

The most commonly seen prisms have bases that are triangles, squares, rectangles, hexagons, or octagons. However, the base can be any type of polygon. If you know the shape of the base of a prism, you can usually name the prism.

Each figure below shows the base of a prism. Name the prism.

a. 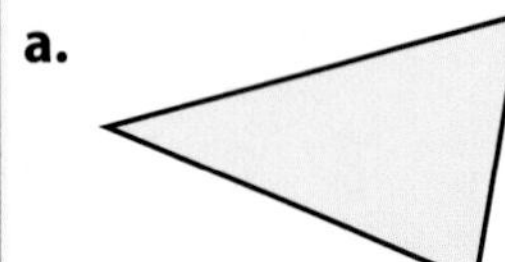

The shape of the base is a triangle, so this is a triangular prism.

b.  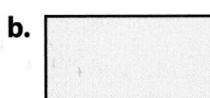

The shape of the base is a rectangle, so this is a rectangular prism.

c. 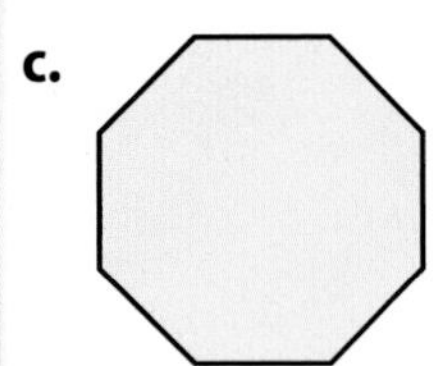

The shape of the base is a hexagon, so this is a hexagonal prism.

d. 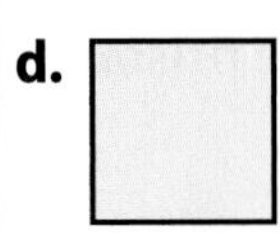

The shape of the base is a square, so this is a square prism with 4 faces that are rectangles. It could be a cube, but since the shape of the other four faces are not known, you do not know this for certain.

SEARCH

To see step-by-step videos of these problems, enter the page number into the SWadvantage.com Search Bar.

EXAMPLE 5

Owen built a wood box shaped like a prism. The bases of the box are shaped as shown at right.

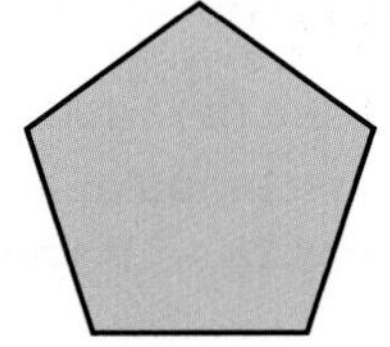

a. How many sides does the box have?

There are 2 bases with 5 sides so the box has 5 more sides. $2 + 5 = 7$. The box has 7 sides.

b. Use what you know about naming prisms to name the shape of the box.

The base is a pentagon so the box is a pentagonal prism.

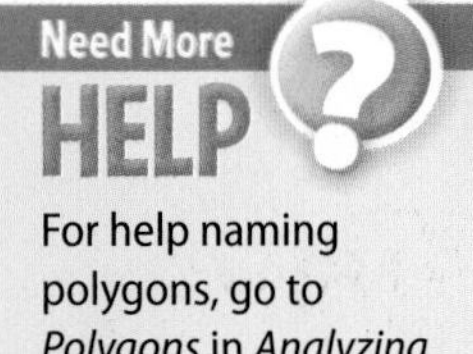

For help naming polygons, go to *Polygons* in *Analyzing Shapes in a Plane* (p. 154).

The prisms shown in the *Got To Know!* box below are *right prisms*. This means that their congruent, parallel bases are aligned directly above and below each other, and the sides are perpendicular to the bases and are rectangles.

Notice that the faces on the *oblique prism* are parallelograms but not rectangles.

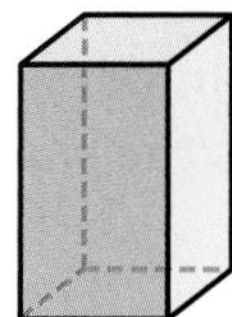
Right Prism

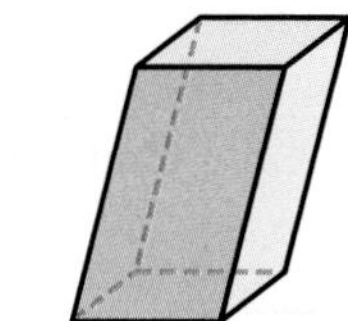
Non-right (oblique) Prism

Characteristics of Right Prisms

Rectangular Prism

Faces: 6 rectangular
Edges: 12
Vertices: 8

Cube (Square Prism)

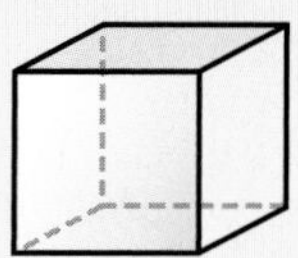

Faces: 6 square
Edges: 12
Vertices: 8

Triangular Prism

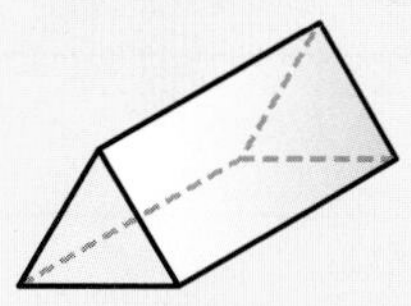

Faces: 2 triangular, 3 rectangular
Edges: 9
Vertices: 6

Hexagonal Prism

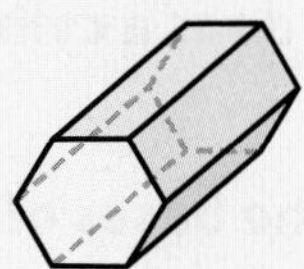

Faces: 2 hexagonal, 6 rectangular
Edges: 18
Vertices: 12

Octagonal Prism

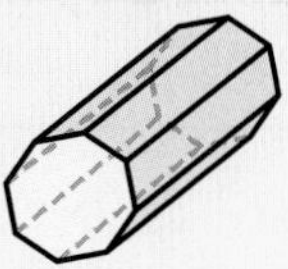

Faces: 2 octagonal, 8 rectangular
Edges: 24
Vertices: 16

Cylinders

Remember, a *geometric solid* is a 3-dimensional figure that has length, width, and height.

What Is a Cylinder?

A **cylinder** is a geometric solid with two congruent circular bases that are opposite and parallel to each other. A curved surface connects the bases.

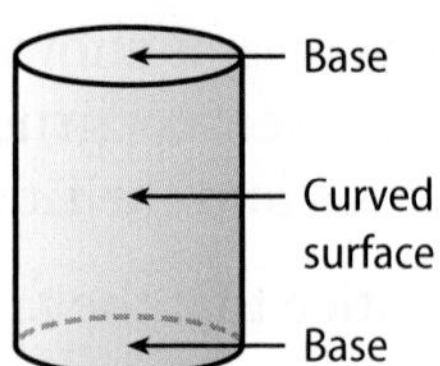

Like prisms, cylinders are 3-dimensional figures. However, the bases of a cylinder are circles, not polygons. Also, instead of rectangular sides, a cylinder has one continuous curved surface that connects the bases.

EXAMPLE 1

Classify each figure as a cylinder or not a cylinder.

a. 

Cylinder. It has two circular bases and a curved side.

b. 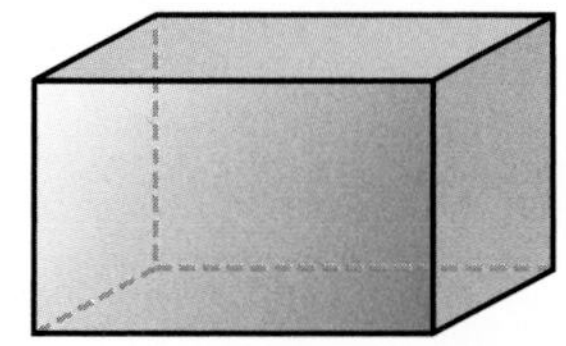

Not a cylinder. It has 6 rectangular sides.

c. 

Cylinder. It has two circular bases and a curved side.

d. 

Not a cylinder. It has only 1 circular base.

EXAMPLE 2

Use the picture of the cylinder at the top of the page to answer these questions.

a. How many bases does a cylinder have? A cylinder has 2 bases.

b. What shape are the bases of a cylinder? The bases are circles.

c. How many sides does a cylinder have? None. A cylinder has a curved surface that connects the bases.

If you cut off the top and the bottom of a cylinder and flattened out the curved surface, it would look like this.

Notice that the curved surface forms a rectangle. The figure formed when the cylinder is cut apart and flattened is called a *net*. If you folded it back up, you would have a cylinder.

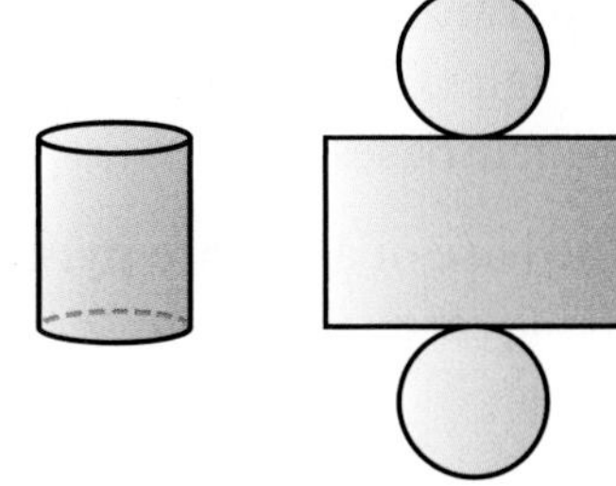

Need More HELP

For more about nets, go to pages 173, 174, or 177, or to *Nets* in *Geometry* (p. 694).

EXAMPLE 3

Look at each net. Tell whether the net is for a cylinder or not.

a.

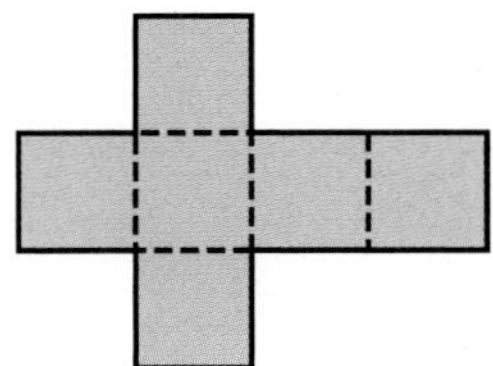

No, this is not a net for a cylinder. It is made up of 6 squares.

b.

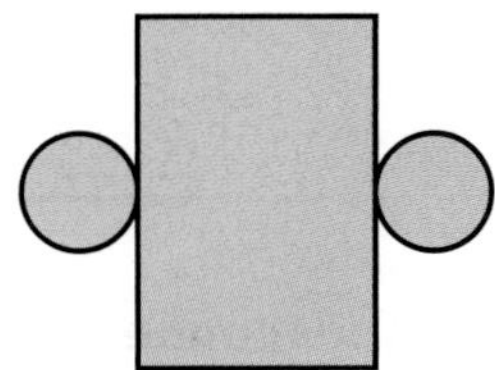

Yes, this is a net of a cylinder. It is made up of 2 circles and 1 rectangle.

SEARCH

To see step-by-step videos of these problems, enter the page number into the SWadvantage.com Search Bar.

EXAMPLE 4

Compare and contrast a cylinder and a prism.

- A cylinder and a prism are both geometric solids and have a height.
- A cylinder has two bases that are circles, and a prism has two bases that are polygons.
- Instead of sides, a cylinder has one curved surface that connects the circular bases. Prisms have three or more sides.

Identifying Cylinders

A **cylinder** is a geometric solid with two bases that are congruent circles and a continuous curved surface that connects the bases. The figures below are cylinders.

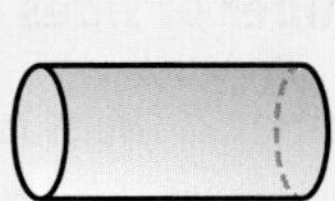

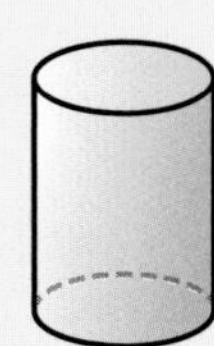

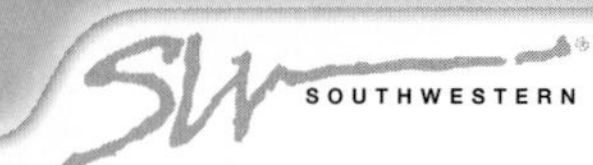

What Is a Pyramid?

Remember, a *geometric solid* is a 3-dimensional figure that has length, width, and height.

A **pyramid** is a geometric solid with one base that is a polygon and faces that are triangles. The triangular faces meet at a vertex. Pyramids are named for the shape of their bases.

The base of a **square pyramid** is a square.

The base of a **triangular pyramid** is a triangle.

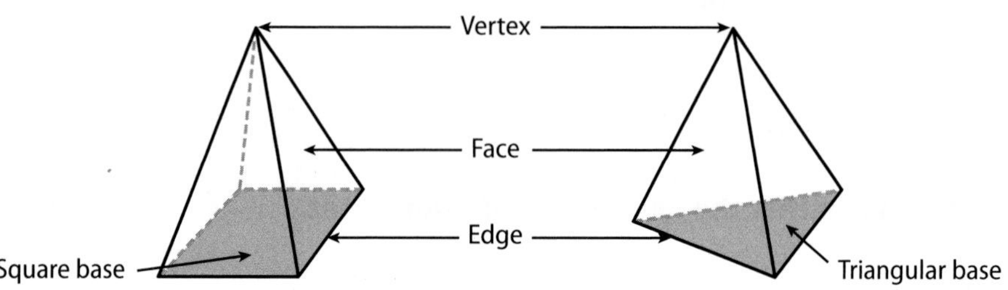

EXAMPLE 1

Need More HELP

Remember, the *base* of a geometric solid is one of its flat faces. Be sure to include the bases in your count of "faces."

A *vertex* is where two edges meet. Include every vertex on the figure in your count of "vertices."

Name each figure and the number of faces, edges, and vertices it has.

a. The figure is a triangular pyramid because its base is a triangle.

There are 4 faces.
There are 6 edges.
There are 4 vertices.

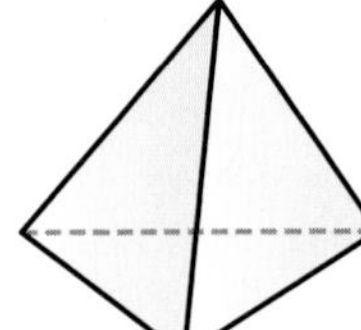

b. The figure is a square pyramid because its base is a square.

There are 5 faces.
There are 8 edges.
There are 5 vertices.

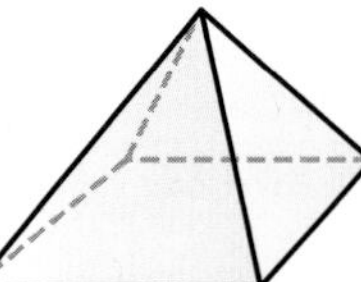

EXAMPLE 2

Use the pictures of the pyramids above to answer these questions.

a. How many bases does a pyramid have?

1 base

b. Compare the number of faces (flat surfaces) on the pyramids.

The triangular pyramid has 4 faces, and the square pyramid has 5 faces.

c. What is the relationship between the number of faces on the solid figure and the number of sides on the flat base?

The number of faces is one more than the number of sides on the base.

EXAMPLE 3

A pentagon has 5 sides, and a hexagon has 6 sides.

a. How many faces does a pentagonal pyramid have?

Since a pentagon has 5 sides, a pentagonal pyramid has $5 + 1 = 6$ faces.

b. How many faces does a hexagonal pyramid have?

Since a hexagon has 6 sides, a hexagonal pyramid has $6 + 1 = 7$ faces.

SEARCH

To see step-by-step videos of these problems, enter the page number into the SWadvantage.com Search Bar.

Net for a Pyramid

If you cut out the triangular pyramid at the right along three of its edges and flattened it out, it would look like this.

This figure is called a *net*. If you folded up the net, you would have a triangular pyramid.

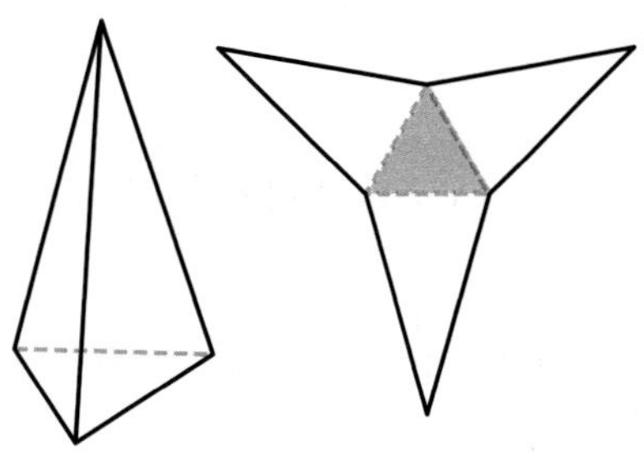

Need More HELP

There are many ways to make a net for a pyramid. For more about nets, go to pages 171, 174, or 177, or to *Nets* in *Geometry* (p. 694).

EXAMPLE 4

Look at each net. Tell whether it is for a square pyramid or a triangular pyramid.

a.

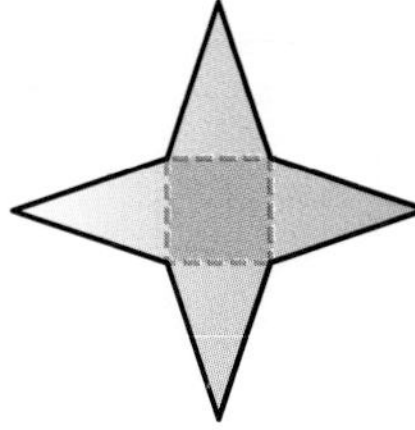

Square pyramid. The net has a square base and four sides that are triangles.

b.

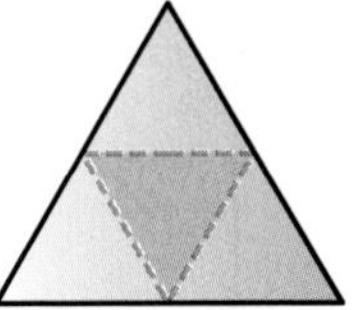

Triangular pyramid. The net has a base that is a triangle. The other three triangles are the sides.

Identifying Pyramids

A pyramid is a geometric solid with 1 base that is a polygon. The faces are triangles. Pyramids are named for the shape of their bases.

Square Pyramid

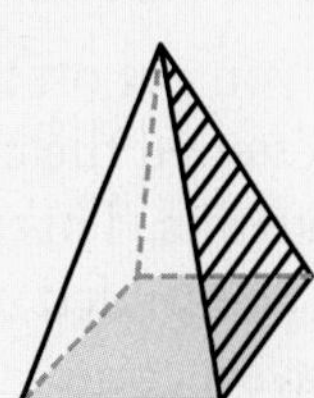

Triangular Pyramid

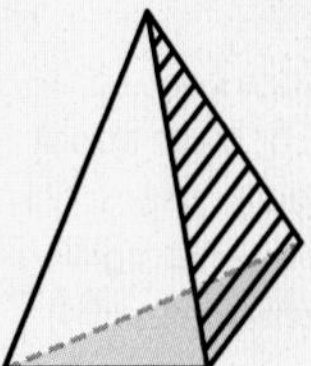

What Is a Cone?

If you are speaking of prisms, the definition of a *vertex* is a point where three or more sides meet. A cone, however, is not a prism so the definition of the vertex of a cone is slightly different. You may also see the vertex of a cone called the *apex*.

A **cone** is a geometric solid figure. A cone has one base that is a circle and a curved surface that connects all points on the circle to a point called the *vertex*.

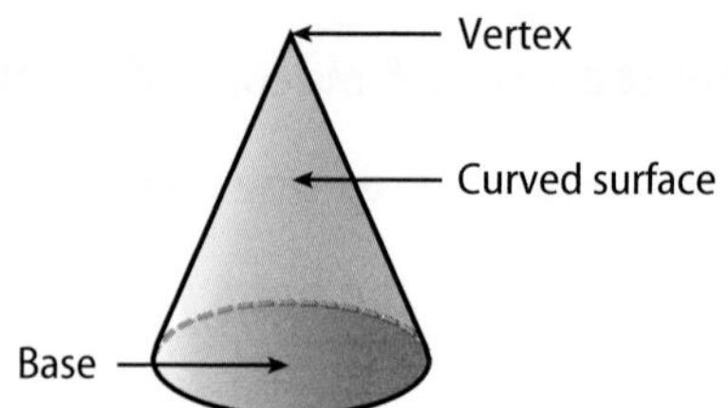

EXAMPLE 1

Use the picture above to answers these questions.

a. **Describe the base(s) of a cone.** A cone has exactly 1 base that is a circle.

b. **How many sides does a cone have?** A cone has 0 sides. It has a curved surface that connects the base to a point called the vertex.

c. **How many vertices does a cone have?** A cone has 1 vertex.

EXAMPLE 2

Classify each figure as a cone or not a cone.

a. 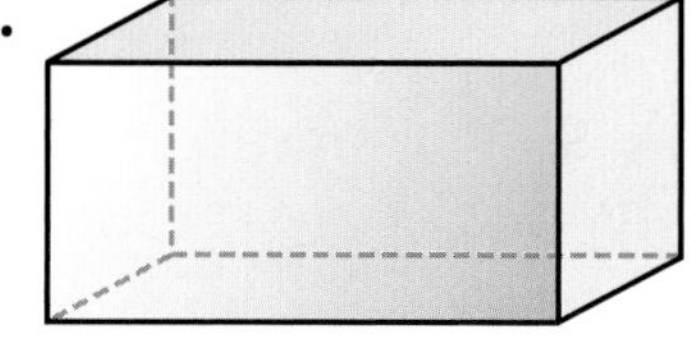

Not a cone. This figure has 6 rectangular sides.

b. 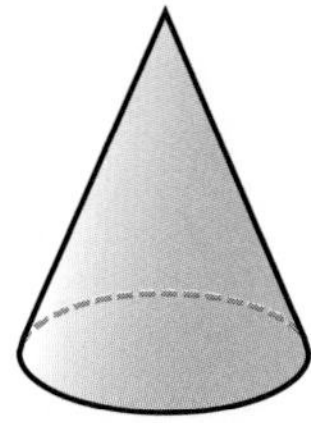

Cone. This figure has 1 base that is a circle, 1 curved surface, and 1 vertex.

c. 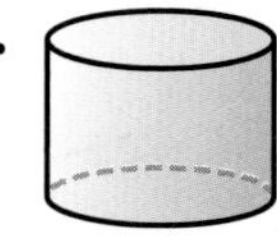

Not a cone. This figure has 2 bases that are circles, 1 curved surface, and no vertex.

Net for a Cone

Nets for a cone can vary. For more about nets, go to pages 171, 173, or 177, or to *Nets* in *Geometry* (p. 694).

If you cut off the base of a cone and flattened the cone out, it would look like this. This figure is called a *net*. If you folded up the net, you would have a cone.

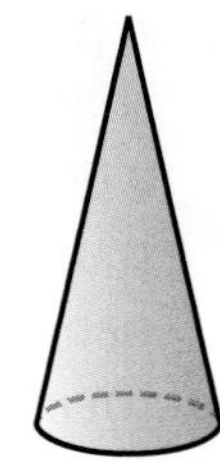

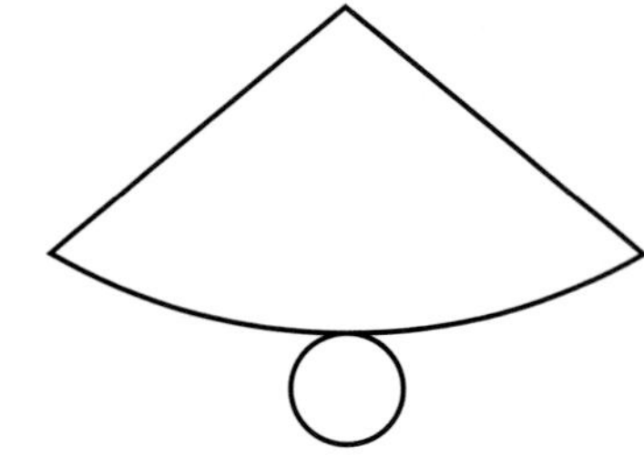

EXAMPLE 3

Look at each net. Tell whether the net would form a cone.

a.

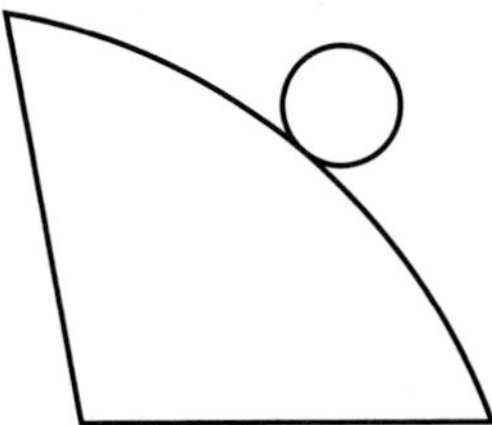

This net would form a cone. It has 1 base that is a circle and its curved surface would taper to 1 vertex.

b.

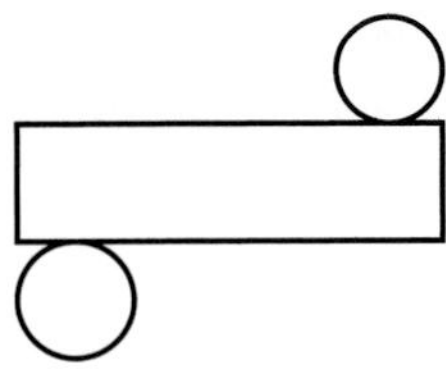

This net would not form a cone. It has 1 curved surface but it has 2 bases that are circles. It would form a cylinder.

SEARCH

To see step-by-step videos of these problems, enter the page number into the SWadvantage.com Search Bar.

EXAMPLE 4

Compare and contrast the cone and the cylinder.

- A cone has 1 circular base. A cylinder has 2 circular bases.
- A cone has 1 curved surface. A cylinder has 1 curved surface.
- A cone has 1 vertex. A cylinder has 0 vertices.

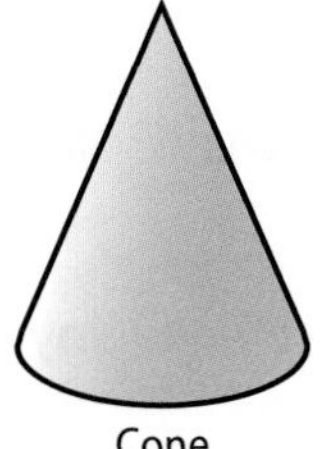

Cone

Cylinder

GOT TO KNOW!

Identifying Cones

A **cone** is a geometric solid with 1 base that is a circle. It has a curved surface that connects all points on the base to a vertex. Both figures below are cones.

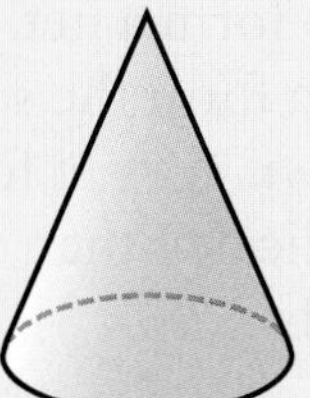

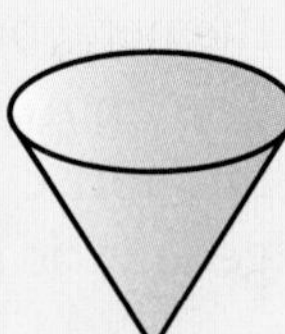

Spheres

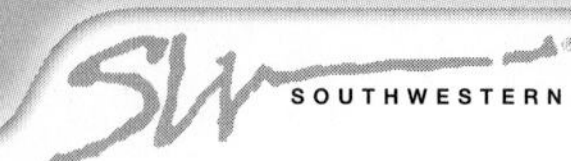

Remember, a *geometric solid* is a 3-dimensional figure that has length, width, and height.

What Is a Sphere?

A **sphere** is a geometric solid with all points on its surface the same distance from the center of the sphere. The distance from the center to any point on the surface of the sphere is a *radius*.

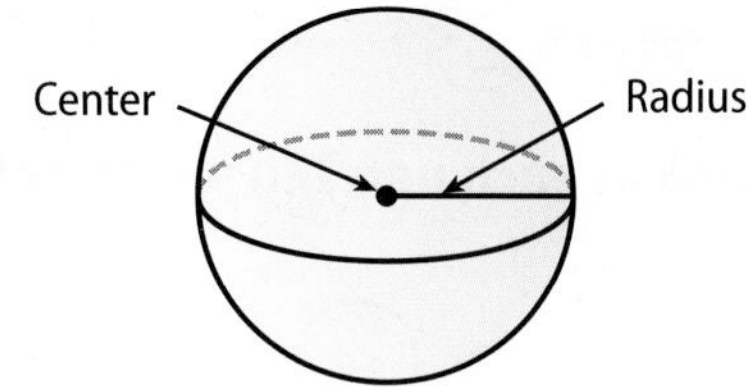

EXAMPLE 1

Use the picture above to answer these questions about a sphere.

a. How many bases does a sphere have? A sphere has 0 bases.

b. How many faces does a sphere have? A sphere has 0 faces. It has only one curved surface.

c. Is a sphere a polygon? No. A polygon is a flat, closed figure with three or more straight sides. A sphere is a solid figure with no sides.

d. Is a sphere a prism? No. A prism has flat faces. A sphere has only 1 curved surface.

e. Does a sphere have any edges or vertices? No. Its surface is curved.

EXAMPLE 2

Suppose you cut a flat section across the center of a sphere. What shape would the section look like—a square, a circle, or a triangle? Explain your answer.

The section would look like a circle. This is because the outside edge of the shape would be a curved line that is always the same distance from the center of the section.

SEARCH

To see step-by-step videos of these problems, enter the page number into the SWadvantage.com Search Bar.

Net for a Sphere

Recall that you can cut apart a solid figure and flatten it to form a net. If you fold up the net, you can form the solid figure again. The figure shown is a net for a sphere. It is a bit more complicated than the nets of other geometric solids.

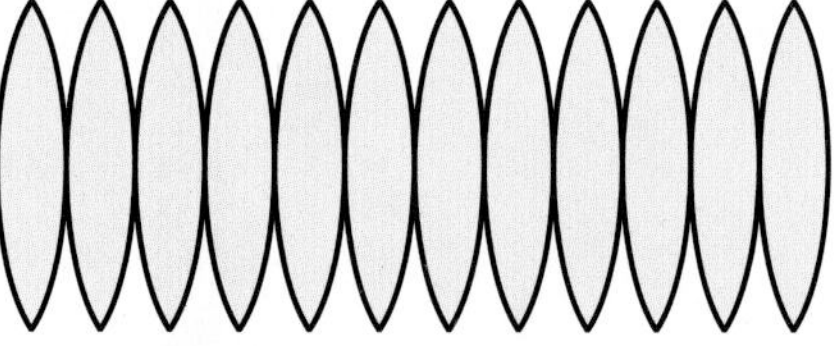

For more about nets, go to pages 171, 173, or 174, or to *Nets* in *Geometry* (p. 694).

Hemispheres

The prefix *hemi–* means "half of," so a hemisphere is half of a sphere. If you cut a sphere into two equal halves, you will have two hemispheres.

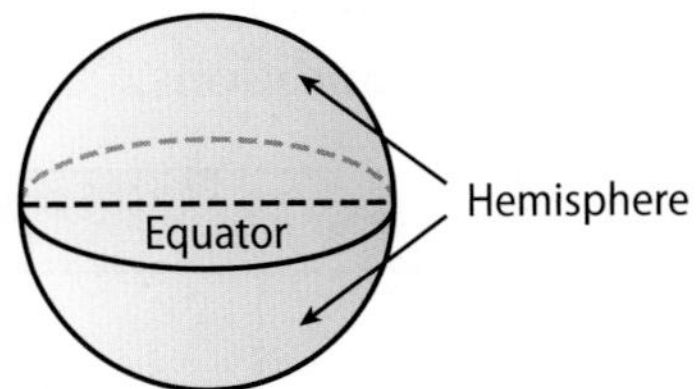

Need More HELP

Earth is actually a spheroid, not a sphere. A *spheroid* is a geometric solid that is almost spherical.

Half the region on the surface of Earth is called a *hemisphere*. You may know that North America and South America are in the Western Hemisphere, or that when it is summer in the Northern Hemisphere, it is winter in the Southern Hemisphere.

Look at the figures closely. Is a hemisphere the same as a circle? Explain your answer.

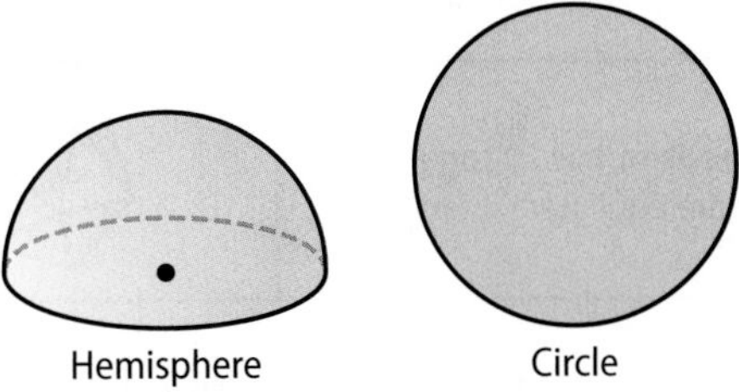

No. A hemisphere is a geometric solid that is half of a sphere. Its base is a circle, which is a flat figure.

GOT TO KNOW!

Identifying a Sphere

A **sphere** is a geometric solid with all points on its surface the same distance from the center of the sphere. A **hemisphere** is half of a sphere with a base that is a circle.

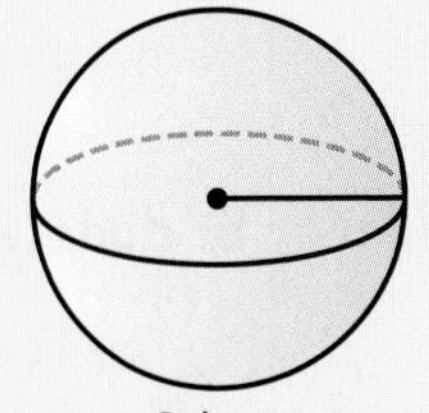
Sphere

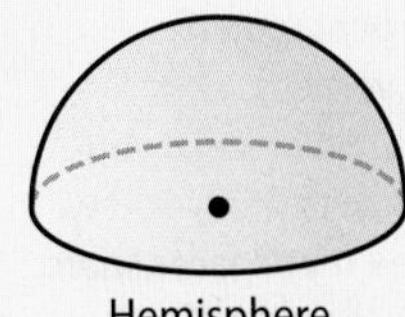
Hemisphere

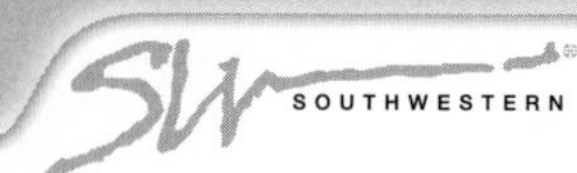

What Are Platonic Solids?

Remember, a *regular polygon* has sides that are equal in length, and all of its angles have the same measure.

The **Platonic solids** are the five *regular polyhedra*. They are named after the Greek philosopher Plato (428–348 B.C.E.). A **regular polyhedron** has faces that are congruent *regular polygons*, and has the same number of faces meet at each vertex. No other polyhedra meet these conditions.

The Five Platonic Solids	
A **tetrahedron** has 4 congruent faces that are equilateral triangles.	
A **cube** has 6 congruent faces that are squares. A cube is also called a hexahedron.	
An **octahedron** has 8 congruent faces that are equilateral triangles.	
A **dodecahedron** has 12 congruent faces that are regular pentagons.	
An **icosahedron** has 20 congruent faces that are equilateral triangles.	

The Swiss mathematician Leonhard Euler developed a formula for the relationship among the vertices, faces, and edges of *any* polyhedron.

$$V + F - E = 2,$$

where V = number of vertices, F = number of faces, and E = number of edges.

EXAMPLE 1

Use the figures above to describe the Platonic solids below. First, name the polygon that forms each face. Then tell the number of faces and vertices.

a. octahedron

The 8 faces are all congruent equilateral triangles. There are 6 vertices.

b. dodecahedron

The 12 faces are all congruent regular pentagons. There are 20 vertices.

c. icosahedron

The 20 faces are all congruent equilateral triangles. There are 12 vertices.

Watch Out!

A *dodecahedron* has 12 congruent faces that are regular pentagons, and a pentagon has 5 vertices: $12 \times 5 = 60$. However, if you look carefully you will see that 3 faces share each vertex. Since $60 \div 3 = 20$, there are 20 vertices.

EXAMPLE 2

Use this variation of Euler's formula to find the number of edges (E) on an icosahedron: $E = F + V - 2$.

Think: An icosahedron has 20 faces (F) and 12 vertices (V).

Substitute what you know.	$E = F + V - 2$
Add.	$= (20 + 12) - 2$
Subtract.	$= 32 - 2$
	$= 30$

An icosahedron has 30 edges.

SEARCH

To see step-by-step videos of these problems, enter the page number into the SWadvantage.com Search Bar.

EXAMPLE 3

Look at each net. Tell which Platonic solid it will form.

a.

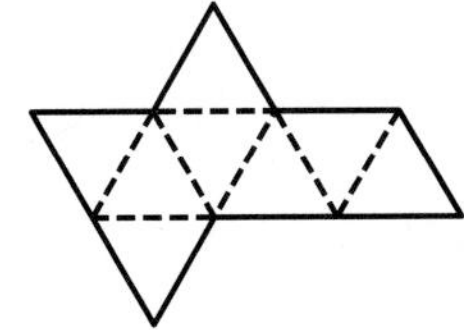

The net has 8 congruent, equilateral triangles. It is a net for an octahedron.

b.

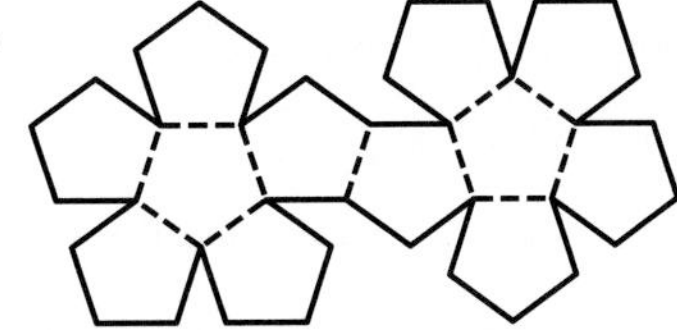

The net has 12 congruent, regular pentagons. It is a net for a dodecahedron.

Need More HELP

Remember, a *net* is a two-dimensional representation of a three-dimensional figure.

For help with nets, go to *Nets* in *Geometry* (p. 694).

Properties of Platonic Solids

Regular Polyhedron	Faces	Edges	Vertices
Tetrahedron – Faces are congruent equilateral triangles.	4	6	4
Cube – Faces are congruent squares.	6	12	8
Octahedron – Faces are congruent equilateral triangles.	8	12	6
Dodecahedron – Faces are congruent regular pentagons.	12	30	20
Icosahedron – Faces are congruent equilateral triangles.	20	30	12

Data and Graphs

What Came Before?

- Comparing, ordering, and operations with whole numbers
- Circles and lines

What's This About?

- Reading and interpreting information on charts and graphs
- Making graphs to display data
- Ways to describe a "middle" value of a data set

Practical Apps

- Financial analysts often use visual displays of information to help people to make sense of numerical information.
- Pollsters may use data displays to show the results of polls.

just for FUN!

I'd rather have a pie chart than a circle graph.

Q: Why, aren't they the same thing?

A: Yes, but the pie chart tastes better.

CONTENTS UPLOAD DOWNLOAD

Foundations of Mathematics

You can find more practice problems online by visiting:
www.SWadvantage.com

Tally Charts

Tally marks are grouped in 5's to help make them easy to count. For each row on a tally chart, count by fives until you get to the single tallies. Then count on by ones. For example, for the tally chart shown at the right, count the row for pennies as: 5, 10, 15, 20, 21, 22.

What Is a Tally Chart?

A **tally chart** is a chart used to record the frequency of data (information). Individual tally marks that look like this, |, represent each piece of information. Tallies are combined in groups of five that look like this, ~~||||~~. When a tally chart includes the frequency of each kind of data, it may be called a **frequency table**.

Carson's coin bank was full. He wondered how much money it held. He emptied it and recorded each coin in this tally chart.

Coin	Tally Marks	Number
Pennies	~~||||~~ ~~||||~~ ~~||||~~ ~~||||~~ ||	22
Nickels	||||	4
Dimes	~~||||~~ ~~||||~~ ||||	14
Quarters	~~||||~~ ~~||||~~ ~~||||~~ ~~||||~~ ~~||||~~ ||	27

Column 1 on the tally chart shows the types of coins that were in the coin bank. Column 2 shows the tally marks that represent the numbers of each type of coin. Column 3 shows the total number of tallies (frequency) for each type of coin.

Using a Tally Chart

SEARCH

To see step-by-step videos of these problems, enter the page number into the SWadvantage.com Search Bar.

EXAMPLE 1

Use the tally chart above to find the total value of the coins in Carson's coin bank.

STEP 1 Multiply to find the total value of each kind of coin.

A penny is worth 1¢. $22 \times 1¢ = \$\ .22$

A nickel is worth 5¢. $4 \times 5¢ = \$\ .20$

A dime is worth 10¢. $14 \times 10¢ = \$1.40$

A quarter is worth 25¢. $27 \times 25¢ = \$6.75$

STEP 2 Add to find the total value of the coins.

$\$.22 + \$.20 + \$1.40 + \$6.75 = \$8.57$

There was $8.57 in Carson's bank.

EXAMPLE 2

Nisha is counting the types of girl's clothing donated for a rummage sale. She recorded the number on a tally chart, as shown below.

Item	Number Donated
Shirts	𝍸 𝍸 𝍸 𝍸 𝍸 𝍸 ||
Dresses	𝍸 𝍸
Pants	𝍸 𝍸 𝍸 𝍸 𝍸 |||
Skirts	𝍸 𝍸 𝍸 ||||
Sweaters	𝍸 𝍸 𝍸 𝍸 |

Use the tally chart to answer each question.

a. How many more skirts than dresses were donated?

Count the tallies for the skirts: 5, 10, 15, 19
Count the tallies for the dresses: 5, 10
Subtract: $19 - 10 = 9$
There are 9 more skirts than dresses donated.

b. How many fewer sweaters than shirts were donated?

Count the tallies for the sweaters: 5, 10, 15, 20, 21
Count the tallies for the shirts: 5, 10, 15, 20, 25, 30, 32
Subtract: $32 - 21 = 11$
There were 11 fewer sweaters than shirts donated.

c. What was the total number of girl's clothing items donated?

METHOD 1

- Find how many of each type of item was donated. From Parts (a) and (b) you already know: 19 skirts, 10 dresses, 21 sweaters, 32 shirts. Pants = 5, 10, 15, 20 25, 28.
- Add the five values:

```
    19 skirts
    10 dresses
    21 sweaters
    32 shirts
 +  28 pants
   110 items total
```

METHOD 2

- Find the value of the groups of 5 tallies. Count the groups of 5. There are 20. Multiply by 5: $20 \times 5 = 100$
- Add the single tallies: $2 + 3 + 4 + 1 = 10$
- Add the two sums: $100 + 10 = 110$

A total of 110 girl's clothing items were donated.

GOT TO KNOW!

Tally Chart

A **tally chart** uses tally marks to record and organize data. The value of a single tally mark is 1 unit. Tally marks are grouped by 5's to make them easier to track and count.

||| = 3
𝍸 𝍸 𝍸 = 15
𝍸 𝍸 || = 12

Using Tally Charts in Surveys

A **survey** is a way of collecting data from a group of people. Each person in the group is asked the same question or questions. Tally charts are often used to record the responses to simple survey questions. When you use a tally chart to record responses, sometimes you only need to compare tally marks rather than find exact answers.

EXAMPLE 3

A survey question asked, "Is your birthday in the summer, fall, winter, or spring?" The person asking the question recorded each response by making a tally mark on the chart below.

Season	Number of Responses	Frequency
Summer	卌 |	?
Fall	卌	?
Winter	卌 ||||	?
Spring	卌 卌	?

Use the information on the tally chart to answer each question.

a. What is the frequency for each category of data?

Count the tally marks for each category.
Summer: $5 + 1 = 6$
Fall: 5
Winter: $5 + 4 = 9$
Spring: $5 + 5 = 10$

The frequency of each category is: Summer, 6; Fall, 5; Winter, 9; and Spring, 10.

b. How many people responded to this survey?

Each tally mark represents a response. Add the frequencies for the categories.
$6 + 5 + 9 + 10 = 30$

Thirty people responded to the survey.

c. What fraction of the people surveyed have a birthday in the spring?

30 people responded to the survey.
10 of the people said their birthday is in the spring.
$30 \div 3 = 10$, so 10 is one-third of 30.

One-third $\left(\frac{1}{3}\right)$ of the people surveyed have a birthday in the spring.

SEARCH

To see step-by-step videos of these problems, enter the page number into the SWadvantage.com Search Bar.

Need More HELP

Remember, data displays organize data into *categories*. This tally chart organizes the birthdays by the season of the year. So each season is a category.

A group of fourth graders were asked to vote for the kinds of TV programs they like best. The frequency table shows their votes.

Type of TV Show	Number of Votes	Frequency
Cartoons	卌 卌 卌 卌 ||||	?
Quiz Shows	卌 |||	?
Reality TV	卌 |	?
Science-Nature	卌 卌 卌	?
Comedies	卌 卌 |||	?
Sports	卌 ||	?

a. Which category of TV show received the most votes?

Think: Do any categories have more groups of 5 tallies than the other categories?

Yes, the category Cartoons has *4 groups* of 5 tallies, so it has at least $4 \times 5 = 20$ votes. No other category has 4 groups of 5 tallies.

The category Cartoons received the most votes.

b. Which category of TV show received the least votes?

Think: Do any categories have less than 5 tallies? No.
Do any categories have only one group of 5 tallies?
Yes, Quiz Shows, Reality TV, and Sports.
Which of these categories has the *least* single tallies?
Reality TV has only 1 single tally.

The category Reality TV received the least votes, 6.

c. Did any categories receive the same number of votes? Explain how you know.

No types of TV shows have *both* the same number of groups of 5 tallies *and* the same number of single tallies.

No categories received the same number of votes.

d. Suppose you were going to display this data on a bar graph. What values would you use for the lengths of the bars?

On a bar graph, the lengths of the bars represent the frequency of the data. To find the length of each bar, count the tallies for that category.

Cartoons: $5 + 5 + 5 + 5 + 4 = 24$ Quiz Shows: $5 + 3 = 8$ Reality TV: $5 + 1 = 6$
Science-Nature: $5 + 5 + 5 = 15$ Comedies: $5 + 5 + 3 = 13$ Sports: $5 + 2 = 7$

The value for the lengths of the bars are: Cartoons = 24, Quiz Shows = 8, Reality TV = 6, Science-Nature = 15, Comedies = 13, and Sports = 7.

For help with bar graphs, go to *Bar Graphs* on p. 188.

Pictographs

Understanding Pictographs

Need More HELP

The **key** on a graph is sometimes called the *legend*. The symbol used in the key is sometimes called the *icon*.

A **pictograph** uses symbols to display data. To read a pictograph, first look at the key to find the value of each symbol. Then, multiply the value of one symbol by the number of symbols in each row. Sometimes a pictograph will show only half of a symbol. In this case, the symbol has half the value shown on the key.

A student asked 25 classmates to vote on the type of music they like the best. The pictograph shows the results.

Favorite Type of Music

Classical	●●
Country	●●●●
Rap	●●●
Rock	●●◖
Other	●

Key: ● = 2 votes

To find the total for each group, use the information in the key.

Classical 2 icons × 2 votes per icon = 4 votes
Country 4 icons × 2 votes per icon = 8 votes
Rap 3 icons × 2 votes per icon = 6 votes
Rock 2 icons × 2 votes per icon = 4 votes plus a half icon = 1 vote
4 votes + 1 vote = 5 votes
Other 1 icon × 2 votes per icon = 2 votes

4 + 8 + 6 + 5 + 2 = 25 votes total

SEARCH

To see step-by-step videos of these problems, enter the page number into the SWadvantage.com Search Bar.

EXAMPLE 1

The workers at Just Like Home Kennels made this pictograph to record the kinds of pets they boarded one week. Use the pictograph to answer the questions.

Pets Boarded This Week

Dogs	♥♥♥♥♥♥♥♥♥♥♥♥♥♥♥♥
Cats	♥♥♥♥♥♥♥♥♥
Birds	♥♥♥♥♥♥
Ferrets	♥♥♥♥
Other	♥♥♥♥

Key: ♥ = 1 pet

a. How many pets were boarded that week?

Each heart stands for one pet. Count the hearts by ones in each row.

Then add: 16 + 9 + 6 + 4 + 4 = 39

There were 39 pets boarded that week.

b. Why might you want to have a symbol represent more than one data item?

You would need fewer symbols to display the data. It may be easier to skip count the number of symbols than to count a long line of symbols by 1.

The table shows the number of cell phone calls made by four students in July.

Cell Phone Calls (July)

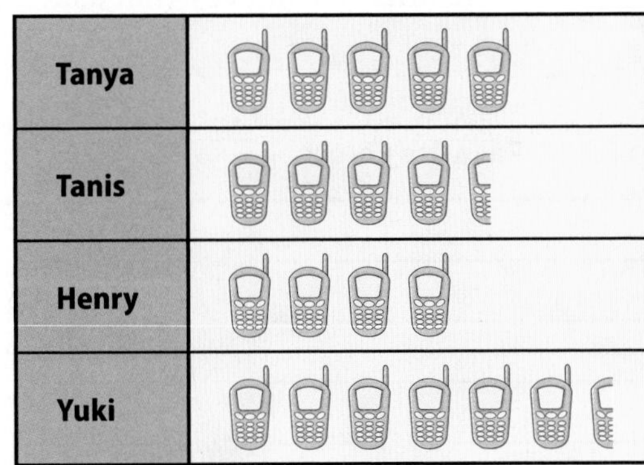

Key: = 10 calls

a. How many calls did each student make?

Think: Each symbol stands for 10 calls, so a half symbol stands for 5 calls.

Tanya – 5 symbols × 10 = 50 calls

Tanis – 4 symbols × 10 = 40 calls + 5 calls = 45 calls

Henry – 4 symbols × 10 = 40 calls

Yuki – 6 symbols × 10 = 60 calls + 5 calls = 65 calls

The number of calls are: Tanya, 50; Tanis, 45; Henry, 40; Yuki, 65

b. If each symbol represented 5 calls, how would you find the number of symbols needed for the students?

Think: The totals are all multiples of 5. *Tanya:* 5 × 10 = 50. *Tanis:* 5 × 9 = 45. *Henry:* 5 × 8 = 40. *Yuki:* 5 × 13 = 65.

If each symbol = 5, use 10 symbols for Tanya, 9 for Tanis, 8 for Henry, and 13 for Yuki.

c. Would having 1 symbol = 20 calls be a good choice for this pictograph?

Think: 50 would be 2 symbols plus half a symbol. 40 would be 2 symbols. However, 45 and 65 both end with 5. Because 20 ÷ 5 = 4, the values 45 and 65 would need a symbol that is one-fourth a cell phone.

It could be confusing to have whole, half, and quarter symbols on the same pictograph, so having 1 symbol = 20 calls is not a good choice for this pictograph.

GOT TO KNOW!

Pictographs

Pictographs use pictures or symbols to represent data. You can use a pictograph to compare amounts.

A key on the graph tells the value of each symbol. To find the exact amount for each category, multiply the number of symbols by the amount each symbol represents.

Watch Out !

The pictograph includes half symbols. Remember that a half symbol has half the value shown on the key.

Bar Graphs

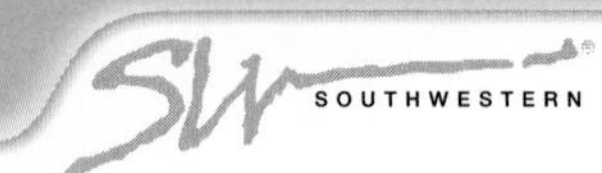

What Is a Bar Graph?

A *data display* is a way to visually organize information. Types of data displays include tally charts, bar graphs, line graphs, and circle graphs.

The *axes* on a graph are the vertical and horizontal lines.

A **bar graph** is a type of data display that uses bars to organize information. You can compare the information on a bar graph by comparing the lengths of the bars.

The vertical bar graph below shows the results of a survey that asked 36 students, "What is your favorite color?"

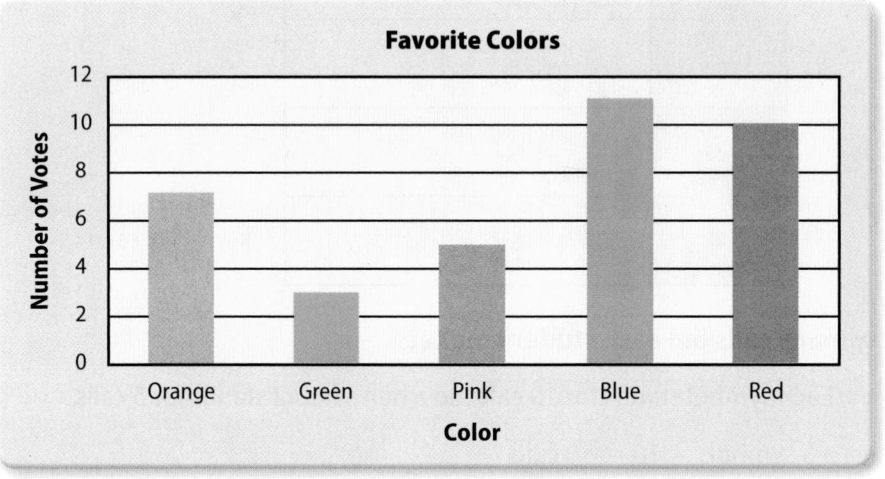

- The *title*, **Favorite Colors**, tells what information is displayed.
- The *vertical axis title*, **Number of Votes**, tells what the heights of the bars represent. The range of the scale is 0 to 12.
- The *horizontal axis title*, **Color**, tells what the bars represent. In addition, each bar has its own label that tells what color it represents.

You use the graph scale to find the number of votes each bar represents. For example, the top of the red bar is even with 10 on the scale. This means that 10 students voted for red. The top of the green bar is halfway between the 2 and the 4 on the scale. This means that 3 students voted for green.

SEARCH

To see step-by-step videos of these problems, enter the page number into the SWadvantage.com Search Bar.

EXAMPLE 1

Use the bar graph above to answer each question. Explain how you know the answers.

a. Which color received the greatest number of votes?
Blue. I know because the blue bar is taller than any other bar.

b. Which color received 10 votes?
Red. I know because the top of the red bar is on the scale line for 10.

c. How could you be certain that the graph represents the result of 36 votes?
Each bar represents the number of votes for a color. If I add the lengths of the five bars, the sum should be 36: $7 + 3 + 5 + 11 + 10 = 36$.

Vertical Bar Graphs

The bars of a *vertical bar graph* go from the bottom axis of the graph upward. The graph scale is always on the left (or vertical) axis.

EXAMPLE 2

Gina and Max have an online store. One of their most popular items is denim jeans. The vertical bar graph below shows the numbers of jeans sold in one month, arranged by price categories. Use the graph to answer each question.

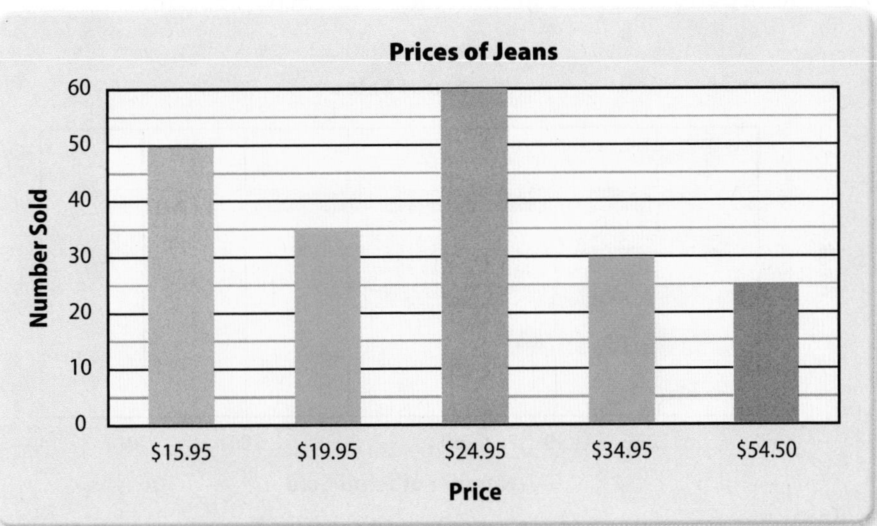

a. Explain how the scale on the graph is set up.
The scale goes from 0 to 60, and is labeled by tens. There are unlabeled lines halfway between the labeled ones. They represent: 5, 15, 25, 35, 45, and 55.

b. How many pairs of jeans that cost $20 or less were sold during this month?
Think: The horizontal axis is labeled "Price." Look for the bars that represent a price of $20 or less.
The bar for $15.95 represents 50 pairs of jeans. The bar for $19.95 represents 35 pairs of jeans. $50 + 35 = 85$.

During this month, 85 pairs of jeans that cost less than $20 were sold.

c. How many total pairs of jeans were sold during this month?
Think: The bars represent the numbers of jeans sold. I can find the number of sales each bar represents. Then I can add to find the total. From left to right, the numbers of pairs of jeans are: $50 + 35 + 60 + 30 + 25 = 200$.

There were 200 pairs of jeans sold during this month.

GOT TO KNOW!

Reading a Bar Graph

The lengths of the bars represent numerical data (information). To read this information on a vertical bar, look at the top of the bar. Then move to the left to the scale. Find where the top of the bar touches the scale. This will tell you the value of the bar.

In the partial graph below, the value of the bar for Dogs is 20. The value of the bar for Cats is 25.

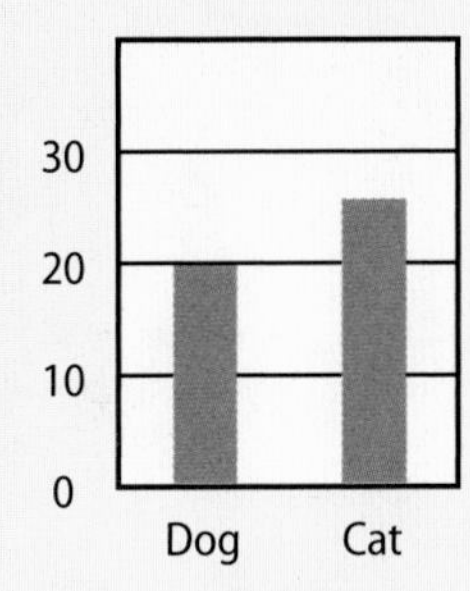

Horizontal Bar Graphs

A **horizontal bar graph** displays the same kind of data as a vertical bar graph. The difference is that the bars run from left to right and the scale is on the horizontal (bottom) axis. To find the vaue of a bar, go to the right end of the bar. Then look to see where the right end touches the scale.

SEARCH

To see step-by-step videos of these problems, enter the page number into the SWadvantage.com Search Bar.

EXAMPLE 3

The horizontal bar graph below shows the numbers of jeans sold each week during a 6-week period. Use the graph to answer each question.

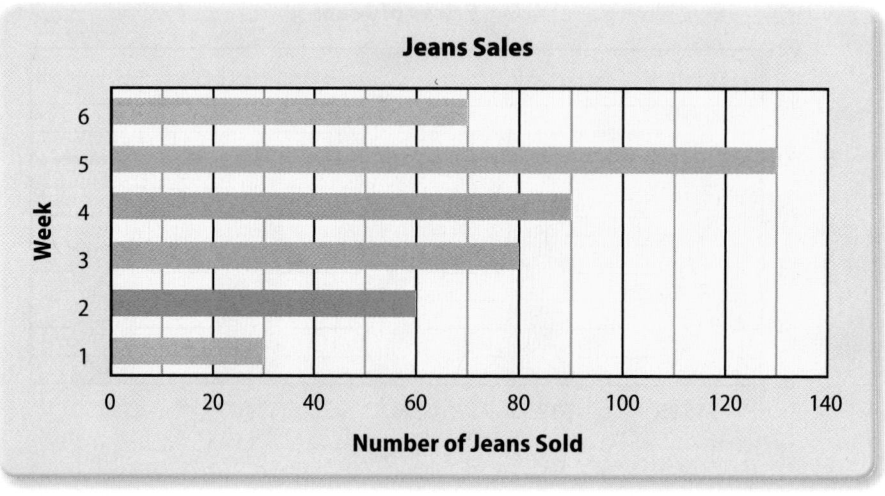

a. Explain how the scale on the graph is set up.
The scale goes from 0 to 140 and is labeled by 20's. There are unlabeled lines halfway between the labeled lines. They represent: 10, 30, 50, 70, 90, 110, and 130.

b. How many pairs of jeans were sold during the first three weeks altogether?
Think: Each bar represents the number of jeans sold for one week. Look at the right end of the bar for weeks 1, 2, and 3. Follow the end of each bar down to the scale, and match it to a number on the scale. If a bar ends halfway between two numbers on the scale, then use the number halfway between the two numbers.
Week 1, 30 pairs sold. Week 2, 60 pairs sold. Week 3, 80 pairs sold.
Add to find the sum of the sales: $30 + 60 + 80 = 170$

During the first three weeks,170 pairs of jeans were sold.

c. How many more pairs of jeans were sold in week 5 than in week 6?
Think: Find the number of jeans sold in weeks 5 and 6. Then subtract the values.
Week 5, 130 pairs of jeans were sold. Week 6, 70 pairs of jeans were sold.
$130 - 70 = 60$

There were 60 more pairs of jeans sold in week 5 than in week 6.

Making a Bar Graph

Once you are familiar with reading bar graphs, you are ready to make one. Use the steps for making a bar graph in the *Got To Know!* box to help you answer the questions in Example 4.

Making a Bar Graph

When you make a bar graph, follow these steps.

- Draw the two axis lines.
- Decide if the bars will be horizontal or vertical.
- Identify what the bars represent.
- Decide what scale to use. Then draw and label the scale.
- Label the axis that shows the scale.
- Draw and label each bar.
- Label the axis that shows what the bars represent.
- Give the graph a title that tells what it represents.

EXAMPLE 4

The frequency table below shows the favorite breakfast foods for 28 students.

Food	Eggs	Hot Cereal	Cold Cereal	Yogurt–Fruit	Toaster Pastry
Frequency	4	6	9	7	2

Suppose you were going to display this data (information) on a bar graph similar to the one started below.

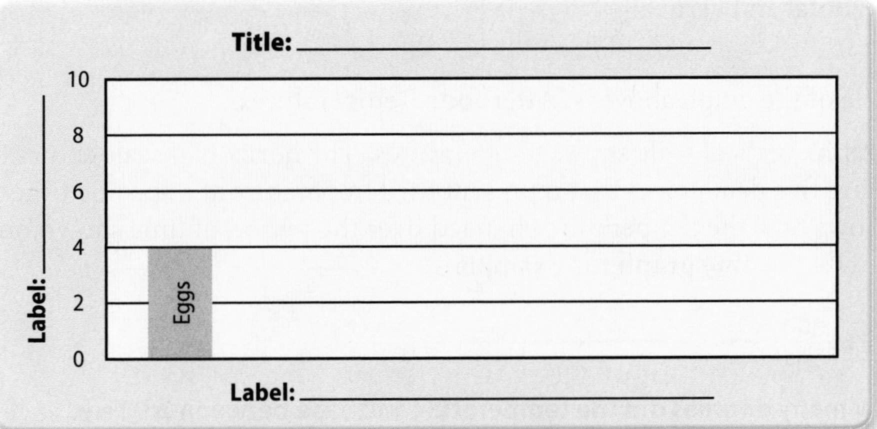

a. What would the length of each bar represent?
The number of times (frequency) a particular food was named as a favorite.

b. What scale could you use on this graph?
The longest bar represents a frequency of 9, so the scale must go from at least 0 to 9. You could use 0–9 or 0–10. You could label every value, or you could label only even values: 0, 2, 4, 6, 8, 10.

c. How could you label the vertical and horizontal axes?
The vertical axis (scale) shows frequency. You could label it *Frequency* or *Number of Times Chosen*. The horizontal axis shows types of food. You could label it *Food Choices*.

d. What is a good title for the graph?
The title tells what the data show. You could use the title *Favorite Breakfast Foods.*

On some bar graphs, such as the one started in Example 4, the labels for the bars are on the bars instead of below the bars.

Reading Line Graphs

For more about line graphs, go to *Choosing an Appropriate Graph* in *Line Graphs* in *Statistics and Probability* (Book 2, p. 1270).

A **line graph** is a data display that shows information as data points connected by line segments. A line graph is usually used to show change over time. To read a line graph:

- Read the graph title and the labels on the horizontal and vertical scales of the graph. Be sure you understand what the graph represents.
- Then decide how each data point relates to the horizontal and vertical scales.

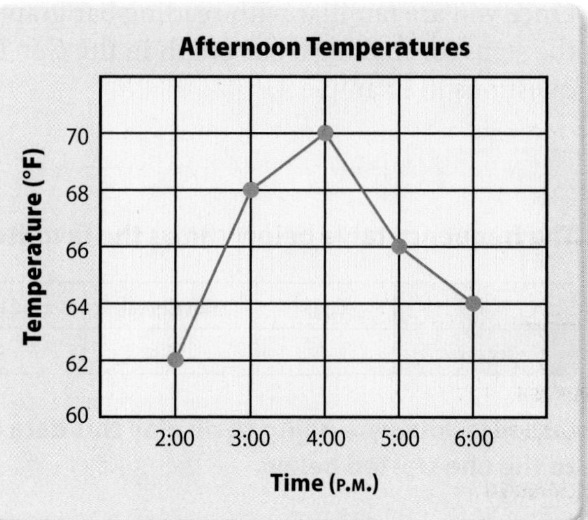

The title of the graph above is "Afternoon Temperatures."

The graph's vertical scale shows temperatures. The horizontal scale shows times. There are five data points that represent the temperature at a specific time. The line shows how the temperature changed over the period of time shown on the graph. Use this **line graph** for Example 1.

EXAMPLE 1

SEARCH

To see step-by-step videos of these problems, enter the page number into the SWadvantage.com Search Bar.

a. How many degrees did the temperature increase between 2:00 P.M. and 3:00 P.M.?

Look at the point above 2:00 P.M. on the horizontal scale. Then move left to the vertical scale. The temperature at 2:00 was 62°.

Look at the point above 3:00 P.M. on the horizontal scale. Then move left to the vertical scale. The temperature at 3:00 was 68°.

$68 - 62 = 6$

The temperature increased by six degrees between 2:00 P.M. and 3:00 P.M.

Need More HELP

An **interval** is a period of time between two or more events. One interval in the "Afternoon Temperatures" graph is the period of time between 3:00 and 4:00.

b. During which 1-hour interval did the temperature *decrease* the most?

Think: Find the line segment with the greatest *downward* slant. The line segment connecting the points for 4:00 P.M. and 5:00 P.M. has the *greatest downward* slant. At 4:00 P.M. it was 70°, and at 5:00 P.M. it was 66°. $70 - 66 = 4$

The temperature *decreased* the most during the 1-hour interval from 4:00 P.M. to 5:00 P.M.

EXAMPLE 2

Daniel kept track of his dog Kella's weight during the first year of her life.

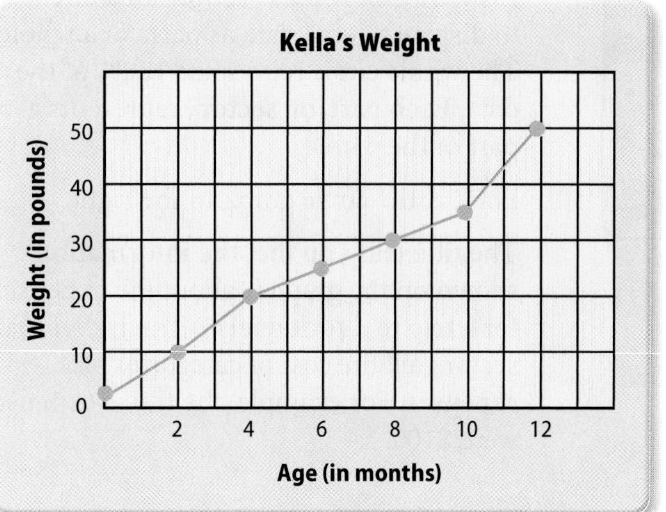

a. What was Kella's approximate weight when she was 3 months old?

The scale shows age in 2-month intervals. At 2 months old, Kella weighed 10 lb. At 4 months old, she weighed 20 lb. The number halfway between 10 and 20 is 15.

When Kella was 3 months old, she weighed about 15 lb.

b. During which 2-month period did Kella gain the most weight? How much weight did she gain during that time?

Think: Find the line segment with the greatest *upward* slant.

The line between 10 and 12 months has the greatest upward slant.

At 10 months, Kella weighed about 35 lb. At 12 months she weighed 50 pounds.

$50 - 35 = 15$

Kella gained the most weight during the 2-month period between 10 and 12 months. She gained 15 lb during this time.

Line Graph

A **line graph** shows information as data points connected by line segments. Each point is a piece of information. Line graphs usually show change over time. Some line graphs, like the graphs in Example 1 and Example 2, have a numeric scale that you read. Others, like the graph at the right, simply show increases and decreases. For example, you can tell that sales increased from January to February, but decreased from February to March.

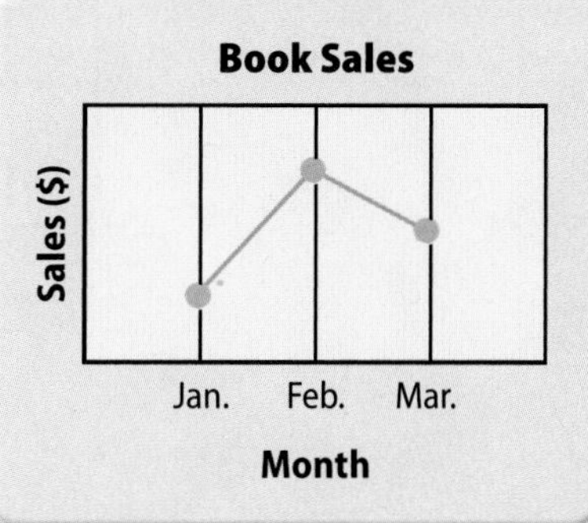

Ways to REMEMBER

A circle graph is sometimes called a *pie chart* because the sectors look like slices of pie.

Reading Circle Graphs

A **circle graph** uses sections of a circle to display a set of data as parts of a whole. The whole circle represents 100% of the data. Each part, or **sector**, represents a part of the whole.

Look at the circle graph to the right.

The title tells you that the information shown on the graph is about the expenses for a trip to a rock quarry. The individual sectors tell the cost of categories of expenses. For example, the travel expenses were $100.

Rock Quarry Trip—Expenses

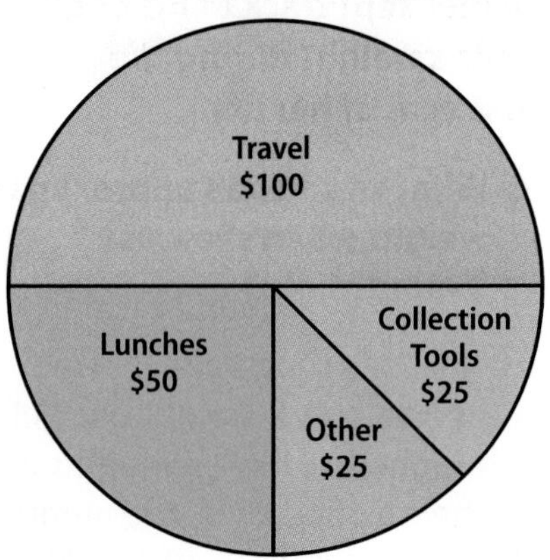

EXAMPLE 1

The circle graph above shows the expenses for a scout trip to a rock quarry.

a. What were the total trip expenses?

Think: A circle graph represents the whole. To find the total expenses, add the four expenses shown on the circle graph.
$\$100 + \$25 + \$25 + \$50 = \$200$

The total trip expenses were $200.

b. What percent of the total was for travel?

Think: The total expenses are $200, and $100 was spent on travel.
100 is one-half of 200. One-half = 50%
You can also see that the sector for expenses is one-half of the circle.

50% of the total was spent on travel.

c. What two categories represent the same amount?

Think: The categories *Collection Tools* and *Other* are both $25. Also, the sectors that represent them are the same size.

The categories *Collection Tools* and *Other* represent the same amounts.

SEARCH

To see step-by-step videos of these problems, enter the page number into the SWadvantage.com Search Bar.

EXAMPLE 2

Hakim earns $48 per week at his after-school job. He made the circle graph below to show how he uses this income.

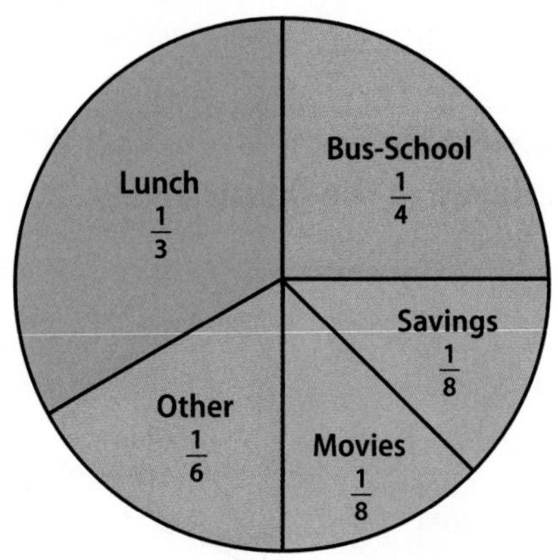

a. According to the graph, how much does Hakim save each week?

The graph shows that he saves $\frac{1}{8}$ of his weekly income of $48.

METHOD 1

Think: $48 \div 8 = 6$

One-eighth of $48 must be $6.

Hakim saves $6 each week.

METHOD 2

Think: What is $\frac{1}{8}$ of 48?

$\frac{1}{\cancel{8}_1} \times \frac{\cancel{48}^6}{1} = 6$

b. How much more does Hakim spend on lunches than on the bus to school?

Hakim spends $\frac{1}{3}$ of $48 on lunches. $\$48 \div 3 = \$16$

He spends $\frac{1}{4}$ of $48 on the bus to school. $\$48 \div 4 = \$12$

$\$16 - \$12 = \$4$

Hakim spends $4 more on lunches than on the bus to school.

c. Which category represents the greater amount of money—*Other* or *Movies*? Explain how you know.

Other $= \frac{1}{6}$ of his weekly income. *Movies* $= \frac{1}{8}$ of his weekly income.

The unit fraction $\frac{1}{6}$ is greater than the unit fraction $\frac{1}{8}$. Also, if you look closely you can see that the sector for *Other* is slightly larger than the sector for *Movies*.

The category *Other* represents the greater amount of money.

GOT TO KNOW!

Circle Graph

A **circle graph** shows how parts of a set of data are related to the whole set of data. The whole is 100% of the data, or 1.

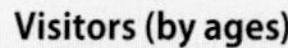

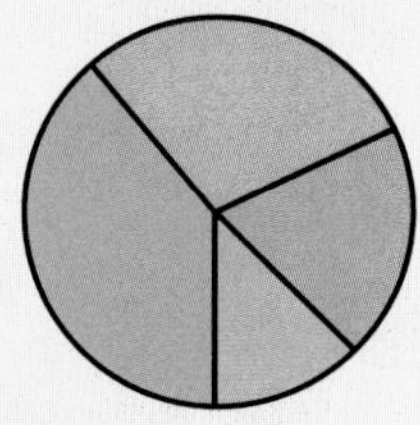

Key (ages)
- 12–15
- 16–20
- 21–25
- over 25

Some circle graphs have a key. Others show all of the information on the graph.

Circle Graphs and Percents

A **percent** is a comparison of a number to 100. The word percent means *per hundred*. You can write any number as a percent by first writing it as a fraction with a denominator of 100. For example, 40% means $\frac{40}{100}$, or 40 out of 100.

Need More HELP

For help with percents, go to *Finding the Percent of a Whole Number* in *Numbers and Operations* (p. 384).

EXAMPLE 3

A student surveyed a group of 100 teachers and asked, "What color is your car?" The 100 responses are displayed in the graph below.

Teachers' Car Colors

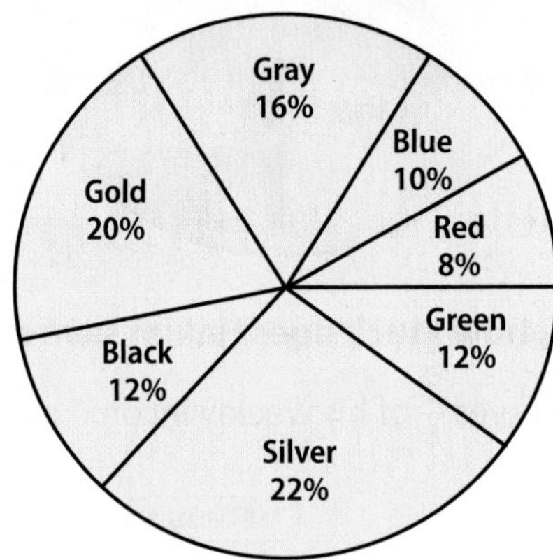

a. What color occurs most frequently? How many cars is this?

The greatest percent shown is 22% for silver. 22% of 100 is 22.

The color silver occurs most frequently. This is 22 silver cars.

b. What two colors occur with the same frequency?

Both green and black show a frequency of 12%.

The colors green and black occur with the same frequency.

c. What color occurs twice as often as red?

8% of the responses are for red. $2 \times 8 = 16$. 16% of the responses are for gray.

The color gray occurs twice as frequently as red.

d. How many of the teachers who responded have a blue car?

10% of 100 cars are blue. This means that 10 out of the 100 cars are blue.

Ten teachers said that they have a blue car.

SEARCH

To see step-by-step videos of these problems, enter the page number into the SWadvantage.com Search Bar.

Making a Circle Graph

The sectors that make up a circle graph have an angle with a vertex at the center of the circle. This type of angle is called a ***central angle***. The sum of the central angles of a circle is always 360°. To make a circle graph, you need to know the measures of the central angles. Sometimes these measures are given to you. At other times, you need to calculate the measures.

Try It This Way

If you "do a 360" on a skateboard, you turn all the way around. Use this expression to remember that there are 360° around the center of a circle.

EXAMPLE 4

A recycling center reported these categories of recycled items: 18% metal, 14% plastic, 10% glass, 42% paper, and 16% yard trimmings.

a. Find the measures of the central angles that represent each category of recycled items.

There are 360° in the whole circle. Multiply each percent by 360° to find the number of degrees in each central angle. Round each product to the nearest whole number.

Multiply the percent of *metal*.	$360° \times 18\% = 64.8° \approx 65°$
Multiply the percent of *plastic*.	$360° \times 14\% = 50.4° \approx 50°$
Multiply the percent of *glass*.	$360° \times 10\% = 36°$
Multiply the percent of *paper*.	$360° \times 42\% = 151.2° \approx 151°$
Multiply the percent of *yard trimmings*.	$360° \times 16\% = 57.6° \approx 58°$
Check to be certain the sum is 360°.	$65° + 50° + 36° + 151° + 58° = 360°$.

b. Draw a circle graph for the data.

- Draw a circle.
- Draw any radius of the circle.
- Use a protractor and the radius as one ray of a central angle of 65°. Draw the other ray. Label it: Metal 18%.
- Continue measuring and marking angles until you have drawn all five angles.
- Give the graph a title.
- Your graph should be similar to the one at the right. While the sectors may be at different locations, the corresponding sectors should be the same size.

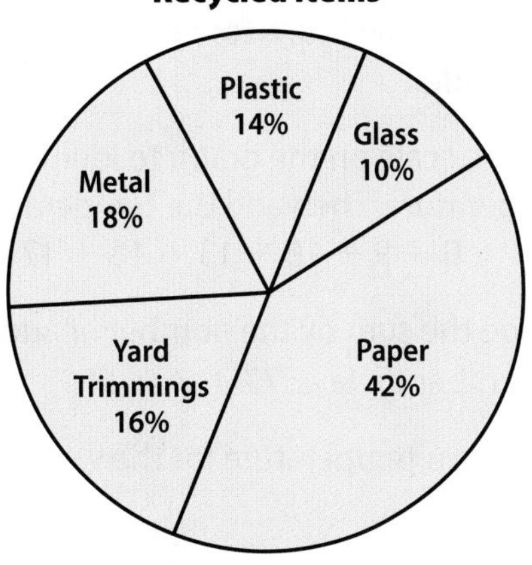

Ways to REMEMBER

Use the percent key on your calculator to find each measure. For example, to find the measure of the central angle for Metal,

Enter: 360
Press: ×
Enter: 18
Press: %
The calculator display will show: 64.8.

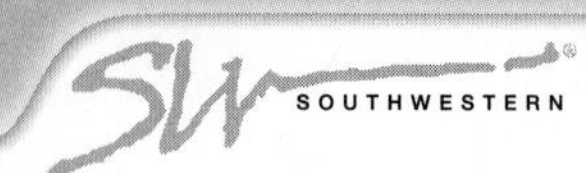

Mean of a Data Set

The mean of a data set is the average of the numbers in the data set. To find the mean, add the data values. Then divide the sum by the number of data values added. The mean will always fall within the range of the data values.

For more information abut the mean of a set of data, go to *The "Center" of a Data Set* in *Statistics and Probability* (Book 2, p. 1294).

EXAMPLE 1

A shopper bought 3 bags of groceries. The weights of the bags were 21 lb, 17 lb, and 25 lb. What is the mean (or average) weight of the three bags?

Find the sum of the weights of the bags.

$21 + 17 + 25 = 63$

Divide the sum by the number of bags.

$63 \div 3 = 21$

CHECK 21 is within the range of 21–25, so the answer is reasonable.

The mean weight of the bags is 21 lb. ✔

EXAMPLE 2

SEARCH

To see step-by-step videos of these problems, enter the page number into the SWadvantage.com Search Bar.

Kim's scores on 4 math tests are 77, 85, 75, and 83. What is Kim's mean score?

Find the sum of the scores.

$77 + 85 + 75 + 83 = 320$

Divide the sum by the number of tests.

$320 \div 4 = 80$

Kim's mean score on the four tests is 80.

EXAMPLE 3

Use the data in the graph to find the mean temperature for the week in Fairbanks.

Use the scale on the graph to identify each temperature. Then add the temperatures.

$4 + 0 + 9 + 16 + 13 + 18 + 17 = 77$

Divide the sum by the number of addends, or number of days. $77 \div 7 = 11$

The mean temperature for the week in March was 11°F.

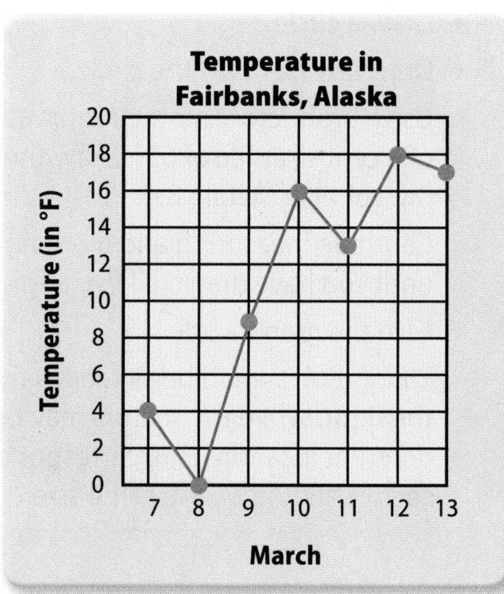

EXAMPLE 4

Five students counted the number of steps they each took to get from their classroom to the front door of the school. The table on the right shows the results.

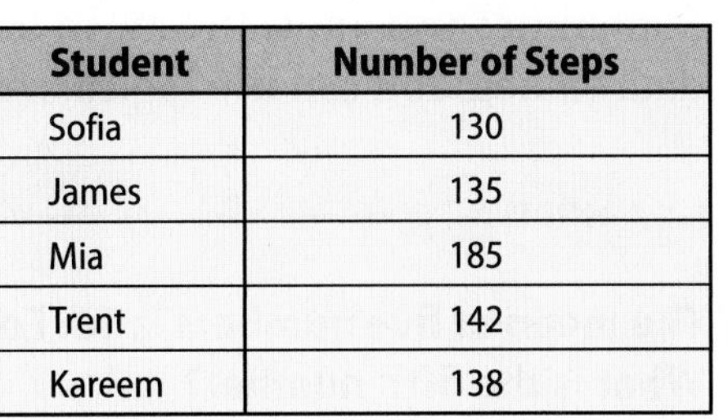

Student	Number of Steps
Sofia	130
James	135
Mia	185
Trent	142
Kareem	138

a. Find the mean number of steps it took to reach the front door of the school.

Find the sum of the numbers of steps.

$130 + 135 + 185 + 142 + 138 = 730$

Divide the sum by the number of addends.

$730 \div 5 = 146$

The mean number of steps was 146.

b. Mia took many more steps than the other students did. Suppose her steps were not included when calculating the mean. Predict how this would change the mean.

Think: If I remove 185 from the list, I will add: 130, 135, 142, and 138. The greatest number in this set is 142. Since $142 < 146$, the average number of steps will decrease.

Without Mia's number of steps, the mean will be less than 146.

c. Find the mean number of steps, leaving out Mia's steps.

Find the sum of the numbers of steps.

$130 + 135 + 142 + 138 = 545$

There are 4 addends. Divide the sum by the number of addends. (Round to the nearest whole number.)

$545 \div 4 = 136.25 \approx 136$

Without Mia's steps, the mean number of steps is about 136.

GOT TO KNOW!

The Mean of a Data Set

The mean is the *average* of the numbers in a set of data.

To find the mean:

- Add the data values.
- Divide the sum by the number of addends.

Example:

Data Set: 5, 3, 8, 8
Sum of Values:
$5 + 3 + 8 + 8 = 24$
Divide by 4:
$24 \div 4 = 6$
Mean: 6

Finding Missing Data Values

Sometimes you know the mean of a set of data but you do not know one of the data values. You can use logical reasoning to find the missing data value.

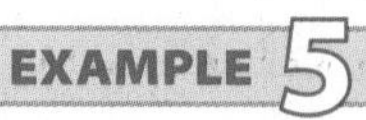

The mean of five numbers is 18. Four of the numbers are: 18, 13, 18, and 17. What is the fifth number?

Think: The mean of the 5 numbers is 18.
So the sum of the 5 numbers is $5 \times 18 = 90$.

- Find the sum of the 4 given numbers:
  $18 + 13 + 18 + 17 = 66$
- Subtract the sum from 90. The difference is the missing data value.
  $90 - 66 = 24$
- To check your answer, add the four given numbers and 24. Then divide by 5.
  $18 + 13 + 18 + 17 + 24 = 90$
  $90 \div 5 = 18$
  Using 24 for the fifth number gives a mean of 18.

The missing number in the data set is 24.

Try It This Way

You can use guess and check to find a missing data value. For Example 5, find the mean of the four given numbers:
$18 + 13 + 18 + 17 = 66$
$66 \div 4 = 16.5$
$16.5 < 18$
Look for a value that will raise the mean to 18. The value will be greater than any of the given values.

EXAMPLE 6

The mean of four amounts of money is \$561. Three of the amounts are \$562, \$535, and \$573. What is the fourth amount?

Think: The mean of the four numbers is \$561.
So the sum of the four numbers is $4 \times \$561 = \$2{,}244$.

- Find the sum of the three given numbers:
  $\$562 + \$535 + \$573 = \$1{,}670$
- Subtract the sum from \$2,244. The difference is the missing data value.
  $\$2{,}244 - 1{,}670 = 574$
- To check your answer, add the three given numbers and 574. Then divide by 4.
  $\$562 + \$535 + \$573 + \$574 = \$2{,}244$
  $\$2{,}244 \div 4 = \$561$
  Using \$574 for the fourth number gives a mean of \$561.

The missing number in the data set is \$574.

SEARCH

To see step-by-step videos of these problems, enter the page number into the SWadvantage.com Search Bar.

EXAMPLE 7

Mr. Wilson has 5 cans marked "Nails" in his workshop. The mean of the number of nails in the cans is 90. The first four cans contain these numbers of nails: 122, 84, 108, and 136. How many nails are in the fifth can?

- The mean of the number of nails in the 5 cans is 90.
  So the total number of nails in the cans is $5 \times 90 = 450$.
- Find the sum of the given numbers of nails:
  $122 + 84 + 108 + 136 = 450$

Think: If the total number of nails in the cans AND the sum of the four given numbers are both 450, there must be 0 nails in the fifth can.

- To check your answer, find the mean of the five numbers using zero as the fifth value.
  $122 + 84 + 108 + 136 + 0 = 450$
  $450 \div 5 = 90$

There are zero nails in the fifth can.

Comparing Means

You may be asked to compare the means of two or more data sets.

Two shoppers bought items that cost these amounts.

Shopper 1: **$42 + $47 + $50 + $37**
Shopper 2: **$44 + $53 + $38**

a. The mean price of which shopper's items was greater?

Find the mean for each set of prices.

Shopper 1:
$42 + $47 + $50 + $37 = $176
Mean: $176 ÷ 4 = $44

Shopper 2:
$44 + $53 + $38 = $135
Mean: $135 ÷ 3 = $45

$45 > $44, so the mean price of Shopper 2's items is greater.

b. Shopper 2 buys a fourth item. Now the means are equal. What was the cost of the fourth item?

Think: Four items with an average cost of $44 would cost: 4 × $44 = $176. The shopper would need to spend $176 − 135 = $41 on the fourth item.

The cost of the fourth item was $41.

Watch Out!

In Example 8, the two data sets contain different numbers of items. Count the number of addends in the set to find the divisor for the set.

Median, Mode, Range

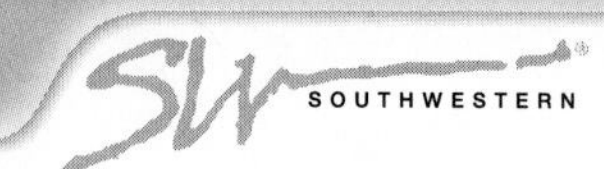

Median

For help finding the *Mean of a Data Set*, go to pages 198–201.

The *median*, the *mode*, and the *mean* of a data set are **measures of central tendency**. They represent different ways to describe the "center" of a data set.

To find the *median*, write the numbers in order, least to greatest or greatest to least. When the data set is an odd number of values, the **median** is the middle number. When the data set is an even number of values, the median is the mean of two middle numbers.

SEARCH

To see step-by-step videos of these problems, enter the page number into the SWadvantage.com Search Bar.

EXAMPLE 1

A theater box office recorded these ticket sales for one week.

Day	Sun.	Mon.	Tues.	Wed.	Thurs.	Fri.	Sat.
Tickets Sold	65	82	37	50	89	110	93

What is the median number of tickets sold?

Write the data values in numerical order.
37, 50, 65, 82, 89, 93, 110

The data set is an odd number of values. Find the middle value.
37, 50, 65, 82, 89, 93, 110

The median number of tickets sold is 82.

EXAMPLE 2

A movie theater box office reported these ticket sales during a six-month period.

Month	Jan.	Feb.	Mar.	Apr.	May	Jun.
Tickets Sold	2,261	1,837	1,909	2,178	2,062	2,475

What is the median number of tickets sold?

Write the data values in numerical order.
2,475; 2,261; 2,178; 2,062; 1,909; 1,837

There is an even number of data values. Find the two middle numbers.
2,475; 2,261; 2,178; 2,062; 1,909; 1,837

Find the mean of the two middle numbers.
$2{,}178 + 2{,}062 = 4{,}240$
$4{,}240 \div 2 = 2{,}120$

The median number of tickets sold is 2,120.

Mode

The **mode** of a data set is the value that occurs most often. A data set may have one mode, more than one mode, or no mode at all.

Measures of Central Tendency

Mean The *mean* is the average of the numbers in a data set.
Median The *median* is the middle number in a data set when the numbers are ordered by numerical value. When a data set contains an even number of values, the median is the mean of two middle numbers.
Mode The *mode* of a data set is the value that occurs most often. A data set may have one mode, more than one mode, or no mode at all.

EXAMPLE 3

The judges on a TV talent show give each performance a score that ranges from 1 to 10. The tables below show the scores of three different contestants. Find the mode of each data set.

a. Tommy sang on eight shows. His scores are shown below.

Show Number	1	2	3	4	5	6	7	8
Score	4	8	7	5	8	6	9	10

Write the scores in numerical order.
4, 5, 6, 7, 8, 8, 9, 10

Find the score that occurs most often.
4, 5, 6, 7, 8, 8, 9, 10

The mode of Tommy's scores is 8.

b. Twila danced on nine shows. Her scores are shown below.

Show Number	1	2	3	4	5	6	7	8	9
Score	8	10	9	10	6	10	8	7	8

Write the scores in numerical order.
6, 7, 8, 8, 8, 9, 10, 10, 10

Find the score that occurs most often.
6, 7, 8, 8, 8, 8, 9, 10, 10, 10

The modes of Twila's scores are 8 and 10.

c. Lin played the piano on seven shows. Her scores are shown below.

Show Number	1	2	3	4	5	6	7
Score	7	4	9	5	10	6	8

Write the scores in numerical order.
4, 5, 6, 7, 8, 9, 10
None of Lin's scores occurred more than once.

There is no mode for Lin's scores.

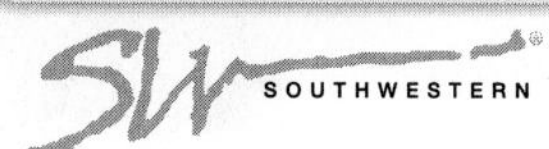

Using Measures of Central Tendency

The best measure of central tendency to use often depends on the data set being studied. It can also depend on what information is needed from the data.

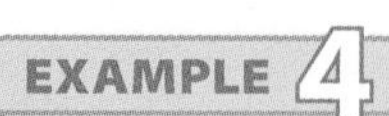

Remember, the *mean* is the average of the data set. To find the mean, find the sum of the values and divide by the number of values in the set.

The table below shows the monthly salaries of five salespeople at a car dealership.

a. Which measure of central tendency—mean, median, or mode—best represents the center of the data?

Salesperson	Nick	Julia	Enrique	Thomas	Lucy
Monthly Salary	\$4,900	\$6,300	\$5,500	\$5,200	\$4,700

STEP 1 Find the mean, median, and mode of the data set.

Mean: Find the sum of the data values.
\$4,900 + \$6,300 + \$5,500 + \$5,200 + \$4,700 = \$26,600
Divide by the number of values in the data set. \$26,600 ÷ 5 = \$5,320
The mean is \$5,320.

Median: Order the values. Then find the middle value.
\$4,700 \$4,900 \$5,200 \$5,500 \$6,300
The median is \$5,200.

Mode: No salaries are the same, so there is no mode.

STEP 2 Compare the measures. Mean − \$5,320 Median − \$5,200
There is no mode. The mean and the median are very close in value.

Both the mean and the median can be used to represent the center of the data.

b. Suppose a sixth sales person earned \$8,800 that month. How would that affect which measure of central tendency best represents the center of the data?

Mean: \$4,900 + \$6,300 + \$5,500 + \$5,200 + \$4,700 + \$8,800 = \$35,400
\$35,400 ÷ 6 = \$5,900

Median: \$4,700 \$4,900 \$5,200 \$5,500 \$6,300 \$8,800
\$5,200 + \$5,500 = \$10,700
\$10,700 ÷ 2 = \$5,350

The new mean, \$5,900, is higher than four of the values in the data set. It is not as close to the center as the new median. In this case, it is best to use the new median, \$5,350, to describe the data.

When one value in a data set is much higher than the other values, the mean may not be the best measure for describing the data set.

Range

The **range** of a set of data is the difference between the greatest and the least value in the data set. To find the range, subtract the least value from the greatest value.

Range of a Data Set

The **range** of a set of data is the difference between the greatest and the least value in the data set. Find the range of a set of data by subtracting the least value from the greatest value.

Gregory worked at a recreation center for six weeks last summer. He worked these numbers of hours each week: 10 hours, 8 hours, 15 hours, 12 hours, 10 hours, and 7 hours. What is the range in the number of hours he worked per week?

The greatest number of hours Gregory worked was 15. The least number was 7. Subtract to find the range of the data. $15 - 7 = 8$

The range of the number of hours Gregory worked is 8 hours.

EXAMPLE 6

Markus and Franco took turns bouncing a ball next to the height chart on the gym wall. They recorded their bounces.

Markus	3 ft	4 ft	7 ft	4 ft	5 ft	6 ft	7 ft
Franco	4 ft	8 ft	7 ft	5 ft	8 ft	6 ft	9 ft

Whose range was greater? What was that range?

Find the range of each data set.
Markus: $7 - 3 = 4$
Franco: $9 - 4 = 5$

Franco's range of 5 feet was greater than Markus's range of 4 feet.

SEARCH

To see step-by-step videos of these problems, enter the page number into the SWadvantage.com Search Bar.

EXAMPLE 7

The table shows the number of calories in one cup of four kinds of juice.

Type of Juice	Apple	Grape	Orange	Pineapple
Calories in 1 Cup	90	114	84	108

Find the range of the number of calories in one cup of juice.

$114 - 84 = 30$

The range of calories per cup is 30.

Foundations of Mathematics

Basic Addition Facts

+	0	1	2	3	4	5	6	7	8	9	10
0	0	1	2	3	4	5	6	7	8	9	10
1	1	2	3	4	5	6	7	8	9	10	11
2	2	3	4	5	6	7	8	9	10	11	12
3	3	4	5	6	7	8	9	10	11	12	13
4	4	5	6	7	8	9	10	11	12	13	14
5	5	6	7	8	9	10	11	12	13	14	15
6	6	7	8	9	10	11	12	13	14	15	16
7	7	8	9	10	11	12	13	14	15	16	17
8	8	9	10	11	12	13	14	15	16	17	18
9	9	10	11	12	13	14	15	16	17	18	19
10	10	11	12	13	14	15	16	17	18	19	20

Basic Subtraction Facts

−	0	1	2	3	4	5	6	7	8	9	10
0	0										
1	1	0									
2	2	1	0								
3	3	2	1	0							
4	4	3	2	1	0						
5	5	4	3	2	1	0					
6	6	5	4	3	2	1	0				
7	7	6	5	4	3	2	1	0			
8	8	7	6	5	4	3	2	1	0		
9	9	8	7	6	5	4	3	2	1	0	
10	10	9	8	7	6	5	4	3	2	1	0

Basic Addition Facts

0 + 0 = 0	1 + 0 = 1	2 + 0 = 2	3 + 0 = 3	4 + 0 = 4	5 + 0 = 5	6 + 0 = 6	7 + 0 = 7	8 + 0 = 8	9 + 0 = 0	10 + 0 = 10
0 + 1 = 1	1 + 1 = 2	2 + 1 = 3	3 + 1 = 4	4 + 1 = 5	5 + 1 = 6	6 + 1 = 7	7 + 1 = 8	8 + 1 = 9	9 + 1 = 10	10 + 1 = 11
0 + 2 = 2	1 + 2 = 3	2 + 2 = 4	3 + 2 = 5	4 + 2 = 6	5 + 2 = 7	6 + 2 = 8	7 + 2 = 9	8 + 2 = 10	9 + 2 = 11	10 + 2 = 12
0 + 3 = 3	1 + 3 = 4	2 + 3 = 5	3 + 3 = 6	4 + 3 = 7	5 + 3 = 8	6 + 3 = 9	7 + 3 = 10	8 + 3 = 11	9 + 3 = 12	10 + 3 = 13
0 + 4 = 4	1 + 4 = 5	2 + 4 = 6	3 + 4 = 7	4 + 4 = 8	5 + 4 = 9	6 + 4 = 10	7 + 4 = 11	8 + 4 = 12	9 + 4 = 13	10 + 4 = 14
0 + 5 = 5	1 + 5 = 6	2 + 5 = 7	3 + 5 = 8	4 + 5 = 9	5 + 5 = 10	6 + 5 = 11	7 + 5 = 12	8 + 5 = 13	9 + 5 = 14	10 + 5 = 15
0 + 6 = 6	1 + 6 = 7	2 + 6 = 8	3 + 6 = 9	4 + 6 = 10	5 + 6 = 11	6 + 6 = 12	7 + 6 = 13	8 + 6 = 14	9 + 6 = 15	10 + 6 = 16
0 + 7 = 7	1 + 7 = 8	2 + 7 = 9	3 + 7 = 10	4 + 7 = 11	5 + 7 = 12	6 + 7 = 13	7 + 7 = 14	8 + 7 = 15	9 + 7 = 16	10 + 7 = 17
0 + 8 = 8	1 + 8 = 9	2 + 8 = 10	3 + 8 = 11	4 + 8 = 12	5 + 8 = 13	6 + 8 = 14	7 + 8 = 15	8 + 8 = 16	9 + 8 = 17	10 + 8 = 18
0 + 9 = 9	1 + 9 = 10	2 + 9 = 11	3 + 9 = 12	4 + 9 = 13	5 + 9 = 14	6 + 9 = 15	7 + 9 = 16	8 + 9 = 17	9 + 9 = 18	10 + 9 = 19
0 + 10 = 10	1 + 10 = 11	2 + 10 = 12	3 + 10 = 13	4 + 10 = 14	5 + 10 = 15	6 + 10 = 16	7 + 10 = 17	8 + 10 = 18	9 + 10 = 19	10 + 10 = 20

Basic Subtraction Facts

0 − 0 = 0										
1 − 0 = 1	1 − 1 = 0									
2 − 0 = 2	2 − 1 = 1	2 − 2 = 0								
3 − 0 = 3	3 − 1 = 2	3 − 2 = 1	3 − 3 = 0							
4 − 0 = 4	4 − 1 = 3	4 − 2 = 2	4 − 3 = 1	4 − 4 = 0						
5 − 0 = 5	5 − 1 = 4	5 − 2 = 3	5 − 3 = 2	5 − 4 = 1	5 − 5 = 0					
6 − 0 = 6	6 − 1 = 5	6 − 2 = 4	6 − 3 = 3	6 − 4 = 2	6 − 5 = 1	6 − 6 = 0				
7 − 0 = 7	7 − 1 = 6	7 − 2 = 5	7 − 3 = 4	7 − 4 = 3	7 − 5 = 2	7 − 6 = 1	7 − 7 = 0			
8 − 0 = 8	8 − 1 = 7	8 − 2 = 6	8 − 3 = 5	8 − 4 = 4	8 − 5 = 3	8 − 6 = 2	8 − 7 = 1	8 − 8 = 0		
9 − 0 = 9	9 − 1 = 8	9 − 2 = 7	9 − 3 = 6	9 − 4 = 5	9 − 5 = 4	9 − 6 = 3	9 − 7 = 2	9 − 8 = 1	9 − 9 = 0	
10 − 0 = 10	10 − 1 = 9	10 − 2 = 8	10 − 3 = 7	10 − 4 = 6	10 − 5 = 5	10 − 6 = 4	10 − 7 = 3	10 − 8 = 2	10 − 9 = 1	10 − 10 = 0

Basic Multiplication Facts

×	0	1	2	3	4	5	6	7	8	9	10
0	0	0	0	0	0	0	0	0	0	0	0
1	0	1	2	3	4	5	6	7	8	9	10
2	0	2	4	6	8	10	12	14	16	18	20
3	0	3	6	9	12	15	18	21	24	27	30
4	0	4	8	12	16	20	24	28	32	36	40
5	0	5	10	15	20	25	30	35	40	45	50
6	0	6	12	18	24	30	36	42	48	54	60
7	0	7	14	21	28	35	42	49	56	63	70
8	0	8	16	24	32	40	48	56	64	72	80
9	0	9	18	27	36	45	54	63	72	81	90
10	0	10	20	30	40	50	60	70	80	90	100

Basic Division Facts

÷	1	2	3	4	5	6	7	8	9	10
1	1	2	3	4	5	6	7	8	9	10
2	2	4	6	8	10	12	14	16	18	20
3	3	6	9	12	15	18	21	24	27	30
4	4	8	12	16	20	24	28	32	36	40
5	5	10	15	20	25	30	35	40	45	50
6	6	12	18	24	30	36	42	48	54	60
7	7	14	21	28	35	42	49	56	63	70
8	8	16	24	32	40	48	56	64	72	80
9	9	18	27	36	45	54	63	72	81	90
10	10	20	30	40	50	60	70	80	90	100

Basic Multiplication Facts

zeros	0 × 0 = 0	1 × 0 = 0	2 × 0 = 0	3 × 0 = 0	4 × 0 = 0	5 × 0 = 0	6 × 0 = 0	7 × 0 = 0	8 × 0 = 0	9 × 0 = 0	10 × 0 = 0
ones	0 × 1 = 0	1 × 1 = 1	2 × 1 = 2	3 × 1 = 3	4 × 1 = 4	5 × 1 = 5	6 × 1 = 6	7 × 1 = 7	8 × 1 = 8	9 × 1 = 9	10 × 1 = 10
twos	0 × 2 = 0	1 × 2 = 2	2 × 2 = 4	3 × 2 = 6	4 × 2 = 8	5 × 2 = 10	6 × 2 = 12	7 × 2 = 14	8 × 2 = 16	9 × 2 = 18	10 × 2 = 20
threes	0 × 3 = 0	1 × 3 = 3	2 × 3 = 6	3 × 3 = 9	4 × 3 = 12	5 × 3 = 15	6 × 3 = 18	7 × 3 = 21	8 × 3 = 24	9 × 3 = 27	10 × 3 = 30
fours	0 × 4 = 0	1 × 4 = 4	2 × 4 = 8	3 × 4 = 12	4 × 4 = 16	5 × 4 = 20	6 × 4 = 24	7 × 4 = 28	8 × 4 = 32	9 × 4 = 36	10 × 4 = 40
fives	0 × 5 = 0	1 × 5 = 5	2 × 5 = 10	3 × 5 = 15	4 × 5 = 20	5 × 5 = 25	6 × 5 = 30	7 × 5 = 35	8 × 5 = 40	9 × 5 = 45	10 × 5 = 50
sixes	0 × 6 = 0	1 × 6 = 6	2 × 6 = 12	3 × 6 = 18	4 × 6 = 24	5 × 6 = 30	6 × 6 = 36	7 × 6 = 42	8 × 6 = 48	9 × 6 = 54	10 × 6 = 60
sevens	0 × 7 = 0	1 × 7 = 7	2 × 7 = 14	3 × 7 = 21	4 × 7 = 28	5 × 7 = 35	6 × 7 = 42	7 × 7 = 49	8 × 7 = 56	9 × 7 = 63	10 × 7 = 70
eights	0 × 8 = 0	1 × 8 = 8	2 × 8 = 16	3 × 8 = 24	4 × 8 = 32	5 × 8 = 40	6 × 8 = 48	7 × 8 = 56	8 × 8 = 64	9 × 8 = 72	10 × 8 = 80
nines	0 × 9 = 0	1 × 9 = 9	2 × 9 = 18	3 × 9 = 27	4 × 9 = 36	5 × 9 = 45	6 × 9 = 54	7 × 9 = 63	8 × 9 = 72	9 × 9 = 81	10 × 9 = 90
tens	0 × 10 = 0	1 × 10 = 10	2 × 10 = 20	3 × 10 = 30	4 × 10 = 40	5 × 10 = 50	6 × 10 = 60	7 × 10 = 70	8 × 10 = 80	9 × 10 = 90	10 × 10 = 100

Basic Division Facts

ones	0 ÷ 1 = 0	1 ÷ 1 = 1	2 ÷ 1 = 2	3 ÷ 1 = 3	4 ÷ 1 = 4	5 ÷ 1 = 5	6 ÷ 1 = 6	7 ÷ 1 = 7	8 ÷ 1 = 8	9 ÷ 1 = 9	10 ÷ 1 = 10
twos	0 ÷ 2 = 0	2 ÷ 2 = 1	4 ÷ 2 = 2	6 ÷ 2 = 3	8 ÷ 2 = 4	10 ÷ 2 = 5	12 ÷ 2 = 6	14 ÷ 2 = 7	16 ÷ 2 = 8	18 ÷ 2 = 9	20 ÷ 2 = 10
threes	0 ÷ 3 = 0	3 ÷ 3 = 1	6 ÷ 3 = 2	9 ÷ 3 = 3	12 ÷ 3 = 4	15 ÷ 3 = 5	18 ÷ 3 = 6	21 ÷ 3 = 7	24 ÷ 3 = 8	27 ÷ 3 = 9	30 ÷ 3 = 10
fours	0 ÷ 4 = 0	4 ÷ 4 = 1	8 ÷ 4 = 2	12 ÷ 4 = 3	16 ÷ 4 = 4	20 ÷ 4 = 5	24 ÷ 4 = 6	28 ÷ 4 = 7	32 ÷ 4 = 8	36 ÷ 4 = 9	40 ÷ 4 = 10
fives	0 ÷ 5 = 0	5 ÷ 5 = 1	10 ÷ 5 = 2	15 ÷ 5 = 3	20 ÷ 5 = 4	25 ÷ 5 = 5	30 ÷ 5 = 6	35 ÷ 5 = 7	40 ÷ 5 = 8	45 ÷ 5 = 9	50 ÷ 5 = 10
sixes	0 ÷ 6 = 0	6 ÷ 6 = 1	12 ÷ 6 = 2	18 ÷ 6 = 3	24 ÷ 6 = 4	30 ÷ 6 = 5	36 ÷ 6 = 6	42 ÷ 6 = 7	48 ÷ 6 = 8	54 ÷ 6 = 9	60 ÷ 6 = 10
sevens	0 ÷ 7 = 0	7 ÷ 7 = 1	14 ÷ 7 = 2	21 ÷ 7 = 3	28 ÷ 7 = 4	35 ÷ 7 = 5	42 ÷ 7 = 6	49 ÷ 7 = 7	56 ÷ 7 = 8	63 ÷ 7 = 9	70 ÷ 7 = 10
eights	0 ÷ 8 = 0	8 ÷ 8 = 1	16 ÷ 8 = 2	24 ÷ 8 = 3	32 ÷ 8 = 4	40 ÷ 8 = 5	48 ÷ 8 = 6	56 ÷ 8 = 7	64 ÷ 8 = 8	72 ÷ 8 = 9	80 ÷ 8 = 10
nines	0 ÷ 9 = 0	9 ÷ 9 = 1	18 ÷ 9 = 2	27 ÷ 9 = 3	36 ÷ 9 = 4	45 ÷ 9 = 5	54 ÷ 9 = 6	63 ÷ 9 = 7	72 ÷ 9 = 8	81 ÷ 9 = 9	90 ÷ 9 = 10
tens	0 ÷ 10 = 0	10 ÷ 10 = 1	20 ÷ 10 = 2	30 ÷ 10 = 3	40 ÷ 10 = 4	50 ÷ 10 = 5	60 ÷ 10 = 6	70 ÷ 10 = 7	80 ÷ 10 = 8	90 ÷ 10 = 9	100 ÷ 10 = 10

Place Value

Billions			Millions			Thousands			Ones		
hundred billions	ten billions	billions	hundred millions	ten millions	millions	hundred thousands	ten thousands	thousands	hundreds	tens	ones
2	3	6,	9	1	7,	4	0	5,	3	8	9

Forms of a Number

Standard form	236,917,405,389
Expanded form	200,000,000,000 + 30,000,000,000 + 6,000,000,000 + 900,000,000 + 10,000,000 + 7,000,000 + 400,000 + 5,000 + 300 + 80 + 9
Word form	two hundred thirty-six billion, nine hundred seventeen million, four hundred five thousand, three hundred eighty-nine
Short word form	236 billion, 917 million, 405 thousand, 389

Hints on Memorizing Facts

1. Focus on the ways to memorize facts that are listed on the next page.
2. Memorize the facts by saying the facts aloud.
   - For 3 + 8, say "Three plus eight equals eleven."
   - For 8 − 3, say "Eight minus three equals five."
   - For 8 × 7, say "Eight times seven equals fifty-six."
   - For 56 ÷ 8, say "Fifty-six divided by eight equals seven."
3. Memorize a few facts at a time. Work on 2 or 3 facts per day. Start with the easier facts.
4. Practice saying the facts in reverse order, so you don't have to memorize so many facts.
   $8 + 5 = 13, 5 + 8 = 13$ $9 - 4 = 5, 9 - 5 = 4$
5. Memorize one set of times tables at a time. Work on the set until you have mastered it. Then move to another set.
6. Use the relationship of multiplication to division. To remember $10 \div 2 = 5$, think $5 \cdot 2 = 10$.
7. Play fact games.
   - Toss two dice and add the dots that come up. Then have a friend toss two dice and add the dots. Then subtract the smaller sum from the larger sum.
   - Play multiplication facts bingo with some friends.
   - Play "Beat the Clock."
8. Make flash cards and use them on your own or with friends and family. Time how long it takes you to say a set of facts. Try this again the next day and see if you can beat your previous time.
9. Every day, review the facts you know or usually know. Then work on two new facts and play games to practice them.
10. Use a calculator. Enter the fact. Before you press ENTER, say the answer. Then press ENTER to see if you are correct.

Go For It!

Addition Facts: Memorize Fewer Than 121 Facts

There are 121 basic facts, but here are some ways to cut down the task.

- 0 plus any number is that number.
- 1 plus any number is the next number when you count.
- 2 plus any even number is the next even number.
- 2 plus any odd number is the next odd number.
- 10 plus any one-digit number is a teen number with the 1 in the tens place and the one-digit number in the ones place.
- If you know $2 + 3$, you know $3 + 2$. This takes care of half of the 121 facts.
- Once you memorize the doubles, the near doubles are easy to remember.
- Any number plus 9 is one less than that number plus ten.

Subtraction Facts: Memorize Fewer Than 121 Facts

There are 121 basic facts, but here are some ways to cut down the task.

- Any number minus 0 is itself.
- Any number minus itself is 0.
- Any number minus 1 is the previous counting number.
- Any even number minus 2 is the previous even number.
- Any odd number minus 2 is the previous odd number.
- Any teen number minus 10 is the digit in the ones place of the teen number.
- If you know $8 - 3 = 5$, you also know $8 - 5 = 3$. This takes care of half of the subtraction facts.
- Nine minus any number is one less than 10 minus the same number.

Multiplication Facts: Memorize Fewer Than 121 Facts

There are 121 basic facts, but here are some ways to cut down the task.

- Any number times 0 is 0.
- Any number times 1 is itself.
- Any number times 10 is that number with a zero to its right.
- Any number times 2 is the double of that number. For example, $2 \cdot 3 = 3 + 3$, or 6.
- The product of any number times 5 will always have 0 or 5 in the ones place.
- Four times a number is its double times 2. For example, $4 \cdot 3 = 2(2 \cdot 3) = 2(6) = 12$.
- Flip the numbers. If you know $3 \cdot 7 = 21$, you also know that $7 \cdot 3 = 21$.
- Think "one group more" or "one group less." If you know that $3 \cdot 4 = 12$, you know that $4 \cdot 4 = 12 + 4 = 16$.

Division Facts: Memorize Fewer Than 100 Facts

There are 100 facts to remember. Here are some ways to reduce the number of facts you need to memorize.

- Any number divided by 1 is the number itself.
- Any number divided by itself is 1.
- When a number that ends in zero is divided by 10, the quotient is the number without the zero. For example, $50 \div 10 = 5$.
- Pairs of facts are related. If you know that $15 \div 3 = 5$, then you know that $15 \div 5 = 3$.

Foundations of Mathematics

Data Graphs

Pictographs

A *pictograph* uses pictures or symbols to represent data. You can use a pictograph to compare amounts.

Favorite Type of Music

Classical	◉◉
Country	◉◉◉◉◉
Rap	◉◉◉
Rock	◉◉◖
Other	◉

Key: ◉ = 2 votes

Bar Graphs

A *bar graph* is a type of data display that uses bars to organize information. You can compare the information on a bar graph by comparing the lengths of the bars.

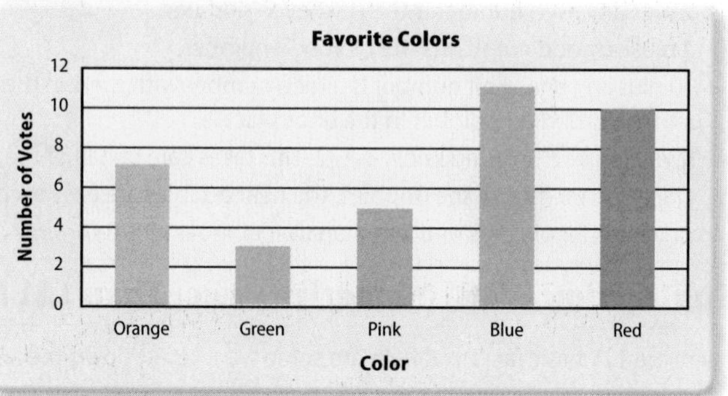

Line Graphs

A *line graph* is a data display that shows information as data points connected by line segments. A line graph usually shows change over time.

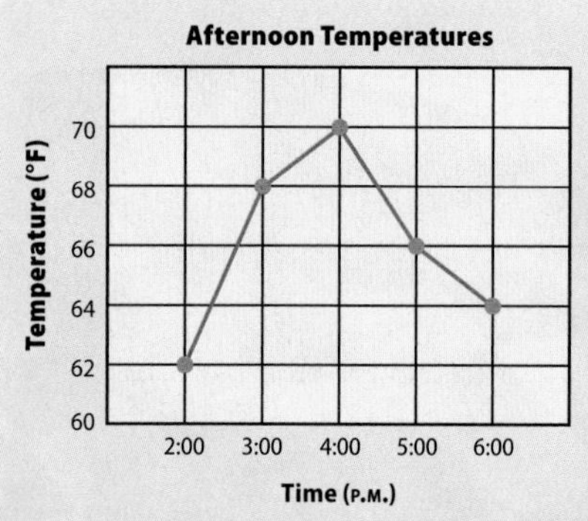

Circle Graphs

A *circle graph* uses sections of a circle to display a set of data as parts of a whole. The whole circle represents 100% of the data.

Rock Quarry Trip—Expenses

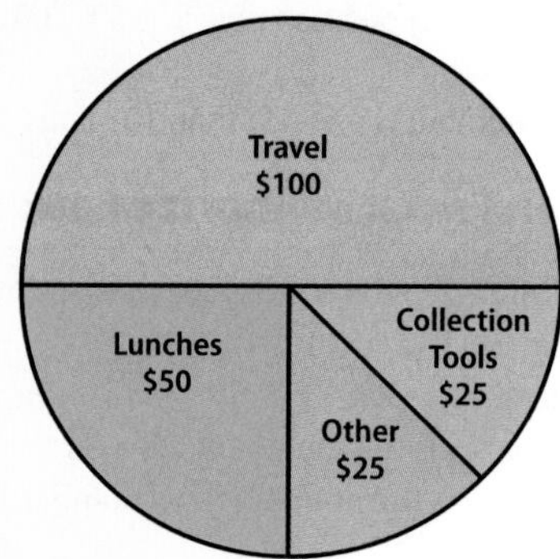

Lines

Points, Lines, Planes

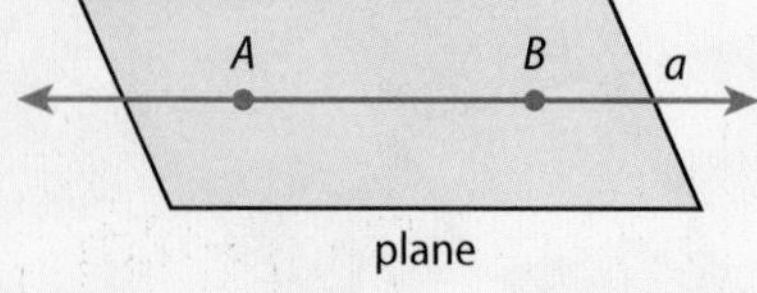

Line Segment

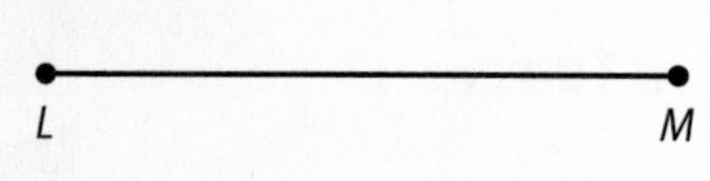

Ray

Intersecting Lines

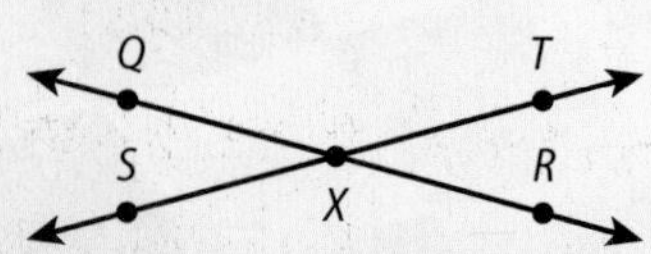

Parallel Lines

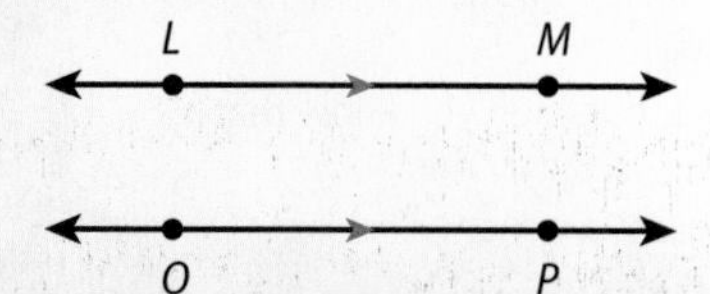

Perpendicular Lines

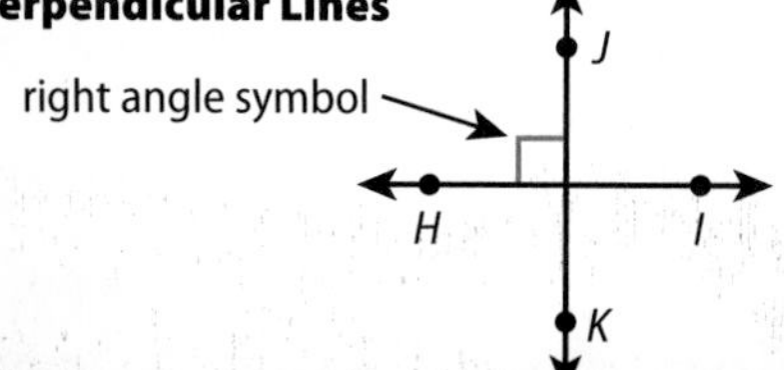

Angles

Angles Classified by Measure

right angle

obtuse angle

acute angle

straight angle

Complementary and Supplementary Angles

Angles *a* and *b* are complementary.

Angles *c* and *d* are supplementary.

Polygons

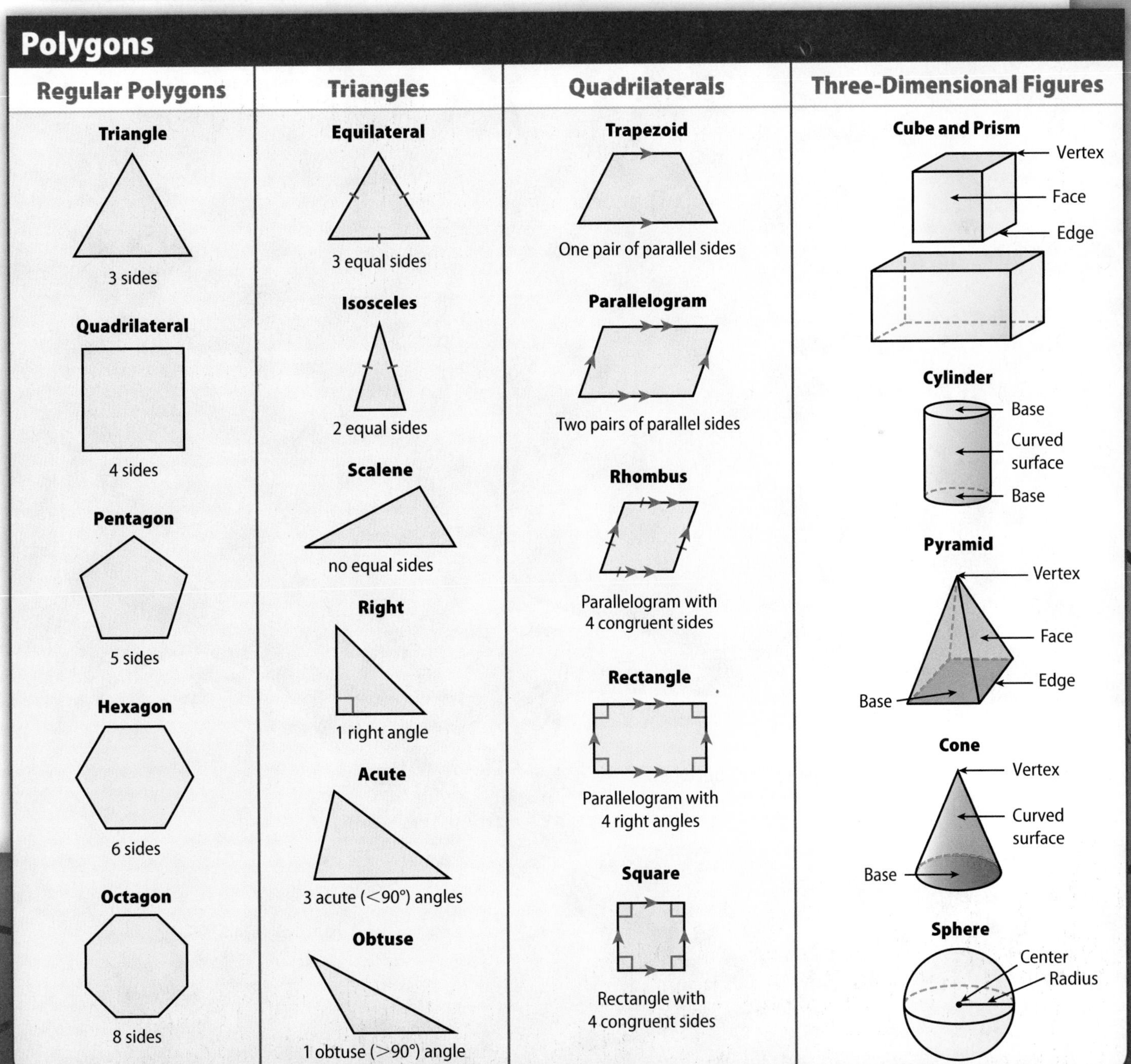

Numbers and Operations

Consumers use unit rates to compare prices between items and to determine which quantity is a better buy.

Decimals

What Came Before?

- Whole numbers—place value, comparing, rounding, operations
- Solving word problems with whole numbers

What's This About?

- Place value and operations with decimals
- Comparing and rounding decimals
- Solving word problems with decimals

Practical Apps

- An optician must understand the decimal numbers on a prescription for a pair of eyeglasses in order to make the lens correctly.
- Consumers need to read and compare decimal numbers when reviewing the energy efficiency ratings of appliances.

just for FUN!

I have 1.5 sisters.

Q: How is that possible?

A: I have one whole sister and one half sister.

CONTENTS UPLOAD DOWNLOAD

Numbers and Operations

You can find more practice problems online by visiting:
www.SWadvantage.com

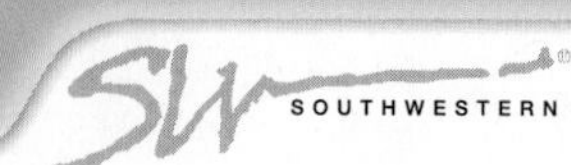

Understanding Decimal Place Values

Need More HELP

For help with whole number place value, go to *Place Value to Billions* on pages 40–41.

Decimal numbers represent values between whole numbers. A decimal point (dot) to the right of the ones place shows where the decimal values begin. You can represent the decimal places on a place-value chart, as shown below. Just as with whole numbers, each decimal place has a value that is *ten times the value of the place to its right* and *one tenth the value of the place to its left.*

EXAMPLE 1

The place value chart shows the number 85.342.

a. **Name the place of the digit 2 in the number 85.342. Then tell its value.** The digit 2 is in the thousandths place. Its value is *two thousandths.*

b. **Name the place of the digit 4 in the number 85.342. Then tell its value.** The digit 4 is in the hundredths place. Its value is *four hundredths.*

Place-Value Chart

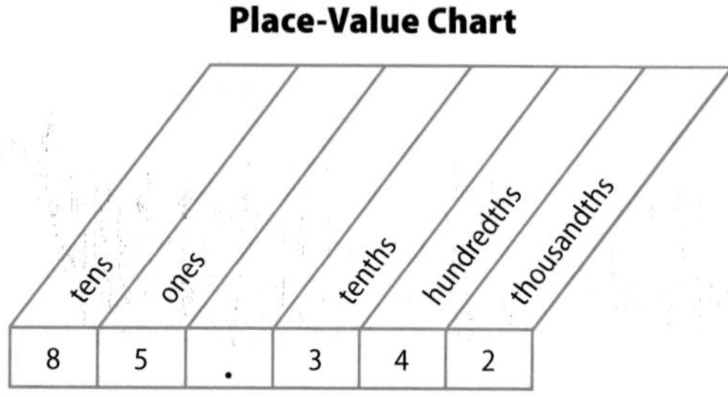

EXAMPLE 2

There are two 6's in the number 5.668. What is the relationship between their values?

The value of the 6 on the left is *six tenths.* The value of the 6 on the right is *six hundredths.*

0.6 is 10 × the value of 0.06. 0.06 is $\frac{1}{10}$ the value of 0.6.

Got to KNOW!

Place Value

Each place has a value that is 10 × the value of the place to its right and $\frac{1}{10}$ the value of the place to its left. In the number shown, the digit 3 has a different value in each place. The values of the places in 3.333 from left to right are:

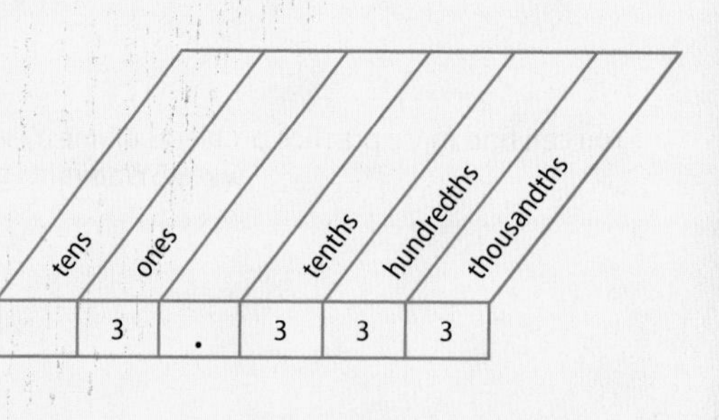

3 ones, 3 tenths, 3 hundredths, 3 thousandths

3 $\frac{3}{10}$ $\frac{3}{100}$ $\frac{3}{1,000}$

Modeling Decimals

You can use a ten by ten grid to model decimal numbers to hundredths. The whole grid represents 1 whole. Each small square represents one hundredth of the whole. Each row or column of ten small squares represents one tenth of the whole.

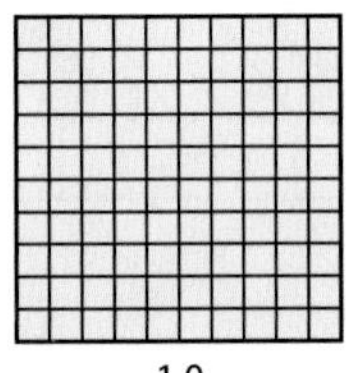
1.0

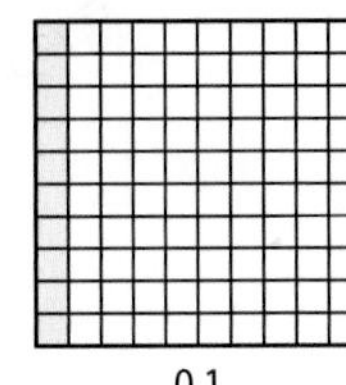
0.1

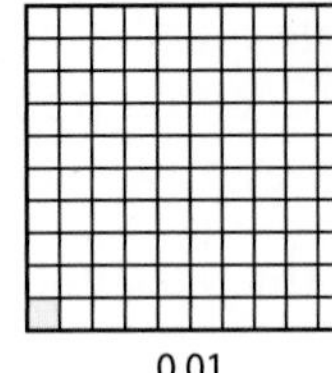
0.01

EXAMPLE 3

Use a ten by ten grid to model 0.15.

0.15 is fifteen hundredths.

Shade 15 squares to model 0.15.

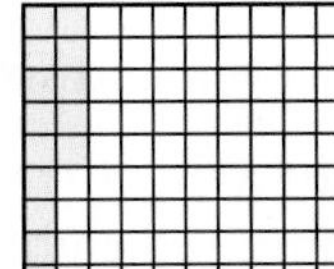

SEARCH

To see step-by-step videos of these problems, enter the page number into the SWadvantage.com Search Bar.

EXAMPLE 4

Use a ten by ten grid to model 0.7.

0.7 is seven tenths.

METHOD 1

Shade 7 rows to model 0.7.

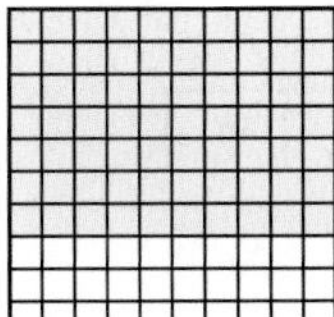

METHOD 2

Shade 7 columns to model 0.7.

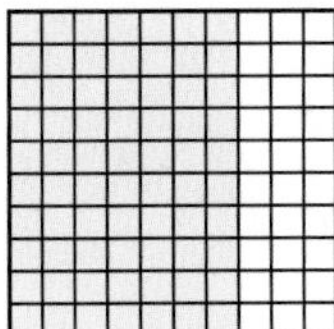

EXAMPLE 5

Complete: 6 tenths = ? hundredths

STEP 1 Model 0.6 on a ten by ten grid.

STEP 2 Count the number of hundredths.

6 tenths = 60 hundredths

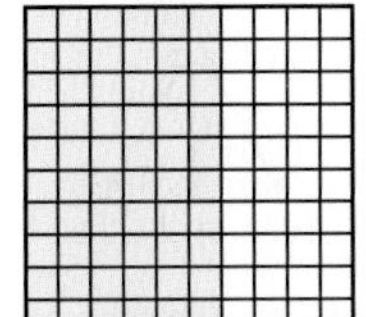

Reading and Writing Decimals

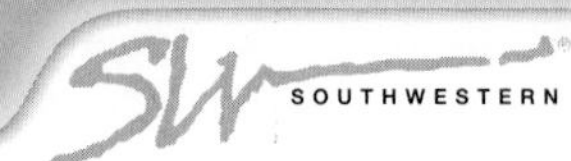

For help with reading whole numbers, go to *Reading Whole Numbers* in *Foundations of Mathematics* (p. 42).

Reading Decimals

The place-value chart shows the decimal number 987.654.

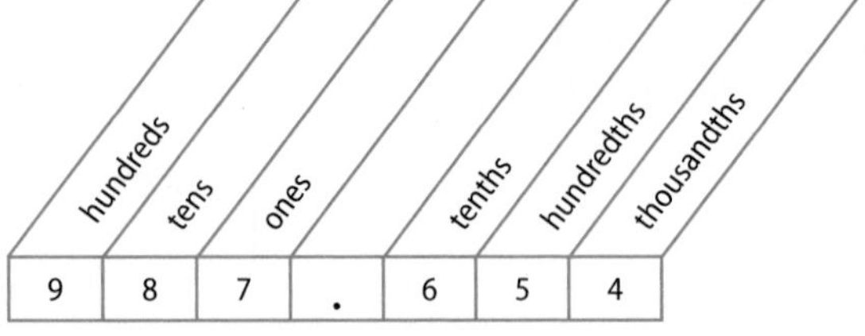

To read this number, follow these steps.

STEP 1 Read the whole number to the left of the decimal point.
nine hundred eighty-seven

STEP 2 Say "and" for the decimal point.
and

STEP 3 Read the number to the right of the decimal point as a whole number.
six hundred fifty-four

STEP 4 Say the place name of the last decimal digit.
thousandths

The number is: nine hundred eighty-seven and six hundred fifty-four thousandths.

Decimal numbers are sometimes read saying the word "point" instead of "and," and saying the names of the digits: nine hundred eighty-seven point six five four.

This method is often used for long decimal numbers because saying the word name might be confusing. Compare the two ways for reading the number 4.8047.

four and eight thousand forty-seven ten thousandths
four point eight zero four seven

EXAMPLE 1

How do you read the decimal 2.56?

The digit 6 is in the hundredths place.

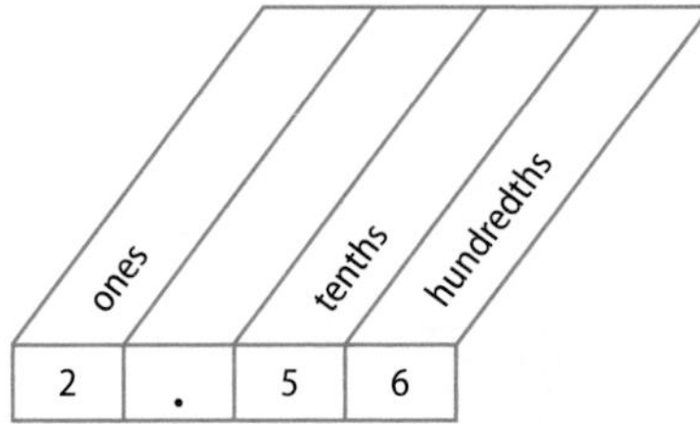

METHOD 1

two and fifty-six hundredths

METHOD 2

two point five six

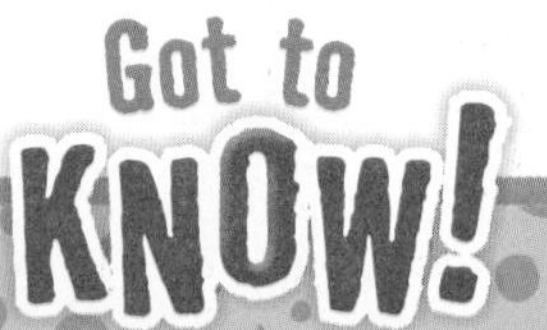

Reading Decimal Numbers

Read the decimal point as "and." Say the place name of the last digit in the number.

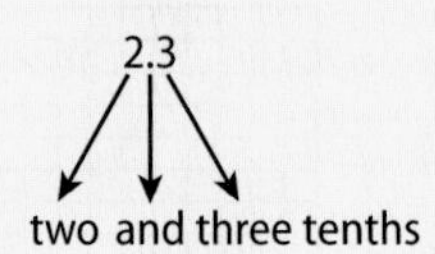

EXAMPLE 2

Read each decimal number in two ways.

a. Jason ran 6.21 miles in a race.

six and twenty-one hundredths six point two one

b. A digital scale shows a weight of 3.205 grams.

three and two hundred five thousandths three point two zero five

c. The length of the board is 5.7 feet.

five and seven tenths five point seven

Watch Out !

When you read a number aloud, you actually say the word form of the number.

Reading Decimals with No Whole Number Part

Some decimal numbers do not have whole number parts. In this case, there is no need to say the word "and" when you read the number. However, if you are reading the number by saying the digits in order, you must still say the word "point."

EXAMPLE 3

How do you read the decimal 0.824?

Use a place-value chart.

METHOD 1

There is no whole number part. The four is in the thousandths place.

Read 0.824 as "eight hundred twenty-four thousandths."

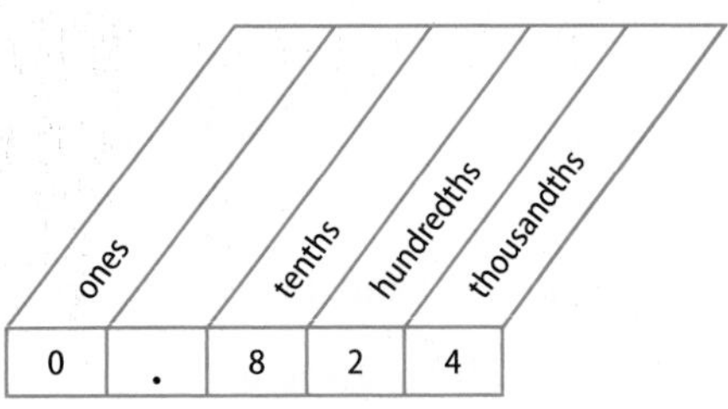

METHOD 2

You can also read 0.824 as "point eight two four."

Got to KNOW!

Decimals Less Than 1

Decimals with a value less than 1 are usually written with a leading zero (0) in the ones place.

0.824

The zero helps the decimal point stand out, so it is not overlooked. It does not change the value of the number.

EXAMPLE 4

How do you read the decimal 0.04?

METHOD 1

There is no whole number part. The 4 is in the hundredths place. Read 0.04 is as "four hundredths."

METHOD 2

You can also read 0.04 as "point zero four."

SEARCH

To see step-by-step videos of these problems, enter the page number into the SWadvantage.com Search Bar.

Writing Decimals

Need More HELP

For help with writing whole numbers and forms of numbers, go to *Writing Whole Numbers* in *Foundations of Mathematics* (p. 44).

A decimal number can be written in different ways called *forms*. Standard form is the most common way.

Form	Example
Standard Form	25.78
Word Form	twenty-five and seventy-eight hundredths
Short Word Form	25 and 78 hundredths
Expanded Form	20 + 5 + 0.7 + 0.08

Notice that the *short word form* simply replaces the name of the whole number and decimal number parts of the number with digits. The *expanded form* shows the number as the sum of the values of the digits.

EXAMPLE 5

Write 10.49 in word form, short form, and expanded form.

Use a place-value chart.

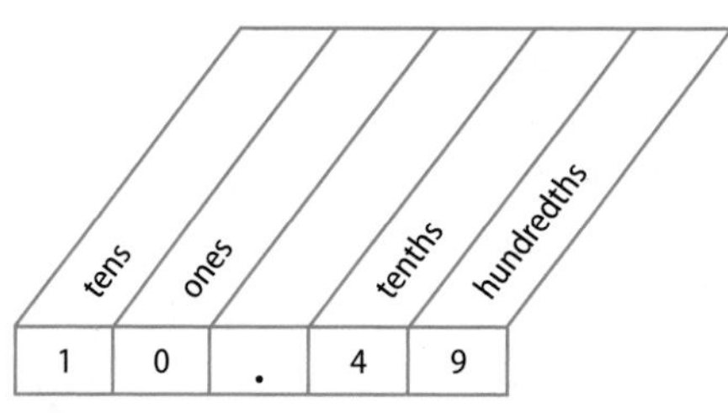

Word form: ten and forty-nine hundredths

Short word form: 10 and 49 hundredths

Expanded form: 10 + 0.4 + 0.09

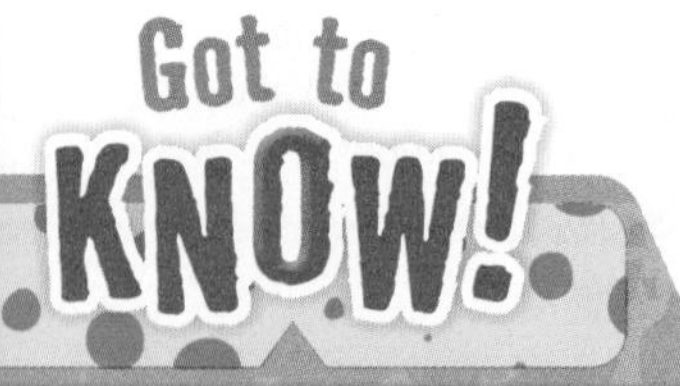

Forms of Numbers

Standard form: 15.67

Word form: fifteen and sixty-seven hundredths

Short word form: 15 and 67 hundredths

Expanded form: 10 + 5 + 0.6 + 0.07

EXAMPLE 6

Write nine tenths in short word form and standard form.

Short word form: Use the digit 9 instead of the word *nine*.
9 tenths

Standard form: Tenths place is the first place to the right of the decimal point. Insert the leading zero and decimal point. Remove the word *tenths*.
0.9

SEARCH

To see step-by-step videos of these problems, enter the page number into the SWadvantage.com Search Bar.

EXAMPLE 7

Write two and three hundredths in standard form.

STEP 1 Write the whole number part of the number and the decimal point. 2.

STEP 2 dentify the location of the last decimal place in the number. Hundredths is two places to the right of the decimal point.

STEP 3 Write the decimal part of the number: 0 tenths and 3 hundredths. 2.03

"Two and three hundredths" written in standard form is 2.03.

Watch Out !

When there is no value in a decimal place, insert a placeholder zero.

2 and 5 hundredths
2.05

2 and 5 thousandths
2.005

2 and 55 thousandths
2.055

2 and 505 thousandths
2.505

EXAMPLE 8

The diameter of a penny is seventy-five hundredths of an inch. Write the decimal in standard form.

STEP 1 Write the leading zero and the decimal point. 0.

STEP 2 Identify the location of the last decimal place in the number. Hundredths is two places to the right of the decimal point.

STEP 3 Write the decimal part of the number: 7 tenths and 5 hundredths. 0.75

"Seventy-five hundredths" written in standard form is 0.75.

EXAMPLE 9

Write thirty-six and four hundred nine thousandths in standard form.

STEP 1 Write the whole number part of the number and the decimal point. 36.

STEP 2 Identify the location of the last decimal place in the number. Thousandths is three places to the right of the decimal point.

STEP 3 Write the decimal part of the number: 4 tenths, 0 hundredths, and 9 thousandths. 36.409

"Thirty-six and four hundred nine thousandths" written in standard form is 36.409.

Comparing and Ordering Decimals

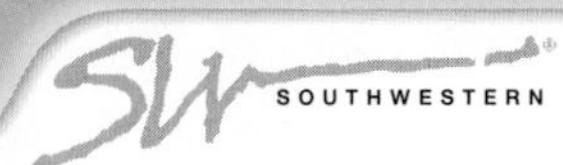

Comparing Decimals

You can use a number line or place value to compare decimals. The numbers on a number line are ordered from least to greatest. As you move right along the number line, the numbers increase in value. To compare two decimals, use the symbols shown in the *Got to Know!* box.

EXAMPLE 1

Use <, >, or = to compare 8.32 and 8.2.

Graph 8.32 and 8.2 on a number line.

8.32 is to the right of 8.2 on the number line, so its value is greater: $8.32 > 8.2$.
You can also say that $8.2 < 8.32$.

Need More HELP

Each comparison can be written in two ways. If $a > b$, then $b < a$.

EXAMPLE 2

Use <, >, or = to compare 0.124 and 0.14.

Use place values and compare the digits.

Align the decimal points.	0.124 0.14
You may find it helpful to add a zero to 0.14 so both numbers have the same number of decimal places.	0.124 0.140
Compare the digits in the decimal places from left to right until the digits are different.	Tenths place: Both the digits are 1. Hundredths place: $4 > 2$

Since 4 hundredths is greater than 2 hundredths, $0.14 > 0.124$.
You can also say that $0.124 < 0.14$.

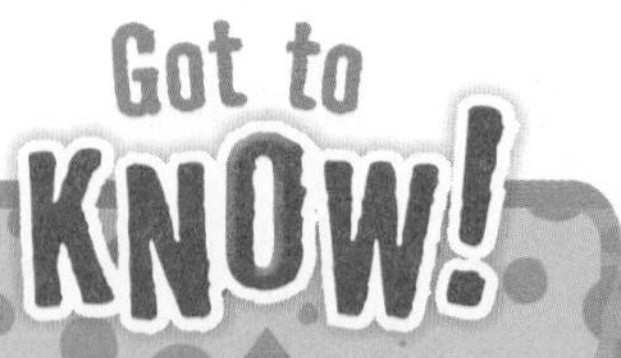

Comparison Symbols

Symbol	Meaning
>	greater than
<	less than
=	equal to

Ordering Decimals

You can use a number line or place value to order decimals. Numbers can be ordered from least to greatest or greatest to least.

EXAMPLE 3

Order from least to greatest: 21.13, 21.43, 21.1

Graph the numbers on a number line.

The numbers are ordered least to greatest as you move left to right along the number line.

Ordered from least to greatest, the numbers are: 21.1, 21.13, 21.43.

Watch Out !

Be sure you understand the scale on the number line. The longer tick marks on these number lines represents tenths. The shorter, unlabeled tick marks represent hundredths.

EXAMPLE 4

The table shows the heights of four students. The height of which student is the least?

Student	Juan	Charlotte	Tomika	Sam
Height (meters)	1.39	1.314	1.309	1.386

Use place values to order the numbers.

Align the decimal points.
Add a zero to 1.39 so all decimals have the same number of decimal places.

1.390
1.314
1.309
1.386

Compare the digits in the decimal places from left to right until the digits are different.

Ones place: All the digits are 1.
Tenths place: All the digits are 3.
Hundredths place: $0 < 1 < 8 < 9$

$1.3\underline{0}9 < 1.3\underline{1}4 < 1.3\underline{8}6 < 1.3\underline{9}$

Tomika's height is the least.

SEARCH

To see step-by-step videos of these problems, enter the page number into the SWadvantage.com Search Bar.

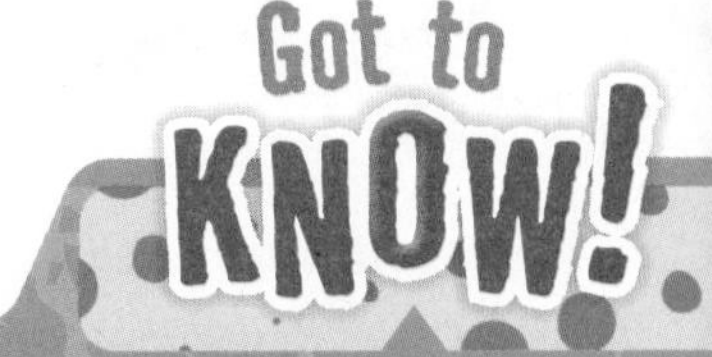

Equivalent Decimals

Equivalent decimals have the same value. Adding a zero to the right of the last decimal place does not change the value of a decimal number.

$4.53 = 4.530$

Rounding Decimals

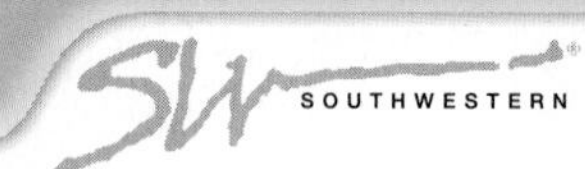

Rounding Decimals Using Rounding Rules

For help with rounding whole numbers, go to *Round Whole Numbers* in *Foundations of Mathematics* (page 50).

When you **round** a number, you express the number to a given place value.

To round decimal numbers, use the same rules you use to round whole numbers. You may find it helpful to write the number in a place-value chart first.

EXAMPLE 1

Round 6.872 to the nearest tenth.

Write the number in a place-value chart.

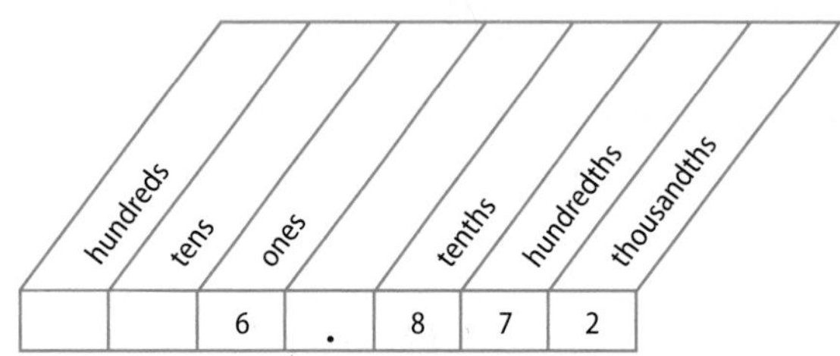

You are rounding to the nearest *tenth*. Identify the digit in the tenths place. The digit is 8.	$6.\underline{8}72$
Look at the digit to its right, 7. 7 is greater than or equal to 5.	$6.\underline{8}72$
Add 1 to the 8 in the tenths place. Drop the digits to the right of the tenths place.	6.9

6.872 rounded to the nearest tenth is 6.9.

Rounding Rules

Underline the digit in the place you are rounding to.

Look at the digit to its right.

- If the digit is greater than or equal to 5, add 1 to the underlined digit.
- If the digit is less than 5, do not change the underlined digit.

Drop the digits to the right of the underlined digit.

EXAMPLE 2

Hiro rode his bike 12.345 kilometers on Saturday. Round this distance to the nearest hundredth of a kilometer (km).

Use a place-value chart and rounding rules.

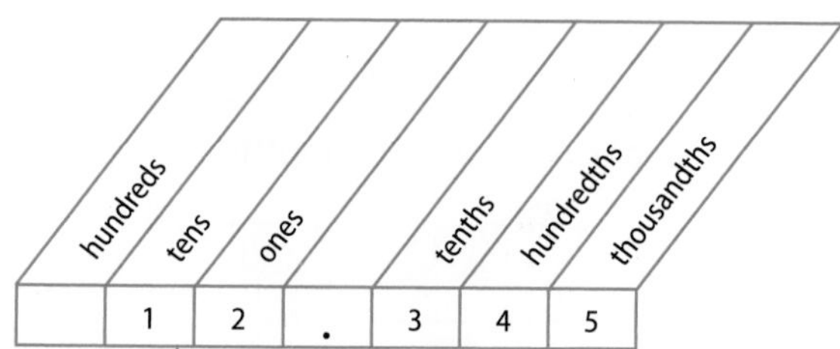

You are rounding to the nearest *hundredth*. The digit 4 is in the hundredths place. 12.345

Look at the digit to the right of 4. The digit is 5, which is ≥ 5. 12.345

Add 1 to the 4. Drop the digits to its right. 12.35

12.345 km rounded to the nearest hundredth is 12.35 km.

Need More **HELP**

You may already know the terms *rounding up* and *rounding down*.

In Example 2, you round 12.345 up to a greater number, 12.35.

In Example 3(a), you round 21.43 down to a lesser number, 21.4.

Rounding Decimals Using a Number Line

Another way to round decimal numbers is to locate the number on a number line. The number line will help you see the number's approximate value.

EXAMPLE 3

Look at the number line below. Each tick mark represents a hundredth. There is a point at 21.43 and a point at 21.46.

a. Round 21.43 to the nearest tenth.

21.43 is closer to 21.40 than to 21.50. It rounds to 21.4.

b. Round 21.46 to the nearest tenth.

21.46 is closer to 21.50 than to 21.40. It rounds to 21.5.

SEARCH

To see step-by-step videos of these problems, enter the page number into the SWadvantage.com Search Bar.

Modeling Decimal Addition

You can use ten by ten grids to model the addition of decimal numbers. The value of each small square in the grid is one hundredth.

SEARCH

To see step-by-step videos of these problems, enter the page number into the SWadvantage.com Search Bar.

EXAMPLE 1

Use a grid to model 0.24 + 0.63.

Shade 24 hundredths of the grid.

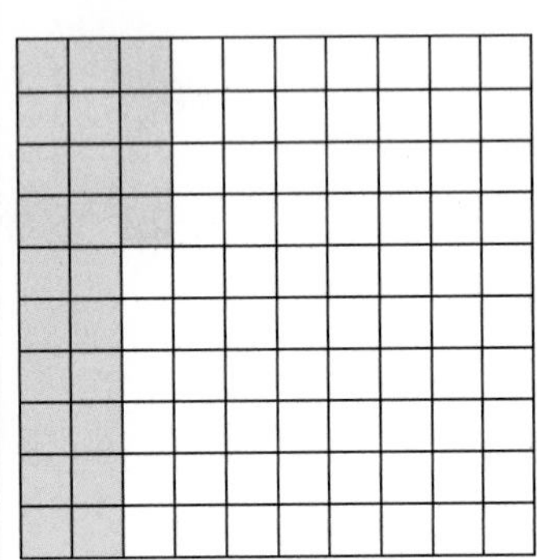

Shade 63 more hundredths.

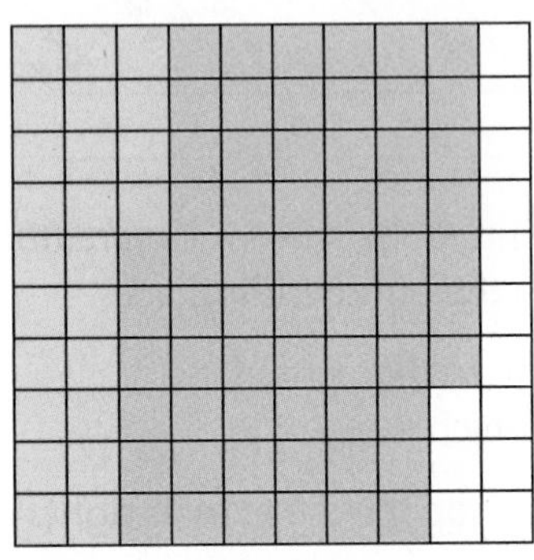

There are 87 hundredths shaded.

0.24 + 0.63 = 0.87

EXAMPLE 2

Use a grid to model 1.35 + 0.29.

Shade 1 whole grid and 35 hundredths of another grid.

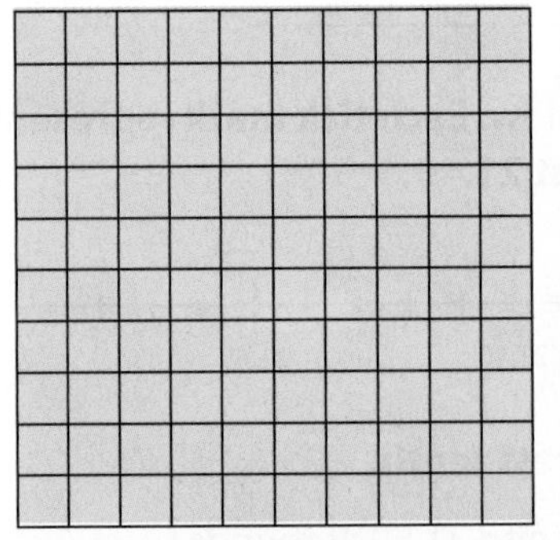

Shade 29 more hundredths.

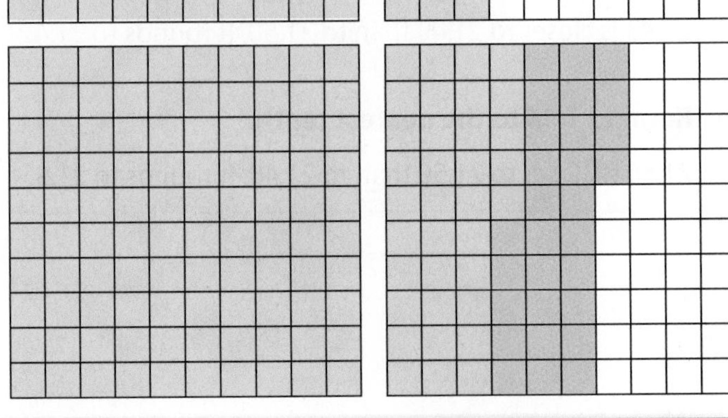

There are 164 hundredths shaded.

1.35 + 0.29 = 1.64

Adding Decimals on a Place-Value Chart

You can also add decimals in a vertical format on a place-value chart. Line up the decimal points in the numbers. The decimal point in the sum will be directly below the decimal points in the addends.

EXAMPLE 3

Add. 11.5 + 5.2

Write the problem vertically on a place-value chart.

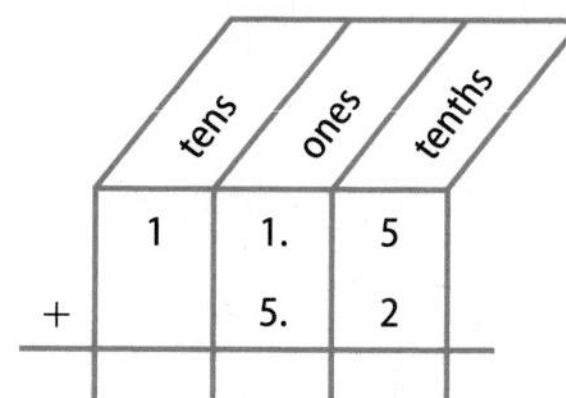

Add from right to left, as you add whole numbers.

Bring the decimal point straight down into the answer.

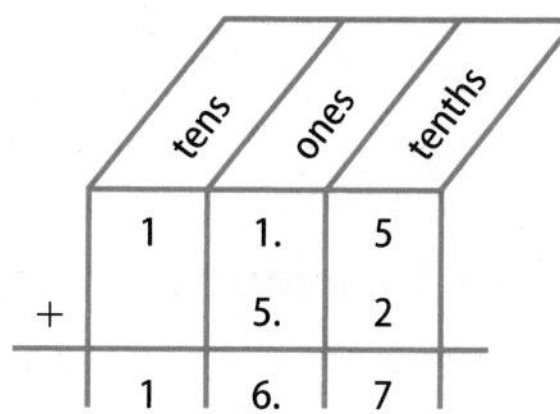

11.5 + 5.2 = 16.7

Try It This Way

You can use mental math to add 11.5 + 5.2.

First, add the whole number parts. Think: 11 + 5 is 16.

Then add the decimal parts. Think: 0.5 + 0.2 is 0.7.

Combine the sums: 16.7

Got to KNOW!

Adding Decimals

When adding decimals vertically, you must align (line up) the decimal points. This keeps each digit in its proper place. The decimal point in the sum is directly below the decimal points in the addends.

$$\begin{array}{r} 11.5 \\ +\ 5.2 \\ \hline 16.7 \end{array}$$

Adding Decimals with Regrouping

When you **regroup**, you organize a value in a different way and rename it. While its name changes, its value remains the same. Suppose you have the sum of 14 tenths. Regroup the tenths as 1 one and 4 tenths. Then place a small 1 above a column of addends to the left to represent the regrouped digits.

Need More HELP

The term *carrying* means the same thing as regrouping. You "carry" a part of the renamed value into the column to its left.

For help with regrouping, go to *Adding Whole Numbers* in *Foundations of Mathematics* (page 82).

EXAMPLE 4

Add. 8.67 + 0.42

Write the problem in vertical format.

Add from right to left, and regroup as needed.

Rename 10 tenths as 1 one and 0 tenths.

Add the whole numbers 8 and 1.

Bring the decimal point straight down into the answer.

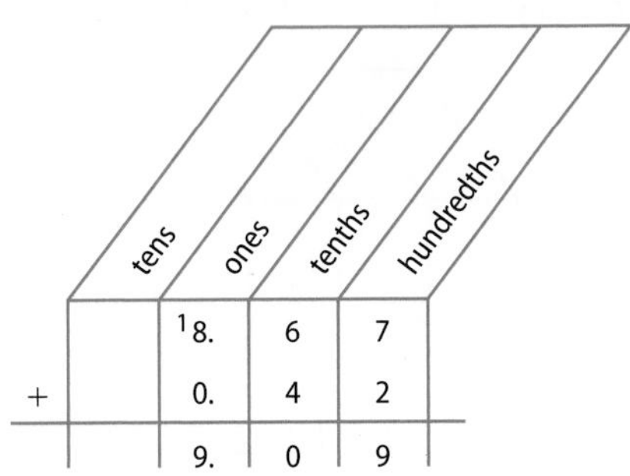

8.67 + 0.42 = 9.09

EXAMPLE 5

Marla bought a DVD for C$15.95 and a bottle of water for C$1.25. How much did she spend in all?

Write the problem in vertical format.

Add from right to left, and regroup as needed.

Rename 10 hundredths as 1 tenth and 0 hundredths.

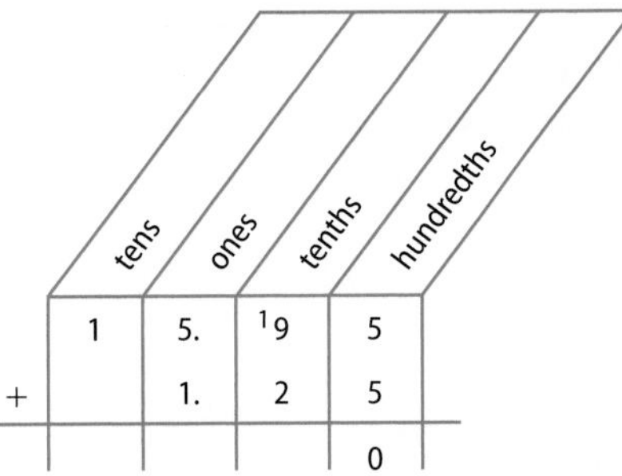

Continue adding.

Rename 12 tenths as 1 one and 2 tenths.

Bring the decimal point straight down into the answer.

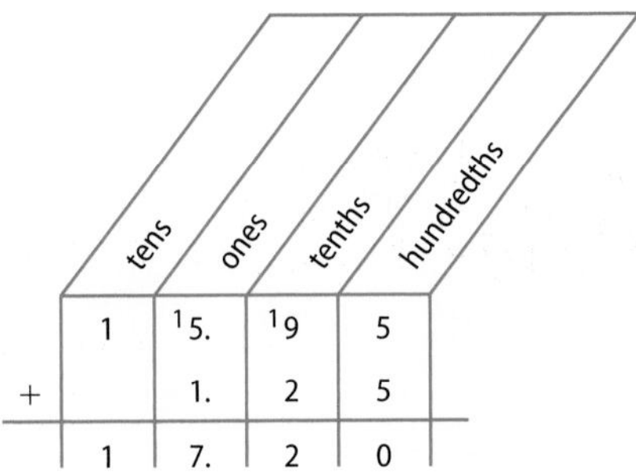

Marla spent C$17.20 in all.

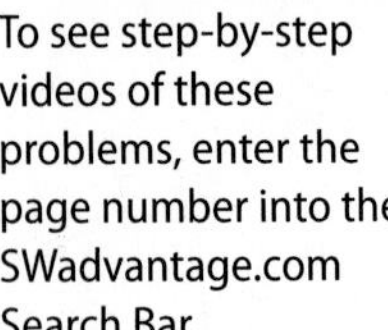

SEARCH

To see step-by-step videos of these problems, enter the page number into the SWadvantage.com Search Bar.

MONEY

NOTE: C$ denotes Canadian dollars.

Adding Decimals with More Than Two Addends

Use a place-value chart. Write the problem in vertical form, being careful to line up the decimal points.

EXAMPLE 6

Add. 43.32 + 4.1 + 1.275

Write the problem in vertical format.

Add from right to left.

Bring the decimal point straight down into the answer.

	tens	ones	tenths	hundredths	thousandths
	4	3.	3	2	
		4.	1		
+		1.	2	7	5
	4	8.	6	9	5

43.32 + 4.1 + 1.275 = 48.695

Try It This Way

For another visual representation of the numbers, add placeholder zeros so each number has two whole number places and three decimal places.

43.320
04.100
01.275

This aligns the decimal points but does not change the value of the numbers.

EXAMPLE 7

Add. 11.037 + 7.843 + 10.46

Write the problem in vertical format.

Add from right to left, and regroup as needed.

Rename the 10 thousandths as 1 hundredth and zero thousandths.

Rename the 14 hundredths as 1 tenth and 4 hundredths.

	T	O	T	H	T
	1	1.	[1]0	[1]3	7
		7.	8	4	3
+	1	0.	4	6	
				4	0

Continue adding.

Rename the 13 tenths as 1 one and 3 tenths.

Add the whole numbers.

Bring the decimal point straight down into the answer.

	T	O	T	H	T
	1	[1]1.	[1]0	[1]3	7
		7.	8	4	3
+	1	0.	4	6	
	2	9.	3	4	0

11.037 + 7.843 + 10.46 = 29.34

Need More HELP

In Example 7, you do not need to include the zero in the thousandths place when you write the final sum. However, if this were a scientific measurement you would include the zero to make the number more precise. The number 29.340 is precise to thousandths, while 29.34 is precise to hundredths.

Adding Three Decimal Numbers

You can also add decimal numbers by simply writing the problem in a vertical format. Use zero as a placeholder as needed.

To help you add the correct digits, use a different color of marker or highlighter to draw a vertical line on each column of numbers. Be sure the color is light enough to see through.

EXAMPLE 8

Add. 3.04 + 5.6 + 0.04

Write the problem in vertical form.

Line up the decimal points.

$$\begin{array}{r} 3.04 \\ 5.60 \\ +\ 0.04 \\ \hline \end{array}$$

Add the numbers from right to left.

Bring the decimal point straight down into the answer.

$$\begin{array}{r} 3.04 \\ 5.60 \\ +\ 0.04 \\ \hline 8.68 \end{array}$$

3.04 + 5.6 + 0.04 = 8.68

EXAMPLE 9

Add. 16.1 + 6.35 + 125.6

Write the problem in vertical format.

Line up the decimal points.

$$\begin{array}{r} 16.10 \\ 6.35 \\ +\ 125.60 \\ \hline \end{array}$$

Add the numbers from right to left. Regroup as needed.

Rename the 10 in the tenths place as 1 one and 0 tenths.

Rename the 18 in the ones place as 1 ten and 8 ones.

Bring the decimal point straight down into the answer.

$$\begin{array}{r} {\scriptstyle 1\,1} \\ 16.10 \\ 6.35 \\ +\ 125.60 \\ \hline 148.05 \end{array}$$

16.1 + 6.35 + 125.6 = 148.05

EXAMPLE 10

At the end of May, Jerome had $125.75 in a savings account. He deposited the amounts shown in the table in June, July, and August.

Month	Amount Deposited
June	$25.50
July	$60.00
August	$72.55

a. What is the total amount of money Jerome deposited in June, July, and August?

Add the amounts for June, July, and August.

Regroup as needed.

Rename 10 tenths as 1 one and 0 tenths.

Bring the decimal point straight down into the answer.

$$\begin{array}{r} \overset{1}{\$25.50} \\ 60.00 \\ +\ 72.55 \\ \hline \$158.05 \end{array}$$

The total amount Jerome deposited is $158.05.

b. What is the total amount of money in Jerome's savings account after he made the three deposits?

Add the amount in the savings account at the end of May and the total amount of the deposits.

Regroup as needed.

Rename 10 hundredths as 1 tenth and 0 hundredths.

Rename 13 ones as 1 ten and 3 ones.

Bring the decimal point straight down into the answer.

$$\begin{array}{r} \$1\overset{1}{2}5.\overset{1}{7}5 \\ +\ 158.05 \\ \hline \$283.80 \end{array}$$

The total amount of money in Jerome's savings account is $283.80.

SEARCH

To see step-by-step videos of these problems, enter the page number into the SWadvantage.com Search Bar.

Subtracting Decimals

Modeling Decimal Subtraction

You can use ten by ten grids to model subtracting decimal numbers. The value of each small square in the grid is one hundredth.

SEARCH

To see step-by-step videos of these problems, enter the page number into the SWadvantage.com Search Bar.

EXAMPLE 1

Subtract 0.51 − 0.16. Use ten by ten grids.

Shade 51 hundredths of the grid.

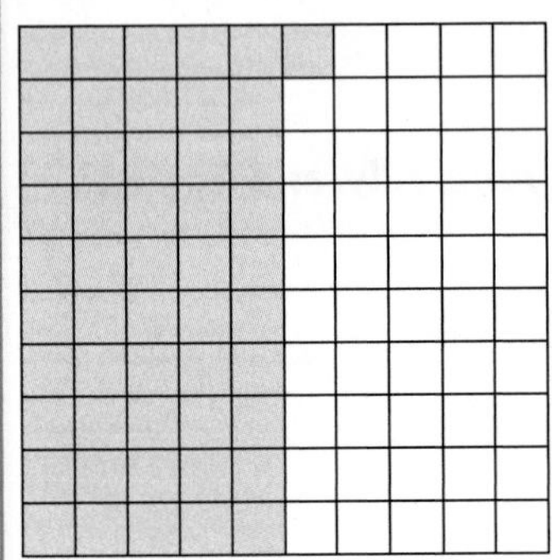

Then mark out 16 hundredths.

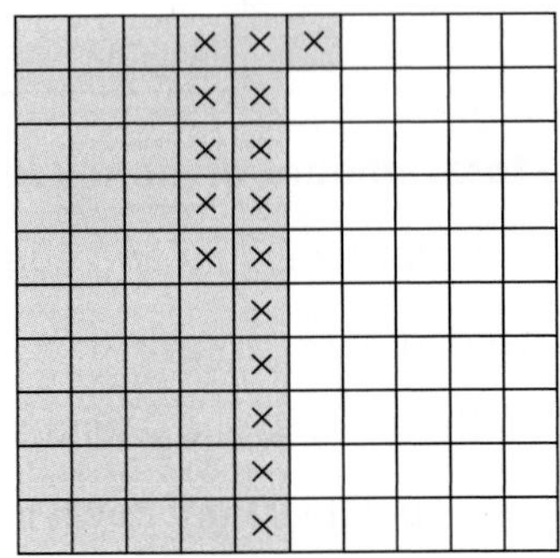

There are 35 hundredths left.

0.51 − 0.16 = 0.35

Subtracting on a Place-Value Chart

Subtracting decimals is almost the same as subtracting whole numbers. The only difference is that you line up the decimal points. A place-value chart can help you with this.

Need More HELP

For help with subtraction, go to *Subtracting Whole Numbers* in *Foundations of Mathematics* (p. 88).

EXAMPLE 2

Subtract 35.8 − 20.5.

Write the problem in vertical form. Align the decimal points vertically.

	tens	ones	tenths
	3	5.	8
−	2	0.	5

Subtract the numbers in the three columns. Keep the decimal point in its position.

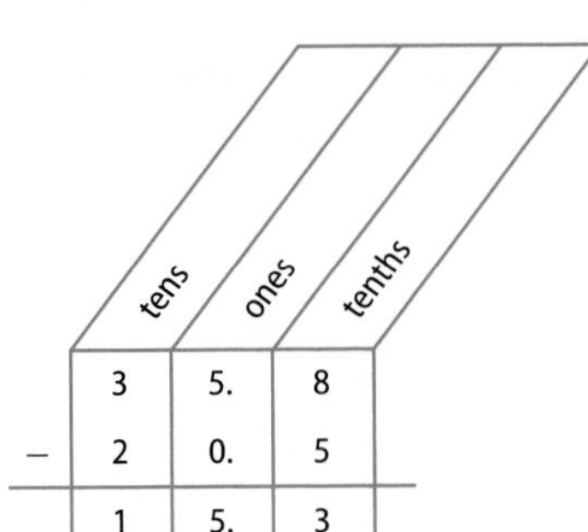

35.8 − 20.5 = 15.3

Subtracting Decimals with Regrouping

Just as with addition, you may need to regroup before you subtract.

EXAMPLE 3

Subtract 6.14 − 2.05.

Use a place-value chart.

Subtract from right to left. You need to regroup.

Rename 1 tenth as 0 tenths and 10 hundredths.

Add 10 hundredths to the 4 hundredths to get 14 hundredths. Place a small zero above the 1 and a small 1 above the 4.

Subtract. Keep the decimal point in its position.

6.14 − 2.05 = 4.09

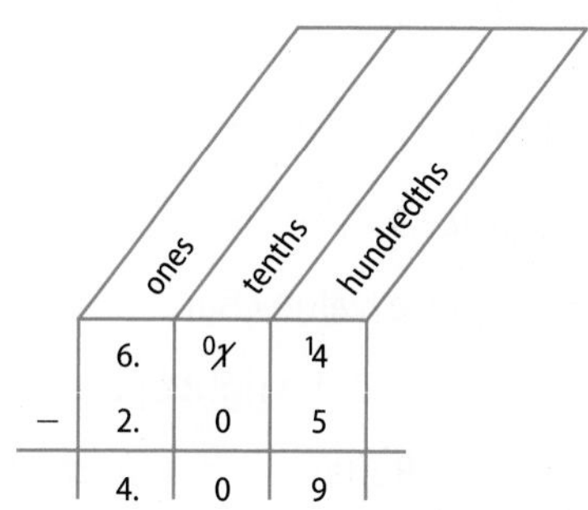

EXAMPLE 4

Subtract 1.51 − 0.86.

Use a place-value chart. In this problem, you will need to regroup twice.

Subtract from right to left. You need to regroup.

Rename 5 tenths as 4 tenths and 10 hundredths.

Now you have 11 hundredths.

Subtract the hundredths.

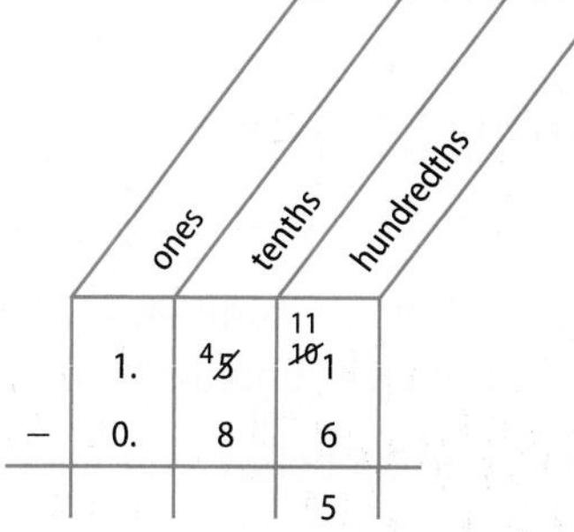

Rename 1 one as 0 ones and 10 tenths.

4 tenths plus 10 regrouped tenths = 14 tenths

Subtract the tenths.

1.51 − 0.86 = 0.65

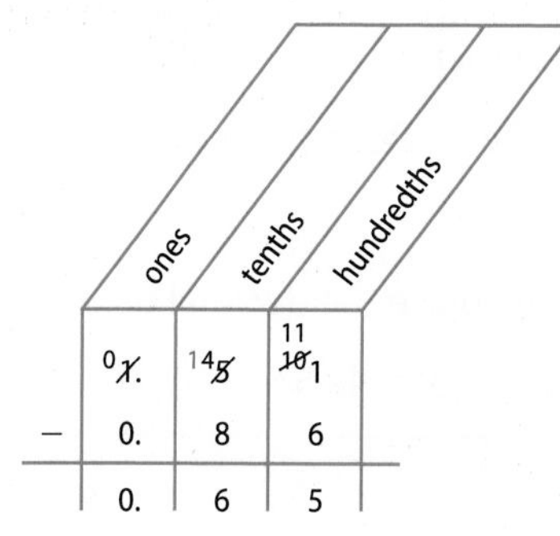

Need More HELP

Sometimes the term *borrow* is used instead of *regroup*. Both terms mean that you rename a value in a column to the left of the column you are subtracting. For example,

$$\begin{array}{r} 4.2 \\ -0.6 \\ \hline \end{array}$$

Rename 1 one as 10 tenths. Now you have 3 ones and 10 tenths + 2 tenths = 3 ones and 12 tenths.

$$\begin{array}{r} \overset{3}{\cancel{4}}.\overset{1}{2} \\ -0.6 \\ \hline 3.6 \end{array}$$

For help with regrouping, go to *Subtract Whole Numbers* in *Foundations of Mathematics* (p. 88).

Subtracting with Regrouping—Placeholder Zeros

In some problems, the decimal numbers do not contain the same number of digits. In the number with fewer decimal digits, add zeros as placeholders. Remember, adding zeros to the right in a decimal number does not change the value of the number.

SEARCH

To see step-by-step videos of these problems, enter the page number into the SWadvantage.com Search Bar.

EXAMPLE 5

Subtract 3.89 − 2.647.

Use a place-value chart.

Add a zero to the right of the 9 in 3.89.

Regroup. Rename 9 hundredths as 8 hundredths and 10 thousandths.

Subtract the thousandths.

Subtract the hundredths.

Subtract the tenths.

Subtract the ones.

Keep the decimal point in its position.

3.89 − 2.647 = 1.243

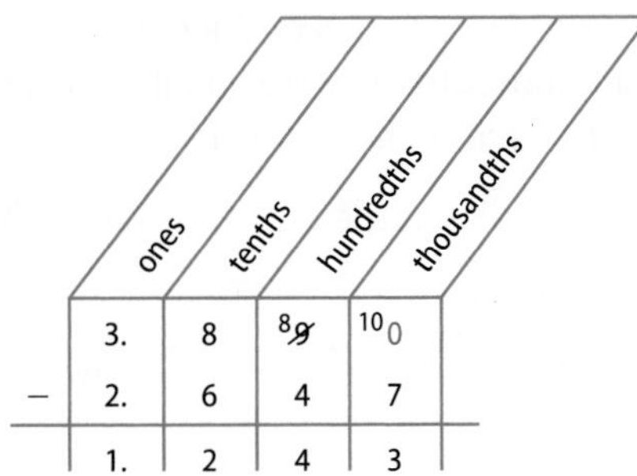

EXAMPLE 6

Subtract 41 − 0.5.

Write the whole number, 41. Add a decimal point and a placeholder zero to the right of the 1.

Now write 0.5 below 41.0, aligning the decimal points.

$$\begin{array}{r} 41.0 \\ -\ 0.5 \\ \hline \end{array}$$

Subtract.

Regroup. Rename 1 one as 0 ones and 10 tenths.

Subtract.

Then place the decimal point.

$$\begin{array}{r} 4\overset{0}{\not 1}.\overset{1}{0} \\ -\ 0.5 \\ \hline 40.5 \end{array}$$

41 − 0.5 = 40.5

EXAMPLE 7

Subtract 26.5 − 0.47.

Write in vertical form. Add a placeholder zero to the right of the 5 in 26.5.

Subtract.

Regroup. Rename 5 tenths as 4 tenths and 10 hundredths.

Subtract. Then place the decimal point.

```
     4 1
  26.5̸0
−  0.47
  26.03
```

26.5 − 0.47 = 26.03

Watch Out !

In Example 7, when you subtract the tenths the difference is zero. You must include this zero in your answer.

EXAMPLE 8

Subtract 1.043 − 0.75.

Write the problem. Write a placeholder zero to the right of the 5 in 0.75.

Subtract the thousandths.

To subtract the hundredths you will have to regroup twice because there are no tenths to regroup.

```
  0 10
  1̸.0̸43
− 0.750
      3
```

First regroup 1 one as 0 ones and 10 tenths.

Then regroup 10 tenths as 9 tenths and 10 hundredths.

Now you have 14 hundredths.

Subtract.

```
     9 14
  0 1̸0̸
  1̸.0̸4̸3
− 0.750
  0.293
```

1.043 − 0.75 = 0.293

Subtracting Across Zeros

When the minuend contains several zeros, you will need to regroup several times before you can begin to subtract.

Need More HELP

The *minuend* is the number from which another number is subtracted.

EXAMPLE 9

Subtract 7.006 − 4.798.

Use a place-value chart.

Rename 7 ones as 6 ones and 10 tenths. Then rename the decimal part of the number.

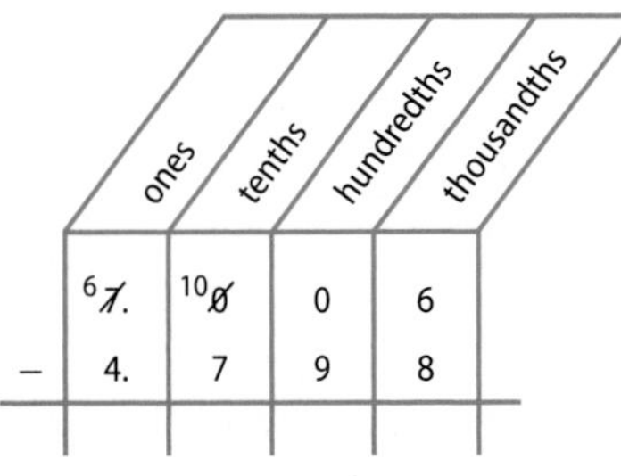

Rename 10 tenths as 9 tenths and 10 hundredths.

Rename 10 hundredths as 9 hundredths and 10 thousandths.

Now you have 16 thousandths. Subtract.

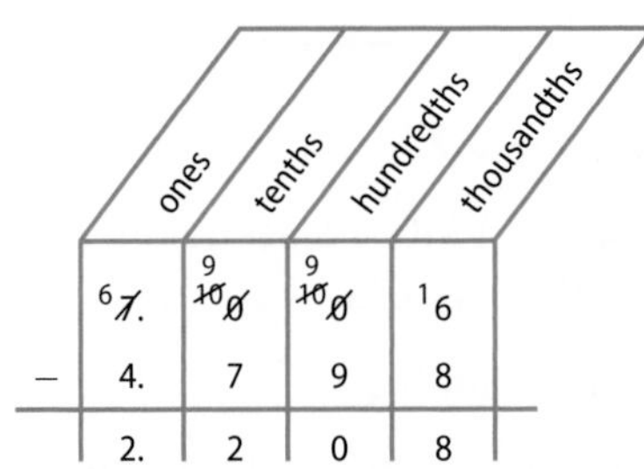

7.006 − 4.798 = 2.208

EXAMPLE 10

Subtract 300 − 1.82.

You could subtract this problem by regrouping the hundreds, then the tens, then the ones, and then the tenths. Here is another way to think about this problem that does not require regrouping as many times.

Think of 300 as 298 + 2.

$$\begin{array}{r} 298 \\ +\quad 2 \\ \hline 300 \end{array}$$

Subtract 2 − 1.82. Write the 2 as 2.00.

Rename 2 ones as 1 one and 10 tenths.

Rename 10 tenths as 9 tenths and 10 hundredths.

Subtract.

$$\begin{array}{r} \overset{1}{\cancel{2}}.\overset{9\,10}{\cancel{0}\cancel{0}} \\ -\ 1.82 \\ \hline 0.18 \end{array}$$

Add the difference to 298.

298 + 0.18 = 298.18

300 − 1.82 = 298.18

EXAMPLE 

A hiking trail is 8.45 kilometers in length. So far, Marcus has hiked 5.86 kilometers. If he hikes the entire length of the trail, how many kilometers does he have left?

Subtract the distance hiked, 5.86 km, from the total length of the trail, 8.45 km.

Rename 8 ones as 7 ones and 10 tenths.

Rename the 10 tenths as 9 tenths and 10 hundredths.

Add 9 tenths to the 4 tenths to get 13 tenths.

Add 10 hundredths to the 5 hundredths to get 15 hundredths.

Now you can subtract.

```
   13 15
  7 1̸0̸
  8̸.45
− 5.86
  2.59
```

Marcus has 2.59 kilometers left to hike.

Watch Out 

In Example 11, when you subtract the 8 tenths you are subtracting from 13 tenths—the 4 tenths that were already in the tenths place plus 9 regrouped tenths.

EXAMPLE 12

The Jefferson family drove from Baltimore, Maryland, to Miami, Florida. They drove the total distance of 1,102.79 miles in three days. The table shows the number of miles they drove on Day 1 and Day 2. How many miles did they drive on Day 3?

Day	1	2
Miles Driven	394.24	393.5

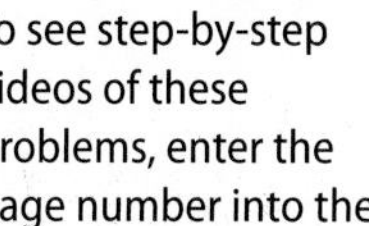

SEARCH

To see step-by-step videos of these problems, enter the page number into the SWadvantage.com Search Bar.

METHOD 1

STEP 1 Add the amounts for Day 1 and Day 2.

```
   1
   394.24
 + 393.50
   787.74
```

STEP 2 Subtract the sum found in Step 1 from the total distance.

```
     9
    0 1̸ 1
   1 1̸0̸2.79
 −   787.74
     315.05
```

METHOD 2

STEP 1 Subtract the number of miles driven on Day 1 from the total distance.

```
     9
    0 1̸ 1
   1 1̸0̸2.79
 −   394.24
     708.55
```

STEP 2 Subtract the miles driven on Day 2 from the difference found in Step 1.

```
   6 1
   7̸08.55
 − 393.50
   315.05
```

The Jefferson family drove 315.05 miles on Day 3 to reach Miami.

For help multiplying whole numbers, go to *Multiply Whole Numbers* in *Foundations of Mathematics* (p. 96).

Multiplying a Decimal by a Whole Number

Multiplying a decimal number by a whole number is actually the same as repeated addition. For example, multiplying 1.2 times 3 is the same as adding 1.2 three times.

$1.2 \times 3 = 1.2 + 1.2 + 1.2$

The multiplication of the numbers is almost the same as multiplying two whole numbers. The only difference is that you must place a decimal point in the product. The number of decimal places in the product is equal to the total number of decimal places in the two factors.

$$\begin{array}{rl} 1.2 & \leftarrow \text{decimal factor, 1 decimal place} \\ \times\ 3 & \leftarrow \text{whole number factor, 0 decimal places} \\ \hline 3.6 & \leftarrow \text{product, 1 decimal place} \end{array}$$

When a decimal number is multiplied by a whole number, the product always has the number of decimal places shown in the decimal factor.

EXAMPLE 1

Multiply 9.12 × 4.

METHOD 1

Use repeated addition.

$$\begin{array}{r} 9.12 \\ 9.12 \\ 9.12 \\ +\ 9.12 \\ \hline 36.48 \end{array}$$

$9.12 \times 4 = 36.48$

METHOD 2

Write the problem in vertical form.

$$\begin{array}{r} 9.12 \\ \times\ \ 4 \\ \hline \end{array}$$

Multiply as for whole numbers.

Count the total number of decimal places in the two factors.

There are two decimal places, so the product is 36.48.

$$\begin{array}{rl} 9.12 & \leftarrow \text{2 decimal places} \\ \times\ \ 4 & \leftarrow \text{0 decimal places} \\ \hline 36.48 & \leftarrow \text{2 decimal places} \end{array}$$

$9.12 \times 4 = 36.48$

EXAMPLE 2

Shannon is making 12 picture frames. Each frame uses 80.8 centimeters of wood. How many centimeters of wood does Shannon need to make the frames?

Multiply the amount of wood needed for each frame by the number of frames.

Write the problem in vertical form.

$$\begin{array}{r} 80.8 \\ \times\ 12 \\ \hline \end{array}$$

Multiply as for whole numbers.

Count the number of decimal places in the decimal factor.

There is one decimal place. Place the decimal point.

$$\begin{array}{r} 80.8 \\ \times\ 12 \\ \hline 1616 \\ 8080 \\ \hline 969.6 \end{array}$$

Shannon needs 969.6 centimeters of wood.

SEARCH

To see step-by-step videos of these problems, enter the page number into the SWadvantage.com Search Bar.

EXAMPLE 3

One pound of potatoes costs $0.89. How much do 3 pounds of potatoes cost?

Multiply the cost per pound by the number of pounds purchased.

Write the problem in vertical form.

Multiply as for whole numbers.

Count the number of decimal places in the decimal factor.

$$\begin{array}{r} 0.89 \\ \times\ 3 \\ \hline 2.67 \end{array}$$

There are two decimal places. Place the decimal point.

Three pounds of potatoes cost $2.67.

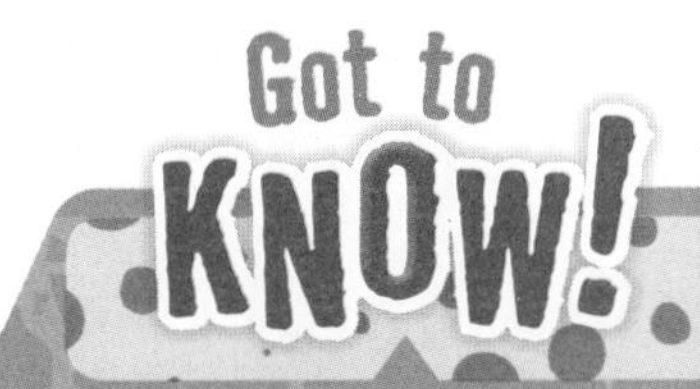

Multiplying a Decimal by a Whole Number

- Multiply as if both numbers were whole numbers.
- Count the number of places in the decimal factor.
- Use this number of decimal places in the product.

Multiplying Decimals by Powers of Ten

It is easy to multiply a decimal by 10, 100, 1,000, or any power of ten. Look for the pattern in the table below.

Watch Out!

$10^0 = 1$. So when you multiply a number by 10^0, you are multiplying the number by 1.

Number	× Power of 10	Is equal to	Decimal point moves
3.6521	$\times 10^0 =$	$3.6521 \times 1 = 3.6521$	0 places to the right.
3.6521	$\times 10^1 =$	$3.6521 \times 10 = 36.521$	1 place to the right.
3.6521	$\times 10^2 =$	$3.6521 \times 100 = 365.21$	2 places to the right.
3.6521	$\times 10^3 =$	$3.6521 \times 1{,}000 = 3{,}652.1$	3 places to the right.
3.6521	$\times 10^4 =$	$3.6521 \times 10{,}000 = 36{,}521$	4 places to the right.
3.6521	$\times 10^5 =$	$3.6521\_ \times 100{,}000 = 365{,}210$	5 places to the right.

Notice that the decimal point shifts to the right the same number of places shown in the power of 10. Sometimes this is called "moving the decimal point."

EXAMPLE 4

Multiply 1.465×10^2.

The power of 10 is 10^2. Move the decimal point 2 places to the right.

$1.465 \times 10^2 = 1.465$

$1.465 \times 10^2 = 146.5$

EXAMPLE 5

Multiply 0.91×10^3.

The power of 10 is 10^3. Move the decimal point 3 places to the right.

There are only 2 decimal places. Add a placeholder zero to make a third decimal place.

$0.91 \times 10^3 = 0.910$

$0.91 \times 10^3 = 910$

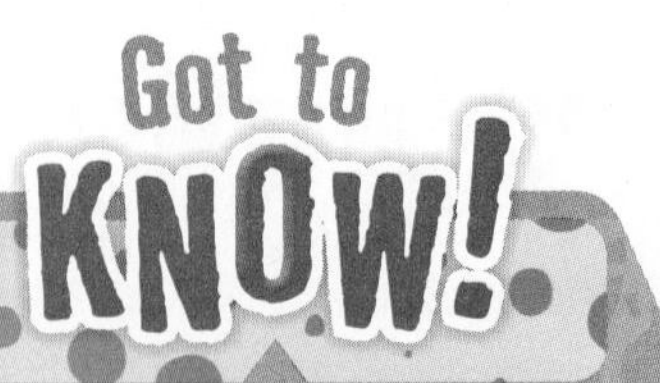

Multiplying a Decimal by Powers of Ten

- Count the number of zeros in the power of ten.
- Move the decimal point to the right the same number of places.

EXAMPLE 6

A restaurant manager orders 100 packages of paper cups. Each package costs $2.59. How much do the 100 packages cost?

Multiply the number of packages by the cost of each package.

METHOD 1

Write the problem in vertical form.

$$\begin{array}{r} \$2.59 \\ \times \quad 100 \\ \hline \$259.00 \end{array}$$

The 100 packages of paper cups cost $259.00.

METHOD 2

Use powers of 10.

Move the decimal point 2 places to the right. $2.59 \times 100 = 2.59$
$= 259$

The 100 packages of paper cups cost $259.00.

Need More HELP

For help with multiplying by powers of ten, go to *Multiply and Divide by 10, 100, etc.* in *Foundations of Mathematics* (p. 94).

Converting Units in the Metric System

To convert metric units from larger units to smaller units, multiply by powers of ten.

EXAMPLE 7

Jason's cat has a mass of 3.6287 kilograms. What is the mass of the cat in grams? (1 kilogram = 1,000 grams.)

A kilogram is larger than a gram. Multiply the mass of the cat in kilograms by 1,000.

Multiply $3.6287 \times 1{,}000$.

Move the decimal point 3 places to the right. $3.6287 \times 1{,}000 = 3.6287$
$= 3{,}628.7$

The cat's mass in grams is 3,628.7 grams.

SEARCH

To see step-by-step videos of these problems, enter the page number into the SWadvantage.com Search Bar.

Multiplying Decimals by Decimals

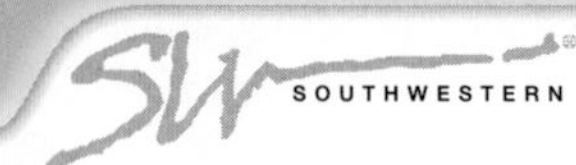

For help with multiplying whole numbers, go to *Multiplying Whole Numbers* in *Foundations of Mathematics* (p. 96).

Modeling Decimal Multiplication

You can use models to multiply decimals. Model the first factor using the columns. Model the second factor using the rows. The area where the shading overlaps will be a different color. This area, the intersection, represents the product.

EXAMPLE 1

Multiply 0.3 × 0.5.

Shade 3 columns on the grid to represent 0.3.

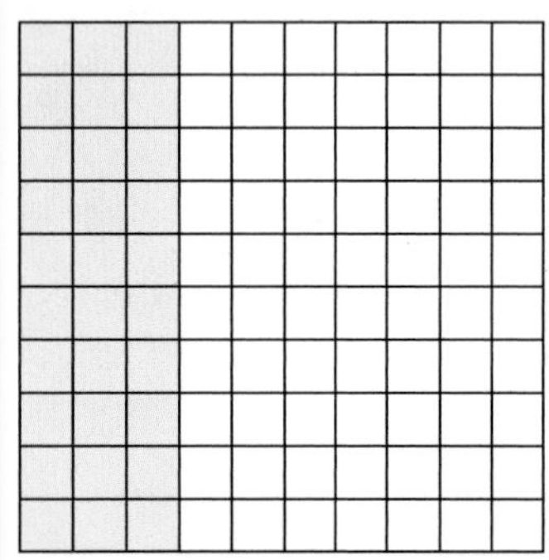

Use a different color and shade 5 rows to represent 0.5.

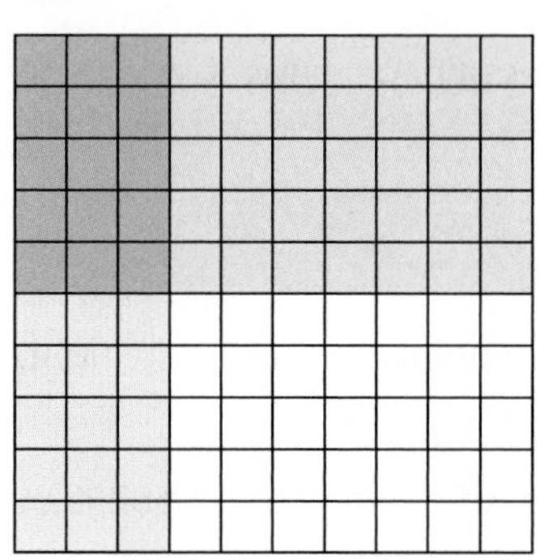

The area where the two colors overlap is the intersection, which is the product. Fifteen squares are in the intersection. They represent 15 hundredths or 0.15.

$0.3 \times 0.5 = 0.15$

EXAMPLE 2

Multiply 0.9 × 0.7.

Shade 9 columns on the grid to represent 0.9.

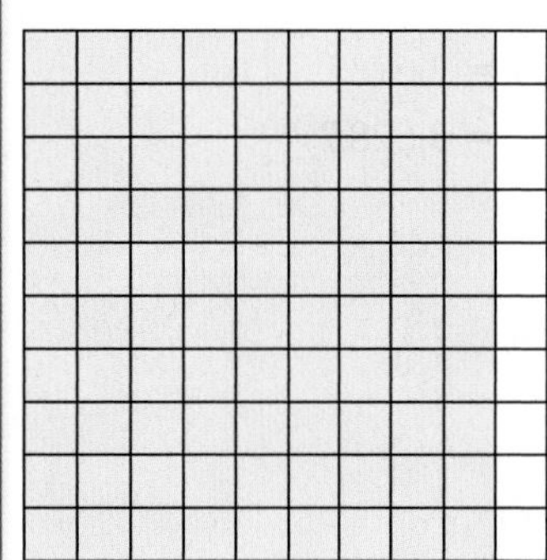

Use a different color and shade 7 rows to represent 0.7.

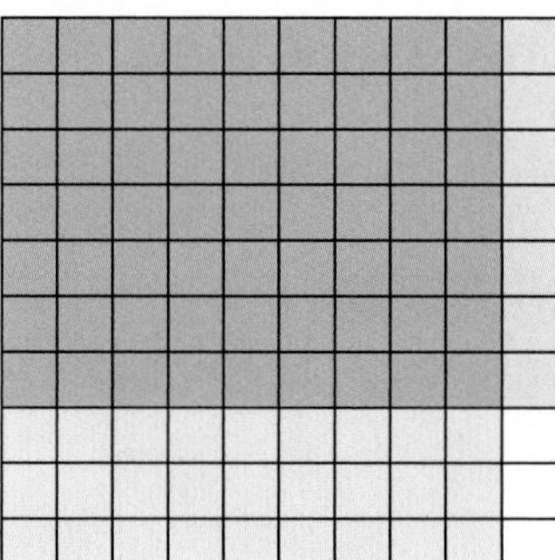

Sixty-three squares are in the intersection.

$0.9 \times 0.7 = 0.63$

SEARCH

To see step-by-step videos of these problems, enter the page number into the SWadvantage.com Search Bar.

Multiplying Decimals

Multiplying two decimal numbers is almost the same as multiplying two whole numbers. The only difference is that you must place a decimal point in the product.

Watch Out!

Make sure you count the number of decimal places to the right of the decimal, not the left.

EXAMPLE 3

Multiply 2.3 × 5.9.

Write the problem in vertical form.

Multiply as you do for whole numbers.

$$\begin{array}{r} 2.3 \\ \times\ 5.9 \\ \hline 207 \\ 1150 \\ \hline 1357 \end{array}$$

Find the number of decimal places in each factor.
Add the number of decimal places: 1 + 1 = 2.

Place the decimal point so there are 2 decimal places in the product.

$$\begin{array}{rl} 2.3 & \text{1 decimal place} \\ \times\ 5.9 & \underline{+1 \text{ decimal place}} \\ \hline 207 & \\ 115 & \\ \hline 13.57 & \text{2 decimal places} \end{array}$$

2.3 × 5.9 = 13.57

EXAMPLE 4

Multiply 12.96 × 1.8.

Write the problem in vertical form.

Multiply as you do for whole numbers.

Find the number of decimal places in each factor.
Add the number of decimal places: 2 + 1 = 3.

Place the decimal point so there are 3 decimal places in the product.

$$\begin{array}{rl} 12.96 & \text{2 decimal places} \\ \times\ \ 1.8 & \underline{+1 \text{ decimal place}} \\ \hline 10368 & \\ 1296\ & \\ \hline 23.328 & \text{3 decimal places} \end{array}$$

12.96 × 1.8 = 23.328

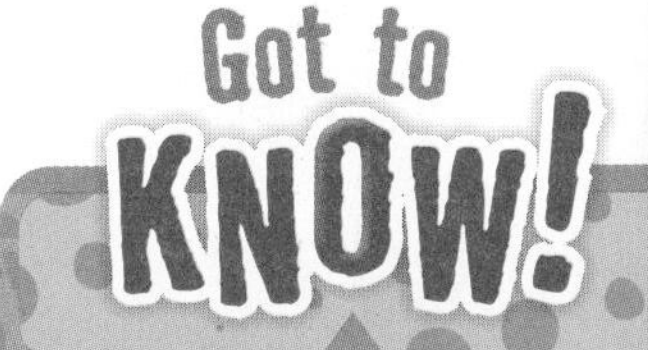

Multiplying Decimal Numbers

When multiplying decimals, the number of decimal places in the product is the same as the total number of decimal places in the factors.

$$\begin{array}{rl} 0.43 & \leftarrow \text{2 decimal places in factor} \\ \underline{\times\ \ 0.3} & \leftarrow \text{1 decimal place in factor} \\ 0.129 & \leftarrow \text{3 decimal places in product} \end{array}$$

Multiplying Decimals

EXAMPLE 5

SEARCH

To see step-by-step videos of these problems, enter the page number into the SWadvantage.com Search Bar.

In one breakfast cereal, one serving contains 3.5 grams of fiber. How much fiber is in 2.75 servings of the cereal?

Multiply the number of servings by the number of grams in each serving.

Write the problem in vertical form.

Multiply.

Find the number of decimal places in each factor.
Add the number of decimal places: $2 + 1 = 3$.

2.75	2 decimal places
× 3.5	+ 1 decimal place
1375	
8250	
9.625	3 decimal places

Place the decimal point so there are 3 decimal places in the product.

There are 9.625 grams of fiber in 2.75 servings of cereal.

Estimating the Product

To estimate a decimal product, round each factor to the nearest whole number. Then multiply. You can use an estimated product to predict the approximate answer and to see where the decimal point should be placed. You can also use an estimated product to decide whether the product you calculate is reasonable.

EXAMPLE 6

Multiply 6.121 × 3.9.

STEP 1 Estimate the product.

6.121 × 3.9 Round each factor to the nearest whole number.

↓ ↓

$6 \times 4 = 24$

The estimated product is 24.

STEP 2 Multiply to find the actual product.

6.121	3 decimal places
× 3.9	+1 decimal place
55089	
183630	
23.8719	4 decimal places

STEP 3 Compare the actual answer to the estimated answer.

23.8719 is close to 24. So, 23.8719 is a reasonable answer.

$6.121 \times 3.9 = 23.8719$

Try It This Way

You can use your estimate to place the decimal point without counting decimal places. Think: 23.87 is close to 24.

Placing Zeros in the Product

Sometimes there are not enough digits to place the decimal point correctly. In these cases you need to add zeros to the *left* of the non-zero digits.

EXAMPLE 7

Multiply 0.2 × 0.4.

Write the problem in vertical form.

Multiply as if the problem were 2 × 4.

$$\begin{array}{r} 0.2 \\ \times\ 0.4 \\ \hline 8 \end{array}$$

Both numbers have one decimal place, so there is a total of 2 decimal places.

There is only one digit in the product of 2 × 4. Another decimal place is needed, so add a zero to the *left* of the 8.

Now you can place the decimal point so there are 2 decimal places in the product.

$$\begin{array}{r} 0.2 \\ \times\ 0.4 \\ \hline 0.08 \end{array}$$

0.2 × 0.4 = 0.08

Watch Out !

Remember, when you place a zero to the right of the last digit in a decimal number you do not change the value of the number. However, the zero placed in Example 7 does change the value of the product because 0.8 ≠ 0.08.

EXAMPLE 8

Multiply 0.005 × 0.07.

Write the problem in vertical form.

Multiply as if the problem were 5 × 7.

$$\begin{array}{r} 0.005 \\ \times\ 0.07 \\ \hline 35 \end{array}$$

The first factor has 3 decimal places. The second factor has 2 decimal places. There is a total of 5 decimal places.

There are only two digits in the product of 5 × 7. Three more decimal places are needed, so add three zeros to the *left* of the 3.

Now you can place the decimal point so there are 5 decimal places in the product.

$$\begin{array}{r} 0.005 \\ \times\ 0.07 \\ \hline 0.00035 \end{array}$$

0.005 × 0.07 = 0.00035

The *dividend* is the number to be divided. The *divisor* is the number you divide by. The *quotient* is the answer.

Modeling Decimal Division

You can use a ten by ten grid to model the division of a decimal number by a whole number. Look at Example 1 and Example 2. Notice the following.

- The quotient has the same number of decimal places as the dividend.
- The quotient is less than the dividend.

Divide 0.75 by 3.

Shade 75 hundredths.

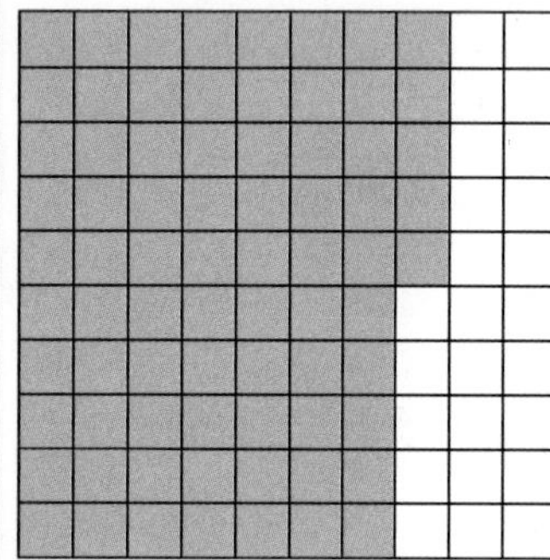

Divide 75 hundredths into 3 equal groups.

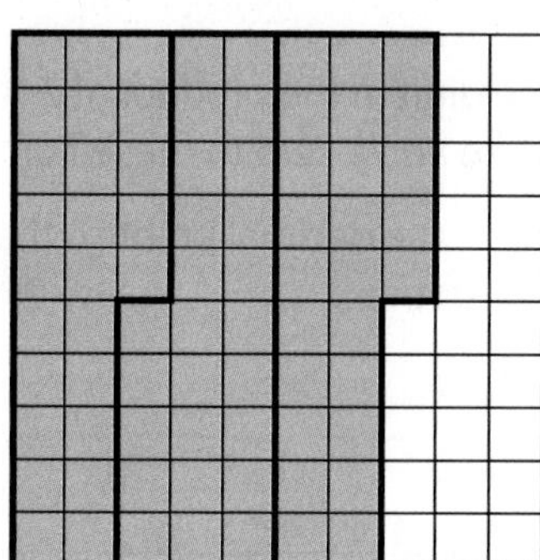

Each group contains 25 hundredths.

$0.75 \div 3 = 0.25$

EXAMPLE 2

Divide 0.6 ÷ 5.

$0.6 = 0.60$

Shade 60 hundredths.

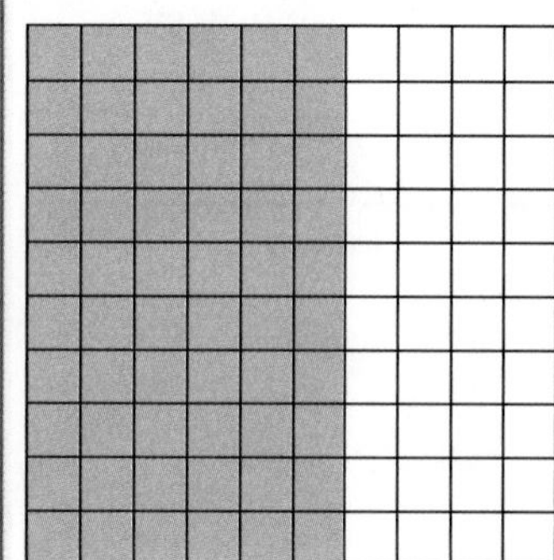

Divide 60 hundredths into 5 equal groups.

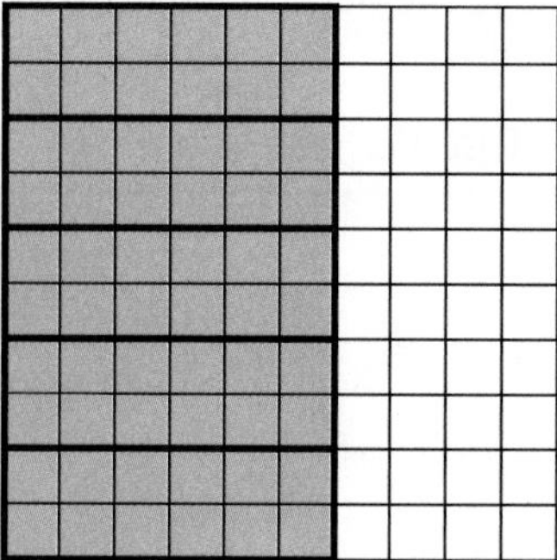

Each group contains 12 hundredths.

$0.6 \div 5 = 0.12$

Got to KNOW!

Dividing a Decimal by a Whole Number

When a decimal number is divided by a whole number, the quotient is always less than the dividend.

$0.60 \div 5 = 0.12$

12 hundredths is less than 60 hundredths.

Dividing Decimals by Whole Numbers

To divide a decimal by a whole number, write the problem in long division form and divide as with whole numbers. Place the decimal point in the quotient directly above the decimal point in the dividend.

Need More HELP

For help with dividing whole numbers, go to *Divide Whole Numbers* in *Foundations of Mathematics* (p. 100).

EXAMPLE 3

Divide 4.68 ÷ 3.

Write the problem in long division form. $3\overline{)4.68}$

Divide as you do for whole numbers. Multiply, subtract, and bring down the next digit in each step.

Place the decimal point in the quotient directly above the decimal point in the dividend.

```
   1.56
3)4.68
  3
  16
  15
   18
   18
    0
```

4.68 ÷ 3 = 1.56

EXAMPLE 4

Mr. Lee bought 18 window shades. The total cost was $179.10. How much did each window shade cost?

Divide the total cost by the number of window shades. 179.10 ÷ 18

Write the problem in long division form. $18\overline{)179.10}$

Divide as you do for whole numbers. Multiply, subtract, and bring down the next digit in each step.

Place the decimal point in the quotient directly above the decimal point in the dividend.

```
      9.95
18)179.10
   162
    171
    162
      90
      90
       0
```

Each window shade cost $9.95.

SEARCH

To see step-by-step videos of these problems, enter the page number into the SWadvantage.com Search Bar.

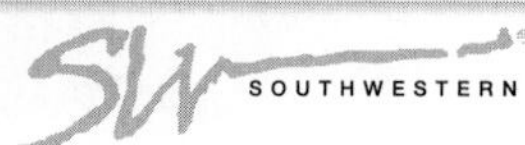

Dividing Decimals by Powers of Ten

It is easy to divide a decimal by 10, 100, 1,000, or any power of ten. Look for the pattern in the table below.

Number	÷ Power of 10	Is equal to	Decimal point moves
872.34	$\div 10^0 =$	$872.34 \div 1 = 872.34$	0 places to the left.
872.34	$\div 10^1 =$	$872.34 \div 10 = 87.234$	1 place to the left.
872.34	$\div 10^2 =$	$872.34 \div 100 = 8.7234$	2 places to the left.
872.34	$\div 10^3 =$	$872.34 \div 1{,}000 = 0.87234$	3 places to the left.
872.34	$\div 10^4 =$	$872.34 \div 10{,}000 = 0.087234$	4 places to the left.

Notice that the decimal point shifts to the left the same number of places shown in the power of 10. Sometimes this is called "moving the decimal point."

Divide 137.5 ÷ 10^3.

The power of 10 is 10^3. Move the decimal point 3 places to the left.

$137.5 \div 10^3 = 137.5 \div 1{,}000$

$= 137.5$

$= 0.1375$

Divide 352 ÷ 10^4.

The power of 10 is 10^4. Move the decimal point 4 places to the left.

$352 \div 10^4 = 352 \div 10{,}000$

$= 0352.0$ Add a zero so you can move the decimal point 4 places.

$= 0.0352$

Dividing by Powers of Ten

To divide a decimal by a power of ten:

- Read the number of zeros in the power of ten. $621.35 \div 10^2 = 6.2135$
- Move the decimal point to the left this many places.

The power of 10 is not always in exponential form. For example, 100 is a power of ten. To divide by 100, count the number of zeros in 100. There are two zeros. Move the decimal point two places to the left.

EXAMPLE 7

Devon bought a pack of 10 CDs for C$6.30. What is the unit price?

The unit price is the cost of 1 CD based on the cost of the pack.

C$6.30 for one pack ÷ 10 CDs per pack = ? per 1 CD

METHOD 1

Write the problem in long division form.

Divide by multiplying, subtracting, and bringing down the next digit in each step.

```
     .63
10)6.30
   60
    30
    30
     0
```

The unit price is C$0.63.

METHOD 2

C$6.30 ÷ 10

Move the decimal point 1 place to the left.

The unit price is C$0.63.

C$6.30 ÷ 10 = .630

= 0.63

SEARCH

To see step-by-step videos of these problems, enter the page number into the SWadvantage.com Search Bar.

MONEY

NOTE: C$ denotes Canadian dollars.

Converting Units in the Metric System

To convert metric units from smaller units to larger units, divide by powers of ten.

EXAMPLE 8

Lan is 137.9 centimeters tall. What is her height in meters? (1 meter = 100 centimeters.)

A meter is larger than a centimeter. To find Lan's height in meters, divide her height in centimeters by 100.

137.9 cm ÷ 100 cm per m

Move the decimal point 2 places to the left.

Lan is 1.379 meters tall.

137.9 ÷ 100 = 137.9

= 1.379

Modeling Decimal Division

You can use a ten by ten grid to model the division of a decimal number by a whole number. When you divide the whole number, you are figuring out how many groups of the decimal number are in the whole number. For instance, in Example 1, you want to know, "How many groups of 0.75 are in 3.0?"

For help with division, go to *Dividing Whole Numbers* in *Foundations of Mathematics* (p. 100).

EXAMPLE 1

Divide 3 by 0.75.

Model the number 3. Shade 3 ten by ten grids completely.

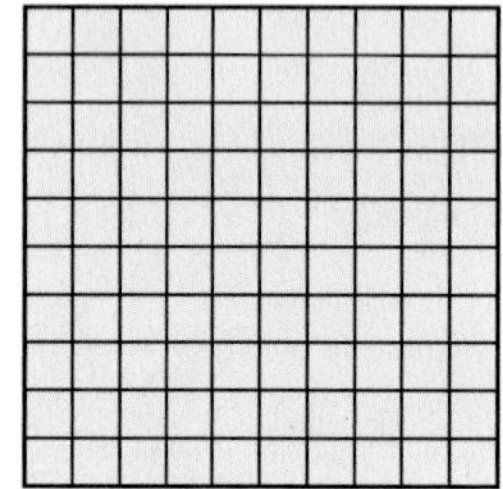

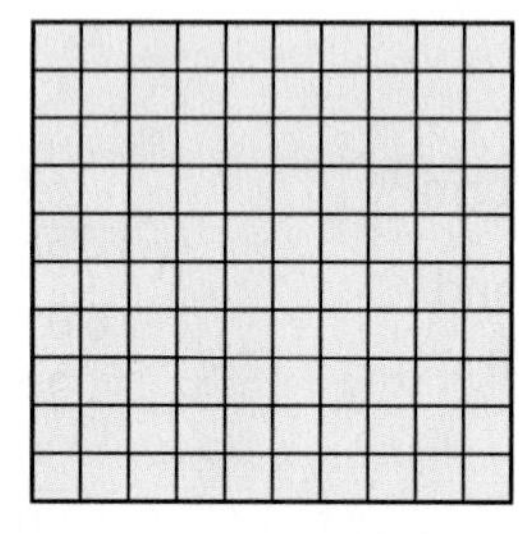

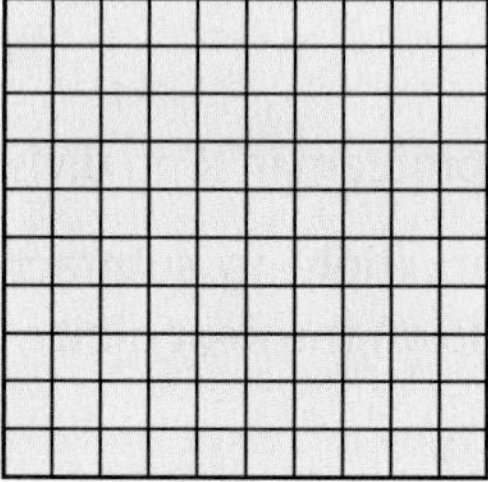

Divide the small squares on the 3 shaded grids into groups of 75 hundredths.

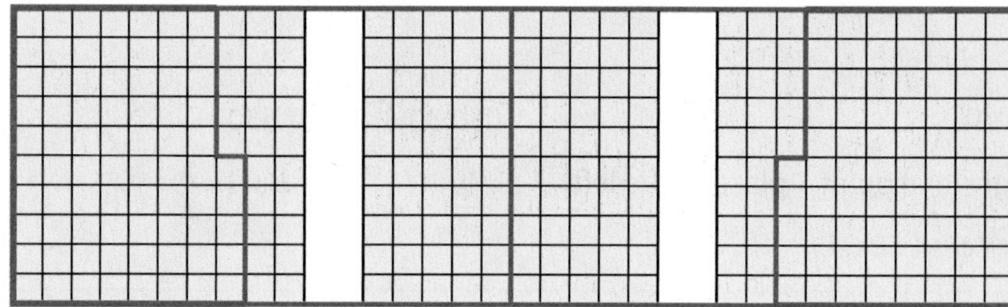

There are 4 equal groups, so $3 \div 0.75 = 4$.

EXAMPLE 2

Divide $1 \div 0.2$.

Shade a 10 by 10 grid. Then divide it into groups of 20 hundredths.

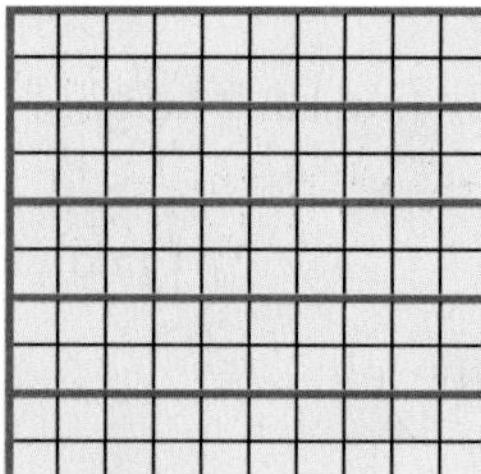

There are 5 equal groups, so $1 \div 0.2 = 5$.

Need More HELP

In Example 2, you divide by 0.2. Remember that $0.2 = 0.20 =$ 20 hundredths.

Dividing Whole Numbers by Decimals

Use long division, just as if you were dividing whole numbers. You will need to insert a decimal point into the whole number, and often you will need to insert placeholder zeros to the right of the decimal point. You can place the decimal point in the quotient before or after you divide.

In a division problem, the *dividend* is the number to be divided. The *divisor* is the number you divide by. The *quotient* is the answer.

EXAMPLE 3

Divide 18 ÷ 1.25.

METHOD 1

Place the decimal point in the quotient first.

Change the divisor to a whole number by multiplying by a power of 10. In this case, use 10^2 or 100. Move the decimal point two places to the right.

$1.25\overline{)18.00}$

$1.25 \times 100 = 125$

Now move the decimal point in the dividend the same number of places.

Place the decimal point in the quotient directly above the decimal point in the dividend.

Divide as you do for whole numbers.

```
         14.4
125)1,800.0
    1 25
      550
      500
       500
       500
         0
```

$18 \div 1.25 = 14.4$

METHOD 2

Place the decimal point in the quotient last.

Divide as you do for whole numbers.

Insert a decimal point to the right of the 18 and insert placeholder zeros as necessary.

```
         144
1.25)18.000
     125
      550
      500
       500
       500
         0
```

To place the decimal point in the quotient, count the number of decimal places in the divisor and the dividend.

1.25 → 2 places
18.000 → 3 places

Subtract the number of decimal places in the divisor from the number of decimal places in the dividend.

$3 - 2 = 1$

Insert 1 decimal place into the quotient.

14.4

$18 \div 1.25 = 14.4$

SEARCH

To see step-by-step videos of these problems, enter the page number into the SWadvantage.com Search Bar.

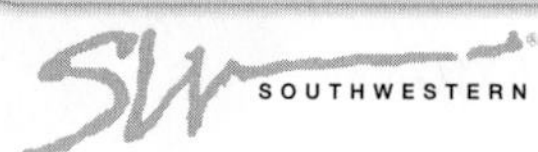

Dividing Whole Numbers by Decimals

As a general rule, to divide a whole number by a decimal follow these steps:

- Write the problem in long division form.
- Change the divisor to a whole number by multiplying by some power of 10.
- Place a decimal point to the right of the whole number and insert placeholder zeros as necessary.

Watch Out!

When the dividend is a whole number, you must continue dividing through the ones place.

EXAMPLE 4

Divide 28 ÷ 0.35.

Write the problem in long division form. $0.35\overline{)28}$

Change the divisor to a whole number. Multiply 0.35 by 100 by moving the decimal point 2 places to the right. $0.35\overline{)28.00}$

Move the decimal point in the dividend the same number of places.

Divide as you do for whole numbers.

The quotient is a whole number.

$$\begin{array}{r} 80 \\ 35\overline{)2{,}800} \\ \underline{280} \\ 00 \\ \underline{0} \\ 0 \end{array}$$

28 ÷ 0.35 = 80

EXAMPLE 5

Rosa has a ribbon that is 72 inches long. She wants to cut the ribbon into smaller pieces that are each 1.5 inches long. How many smaller pieces can she cut from the ribbon?

Divide the total length of the ribbon by the length of each smaller piece.

Write the problem in long division form. $1.5\overline{)72.0}$

Change the divisor to a whole number. Multiply 1.5 by 10 by moving the decimal point 1 place to the right.

Move the decimal point in the dividend the same number of places.

Divide as you do for whole numbers.

The quotient is a whole number.

$$\begin{array}{r} 48 \\ 15\overline{)720} \\ \underline{60} \\ 120 \\ \underline{120} \\ 0 \end{array}$$

Rosa can cut 48 smaller pieces of ribbon.

Rounding Quotients

Remainders are not used in decimal division. The division is continued until the remainder is zero or until you reach one decimal place beyond the number of decimal places desired. Then the quotient is rounded to the given decimal place.

EXAMPLE 6

Divide 116 by 2.8. Round your answer to the nearest tenth.

You are asked for an answer rounded to the nearest tenth, so you must divide to hundredths.

Write the problem in long division form. $2.8\overline{)116.0}$

Change the divisor to a whole number. Multiply 2.8 by 10 by moving the decimal point 1 place to the right.

Divide as you do for whole numbers.

Place the decimal point in the quotient directly above the decimal point in the dividend.

Round 41.42 to the nearest tenth. Because the 2 in the hundredths place is less than 5, round to 41.4.

```
     41.42
28)1160.00
   112
    40
    28
    120
    112
      80
      56
      24
```

116 ÷ 2.8 rounded to the nearest tenth is 41.4.

SEARCH

To see step-by-step videos of these problems, enter the page number into the SWadvantage.com Search Bar.

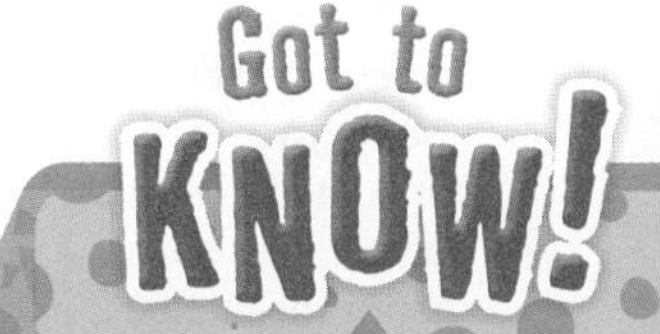

Dividing Whole Numbers by Decimals

When you divide a whole number by a decimal number that is less than 1, the quotient is greater than the dividend.

$28 \div 0.25 = 112$ $0.25 < 1$ $112 > 28$

When you divide a whole number by a decimal number that is greater than 1, the quotient is less than the dividend.

$28 \div 1.25 = 22.4$ $1.25 > 1$ $22.4 < 28$

Dividing Decimals by Decimals

Modeling Decimal Division

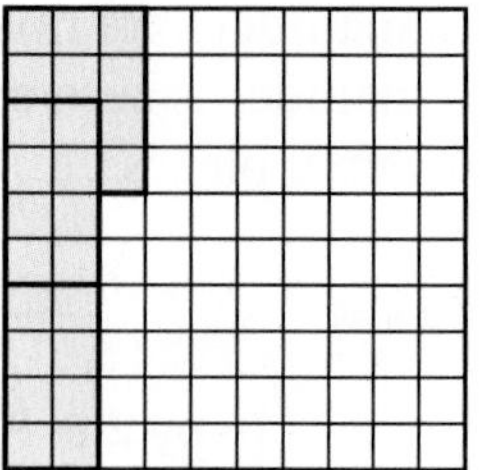

You can use a ten by ten grid to model the division of a decimal number by a decimal number.

Suppose you want to divide 0.24 by 0.8. What you need to know is, "How many groups of 0.8 are in 0.24?" Notice that 0.8 is greater than 0.24. Since there is 1 group of 0.8 in 0.8, there must be fewer than 1 group of 0.8 in 0.24.

It is tempting to say there are 3 groups, but you know there is fewer than 1 group. There are 0.3 groups of 0.8 in 0.24. Multiply to check: $0.3 \times 0.8 = 0.24$.

You can also use a model to show the division of mixed decimal numbers.

To see step-by-step videos of these problems, enter the page number into the SWadvantage.com Search Bar.

EXAMPLE 1

Divide 3.9 by 1.3.

STEP 1 Model the number 3.9.
Shade 3 ten by ten grids completely to represent 3 ones.
Shade 90 small squares of another grid to represent 0.9.

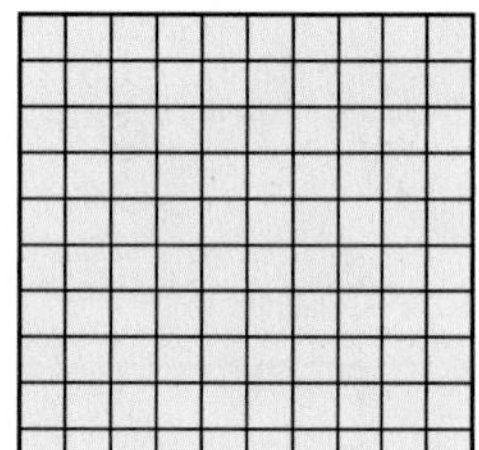 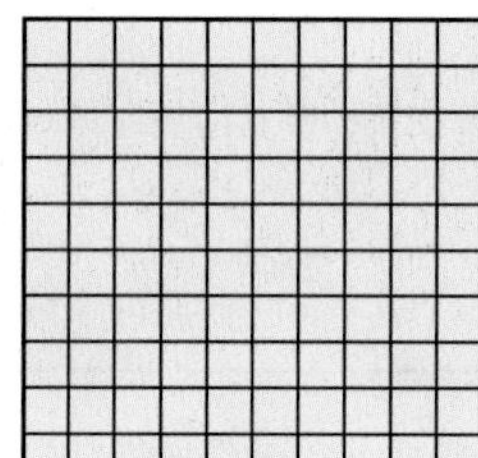 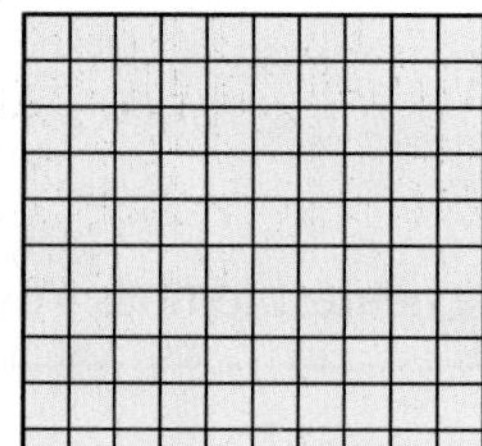 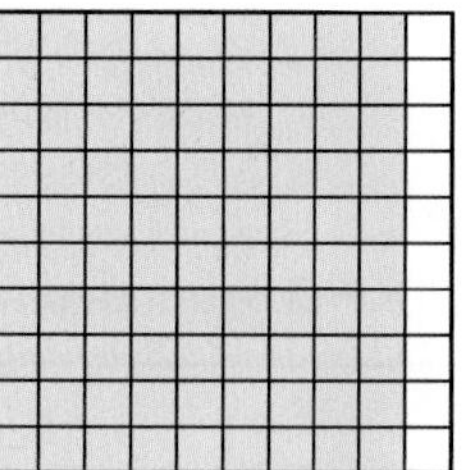

Remember that inserting a zero to the right of a decimal number does not change the number's value.

$0.9 = 0.90$

9 tenths
= 90 hundredths

STEP 2 Divide the shaded squares into groups of 1.3 small squares. You already have three groups of 1. Regroup the 90 small squares. Since $90 \div 3 = 30$, place 30 small squares below each of the grids that are completely shaded.

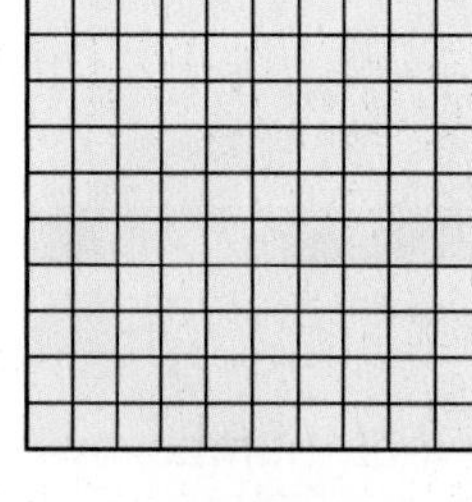 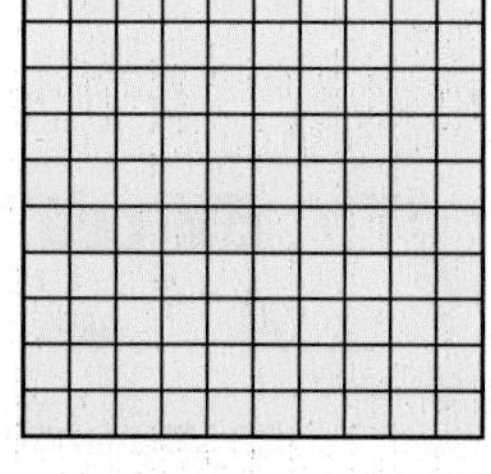 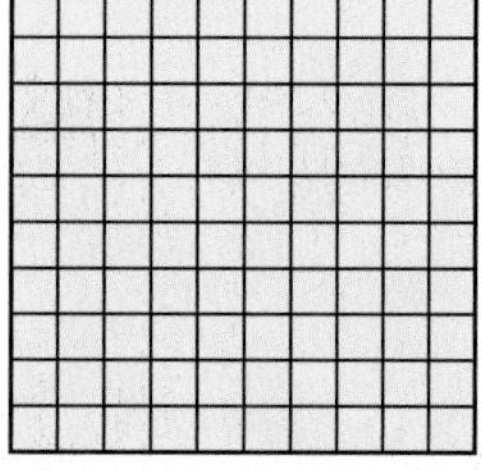

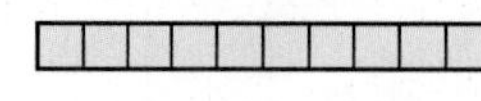 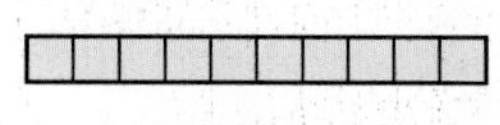 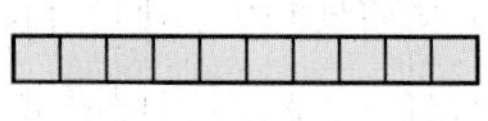

 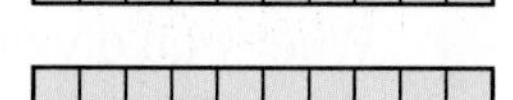 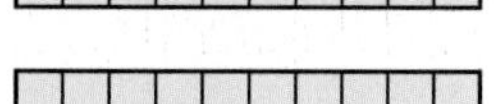

You now have 3 groups of equal size. Each group contains 1.30 small squares.

$3.9 \div 1.3 = 3$

Dividing Decimals by Decimals

Divide just as if you were dividing whole numbers. The most common method is to change the decimal divisor to a whole number, as shown in Example 2.

Need More HELP

In a division problem, the *dividend* is the number to be divided. The *divisor* is the number you divide by. The *quotient* is the answer.

EXAMPLE 2

Divide 14.64 ÷ 1.2.

Change the divisor to a whole number by multiplying by a power of 10. In this case, use 10^1 or 10. Move the decimal point 1 place to the right.

$1.2\overline{)14.64}$

$1.2 \times 10 = 12$

Now move the decimal point in the dividend the same number of places.

Divide as you do for whole numbers.

Place the decimal point in the quotient directly above the decimal point in the dividend.

```
    12.2
12)146.4
   12
    26
    24
     24
     24
      0
```

$14.64 \div 1.2 = 12.2$

EXAMPLE 3

Divide 0.1464 ÷ 0.0002.

Change the divisor to a whole number by multiplying by a power of 10. In this case, use 10^4 or 10,000. Move the decimal point 4 places to the right.

```
             732
0.0002)0.1464
```

$0.0002 \times 10{,}000 = 2$

Move the decimal point in the dividend the same number of places.

Divide using short division. Then bring the decimal point straight up into the quotient.

$0.1464 \div 0.0002 = 732$

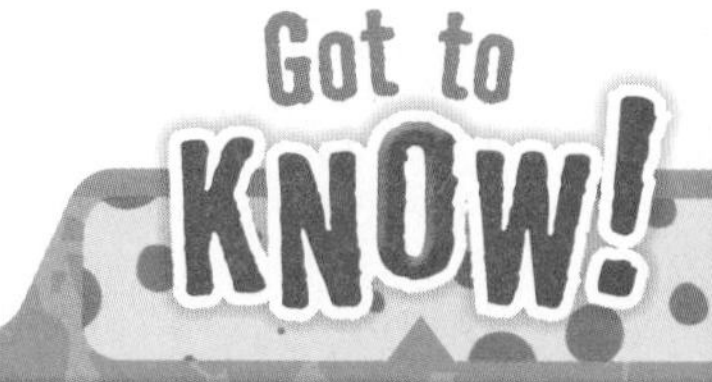

Dividing a Decimal by a Decimal

1. Change the divisor to a whole number by multiplying it by a power of 10.
2. Multiply the dividend by the same power of 10.
3. Divide as for whole numbers.
4. Bring the decimal point straight up into the quotient.

Dividing Decimals by Decimals

As a general rule, to divide a decimal by a decimal, follow these steps:

- Write the problem in long division form.
- Change the divisor to a whole number by multiplying by a power of 10.
- Multiply the dividend by the same power of 10.
- Bring the decimal point straight up into the quotient.

SEARCH

To see step-by-step videos of these problems, enter the page number into the SWadvantage.com Search Bar.

EXAMPLE 4

Divide 180.7 ÷ 3.25.

METHOD 1

Write the problem in long division form. $3.25\overline{)180.7}$

Change the divisor to a whole number. Multiply 3.25 by 100 by moving the decimal point 2 places to the right. $3.25\overline{)180.700}$

Move the decimal point in the dividend the same number of places.

Divide as you do for whole numbers.

This division is complete at tenths.

Place the decimal point in the quotient directly above the decimal point in the dividend.

```
        55.6
325)18,070.0
    1625
     1820
     1625
      1950
      1950
         0
```

180.7 ÷ 3.25 = 55.6

METHOD 2

Write the problem as a fraction. $\frac{180.7}{3.25}$

Multiply by $\frac{100}{100}$ to make the divisor a whole number.

$\frac{180.7}{3.25} \times \frac{100}{100} = \frac{18{,}070}{325}$

Divide as you do for whole numbers, as shown in Method 1 above.

180.7 ÷ 3.25 = 55.6

Remember that the fraction bar shows division. So $\frac{180.7}{3.25}$ means the same thing as 180.7 ÷ 3.25. Multiplying the fraction by $\frac{100}{100}$ is the same as moving the decimal point two places to the right in the divisor and in the dividend.

Rounding Quotients and Repeating Decimals

Remainders are not used in decimal division. The division is continued until the remainder is zero or until you have divided to one decimal place beyond the given number of decimal places. Then the quotient is *rounded* to the given decimal place.

Sometimes the quotient is a repeating decimal. A **repeating decimal** is a decimal in which one or more digits repeat indefinitely. When there is a repeating decimal in the quotient, the division will never come out evenly.

For help with rounding, go to *Round Whole Numbers* in *Foundations of Mathematics* (p. 50).

For help with repeating decimals, go to *Rational Numbers and Number Sets* in *Numbers and Operations* (p. 268).

EXAMPLE 5

Divide 15.8 by 1.2.

a. Round your answer to the nearest hundredth.

You are asked to round to the nearest hundredth, so you must divide to thousandths.

Write the problem in long division form. $1.2\overline{)15.8}$

Change the divisor to a whole number. Multiply 15.8 by 10 by moving the decimal point 1 place to the right.

Divide as you do for whole numbers.

Place the decimal point in the quotient directly above the decimal point in the dividend.

Round 13.166 to the nearest hundredth. Because the 6 in the thousandths place is greater than 5, round to 13.17.

```
       13.166
  12)158.000
     12
      38
      36
       20
       12
        80
        72
         80
         72
          8
```

15.8 ÷ 1.2 rounded to the nearest hundredth is 13.17.

b. Express the quotient as a repeating decimal.

If you use a calculator to divide, you will see that the 6 repeats indefinitely, 13.166666.

Show that the digit repeats by writing 3 dots after the digit, or by placing a bar over the digit that repeats.

$15.8 \div 1.2 = 13.166...$

$15.8 \div 1.2 = 13.1\overline{6}$

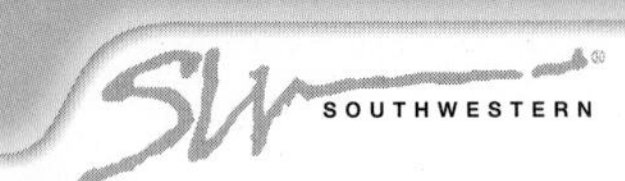

Solving Decimal Word Problems

Often, there is more than one way to solve a word problem. Find the method that works best for you. You may find it helpful to follow the steps shown in *Got To Know!* below. The examples show an application of the steps.

Need More HELP

For help solving word problems, go to *Problem Solving* on pages 448–469. You will find a four-step problem-solving process and strategies for problem solving.

The *Check* in Example 1 uses the strategy *Use Logical Reasoning* on page 460.

EXAMPLE 1

Sarah has a watermelon that has a mass of 7.3 kilograms. Water makes up 6.716 kilograms of the mass. How many kilograms of the watermelon's mass are not water?

READ Read the problem carefully. Identify what you know and what you need to find out, or need to know.
Know: Total mass is 7.3 kg, and 6.716 kg of the mass is water.
Need to Know: the part of the watermelon's mass that is not made up of water

PLAN Think about how you can find the information you need to know. You could subtract the mass that is water from the entire mass of the watermelon.

SOLVE Write the problem in vertical form. Add zeros for placeholders and subtract.

7.300 kg	total mass of watermelon	7.300 (regrouped: 6 12 9 10 1... as 6, 12, 9/1)
− 6.716 kg	mass that is water	− 6.716
? kg	mass that is not water	0.584 kg is not water

CHECK Did I answer the question? Is my answer reasonable?
$6.716 \text{ kg} + 1 \text{ kg} = 7.716 \text{ kg}$, which is greater than the total mass of the watermelon. Therefore, the mass of the watermelon that is not water must be less than 1 kg. The answer of 0.584 kg is a reasonable answer.

0.584 kg of the watermelon's mass is not water.

If you state your answer in terms of the question, you will know you answered the correct question. The question in Example 1 asks, "How many kilograms of the watermelon's mass are not water?" The answer states "0.584 kg of the watermelon's mass is not water."

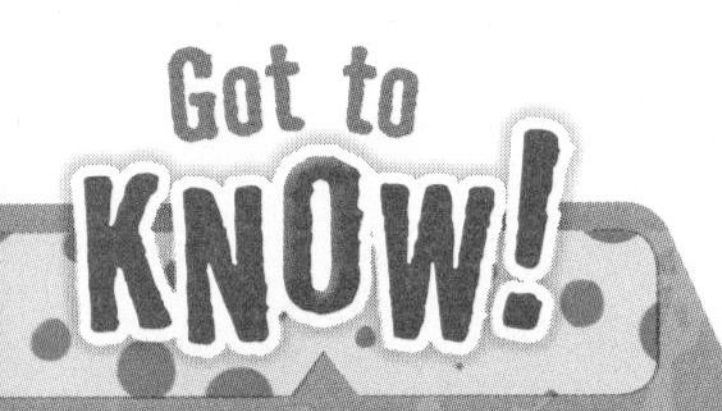

Problem-Solving Process

To solve a word problem, you can use this process.

1. **Read** the problem carefully. Identify what you know and what you need to find out.
2. **Plan** how to find the solution.
3. **Solve** the problem using your plan.
4. **Check** your work and ask if your answer makes sense.

EXAMPLE 2

Jamal bought two T-shirts and a DVD. The T-shirts cost $15.50 each and the DVD cost $14.99. How much did Jamal spend?

READ Know: 2 T-shirts cost $15.50 each, 1 DVD cost $14.99.
Need to Know: Total cost of the 3 items

PLAN There are two ways to solve this problem.

METHOD 1

Multiply to find the total of the T-shirts.
Then add the cost of the DVD to the product.

METHOD 2

Add the cost of the 3 items.

SOLVE

METHOD 1

$$\begin{array}{r} \overset{1\,1}{\$15.50} \\ \times \quad 2 \\ \hline \$31.00 \end{array} \qquad \begin{array}{r} \$31.00 \\ +\ \$14.99 \\ \hline \$45.99 \end{array}$$

METHOD 2

$$\begin{array}{r} \overset{1\,1}{\$15.50} \\ \$15.50 \\ +\ \$14.99 \\ \hline \$45.99 \end{array}$$

CHECK You can estimate each price and then find the sum.
$15.50 is about $15. $15.50 is about $15. $14.99 is about $15.
Use mental math: $15 \times 3 = 45$
The calculated answer of $45.99 is reasonable.

Jamal spent $45.99 on the 3 items.

SEARCH

To see step-by-step videos of these problems, enter the page number into the SWadvantage.com Search Bar.

Need More HELP

For help with estimating to check, go to *Estimating to Predict or Check* on page 410.

EXAMPLE 3

Carolina bought 3.62 pounds of grapes. Each pound of grapes costs C$1.49. How much did Carolina spend?

READ Know: 3.62 lb at C$1.49 per lb
Need to Know: Total cost

PLAN Multiply to find how much Carolina spent.

SOLVE

$$\begin{array}{rl} 3.62 & \text{pounds of grapes} \\ \times\ 1.49 & \text{for 1 pound} \\ \hline 3258 & \\ 1448 & \\ 362 & \\ \hline 5.3938 & \text{rounds to C\$5.39} \end{array}$$

CHECK $1.5 \times 4 = 6$ and $1.5 \times 3 = 4.5$
$6 > 5.39 > 4$
C$5.39 is a reasonable answer.

Carolina spent C$5.39 for the grapes.

MONEY

NOTE: C$ denotes Canadian dollars.

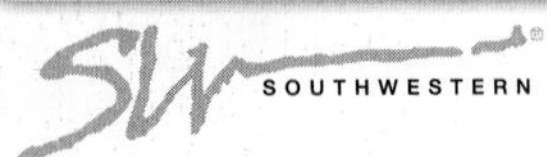

Solving Decimal Word Problems

SEARCH

To see step-by-step videos of these problems, enter the page number into the SWadvantage.com Search Bar.

EXAMPLE 4

Marla is making sandwiches. She has 4 pounds of turkey. Each sandwich uses 0.25 pounds of turkey. What is the greatest number of sandwiches Marla can make?

READ Know: 4 lb of turkey, 0.25 lb per sandwich
Need to Know: Number of sandwiches Marla can make

PLAN Divide the number of pounds of turkey by the amount needed for sandwich.

SOLVE Divide. Move the decimal point to the right two places.

$$\begin{array}{r} 16. \\ 0.25.\overline{)4.00.} \\ -25 \\ \hline 150 \\ -150 \\ \hline 0 \end{array}$$

CHECK Use logical reasoning and mental math.
Think: $16 \div 4 = 4$
If she can make 16 sandwiches per 4 lb turkey, then she can make 4 sandwiches with 1 lb of turkey.
$1 \text{ lb} \div 4 = \frac{1}{4} \text{ lb} = 0.25 \text{ lb}$
The answer is reasonable.

The greatest number of sandwiches Marla can make is 16.

EXAMPLE 5

Sam bought three lemons for $0.20 each and four oranges for $0.65 each. He gave the clerk a $10.00 bill. How much change did he receive?

READ Know: 3 lemons at $0.20 each, 4 oranges at $0.65 each, gave clerk $10
Need to Know: Amount of change received

PLAN Multiply twice and then add to find total cost of the items. Subtract to find the change.

SOLVE Perform the operations in the plan.

Cost of lemons	Cost of oranges	Total cost
$0.20 per lemon	$0.65 per orange	$0.60
× 3 lemons	× 4 oranges	+ $2.60
$0.60	$2.60	$3.20

Find the change.

$$\begin{array}{r} \$10.00 \\ -\ \$\ 3.20 \\ \hline \$\ 6.80 \end{array}$$

CHECK Review your multiplication. To estimate the change, think: $10 - 3 = 7$, so $6.80 in change is reasonable.

Sam received $6.80 in change.

EXAMPLE 6

Feng is building a fence around his garden. He needs a total of 46.28 meters of fencing. He has one piece of fencing that is 24.65 meters in length and another piece that is 21.75 meters in length. Does Feng have enough fencing for his garden?

READ Know: Feng has 24.65 m and 21.75 m of fencing.
Need to Know: Is this length equal to or greater than 46.28 m?

PLAN Add to find the total amount of fencing Feng has. Compare the sum to what he needs.

SOLVE Perform the operations in the plan.

Add.

$$\begin{array}{r} {}^{1\ 1} \\ 24.65 \\ +\ 21.75 \\ \hline 46.40 \end{array}$$

Compare.

46.40 m > 46.28 m
has > needs

The amount of fencing Feng has is greater than the amount he needs.

Feng has 46.40 meters of fencing.

CHECK Rounding shows that 24 + 21 = 45 and 25 + 22 = 47. This tells you that your answer is reasonable, but for this problem you need a precise comparison. Use a calculator to check your addition, or subtract 46.40 − 21.75 to see if the difference is 24.65.

Feng has enough fencing for his garden.

When a problem asks if some quantity is enough, rounding is not the best way to check the answer.

EXAMPLE 7

An orange juice carton is labeled: 1.92 liters, 8 servings. How many milliliters of juice are in a serving?

READ Know: 1.92 L of juice will make 8 servings.
Need to Know: Number of mL in each serving

PLAN Divide the amount of juice by the number of servings. Convert the answer to mL.

SOLVE Perform the operations in the plan.

Divide.

$$\begin{array}{r} .24 \\ 8\overline{)1.92} \\ -1\underline{6} \\ 32 \\ -\underline{32} \\ 0 \end{array}$$

Convert liters to milliliters.

1 liter = 1,000 milliliters

Multiply 0.24 by 1,000 by moving the decimal point three places to the right.

0.24 L = 240 mL

There are 0.24 liters per serving.

CHECK Use compatible numbers. Divide: 1.6 ÷ 8 = 0. 2 L per serving. Express 0.2 L as 200 mL. 200 mL is close to 240 mL. The answer is reasonable.

There are 240 milliliters of juice in each serving.

Need More HELP

For help with compatible numbers, go to *Estimating Decimal Sums and Differences* on page 414.

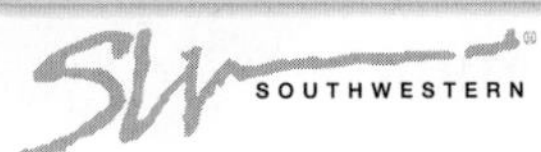

Solving Decimal Word Problems

SEARCH

To see step-by-step videos of these problems, enter the page number into the SWadvantage.com Search Bar.

EXAMPLE 8

Ashley is making pizzas. She has 7.75 pounds of cheese. Each pizza uses 0.75 pounds of cheese. What is the greatest number of pizzas Ashley can make?

READ Know: 7.75 lb of cheese, 0.75 lb per pizza
Need to Know: The number of pizzas that can be made

PLAN Divide the number of pounds of cheese by the amount used on each pizza.

SOLVE Move the decimal point two places to the right and divide.

You can stop dividing as soon as you know the digit in the ones place. You know that she can make 10 pizzas, and there will be some cheese left over.

$$\begin{array}{r} 10. \\ 0.75.\overline{)7.75.} \\ \underline{-7\,5} \\ 25 \end{array}$$

CHECK Mentally multiply 0.75 lb $\times$ 10 pizzas $=$ 7.5 lb for 10 pizzas. Since 7.5 is close to 7.75 and you know there was some cheese left over, 10 pizzas is a reasonable answer.

The greatest number of pizzas Ashley can make is 10.

EXAMPLE 9

Mrs. Dawson made 15 liters of spaghetti sauce. She pours the sauce into identical 0.47-L jars. There is no sauce left over. How many jars did she use?

READ Know: 15 L of sauce, 0.47 L jars
Need to Know: Number of jars needed

PLAN Divide the total amount of sauce by the amount each jar will hold.

SOLVE Move the decimal point two places to the right and divide.

You can stop dividing as soon as you know that the quotient is greater than 31. The quotient tells you that she will need an additional jar. 31 + 1 = 32 jars.

$$\begin{array}{r} 31. \\ 0.47.\overline{)15.00.} \\ \underline{-141} \\ 90 \\ \underline{-47} \\ 43 \end{array}$$

CHECK Round and multiply to check the answer. 32 jars $\times$ 0.5 L per jar $=$ 16 L. Since 16 L is close to 15 L, the answer is reasonable.

Mrs. Dawson used 32 jars.

EXAMPLE 10

Chantal is making a holder for a hanging plant. She needs four 12-foot pieces of cord and two 1.5-foot pieces of cord. She has 50 feet of cord. Is this enough to make the plant holder?

READ Know: Need four 12 foot-pieces, and two 1.5-foot pieces, has 50 feet
Need to Know: Does she have enough cord?

PLAN Find the total length of cord needed. Compare it to 50 feet.

SOLVE Perform the operations in the plan.

Find the total length of the 12-ft pieces.

$$\begin{array}{r} 12\text{ ft} \\ \times 4 \\ \hline 48\text{ ft} \end{array}$$

Find the total length of the 1.5-ft pieces.

$$\begin{array}{r} 1.5\text{ ft} \\ \times 2 \\ \hline 3.0\text{ ft} \end{array}$$

Find the total amount needed.

$$\begin{array}{r} \overset{1}{4}8\text{ ft} \\ +\ 3\text{ ft} \\ \hline 51\text{ ft} \end{array}$$

Compare the amounts. 50 ft < 51 ft

The amount of cord Chantal has is less than the amount she needs.

CHECK Rounding is not the best choice for checking the answer because you need to know a precise length. Use a calculator to check your multiplication. Or, mentally add the six individual lengths: 12 + 12 + 12 + 12 + 1.5 + 1.5.

Since 50 ft is less than 51 ft, Chantal does not have enough cord.

EXAMPLE 11

Jason purchased a can of corn for $0.79, a can of beans for $0.65, a can of tomato juice for $1.99, and a red pepper for $1.49. How much money did he spend in all?

READ Know: Price of four items: $0.79, $0.65, $1.99, and $1.49
Need to Know: Total price of the items

PLAN Add the prices of the items.

SOLVE Add. Regroup as needed.

$$\begin{array}{r} \$\overset{2}{0}.\overset{3}{7}9 \\ 0.65 \\ 1.99 \\ +\ 1.49 \\ \hline \$4.92 \end{array}$$

Jason spent $4.92 in all.

CHECK Round each price to the nearest dollar or half dollar and mentally add.

$$\begin{array}{r} 1.00 \\ 0.50 \\ 2.00 \\ +\ 1.50 \\ \hline 5.00 \end{array}$$

$5.00 is close to $4.92, so the answer is reasonable.

Solving Decimal Word Problems

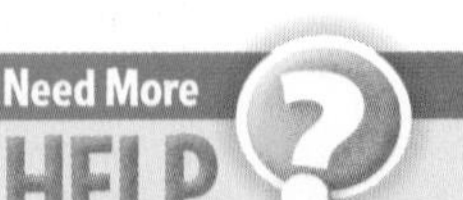

To solve this problem, use the problem solving strategy *Write a Number Sentence* on page 450.

SEARCH

To see step-by-step videos of these problems, enter the page number into the SWadvantage.com Search Bar.

EXAMPLE 12

Daniel has \$2.15 in coins: nickels, dimes, and quarters. He has four nickels. He has three times as many dimes as nickels. If the rest of the coins are quarters, how many dimes and quarters does he have?

READ Know: \$2.15 in coins, 4 are nickels, 3 × as many dimes as nickels, rest are quarters
Need to Know: The number of dimes and quarters

PLAN AND SOLVE This problem requires several steps.

- Think: You know there are 4 nickels and there are 3 times as many dimes. Write a number sentence to find the number of dimes.

  number of nickels × 3 = number of dimes
  4 nickels × 3 = 12 dimes

- Find the amount of money that is nickels and the amount of money that is dimes.

  4 nickels × \$0.05 per nickel = \$0.20 in nickels
  12 dimes × \$.10 per dime = \$1.20 in dimes

- You need to know how much of the money is in quarters. Use the information you were given and the information you found above to write a number sentence that represents the amount of money that is quarters.

total amount of money − (*money in nickels* + *money in dimes*) = *money in quarters*

\$2.15 − (\$0.20 + \$1.20) = ?
\$2.15 − \$1.40 = \$0.75 in quarters

- Divide to find the number of quarters.

  \$0.75 in quarters ÷ \$0.25 per quarter = 3 quarters

CHECK Write a number sentence to check your answer. If the answer is correct, the value of the number sentence will be \$2.15.

value of nickels + *value of dimes* + *value of quarters* $\stackrel{?}{=}$ \$2.15

\$0.20 + \$1.20 + \$0.75 = \$2.15 ✔

Daniel has 12 dimes and 3 quarters.

EXAMPLE 13

Casey bought a CD for $12.95. The sales tax rate is $0.08 per dollar. What was the cost of the CD including the sales tax?

READ Know: CD cost $12.95; sales tax is $0.08 on the dollar
Need to Know: Total cost of CD

PLAN There are two ways to solve this problem.

METHOD 1

Multiply the price of the CD by 0.08 to find the tax. Then add the tax to the cost of the CD.

METHOD 2

A sales tax is a *percent of increase.* You pay 100% of the cost of the item plus some percent sales tax. In this problem the total cost is:

100% + 0.08% = 1.08%

Multiply the price of the CD by 1.08%, or 1.08.

SOLVE

METHOD 1

$12.95	cost of CD
× 0.08	tax per dollar
$1.036	tax on CD

Round $1.036 to $1.04.

$12.95	cost of CD
+ 1.04	tax
$13.99	total cost of CD

METHOD 2

$12.95	pretax cost of CD
× 1.08	total cost of CD
10360	
00000	
+ 1295	
$13.9860	

Round $13.9860 to $13.99.

CHECK Round to check.

The price of the CD is about $13.00. The tax is close to $0.10 on each dollar.

$13.00 × $0.10 = $1.30

$13.00 + $1.30 = $14.30

$13.99 is close to but less than $14.30. However, you rounded 0.08 up to 0.10, so the answer is reasonable.

The total cost of the CD including the sales tax was $13.99.

Need More HELP

For help with percents of increase, go to *Percent Increase and Decrease* on page 394.

For help with the relationship between decimals and percents, go to *Decimals, Fractions, and Percent* on page 272.

Number Theory

What Came Before?

- Operations with whole numbers and decimals
- Comparing and ordering whole numbers and decimals

What's This About?

- Different types of numbers—fractions, decimals, and percents
- Multiples, factors, and divisibility of numbers
- Exponents

Practical Apps

- Security experts use very large prime numbers to encrypt (transfer) electronic information into a form that only people with valid security codes can access.
- The inventor of bar codes used number theory to develop the "final check" digit that ensures that the code was scanned and read correctly.

just for FUN!

Stay away from the square root of 2.

Q: Why?

A: It's a very irrational number!

CONTENTS UPLOAD DOWNLOAD

Numbers and Operations

You can find more practice problems online by visiting:
www.SWadvantage.com

Sometimes the *set of rational numbers* is defined as numbers that can be expressed as the *ratio* of two integers.

Sets of Numbers

A **set** is a collection of objects. You can represent sets in different ways. Here are two examples that name the same set:

- the set of all the colors on a traffic light
- $C = \{\text{red, yellow, green}\}$

Mathematicians work with the following sets of numbers.

Set	Symbol	Examples
Real numbers All of the numbers that can be represented by a point on a number line. This set contains the set of rational numbers and the set of irrational numbers.	*R*	$0, 5, -8, \frac{3}{7}, \pi, \sqrt{2},$ 1.0100100010001,... $-\sqrt{137}$
Rational numbers Numbers that can be written as the quotient of two integers, $\frac{n}{d}$, where $d \neq 0$.	*Q*	$0, 3, \frac{1}{2}, \frac{3}{4}, 3.2, -\frac{7}{8}, -57,$ $-0.0001, -6\frac{2}{3}, 1{,}000{,}0001$
Integers Whole numbers and their opposites.	*Z*	$\ldots -3, -2, -1, 0, 1, 2, 3, \ldots$
Whole numbers The set of natural numbers and 0 (the number of members in an empty set).	*W*	$0, 1, 2, 3, \ldots$
Natural numbers (counting numbers): The numbers with which we count. The number of members in a nonempty set.	*N*	$1, 2, 3, \ldots$
Irrational numbers Numbers that cannot be written as the quotient of two integers. Their decimal form is nonrepeating and nonterminating.	No symbol	$\sqrt{2}, \pi$ (3.14159...), $\sqrt{7},$ 2.718281828...

The Venn diagram shows the relationships among these sets of numbers. Each set of numbers contains all of the sets below it. For example, the set of integers contains the set of whole numbers and the set of natural numbers.

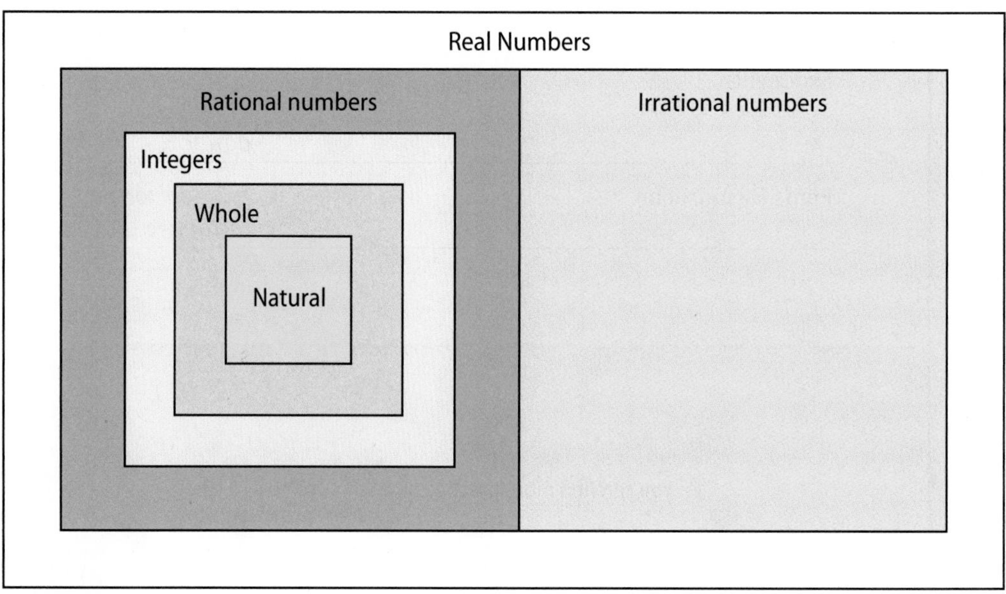

Use the table and the Venn diagram on the facing page to identify the sets to which each number belongs.

EXAMPLE 1

To which sets of numbers does $\frac{1}{5}$ belong?

The number $\frac{1}{5}$ belongs to the following sets.

Set	**Why does it belong?**
Rational numbers	The number $\frac{1}{5}$ is the quotient of two integers. $(1 \div 5 = 0.2)$
Real numbers	The set of real numbers contains the set of rational numbers.

EXAMPLE 2

To which sets of numbers does 0.4 belong?

The number 0.4 belongs to the following sets.

Set	**Why does it belong?**
Rational numbers	$0.4 = \frac{4}{10}$, so it is the quotient of two integers.
Real numbers	The set of real numbers contains the set of rational numbers.

EXAMPLE 3

To which sets of numbers does 0 belong?

The number 0 belongs to the following sets.

Set	**Why does it belong?**
Whole numbers	The set of whole numbers contains the natural numbers and 0.
Integers	The set of integers contains the set of whole numbers and their opposites, and zero.
Rational numbers	Zero can be written as the ratio of two integers: $\frac{0}{5}$
Real numbers	The set of real numbers contains the set of rational numbers.

SEARCH

To see step-by-step videos of these problems, enter the page number into the SWadvantage.com Search Bar.

Rational Numbers: Terminating and Repeating Decimals

Decimals that terminate or repeat are rational numbers.

A **terminating decimal** has a finite, or limited, number of decimal places. For example, $\frac{1}{4} = 0.25$.

A **repeating decimal** repeats infinitely the same digits or set of digits. For example, $\frac{7}{9} = 0.777\ldots = 0.\overline{7}$, and $\frac{8}{11} = 0.727272\ldots = 0.\overline{72}$

SEARCH

To see step-by-step videos of these problems, enter the page number into the SWadvantage.com Search Bar.

EXAMPLE 4

Classify the decimal form of $\frac{3}{4}$ as terminating or repeating.

Express the fraction in decimal form by dividing the numerator by the denominator.

$$\begin{array}{r} 0.75 \\ 4\overline{)3.00} \\ \underline{28} \\ 20 \\ \underline{20} \\ 0 \end{array}$$

There is no remainder.

The decimal form of $\frac{3}{4}$ is a terminating decimal.

EXAMPLE 5

Classify the decimal form of $\frac{2}{11}$ as terminating or repeating.

Express the fraction in decimal form by dividing the numerator by the denominator.

$$\begin{array}{r} 0.1818 \\ 11\overline{)2.0000} \\ \underline{11} \\ 90 \\ \underline{88} \\ 20 \\ \underline{11} \\ 90 \\ \underline{88} \\ 2 \end{array}$$

The quotient repeats the digits 1 and 8.

The decimal form of $\frac{2}{11}$ is a repeating decimal.

Rational and Irrational Numbers

EXAMPLE 6

Classify $\frac{8}{9}$ as rational or irrational.

The number $\frac{8}{9}$ is the quotient of two integers.

$\frac{8}{9}$ is a rational number.

EXAMPLE 7

Classify $\sqrt{25}$ as rational or irrational.

Since $5 \times 5 = 25$, $\sqrt{25} = 5$.

The number 5 can be written as the quotient of two integers: $\frac{5}{1}$

$\sqrt{25}$ is a rational number.

EXAMPLE 8

Classify $0.3\overline{18}$ as rational or irrational.

The overbar means that the digits 18 repeat.

The number $0.3\overline{18}$ can be written as 0.3181818...

$0.3\overline{18}$ is a rational number.

EXAMPLE 9

Classify π (3.14159...) as rational or irrational.

π is a nonterminating, nonrepeating decimal.

π is an irrational number.

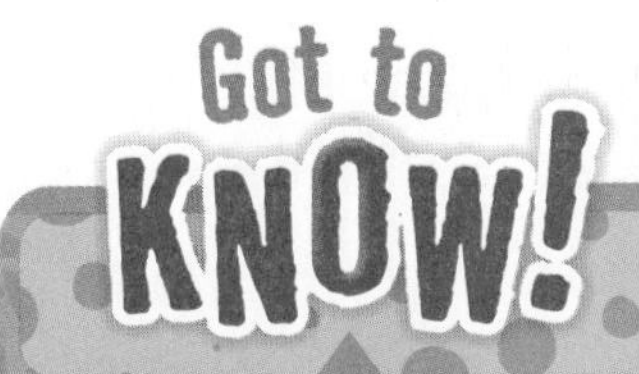

Rational and Irrational Numbers

A **rational number** can be written as a quotient of two integers. Terminating decimals and repeating decimals are rational numbers.

An **irrational number** cannot be written as a quotient of two integers. Nonterminating, nonrepeating decimals are irrational numbers.

Relating Fractions and Decimals

Sometimes you need to express a fraction as a decimal. At other times, you need to express a decimal as a fraction. When you *express* something, you say or write it in a certain way.

You can use a model to help you relate fractions and decimals.

EXAMPLE 1

Express $\frac{1}{2}$ as a decimal.

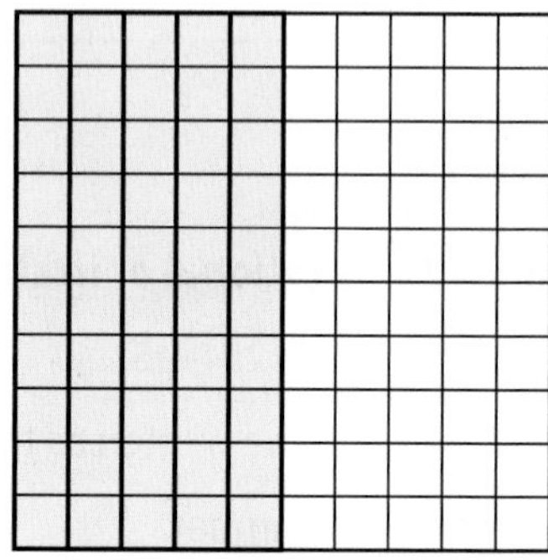

Look at the model.

The model shows 50 out of 100 small squares shaded, which is the same as 5 out of 10 columns shaded.

Write a 5 in the tenths place: 0.5

$\frac{1}{2} = 0.5$

EXAMPLE 2

Express $\frac{6}{10}$ as a decimal.

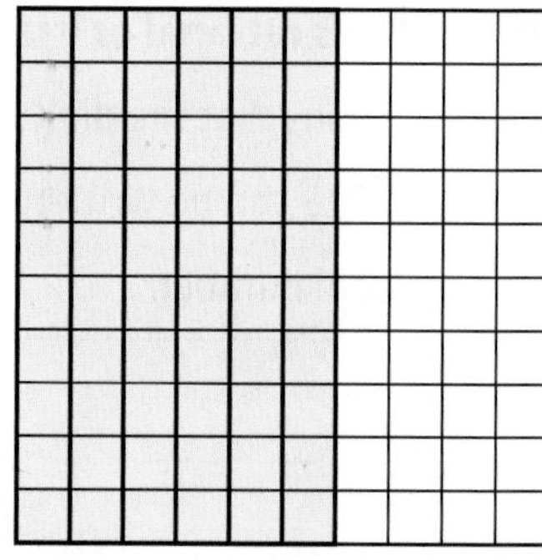

Use a model.

The model shows 60 out of 100 small squares shaded, which is the same as 6 out of 10 columns shaded.

Write a 6 in the tenths place.

$\frac{6}{10} = 0.6$

Need More HELP

For help with percents, go to page 277 and to *Percent* starting on p. 378.

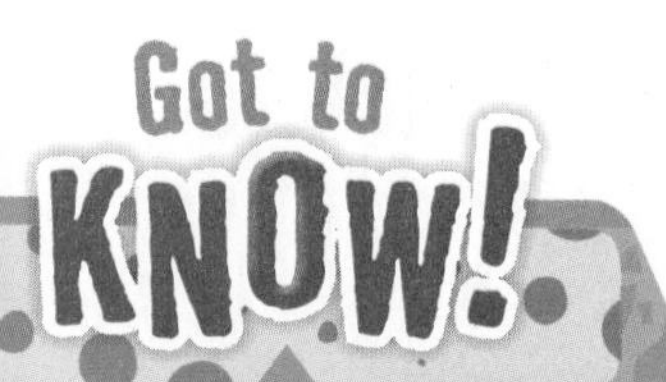

Common Equivalent Fractions, Decimals, and Percents

Fraction	$\frac{1}{100}$	$\frac{1}{10}$	$\frac{1}{4}$	$\frac{1}{2}$	$\frac{3}{4}$	$\frac{100}{100}$
Decimal	0.01	0.1	0.25	0.5	0.75	1
Percent	1%	10%	25%	50%	75%	100%

EXAMPLE 3

Express 0.23 as a fraction.

Use a model.

The model shows 23 out of 100 small squares shaded.

Use 100 as the denominator.

Use 23 as the numerator.

$0.23 = \frac{23}{100}$

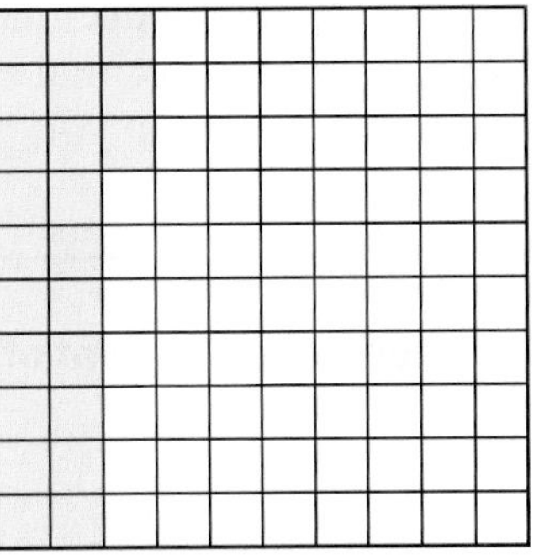

SEARCH

To see step-by-step videos of these problems, enter the page number into the SWadvantage.com Search Bar.

EXAMPLE 4

Write 0.9 as a fraction in simplest form.

Use a model.

The model shows 90 out of 100 small squares shaded.

Use 90 as the numerator.

Use 100 as the denominator.

Then simplify the fraction.

$\frac{90}{100} = \frac{9}{10}$

$0.9 = \frac{9}{10}$

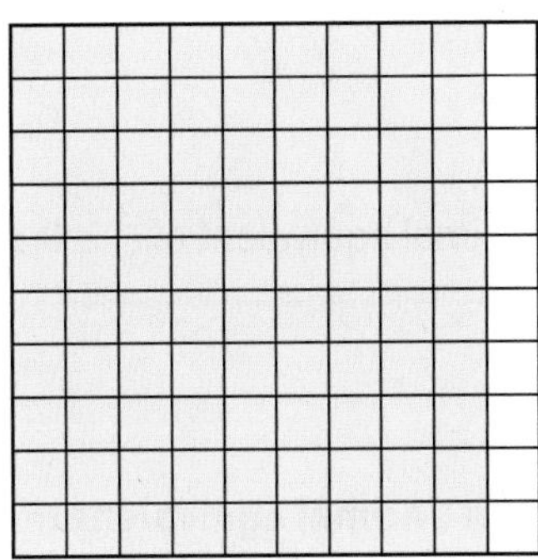

Need More HELP

For help with simplifying fractions, go to *Equivalent Fractions* on page 308.

EXAMPLE 5

Write 0.75 as a fraction in simplest form.

Use a model.

The model shows 75 out of 100 small squares shaded.

Use 75 as the numerator.

Use 100 as the denominator.

Simplify the fraction.

$\frac{75}{100} = \frac{75 \div 25}{100 \div 25} = \frac{3}{4}$

$0.75 = \frac{3}{4}$

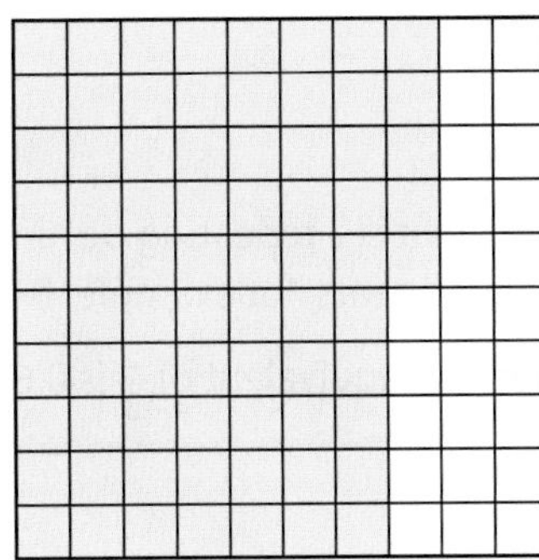

Decimal Equivalents of Fractions

When a fraction and a decimal represent the same quantity, they are **equivalent** in value. To find the decimal equivalent of a fraction, divide the numerator of the fraction by the denominator.

Need More HELP

For help with division, go to *Dividing Whole Numbers* in *Foundations of Mathematics* on page 100.

EXAMPLE 6

Find the decimal equivalent of $\frac{3}{8}$.

Divide 8 into 3.

$$\begin{array}{r} 0.375 \\ 8\overline{)3.000} \\ \underline{24} \\ 60 \\ \underline{56} \\ 40 \\ \underline{40} \\ 0 \end{array}$$

The decimal equivalent of $\frac{3}{8}$ is 0.375.

Need More HELP

For help with repeating decimals, go to page 270.

EXAMPLE 7

Find the decimal equivalent of $\frac{2}{3}$.

Divide 3 into 2.

$$\begin{array}{r} 0.666 \\ 3\overline{)2.000} \\ \underline{18} \\ 20 \\ \underline{18} \\ 20 \\ \underline{18} \\ 2 \end{array}$$

The quotient is a repeating decimal. You can write this decimal by inserting a line above the digit that repeats, for example: $0.\overline{6}$.

The decimal equivalent of $\frac{2}{3}$ is $0.\overline{6}$.

Fraction Equivalents of Decimals

To express a nonrepeating decimal as a fraction:

- Identify the least decimal place value in the number.
- Use this place value as the denominator of the fraction.
- Write the fraction in simplest form.

To express a repeating decimal as a fraction:

- Use the method described in Example 9.

EXAMPLE 8

Write 0.12 as a fraction.

STEP 1 The least place value is hundredths. 0.12

STEP 2 Use 12 as the numerator and 100 as the denominator. $\frac{12}{100}$

STEP 3 Simplify. $\frac{12 \div 4}{100 \div 4} = \frac{3}{25}$

$0.12 = \frac{3}{25}$

Need More HELP

For help with simplifying fractions, go to *Equivalent Fractions* on page 308.

EXAMPLE 9

Write 0.312312312... as a fraction.

STEP 1 Set the decimal number equal to n.

$n = 0.312312312...$

STEP 2 Multiply n and the decimal number by a power of 10 equal to the number of repeating digits. In this case three digits repeat—312. Multiply by 10^3 or 1,000.

$1{,}000 \times n = 1{,}000 \times 0.312312312$

$1{,}000n = 312.312312$

STEP 3 Remove the repeating digits by subtracting the equation in Step 1 from the equation in Step 2.

$$\begin{array}{rl} 1{,}000n &= 312.312312312... \\ - \quad n &= 000.312312312... \\ \hline 999n &= 312 \end{array}$$

STEP 4 Find the value of n by dividing both sides of the equation by 999.

$$\frac{\cancel{999}n}{\cancel{999}} = \frac{312}{999}$$

$$n = \frac{312 \div 3}{999 \div 3} = \frac{104}{333}$$

$0.312312312... = \frac{104}{333}$

SEARCH

To see step-by-step videos of these problems, enter the page number into the SWadvantage.com Search Bar.

Writing Mixed Numbers

You can use what you know about fraction and decimal equivalents to change the form of a mixed number.

EXAMPLE 10

Write $3\frac{4}{5}$ as a mixed decimal number.

Whole number part: 3.0

Fractional part: Express the fraction as an equivalent decimal.

METHOD 1

To express the fraction as a decimal, divide 4 by 5.

$$5\overline{)4.0} = 0.8$$
$$\begin{array}{r} 4.0 \\ \underline{40} \\ 0 \end{array}$$

METHOD 2

Express $\frac{4}{5}$ as an equivalent fraction with a denominator of 10.

$$\frac{4 \times 2}{5 \times 2} = \frac{8}{10}$$

Express the fraction as 0.8.

$$3\frac{4}{5} = 3.8$$

SEARCH

To see step-by-step videos of these problems, enter the page number into the SWadvantage.com Search Bar.

EXAMPLE 11

Write 7.425 as a mixed number.

Whole number part: 7

Decimal part: Express the decimal as an equivalent fraction.

Identify the least decimal place value. The least decimal place is the thousandths. $0.42\underline{5}$

Use 1,000 as the denominator. $\frac{425}{1{,}000}$

Express the fraction in simplest form. $\frac{425 \div 25}{1{,}000 \div 25} = \frac{17}{40}$

$$7.425 = 7\frac{17}{40}$$

Need More HELP

Make sure you find the correct decimal place. Remember that the places to the right of the decimal point are, in order:

- tenths
- hundredths
- thousandths
- ten-thousandths

Percents

A **percent** is a ratio of some quantity to 100. Percents are usually written with a percent sign (%) instead of as a fraction. You can express a percent as an equivalent fraction or decimal.

Need More HELP

For help with percents, go to *Meaning of Percents* on page 380.

EXAMPLE 12

Write 37% as a fraction.

Write the percent as a fraction with a denominator of 100. $37\% = \frac{37}{100}$

$37\% = \frac{37}{100}$

EXAMPLE 13

Write 40% as a fraction in simplest form.

Write the percent as a fraction with a denominator of 100. $40\% = \frac{40}{100} = \frac{40 \div 10}{100 \div 10} = \frac{4}{10}$

$40\% = \frac{4}{10}$

EXAMPLE 14

Write 0.75 as a percent.

Write the decimal as a fraction. $0.75 = \frac{75}{100}$

Express the fraction as a percent. $\frac{75}{100} = 75\%$

$0.75 = 75\%$

EXAMPLE 15

Write $\frac{1}{2}$ as a percent.

Multiply the numerator and denominator by 50 so that the denominator is equal to 100. $\frac{1 \times 50}{2 \times 50} = \frac{50}{100}$

Write the fraction as a percent. $\frac{50}{100} = 50\%$

$\frac{1}{2} = 50\%$

Graphing Rational Numbers on a Number Line

Every rational number can be represented on a number line. Before you graph a number on a number line, be certain you understand the meaning of the intervals (shown by tick marks) between the labeled numbers.

Need More HELP

For help with rational numbers, go to *Rational Numbers and Number Sets* on page 268.

EXAMPLE 1

Graph 5.2 on a number line.

The intervals between the whole numbers are divided into tenths, and each tick mark represents 1 tenth.

Find 5 on the number line.

Move 2 tick marks to the right.

Place a point at 5.2.

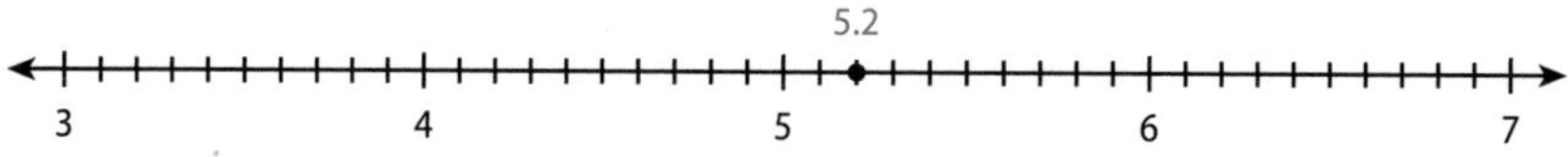

EXAMPLE 2

Graph $1\frac{1}{2}$ on a number line.

The intervals between the whole numbers are divided into tenths, and each tick mark represents 1 tenth.

Write $1\frac{1}{2}$ in decimal form. $1\frac{1}{2} = 1.5$

Find 1 on the number line.

Move 5 tick marks to the right.

Place a point at 1.5.

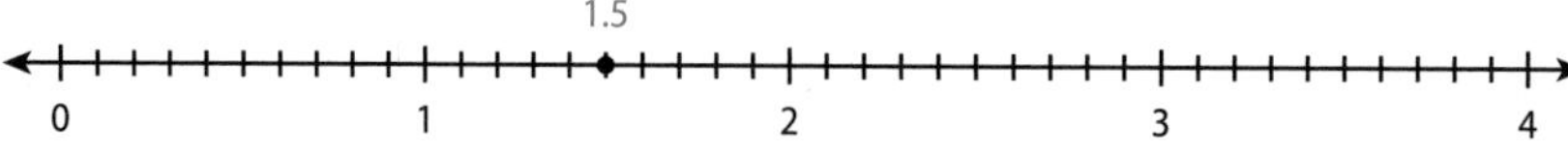

Got to KNOW!

Estimating the Position of a Number on a Number Line

1. Identify the intervals the given number is between.
2. Name the halfway point between the intervals.
3. Decide whether the given number comes before the halfway point or after the halfway point.
4. Based on this information, estimate the position of the number.

Estimating to Graph Rational Numbers

Sometimes a number line does not have intervals that are precise enough to graph a number exactly. In this case, you must estimate the position of the number.

EXAMPLE 3

Graph 4.86 on a number line.

Each tick mark between the whole numbers represents 1 tenth, but the decimal is to the hundredths place.

Think: $4.8 < 4.86 < 4.9$

Locate 4.8 and 4.9 on the number line.

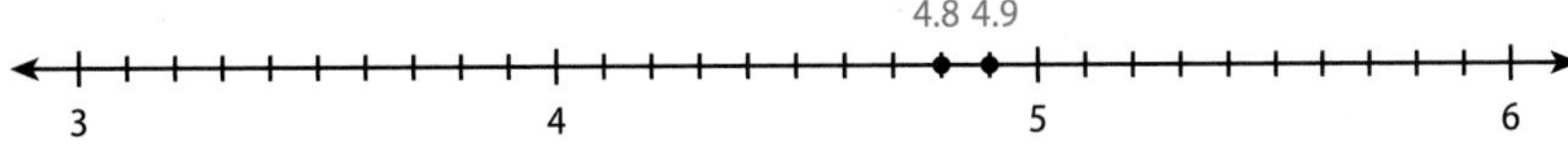

Think: 4.85 is halfway between 4.8 and 4.9, so 4.86 is a *little more* than halfway between 4.8 and 4.9.

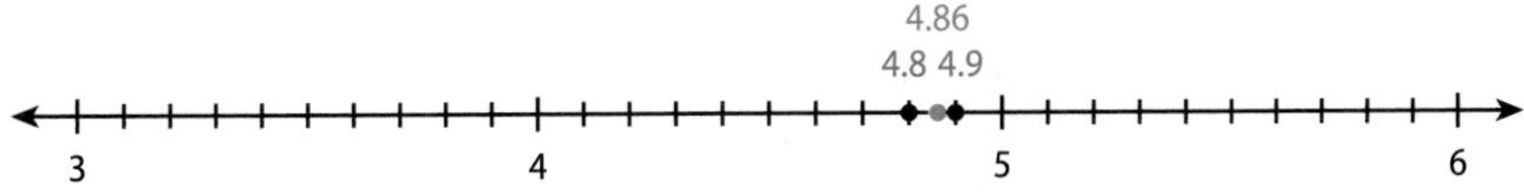

SEARCH

To see step-by-step videos of these problems, enter the page number into the SWadvantage.com Search Bar.

You may need to graph a repeating decimal on a number line. You must estimate its position on the number line.

Need More HELP

Remember, a repeating decimal is a rational number that repeats infinitely the same decimal digits or set of digits.

EXAMPLE 4

Graph $5\frac{1}{3}$ on a number line.

Write $5\frac{1}{3}$ in decimal form. $5\frac{1}{3} = \frac{16}{3} = 16 \div 3 = 5.333...$

Think: $5.3 < 5.\overline{3} < 5.4$

Locate 5.3 and 5.4 on the number line.

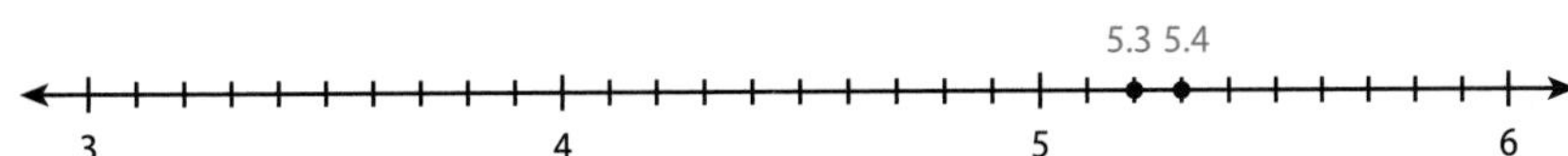

Think: 5.35 is halfway between 5.3 and 5.4, so $5.\overline{3}$ is a *little less* than halfway between 5.3 and 5.4.

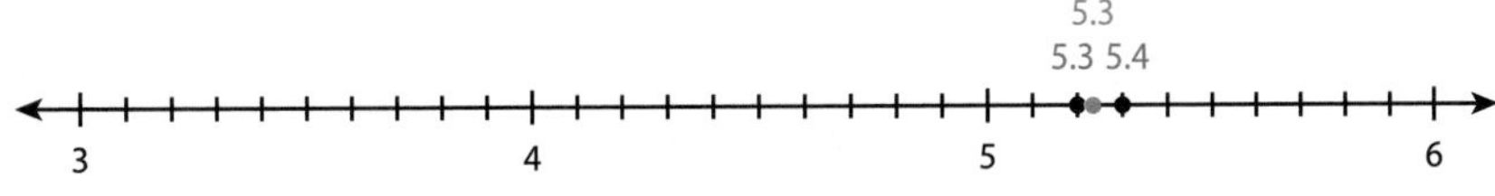

Comparing and Ordering Rational Numbers

Comparing Rational Numbers

You can use a number line to compare a set of rational numbers. Remember, as you move from left to right along the number line the numbers increase in value. When you compare numbers, use the comparison symbols $<$, $=$, and $>$.

For help with comparing and ordering decimals, go to *Comparing and Ordering Decimals* on page 222.

EXAMPLE 1

Graph the numbers 11 and 11.25 on a number line. Use symbols to compare them.

STEP 1 Graph the numbers. 11.25 is halfway between 11.2 and 11.3.

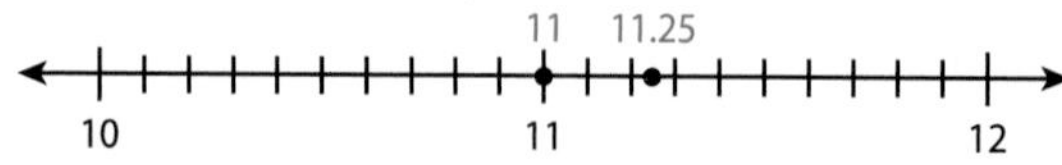

STEP 2 Compare. 11.25 is to the right of 11, so it has a greater value.

$11.25 > 11$ and $11 < 11.25$

Watch Out !

The decimals 1.6 and $1.\overline{6}$ are not the same number. The number 1.6 is a terminating decimal. The number $1.\overline{6}$ is a repeating decimal that means 1.666... .

EXAMPLE 2

Graph the numbers $1.\overline{6}$ and 1.6 on a number line. Use symbols to compare them.

STEP 1 Graph the numbers.

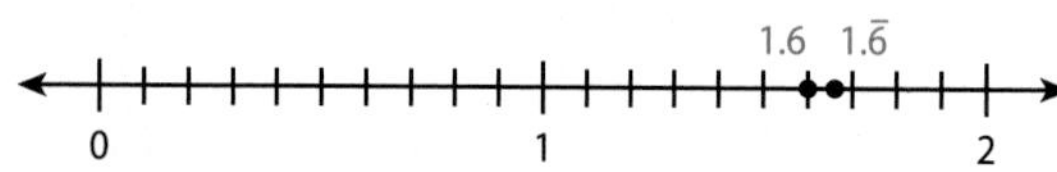

STEP 2 Compare. $1.\overline{6}$ is to the right of 1.6 on the number line, so it has a greater value.

$1.\overline{6} > 1.6$ and $1.6 < 1.\overline{6}$

SEARCH

To see step-by-step videos of these problems, enter the page number into the SWadvantage.com Search Bar.

EXAMPLE 3

Use $<$, $>$, or $=$ to compare 0.65 and $\frac{13}{20}$.

Express $\frac{13}{20}$ as a decimal.

```
      0.65
20)13.00
   -12 0
     1 00
    -1 00
        0
```

$0.65 = \frac{13}{20}$

EXAMPLE 4

Use <, >, or = to compare $2\frac{3}{4}$ and 2.7.

For help with writing fractions as decimals, go to *Decimals, Fractions, and Percents* on page 272.

METHOD 1

Use a number line. It is usually easier to graph numbers if they are written in decimal form.

STEP 1 Express $2\frac{3}{4}$ as a decimal. $2\frac{3}{4} = 2.75$

STEP 2 Graph 2.75 and 2.7 on a number line.

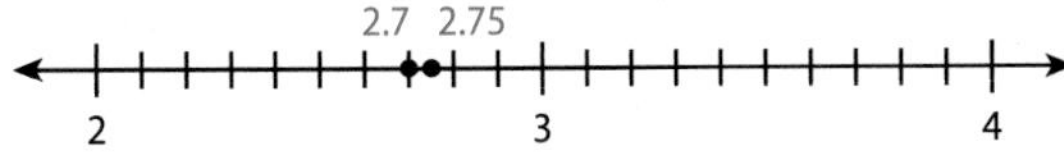

STEP 3 Compare. 2.75 is to the right of 2.7 on the number line, so it has the greater value.

$2\frac{3}{4} > 2.7$ and $2.7 < 2\frac{3}{4}$

METHOD 2

Solve a simpler problem by relating the numbers to money.

Think: $2\frac{3}{4}$ is two dollars plus three-fourths of a dollar.

Three-fourths of a dollar is \$0.75, so, $2\frac{3}{4}$ dollars is \$2.75.

Think: 2.7 is two dollars and seventy cents, or \$2.70.

\$2.75 > \$2.70, so $2\frac{3}{4} > 2.7$.

Comparing Rational Numbers

To compare most numbers, the numbers need to be in the same form.

For example, to compare 0.65 and $\frac{13}{20}$, express both numbers as a fraction or as a decimal.

Express repeating decimals with as many decimal digits as necessary.

For example, $0.\overline{6} = 0.66$ or 0.666 or 0.6666, and so on.

Use the comparison symbols to compare two or more numbers.

> means *greater than* = means *is equal to* < means *less than*

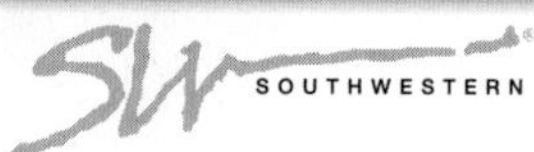

Ordering Rational Numbers

You can use a number line to order rational numbers from least to greatest or greatest to least.

EXAMPLE 5

Order from least to greatest on a number line: 1.5, $\frac{3}{5}$, 0.55

STEP 1 Express $\frac{3}{5}$ as a decimal.

$$\frac{3 \times 2}{5 \times 2} = \frac{6}{10} = 0.6$$

STEP 2 Graph the numbers on a number line.

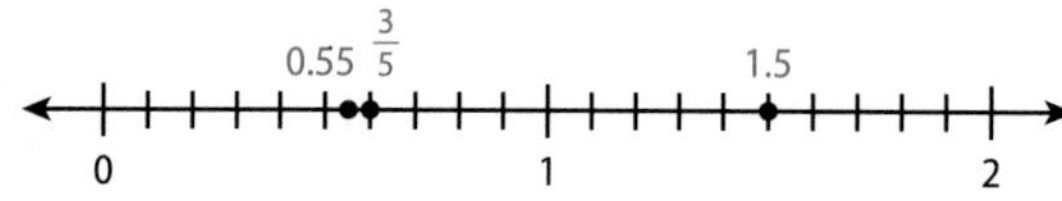

As you move from left to right along the number line, the numbers are ordered least to greatest.

The numbers ordered from least to greatest are: 0.55, $\frac{3}{5}$, 1.5

Need More HELP

For help with converting fractions to decimals, go to *Decimals, Fractions, and Percents* on page 272.

EXAMPLE 6

Order from least to greatest on a number line: $2\frac{1}{3}$, $\frac{14}{5}$, 2.7

STEP 1 Express $2\frac{1}{3}$ and $\frac{14}{5}$ as decimals.

$$2\frac{1}{3} = 2.\overline{3}$$

$$\frac{14}{5} = 14 \div 5 = 2.8$$

STEP 2 Graph the numbers on a number line.

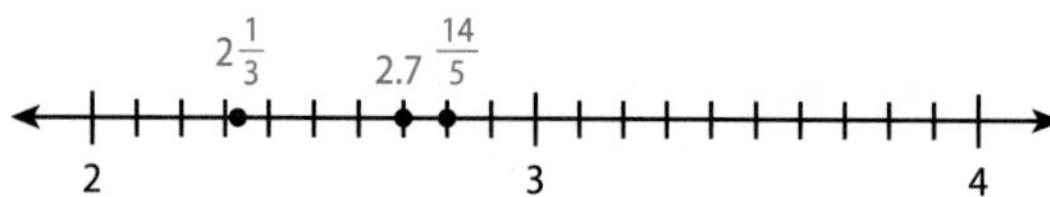

The numbers ordered from least to greatest are: $2\frac{1}{3}$, 2.7, $\frac{14}{5}$

You can also use place value to compare and order rational numbers. This method is useful when the numbers have several decimal places and are close in value.

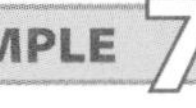

EXAMPLE 7

Use place value to order from greatest to least: $\frac{3}{16}, \frac{2}{9}, \frac{1}{6}$, 0.21

STEP 1 Write the fractions as decimals.

$\frac{3}{16} = 0.1875$

$\frac{2}{9} = 0.\overline{2}$

$\frac{1}{6} = 0.1\overline{6}$

STEP 2 Write the decimal numbers in a column and compare the digits from left to right.

0.1875

0.222...

0.1666...

0.21

STEP 3 Compare: $0.\underline{2}22$ and $0.\underline{2}1$

There is a 2 in the tenths place.

Compare the hundredths place.

Since $2 > 1$, then $0.2\underline{2}2... > 0.2\underline{1}$.

Compare: $0.\underline{1}875$ and $0.\underline{1}66$

There is a 1 in the tenths place.

Compare the hundredths place.

Since $8 > 6$, then $0.1\underline{8}75 > 0.1\underline{6}66...$.

STEP 4 Order the numbers from greatest to least.

$0.222... > 0.21 > 0.1875 > 0.1666...$

STEP 5 Substitute the original number into the ordered list.

$\frac{2}{9} > 0.21 > \frac{3}{16} > \frac{1}{6}$

The numbers ordered from greatest to least are: $\frac{2}{9}$, 0.21, $\frac{3}{16}$, $\frac{1}{6}$

SEARCH

To see step-by-step videos of these problems, enter the page number into the SWadvantage.com Search Bar.

EXAMPLE 8

The table shows the gold medal scores for four women's gymnastics events at the Summer Olympic Games. Order the scores from greatest to least.

Event	Score
Floor Exercise	$9\frac{3}{4}$
Vault	9.656
Balance Beam	9.787
Uneven Bars	9.687

STEP 1 Express $9\frac{3}{4}$ as a decimal.

$9\frac{3}{4} = 9.75$

STEP 2 Think: $7 > 6$ so 9.75 and 9.787 are the two greatest numbers.

Think: $8 > 5$, so $9.7\underline{8}7 > 9.7\underline{5}$ and $9.6\underline{8}7 > 9.6\underline{5}6$

The scores ordered from greatest to least are: 9.787, $9\frac{3}{4}$, 9.687, 9.656

Prime and Composite Numbers

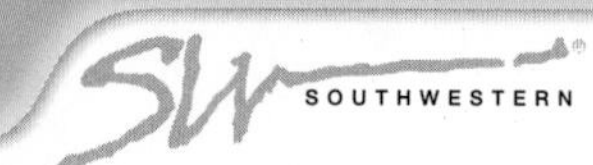

For help with factors, go to *Factors* on pages 286–287.

Identifying Prime and Composite Numbers

Every counting number can be classified as a *prime number* or a *composite number*. A **prime number** has *exactly* two different factors, 1 and the number itself. A **composite number** has more than two factors.

EXAMPLE 1

Classify 6 as a prime or a composite number.

Identify the factors of 6.

$1 \times 6 = 6 \qquad 6 \times 1 = 6$

$2 \times 3 = 6 \qquad 3 \times 2 = 6$

The factors of 6 are: 1, 2, 3, and 6.

Since 6 has more than two factors, 6 is a composite number.

The Greek mathematician Eratosthenes developed a method for finding prime numbers. Follow these steps to create Eratosthenes' Sieve for finding all of the prime numbers in 1–100.

- Write the whole numbers from 1 to 100. Since 1 is neither prime nor composite, cross it out.
- Circle 2. Then cross out every following even number, which is every number divisible by 2.
- Circle 3. Then cross out every following third number, which is every number divisible by 3.
- Circle 5. Then cross out every fifth number, which is every number divisible by 5.
- Continue in this way until every number that is divisible is crossed out and every prime number is circled.

1	**2**	**3**	4	**5**	6	**7**	8	9	10
11	12	**13**	14	15	16	**17**	18	**19**	20
21	22	**23**	24	25	26	27	28	**29**	30
31	32	33	34	35	36	**37**	38	39	40
41	42	**43**	44	45	46	**47**	48	49	50
51	52	**53**	54	55	56	57	58	**59**	60
61	62	63	64	65	66	**67**	68	69	70
71	72	**73**	74	75	76	77	78	**79**	80
81	82	**83**	84	85	86	87	88	**89**	90
91	92	93	94	95	96	**97**	98	99	100

You can use Eratosthenes' Sieve to identify prime and composite numbers. If you make your own copy, notice that you can use skip-counting to count by 2s, 3s, 5s, and so on.

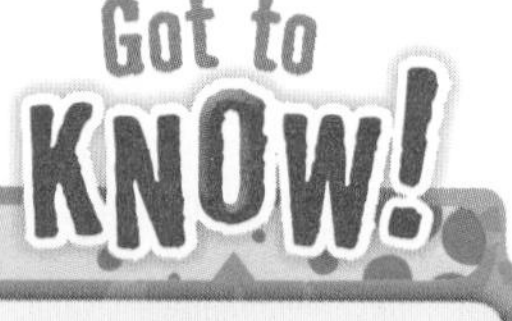

Prime and Composite Numbers

A **prime number** has *exactly* two factors, 1 and itself.

A **composite number** has more than two factors.

EXAMPLE 2

a. Classify 36 as a prime or a composite number.

Identify the factors of 36.

$1 \times 36 = 36$ $2 \times 18 = 36$
$3 \times 12 = 36$ $4 \times 9 = 36$

36 has eight factors, 1, 2, 3, 4, 9, 12, 18, and 36.

36 is a composite number.

b. Classify 53 as a prime or a composite number.

Identify the factors of 53.

$1 \times 53 = 53$

Since 53 has exactly two factors, 1 and itself, 53 is a prime number.

c. Classify 27 as a prime or a composite number.

Identify the factors of 27.

$1 \times 27 = 27$ $3 \times 9 = 27$

Since 27 has four factors, 1, 3, 9, and 27, 27 is a composite number.

Try It This Way

Use counters to represent a number. Start with the counters in one group. This represents the number itself $\times$ 1. If you can group the counters into more than one group, with an equal number of counters in each group, the number is a composite number.

EXAMPLE 3

Use Eratosthenes' Sieve to list the prime numbers between 1 and 100.

The prime numbers between 1 and 100 are:
2, 3, 5, 7, 11, 13, 17, 19, 23, 29, 31, 37, 41, 43, 47,
53, 59, 61, 67, 71, 73, 79, 83, 89, 97.

EXAMPLE 4

Jerome cannot remember the last number in the combination for his lock. He knows the number is between 30 and 50 and is prime. He also knows the sum of the digits of the number is 11. What is the last number of the combination?

Use logical reasoning and Eratosthenes' Sieve to solve the problem.

STEP 1 List the prime numbers between 30 and 50.
31, 37, 41, 43, 47

STEP 2 Find the number whose digits have a sum of 11.
31: $3 + 1 = \not{4}$ 37: $3 + 7 = \not{10}$ 41: $4 + 1 = \not{5}$
43: $4 + 3 = \not{7}$ 47: $4 + 7 = 11$
The last number in the combination is 47.

SEARCH

To see step-by-step videos of these problems, enter the page number into the SWadvantage.com Search Bar.

Factors

What Is a Factor?

In multiplication, a **factor** is a number that is multiplied by another number to find a product. You can also think of a *factor* as a whole number that divides evenly into another whole number.

What are the factors of 12?

$1 \times 12 = 12$ $2 \times 6 = 12$ $3 \times 4 = 12$

$12 \div 1 = 12$ $12 \div 2 = 6$ $12 \div 3 = 4$

So, the factors of 12 are: 1, 2, 3, 4, 6, and 12.

On the other hand, there is no whole number that can be multiplied by 5 to give the product 12, and 5 does not divide evenly into 12. So, 5 is not a factor of 12.

Try It This Way

Think of each multiplication as going both directions.

$1 \leftarrow \times \rightarrow 18$

$2 \leftarrow \times \rightarrow 9$

$3 \leftarrow \times \rightarrow 6$

4 not a factor

5 not a factor

Count down the left column and up the right column: 1, 2, 3, 4, 5, **6**. When the number at the bottom of the right column is the next counting number, you have found all of the factors of a number.

EXAMPLE 1

Find the factors of 18.

List all the ways 18 can be expressed as the product of two numbers. Start with 1, then use 2, and so on.

$1 \times 18 = 18$ $2 \times 9 = 18$ $3 \times 6 = 18$

The numbers 4 and 5 do not divide evenly into 18. They are not factors of 18.

The number 6 is the next factor, but the factor 6 was already used in $3 \times 6 = 18$.

As soon as a factor repeats, as 6 does in $6 \times 3 = 18$, you have found all of the factors.

The factors of 18 are 1, 2, 3, 6, 9, and 18.

EXAMPLE 2

Find the factors of 30.

METHOD 1

List all the ways 30 can be expressed as the product of two numbers.

$1 \times 30 = 30$

$2 \times 15 = 30$

$3 \times 10 = 30$

($4 \times$ no number is equal to 30)

$5 \times 6 = 30$

METHOD 2

List all the ways 30 can be evenly divided by another number.

$30 \div 1 = 30$

$30 \div 2 = 15$

$30 \div 3 = 10$

($30 \div 4$, no even division)

$30 \div 5 = 6$

The factors of 30 are 1, 2, 3, 5, 6, 10, 15, and 30.

SEARCH

To see step-by-step videos of these problems, enter the page number into the SWadvantage.com Search Bar.

Finding the Greatest Common Factor (GCF)

A **common factor** is a factor shared by two or more numbers. The **greatest common factor** (GCF) of two or more numbers is the greatest factor shared by (common to) the numbers.

Knowing the divisibility rules can help you find factors of greater numbers. For help with the divisibility rules, go to *Divisibility Rules* on page 290.

Find the GCF of 12 and 20.

STEP 1 Write the factors of both numbers.

The factors of 12 are: 1, 2, 3, 4, 6, 12

The factors of 20 are: 1, 2, 4, 5, 10, 20

STEP 2 Compare the factors of 12 and 20. Circle the common factors.

12: (1), (2), 3, (4), 6, 12 **20:** (1), (2), (4), 5, 10, 20

The common factors are 1, 2, and 4.

STEP 3 Identify the GCF. $4 > 2 > 1$

The GCF of 12 and 20 is 4.

EXAMPLE 4

Find the GCF of 18 and 24.

STEP 1 Write the factors of both numbers.

The factors of 18 are: 1, 2, 3, 6, 9, 18

The factors of 24 are: 1, 2, 3, 4, 6, 8, 12, 24

STEP 2 Compare the factors of 12 and 20. Circle the common factors.

18: (1), (2), (3), (6), 9, 18 **24:** (1), (2), (3), 4, (6), 8, 12, 24

The common factors are 1, 2, 3, and 6.

STEP 3 Identify the GCF. $6 > 3 > 2 > 1$

The GCF of 18 and 24 is 6.

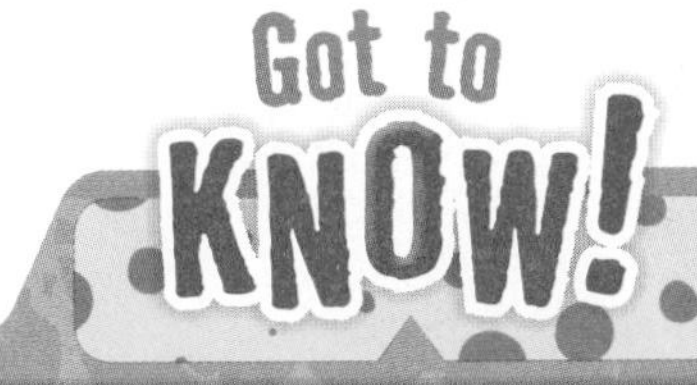

Factors of Numbers

- Any whole number that divides evenly into a given whole number is a **factor** of the given number. Example: $6 \div 3 = 2$, so 3 is a factor of 6.
- A **common factor** is a factor shared by a set of numbers.
- The **greatest common factor (GCF)** of a set of numbers is the greatest factor shared by all of the numbers in the set.

Multiples

What Is a Multiple?

Ways to REMEMBER

Think: A number's *factors are smaller* than the number. Its *multiples are larger*. Make up a sentence that can help you remember:

Factors	Frank
smaller	saw
multiples	many
larger	lions.

A **multiple** is the product of a counting number and a positive integer. For example,

$2 \times 1 = 2, 2 \times 2 = 4, 2 \times 3 = 6, \ldots$ The first three multiples of 2 are: 2, 4, 6.
$3 \times 1 = 3, 3 \times 2 = 6, 3 \times 3 = 9, \ldots$ The first three multiples of 3 are: 3, 6, 9.

The multiples of a number are infinite, so you cannot write a list of all the multiples of a number.

EXAMPLE 1

a. List the first six multiples of 6.

$6 \times 1 = 6$ $6 \times 4 = 24$
$6 \times 2 = 12$ $6 \times 5 = 30$
$6 \times 3 = 18$ $6 \times 6 = 36$

The first six multiples of 6 are 6, 12, 18, 24, 30, and 36.

b. List the first six multiples of 9.

$9 \times 1 = 9$ $9 \times 4 = 36$
$9 \times 2 = 18$ $9 \times 5 = 45$
$9 \times 3 = 27$ $9 \times 6 = 54$

The first six multiples of 9 are 9, 18, 27, 36, 45, and 54.

Finding the Least Common Multiple (LCM)

A **common multiple** is a multiple that is shared by two or more numbers. The **least common multiple** (LCM) of two or more numbers is their common multiple that has the least (smallest) value. You can find a common multiple of two or more numbers by multiplying the numbers, but the product may not be the LCM.

EXAMPLE 2

Find the LCM of 3 and 5.

List the multiples of both numbers, one at a time, until you get to a multiple that is common to both numbers.

Multiply by 1.
3: 3
5: 5

Multiply by 2.
3: 3, 6
5: 5, 10

Multiply by 3.
3: 3, 6, 9
5: 5, 10, 15

Multiply by 4.
3: 3, 6, 9, 12
5: 5, 10, 15, 20

Multiply by 5.
3: 3, 6, 9, 12, 15
5: 5, 10, 15, 20, 25

The least common multiple of 3 and 5 is 15. In this case, $3 \times 5 = 15$ gives the LCM.

EXAMPLE 3

Find the LCM of 6, 9, and 12.

List multiples of the three numbers, one at a time, until you get to a multiple that is common to all three numbers. You may find a table format helpful.

	×1	×2	×3	×4	×5	×6
6:	6	12	18	24	30	36
9:	9	18	27	36	45	54
12:	12	24	36	48	60	72

The LCM of 6, 9, and 12 is 36. In this case, $6 \times 9 \times 12 = 648$ does not give the LCM.

SEARCH

To see step-by-step videos of these problems, enter the page number into the SWadvantage.com Search Bar.

Finding the Least Common Denominator (LCD)

The **least common denominator** (LCD) of two or more fractions is the least common multiple (LCM) of the denominators of the fractions. Understanding the relationship between the least common multiple (LCM) and the least common denominator (LCD) is important when finding equivalent fractions.

EXAMPLE 4

a. Find the LCD of $\frac{3}{4}$ and $\frac{5}{6}$.

The denominators are 4 and 6. Find the LCM of 4 and 6.

4: 4, 8, 12
6: 6, 12, 18

The LCM of 4 and 6 is 12,

so the LCD of $\frac{3}{4}$ and $\frac{5}{6}$ is 12.

b. Find the LCD of $\frac{1}{2}$, $\frac{2}{3}$, and $\frac{1}{6}$.

The denominators are: 2, 3, and 6. Find the LCM of 2, 3, and 6.

2: 2, 4, 6
3: 3, 6, 9
6: 6, 12, 18

The LCM of 2, 3, and 6 is 6,

so the LCD of $\frac{1}{2}$, $\frac{2}{3}$, and $\frac{1}{6}$ is 6.

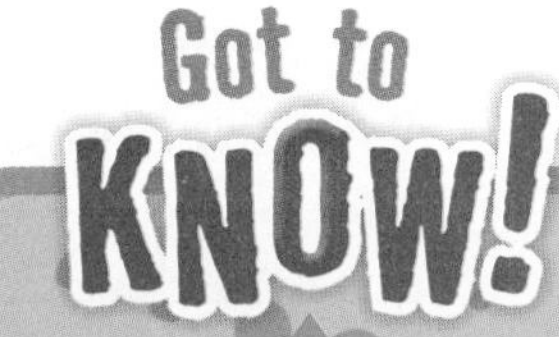

Multiples of Numbers

A **multiple** is the product of a counting number and a positive integer.

A **common multiple** is a multiple that is shared by two or more numbers.

The **least common multiple (LCM)** of a set of numbers is their smallest common multiple.

The **least common denominator (LCD)** of a set of fractions is the LCM of the fractions' denominators.

Divisibility Rules

For help with divisibility, go to *Division Facts* in *Foundations of Mathematics* (p. 800).

Using Divisibility Rules

A whole number is **divisible** by another whole number if there is no remainder when the first number is divided by the second. Use the divisibility rules in the *Got to Know!* box to determine if a number is divisible by the numbers 2 through 10.

EXAMPLE 1

Use the divisibility rules to answer the following questions.

a. Is 342 divisible by 2?

Check to see if the digit in the ones place is an even digit.

The digit is 2. Two is an even number, so…

342 is divisible by 2.

b. Is 207 divisible by 5?

Check to see if the digit in the ones place is 0 or 5.

The digit in the ones place is neither 0 nor 5, so…

207 is not divisible by 5.

c. Is 531 divisible by 3?

Check to see if the sum of the digits of 531 is divisible by 3.

$5 + 3 + 1 = 9$ and $9 \div 3 = 3$. Nine is divisible by 3, so…

531 is divisible by 3.

d. Is 5,236 divisible by 4?

Check to see if the number formed by the last two digits is divisible by 4.

$36 \div 4 = 9$. Thirty-six is divisible by 4, so…

5,236 is divisible by 4.

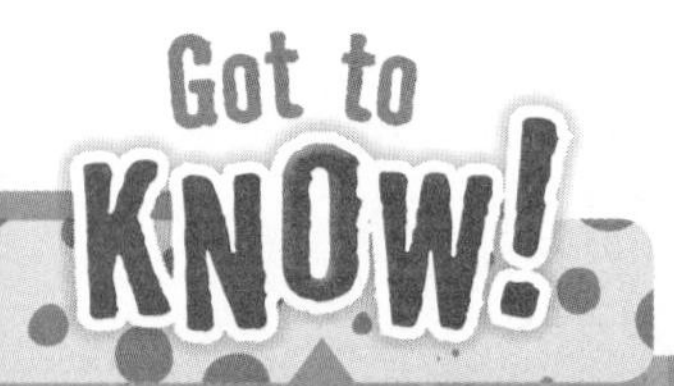

Tests for Divisibility

Divisible by	Rule
2	The digit in the ones place is an even digit: 0, 2, 4, 6, or 8.
3	The sum of the digits is divisible by 3.
4	The number formed by the last two digits is divisible by 4.
5	The digit in the ones place is 0 or 5.
6	The number is divisible by both 2 and 3.
8	The number formed by the last three digits is divisible by 8.
9	The sum of the digits is divisible by 9.
10	The digit in the ones place is 0.

EXAMPLE 2

Is 3,463 divisible by 9?

METHOD 1

Use long division.

Divide 3,463 by 9.

```
    384
9)3,463
 - 27
    76
  - 72
     43
   - 36
      7
```

There is a remainder of 7, so 3,463 is not divisible by 9.

METHOD 2

Use divisibility rules.

Check to see if the sum of the digits is divisible by 9.

$3 + 4 + 6 + 3 = 16$

The number 16 is not divisible by 9, so 3,463 is not divisible by 9.

Watch Out !

Using long division usually takes more time than using divisibility rules.

EXAMPLE 3

A total of 132 people have joined a bowling league. If each team must have 6 people, can everyone who has joined be placed on a team?

To answer the question, you need to know if 132 is divisible by 6. Use divisibility rules.

If a number is divisible by both 2 and 3, it is divisible by 6.

Use divisibility rules to find out if 132 is divisible by both 2 and 3.

Divisibility by 2:	Divisibility by 3:
Check the digit in the ones place.	Find the sum of the digits of 132.
The digit 2 is even.	$1 + 3 + 2 = 6$, and $6 \div 3 = 2$
132 is divisible by 2.	132 is divisible by 3.

The number 132 is divisible by both 2 and 3, so it is divisible by 6.

Everyone who joined the bowling league can be placed on a team.

SEARCH

To see step-by-step videos of these problems, enter the page number into the SWadvantage.com Search Bar.

Using Divisibility Rules

You can combine some divisibility rules as shown in the *Got to Know!* box below. Use these rules and the rules on page 290 in Example 4 and Example 5.

SEARCH

To see step-by-step videos of these problems, enter the page number into the SWadvantage.com Search Bar.

EXAMPLE 4

Tell whether 105 is divisible by 2, 3, 4, 5, 6, 8, 9, and 10.

2	The digit in the ones place, 5, is not even.	Not divisible by 2
3	The sum of the digits, 6, is divisible by 3.	Divisible by 3
4	The number formed by the last two digits, 5, is not divisible by 4.	Not divisible by 4
5	The digit in the ones place is 5.	Divisible by 5
6	The number is divisible by 3 but not by 2.	Not divisible by 6
8	The number is not divisible by 2 or 4.	Not divisible by 8
9	The sum of the digits, 6, is not divisible by 9.	Not divisible by 9
10	The digit in the ones place is not a 0.	Not divisible by 10

The number 105 is divisible by 3 and 5.

EXAMPLE 5

Tell whether 35,712 is divisible by 2, 3, 4, 5, 6, 8, 9, and 10.

2	The digit in the ones place, 2, is even.	Divisible by 2
3	The sum of the digits, 18, is divisible by 3.	Divisible by 3
4	The number formed by the last two digits, 12, is divisible by 4.	Divisible by 4
5	The digit in the ones place is not a 5 or 0.	Not divisible by 5
6	The number is divisible by 2 and 3.	Divisible by 6
8	The number is divisible by 2 and 4.	Divisible by 8
9	The sum of the digits, 18, is divisible by 9.	Divisible by 9
10	The digit in the ones place is not a 0.	Not divisible by 10

The number 35,712 is divisible by 2, 3, 4, 6, 8, and 9.

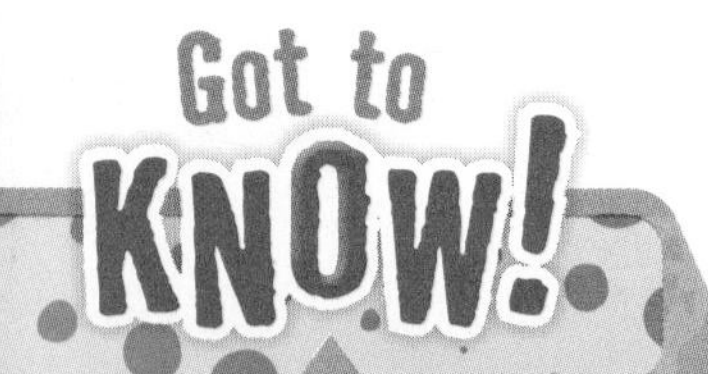

Combining Rules

If a number is divisible by 8 (2×4), then it is also divisible by 2 and 4.

If a number is divisible by 9 (3×3), then it is also divisible by 3.

If a number is divisible by 10 (2×5), then it is also divisible by 2 and 5.

Using Divisibility Rules to Find Factors

You can use divisibility rules to help you find factors of a number.

Need More HELP

Remember that a *factor* of a whole number is a whole number that divides evenly into the number. For help with factors, go to pages 286–287.

EXAMPLE 6

Tell whether 2, 3, 4, 5, 6, 8, 9, and 10 are factors of 530.

Use divisibility rules to test each number.

2	The digit in the ones place, 0, is even.	2 is a factor
3	The sum of the digits, 8, is not divisible by 3.	3 is not a factor
4	The number formed by the last two digits, 30, is not divisible by 4.	4 is not a factor
5	The digit in the ones place is a 0.	5 is a factor
6	The number is divisible by 2 but not by 3.	6 is not a factor
8	The number is divisible by 2 but not by 4.	8 is not a factor
9	The sum of the digits, 8, is not divisible by 9.	9 is not a factor
10	The digit in the ones place is a 0.	10 is a factor

The numbers 2, 5, and 10 are factors of 530.

EXAMPLE 7

The first two digits of a three-digit number are 2 and 4. Nine is a factor of the number. What is the number?

Because 9 is a factor, the sum of the digits of the number must be divisible by 9.

$2 + 4 + 3 = 9$, so the missing digit is 3.

The number is 243.

EXAMPLE 8

Juanita knows that the first three digits of her four-digit PIN are 1-8-5. She also knows that 2 and 3 are factors of her PIN. What is Juanita's PIN?

- Because 2 is a factor, the missing digit in 1-8-5-__ must be an even number. The PIN could be 1850, 1852, 1854, 1856, or 1858.
- Because 3 is also a factor, the sum of the digits must be divisible by 3.

$1 + 8 + 5 + 0 = \cancel{14}$ $\quad 1 + 8 + 5 + 2 = \cancel{16}$ $\quad 1 + 8 + 5 + 4 = 18$

$1 + 8 + 5 + 6 = \cancel{20}$ $\quad 1 + 8 + 5 + 8 = \cancel{22}$

Only the sum 18 is divisible by 3, so Juanita's PIN is 1854.

Exponents

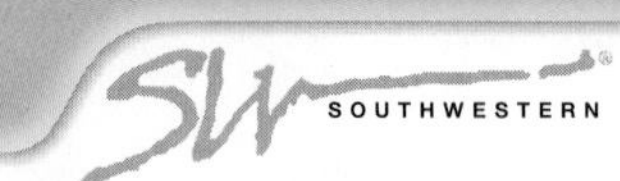

Some other ways to read 3^4 are:
"three to the power of four,"
"three to the fourth,"
and
"the fourth power of three."

Exponents and Repeated Multiplication

One way to show repeated multiplication is to use an *exponent*. The number that is multiplied is called the **base**. The **exponent** tells how many times the base is used as a factor. When a number is written as a base and an exponent, it is called a **power**.

$\underbrace{3 \times 3 \times 3 \times 3}= 3^4$ base $\rightarrow 3^4 \leftarrow$ exponent

3 is multiplied by itself 4 times. Read 3^4 as "three to the fourth power."

Any base raised to the exponent 1 equals the base. For example, $3^1 = 3$.

Any base raised to the exponent 0 equals 1. For example, $3^0 = 1$.

SEARCH

To see step-by-step videos of these problems, enter the page number into the SWadvantage.com Search Bar.

EXAMPLE 1

Write each expression, using an exponent. Identify the base and the exponent.

a. $2 \times 2 \times 2 \times 2 \times 2$

In the expression, 2 is used as a factor 5 times.

The number 2 is the base, and 5 is the exponent.

$2 \times 2 \times 2 \times 2 \times 2 = 2^5$

b. $9 \times 9 \times 9$

In the expression, 9 is used as a factor 3 times.

The number 9 is the base, and 3 is the exponent.

$9 \times 9 \times 9 = 9^3$

c. $25 \times 25 \times 25 \times 25 \times 25 \times 25$

In the expression, 25 is used as a factor 6 times.

The number 25 is the base, and 6 is the exponent.

$25 \times 25 \times 25 \times 25 \times 25 \times 25 = 25^6$

Simplifying Exponential Expressions

To *simplify* an expression, perform all possible operations to the expression to find its value. Here is how you simplify an expression with an exponent, such as 8^4.

- Write 8^4 as repeated multiplication: $8 \times 8 \times 8 \times 8$
- Multiply to find its value: $8 \times 8 \times 8 \times 8 = 4{,}096$

Watch Out!

A common mistake is to multiply the base times the exponent.

$8 \times 4 = 32$, which is much less than 4,096.

EXAMPLE 2

Simplify each expression.

a. 6^3

Write the expression as repeated multiplication: $6 \times 6 \times 6$
Multiply: $6 \times 6 \times 6 = 216$

b. 21^1

Any base raised to the exponent 1 equals the base.
$21^1 = 21$

c. 9^0

Any base raised to the exponent 0 equals 1.
$9^0 = 1$

d. 10^8

METHOD 1

Write the 10^8 as repeated multiplication. Then multiply.
$10^8 = 10 \times 10 \times 10 \times 10 \times 10 \times 10 \times 10 \times 10$
$= 100{,}000{,}000$

METHOD 2

10^8 is a power of 10.

Write a 1 followed by 8 zeros.
$10^8 = 100{,}000{,}000$

Need More HELP

For help with multiplying by multiples of 10, go to *Multiplying and Dividing by 10, 100, etc.* in *Foundations of Mathematics* (p. 94) or *Multiplying Decimals by Whole Numbers* (p. 238).

EXAMPLE 3

On day 1, you save 2 pennies. Each day you double the number of pennies you save. How many pennies will you save on the tenth day?

STEP 1 Determine the number of pennies you save on days 1–4.

Day 1	Day 2	Day 3	Day 4
2	4	8	16

STEP 2 Express each number of pennies in exponential form. Look at the pattern.

Day 1	Day 2	Day 3	Day 4
2	4	8	16
2^1	2^2	2^3	2^4

So, on day 10 you will save 2^{10} or 1,024 pennies.

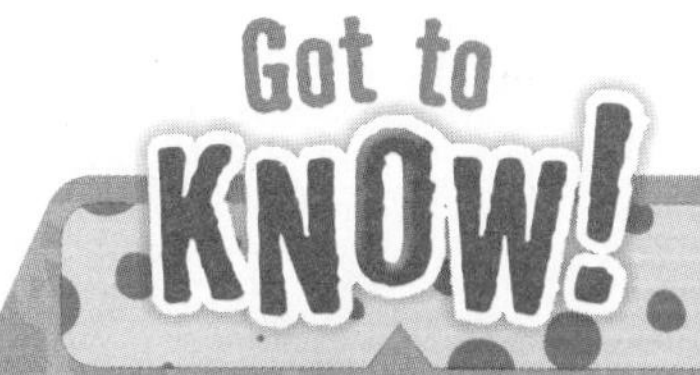

Powers of 10—Look at the Pattern of Zeros

Power of 10	Value	Zeros
10^0	1	0
10^1	10	1
10^2	100	2
10^3	1,000	3

Power of 10	Value	Zeros
10^4	10,000	4
10^5	100,000	5
10^6	1,000,000	6
10^7	10,000,000	7

Prime Factorization

Need More HELP

For help understanding prime and composite numbers or factors, go to *Prime and Composite Numbers* or *Factors* on page 284.

Understanding Prime Factorization

The **prime factorization** of a number is the number written as the product of its prime number factors. You can use different methods to find the prime factorization of a number. One of the methods is called the *factor tree method.*

A **factor tree** is a diagram that shows how to break a number down into its prime factors. Here are the steps for making a factor tree for a composite number, using the number 12 as an example.

- Write the composite number at the top of the factor tree. **12**
- "Branch" down, using any two factors of the number. 4 × 3
- Circle the prime factors as they occur.
- Continue branching until all the numbers on the tips of the branches are prime numbers. 2 × 2

12
4 × (3) ← 4 and 3 are factors of 12.
(2) × (2) ← 2 and 2 are factors of 4.

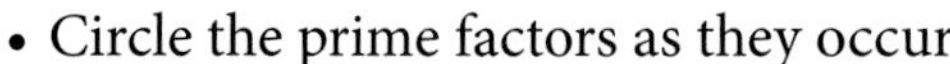

The prime factorization of 12 is 2 × 2 × 3.

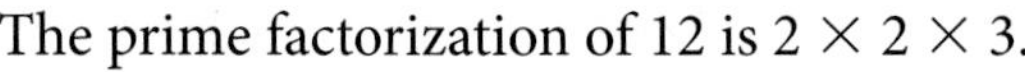

SEARCH

To see step-by-step videos of these problems, enter the page number into the SWadvantage.com Search Bar.

You can start a factor tree with any factor pair for a number. Here are two different factor trees for the number 36.

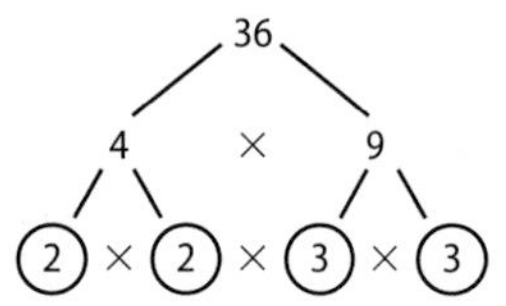

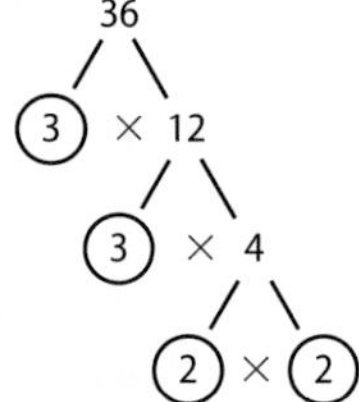

Prime factorization: 2 × 2 × 3 × 3 Prime factorization: 2 × 2 × 3 × 3

When the prime factors are ordered from least to greatest you can see that both trees result in the same prime factorization. This is because every positive counting number greater than 1 has only one prime factorization.

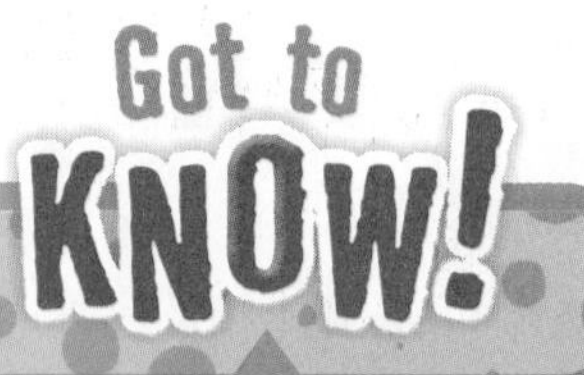

Prime and Composite Numbers

A **prime number** is a counting number that has *exactly* two factors, one and itself.

A **composite number** is a counting number that has more than two factors.

A *composite* number can be expressed as the product of its prime factors. This is called the **prime factorization** of the number.

Using the Factor Tree Method

When you *factor* a number, you write it as a product of its prime factors. Another way to say this is that you find the prime factorization of the number.

EXAMPLE 1

Use a factor tree to find the prime factorization of 70.

METHOD 1

Since 70 is divisible by 7, you can use 7 × 10 for the first branch.

- Write 70 at the top of the factor tree.
- Write the first branch: 7 × 10
- Circle 7 because it is prime.
- Ten is not prime. Write a factor pair of 10.
- Circle 2 and 5 because they are prime.

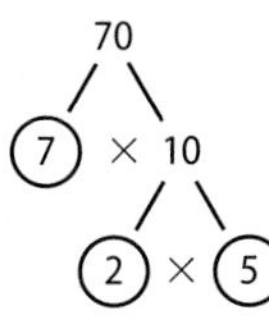

All of the factors at the tips are prime, so the prime factorization is complete.

The prime factorization of 70 is 2 × 5 × 7.

METHOD 2

Since 70 is divisible by 2, you can use 2 × 35 for the first branch.

- Write 70 at the top of the factor tree.
- Write the first branch: 2 × 35
- Circle 2 because it is prime.
- Thirty-five is not prime. Write a factor pair of 35.
- Circle 5 and 7 because they are prime.

70
2 × 35
5 × 7

All of the factors at the tips are prime, so the prime factorization is complete.

The prime factorization of 70 is 2 × 5 × 7.

Need More HELP

For help with finding factors of a composite number, go to *Divisibility Rules* on page 290.

Watch Out!

Make sure that the last branches of the factor tree contain only prime numbers. If one of the numbers is composite, make another branch.

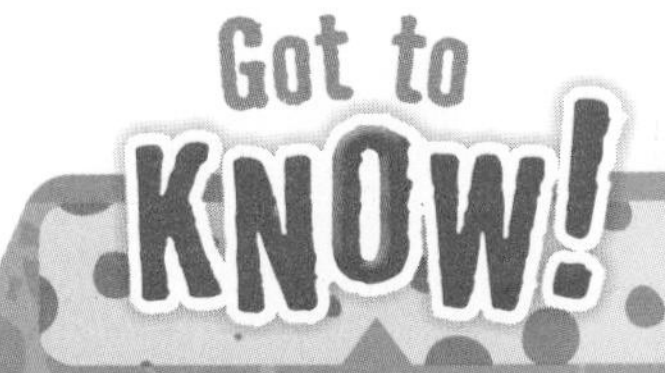

The Fundamental Theorem of Arithmetic

Every positive integer greater than 1 has exactly one set of prime factors (one prime factorization).

Using the Factor Tree Method

EXAMPLE 2

Use a factor tree to find the prime factorization of 1,440.

SEARCH

To see step-by-step videos of these problems, enter the page number into the SWadvantage.com Search Bar.

Write 1,440 at the top of the factor tree.

Choose any two factors whose product is 1,440. The number 1,440 ends in 0 so it is divisible by 10. You can choose 144×10.

Continue until all numbers at the tips of the branches are prime.

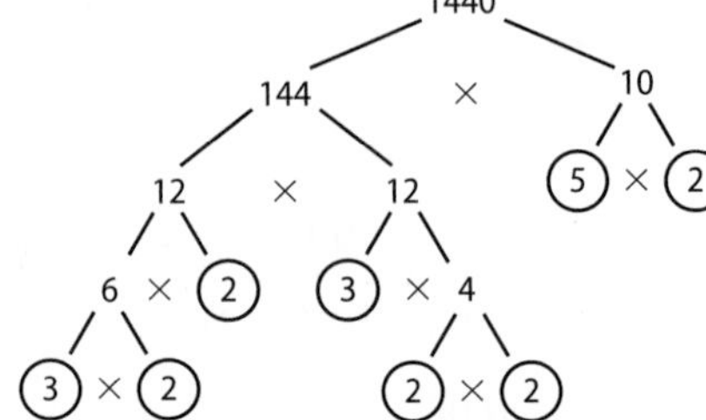

Write the prime factorization. $2 \times 2 \times 2 \times 2 \times 2 \times 3 \times 3 \times 5$

Express the prime factorization in exponential form. $2^5 \times 3^2 \times 5$

The prime factorization of 1,440 is $2^5 \times 3^2 \times 5$.

Using the Repeated Division Method

Another method for factoring a composite number into a product of primes is called the *repeated division method*. With this method, you keep dividing by prime factors of the number until the quotient is 1.

EXAMPLE 3

Use repeated division to find the prime factorization of 42.

Choose a prime factor of 42. This example starts with 2.

Keep dividing by prime factors until the quotient is 1.

The divisors represent the prime factorization.

Divisor	Dividend
2	42
3	21
7	7
	1

The prime factorization of 42 is $2 \times 3 \times 7$.

EXAMPLE 4

Use repeated division to find the prime factorization of 648.

METHOD 1

648 is divisible by 2. Choose 2 as the first prime factor.

Use 2 as a divisor until the dividend is no longer divisible by 2.

Keep dividing by prime factors until the quotient is 1.

The divisors represent the prime factorization.

The prime factorization of 648 is $2^3 \times 3^4$.

$$
\begin{array}{r|l}
2 & 6\ 4\ 8 \\
2 & 3\ 2\ 4 \\
2 & 1\ 6\ 2 \\
3 & 8\ 1 \quad \leftarrow \text{Not divisible by 2.} \\
3 & 2\ 7 \\
3 & 9 \\
3 & 3 \\
 & 1
\end{array}
$$

METHOD 2

$6 + 4 + 8 = 18$, which is divisible by 3, so 648 is divisible by 3. Choose 3 as the first prime factor.

Use 3 as a divisor until the dividend is no longer divisible by 3.

Keep dividing by prime factors until the quotient is 1.

The divisors represent the prime factorization.

The prime factorization of 648 is $2^3 \times 3^4$.

$$
\begin{array}{r|l}
3 & 6\ 4\ 8 \\
3 & 2\ 1\ 6 \\
3 & 7\ 2 \\
3 & 2\ 4 \\
2 & 8 \quad \leftarrow \text{Not divisible by 3.} \\
2 & 4 \\
2 & 2 \\
 & 1
\end{array}
$$

Division ladders like those above are a good choice for large numbers. But notice that because 648 is divisible by 3, it is also divisible by any number that is divisible by 3, such as 18. *You could also find the prime factorization of 648 by using a factor tree that starts with 18×36.*

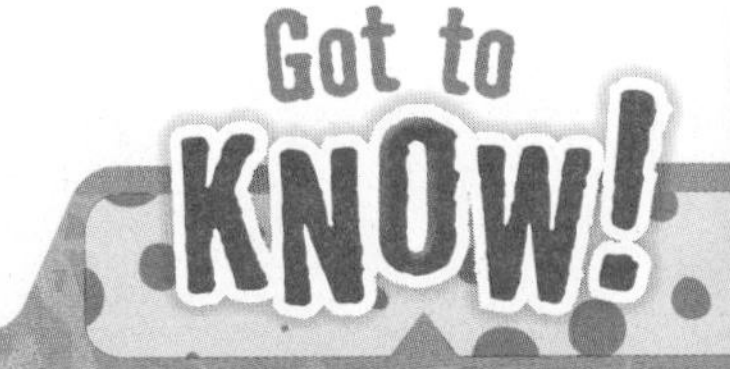

Prime Factorizations

When you use factor trees or repeated division to factor a number, the order of the prime factors may vary. However, there is only one prime factorization for the numbers.

$3 \times 3 \times 2$ is the same as $2 \times 3 \times 3$

$3^2 \times 2$ is the same as 2×3^2

Fractions and Mixed Numbers

What Came Before?

- Factors and multiples of whole numbers
- Converting between fractions, decimals, and percents

What's This About?

- Understanding fractions as parts of a whole or of a set
- Comparing and ordering fractions and mixed numbers
- Operations with fractions and mixed numbers

Practical Apps

- Cooks needs to multiply by fractions and mixed numbers to adjust recipes to serve given numbers of people.
- Construction workers need to understand fractions when cutting boards to frame houses.

just for FUN!

Q: Why are you shaking up those number tiles?

A: We're studying mixed numbers.

CONTENTS UPLOAD DOWNLOAD

Numbers and Operations

You can find more practice problems online by visiting: **www.SWadvantage.com**

Fractions—Part of a Whole

Modeling Fractions as Part of a Whole

A **fraction** is a number that names a part of a whole or a part of a set. The **numerator** of a fraction names the number of parts being considered. The **denominator** names the total number of equal parts.

The pizza below is divided into three equal parts. Each part is one-third of the pizza. Two of the parts are shaded, so two-thirds of the pizza is shaded.

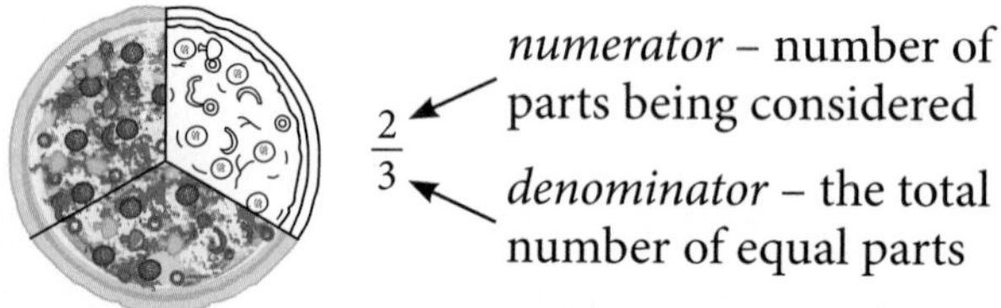

A **unit fraction** is a fraction whose numerator is 1. The fractions $\frac{1}{2}$, $\frac{1}{3}$, $\frac{1}{4}$, $\frac{1}{5}$, and so on are unit fractions.

SEARCH

To see step-by-step videos of these problems, enter the page number into the SWadvantage.com Search Bar.

EXAMPLE 1

Draw a model for each fraction.

a. Use a circle to model $\frac{1}{10}$ of a whole.

$\frac{\text{number of shaded parts}}{\text{total number of parts}} \rightarrow \frac{1}{10}$

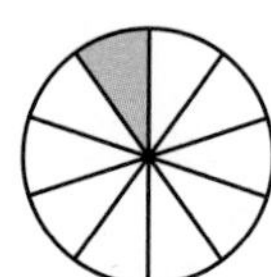

b. Use a rectangle to model $\frac{3}{4}$ as part of a whole.

$\frac{\text{number of shaded parts}}{\text{total number of parts}} \rightarrow \frac{3}{4}$

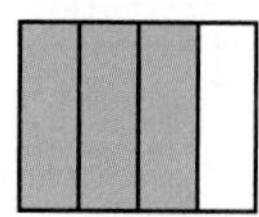

Naming a Part of a Whole

EXAMPLE 2

Name the fraction represented by the shaded region of each figure.

a. 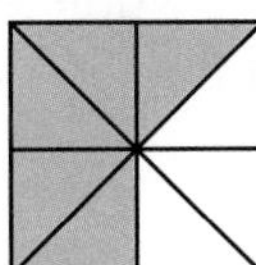

Five parts are shaded. ⟶ 5

There is a total of 8 parts. ⟶ 8

The model represents the fraction $\frac{5}{8}$.

b. 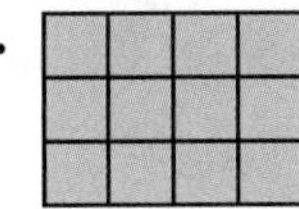

Twelve parts are shaded. ⟶ 12

There is a total of 12 parts. ⟶ 12

The model represents $\frac{12}{12}$ or 1.

Watch Out !

The fraction represented by the unshaded region is different than the fraction represented by the shaded region.

EXAMPLE 3

A pan of lasagna is divided into 24 equal pieces. The members of the Gomez family eat 11 pieces of lasagna. What fraction of the lasagna is *not* eaten?

STEP 1 Find the number of pieces that are not eaten.

Subtract: 24 total − 11 eaten = 13 not eaten

STEP 2 Write a fraction.

13 pieces not eaten. ⟶ 13
24 pieces in all. ⟶ 24

So, $\frac{13}{24}$ of the lasagna was not eaten.

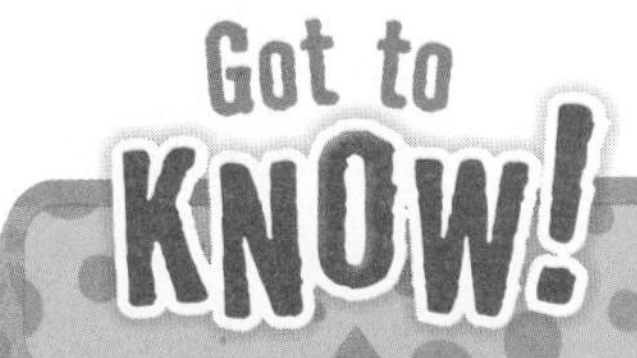

Special Fractions

When the numerator is equal to the denominator, the ***fraction is equal to 1.***

$\frac{2}{2} = \frac{3}{3} = \frac{4}{4} = \frac{6}{6} = \frac{100}{100} = 1$

When the numerator is 1, the fraction is a ***unit fraction.*** Examples:

$\frac{1}{2}, \frac{1}{8}, \frac{1}{10}, \frac{1}{15}$, and $\frac{1}{23}$

Modeling Fractions as Part of a Set

A **fraction** is a number that names a part of a whole or a part of a set.
The **numerator** of a fraction names the number of parts being considered.
The **denominator** names the total number of equal parts.

When a fraction names a part of a set, all of the items in the set make up 1 whole set. For example, the set below contains 2 oranges. One orange is one-half of the set.

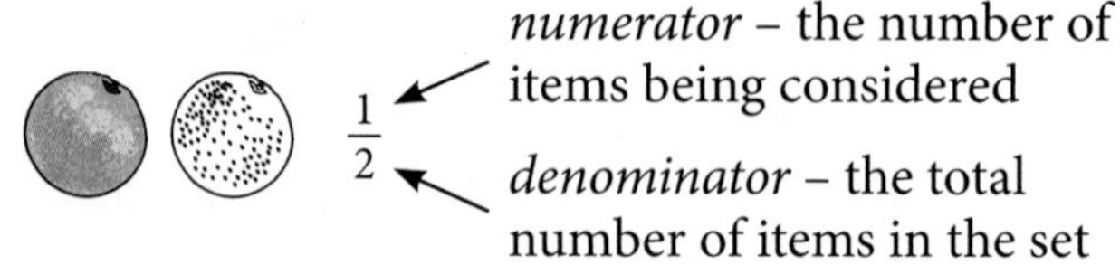

Suppose there were six oranges in the set. You would model four-sixths of the set as shown below.

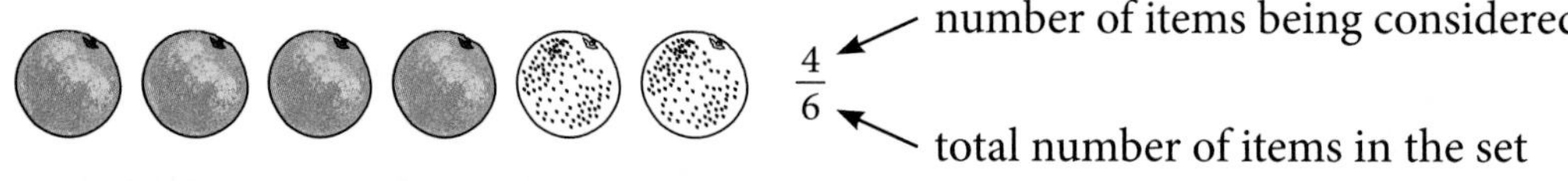

Watch Out !

Remember, the denominator is the total number of items in a set, not the number of unshaded items.

EXAMPLE 1

Draw a model for each fraction of a set.

a. Use stars to model $\frac{4}{8}$ of a set.

number of shaded parts → 4
total number of parts → 8

b. Use triangles to model $\frac{2}{9}$ of a set.

number of shaded parts → 2
total number of parts → 9

c. Use hearts to model $\frac{18}{20}$ of a set.

number of shaded parts → 18
total number of parts → 20

Naming a Part of a Set

EXAMPLE 2

Name the fraction represented by the shaded parts of each set.

a.  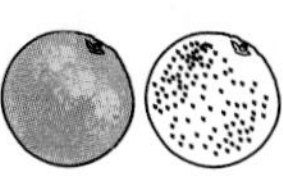 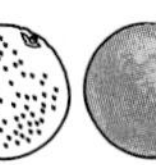 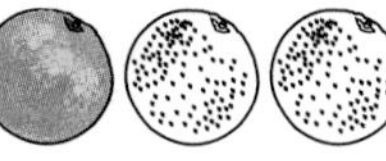  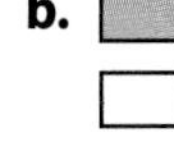

Three oranges are shaded. ⟶ 3

There are 6 oranges in the set. ⟶ 6

The model represents the fraction $\frac{3}{6}$.

b. 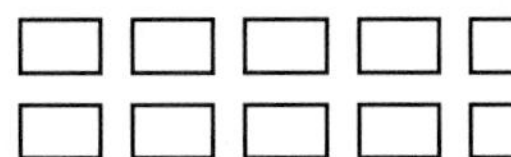

One rectangle is shaded. ⟶ 1

There are 15 rectangles in the set. ⟶ 15

The model represents $\frac{1}{15}$.

SEARCH

To see step-by-step videos of these problems, enter the page number into the SWadvantage.com Search Bar.

EXAMPLE 3

Cheryl downloaded some music to her MP3 player. She downloaded 5 country songs, 6 rock songs, and 3 reggae songs. What fraction of the downloaded songs are country songs?

STEP 1 Find the total number of songs downloaded.

Add: $5 + 6 + 3 = 14$

STEP 2 Write a fraction.

5 country songs downloaded ⟶ 5
14 songs downloaded ⟶ 14

$\frac{5}{14}$

So, $\frac{5}{14}$ of the songs Cheryl downloaded are country songs.

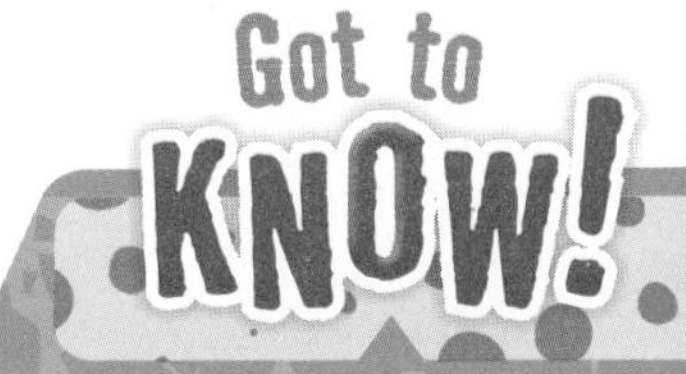

Fractions of Sets

When the numerator is equal to the denominator, the fraction is equal to 1. All the items in the set represent 1 whole.

The model represents $\frac{10}{10}$, or 1.

The order of the shaded parts of a set does not matter. Both models below represent $\frac{2}{5}$ of a set.

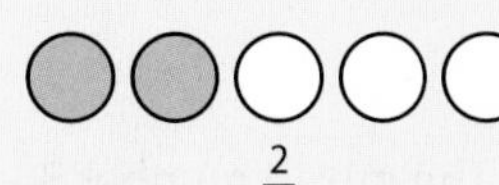

$\frac{2}{5}$

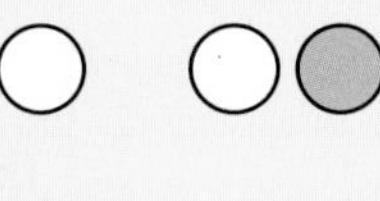 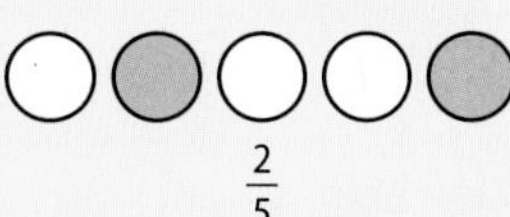

$\frac{2}{5}$

Understanding Mixed Numbers and Improper Fractions

A **proper fraction** has a numerator that is less than its denominator. Examples: $\frac{1}{2}, \frac{3}{4}, \frac{5}{9}$

An **improper fraction** has a numerator that is greater than or equal to its denominator. Examples: $\frac{7}{2}, \frac{15}{7}, \frac{10}{10}$

A **mixed number** contains a whole number and a proper fraction. Mixed numbers name the sum of a whole and a part of a whole. Examples: $1\frac{1}{3}, 2\frac{3}{8}, 4\frac{1}{6}$

SEARCH

To see step-by-step videos of these problems, enter the page number into the SWadvantage.com Search Bar.

EXAMPLE 1

Liam and his friends ate three and one-half pizzas. Write a mixed number to represent the number of pizzas eaten.

Use a model to help you.

Three whole pizzas and one-half of another pizza are shaded.

Liam and his friends ate $3\frac{1}{2}$ pizzas.

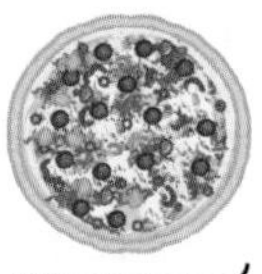

$3 + \frac{1}{2}$

Expressing Mixed Numbers as Improper Fractions

Sometimes it is necessary to express a mixed number as an improper fraction.

EXAMPLE 2

Write $3\frac{1}{2}$ as an improper fraction.

METHOD 1

Use a diagram to model $3\frac{1}{2}$.

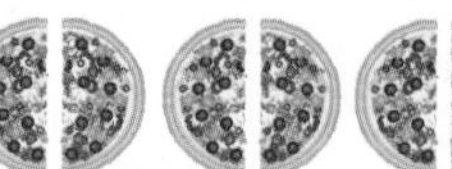

There are seven half-pizzas shown in the diagram.

METHOD 2

Think: There are 2 halves in 1 pizza, so there are $2 \times 3 = 6$ halves in 3 pizzas: $\frac{6}{2}$

Add this fraction to one-half.

$\frac{6}{2} + \frac{1}{2} = \frac{7}{2}$

METHOD 3

Multiply the whole number by the denominator.

Then add the numerator.

$3\frac{1}{2} = \frac{(3 \times 2) + 1}{2}$

$= \frac{7}{2}$

The mixed number $3\frac{1}{2}$ written as an improper fraction is $\frac{7}{2}$.

Expressing Improper Fractions as Mixed Numbers

To change an improper fraction to a mixed number, follow these steps.

- Divide the numerator by the denominator.
- Use the quotient as the whole number part of the mixed number.
- Use the remainder as the numerator of the fraction in the mixed number.
- Keep the original denominator that you used as the divisor.

For help with division, go to *Dividing Whole Numbers* in *Foundations of Mathematics* (p. 100).

EXAMPLE 3

Express each improper fraction as a mixed number.

a. $\frac{5}{3}$

The quotient 1 is the whole number part of the mixed number.

The remainder 2 is the numerator of the proper fraction.

The improper fraction $\frac{5}{3}$ written as a mixed number is $1\frac{2}{3}$.

$$\begin{array}{r} 1 \\ 3\overline{)\ 5} \\ -3 \\ \hline 2 \end{array} \rightarrow 1\frac{2}{3}$$

b. $\frac{17}{5}$

The quotient 3 is the whole number part of the mixed number.

The remainder 2 is the numerator of the proper fraction.

The improper fraction $\frac{17}{5}$ written as a mixed number is $3\frac{2}{5}$.

$$\begin{array}{r} 3 \\ 5\overline{)\ 17} \\ -15 \\ \hline 2 \end{array} \rightarrow 3\frac{2}{5}$$

c. $\frac{109}{4}$

The quotient 27 is the whole number part of the mixed number.

The remainder 1 is the numerator of the proper fraction.

The improper fraction $\frac{109}{4}$ written as a mixed number is $27\frac{1}{4}$.

$$\begin{array}{r} 27 \\ 4\overline{)109} \\ -8 \\ \hline 29 \\ -28 \\ \hline 1 \end{array} \rightarrow 27\frac{1}{4}$$

Try It This Way

For Example 3a, take 5 counters and divide them into groups of 3. You can make 1 group of 3. There are 2 counters left over that represent $\frac{2}{3}$ of the whole.

Try this method for Example 3(b), starting with 17 counters and making groups of 5.

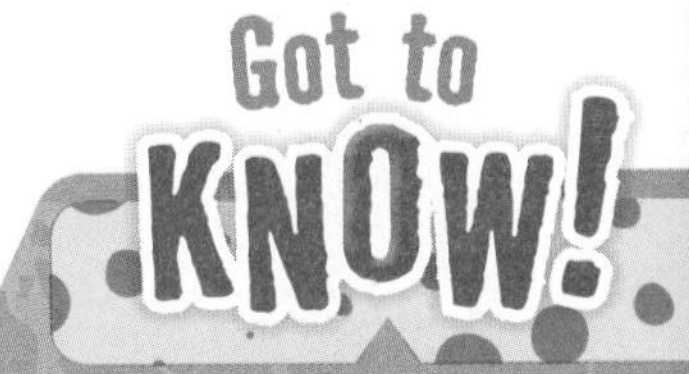

Renaming Mixed Numbers and Improper Fractions

Mixed number → Improper fraction

- Multiply the whole number by the denominator.
- Then add the numerator.

Improper fraction → Mixed number

- Divide the numerator by the denominator.
- Use the quotient as the whole number.
- Use the remainder as the numerator.

Modeling Equivalent Fractions

Equivalent fractions are fractions that name the same value, or amount. You can model equivalent fractions using fraction strips or a number line. The models below use equivalent fractions to name the same quantity: $\frac{1}{2} = \frac{2}{4} = \frac{4}{8}$.

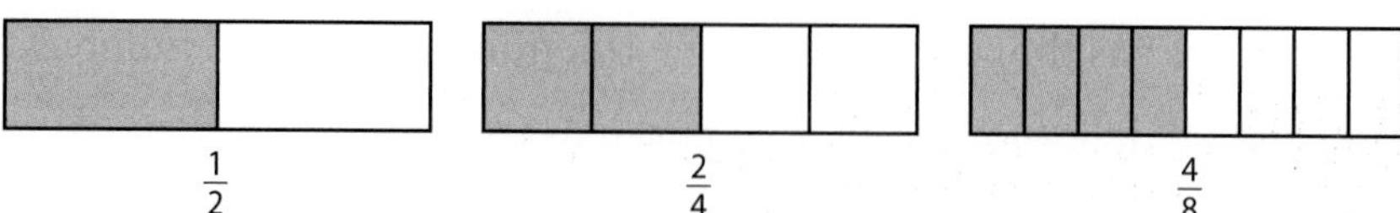

EXAMPLE 1

Use fraction strips to write two fractions that are equivalent to $\frac{3}{4}$.

STEP 1 Model $\frac{3}{4}$ using fourths strips.

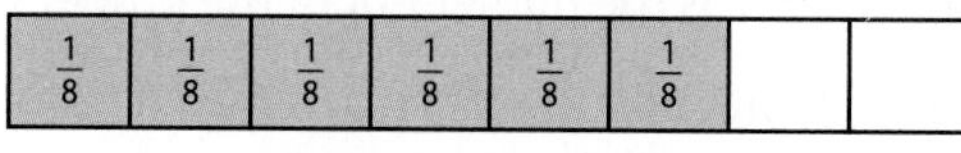

STEP 2 It takes 6 eighths to make a strip of equal length.

$\frac{1}{8}$	$\frac{1}{8}$	$\frac{1}{8}$	$\frac{1}{8}$	$\frac{1}{8}$	$\frac{1}{8}$		

STEP 3 It takes 9 twelfths to make a strip of equal length.

$\frac{1}{12}$	$\frac{1}{12}$	$\frac{1}{12}$	$\frac{1}{12}$	$\frac{1}{12}$	$\frac{1}{12}$	$\frac{1}{12}$	$\frac{1}{12}$	$\frac{1}{12}$			

The fractions $\frac{3}{4}$, $\frac{6}{8}$, and $\frac{9}{12}$ are equivalent fractions.

To see step-by-step videos of these problems, enter the page number into the SWadvantage.com Search Bar.

EXAMPLE 2

Use a number line to write a fraction equivalent to $4\frac{1}{3}$.

Divide the distance between 4 and 5 into thirds.

Graph $4\frac{1}{3}$ on a number line.

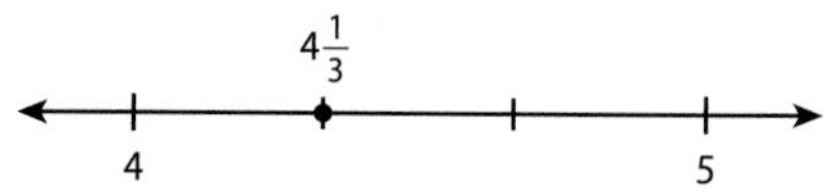

Divide the distance between 4 and 5 into sixths.

Graph $4\frac{2}{6}$ on a number line.

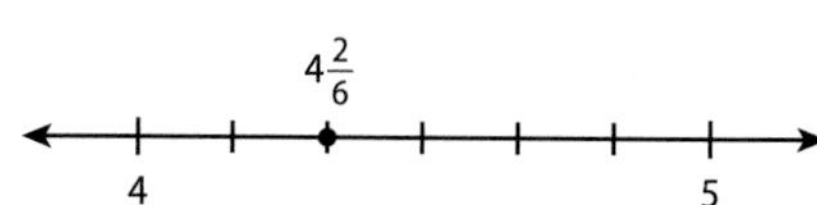

The fractions $4\frac{1}{3}$ and $4\frac{2}{6}$ name the same point on a number line. They are equivalent fractions.

Naming Equivalent Fractions

EXAMPLE 3

Write the equivalent fractions shown in the model.

a.

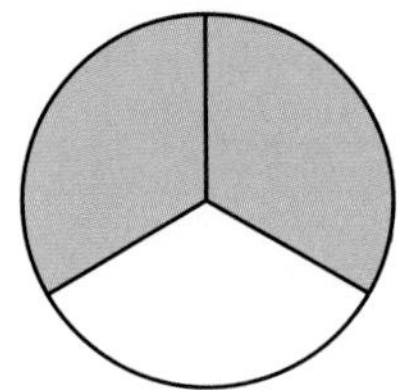

=

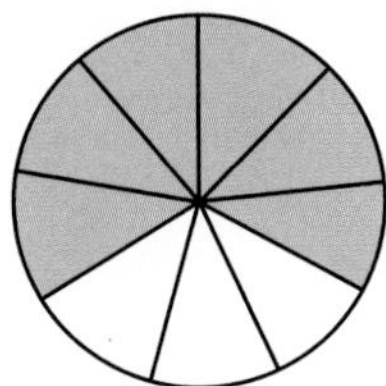

The circle on the left is divided into thirds. Two-thirds are shaded.

The circle on the right is divided into ninths. Six-ninths are shaded.

So, $\frac{2}{3} = \frac{6}{9}$.

b.

=

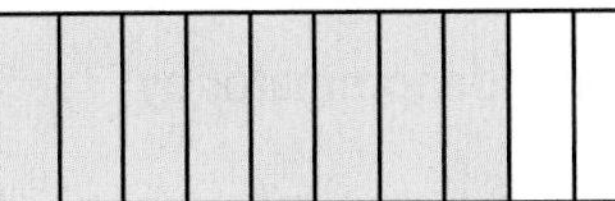

The rectangle on the left is divided into fifths. Four-fifths are shaded.

The rectangle on the right is divided into tenths. Eight-tenths are shaded.

So, $\frac{4}{5} = \frac{8}{10}$.

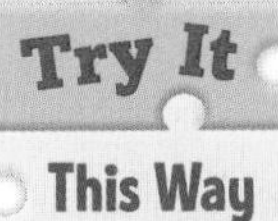

In Example 4, the numerators are multiples of 2, and the denominators are multiples of 5.

You may find it easier to skip count to find equivalent fractions: $\frac{2}{5}, \frac{4}{10}, \frac{6}{15}, \frac{8}{20}, \frac{10}{25}$

Each pair of multiples forms a fraction equivalent to two-fifths.

Writing Equivalent Fractions

If you multiply or divide the numerator and the denominator of a fraction by the same non-zero number, the result is an equivalent fraction.

EXAMPLE 4

Write four fractions that are equivalent to $\frac{2}{5}$.

$\frac{2 \times 2}{5 \times 2} = \frac{4}{10}$ $\frac{2 \times 3}{5 \times 3} = \frac{6}{15}$ $\frac{2 \times 4}{5 \times 4} = \frac{8}{20}$ $\frac{2 \times 5}{5 \times 5} = \frac{10}{25}$

The fractions $\frac{4}{10}, \frac{6}{15}, \frac{8}{20}$, and $\frac{10}{25}$ are equivalent to $\frac{2}{5}$. They are equivalent fractions.

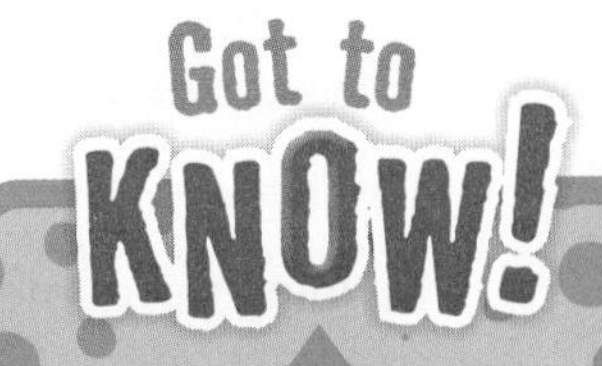

Multiplying to Find Equivalent Fractions

Multiplication by 1 does not change the value of a number.

Multiplying the numerator and denominator of a fraction by the same number is the same as multiplying the fraction by 1.

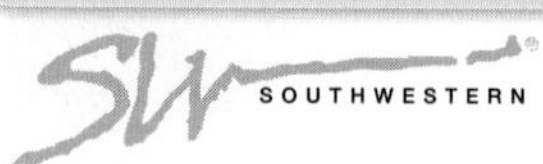

Writing Equivalent Fractions

EXAMPLE 5

Write two equivalent fractions for each given fraction.

a. $\frac{5}{8}$

Multiply the numerator and denominator by the same number.

$\frac{5}{8} = \frac{5 \times 2}{8 \times 2} = \frac{10}{16}$

$\frac{5}{8} = \frac{5 \times 3}{8 \times 3} = \frac{15}{24}$

The fractions $\frac{10}{16}$ and $\frac{15}{24}$ are equivalent to $\frac{5}{8}$.

b. $\frac{15}{25}$

Multiply the numerator and denominator by the same number.

$\frac{15}{25} = \frac{15 \times 4}{25 \times 4} = \frac{60}{100}$

Divide the numerator and denominator by the same number.

$\frac{15}{25} = \frac{15 \div 5}{25 \div 5} = \frac{3}{5}$

The fractions $\frac{60}{100}$ and $\frac{3}{5}$ are equivalent to $\frac{15}{25}$.

Try It This Way

When finding a missing numerator or denominator, as in Example 6, setting up the problem first will help you visualize it.

Since $50 > 5$, you must multiply.

$\frac{5 \times ?}{7 \times ?} = \frac{50}{?}$

In the problem below, $4 < 16$, so you must divide.

$\frac{12 \div ?}{16 \div ?} = \frac{?}{4}$

EXAMPLE 6

What denominator would make these fractions equivalent? $\frac{5}{7} = \frac{50}{?}$

Think: What number multiplied by 5 is equal to 50?

$5 \times 10 = 50$

$\frac{5}{7} = \frac{5 \times 10}{7 \times 10} = \frac{50}{70}$

Multiply the denominator, 7, by the same number.

So, $\frac{5}{7} = \frac{50}{70}$. The denominator 70 makes the fractions equivalent.

Dividing to Find Equivalent Fractions

Dividing the numerator and denominator of a fraction by the same number is the same as dividing by 1.

$\frac{15}{25} = \frac{15 \div 5}{25 \div 5} = \frac{3}{5}$

If you cannot divide the numerator and denominator of a fraction by the same number, the fraction is in *simplest form.*

$\frac{11}{25}$ 11 and 25 have no common factors.

Simplest Form of a Fraction

A fraction is in **simplest form** when the numerator and denominator have no common factor other than one. To write a fraction in simplest form, divide the numerator and denominator repeatedly by their common factors or once by their greatest common factor.

EXAMPLE 7

Write $\frac{24}{30}$ in simplest form.

METHOD 1

Find the GCF of 18 and 24. 18: 1, 2, 3, 6, 9, 18

List factors of 18 and 24. 24: 1, 2, 3, 4, 6, 8, 12, 24

The GCF is 6.

Divide the numerator and denominator by 6. $\frac{24}{30} = \frac{24 \div 6}{30 \div 6} = \frac{4}{5}$

The numbers 4 and 5 have no common factors other than 1. The fraction is in simplest form.

The fraction $\frac{24}{30}$ written in simplest form is $\frac{4}{5}$.

METHOD 2

Find a common factor of 24 and 30. Both numbers are divisible by 2. $\frac{24}{30} = \frac{24 \div 2}{30 \div 2} = \frac{12}{15}$

Divide the numerator and denominator by 2.

The numbers 12 and 15 share a common factor, 3.

Divide the numerator and denominator by 3. $\frac{12}{15} = \frac{12 \div 3}{15 \div 3} = \frac{4}{5}$

The numbers 4 and 5 have no common factors other than 1. The fraction is in simplest form.

The fraction $\frac{24}{30}$ written in simplest form is $\frac{4}{5}$.

Need More HELP

For help with finding the GCF, go to *Factors* on page 286.

EXAMPLE 8

Write $2\frac{14}{21}$ in simplest form.

Find the simplest form of the fraction part of the mixed number.

The GCF of 14 and 21 is 7, so $\frac{14}{21} = \frac{14 \div 7}{21 \div 7} = \frac{2}{3}$.

The mixed number $2\frac{14}{21}$ written in simplest form is $2\frac{2}{3}$.

SEARCH

To see step-by-step videos of these problems, enter the page number into the SWadvantage.com Search Bar.

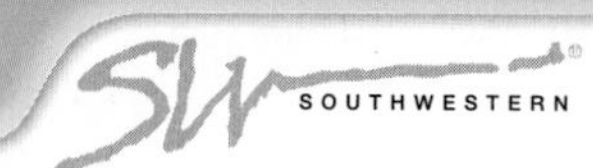

Comparing Fractions and Mixed Numbers

You can use models and number lines to compare fractions. As you move to the right along a number line, the numbers increase in value. To compare two fractions, use the symbols shown in the *Got to Know!* box.

EXAMPLE 1

Use <, >, or = to compare $\frac{2}{3}$ and $\frac{5}{9}$.

Use fraction strips to model $\frac{2}{3}$ and $\frac{5}{9}$.

$\frac{1}{3}$	$\frac{1}{3}$	

$\frac{1}{9}$	$\frac{1}{9}$	$\frac{1}{9}$	$\frac{1}{9}$	$\frac{1}{9}$				

The model for $\frac{2}{3}$ is longer than the model for $\frac{5}{9}$, so its value is greater.

$\frac{2}{3} > \frac{5}{9}$. You can also say that $\frac{5}{9} < \frac{2}{3}$.

Need More HELP

Remember, when you *compare* two or more numbers you decide if they are less than, equal to, or greater than each other.

EXAMPLE 2

Use <, >, or = to compare $3\frac{1}{2}$ and $3\frac{5}{8}$.

Graph $3\frac{1}{2}$ and $3\frac{5}{8}$ on a number line.

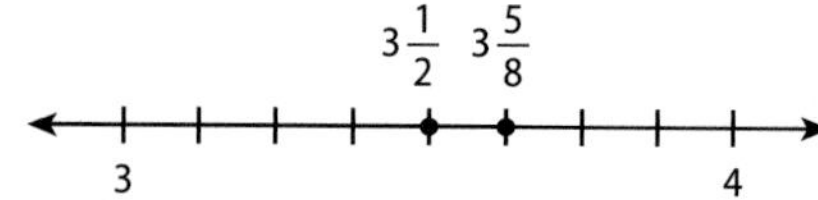

$3\frac{5}{8}$ is to the right of $3\frac{1}{2}$ on the number line, so its value is greater.

$3\frac{5}{8} > 3\frac{1}{2}$. You can also say that $3\frac{1}{2} < 3\frac{5}{8}$.

SEARCH

To see step-by-step videos of these problems, enter the page number into the SWadvantage.com Search Bar.

Got to KNOW!

Comparison Symbols

Symbol	<	>	=
Meaning	less than	greater than	equal to

Comparing Fractions with Like Denominators

To compare fractions with like, or the same, denominators, compare the numerators. The fraction with the greater numerator has the greater value.

Use $<$, $>$, or $=$ to compare $\frac{11}{15}$ and $\frac{14}{15}$.

The fractions have the same denominators, 15.

Compare the numerators. $11 < 14$

So, $\frac{11}{15} < \frac{14}{15}$.

Comparing Fractions with Unlike Denominators

To compare fractions with unlike, or different, denominators, rename the fractions so they have the same denominator. Sometimes you need to rename only one of the fractions. (For example, to compare $\frac{1}{4}$ and $\frac{3}{8}$, rename $\frac{1}{4}$ as the equivalent fraction $\frac{2}{8}$.) At other times, you may need to rename both fractions.

EXAMPLE 4

Use $<$, $>$, or $=$ to compare $\frac{5}{6}$ and $\frac{13}{15}$.

STEP 1 Find the least common denominator (LCD).

List multiples of each denominator until you find a common multiple.

6: 6, 12, 18, 24, 30, ...
15: 15, 30, 45, 60, ...

The least common multiple of the numbers is the LCD.

The LCD is 30.

STEP 2 Write equivalent fractions using the LCD.

$\frac{5}{6} = \frac{5 \times 5}{6 \times 5} = \frac{25}{30}$ $\qquad \frac{13}{15} = \frac{13 \times 2}{15 \times 2} = \frac{26}{30}$

STEP 3 Compare the numerators: $25 < 26$

Because $25 < 26$, $\frac{25}{30} < \frac{26}{30}$.

So, $\frac{5}{6} < \frac{13}{15}$.

For help with finding least common multiples, go to *Multiples* on page 288.

Try It This Way

Use a calculator to find equivalent fractions.

Multiply $15 \times 6 = 90$ to find a common denominator.

Divide: $90 \div 6 = 15$

Multiply: $15 \times 5 = 75$

$15 \times 5 = 75$

$\frac{5}{6} = \frac{75}{90}$

$90 \div 6 = 15$

Ordering Fractions and Mixed Numbers

You can order fractions from least to greatest, or from greatest to least. One way to order fractions is to use a number line. When the fractions have like denominators, you can order the fractions by the value of their numerators.

Try It This Way

Use a calculator to find the decimal equivalent of a fraction. For the fraction $\frac{5}{6}$, on your calculator enter:

The display will show the decimal equivalent: 0.8333333, which you can write as $0.8\overline{3}$.

EXAMPLE 5

Order from least to greatest: $\frac{5}{6}, \frac{2}{3}, \frac{3}{4}$

METHOD 1

Use a number line. First, express each fraction as a decimal.

$$\frac{5}{6} = 6\overline{)5.00} = 0.8\overline{3} \quad \begin{array}{r} 5.00 \\ -\,48 \\ \hline 20 \\ -\,18 \\ \hline 2 \end{array} \qquad \frac{2}{3} = 3\overline{)2.0} = 0.\overline{6} \quad \begin{array}{r} 2.0 \\ -\,18 \\ \hline 2 \end{array} \qquad \frac{3}{4} = 4\overline{)3.00} = 0.75 \quad \begin{array}{r} 3.00 \\ -\,28 \\ \hline 20 \\ -\,20 \\ \hline 0 \end{array}$$

Then graph $0.8\overline{3}$, $0.\overline{6}$, and 0.75 on a number line.

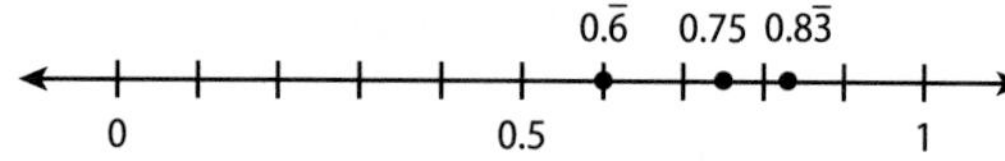

$0.\overline{6} < 0.75 < 0.8\overline{3}$

Ordered from least to greatest the fractions are: $\frac{2}{3}, \frac{3}{4}, \frac{5}{6}$.

METHOD 2

Rename the fractions so they have a common denominator.

STEP 1 Use the least common multiple (LCM) of the numbers as the denominator. The LCM of 3, 4, and 6 is 12. So, the least common denominator (LCD) is 12.

STEP 2 Write equivalent fractions.

$$\frac{5}{6} = \frac{5 \times 2}{6 \times 2} = \frac{10}{12} \qquad \frac{2}{3} = \frac{2 \times 4}{3 \times 4} = \frac{8}{12} \qquad \frac{3}{4} = \frac{3 \times 3}{4 \times 3} = \frac{9}{12}$$

STEP 3 Now the fractions have like denominators. Compare the numerators.

$8 < 9 < 10$, so $\frac{8}{12} < \frac{9}{12} < \frac{10}{12}$

Ordered from least to greatest the fractions are: $\frac{2}{3}, \frac{3}{4}, \frac{5}{6}$.

Need More HELP

Remember, the least common multiple (LCM) of the denominators of a set of fractions is also the least common denominator (LCD) of the fractions.

EXAMPLE 6

Order from greatest to least: $2\frac{7}{12}, 2\frac{8}{15}, 1\frac{2}{3}$

STEP 1 Compare the whole number part of the mixed numbers.

Since $1 < 2$, $1\frac{2}{3}$ is the least number.

STEP 2 Compare the fraction part of $2\frac{7}{12}$ and $2\frac{8}{15}$.

The LCM of 12 and 15 is 60. So, the LCD is 60.

STEP 3 Write equivalent fractions.

$\frac{7}{12} = \frac{7 \times 5}{12 \times 5} = \frac{35}{60}$ $\frac{8}{15} = \frac{8 \times 4}{15 \times 4} = \frac{32}{60}$

STEP 4 Compare the numerators.

$35 > 32$, so $\frac{35}{60} > \frac{32}{60}$ <. This means that $2\frac{7}{12} > 2\frac{8}{15}$.

Ordered from *greatest to least* the mixed numbers are: $2\frac{7}{12}, 2\frac{8}{15}, 1\frac{2}{3}$.

Need More HELP

Remember, the least common multiple (LCM) of the denominators of a set of fractions is the least common denominator (LCD) of the fractions.

EXAMPLE 7

John walked $\frac{3}{8}$ mile on Monday, $\frac{1}{4}$ mile on Tuesday, and $\frac{5}{16}$ mile on Wednesday. On which day did he walk the greatest distance?

The LCD of 8, 4, and 16 is 16. Write equivalent fractions using the LCD.

$\frac{3}{8} = \frac{3 \times 2}{8 \times 2} = \frac{6}{16}$ $\frac{1}{4} = \frac{1 \times 4}{4 \times 4} = \frac{4}{16}$ $\frac{5}{16}$ already has the LCD

The greatest distance is $\frac{6}{16}$ or $\frac{3}{8}$ mile. John walked the greatest distance on Monday.

SEARCH

To see step-by-step videos of these problems, enter the page number into the SWadvantage.com Search Bar.

Comparing and Ordering Fractions

Use Fractions

1. Express the fractions as equivalent fractions with the same denominator.
2. To compare or order the fractions, compare their numerators.

Use Decimals

1. Find the decimal equivalent of each fraction.
2. Compare and order the decimal numbers. Use this order for the fractions.

Rounding Fractions and Mixed Numbers

Rounding Fractions

A **benchmark** is a reference number to which you can compare other numbers. The benchmark numbers 0, $\frac{1}{2}$, and 1 are useful when rounding or estimating fractions.

EXAMPLE 1

Use a number line to decide if $\frac{2}{9}$ rounds to 0, $\frac{1}{2}$, or 1.

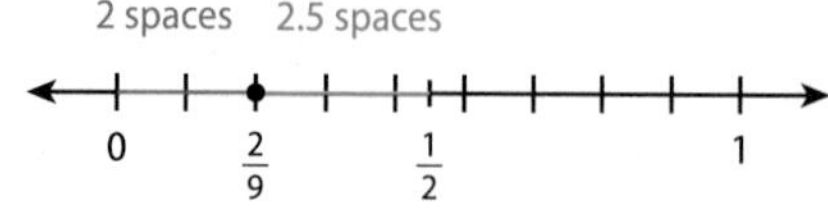

The number line is divided into ninths.

Graph $\frac{2}{9}$ on a number line.

$\frac{2}{9}$ is closer to 0 than to $\frac{1}{2}$.

The fraction $\frac{2}{9}$ rounds to 0.

SEARCH

To see step-by-step videos of these problems, enter the page number into the SWadvantage.com Search Bar.

EXAMPLE 2

Does $\frac{7}{12}$ round to 0, $\frac{1}{2}$, or 1?

STEP 1 Write equivalent fractions for 0, $\frac{1}{2}$, and 1 with denominators of 12.

$$0 = \frac{0}{12} \qquad \frac{1}{2} = \frac{1 \times 6}{2 \times 6} = \frac{6}{12} \qquad 1 = \frac{1}{1} = \frac{1 \times 12}{1 \times 12} = \frac{12}{12}$$

STEP 2 Compare the numerator 7 with each benchmark numerator: $0 < 6 < 7 < 12$

7 is closer to 6 than to 12, so $\frac{7}{12}$ is closest to $\frac{1}{2}$.

The fraction $\frac{7}{12}$ rounds to $\frac{1}{2}$.

Need More HELP

Remember, when a fraction's denominator is exactly twice its numerator, the fraction is equivalent to one-half. For example, $\frac{2}{4}$, $\frac{3}{6}$, $\frac{9}{18}$, and $\frac{50}{100}$ are all equivalent to $\frac{1}{2}$.

Ways to Round Fractions

You can use a number line, equivalent fractions, and number sense to round fractions.

The benchmarks 0, $\frac{1}{2}$, and 1 are also helpful when rounding fractions.

Rounding Mixed Numbers

When rounding a mixed number, first look at the whole number part of the mixed number. For example, the value of the mixed number $2\frac{1}{8}$ is between 2 and 3.

When you graph $2\frac{1}{8}$ on a number line, you can see that it is closer to 2 than to $2\frac{1}{2}$ or 3. So $2\frac{1}{8}$ rounds to 2.

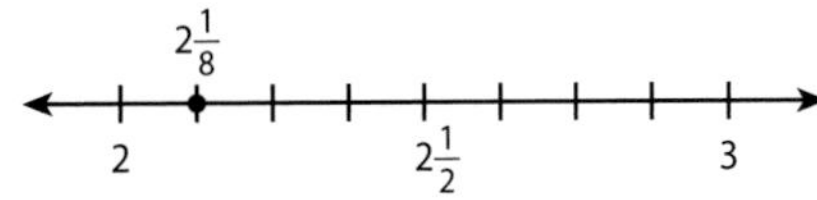

Try It This Way

Run your finger or the tip of your pencil along the distance between 2 and $2\frac{1}{8}$. Then run it between $2\frac{1}{8}$ to $2\frac{1}{2}$.

You can feel that one distance is longer than the other.

EXAMPLE 3

Use a number line to decide if $6\frac{4}{5}$ rounds to 6, $6\frac{1}{2}$, or 7.

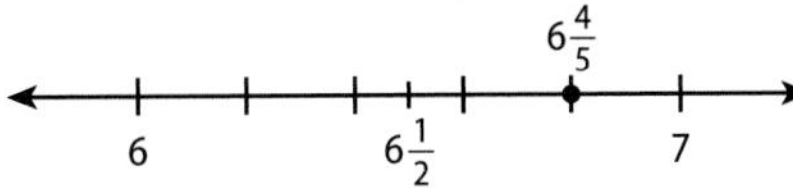

The number line is divided into fifths. $6\frac{1}{2}$ is also marked.

Graph $6\frac{4}{5}$ on a number line.

$6\frac{4}{5}$ is closer to 7 than to $6\frac{1}{2}$.

The fraction $6\frac{4}{5}$ rounds to 7.

Estimating with Fractions and Mixed Numbers

EXAMPLE 4

Sara will make two kinds of granola. One recipe uses $2\frac{1}{4}$ cups of rolled oats. The other recipe uses $2\frac{2}{3}$ cups. Use number sense to estimate the number of cups of rolled oats Sara will need.

STEP 1 Think: $\frac{1}{4}$ is less than $\frac{1}{2}$, and $\frac{2}{3}$ is greater than $\frac{1}{2}$.

STEP 2 Round each mixed number.

Round $2\frac{1}{4}$ cups to 2 cups, not $2\frac{1}{2}$ cups.

Round $2\frac{2}{3}$ cups to 3 cups, not $2\frac{1}{2}$ cups.

STEP 3 Add to estimate the amount of oats: 2 cups + 3 cups = 5 cups

Sara needs about 5 cups of rolled oats to make the two kinds of granola.

Need More HELP

When you know from memory the relationship between fractions such as $\frac{1}{8}$, $\frac{1}{4}$, $\frac{1}{3}$, $\frac{1}{2}$, $\frac{2}{3}$, and $\frac{3}{4}$, it is easier to round fractions or estimate the sums and differences.

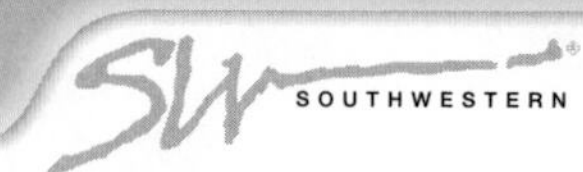

Modeling Adding Fractions with Like Denominators

You can model adding fractions with like denominators using fraction strips or diagrams.

EXAMPLE 1

Use fraction strips to model $\frac{1}{5} + \frac{3}{5}$.

Model $\frac{1}{5}$ plus $\frac{3}{5}$.

Count the number of fifths.
There are 4 fifths.

$\frac{1}{5} + \frac{3}{5} = \frac{4}{5}$

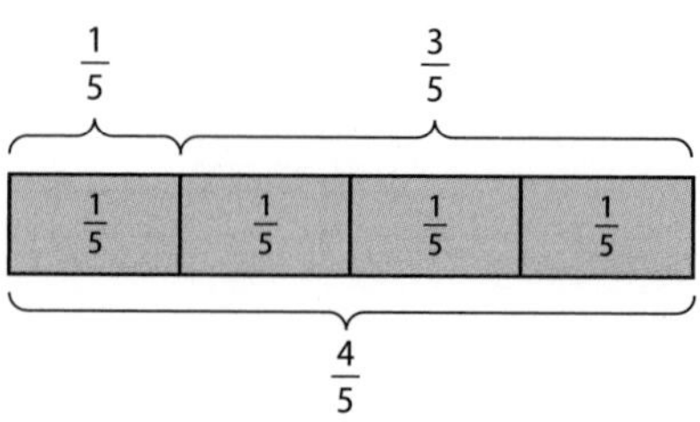

SEARCH

To see step-by-step videos of these problems, enter the page number into the SWadvantage.com Search Bar.

EXAMPLE 2

Use fraction strips to model $\frac{1}{8} + \frac{5}{8}$.

STEP 1 Model $\frac{1}{8}$ plus $\frac{5}{8}$.

Count the number of eighths.
There are 6 eighths.

$\frac{1}{8} + \frac{5}{8} = \frac{6}{8}$

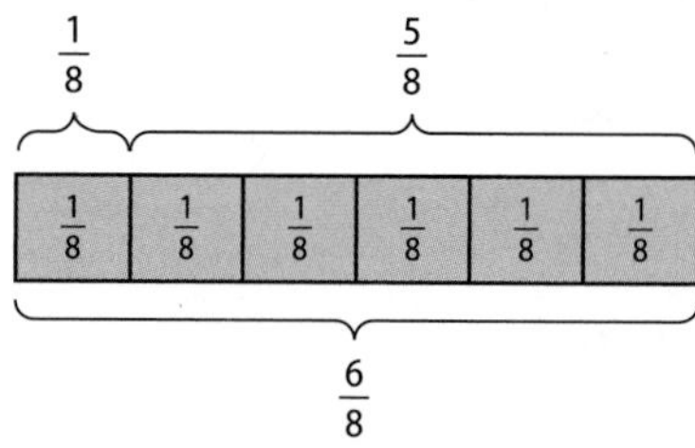

STEP 2 Simplify.

$\frac{6 \div 2}{8 \div 2} = \frac{3}{4}$

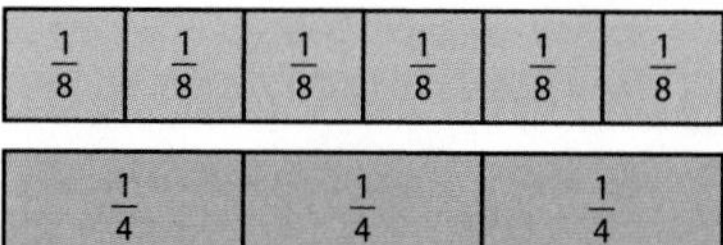

$\frac{1}{8} + \frac{5}{8} = \frac{3}{4}$

Need More HELP

For help with simplifying fractions, go to *Simplest Form of a Fraction* on page 311.

EXAMPLE 3

Use fraction strips to model $\frac{3}{4} + \frac{2}{4}$.

Model $\frac{3}{4}$ plus $\frac{2}{4}$.

There are 5 fourths.

Simplify: $\frac{5}{4} = \frac{4}{4} + \frac{1}{4}$, or $1\frac{1}{4}$

$\frac{3}{4} + \frac{2}{4} = 1\frac{1}{4}$

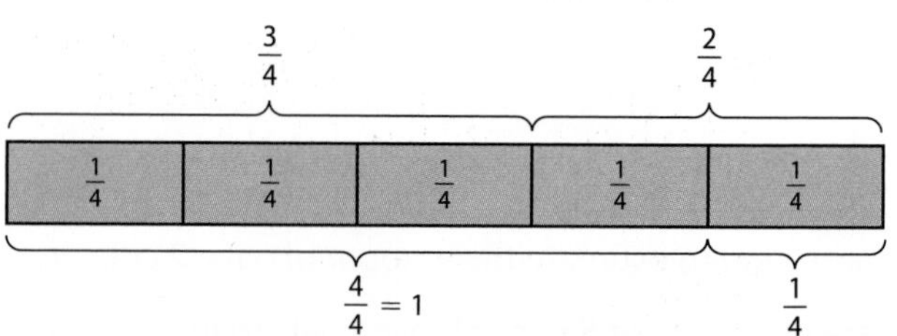

EXAMPLE 4

A round pizza is divided into ten equal slices. Ben eats 3 slices, or $\frac{3}{10}$ of the pizza. Sonia eats 2 slices, or $\frac{2}{10}$ of the pizza. What fraction represents the part of the pizza that was eaten?

STEP 1 Draw a diagram to represent the situation. Shade the part of the pizza that was eaten.

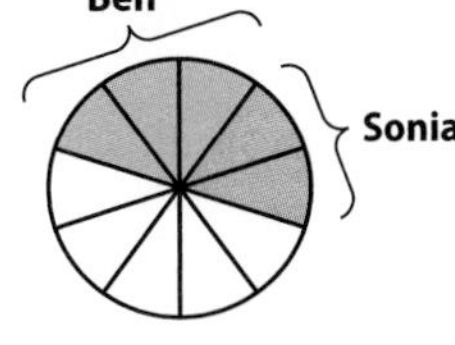

STEP 2 Count the number of slices eaten. 5.

$\frac{3}{10} + \frac{2}{10} = \frac{5}{10}$

STEP 3 Write the sum in simplest form.
Divide the numerator and denominator by 5: $\frac{5 \div 5}{10 \div 5} = \frac{1}{2}$

Ben and Sonia ate one-half of the pizza.

Adding Fractions

Like fractions are fractions with the same denominator. To add like fractions, add the numerators and put the sum over the common denominator.

EXAMPLE 5

Add. $\frac{2}{7} + \frac{3}{7}$

The fractions are like fractions. Add the numerators: $2 + 3 = 5$

$\frac{2}{7} + \frac{3}{7} = \frac{5}{7}$

Adding Fractions with Like Denominators

- Add the numerators. $\frac{5}{12} + \frac{3}{12}$
- Write the sum over their common denominator. $= \frac{8}{12}$
- Simplify if possible. $= \frac{8 \div 4}{12 \div 4}$

$= \frac{2}{3}$

Adding Fractions

Need More HELP

Remember, the *numerator* is above the fraction bar. It is the number of parts being considered. The *denominator* is below the fraction bar. It is the total number of equal parts.

EXAMPLE 6

Add. $\frac{1}{9} + \frac{5}{9} + \frac{2}{9}$

Add the numerators of the like fractions. $1 + 5 + 2 = 8$

Put the sum over the denominator. $\frac{8}{9}$

$\frac{1}{9} + \frac{5}{9} + \frac{2}{9} = \frac{8}{9}$

EXAMPLE 7

Add. $\frac{11}{12} + \frac{7}{12}$

Add the numerators of the like fractions. $11 + 7 = 18$

Put the sum over the denominator. $\frac{18}{12}$

The sum is an improper fraction. Write the improper fraction as a mixed number. $= \frac{12}{12} + \frac{6}{12} = 1\frac{6}{12}$

Simplify the fraction. Divide the numerator and denominator by their GCF, 6. $\frac{6}{12} = \frac{6 \div 6}{12 \div 6} = \frac{1}{2}$

$\frac{11}{12} + \frac{7}{12} = 1\frac{1}{2}$

EXAMPLE 8

Add. $\frac{8}{15} + \frac{4}{15} + \frac{7}{15}$

Add the numerators of the like fractions. $8 + 4 + 7 = 19$

Put the sum over the denominator. $\frac{19}{15}$

The sum is an improper fraction. Write the improper fraction as a mixed number.

METHOD 1

$\frac{19}{15} = \frac{15}{15} + \frac{4}{15}$

$= 1\frac{4}{15}$

METHOD 2

Divide the numerator by the denominator.

$$\begin{array}{r} 1 \\ 15\overline{)19} \\ \underline{15} \\ 4 \end{array}$$

$1R4 = 1\frac{4}{15}$

Adding Mixed Numbers

To add mixed numbers, add the whole number parts and the fraction parts separately.

EXAMPLE 9

Add. $2\frac{2}{15} + 5\frac{11}{15}$

Write the problem in vertical form.

Add the whole number parts.

Add the numerators of the like fractions.

$$\begin{array}{r} 2\frac{2}{15} \\ +5\frac{11}{15} \\ \hline 7\frac{13}{15} \end{array}$$

$2\frac{2}{15} + 5\frac{11}{15} = 7\frac{13}{15}$

SEARCH

To see step-by-step videos of these problems, enter the page number into the SWadvantage.com Search Bar.

EXAMPLE 10

Farrah bought $1\frac{1}{4}$ pounds of Swiss cheese, $\frac{3}{4}$ pound of American cheese, and $2\frac{1}{4}$ pounds of provolone cheese. How much cheese did she buy in all?

Add the amounts of cheese.

Write the problem in vertical form.

Add the whole number parts.

Add the numerators of the like fractions.

$$\begin{array}{r} 1\frac{1}{4} \\ \frac{3}{4} \\ +2\frac{1}{4} \\ \hline 3\frac{5}{4} \end{array}$$

Simplify the improper fraction in the sum.

$$3\frac{5}{4} = 3 + \frac{4}{4} + \frac{1}{4}$$
$$= 3 + 1 + \frac{1}{4}$$
$$= 4\frac{1}{4}$$

Farrah bought $4\frac{1}{4}$ pounds of cheese in all.

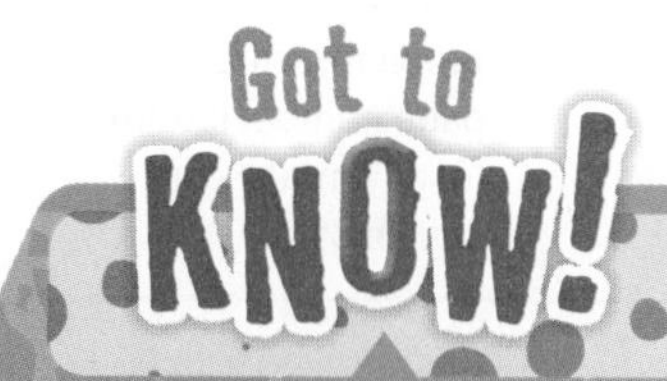

Adding Mixed Numbers

- Add the whole number parts.
- Add the fraction parts.
- Simplify the sum if necessary.

Modeling Addition with Unlike Fractions

Sometimes you need to add fractions with different denominators, or **unlike fractions**. These fractions do not have a common denominator so we say they have unlike denominators. You can use fraction strips to model adding fractions with unlike denominators.

Watch Out!

When you line up the equivalent fraction strips, make certain that they align with the left edge of the strips above them.

EXAMPLE 1

Use fraction strips to model $\frac{3}{8} + \frac{1}{2}$.

METHOD 1

Model the addition with fraction strips.

Use eighths fraction strips to rename $\frac{1}{2}$.

Count the number of eighths. $\frac{1}{2} + \frac{3}{8} = \frac{7}{8}$

$\frac{1}{8}$ $\frac{1}{8}$ $\frac{1}{8}$ + $\frac{1}{2}$

$\frac{1}{8}$ $\frac{1}{8}$ $\frac{1}{8}$ + $\frac{1}{8}$ $\frac{1}{8}$ $\frac{1}{8}$ $\frac{1}{8}$

$\frac{3}{8}$ + $\frac{4}{8}$ $= \frac{7}{8}$

METHOD 2

Model the addition without folding fraction strips.

Model the sum using eighths. strips Count the number of eighths.

$\frac{1}{2} + \frac{3}{8} = \frac{7}{8}$

$\frac{1}{2}$ $\frac{1}{2}$

$\frac{1}{8}$ $\frac{1}{8}$ $\frac{1}{8}$ $\frac{1}{8}$ $\frac{1}{8}$ $\frac{1}{8}$ $\frac{1}{8}$ $\frac{1}{8}$

$\frac{1}{8}$ $\frac{1}{8}$ $\frac{1}{8}$ $\frac{1}{8}$ $\frac{1}{8}$ $\frac{1}{8}$ $\frac{1}{8}$ $\frac{1}{8}$ $= \frac{7}{8}$

EXAMPLE 2

SEARCH

To see step-by-step videos of these problems, enter the page number into the SWadvantage.com Search Bar.

Use fraction strips to model $\frac{5}{6} + \frac{3}{4}$.

Model the addition with fraction strips.

Use twelfths fraction strips to rename both fractions.

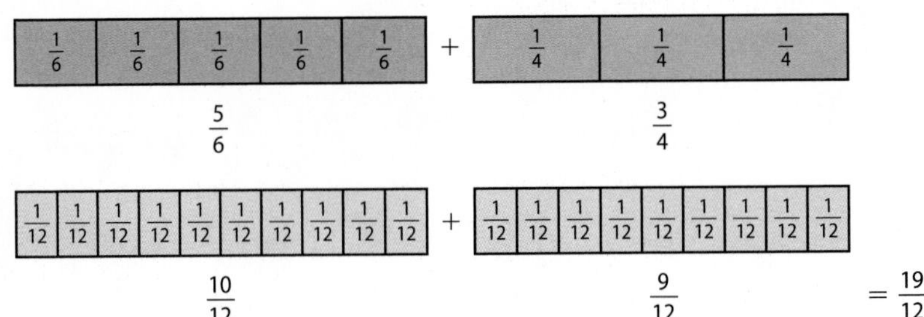

Simplify the improper fraction.

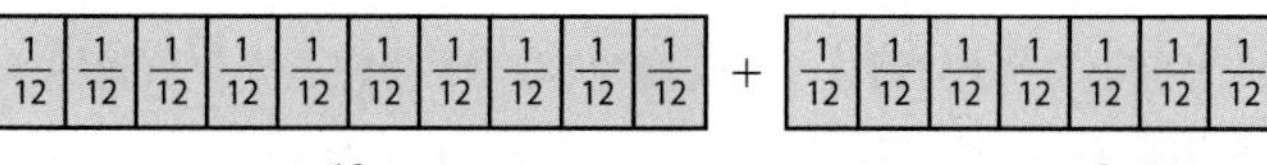

Write the sum as a mixed number.

$\frac{10}{12}$ $\frac{9}{12}$

$\frac{12}{12} = 1 \quad + \quad \frac{7}{12} \quad = 1\frac{7}{12}$

$\frac{5}{6} + \frac{3}{4} = 1\frac{7}{12}$

Using Equivalent Fractions to Add

Other ways to add unlike fractions include finding the least common denominator (LCD) of the fractions and drawing a diagram.

EXAMPLE 3

Add. $\frac{2}{5} + \frac{3}{10}$

METHOD 1

Write equivalent fractions for $\frac{2}{5}$ and $\frac{3}{10}$ using their least common denominator (LCD).

The LCD of two fractions is its LCM (least common multiple). — Multiples of 5: 5, 10, …
Multiples of 10: 10, 20, …

Find the LCM of 5 and 10. — LCM = 10

Rename $\frac{2}{5}$ using the denominator 10. — $\frac{2}{5} = \frac{2 \times 2}{5 \times 2} = \frac{4}{10}$

Now the fractions are like.

Add the numerators and put the sum over the denominator. — $\frac{4}{10} + \frac{3}{10} = \frac{4+3}{10} = \frac{7}{10}$

$\frac{2}{5} + \frac{3}{10} = \frac{7}{10}$

METHOD 2

Use a diagram.

STEP 1 Draw a diagram to model the problem.

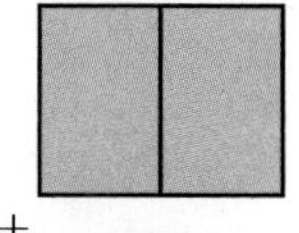

$\frac{2}{5}$

+

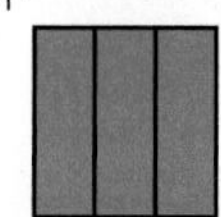

$\frac{3}{10}$

STEP 2 Change the model for $\frac{2}{5}$ into tenths.

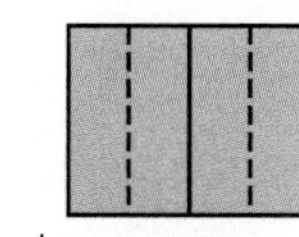

$\frac{2}{5} = \frac{4}{10}$

+

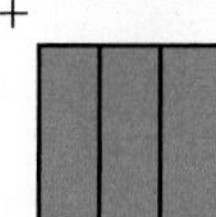

$\frac{3}{10}$

STEP 3 Count the sections. 7

$\frac{2}{5} + \frac{3}{10} = \frac{7}{10}$

Need More HELP

For help with least common multiples and least common denominators, go to *Multiples* on page 288.

Simplifying Sums with Improper Fractions

Sometimes the sum of two or more proper fractions is an improper fraction. When this happens, simplify the sum by expressing it as a mixed number.

EXAMPLE 4

Add. $\frac{5}{12} + \frac{8}{9}$

Write equivalent fractions for $\frac{5}{12}$ and $\frac{8}{9}$ using their LCD (least common denominator).

List the multiples of 12 and 9 until you find the first, or least, common multiple (LCM).

Multiples of 12: 12, 24, 36, 48, …
Multiples of 9: 9, 18, 27, 36, …

The LCM, 36, is the LCD.

Write equivalent fractions using the LCD.

$\frac{5}{12} = \frac{5 \times 3}{12 \times 3} = \frac{15}{36}$ $\quad \frac{8}{9} = \frac{8 \times 4}{9 \times 4} = \frac{32}{36}$

Add the numerators of the like fractions. Put the sum over the denominator.

$\frac{15}{36} + \frac{32}{36} = \frac{15 + 32}{36} = \frac{47}{36}$

The sum is an improper fraction.

Rename the improper fraction as a mixed number.

$$\begin{array}{r} 1 \\ 36\overline{)47} \\ -36 \\ \hline 11 \end{array}$$

$1R11 = 1\frac{11}{36}$

$\frac{5}{12} + \frac{8}{9} = 1\frac{11}{36}$

Need More HELP

For help writing improper fractions as mixed numbers, go to *Improper Fractions and Mixed Numbers* on pages 306–307.

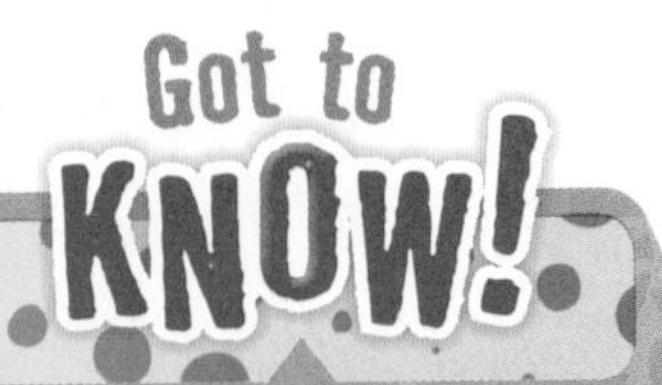

Adding Fractions with Unlike Denominators

To add fractions with different denominators:

1. Rename the fractions so they have the same denominator.
2. Add the numerators of the like fractions.
3. Write the sum of the numerators over their common denominator.
4. Simplify the sum if necessary.

$$\begin{aligned} \frac{3}{4} + \frac{1}{2} &= \frac{3 \times 3}{4 \times 3} + \frac{1 \times 6}{2 \times 6} \\ &= \frac{9}{12} + \frac{6}{12} \\ &= \frac{15}{12} \\ &= \frac{12}{12} + \frac{3}{12} \\ &= 1 + \frac{3 \div 3}{12 \div 3} \\ &= 1\frac{1}{4} \end{aligned}$$

Adding Mixed Numbers

To add mixed numbers, add the whole number parts and the fraction parts separately. It may help to write the addition problem in vertical form.

EXAMPLE 5

Add. $4\frac{5}{6} + 1\frac{1}{3} + 5\frac{1}{2}$

Write the problem in vertical form.

Rename the fraction parts so they have a common denominator.

The LCM of 6, 3, and 2 is 6. Use 6 as the LCD.

$$\begin{array}{rcr} 4\frac{5}{6} & \rightarrow & 4\frac{5}{6} \\ 1\frac{1}{3} & \rightarrow & 1\frac{2}{6} \\ +5\frac{1}{2} & \rightarrow & +5\frac{3}{6} \end{array}$$

Add the whole number parts.

Then add the fractions.

$$\begin{array}{r} 4\frac{5}{6} \\ 1\frac{2}{6} \\ +5\frac{3}{6} \\ \hline 10\frac{10}{6} \end{array}$$

Rename $\frac{10}{6}$ as a mixed number.

$$10\frac{10}{6} = 10 + \frac{6}{6} + \frac{4}{6}$$
$$= 10 + 1 + \frac{4}{6}$$
$$= 11\frac{4}{6}$$

Simplify the fraction part of the sum.

$$\frac{4}{6} = \frac{4 \div 2}{6 \div 2} = \frac{2}{3}$$

$4\frac{5}{6} + 1\frac{1}{3} + 5\frac{1}{2} = 11\frac{2}{3}$

Need More HELP

Use mental math to find equivalent fractions when the common denominator is a small number such as 6. Think:
3 divides into 6,
2 times: $2 \times 1 = 2$
2 divides into 6,
3 times: $3 \times 1 = 3$

SEARCH

To see step-by-step videos of these problems, enter the page number into the SWadvantage.com Search Bar.

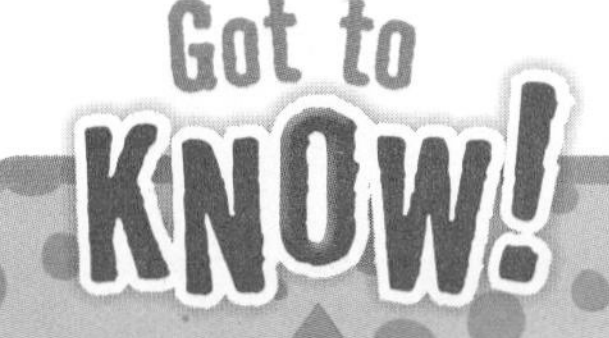

Simplifying Mixed Number Sums

If the sum includes an improper fraction, simplify the sum.

- You may only need to simplify the fraction part of the sum.
  $4\frac{6}{8} = 4\frac{3}{4}$
- You may need to express the fraction part of the sum as a mixed number.
  $4\frac{9}{8} = 4 + 1 + \frac{1}{8} = 5\frac{1}{8}$

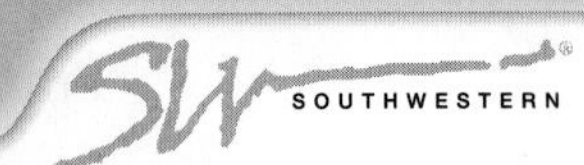

Modeling Subtracting Fractions with Like Denominators

When fractions have *like denominators,* the denominators are the same number. You can model subtracting fractions with like denominators using fraction strips or diagrams.

SEARCH

To see step-by-step videos of these problems, enter the page number into the SWadvantage.com Search Bar.

EXAMPLE 1

Use fraction strips to model $\frac{5}{6} - \frac{2}{6}$.

Model $\frac{5}{6}$.

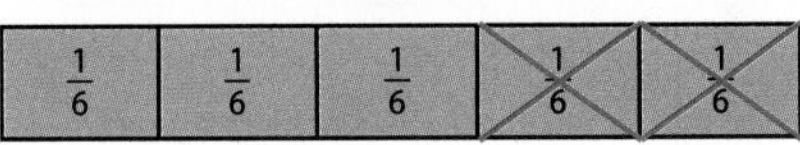

Remove $\frac{2}{6}$.

$\frac{1}{6}$	$\frac{1}{6}$	$\frac{1}{6}$	~~$\frac{1}{6}$~~	~~$\frac{1}{6}$~~

Count the number of sixths that remain. 3

$\frac{5}{6} - \frac{2}{6} = \frac{3}{6}$

EXAMPLE 2

Use fraction strips to model $\frac{11}{12} - \frac{5}{12}$.

STEP 1 Model $\frac{11}{12}$.

$\frac{1}{12}$	$\frac{1}{12}$	$\frac{1}{12}$	$\frac{1}{12}$	$\frac{1}{12}$	$\frac{1}{12}$	$\frac{1}{12}$	$\frac{1}{12}$	$\frac{1}{12}$	$\frac{1}{12}$	$\frac{1}{12}$

Remove $\frac{5}{12}$.

$\frac{1}{12}$	$\frac{1}{12}$	$\frac{1}{12}$	$\frac{1}{12}$	$\frac{1}{12}$	$\frac{1}{12}$	~~$\frac{1}{12}$~~	~~$\frac{1}{12}$~~	~~$\frac{1}{12}$~~	~~$\frac{1}{12}$~~	~~$\frac{1}{12}$~~

Count the number of twelfths that remain. 6

$\frac{11}{12} - \frac{5}{12} = \frac{6}{12}$

STEP 2 Simplify.

$\frac{6}{12} = \frac{1}{2}$

$\frac{1}{12}$	$\frac{1}{12}$	$\frac{1}{12}$	$\frac{1}{12}$	$\frac{1}{12}$	$\frac{1}{12}$

$\frac{1}{2}$

$\frac{11}{12} - \frac{5}{12} = \frac{1}{2}$

Need More HELP

For help with simplifying fractions, go to page 311.

Subtracting the Numerators

To subtract like fractions, subtract the numerators. Then put the difference over the common denominator. Always express the difference in simplest form.

Remember, the *numerator* is above the fraction bar. It is the number of parts being considered.

The *denominator* is below the fraction bar. It is the total number of equal parts.

EXAMPLE 3

Subtract. $\frac{13}{15} - \frac{11}{15}$

METHOD 1

Subtract the numerators. Then put the difference over the common denominator.

$$\frac{13}{15} - \frac{11}{15} = \frac{13 - 11}{15} = \frac{2}{15}$$

$$\frac{13}{15} - \frac{11}{15} = \frac{2}{15}$$

METHOD 2

Draw a diagram to model $\frac{13}{15}$. Shade 13 of the 15 squares.

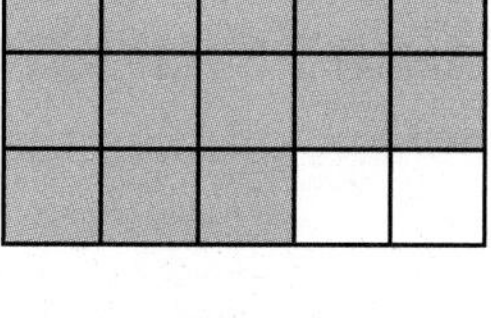

Unshade 11 squares to show "taking away" 11 from the 13 shaded squares. Two of the 15 squares remain shaded.

$$\frac{13}{15} - \frac{11}{15} = \frac{2}{15}$$

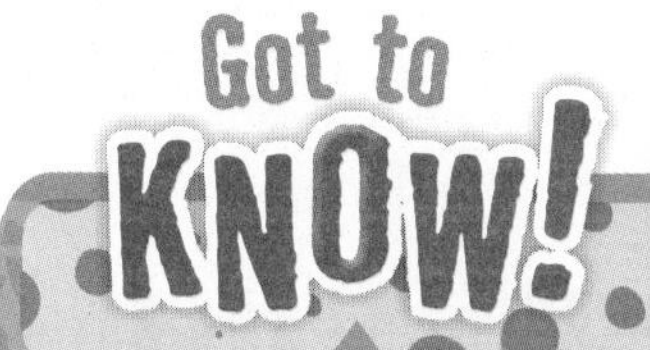

Subtracting Fractions with Like Denominators

1. Subtract the numerators and write the sum over their common denominator.
2. Simplify if possible.

$$\frac{5}{12} - \frac{3}{12} = \frac{2}{12}$$
$$= \frac{2 \div 2}{12 \div 2}$$
$$= \frac{1}{6}$$

Subtracting Fractions

Need More HELP

For help with finding the greatest common factor, go to *Factors* on page 286.

EXAMPLE 4

Subtract. $\frac{9}{10} - \frac{7}{10}$

Subtract the numerators of the fractions.	$9 - 7 = 2$
Put the sum over the common denominator.	$\frac{2}{10}$
Simplify the difference. Divide the numerator and denominator by their greatest common factor (GCF), 2.	$\frac{2}{10} = \frac{2 \div 2}{10 \div 2} = \frac{1}{5}$

$\frac{9}{10} - \frac{7}{10} = \frac{1}{5}$

Subtracting Mixed Numbers

To subtract mixed numbers, subtract the whole number parts and the fraction parts separately.

SEARCH

To see step-by-step videos of these problems, enter the page number into the SWadvantage.com Search Bar.

EXAMPLE 5

Subtract. $15\frac{7}{20} - 9\frac{3}{20}$

Write the problem in vertical form.	$15\frac{7}{20}$
Subtract the whole number parts.	$-9\frac{3}{20}$
Subtract the numerators of the like fractions.	$6\frac{4}{20}$
Simplify the fraction part of the difference. Divide the numerator and denominator by their GCF, 4.	$\frac{4}{20} = \frac{4 \div 4}{20 \div 4} = \frac{1}{5}$

$15\frac{7}{20} - 9\frac{3}{20} = 6\frac{1}{5}$

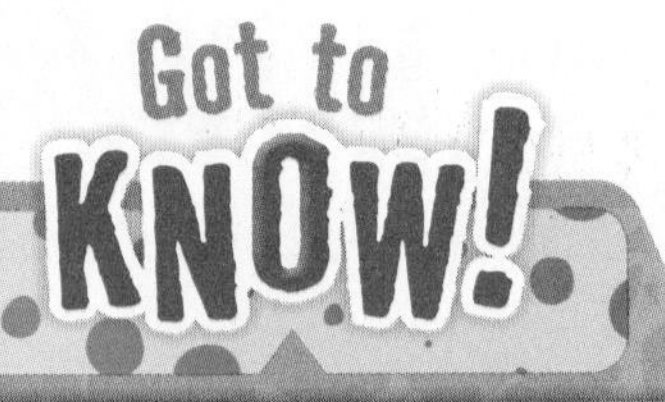

Subtracting Mixed Numbers

1. Subtract the whole number parts.
2. Subtract the fraction parts.
3. Simplify the difference if necessary.

EXAMPLE 6

Keiji bought $5\frac{3}{4}$ pounds of peanuts. He used $2\frac{1}{4}$ pounds to make peanut butter. How many pounds of peanuts are left?

Subtract the amount of peanuts Keiji used from the amount he bought.

Write the problem in vertical form.

Subtract the whole number parts.

Subtract the numerators of the like fractions.

$$\begin{array}{r} 5\frac{3}{4} \\ -2\frac{1}{4} \\ \hline 3\frac{2}{4} \end{array}$$

Simplify the fraction part of the difference. Divide the numerator and denominator by their GCF, 2.

$$\frac{2}{4} = \frac{2 \div 2}{4 \div 2} = \frac{1}{2}$$

There are $3\frac{1}{2}$ pounds of peanuts left.

Try It This Way

You may find it easier to understand the problem if you write it as two problems. Then combine the answers.

$$\begin{array}{r} 5 \\ -2 \\ \hline 3 \end{array} \qquad \begin{array}{r} \frac{3}{4} \\ -\frac{1}{4} \\ \hline \frac{2}{4} \end{array}$$

The difference is $3\frac{2}{4}$, which simplifies to $3\frac{1}{2}$.

Subtracting a Mixed Number from a Whole Number

To subtract a mixed number from a whole number, rename the whole number as a mixed number with an improper fraction. When you rename the whole number, use the same denominator shown in the fraction you will subtract. For example:

$8 - 2\frac{1}{2} = ?$ You need to subtract halves. Rename 8 as 7 + 1, or $7\frac{2}{2}$.

$7\frac{2}{2} - 2\frac{1}{2} = 5\frac{1}{2}$ Now you can subtract the whole numbers and the like fractions.

Need More HELP

Remember, when the numerator and the denominator are the same number, the fraction is equal to 1.

$\frac{2}{2} = \frac{9}{9} = 1$

EXAMPLE 7

Subtract. $17 - 10\frac{5}{9}$

Write the problem in vertical form.

You need to subtract ninths. Rename 17 as 16 + 1, or $16 + \frac{9}{9}$.

Subtract the whole number parts. Then subtract the fractions.

$$\begin{array}{r} 17 \\ -10\frac{5}{9} \\ \hline \end{array} \rightarrow \begin{array}{r} 16\frac{9}{9} \\ -10\frac{5}{9} \\ \hline 6\frac{4}{9} \end{array}$$

$17 - 10\frac{5}{9} = 6\frac{4}{9}$

Modeling Subtraction with Unlike Denominators

You can model subtracting fractions with unlike denominators by using fraction strips.

Need More HELP

Remember, *unlike fractions* are fractions with different denominators.

EXAMPLE 1

Use fraction strips to model $\frac{1}{3} - \frac{1}{6}$.

METHOD 1

You can see that $\frac{1}{3} = \frac{2}{6}$.

Model $\frac{1}{3}$ and $\frac{2}{6}$.

Remove $\frac{1}{6}$.

There is 1 sixth remaining.

$\frac{1}{3} - \frac{1}{6} = \frac{1}{6}$

METHOD 2

Model $\frac{1}{3}$.

Model $\frac{1}{6}$ just below it.

The space that remains is the *difference*. Find the number of sixths that will fit in this space.

1 sixth fits into the space.

$\frac{1}{3} - \frac{1}{6} = \frac{1}{6}$

Difference

SEARCH

To see step-by-step videos of these problems, enter the page number into the SWadvantage.com Search Bar.

Subtracting by Modeling and Using Equivalent Fractions

Another way to subtract unlike fractions is to rename the fractions so they are like fractions, or fractions with the same denominator. If one denominator is a multiple of the other, you will need to rename only one of the fractions, as shown in Example 2. If not, you will need to rename both fractions, as shown in Example 3.

EXAMPLE 2

Subtract $\frac{5}{9} - \frac{1}{3}$.

METHOD 1

Use a diagram to rename the fractions.

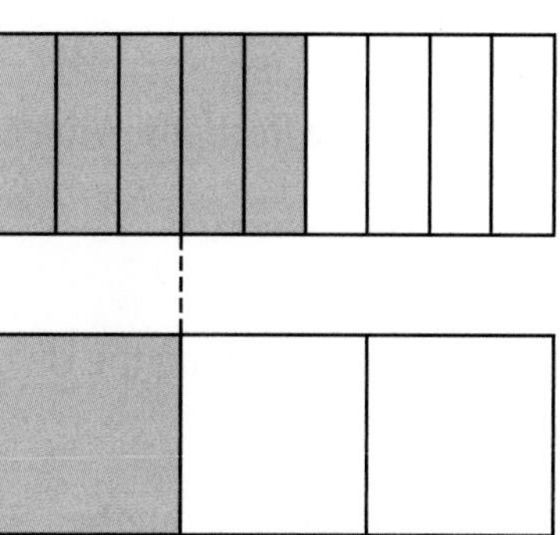

STEP 1 Draw a diagram to model the problem.

The model shows that $\frac{1}{3} = \frac{3}{9}$.

STEP 2 Subtract the like fractions.

$\frac{5}{9} - \frac{3}{9} = \frac{5-3}{9} = \frac{2}{9}$

$\frac{5}{9} - \frac{1}{3} = \frac{2}{9}$

Need More HELP

For help with writing equivalent fractions, go to *Equivalent Fractions* on page 310.

METHOD 2

Write equivalent fractions for $\frac{5}{9}$ and $\frac{1}{3}$ using their least common denominator (LCD).

STEP 1 Find the LCD. The LCD of two or more fractions is the same as their least common multiple (LCM).

Find the LCM of 9 and 3. Multiples of 9: 9, 18, 27, . . .

The LCD of 3 and 9 is 9. Multiples of 3: 3, 6, 9, . . .

Need More HELP

For help finding the LCD and the LCM, go to *Multiples* on page 288.

STEP 2 Rename the fractions to have 9 as the denominator.

The fraction $\frac{5}{9}$ already has 9 as its denominator.

Rename $\frac{1}{3}$ as an equivalent fraction with 9 as the denominator.

$\frac{1}{3} = \frac{1 \times 3}{3 \times 3} = \frac{3}{9}$

STEP 3 Subtract the like fractions.

$\frac{5}{9} - \frac{3}{9} = \frac{5-3}{9} = \frac{2}{9}$

$\frac{5}{9} - \frac{1}{3} = \frac{2}{9}$

Subtracting by Writing Equivalent Fractions

EXAMPLE 3

Subtract $\frac{7}{8} - \frac{5}{6}$.

The fractions are unlike fractions. Write equivalent fractions for $\frac{7}{8}$ and $\frac{5}{6}$ using their LCD.

Find the LCM of 8 and 6.
The LCD is 24.

Multiples of 8: 8, 16, 24, 32, . . .
Multiples of 6: 6, 12, 18, 24, . . .

Write equivalent fractions using the LCD. $\frac{7}{8} = \frac{7 \times 3}{8 \times 3} = \frac{21}{24}$ $\frac{5}{6} = \frac{5 \times 4}{6 \times 4} = \frac{20}{24}$

Now the fractions are like.

Subtract the numerators and put the difference over the denominator. $\frac{21}{24} - \frac{20}{24} = \frac{21 - 20}{24} = \frac{1}{24}$

$\frac{7}{8} - \frac{5}{6} = \frac{1}{24}$

SEARCH

To see step-by-step videos of these problems, enter the page number into the SWadvantage.com Search Bar.

EXAMPLE 4

Danielle has a piece of ribbon $\frac{5}{6}$ yard long. She cuts off a piece that is $\frac{7}{12}$ yard long. How much ribbon does she have left?

Subtract $\frac{5}{6} - \frac{7}{12}$.

The fractions are unlike fractions. Write equivalent fractions for $\frac{5}{6}$ and $\frac{7}{12}$ using their LCD.

Find the LCM of 6 and 12.
The LCD is 12.

Multiples of 6: 6, 12, 18, 24, 30, 36, 42, . . .
Multiples of 12: 12, 24, 36, 48, . . .

The fraction $\frac{7}{12}$ already has 12 as a denominator. Rename $\frac{5}{6}$ with 12 as the denominator.

$\frac{5}{6} = \frac{5 \times 2}{6 \times 2} = \frac{10}{12}$

Subtract the like fractions. $\frac{10}{12} - \frac{7}{12} = \frac{10 - 7}{12} = \frac{3}{12}$

Write the difference in simplest form. Divide the numerator and denominator by the GCF of 3 and 12. $\frac{3}{12} = \frac{3 \div 3}{12 \div 3} = \frac{1}{4}$

Danielle has $\frac{1}{4}$ yard of ribbon left.

Got to KNOW!

Subtracting Fractions with Unlike Denominators

1. Rename the fractions as like fractions, fractions with the same denominator.
2. Subtract the numerators of the like fractions and write the difference over their common denominator.
3. Simplify the fraction, if possible.

Subtracting Mixed Numbers

To subtract mixed numbers, subtract the whole number parts and the fraction parts separately. Rename the fractions so they are like fractions.

In some mixed numbers, the fraction part of the *subtrahend* is greater than the fraction part of the *minuend*. For example, in

$3\frac{1}{4} - 1\frac{2}{4}, \frac{2}{4} > \frac{1}{4}$.

When this is the case, rename the mixed number in the minuend.

Rename $3\frac{1}{4}$ as

$\left(2 + 1 + \frac{1}{4}\right) = \left(2 + \frac{4}{4} + \frac{1}{4}\right) = 2\frac{5}{4}$

For help writing mixed numbers as improper fractions, go to *Improper Fractions and Mixed Numbers* on page 306.

EXAMPLE 5

Subtract $8\frac{3}{4} - 6\frac{5}{8}$.

You can write the problem in vertical form.

The fraction parts of the mixed numbers are unlike fractions.

The LCM of 4 and 8 is 8. Write equivalent fractions using 8 as the LCD.

$$\begin{array}{rcr} 8\frac{3}{4} & \rightarrow & 8\frac{6}{8} \\ -\,6\frac{5}{8} & \rightarrow & -\,6\frac{5}{8} \\ \hline & & 2\frac{1}{8} \end{array}$$

$8\frac{3}{4} - 6\frac{5}{8} = 2\frac{1}{8}$

EXAMPLE 6

Subtract $6\frac{1}{4} - 1\frac{2}{3}$.

You can write the problem in vertical form.

The fraction parts of the mixed numbers are unlike fractions.

$$\begin{array}{rcr} 6\frac{1}{4} & \rightarrow & 6\frac{3}{12} \\ -\,1\frac{2}{3} & \rightarrow & -\,1\frac{8}{12} \\ \hline \end{array}$$

The LCM of 4 and 3 is 12. Write equivalent fractions using 12 as the LCD.

Since $8 > 3$, rename $6\frac{3}{12}$ as

$\left(5 + 1 + \frac{3}{12}\right) = \left(5 + \frac{12}{12} + \frac{3}{12}\right) = 5\frac{15}{12}$.

$$\begin{array}{rcr} 6\frac{3}{12} & \rightarrow & 5\frac{15}{12} \\ -\,1\frac{8}{12} & \rightarrow & -\,1\frac{8}{12} \\ \hline & & 4\frac{7}{12} \end{array}$$

$6\frac{1}{4} - 1\frac{2}{3} = 4\frac{7}{12}$

Multiplying Fractions by Fractions

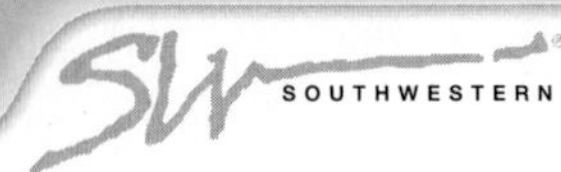

Modeling Multiplication of Fractions

A diagram can be used to model multiplication of fractions.

EXAMPLE 1

Draw a diagram to model the problem $\frac{1}{4} \times \frac{3}{8}$.

STEP 1 Divide a rectangle into fourths. Shade one fourth in blue.

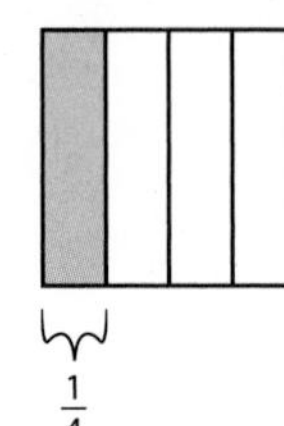

STEP 2 Divide each fourth into eighths. Shade three eighths in yellow.

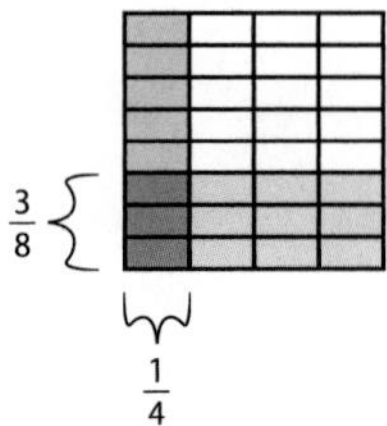

STEP 3 The model is now divided into 32 equal sections. Each section is $\frac{1}{32}$. The area where the blue and yellow shading overlap represents the product. Since there are 3 sections that overlap, the product is $\frac{3}{32}$.

$\frac{1}{4} \times \frac{3}{8} = \frac{3}{32}$

Need More HELP

This type of diagram is sometimes called an *area model.*

To see step-by-step videos of these problems, enter the page number into the SWadvantage.com Search Bar.

Multiplying Fractions

When you multiply fractions, multiply the numerators and multiply the denominators. Simplify the product, if necessary.

EXAMPLE 2

Multiply $\frac{3}{8} \times \frac{2}{5}$.

METHOD 1

Multiply the numerators.

Multiply the denominators.

$$\frac{3}{8} \times \frac{2}{5} = \frac{3 \times 2}{8 \times 5} = \frac{6}{40}$$

Simplify. Divide the numerator and the denominator by their greatest common factor (GCF).

$$\frac{6}{40} = \frac{6 \div 2}{40 \div 2} = \frac{3}{20}$$

$\frac{3}{8} \times \frac{2}{5} = \frac{3}{20}$

Need More HELP

For help with writing fractions in simplest form, go to *Equivalent Fractions* on page 308.

METHOD 2

Simplify first. Eliminate common factors in the numerator and denominator of the product before you multiply. Then multiply the numerators and denominators.

Simplify first.

Divide 2 and 8 by their GCF, 2. $\frac{3}{8} \times \frac{2}{5} = \frac{3}{\cancel{8}_4} \times \frac{\cancel{2}^1}{5}$

Multiply the numerators. $\frac{3}{4} \times \frac{1}{5} = \frac{3 \times 1}{4 \times 5} = \frac{3}{20}$

Multiply the denominators.

$\frac{3}{8} \times \frac{2}{5} = \frac{3}{20}$

EXAMPLE 3

In Janelle's flower garden, $\frac{4}{9}$ of the flowers are pansies, and $\frac{3}{4}$ of the pansies are yellow. What part of the flowers in the garden are yellow pansies?

You need to find $\frac{4}{9}$ of $\frac{3}{4}$. The word *of* means "times," so find $\frac{4}{9} \times \frac{3}{4}$.

Simplify first.

Divide 3 and 9 by their GCF, 3. $\frac{4}{9} \times \frac{3}{4} = \frac{\cancel{4}^1}{\cancel{9}_3} \times \frac{\cancel{3}^1}{\cancel{4}_1}$

Divide 4 and 4 by their GCF, 4.

Multiply the numerators. $\frac{1}{3} \times \frac{1}{1} = \frac{1 \times 1}{3 \times 1} = \frac{1}{3}$

Multiply the denominators.

So, $\frac{1}{3}$ of the flowers in the garden are yellow pansies.

Watch Out!

You know that $1 \times 1 = 1$. When both of the factors are less than 1, the product will be *less* than either factor. This is because you are multiplying a number less than 1 by another number less than 1.

Try It This Way

Draw a diagram to solve the problem.

- Draw 9 flowers.
- Label 4 flowers pansies.
- Color 3 of the pansies yellow.

3 out of 9 flowers are yellow pansies.

$\frac{3}{9} = \frac{1}{3}$

You can also draw a diagram as shown in Example 1.

Got to KNOW!

Multiplying Fractions by Fractions

1. Multiply the numerators and multiply the denominators.
   $\frac{1}{3} \times \frac{3}{5} = \frac{3}{15}$
2. Simplify the result, if necessary. Use the greatest common factor (GCF) of the numerator and the denominator.
   $\frac{3}{15} = \frac{3 \div 3}{15 \div 3} = \frac{1}{5}$

Alternate method:

1. Simplify first by factoring out common factors in the numerator and denominator of the product before you multiply.
2. Then multiply the numerators and denominators.

Multiplying Whole Numbers and Fractions

Modeling Multiplication of a Whole Number and a Fraction

You can use fraction strips, diagrams, and fraction circles to model multiplying a whole number by a fraction.

EXAMPLE 1

Multiply $2 \times \frac{1}{9}$.

Model the problem as addition using fraction strips.

$$2 \times \frac{1}{9} = \underbrace{\frac{1}{9} + \frac{1}{9}}_{2}$$

$$2 \times \frac{1}{9} = \frac{2}{9}$$

$\frac{1}{9}$ + $\frac{1}{9}$

$\underbrace{\frac{1}{9}\ \frac{1}{9}}_{\frac{2}{9}}$

EXAMPLE 2

Multiply $3 \times \frac{1}{2}$.

Model the problem as addition.

 +  + 

$$3 \times \frac{1}{2} = \underbrace{\frac{1}{2} + \frac{1}{2} + \frac{1}{2}}_{3}$$

Combine the parts.

$$3 \times \frac{1}{2} = \frac{3}{2} = 1\frac{1}{2}$$

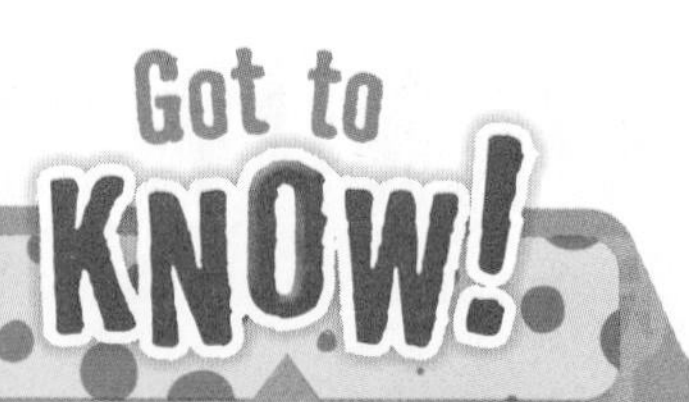

Multiplication as Repeated Addition

The multiplication of a whole number by a whole number is the same as repeated addition.

The same is true of the multiplication of a whole number by a fraction.

$$3 \times \frac{2}{5} = \frac{2}{5} + \frac{2}{5} + \frac{2}{5}$$

EXAMPLE 3

Multiply $5 \times \frac{2}{3}$.

Model the problem as addition using fraction circles.

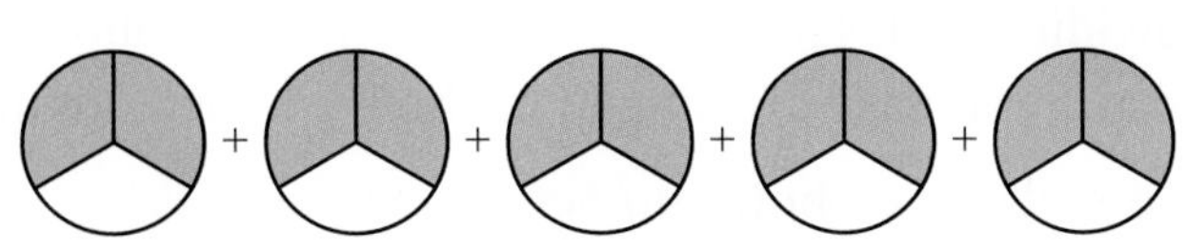

$$5 \times \frac{2}{3} = \underbrace{\frac{2}{3} + \frac{2}{3} + \frac{2}{3} + \frac{2}{3} + \frac{2}{3}}_{5}$$

Combine the parts into whole circles.

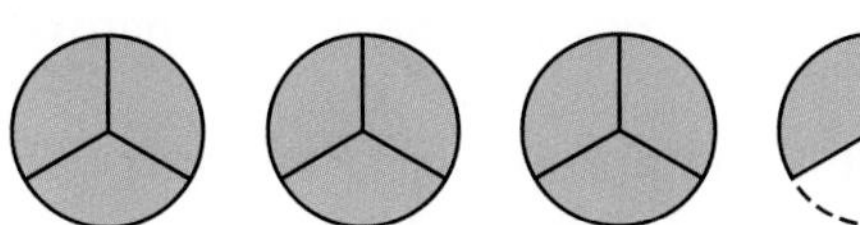

$$5 \times \frac{2}{3} = \frac{10}{3} = 3\frac{1}{3}$$

SEARCH

To see step-by-step videos of these problems, enter the page number into the SWadvantage.com Search Bar.

EXAMPLE 4

Use models to show that $\frac{1}{4} \times 4$ is equivalent to $4 \times \frac{1}{4}$.

STEP 1 Model $\frac{1}{4} \times 4$.

Draw four boxes to represent the 4.

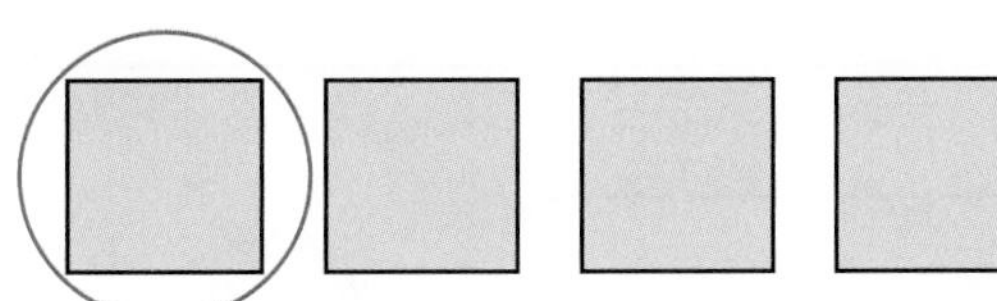

The circle marks $\frac{1}{4}$ of a group of 4.

$\frac{1}{4} \times 4 = 1$

STEP 2 Model $4 \times \frac{1}{4}$.

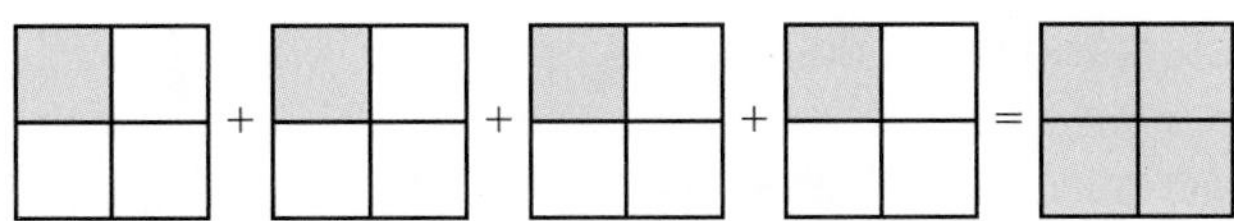

The model shows one-fourth taken four times.

$4 \times \frac{1}{4} = 1$

Since both products equal 1, then $\frac{1}{4} \times 4$ is equivalent to $4 \times \frac{1}{4}$.

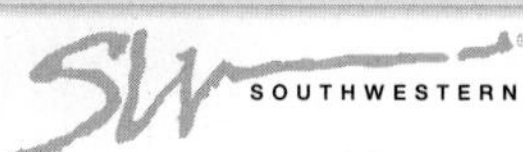

Need More HELP

For help with multiplying fractions, go to *Multiplying Fractions by Fractions* on page 334.

Multiplying a Whole Number by a Fraction

You may have learned to find $\frac{1}{2}$ of 6 by dividing 6 by 2, or to find $\frac{1}{4}$ of 16 by dividing by 4. This method works when the numerator of the fraction is 1, but you are actually dividing by a whole number, not multiplying by a fraction.

To multiply a whole number by a fraction:

- Write the whole number as a fraction with a denominator of 1. $\frac{1}{2} \times \frac{6}{1}$
- Multiply the numerators and the denominators. $= \frac{1}{2} \times \frac{6}{1}$
- If the product is an improper fraction, rewrite it as a mixed number and simplify if necessary. $= \frac{6}{2}$

$= 3$

EXAMPLE 5

SEARCH

To see step-by-step videos of these problems, enter the page number into the SWadvantage.com Search Bar.

Multiply $7 \times \frac{2}{15}$.

Write 7 as $\frac{7}{1}$. $\frac{7}{1} \times \frac{2}{15}$

Multiply the numerators and the denominators. $= \frac{14}{15}$

$7 \times \frac{2}{15} = \frac{14}{15}$

EXAMPLE 6

Multiply $6 \times \frac{3}{8}$.

Need More HELP

For help with improper fractions and mixed numbers, go to *Improper Fractions and Mixed Numbers* on page 306.

METHOD 1

Multiply, and then simplify.

Write 6 as $\frac{6}{1}$. $\frac{6}{1} \times \frac{3}{8}$

Multiply the numerators and the denominators. $= \frac{18}{8}$

$\frac{18}{8}$ is an improper fraction. Rewrite it as a mixed number. $= 2\frac{2}{8}$

Simplify. $= 2\frac{1}{4}$

$6 \times \frac{3}{8} = 2\frac{1}{4}$

METHOD 2

Simplify, and then multiply.

Write 6 as $\frac{6}{1}$.	$\frac{6}{1} \times \frac{3}{8}$
Simplify. Divide 6 and 8 by their greatest common factor (GCF), 2.	$= \frac{\overset{3}{\cancel{6}}}{1} \times \frac{3}{\underset{4}{\cancel{8}}}$
Multiply.	$= \frac{9}{4}$
Write the improper fraction $\frac{9}{4}$ as a mixed number.	$= 2\frac{1}{4}$

$6 \times \frac{3}{8} = 2\frac{1}{4}$

EXAMPLE 7

There are 36 pieces of chocolate candy in a box. Two-ninths of them contain cherries. How many of the chocolates contain cherries?

The 36 pieces in the box of chocolates represent the whole. Only a part of them, $\frac{2}{9}$, contain cherries. To find the number of chocolates that contain cherries, multiply 36 by $\frac{2}{9}$.

Write 36 as $\frac{36}{1}$.	$\frac{36}{1} \times \frac{2}{9}$
Simplify. Divide 36 and 9 by their GCF, 9.	$= \frac{\overset{4}{\cancel{36}}}{1} \times \frac{2}{\underset{1}{\cancel{9}}}$
Multiply.	$= \frac{8}{1}$
	$= 8$

Eight of the chocolates contain cherries.

Try It This Way

Use 36 counters to model the chocolates. Arrange the counters into 9 equal groups. Then count the number of counters in 2 of the groups.

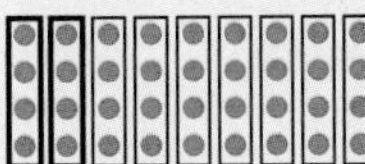

There are 8 counters in the two groups, so 8 of the chocolates contain cherries.

Multiplying Whole Numbers by Fractions

1. Write the whole number as a fraction with a denominator of 1.
2. Multiply the numerators and multiply the denominators.
3. Simplify the fraction if possible.

Multiplying Mixed Numbers

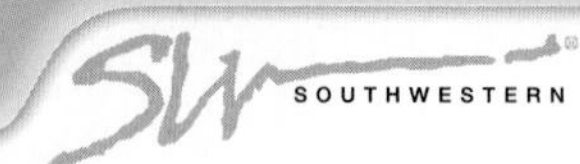

Modeling Multiplying Mixed Numbers and Whole Numbers

You can use a diagram to model multiplying a whole number by a mixed number.

SEARCH

To see step-by-step videos of these problems, enter the page number into the SWadvantage.com Search Bar.

EXAMPLE 1

Multiply $2 \times 1\frac{1}{4}$.

Model the problem as addition using a diagram.

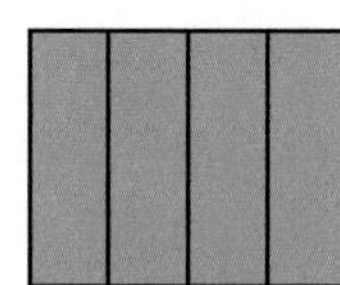
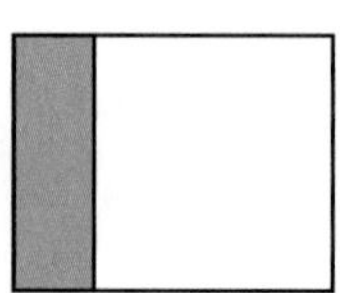
+
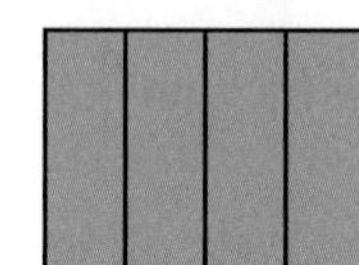
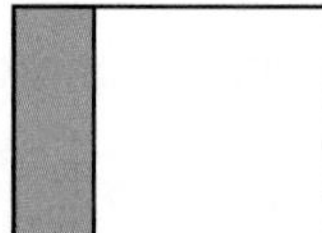

$$2 \times 1\frac{1}{4} = \underbrace{1\frac{1}{4} + 1\frac{1}{4}}_{2}$$

Combine the parts.

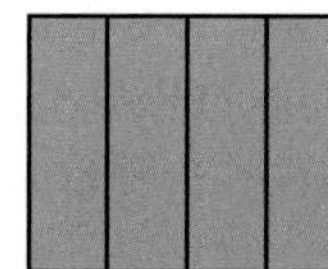
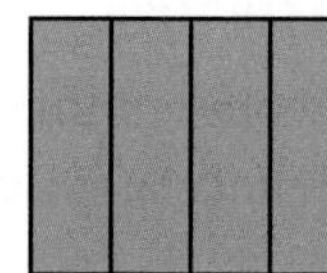
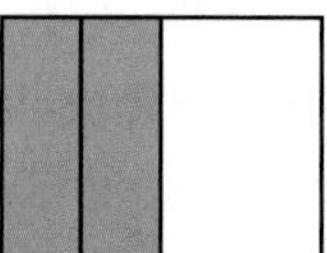

$$2 \times 1\frac{1}{4} = 2\frac{1}{2}$$

Multiplying Mixed Numbers and Whole Numbers

To multiply a mixed number by a whole number, first express the mixed number and the whole number as improper fractions. Then multiply the fractions.

Need More HELP

Remember, the term *express* means to state in a certain way. You could also say *write* or *rename* a mixed number as an improper fraction.

For help writing mixed numbers as improper fractions, go to *Improper Fractions and Mixed Numbers* on page 306.

EXAMPLE 2

Multiply $1\frac{2}{3} \times 4$.

Express $1\frac{2}{3}$ as the improper fraction $\frac{5}{3}$.	$\frac{5}{3} \times \frac{4}{1}$
Express 4 as a fraction with a denominator of 1: $\frac{4}{1}$.	
Multiply the numerators and the denominators.	$= \frac{5 \times 4}{3 \times 1}$
Write $\frac{20}{3}$ as a mixed number.	$= \frac{20}{3}$
	$= 6\frac{2}{3}$

$$1\frac{2}{3} \times 4 = 6\frac{2}{3}$$

EXAMPLE 3

Multiply $5\frac{3}{8} \times 2$.

Express $5\frac{3}{8}$ as $\frac{43}{8}$ and 2 as $\frac{2}{1}$.	$\frac{43}{8} \times \frac{2}{1}$
Simplify. Divide 8 and 2 by their greatest common factor (GCF), 2.	$= \frac{43}{\cancel{8}_4} \times \frac{\cancel{2}^1}{1}$
Multiply the numerators and the denominators.	$= \frac{43 \times 1}{4 \times 1}$
Express $\frac{43}{4}$ as a mixed number.	$= \frac{43}{4}$
	$= 10\frac{3}{4}$

$5\frac{3}{8} \times 2 = 10\frac{3}{4}$

Need More HELP

For help finding the GCF, go to *Factors* on page 286.

EXAMPLE 4

Mrs. Chen bought 3 packages of carrots. Each package weighs $1\frac{1}{4}$ pounds. How many pounds of carrots did Mrs. Chen buy in all?

Multiply the number of packages by the weight of each package: $3 \times 1\frac{1}{4}$

METHOD 1

Express 3 as $\frac{3}{1}$ and $1\frac{1}{4}$ as $\frac{5}{4}$.	$\frac{3}{1} \times \frac{5}{4}$
Multiply the numerators and the denominators.	$= \frac{3 \times 5}{1 \times 4}$
Express $\frac{15}{4}$ as a mixed number.	$= \frac{15}{4}$
Simplify.	$= 3\frac{3}{4}$

Mrs. Chen bought $3\frac{3}{4}$ pounds of carrots.

METHOD 2

Write $3 \times 1\frac{1}{4}$ as repeated addition.	$3 \times 1\frac{1}{4} = 1\frac{1}{4} + 1\frac{1}{4} + 1\frac{1}{4}$
Add the whole numbers, and then add the fractions.	$= 3\frac{3}{4}$

Mrs. Chen bought $3\frac{3}{4}$ pounds of carrots.

Got to KNOW!

Multiplying a Mixed Number by a Whole Number

1. Express the whole number as a fraction with 1 as the denominator.
2. Express the mixed number as an improper fraction.
3. Multiply the two fractions by multiplying the numerators and multiplying the denominators.
4. Simplify the fraction if possible.

Modeling Multiplying Mixed Numbers and Fractions

When you multiply a mixed number by a fraction, you are multiplying by a value that is less than 1. The product will always be less than the mixed number factor. Check your answer to be sure it is not greater than the mixed number factor.

SEARCH

To see step-by-step videos of these problems, enter the page number into the SWadvantage.com Search Bar.

EXAMPLE 5

Multiply $\frac{1}{3} \times 1\frac{1}{2}$.

Remember, $\frac{1}{3} \times 1\frac{1}{2}$ means the same thing as $\frac{1}{3}$ of $1\frac{1}{2}$.

METHOD 1

STEP 1 Model the fraction $1\frac{1}{2}$.

Draw two squares and divide them in half. Shade 1 whole square and $\frac{1}{2}$ of the other square.

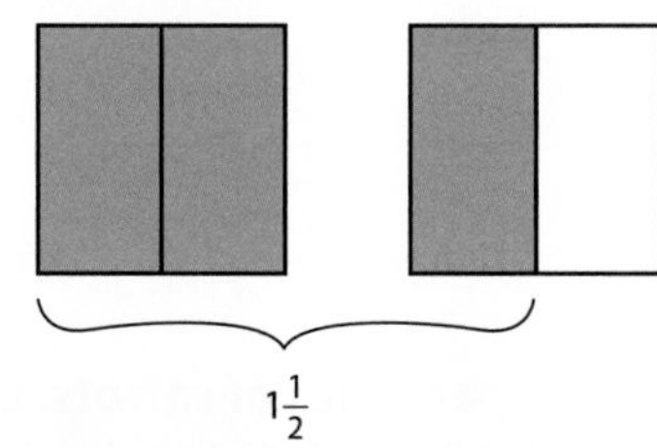

STEP 2 Divide each half into thirds and shade $\frac{1}{3}$ of each half.

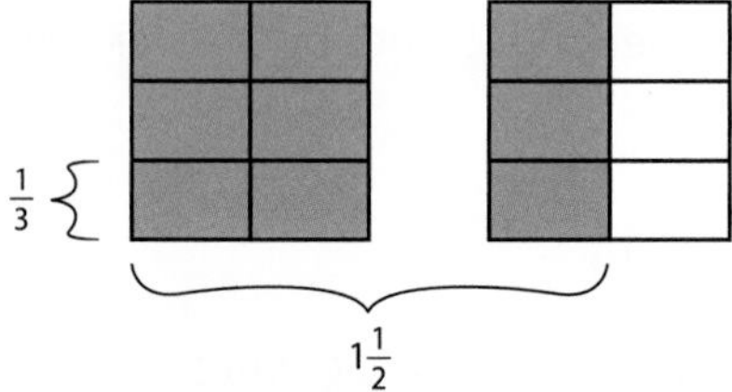

STEP 3 Each whole square is now divided into six equal sections. Each section is $\frac{1}{6}$ of the whole. The area where the shading overlaps represents the product. Since there are 3 sections that overlap, the product is $\frac{3}{6}$. Simplify the product: $\frac{3}{6} = \frac{1}{2}$

$\frac{1}{3} \times 1\frac{1}{2} = \frac{1}{2}$

METHOD 2

Model the fraction $1\frac{1}{2}$ using a diagram.

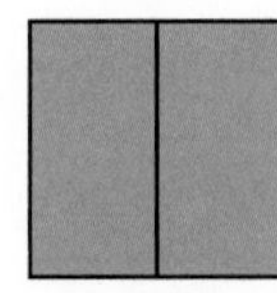 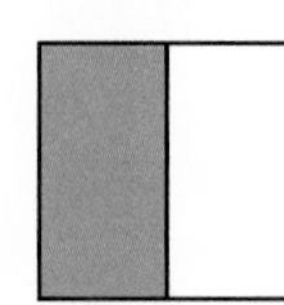 = 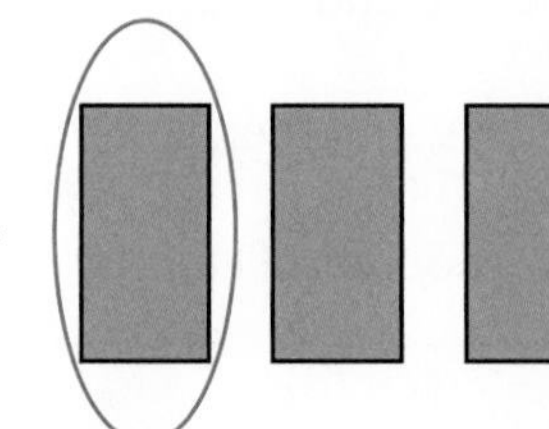

Divide $1\frac{1}{2}$ into 3 equal groups.

$\frac{1}{3} \times 1\frac{1}{2} = \frac{1}{2}$

Multiplying Mixed Numbers and Fractions

To multiply a mixed number by a fraction, first express the mixed number as an improper fraction. Then multiply the two fractions.

EXAMPLE 6

Multiply $2\frac{5}{12} \times \frac{3}{7}$.

Express $2\frac{5}{12}$ as $\frac{29}{12}$.	$\frac{29}{12} \times \frac{3}{7}$
Simplify. Divide 12 and 3 by their GCF, 3.	$= \frac{29}{\cancel{12}_4} \times \frac{\cancel{3}^1}{7}$
Multiply the numerators and the denominators.	$= \frac{29 \times 1}{4 \times 7}$
Write $\frac{29}{28}$ as a mixed number.	$= \frac{29}{28}$
	$= 1\frac{1}{28}$

$2\frac{5}{12} \times \frac{3}{7} = 1\frac{1}{28}$

EXAMPLE 7

Filipe ran $2\frac{1}{4}$ miles around a track. Pamela ran one-third of the distance Filipe ran. How far did Pamela run?

The word "of" means "times." Multiply the distance Filipe ran by $\frac{1}{3}$. $2\frac{1}{4} \times \frac{1}{3}$

Remember, the product will be less than the mixed number factor.

Write $2\frac{1}{4}$ as $\frac{9}{4}$.	$\frac{9}{4} \times \frac{1}{3}$
Simplify. Divide 3 and 9 by their GCF, 3.	$= \frac{^3\cancel{9}}{4} \times \frac{1}{\cancel{3}_1}$
Multiply the numerators and the denominators.	$= \frac{3 \times 1}{4 \times 1} = \frac{3}{4}$

Pamela ran $\frac{3}{4}$ of a mile.

CHECK Is your answer reasonable? $2\frac{1}{4}$ rounds to 2. One-third of 2 is less than 1. Since $\frac{3}{4}$ is less than 1, the answer is reasonable. ✔

Multiplying Mixed Numbers and Mixed Numbers

To multiply a mixed number by a mixed number, first express both mixed numbers as improper fractions. Then multiply the improper fractions.

Watch Out !

When multiplying two mixed numbers, you CANNOT multiply the whole numbers and the fractions separately. Remember a mixed number is the *sum* of a whole number and a fraction, not the *product*.

EXAMPLE 8

Multiply $2\frac{1}{4} \times 5\frac{1}{2}$.

Express $2\frac{1}{4}$ as $\frac{9}{4}$ and $5\frac{1}{2}$ as $\frac{11}{2}$.	$\frac{9}{4} \times \frac{11}{2}$
Multiply the numerators and the denominators.	$= \frac{9 \times 11}{4 \times 2}$
Write $\frac{99}{8}$ as a mixed number.	$= \frac{99}{8}$
	$= 12\frac{3}{8}$

$2\frac{1}{4} \times 5\frac{1}{2} = 12\frac{3}{8}$

EXAMPLE 9

Multiply $1\frac{2}{5} \times 3\frac{1}{3}$.

Write $1\frac{2}{5}$ as $\frac{7}{5}$ and $3\frac{1}{3}$ as $\frac{10}{3}$.	$\frac{7}{5} \times \frac{10}{3}$
Simplify. Divide 5 and 10 by their GCF, 5.	$= \frac{7}{\cancel{5}_1} \times \frac{\cancel{10}^2}{3}$
Multiply the numerators and the denominators.	$= \frac{7 \times 2}{1 \times 3}$
Write $\frac{14}{3}$ as a mixed number.	$= \frac{14}{3}$
	$= 4\frac{2}{3}$

$1\frac{2}{5} \times 3\frac{1}{3} = 4\frac{2}{3}$

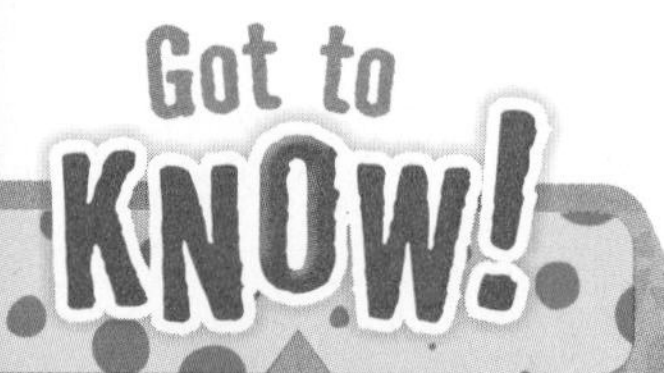

Multiplying Mixed Numbers

1. Express both of the numbers as improper fractions.
2. Then multiply as you would multiply proper fractions.

EXAMPLE 10

Kevin is having some friends over for dinner. He plans to make one and one-half times his favorite chili recipe.

Kevin's Super Good Chili
Ingredients
1 onion, chopped
1 green pepper, chopped
1 tbsp oil
$2\frac{3}{4}$ cups kidney beans
2 16-oz cans of tomatoes
$\frac{1}{2}$ lb ground turkey
2 tsp chili powder
1 tsp salt

a. He has 5 cups of kidney beans. Is this enough?

The recipe uses $2\frac{3}{4}$ cups of kidney beans.

Multiply this quantity by $1\frac{1}{2}$.

$2\frac{3}{4} \times 1\frac{1}{2}$

Write $2\frac{3}{4}$ as $\frac{11}{4}$ and $1\frac{1}{2}$ as $\frac{3}{2}$. $\quad \frac{11}{4} \times \frac{3}{2}$

Multiply the numerators and the denominators. $\quad = \frac{11 \times 3}{4 \times 2}$

$= \frac{33}{8}$

Write $\frac{33}{8}$ as a mixed number. $\quad = 4\frac{1}{8}$

Kevin needs $4\frac{1}{8}$ cup of kidney beans. Since $4\frac{1}{8} < 5$, Kevin has enough kidney beans.

b. How many teaspoons of chili power will he need?

The recipe uses 2 teaspoons of chili powder. Multiply this quantity by $1\frac{1}{2}$: $2 \times 1\frac{1}{2}$

METHOD 1

Write 2 as $\frac{2}{1}$ and $1\frac{1}{2}$ as $\frac{3}{2}$. $\quad \frac{2}{1} \times \frac{3}{2}$

Simplify and multiply. $\quad = \frac{\cancel{2}^{1}}{1} \times \frac{3}{\cancel{2}_{1}} = \frac{3}{1} = 3$

METHOD 2

Use the distributive property.

$2 \times 1\frac{1}{2} = 2 \times \left(1 + \frac{1}{2}\right) = (2 \times 1) + \left(2 \times \frac{1}{2}\right) = 2 + 1 = 3$

Both methods show that Kevin needs 3 teaspoons of chili powder.

SEARCH

To see step-by-step videos of these problems, enter the page number into the SWadvantage.com Search Bar.

Need More HELP

For help with the distributive property, go to *The Distributive Property* in *Algebra* (Book 2, p. 1410).

Dividing Fractions by Fractions

Modeling Division of Fractions

When you divide a fraction by a fraction, such as $\frac{1}{2} \div \frac{1}{4}$, you are actually asking, "How many one-fourths are in one-half?" You can use fraction circles to model this division.

EXAMPLE 1

One-half of a round pizza is left over. Jackson will eat $\frac{1}{4}$ of a pizza each day for lunch. How many lunches of leftover pizza will Jackson eat?

You need to find $\frac{1}{2} \div \frac{1}{4}$.

STEP 1 Model one-half of a pizza.

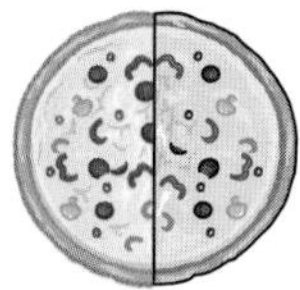

STEP 2 Divide the whole pizza into fourths, or lunch-sized pieces.

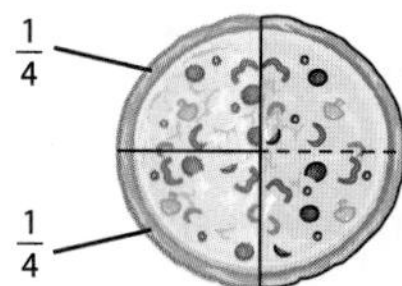

STEP 3 Count the number of lunches. There are two pieces that are each $\frac{1}{4}$ of a pizza.

Since $\frac{1}{2} \div \frac{1}{4} = 2$, Jackson will have 2 lunches of leftover pizza.

SEARCH

To see step-by-step videos of these problems, enter the page number into the SWadvantage.com Search Bar.

Reciprocals

Two numbers are **reciprocals** if their product is one.

For example, the product of $\frac{2}{5}$ and $\frac{5}{2}$ is 1, so they are reciprocals.

$$\frac{\overset{1}{\cancel{2}}}{\underset{1}{\cancel{5}}} \times \frac{\overset{1}{\cancel{5}}}{\underset{1}{\cancel{2}}} = \frac{1}{1} = 1$$

To find the reciprocal of a fraction, switch the fraction's numerator and denominator.

EXAMPLE 2

Find each reciprocal.

a. $\frac{2}{9}$

The reciprocal of $\frac{2}{9}$ is $\frac{9}{2}$.

b. $\frac{1}{5}$

The reciprocal of $\frac{1}{5}$ is $\frac{5}{1}$.

Dividing Fractions

When you divide by a fraction, you actually multiply by the reciprocal (multiplicative inverse) of the fraction. Notice that when you divide by a fraction, the quotient is always greater than the dividend (number divided). This is because you are dividing by a number that is less than 1.

EXAMPLE 3

Divide $\frac{2}{3} \div \frac{5}{6}$.

$$\frac{2}{3} \div \frac{5}{6}$$

Multiply $\frac{2}{3}$ by the reciprocal of $\frac{5}{6}$.

$$= \frac{2}{3} \times \frac{6}{5}$$

Simplify.

$$= \frac{2}{\cancel{3}_1} \times \frac{\cancel{6}^2}{5}$$

$$= \frac{4}{5}$$

$\frac{2}{3} \div \frac{5}{6} = \frac{4}{5}$

EXAMPLE 4

Divide $\frac{7}{8} \div \frac{1}{4}$.

$$\frac{7}{8} \div \frac{1}{4}$$

Multiply $\frac{7}{8}$ by the reciprocal of $\frac{1}{4}$.

$$= \frac{7}{8} \times \frac{4}{1}$$

Simplify.

$$= \frac{7}{\cancel{8}_2} \times \frac{\cancel{4}^1}{1}$$

Simplify again to express $\frac{7}{2}$ as a mixed number.

$$= \frac{7}{2}$$

$$= 3\frac{1}{2}$$

$\frac{7}{8} \div \frac{1}{4} = 3\frac{1}{2}$

Got to KNOW!

Reciprocals and Division

Reciprocals are numbers whose product is 1.

To divide by a fraction, multiply by the reciprocal of the divisor.

$\frac{3}{4} \div \frac{5}{7}$

$= \frac{3}{4} \times \frac{7}{5}$

Ways to REMEMBER

Use this sentence to remember the process for dividing fractions.

Kangaroos **C**hase **F**urry **M**ice

Keep the 1st fraction.

Change ÷ to ×.

Flip the 2nd fraction.

Multiply.

Model Division With Fraction Strips

You can use fraction strips to model division of a whole number by a fraction and a fraction by a whole number.

EXAMPLE 1

Divide $2 \div \frac{1}{3}$.

Model the number 2 using whole fraction strips.

1	1

Place one-third fraction strips below the two whole strips.

1			1		
$\frac{1}{3}$	$\frac{1}{3}$	$\frac{1}{3}$	$\frac{1}{3}$	$\frac{1}{3}$	$\frac{1}{3}$

Then count the number of one-third fraction strips needed to equal two whole strips.

There are 6 one-third fraction strips in all.

$2 \div \frac{1}{3} = 6$

EXAMPLE 2

Divide $\frac{3}{4} \div 3$.

Model $\frac{3}{4}$ using fraction strips.

$\frac{1}{4}$	$\frac{1}{4}$	$\frac{1}{4}$

Divide $\frac{3}{4}$ into 3 equal groups.

$\frac{1}{4}$ $\quad$ $\frac{1}{4}$ $\quad$ $\frac{1}{4}$

The value of each group is $\frac{1}{4}$.

$\frac{3}{4} \div 3 = \frac{1}{4}$

SEARCH

To see step-by-step videos of these problems, enter the page number into the SWadvantage.com Search Bar.

Model Division With Fraction Circles

You can also use fraction circles to model the division of a whole number by a fraction and a fraction by a whole number.

EXAMPLE 3

Divide $6 \div \frac{1}{3}$.

Model the number 6 using the thirds fraction circles.

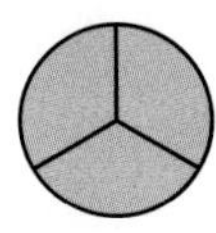 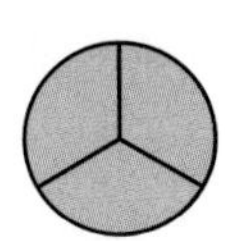 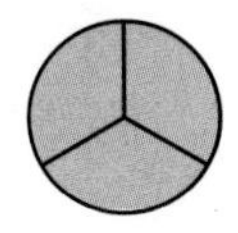 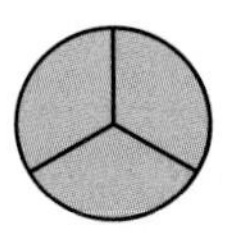 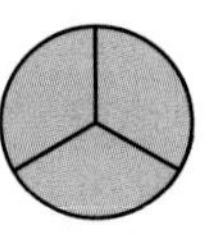 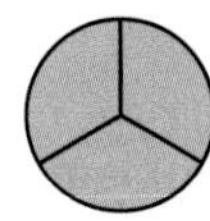

Count the number of thirds in 6.

 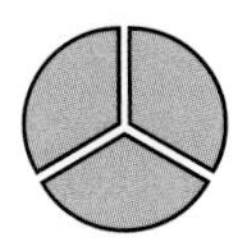 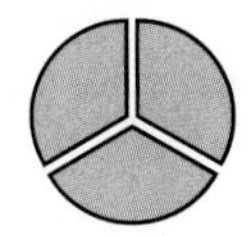   

There are 18 one-third pieces.

$6 \div \frac{1}{3} = 18$

Try It This Way

You can visualize this problem by thinking of a tricycle, which has three wheels.

If you have 6 tricycles and you count the number of wheels (a third of each tricycle's wheels), you get 18 wheels in all.

EXAMPLE 4

The model below shows that $4 \div \frac{1}{4} = 16$.

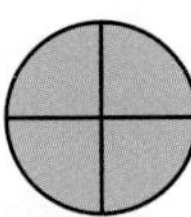 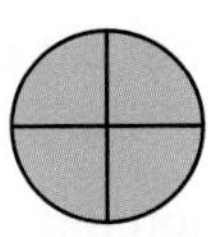 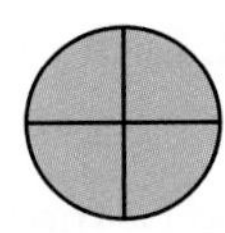 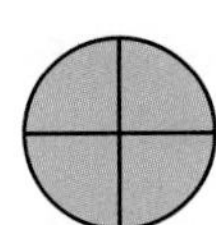

Use models to show that $\frac{1}{4} \div 4$ is not equivalent to $4 \div \frac{1}{4}$.

Model $\frac{1}{4}$ using fraction circles.

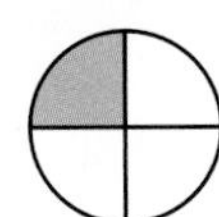 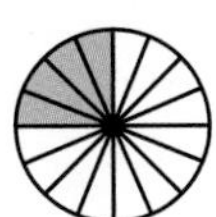

Divide $\frac{1}{4}$ into 4 equal parts.

The value of each shaded part is $\frac{1}{16}$.

$\frac{1}{4} \div 4 = \frac{1}{16}$

$4 \div \frac{1}{4} = 16$ and $\frac{1}{4} \div 4 = \frac{1}{16}$.

The division expressions are not equivalent.

Dividing a Whole Number by a Fraction

To divide a whole number by a fraction, write the whole number as a fraction with a denominator of 1. Then multiply by the multiplicative inverse, or reciprocal, of the fraction. Simplify, if necessary.

Need More HELP

Fractions are *reciprocals* if their product is 1.

The reciprocal of a fraction is found by switching the numerator and denominator. For example, the reciprocal of $\frac{2}{3}$ is $\frac{3}{2}$.

EXAMPLE 5

Divide $15 \div \frac{5}{9}$.

Write 15 as $\frac{15}{1}$.	$\frac{15}{1} \div \frac{5}{9}$
Rewrite the problem as multiplication.	$= \frac{15}{1} \times \frac{9}{5}$
Simplify.	$= \frac{{}^{3}\cancel{15}}{1} \times \frac{9}{\cancel{5}_{1}}$
Multiply.	$= \frac{3 \times 9}{1 \times 1} = 27$

$15 \div \frac{5}{9} = 27$

CHECK You can check your answer by multiplying the quotient by the divisor. The answer should be the dividend of the division problem:

$$27 \times \frac{5}{9} = \frac{27}{1} \times \frac{5}{9} = \frac{{}^{3}\cancel{27}}{1} \times \frac{5}{\cancel{9}_{1}} = 15 \checkmark$$

EXAMPLE 6

Esmeralda has 12 cups of cat food. Each day her cat eats $\frac{3}{4}$ cup of cat food. How many days will the cat food last?

Divide the number of cups of cat food by the amount the cat eats each day.

Find $12 \div \frac{3}{4}$.

Write 12 as $\frac{12}{1}$.	$\frac{12}{1} \div \frac{3}{4}$
Rewrite the problem as multiplication.	$= \frac{12}{1} \times \frac{4}{3}$
Simplify and multiply.	$= \frac{{}^{4}\cancel{12}}{1} \times \frac{4}{\cancel{3}_{1}} = 16$

The cat food will last for 16 days.

SEARCH

To see step-by-step videos of these problems, enter the page number into the SWadvantage.com Search Bar.

Divide a Fraction by a Whole Number

To divide a fraction by a whole number, write the whole number as a fraction with a denominator of 1. Then multiply the fractional *dividend* by the multiplicative inverse, or reciprocal, of the whole number *divisor*. Simplify, if necessary.

Remember, the **dividend** is the number being divided. The **divisor** is the number you divide by.

EXAMPLE 7

Divide $\frac{5}{7} \div 2$.

Write 2 as $\frac{2}{1}$.	$\frac{5}{7} \div \frac{2}{1}$
Rewrite the problem as multiplication.	$= \frac{5}{7} \times \frac{1}{2}$
Multiply $\frac{5}{7}$ by the reciprocal of $\frac{2}{1}$.	$= \frac{5 \times 1}{7 \times 2} = \frac{5}{14}$

$\frac{5}{7} \div 2 = \frac{5}{14}$

EXAMPLE 8

Patrick has 4 bird feeders. He will divide $\frac{1}{2}$ pound of birdseed equally among the 4 bird feeders. How much seed will he put in each bird feeder?

Divide the total amount of seed by the number of bird feeders.

Find $\frac{1}{2} \div 4$.

Write 4 as $\frac{4}{1}$.	$\frac{1}{2} \div \frac{4}{1}$
Rewrite the problem as multiplication.	$= \frac{1}{2} \times \frac{1}{4}$
Multiply.	$= \frac{1}{8}$

Patrick will put $\frac{1}{8}$ pound of seed in each bird feeder.

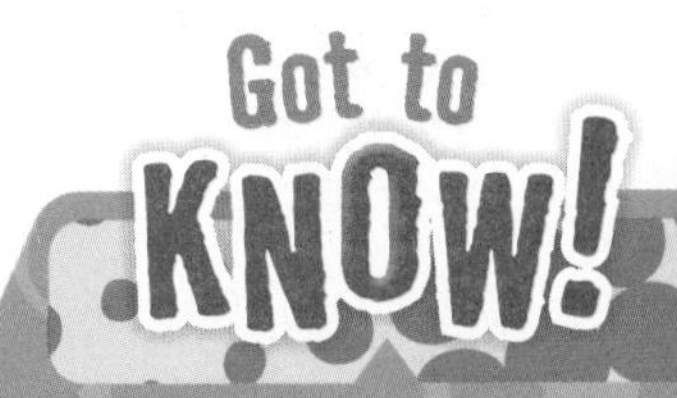

Division as Multiplication by the Reciprocal

To divide a fraction by a whole number or a whole number by a fraction:

1. Write the whole number as a fraction with a denominator of 1.
2. Multiply the dividend by the reciprocal of the divisor.

Dividing Mixed Numbers

Modeling Dividing a Mixed Number by a Fraction

You can use a model to divide a mixed number by a fraction.

EXAMPLE 1

Divide $2\frac{1}{2} \div \frac{1}{2}$.

Use fraction circles to model the *dividend*, $2\frac{1}{2}$.

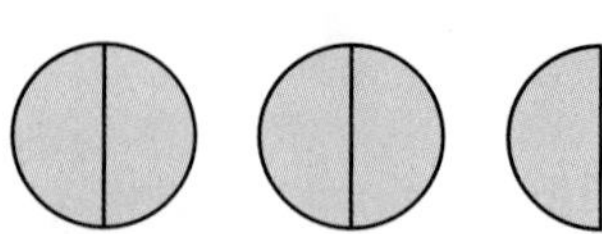

The *divisor* is $\frac{1}{2}$. Divide $2\frac{1}{2}$ into halves.

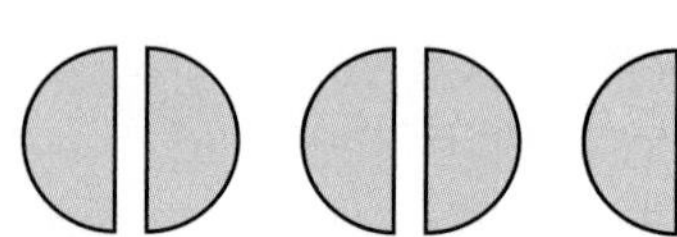

Count the number of halves.

Since there are 5 halves, $2\frac{1}{2} \div \frac{1}{2} = 5$.

Watch Out!

As in all divisions by a fraction, $2\frac{1}{2} \div \frac{1}{2}$ asks, "How many $\frac{1}{2}$'s are in $2\frac{1}{2}$?"

Dividing a Mixed Number by a Fraction

To divide a mixed number by a fraction, write the mixed number as an improper fraction. Then multiply the dividend by the *reciprocal* of the divisor. Write the reciprocal (multiplicative inverse) by switching the numerator and the denominator.

EXAMPLE 2

Divide $2\frac{5}{7} \div \frac{1}{3}$.

Express $2\frac{5}{7}$ as an improper fraction.	$\frac{19}{7} \div \frac{1}{3}$
Rewrite the problem as multiplication.	$= \frac{19}{7} \times \frac{3}{1}$
Multiply the numerators and the denominators.	$= \frac{19 \times 3}{7 \times 1}$
Multiply.	$= \frac{57}{7}$
Simplify by expressing $\frac{57}{7}$ as a mixed number.	$= 8\frac{1}{7}$

$2\frac{5}{7} \div \frac{1}{3} = 8\frac{1}{7}$

Need More HELP

For help writing improper fractions and mixed numbers, go to *Improper Fractions and Mixed Numbers* on page 306.

EXAMPLE 3

Divide $3\frac{1}{6} \div \frac{1}{2}$.

Write $3\frac{1}{6}$ as an improper fraction. $\frac{19}{6} \div \frac{1}{2}$

Rewrite the problem as multiplication. $= \frac{19}{6} \times \frac{2}{1}$

Simplify. Then multiply the numerators and the denominators. $= \frac{19}{\not{6}_3} \times \frac{\not{2}^1}{1}$

$= \frac{19}{3}$

Express $\frac{19}{3}$ as a mixed number. $= 6\frac{1}{3}$

$3\frac{1}{6} \div \frac{1}{2} = 6\frac{1}{3}$

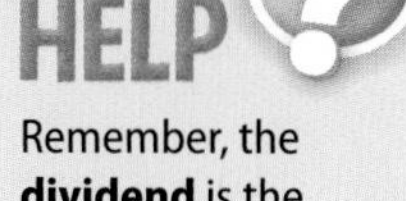

Remember, the **dividend** is the number being divided. In this lesson, the dividend is a mixed number.

The **divisor** is the number divided by. In this lesson, the divisor is a fraction, a whole number, or a mixed number.

The **quotient** is the answer.

EXAMPLE 4

Shauna has $3\frac{1}{2}$ cups of uncooked rice. Her recipe says to use $\frac{1}{4}$ cup of rice per serving. How many servings of rice can she make?

Divide the amount of rice Shauna has by the amount needed per serving: $3\frac{1}{2} \div \frac{1}{4}$

Write $3\frac{1}{2}$ as an improper fraction. $\frac{7}{2} \div \frac{1}{4}$

Rewrite the problem as multiplication. $= \frac{7}{2} \times \frac{4}{1}$

Simplify. $= \frac{7}{\not{2}_1} \times \frac{\not{4}^2}{1}$

Multiply the numerators and the denominators. $= \frac{7 \times 2}{1 \times 1}$

$= 14$

Shauna can make 14 servings of rice.

CHECK Is your answer reasonable? You want to know how many one fourths there are in $3\frac{1}{2}$. Think: There are four fourths in 1, so there are $3 \times 4 = 12$ fourths in 3. There will be a few more fourths in $3\frac{1}{2}$. $14 > 12$, so the answer is reasonable. ✔

SEARCH

To see step-by-step videos of these problems, enter the page number into the SWadvantage.com Search Bar.

Modeling Dividing a Mixed Number by a Whole Number

You can use a model to divide a mixed number by a whole number.

Watch Out !

Be sure you understand the model. The rectangles represent the *dividend,* $5\frac{1}{4}$. The 3 groups represent the *divisor*. The size of each group, $1\frac{3}{4}$, represents the *quotient*. Since you are dividing $5\frac{1}{4}$ into smaller groups, the quotient will be smaller than the dividend.

EXAMPLE 5

Divide $5\frac{1}{4} \div 3$.

Use equal-size rectangles to model the dividend, $5\frac{1}{4}$.

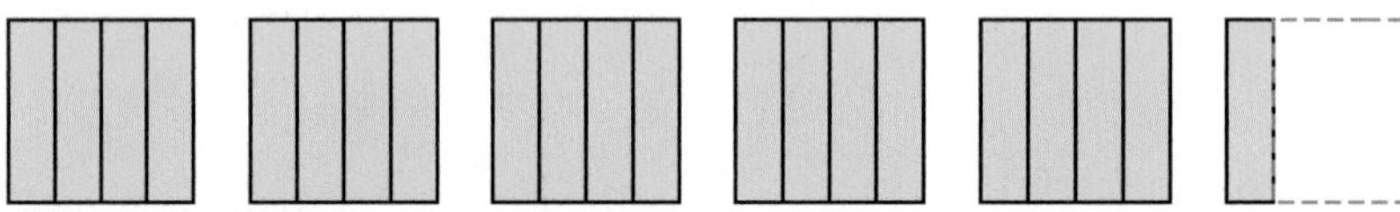

Divide $5\frac{1}{4}$ into 3 equal groups.

There are seven fourths in each group. $\frac{7}{4} = 1\frac{3}{4}$ rectangles in each group.

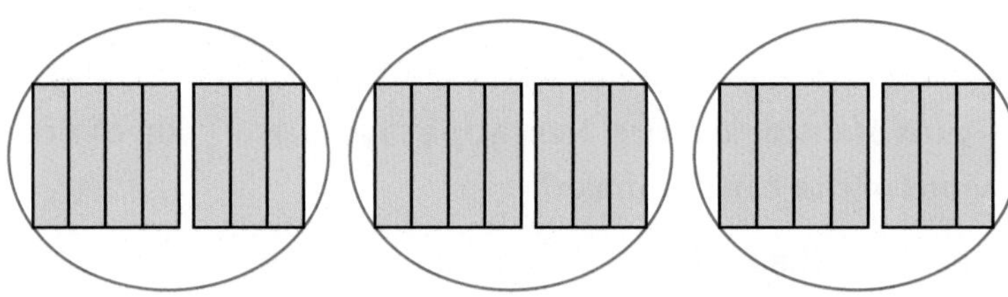

$5\frac{1}{4} \div 3 = 1\frac{3}{4}$

Dividing a Mixed Number by a Whole Number

To divide a mixed number by a whole number, write the mixed number and the whole number as improper fractions. Then multiply the dividend by the reciprocal of the divisor.

SEARCH

To see step-by-step videos of these problems, enter the page number into the SWadvantage.com Search Bar.

EXAMPLE 6

Divide $4\frac{3}{8} \div 2$.

Express $4\frac{3}{8}$ and 2 as improper fractions.	$\frac{35}{8} \div \frac{2}{1}$
Rewrite the problem as multiplication.	$= \frac{35}{8} \times \frac{1}{2}$
Multiply the numerators and the denominators.	$= \frac{35 \times 1}{8 \times 2}$
Multiply.	$= \frac{35}{16}$
Express $\frac{35}{16}$ as a mixed number.	$= 2\frac{3}{16}$

$4\frac{3}{8} \div 2 = 2\frac{3}{16}$

EXAMPLE 7

Divide $1\frac{3}{5} \div 4$.

Express $1\frac{3}{5}$ and 4 as improper fractions. $\frac{8}{5} \div \frac{4}{1}$

Rewrite the problem as multiplication. $= \frac{8}{5} \times \frac{1}{4}$

Simplify. $= \frac{\overset{2}{\cancel{8}}}{5} \times \frac{1}{\underset{1}{\cancel{4}}}$

Multiply the numerators and the denominators. $= \frac{2 \times 1}{5 \times 1}$

$= \frac{2}{5}$

$1\frac{3}{5} \div 4 = \frac{2}{5}$

EXAMPLE 8

Mrs. Gomez has $9\frac{1}{4}$ ounces of snack mix to divide equally among 3 people. How much snack mix does each person receive?

Divide the amount of snack mix into 3 equal groups: $9\frac{1}{4} \div 3$

Express $9\frac{1}{4}$ and 3 as improper fractions. $9\frac{1}{4} \div 3 = \frac{37}{4} \div \frac{3}{1}$

Rewrite the problem as multiplication. $= \frac{37}{4} \times \frac{1}{3}$

Multiply the numerators and the denominators. $= \frac{37}{12}$

Express $\frac{37}{12}$ as a mixed number. $= 3\frac{1}{12}$

Each person receives $3\frac{1}{12}$ ounces of snack mix.

CHECK Is your answer reasonable? The mixed number $9\frac{1}{4}$ rounds to 9. Nine divided by 3 is 3. Because you rounded down, the answer will be a little more than 3. So, $3\frac{1}{12}$ ounces is a reasonable answer. ✔

Try It This Way

You can use fraction circles, fraction strips, or hand-drawn models to model any of the division problems. Remember,

- Model the dividend first.
- If the *divisor is a whole number,* regroup the model into the given number of groups. The *size of the groups is the answer.*
- If the *divisor is a fraction*, regroup the model into groups that contain that fraction. The *number of groups is the answer.*

Watch Out !

In Example 5, the number of circles represents the *divisor*. In Example 9, the size of each group, $2\frac{1}{4}$, represents the *divisor*. The number of circles represents the *quotient*.

Modeling Dividing a Mixed Number by a Mixed Number

You can use a model to divide a mixed number by a mixed number.

EXAMPLE 9

Divide $6\frac{3}{4} \div 2\frac{1}{4}$.

Use equal-size rectangles to model the dividend, $6\frac{3}{4}$.

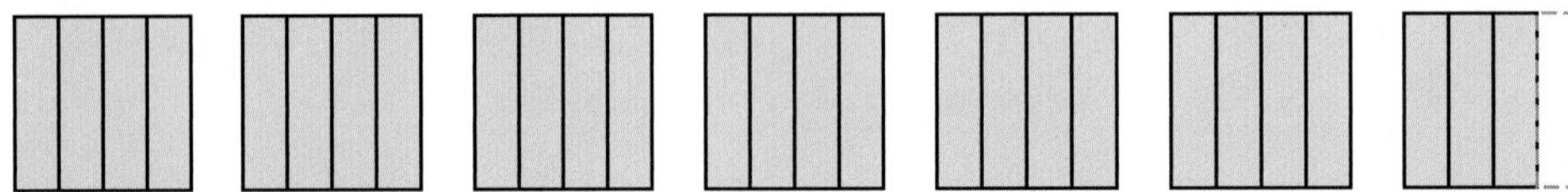

Divide $6\frac{3}{4}$ into groups of $2\frac{1}{4}$.

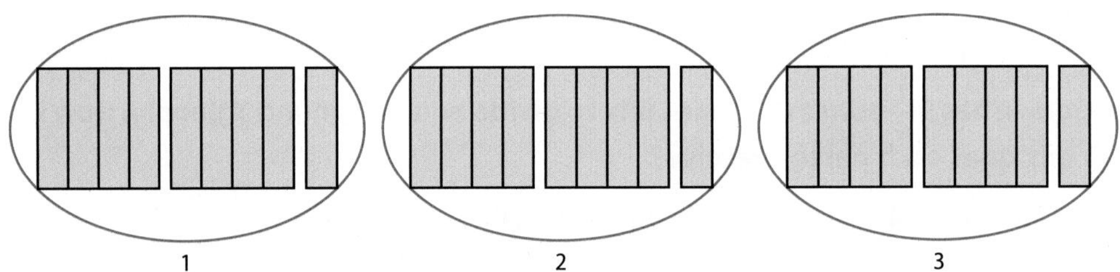

Count the number of groups.

Since there are 3 groups, $6\frac{3}{4} \div 2\frac{1}{4} = 3$.

SEARCH

To see step-by-step videos of these problems, enter the page number into the SWadvantage.com Search Bar.

Dividing a Mixed Number by a Mixed Number

To divide a mixed number by a mixed number, express the dividend *and* the divisor as improper fractions. Then multiply the dividend by the reciprocal of the divisor.

Watch Out !

Simplify *after* you write the division problem as a multiplication problem, not *before*. In Example 10, if you simplify first, you will get a quotient of 5. This is not a reasonable answer because the division asks, "How many groups of $3\frac{1}{3}$ are in $2\frac{1}{2}$? The quotient must be less than 1.

EXAMPLE 10

Divide $2\frac{1}{2} \div 3\frac{1}{3}$.

Express $2\frac{1}{2}$ and $3\frac{1}{3}$ as improper fractions. $\frac{5}{2} \div \frac{10}{3}$

Rewrite the problem as multiplication and simplify. $= \frac{\overset{1}{\cancel{5}}}{2} \times \frac{3}{\underset{2}{\cancel{10}}}$

Multiply the numerators and the denominators. $= \frac{1 \times 3}{2 \times 2}$

$= \frac{3}{4}$

$2\frac{1}{2} \div 3\frac{1}{3} = \frac{3}{4}$

EXAMPLE 11

Divide $8\frac{1}{10} \div 1\frac{4}{5}$.

Express $8\frac{1}{10}$ and $1\frac{4}{5}$ as improper fractions.	$\frac{81}{10} \div \frac{9}{5}$
Rewrite the problem as multiplication.	$= \frac{81}{10} \times \frac{5}{9}$
Simplify.	$= \frac{\cancel{81}^{\,9}}{\cancel{10}_{\,2}} \times \frac{\cancel{5}^{\,1}}{\cancel{9}_{\,1}}$
Multiply the numerators and the denominators.	$= \frac{9}{2}$
Express $\frac{9}{2}$ as a mixed number.	$= 4\frac{1}{2}$

$8\frac{1}{10} \div 1\frac{4}{5} = 4\frac{1}{2}$

EXAMPLE 12

Samantha is making bookmarks using a ribbon that is $154\frac{1}{4}$ inches long. Each bookmark is $12\frac{7}{8}$ inches long. What is the greatest number of bookmarks Samantha can make with the ribbon?

Divide the length of the ribbon by the amount of ribbon needed to make each bookmark. $154\frac{1}{4} \div 12\frac{7}{8}$. If the answer is a mixed number, round to the lesser whole number.

Express $154\frac{1}{4}$ and $12\frac{7}{8}$ as improper fractions.	$\frac{617}{4} \div \frac{103}{8}$
Rewrite the problem as multiplication.	$= \frac{617}{4} \times \frac{8}{103}$
Simplify.	$= \frac{617}{\cancel{4}_{\,1}} \times \frac{\cancel{8}^{\,2}}{103}$
Multiply the numerators and the denominators.	$= \frac{617 \times 2}{1 \times 103}$
Mulitply.	$= \frac{1{,}234}{103}$
Express $\frac{1{,}234}{103}$ as a mixed number.	$= 11\frac{101}{103}$

The greatest number of bookmarks Samantha can make is 11.

Got to KNOW!

Dividing Mixed Numbers

1. Write the mixed number and the divisor as improper fractions.
2. Rewrite the division problem as a multiplication problem, and multiply by the reciprocal of the divisor.
3. Simplify the quotient.

For help dividing whole numbers, go to *Divide Whole Numbers* in *Foundations of Mathematics* (p. 100).

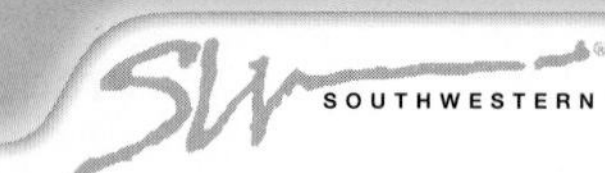

Solving Fraction and Mixed Number Word Problems

There is more than one way to solve many word problems. Find the method that works best for you. You may find it helpful to follow the steps in the *Got to Know!* box on the facing page. Examples 1 and 2 show a formal application of the steps.

For help solving word problems, go to *Problem Solving* starting on p. 446. You will find a four-step problem solving process and strategies for problem solving.

The Check in Example 1 uses the strategy *Use Logical Reasoning* found on page 460.

EXAMPLE 1

Simon checked out a book from the library. He read $\frac{1}{5}$ of the book on Tuesday, $\frac{1}{3}$ of the book on Wednesday, and $\frac{1}{6}$ of the book on Thursday. How much of the book has Simon read in all?

READ Read the problem carefully. Identify what you know and what you need to find out.

Know: He read $\frac{1}{5}$, $\frac{1}{3}$, and $\frac{1}{6}$ of the book.

Need to Know: The fraction of the book he read altogether.

PLAN Think about how you can find the information you need to know. The phrase "in all" usually means addition. You could add the three fractions.

SOLVE Write the problem in vertical form. Find the common denominator and add.

The LCD of 5, 3, and 6 is 30. $\quad \frac{1}{5} = \frac{6}{30}$

Write equivalent fractions using the LCD. $\quad \frac{1}{3} = \frac{10}{30}$

Add the numerators. $\quad +\frac{1}{6} = \frac{5}{30}$

Simplify the sum. $\quad \frac{21}{30} = \frac{7}{10}$

CHECK Did I answer the question? Is my answer is reasonable?

Simon has not read the entire book, so the answer must be less than 1. The fractions $\frac{1}{5}$ and $\frac{1}{6}$ are both a little less than $\frac{1}{4}$, so they represent not quite $\frac{1}{2}$ of the book. The fraction $\frac{1}{3}$ is a little greater than $\frac{1}{4}$. So Simon has read a little over half of the book. Since $\frac{1}{2} = \frac{5}{10}$, then $\frac{7}{10}$ is a reasonable answer.

Simon has read $\frac{7}{10}$ of the book.

SEARCH

To see step-by-step videos of these problems, enter the page number into the SWadvantage.com Search Bar.

EXAMPLE 2

Alejandro and Heather made cardboard decorations. Alejandro made a decoration $2\frac{3}{4}$ inches long. Heather made a decoration $1\frac{1}{4}$ inches long. How much longer was Alejandro's decoration than Heather's?

READ Know: Alejandro's decoration was $2\frac{3}{4}$ inches. Heather's was $1\frac{1}{4}$ inches.

Need to Know: The difference in the lengths of the decorations.

PLAN There are two ways to solve the problem.

METHOD 1

Subtract the whole number parts of the mixed numbers.

Then subtract the fractions.

METHOD 2

Write the mixed numbers as improper fractions.

Then subtract.

SOLVE

METHOD 1

$$\begin{array}{r} 2\frac{3}{4} \\ -1\frac{1}{4} \\ \hline 1\frac{2}{4} = 1\frac{1}{2} \end{array}$$

METHOD 2

$$2\frac{3}{4} = \frac{11}{4}$$
$$-1\frac{1}{4} = \frac{5}{4}$$
$$\frac{6}{4} = 1\frac{2}{4} = 1\frac{1}{2}$$

CHECK Estimate each length. Then find an estimated difference.

$2\frac{3}{4}$ is about 3, and $1\frac{1}{4}$ is about 1. Subtract: $3 - 1 = 2$. Since $1\frac{1}{4}$ is actually a little more than 1, the answer will be less than 2, so $1\frac{1}{2}$ is a reasonable answer.

Alejandro's decoration was $1\frac{1}{2}$ inches longer than Heather's.

For help with estimating, go to *Estimating to Predict or Check* on page 410.

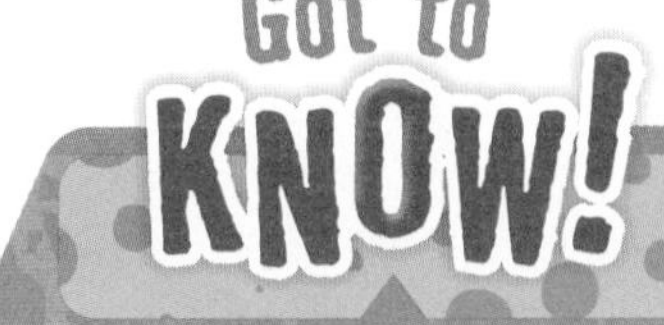

Problem Solving Process

To solve a word problem, you can use this process:

1. **Read** the problem carefully. Identify what you know and what you need to find out.
2. **Plan** how to find the solution.
3. **Solve** the problem using your plan.
4. **Check** your work, and ask if your answer makes sense.

Solving Fraction and Mixed Number Word Problems

Watch Out !

In Example 3, the problem asks how many apples are red, so your answer should be a whole number.

For the check, you could confirm that 10 is two thirds of 15: $\frac{10}{15} = \frac{10 \div 5}{15 \div 5} = \frac{2}{3}$

EXAMPLE 3

A bowl of apples contains 15 apples. Two-thirds of the apples are red. How many apples are red?

READ Know: 15 apples in all and $\frac{2}{3}$ are red.

Need to Know: How many are red?

PLAN Multiply to find $\frac{2}{3}$ of 15 apples.

SOLVE Multiply.

$$\frac{2}{3} \times 15 = \frac{2}{3} \times \frac{15}{1}$$
$$= \frac{2}{\cancel{3}_1} \times \frac{\cancel{15}^5}{1}$$
$$= 10$$

CHECK Use logical reasoning and mental math.

If you arranged 15 apples into 3 equal groups, there would be 5 in each group. Two-thirds of the apples would be $2 \times 5 = 10$. The answer is reasonable.

Ten of the apples are red.

EXAMPLE 4

A pizza maker has $4\frac{1}{2}$ cups of cheese to divide equally among 3 pizzas. How many cups of cheese will be on each pizza?

READ Know: $4\frac{1}{2}$ cups of cheese; 3 pizzas; same amount of cheese on each pizza.

Need to Know: Amount of cheese on each pizza.

PLAN Divide to find the amount of cheese on each pizza.

SOLVE Divide.

$$4\frac{1}{2} \div 3 = \frac{9}{2} \div \frac{3}{1}$$
$$= \frac{\cancel{9}^3}{2} \times \frac{1}{\cancel{3}_1}$$
$$= \frac{3}{2}$$
$$= 1\frac{1}{2}$$

CHECK Add to check your answer.

$$1\frac{1}{2} + 1\frac{1}{2} + 1\frac{1}{2}$$
$$= 3\frac{3}{2}$$
$$= 3 + 1\frac{1}{2}$$
$$= 4\frac{1}{2}\text{, the original amount of cheese}$$

There are $1\frac{1}{2}$ cups of cheese on each pizza.

EXAMPLE 5

A box contains 24 muffins. One-sixth of the muffins are banana muffins. One-half of the banana muffins contain nuts. How many muffins are banana muffins with nuts?

READ Know: 24 muffins, $\frac{1}{6}$ are banana, $\frac{1}{2}$ of the banana muffins contain nuts.
Need to Know: How many are banana muffins with nuts?

PLAN **STEP 1** Multiply to find the number of banana muffins.
STEP 2 Multiply the number of banana muffins by $\frac{1}{2}$.

SOLVE **STEP 1** $\frac{\overset{4}{\cancel{24}}}{1} \times \frac{1}{\underset{1}{\cancel{6}}} = 4$ **STEP 2** $\frac{1}{\underset{1}{\cancel{2}}} \times \frac{\overset{2}{\cancel{4}}}{1} = 2$

CHECK Use another method to check. Multiply $\frac{1}{6} \times \frac{1}{2} = \frac{1}{12}$ to find the fraction of the muffins that are banana nut muffins. Then multiply $\frac{1}{12} \times 24 = 2$ muffins are banana with nuts. ✔

Two of the muffins are banana muffins with nuts.

SEARCH

To see step-by-step videos of these problems, enter the page number into the SWadvantage.com Search Bar.

EXAMPLE 6

Rajat walked $3\frac{3}{4}$ miles. Marian walked $\frac{2}{5}$ as far as Rajat. How many more miles did Rajat walk than Marian?

READ Know: Rajat walked $3\frac{3}{4}$ miles. Marian walked $\frac{2}{5}$ of the distance Rajat walked.
Need to Know: How much farther Rajat walked.

PLAN

STEP 1 Multiply to find the distance Marian walked.

STEP 2 Subtract this distance from the distance Rajat walked.

SOLVE

STEP 1

$$\frac{2}{5} \text{ of } 3\frac{3}{4} = \frac{\overset{1}{\cancel{2}}}{\underset{1}{\cancel{5}}} \times \frac{\overset{3}{\cancel{15}}}{\underset{2}{\cancel{4}}} = \frac{3}{2} = 1\frac{1}{2} \text{ miles}$$

STEP 2

$$3\frac{3}{4} - 1\frac{1}{2} = \frac{15}{4} - \frac{3}{2} = \frac{15}{4} - \frac{6}{4} = \frac{9}{4} = 2\frac{1}{4} \text{ miles}$$

CHECK Round and estimate to check. Rajat walked about 4 miles. Two-fifths is about one-half. So Marian walked about one-half of 4, or 2 miles. Since $4 - 2 = 2$, Rajat walked about 2 miles more than Marian. The answer is reasonable.

Rajat walked $2\frac{1}{4}$ miles more than Marian.

Ratio and Proportion

What Came Before?
- Operations with fractions and mixed numbers
- Finding equivalent fractions

What's This About?
- Understanding ratios, rates, and unit rates
- Setting up and solving proportions
- Scale drawings and real-life applications of proportions

Practical Apps
- Artists use proportions to give a sense of depth and distance in a painting.
- A birdseed manufacturer uses proportions to mix several varieties of seeds in a birdseed mix.

just for FUN!

Q: Guess how many people have trouble with ratios.

A: 7 out of 5?

CONTENTS UPLOAD DOWNLOAD

You can find more practice problems online by visiting:
www.SWadvantage.com

Writing and Simplifying Ratios

Writing Ratios

A **ratio** is a comparison of two quantities by division. The **terms** are the numbers in a ratio. There are three types of ratios and three ways to write each type of ratio.

Type of Ratio	Words	Model	Ways to Write the Ratio
Part to Part	the ratio of the number of yellow counters to the number of red counters		2 to 3 2 : 3 $\frac{2}{3}$ 2 and 3 are the terms in this ratio.
Part to Whole	the ratio of the number of yellow counters to the total number of counters		2 to 5 2 : 5 $\frac{2}{5}$ 2 and 5 are the terms in this ratio.
Whole to Part	the ratio of the total number of counters to the number of yellow counters		5 to 2 5 : 2 $\frac{5}{2}$ 5 and 2 are the terms in this ratio.

Got to KNOW!

What Is a Ratio?

A **ratio** is a comparison of two numbers by division.

There are 4 green squares and 3 blue squares. The ratio of green to blue is 4 to 3, 4 : 3, or $\frac{4}{3}$. Read each ratio as "four to three."

SEARCH

To see step-by-step videos of these problems, enter the page number into the SWadvantage.com Search Bar.

EXAMPLE 1

Write each ratio in three ways.

a. the number of yellow counters to the number of red counters

There are 6 yellow counters and 8 red counters. Write the ratio as: 6 to 8, 6 : 8, or $\frac{6}{8}$.

b. the number of open boxes to the total number of boxes

There are 2 open boxes and 6 boxes total.

Write the ratio as: 2 to 6, 2 : 6, or $\frac{2}{6}$.

c. the total number of cookies to the number of star cookies

There are 9 cookies, and 2 are shaped like stars.

Write the ratio as: 9 to 2, or 9 : 2, or $\frac{9}{2}$.

EXAMPLE 2

An aquarium contains three kinds of fish—guppies, angelfish, and tetras. There are 15 guppies, 8 angelfish, and 10 tetras.

a. What is the ratio of angelfish to guppies? Write the ratio in three ways.

There are 8 angelfish and 15 guppies. Write the ratio as: 8 to 15, 8 : 15, or $\frac{8}{15}$.

b. What is the ratio of tetras to guppies? Write the ratio in three ways.

There are 10 tetras and 15 guppies. Write the ratio as: 10 to 15, 10 : 15, or $\frac{10}{15}$.

c. What is the ratio of guppies to the total number of fish in the aquarium? Write the ratio in three ways.

There are 15 guppies. There are $15 + 8 + 10 = 33$ total fish in the aquarium.

Write the ratio as: 15 to 33, 15 : 33, or $\frac{15}{33}$.

Watch Out !

The order of the terms in a ratio is important. For example, the ratio 8 to 15 is not the same as the ratio 15 to 8.

Simplifying Ratios

To write a ratio in simplest form, divide the terms by their greatest common factor (GCF).

EXAMPLE 3

Write each ratio in simplest form.

a. the number of baseballs to the number of gloves

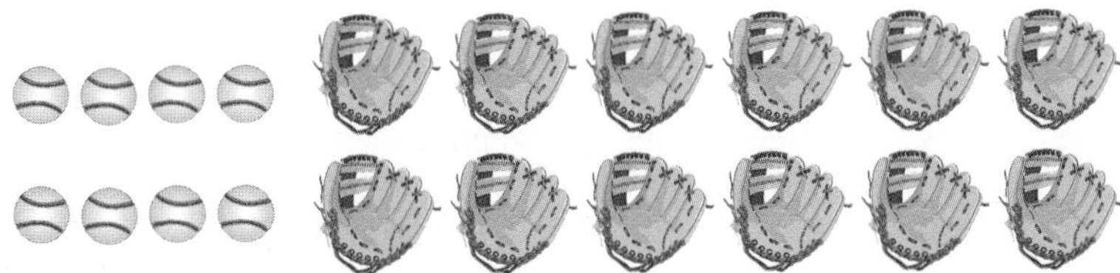

There are 8 baseballs and 12 gloves. The ratio is $\frac{8}{12}$.

Divide 8 and 12 by their GCF, 4. $\frac{8 \div 4}{12 \div 4} = \frac{2}{3}$

The ratio in simplest form is $\frac{2}{3}$.

b. the total number of hearts to the number of red hearts

There are 18 hearts and 9 are red. The ratio is $\frac{18}{9}$.

Divide 18 and 9 by their GCF, 9. $\frac{18 \div 9}{9 \div 9} = \frac{2}{1}$

The ratio in simplest form is $\frac{2}{1}$.

Need More HELP ?

For help finding the GCF of two or more numbers, go to *Factors* (p. 286).

Writing Rates

For help understanding ratios, go to *Writing and Simplifying Ratios* on page 364.

Rates

A **rate** is a ratio that compares quantities with different units of measure. For example, suppose you walk 3 miles in 45 minutes. This means you are walking at a rate of 3 miles every 45 minutes. Expressed as a ratio, this is $\frac{3 \text{ miles}}{45 \text{ minutes}}$.

EXAMPLE 1

Write each rate as a ratio.

a. 120 miles every 3 hours

$\frac{120 \text{ miles}}{3 \text{ hours}}$

b. $10.50 for 2 pounds of cheese

$\frac{\$10.50}{2 \text{ pounds}}$

c. 180 heartbeats every 2 minutes

$\frac{180 \text{ heartbeats}}{2 \text{ minutes}}$

d. 750 calories in 4 servings

$\frac{750 \text{ calories}}{4 \text{ servings}}$

Unit Rates

A **unit rate** is the rate for one unit of a given quantity. Unit rates are most often read and written using the word "per." Per means "for each." Suppose you drive 65 miles in one hour. The unit rate is read as "65 miles per hour." A **unit price** is a unit rate that gives a cost per unit.

EXAMPLE 2

Write each unit rate as a ratio.

a. 30 miles per hour

$\frac{30 \text{ miles}}{1 \text{ hour}}$

b. C$7.99 per pound

$\frac{\text{C\$7.99}}{1 \text{ pound}}$

c. 3 ounces per serving

$\frac{3 \text{ ounces}}{1 \text{ serving}}$

d. 1 inch per 50 miles

$\frac{1 \text{ inch}}{50 \text{ miles}}$

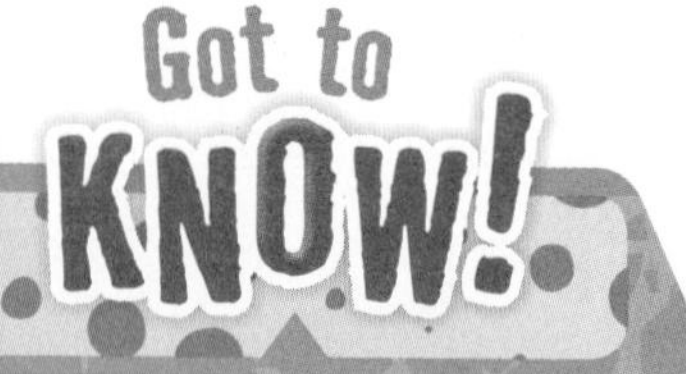

Unit Prices

A **unit price** is a special kind of **unit rate**. It gives the cost of one unit of an item, such as one pound or one ounce.

You can use unit prices to help compare costs and to determine which items are better buys.

Finding Unit Rates

To find a unit rate, divide the first quantity by the second.

EXAMPLE 3

Find the unit rate for each given rate.

a. $2.50 for 2 cups

Write the rate as a ratio. $\frac{\$2.50}{2 \text{ cups}}$

Divide the first quantity by the second. $\frac{\$2.50}{2} = \$1.25$

The unit price is $1.25 per cup.

b. 420 pages every 15 minutes

Write the rate as a ratio. $\frac{420 \text{ pages}}{15 \text{ minutes}}$

Divide the first quantity by the second. $\frac{420}{15} = 15\overline{)420}$ = 28

$$\begin{array}{r} 28 \\ 15\overline{)420} \\ -30 \\ \hline 120 \\ -120 \\ \hline 0 \end{array}$$

The unit rate is 28 pages per minute.

EXAMPLE 4

One package of cookies costs $3.60 and contains 24 cookies. Another package of cookies costs $2.40 and contains 12 cookies. Which package is the better buy?

STEP 1 Write each rate as a ratio.

Package 1: $\frac{\$3.60}{24 \text{ cookies}}$

Package 2: $\frac{\$2.40}{12 \text{ cookies}}$

STEP 2 Divide to find each unit price.

$\frac{\$3.60}{24} = \$0.15$ $\frac{\$2.40}{12} = \$0.20$

STEP 3 Compare the unit prices.

The cookies in Package 1 cost 15 cents each, and the cookies in Package 2 cost 20 cents each.

The package that costs $3.60 is the better buy because the unit price is less.

SEARCH

To see step-by-step videos of these problems, enter the page number into the SWadvantage.com Search Bar.

Try It This Way

You can use mental math to solve this problem.

There are twice as many cookies in Package 1. If you double the price of Package 2, the amount is $4.80, which is greater than the cost of Package 1, $3.60. So Package 1 is the better buy.

Writing Equivalent Ratios

Remember, a *ratio* compares two quantities by division.

Equivalent ratios are ratios that have the same value. You can write equivalent ratios by multiplying or dividing each term of a ratio by the same nonzero number.

EXAMPLE 1

Write two equivalent ratios for the ratio $\frac{10}{12}$.

Equivalent Ratio 1:

Multiply each term by 3.

$$\frac{10}{12} = \frac{10 \times 3}{12 \times 3} = \frac{30}{36}$$

Equivalent Ratio 2:

Divide each term by 2.

$$\frac{10}{12} = \frac{10 \div 2}{12 \div 2} = \frac{5}{6}$$

The ratios $\frac{30}{36}$ and $\frac{5}{6}$ are equivalent to $\frac{10}{12}$.

EXAMPLE 2

SEARCH

To see step-by-step videos of these problems, enter the page number into the SWadvantage.com Search Bar.

Write three equivalent ratios to compare the number of moons to the number of stars.

There are 6 moons and 18 stars. The ratio of moons to stars is 6 to 18.

Equivalent Ratio 1:

Divide each term by 6.

$$\frac{6}{18} = \frac{6 \div 6}{18 \div 6} = \frac{1}{3}$$

Equivalent Ratio 2:

Multiply each term by 5.

$$\frac{6}{18} = \frac{6 \times 5}{18 \times 5} = \frac{30}{90}$$

Equivalent Ratio 3:

Divide each term by 2.

$$\frac{6}{18} = \frac{6 \div 2}{18 \div 2} = \frac{3}{9}$$

The ratios $\frac{1}{3}$, $\frac{30}{90}$, and $\frac{3}{9}$ are equivalent to $\frac{6}{18}$.

EXAMPLE 3

A laser printer prints 160 pages in 5 minutes. What is the unit rate?

METHOD 1

Divide the first quantity by the second. Place the quotient over the denominator 1.

$$\frac{160}{5} = 5\overline{)160}^{\,32} \quad \frac{32}{1}$$

The unit rate is $\frac{32}{1}$.

METHOD 2

Write an equivalent ratio. Divide each term by 5.

$$\frac{160}{5} = \frac{160 \div 5}{5 \div 5} = \frac{32}{1}$$

Writing Proportions

A **proportion** is an equation that states two ratios are equal. Two ratios form a proportion if, and only if, they are equivalent. You can use the *cross products,* as shown in the *Got to Know!* box, to determine whether two ratios form a proportion.

Need More HELP

Read the proportion $\frac{a}{b} = \frac{c}{d}$ as, "a is to b as c is to d." If $ad = bc$, where $b \neq 0$ and $c \neq 0$, then the ratios form a proportion.

The numbers a and d are called the **extremes**, and b and c are called the **means**.

EXAMPLE 4

Determine whether each pair of ratios forms a proportion.

a. $\frac{8}{12}$ **and** $\frac{28}{42}$

Use cross products. $\frac{8}{12} = \frac{28}{42}$

Multiply the numerators of each ratio by the denominators of the other.

$8 \times 42 = 12 \times 28$

$336 = 336$

The cross products are equal, so the ratios $\frac{8}{12}$ and $\frac{28}{42}$ form a proportion.

b. $\frac{6}{10}$ **and** $\frac{24}{40}$

METHOD 1

Multiply each term by 4 to write equivalent ratios.

$\frac{6}{10} = \frac{6 \times 4}{10 \times 4} = \frac{24}{40}$

METHOD 2

Use cross products.

$\frac{6}{10} = \frac{24}{40}$

$6 \times 40 = 10 \times 24$

$240 = 240$

The ratios $\frac{6}{10}$ and $\frac{24}{40}$ are equivalent and the cross products are equal. The ratios form a proportion.

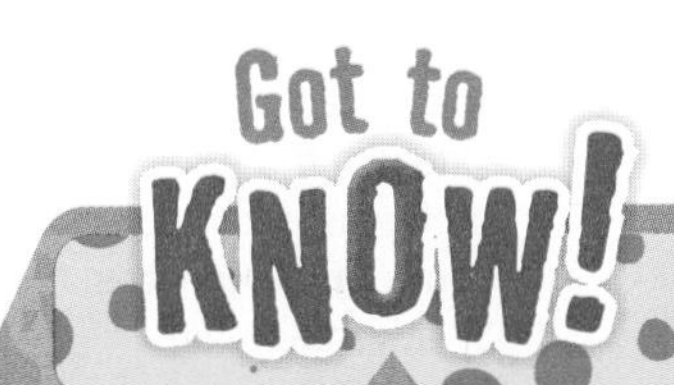

Cross Products

The **cross products** of two fractions are the products of the numerator of one fraction and the denominator of the other fraction. If the cross products of two ratios (fractions) are equal, then the ratios form a proportion.

Proportion	**Not a Proportion**
$\frac{2}{3} = \frac{10}{15}$	$\frac{2}{3} \neq \frac{6}{12}$
$3 \times 10 = 30$	$3 \times 6 = 18$
$2 \times 15 = 30$	$2 \times 12 = 24$

Solving Proportions

Writing Equivalent Ratios to Solve Proportions

When you are asked to solve a proportion, one of the numbers in the proportion is unknown. Remember that the ratios that form a proportion are equivalent, so you can solve a proportion by multiplying or dividing both terms of one of the ratios by the same number.

For help understanding proportions, go to *Equivalent Ratios and Proportions* on page 368.

EXAMPLE 1

Solve each proportion by writing equivalent ratios.

a. $\frac{3}{4} = \frac{n}{16}$

Write a ratio with a denominator of 16 that is equivalent to $\frac{3}{4}$.

Multiply both terms of the ratio $\frac{3}{4}$ by 4. $\frac{3}{4} = \frac{3 \times 4}{4 \times 4} = \frac{12}{16}$, so $n = 12$

When $n = 12$, the ratios form a proportion.

b. $\frac{18}{24} = \frac{3}{x}$

Write a ratio with a numerator of 3 that is equivalent to $\frac{18}{24}$.

Divide both terms of the ratio $\frac{18}{24}$ by 6. $\frac{18}{24} = \frac{18 \div 6}{24 \div 6} = \frac{3}{4}$, so $x = 4$

When $x = 4$, the ratios form a proportion.

EXAMPLE 2

William can drive 385 miles on one tank of gasoline. If his gas tank holds 11 gallons, how many miles can he drive on 33 gallons of gasoline?

Write a proportion that compares the number of miles driven to the number of gallons of gasoline. Let m equal the number of miles he can drive on 33 gallons of gasoline. Then solve the proportion.

SEARCH

To see step-by-step videos of these problems, enter the page number into the SWadvantage.com Search Bar.

STEP 1 Write the proportion.

$$\frac{\text{miles}}{\text{gallons}} \quad \frac{385}{11} = \frac{m}{33} \quad \frac{\text{miles}}{\text{gallons}}$$

STEP 2 Solve the proportion.

Write a ratio with a denominator of 33 that is equivalent to $\frac{385}{11}$.

Multiply both terms of the ratio $\frac{385}{11}$ by 3. $\frac{385}{11} = \frac{385 \times 3}{11 \times 3} = \frac{1{,}155}{33}$, so $m = 1{,}155$

William can drive 1,155 miles on 33 gallons of gasoline.

Using Cross Products to Solve Proportions

You can use the Cross Products Property, shown in the *Got to Know!* box, to solve proportions.

EXAMPLE 3

Solve each proportion using cross products.

a. $\frac{6}{9} = \frac{4}{x}$

Write the proportion. $\frac{6}{9} = \frac{4}{x}$

Use the Cross Products Property. $6x = 36$

Divide both sides by 6. $\frac{6x}{6} = \frac{36}{6}$

$x = 6$

When $x = 6$, the ratios form a proportion.

b. $\frac{21}{x} = \frac{7}{15}$

Write the proportion. $\frac{21}{x} = \frac{7}{15}$

Use the Cross Products Property. $315 = 7x$

Divide both sides by 7. $\frac{315}{7} = \frac{7x}{7}$

$45 = x$

When $x = 45$, the ratios form a proportion.

Remember, when you use the Cross Products Property, you multiply the numerator of one fraction (ratio) and the denominator of the other fraction (ratio).

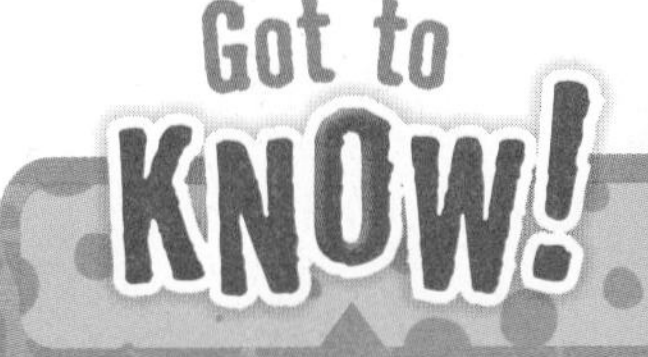

Proportions with an Unknown Value

You can use an *equivalent ratio* or *cross products* to find an unknown value in a ratio.

Use an Equivalent Ratio	**Use Cross Products**
$\frac{2}{3} = \frac{8}{x}$	$\frac{2}{3} = \frac{8}{x}$
$\frac{2 \times 4}{3 \times 4} = \frac{8}{12}$	$2 \cdot x = 3 \times 8$
	$2x = 24$
$x = 12$	$x = 12$

Finding Lengths Using a Scale Drawing

A **scale drawing** is an enlarged or reduced drawing of a real object. The dimensions of a scale drawing are proportional to the dimensions of the object. Architects and interior designers often use scale drawings in their work. A **scale** is a ratio between the measurements in a scale drawing and the measurements of an object.

EXAMPLE 1

The diagram shows a scale drawing of the floor plan of a living room. Use the drawing to answer each question.

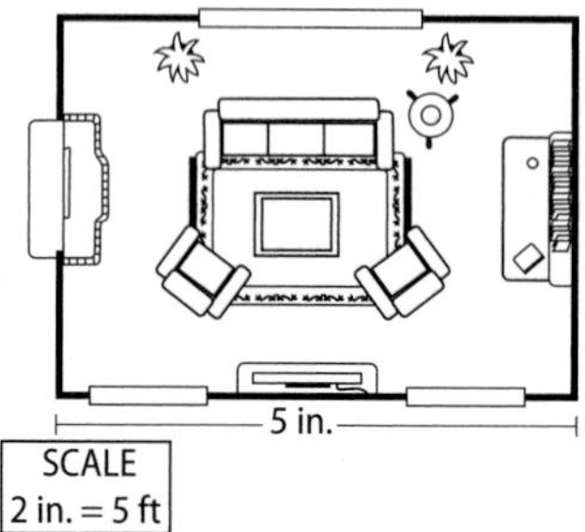

a. Write the scale as a ratio.

The scale shown says 2 in. = 5 ft. This means that every 2 inches on the scale drawing are equal to 5 feet in the actual room. The ratio is $\frac{2 \text{ in.}}{5 \text{ ft}}$.

Watch Out!

A scale is actually a *rate* that compares two different measures. When you set up a proportion using a scale, make sure each ratio is a rate.

b. The length of the living room on the scale drawing is 5 inches. What is the actual length of the living room?

Use the scale to write a proportion. Let x represent the actual length of the living room.

STEP 1 Write the proportion.

$$\frac{\text{scale drawing length (in.)}}{\text{actual length (ft)}} \quad \frac{2}{5} = \frac{5}{x} \quad \frac{\text{scale drawing length (in.)}}{\text{actual length (ft)}}$$

STEP 2 Solve the proportion.

Use the Cross Products Property. $2x = 25$

Divide both sides by 2. $\frac{2x}{2} = \frac{25}{2}$

$x = 12.5$

The length of the living room is 12.5 feet.

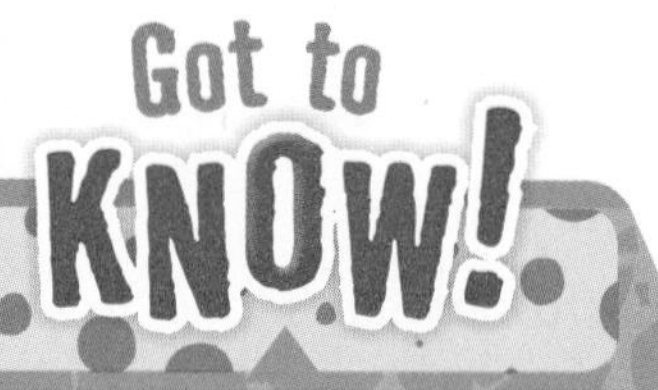

Scale Drawings

- The measurements of a scale drawing or scale model are proportional to the actual measurements of an object.
- If you know the scale and any measurement on a scale drawing, you can use a proportion to find the corresponding measurement on the actual object.

Finding Distances on a Map

A map is a special kind of scale drawing. All maps have scales. You use the scale to find the actual distances between locations on the map.

EXAMPLE 2

Waylen lives in Harrisburg, Pennsylvania. He will go to Philadelphia to visit his cousin. He measures the distance between Harrisburg and Philadelphia on a map as 1.5 inches. The map scale reads "1 in. = 100 km."

a. What is the map scale written as a ratio?

The scale is 1 in. = 100 km. This means that 1 inch on the map is equal to 100 kilometers in actual distance. The ratio is $\frac{1\text{ in.}}{100\text{ km}}$.

b. Based on Waylen's measurement, what is the actual distance between Harrisburg and Philadelphia?

STEP 1 Write a proportion. Let x represent the actual distance.

$$\frac{\text{map distance (in.)}}{\text{actual distance (km)}} \quad \frac{1}{100} = \frac{1.5}{x} \quad \frac{\text{map distance (in.)}}{\text{actual distance (km)}}$$

STEP 2 Solve the proportion.

Use the Cross Products Property. $1x = 100 \times 1.5$

Multiply. $x = 150$

The actual distance between Harrisburg and Philadelphia is about 150 kilometers.

SEARCH

To see step-by-step videos of these problems, enter the page number into the SWadvantage.com Search Bar.

Need More HELP

For help solving proportions, go to *Solving Proportions* on page 370.

EXAMPLE 3

On a map, the distance between two cities is 3 inches. The actual distance between the cities is 195 miles. What is the scale for the map, written in simplest form?

You know the map distance and the actual distance between two cities. Express this distance as a ratio.

$$\frac{\text{map distance (in.)}}{\text{actual distance (mi)}} = \frac{3}{195}$$

Simplify. Divide both numerator and denominator by 3. $\frac{3 \div 3}{195 \div 3} = \frac{1}{65}$

The map scale is 1 in. = 65 mi.

Solving Ratio and Proportion Word Problems

There is more than one way to solve many word problems. Find the method that works best for you. You may find it helpful to follow the steps in the *Got to Know!* box below to solve word problems. Examples 1 and 2 show a formal application of the steps.

Need More HELP

For help solving word problems, go to *Problem Solving* starting on p. 446. You will find a four-step problem solving process and strategies for problem solving.

The Check in Example 1 uses the strategy *Use Logical Reasoning* on page 460.

EXAMPLE 1

The directions on a box of instant mashed potatoes specify using 1 tablespoon of butter for every 2 servings of potatoes. How much butter is needed for 8 servings of potatoes?

READ Read the problem carefully. Identify what you know and what you need to find out.

Know: One tablespoon of butter is used in every 2 servings.

Need to Know: The amount of butter for 8 servings.

PLAN Write a ratio and an equivalent ratio for the amount of butter to servings.

SOLVE Write the ratio of butter to servings. $\frac{1 \text{ tablespoon}}{2 \text{ servings}} = \frac{1}{2}$

Write a ratio with a denominator of 8 that is equivalent to the ratio. $\frac{1}{2}$

Multiply both terms of the ratio $\frac{1}{2}$ by 4. $\frac{1 \text{ tablespoon}}{2 \text{ servings}} = \frac{1 \times 4}{2 \times 4} = \frac{4 \text{ tablespoons}}{8 \text{ servings}}$

CHECK Did I answer the question? Is my answer reasonable?

The ratio of butter to servings is 1 Tbs to 2 servings. Since $2 \times 4 = 8$, 8 servings are 4 times as many as 2 servings. Similarly, 1 Tbs butter $\times$ 4 servings $=$ 4 Tbs butter. I answered the question, and my answer is reasonable.

Four tablespoons of butter are needed for 8 servings of potatoes.

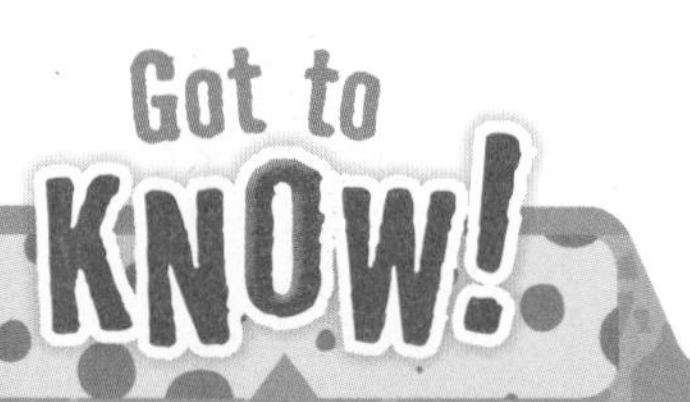

Problem Solving Process

To solve a word problem, you can use this process.

1. **Read** the problem carefully. Identify what you know and what you need to find out.
2. **Plan** how to find the solution.
3. **Solve** the problem using your plan.
4. **Check** your work, and ask if your answer makes sense.

EXAMPLE 2

A French high-speed train traveled 560 kilometers in 4 hours. If it continued at this speed, how many kilometers could it travel in 5 hours?

READ Know: The train traveled at a rate of 560 kilometers in 4 hours.

Need to Know: How many kilometers the train could travel in 5 hours.

PLAN Write a proportion. Let x equal the number of kilometers the train could travel in 5 hours.

$$\frac{\text{kilometers}}{\text{hours}}\ \frac{560}{4} = \frac{x}{5}\ \frac{\text{kilometers}}{\text{hours}}$$

SOLVE Solve the proportion.

Write the proportion. $\frac{560}{4} = \frac{x}{5}$

Use the Cross Products Property. $560 \times 5 = 4x$

Multiply. $2{,}800 = 4x$

Simplify. Divide both sides by 4. $\frac{2{,}800}{4} = \frac{4x}{4}$

$700 = x$

CHECK To check your answer, substitute 700 for x in the proportion $\frac{560}{4} = \frac{x}{5}$. Then use the Cross Products Property to see if the two ratios are a proportion.

$$\frac{560}{4} \stackrel{?}{=} \frac{700}{5}$$

$$560 \times 5 \stackrel{?}{=} 4 \times 700$$

$$2{,}800 = 2{,}800\ ✔$$

The two ratios form a proportion, so the answer checks.

The train could travel 700 kilometers in 5 hours.

SEARCH

To see step-by-step videos of these problems, enter the page number into the SWadvantage.com Search Bar.

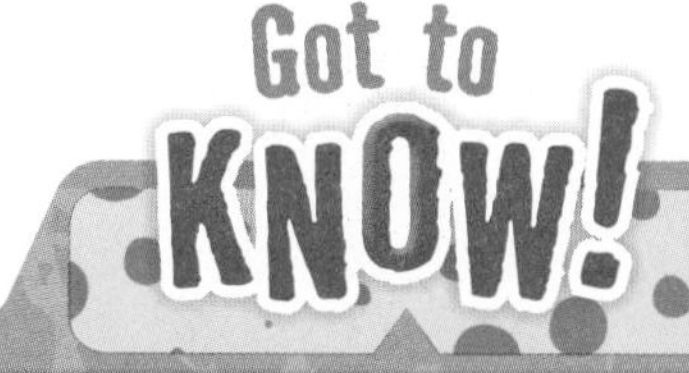

Checking a Proportion

- When you solve a proportion, check your answer by substituting the value you found for the unknown term back into the proportion.
- Then use the Cross Products Property to verify that your answer is correct.

Need More HELP

Remember, a **rate** is a ratio that compares two different quantities. In Example 3, the rate 6 to 5 compares wins to losses.

EXAMPLE 3

The Panthers basketball team started the season with 6 wins and 5 losses. If the team continues to win at the same rate, how many games will the team have won after a total of 33 games?

READ Know: The Panthers have won 6 games and lost 5.

Need to Know: If they play a total of 33 games, and win at the same rate, how many games will they win?

PLAN
1. Find the total number of games played so far. Write a ratio that compares wins so far to the total number of games played so far.
2. Write a ratio that compares total wins in 33 games, w, to 33 games played.
3. Set the ratios as a proportion and solve.

1. Total number wins *so far* to total games *so far*: 6 wins to 11 games (6 wins + 5 losses).
Ratio: $\frac{6}{11}$

2. Total number of wins w to total number of games, 33.
Ratio: $\frac{w}{33}$

3. Proportion:
$\frac{6}{11} = \frac{w}{33}$

SOLVE

Write the proportion. $\frac{6}{11} = \frac{w}{33}$

Use the Cross Products Property. $6 \times 33 = 11w$

Multiply. $198 = 11x$

Simplify. Divide both sides by 11. $\frac{198}{11} = \frac{11w}{11}$

$18 = w$

CHECK

Substitute 18 for w in the proportion.

$\frac{6}{11} \stackrel{?}{=} \frac{18}{33}$

$6 \times 33 \stackrel{?}{=} 11 \times 18$

$198 = 198$ ✔

If the Panthers continue to win at this rate, they will have won 18 games after 33 are played.

EXAMPLE 4

On a scale drawing, the length of a kitchen counter is 3 inches. The actual length of the counter is 72 inches. What is the scale for the drawing?

READ Know: Length of the counter on the drawing is 3 in., the actual length is 72 in.

Need to Know: The scale for the drawing.

PLAN Write the ratio of the length on the drawing to the actual length in simplest form.

SOLVE Write the ratio and simplify.

$\frac{\text{scale drawing (in.)}\ 3}{\text{actual length (in.)}\ 72} = \frac{3 \div 3}{72 \div 3} = \frac{1}{24}$

CHECK

Multiply 24 by 3 to check.

$24 \times 3 = 72$ ✔

The scale is 1 in. = 24 in.

EXAMPLE 5

The Chin family is planning a vacation. They will drive from their home in Naples, Florida, to Fort Lauderdale, Florida.

a. Sonia Chin has a map of Florida. The scale reads, "1 in. = 36 mi." She measures the distance from Naples to Ft. Lauderdale. It is about 2.75 inches. What is the actual distance between the two cities?

READ Know: Map scale is "1 in. = 36 mi." The map distance is 2.75 inches.

Need to Know: The distance, in miles between Naples, Florida and Fort Lauderdale.

PLAN Write and solve a proportion to find the actual distance.

SOLVE Write and solve a proportion. Let x represent the actual distance.

$$\frac{1}{36} = \frac{2.75}{x}$$

Use the Cross Products Property. $1 \cdot x = 36(2.75)$

$$1x = 99$$

The actual distance between Naples and Fort Lauderdale is about 99 miles.

CHECK Substitute 99 for w. Use your calculator to see if the proportion is true.

$$\frac{1}{36} = \frac{2.75}{99}$$

$99 = 99$ ✔

The actual distance is about 99 miles.

b. If they drive at an average speed of 50 miles per hour (mph), about how many hours will it take them to get to Fort Lauderdale?

READ Know: The distance is about 99 miles. The average driving speed is 50 mph.

Need to Know: The driving time in hours.

PLAN Write and solve a proportion to find the driving time. Let x represent the time it will take to drive.

SOLVE Write and solve the proportion.

$$\frac{\text{miles}}{\text{hours}}\ \frac{50}{1} = \frac{99}{x}\ \frac{\text{miles}}{\text{hours}}$$

Use the Cross Products Property. $\frac{50}{1} = \frac{99}{x}$

Simplify. Divide both sides by 50. $50x = 99$

$$x = 1.98$$

CHECK Round 1.98 to 2. 2 hours × 50 miles per hour = 100 miles. This is close to the actual distance of 99 miles so the answer is reasonable.

It will take the Chins about 2 hours to reach Ft. Lauderdale if they drive at an average speed of 50 mph.

SEARCH

To see step-by-step videos of these problems, enter the page number into the SWadvantage.com Search Bar.

Percent

What Came Before?

- Converting between decimals, fractions, and percents
- Finding equivalent fractions

What's This About?

- Finding percents of numbers and numbers from percents
- Finding percent increase and decrease
- Solving problems using percents

Practical Apps

- Store managers use percents to offer discounts and to price items.
- Income tax practitioners, such as enrolled agents, use percents when preparing income tax returns.

just for FUN!

Q: What happened when the student didn't calculate the percent increase correctly?

A: The answer was discounted.

CONTENTS | UPLOAD | DOWNLOAD | *Numbers and Operations*

You can find more practice problems online by visiting:
www.SWadvantage.com

Meaning of Percents

Understanding and Modeling Percents

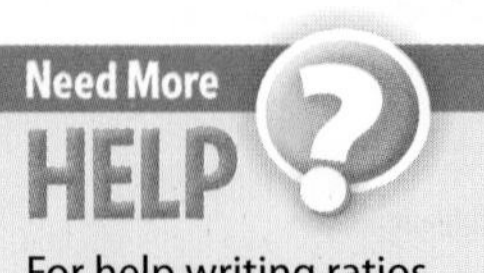

For help writing ratios, go to *Writing and Simplifying Ratios* (p. 364).

In Latin, *percent* means "for each hundred" or "per hundred." A **percent** is a ratio of some quantity to 100. Percents are usually written with a percent sign, %, instead of as fractions. So, 25% means the ratio of 25 to 100, or 25 ÷ 100. Ten by ten grids are a good way to model percents because $10 \times 10 = 100$.

EXAMPLE 1

Use a ten by ten grid to model each percent.

a. 10%

Ten percent is the ratio $\frac{10}{100}$.

Shade 10 of the 100 squares.

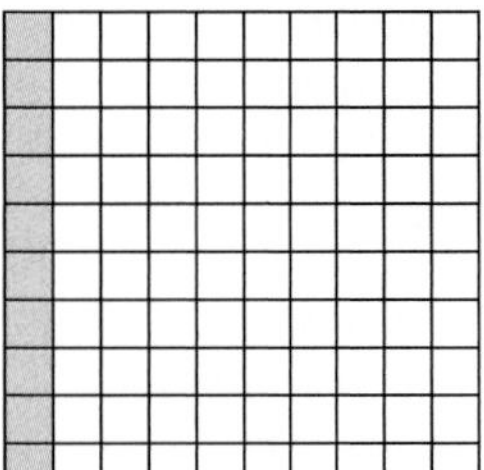

b. 50%

Fifty percent is the ratio $\frac{50}{100}$.

Shade 50 of the 100 squares.

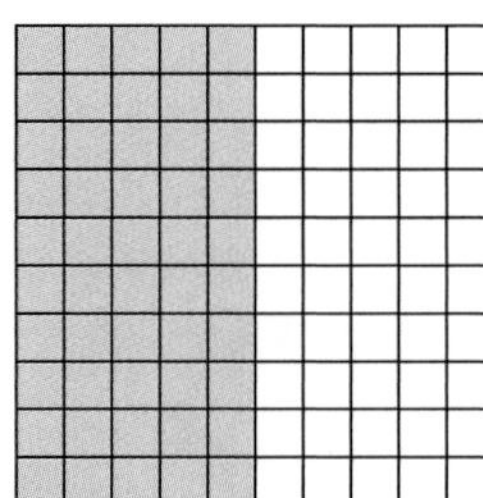

c. 75%

Seventy-five percent is the ratio $\frac{75}{100}$.

Shade 75 squares.

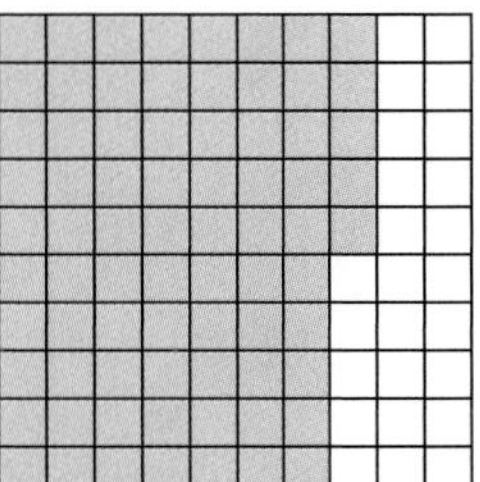

d. 19%

Nineteen percent is the ratio $\frac{19}{100}$.

Shade 19 squares.

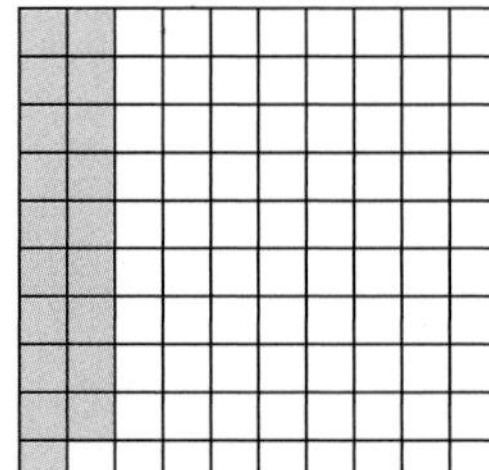

EXAMPLE 2

What percent does each grid model?

a.

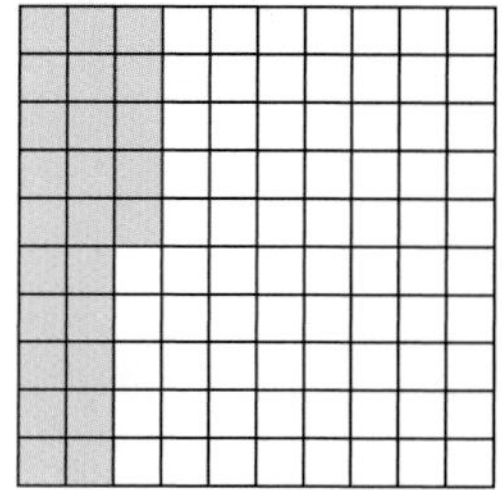

Twenty-five of the 100 squares are shaded.

The grid models 25%.

b.

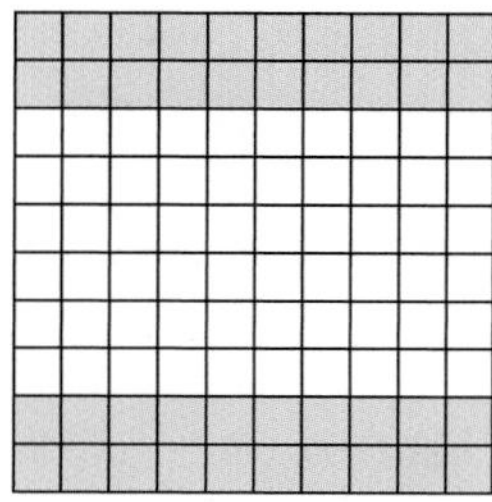

Forty of the 100 squares are shaded.

The grid models 40%.

c.

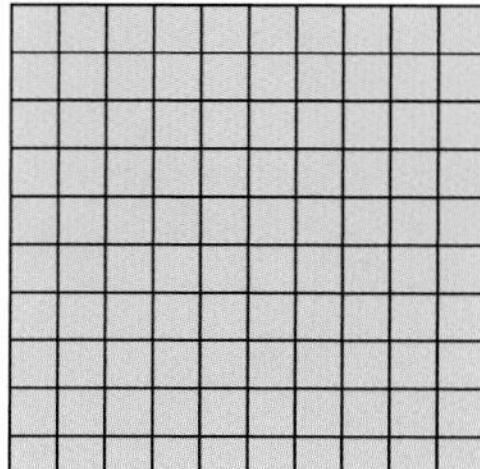

All of the 100 squares are shaded.

The grid models 100%.

d.

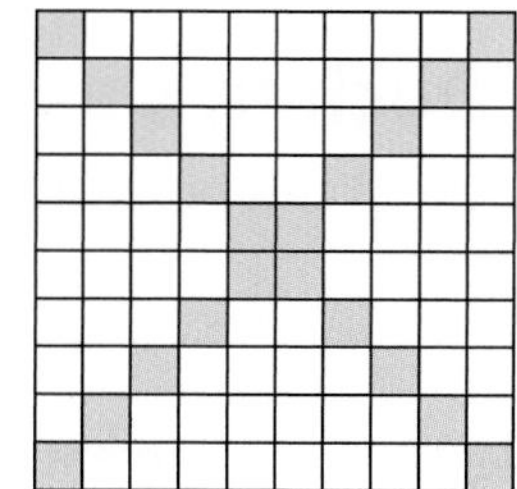

Twenty of the 100 squares are shaded.

The grid models 20%.

Any ratio with a denominator that is a factor of 100 can easily be written as a percent by writing an equivalent ratio with a denominator of 100.

SEARCH

To see step-by-step videos of these problems, enter the page number into the SWadvantage.com Search Bar.

Need More HELP

Remember: Any whole number that divides evenly into 100 is a factor of 100.

EXAMPLE 3

What percent does each shaded region model?

a.

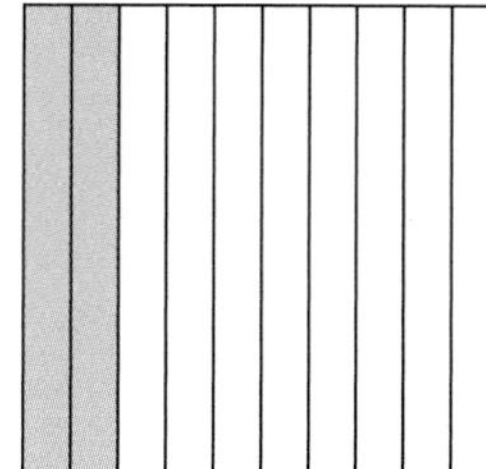

There are 10 equal-sized columns.

The shaded region models $\frac{2}{10}$.

Write an equivalent ratio.

$\frac{2}{10} = \frac{2 \times 10}{10 \times 10} = \frac{20}{100} = 20\%$

b.

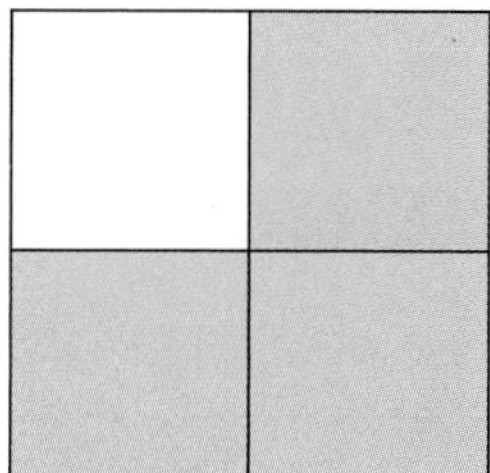

There are 4 equal-sized areas.

The shaded region models $\frac{3}{4}$.

Write an equivalent ratio.

$\frac{3}{4} = \frac{3 \times 25}{4 \times 25} = \frac{75}{100} = 75\%$

Writing Percents as Decimals

To write a percent as a decimal, write the percent as a fraction with a denominator of 100. Then divide the numerator by the denominator.

Need More HELP

Remember: To *divide* a number by 100, move the decimal point 2 places to the left. To *multiply* a number by 100, move the decimal point 2 places to the right.

EXAMPLE 4

Write each percent as a decimal.

a. 62%

Write as a fraction. $62\% = \frac{62}{100}$

Divide. $= 0.62$

$62\% = 0.62$

b. 3%

Write as a fraction. $3\% = \frac{3}{100}$

Divide. $= 0.03$

$3\% = 0.03$

Writing Decimals as Percents

To write a decimal as a percent, multiply the decimal by 100.

EXAMPLE 5

Write each decimal as a percent.

a. 0.4325

Multiply by 100. Move the decimal point 2 places to the right. $0.4325 \times 100 = 43.25$

$0.4325 = 43.25\%$

b. 0.01

Multiply by 100. Move the decimal point 2 places to the right. $0.01 \times 100 = 1$

$0.01 = 1\%$

Got to KNOW!

Percents, Fractions, and Decimals

To write a ...	Example
percent as a ***decimal***, divide by 100.	$25\% = \frac{25}{100} = 0.25$
decimal as a ***percent***, multiply by 100.	$0.10 \times 100 = 10\%$
percent as a ***fraction***, write the percent as a fraction with a denominator of 100. Then simplify the fraction.	$50\% = \frac{50}{100} = \frac{1}{2}$
fraction as a ***percent***, first write the fraction as a decimal. Then express the decimal as a percent.	$\frac{75}{100} = 0.75 = 75\%$

Writing Percents as Fractions

To write a percent as a fraction, write the percent as a fraction with a denominator of 100. Then simplify the fraction.

EXAMPLE 6

Write each percent as a fraction in simplest form.

a. 28%

Write as a fraction. $28\% = \frac{28}{100}$

Simplify. $= \frac{28 \div 4}{100 \div 4}$

$= \frac{7}{25}$

$28\% = \frac{7}{25}$

b. 107%

Write as a fraction. $107\% = \frac{107}{100}$

Write as a mixed number. $= 1\frac{7}{100}$

$107\% = 1\frac{7}{100}$

SEARCH

To see step-by-step videos of these problems, enter the page number into the SWadvantage.com Search Bar.

Writing Fractions as Percents

If the denominator of the fraction is a factor of 100, you can write an equivalent fraction with a denominator of 100. Then express the fraction as a percent. If the denominator is not a factor of 100, write the fraction as a decimal. Then express the decimal as a percent.

EXAMPLE 7

Write $\frac{3}{25}$ as a percent.

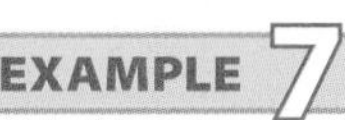

Write $\frac{3}{25}$ as an equivalent fraction with a denominator of 100. $\frac{3}{25} = \frac{3 \times 4}{25 \times 4}$

Express the fraction as a percent. $= \frac{12}{100}$

$= 12\%$

$\frac{3}{25} = 12\%$

METHOD 2

Write $\frac{3}{25}$ as a decimal. $\frac{3}{25} = 0.12$

Multiply by 100, and add a % sign. $0.12 \times 100 = 12$

$\frac{3}{25} = 12\%$

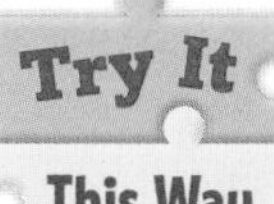

You can use a calculator to express $\frac{3}{25}$ as a decimal.

Press 3 ÷ 2 5 =.

The display will show

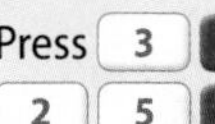

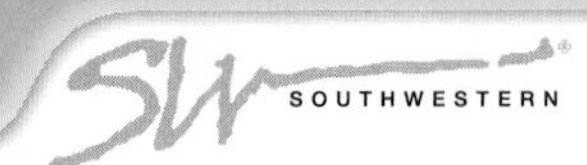

Finding a Percent of a Number

Recall that *of* means "times." When you are asked to find a percent of a number, multiply the percent by the number. You can use the formula in the *Got to Know!* box to help you.

SEARCH

To see step-by-step videos of these problems, enter the page number into the SWadvantage.com Search Bar.

EXAMPLE 1

Find 50% of 200.

Use mental math.

Think: 50% is one-half. $50\% = \frac{50}{100} = \frac{1}{2}$

One-half of 200 is 100.

50% of 200 is 100.

Need More HELP

You may see that the formula in the *Got to Know!* box uses letters as variables. You can use any variable to represent the three parts of the formula:

- the number that is a given percent of another number (the base number)
- the percent
- the base number

EXAMPLE 2

Find 40% of 150.

METHOD 1

Rewrite 40% as a fraction in simplest form. $40\% = \frac{40}{100} = \frac{2}{5}$

Multiply. $\frac{2}{5} \times 150 = \frac{2}{\cancel{5}_1} \times \frac{\cancel{150}^{30}}{1}$

40% of 150 is 60. $= 60$

METHOD 2

Rewrite 40% as a decimal. $40\% = 0.40 = 0.4$

Multiply.

$$\begin{array}{r} 150 \\ \times\ 0.4 \\ \hline 60.0 \end{array}$$

40% of 150 is 60.

Got to KNOW!

Formula for Finding What Number Is a Given Percent of Another Number

Use this formula to find what number (n) is a given percent (p) of a given base number (b)

$$n = p \times b$$

Suppose you are given $p = 30\%$ and $b = 120$ and you want to know what number (n) is 30% of 120. Substitute into the formula and solve for n: $n = 30\% \times 120$, $n = 0.3 \times 120$, $n = 36$.

EXAMPLE 3

In one town, 5% of the 840 businesses lost money last year. How many of the businesses lost money?

METHOD 1

You need to find 5% of 840. You can use the formula $n = p \times b$.

Substitute 5% for p and 840 for b.	$n = 5\% \times 840$
Write 5% as a decimal.	$n = 0.05 \times 840$
Multiply.	$n = 42$

Forty-two businesses lost money last year.

METHOD 2

The formula $n = p \times b$ can be written as the proportion $\frac{n}{b} = \frac{p}{100}$. Use the proportion to solve the problem.

Substitute 840 for b and 5 for p.	$\frac{n}{840} = \frac{5}{100}$
Use the Cross Products Property.	$100n = 840 \times 5$
Multiply.	$100n = 4200$
Divide both sides by 100.	$n = 42$

Forty-two businesses lost money last year.

Need More HELP

For help writing and solving proportions and using the Cross Products Property, go to *Solving Proportions* (p. 368).

EXAMPLE 4

This year Mona saved 115% of the amount she saved last year. Last year she saved $2,350. How much did she save this year?

Find 115% of $2,350.

Write 115% as a decimal.	$115\% = 1.15$
Multiply. Use a calculator.	$2,350 \times 1.15 = 2,702.50$

Mona saved $2,702.50 this year.

Watch Out!

In Example 4, 115% is greater than 100%, so expressed as a decimal its value will be greater than 1.

$100\% + 15\% =$
$1.0 + 0.15 =$
$1.15.$

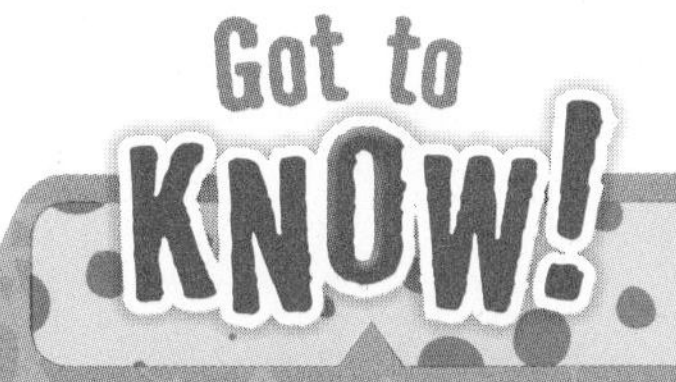

Calculator Tip

Most calculators have a percent key. The [%] key automatically changes the percent to a decimal before multiplying. Here is how to find 17% of 6,978 with and without a [%] key.

With a % calculator key:

Press [6] [9] [7] [8] → [×] → [1] [7] → [%]. The display will show [1186.26]. If it doesn't, press [=].

Without a % calculator key:

Press [6] [9] [7] [8] → [×] → [.] [1] [7] → [ENTER].

Finding a Percent

Sometimes you will need to solve a problem in which you know two numbers and you want to find out what percent one number is of the other number. You can solve a percent problem by returning to the definition of a percent as a ratio.

Remember: A *percent* is a ratio of some number to 100. For help with percents, go to *Meaning of Percents* (p. 380).

EXAMPLE 1

What percent of 80 is 20?

Use mental math. $\frac{1}{4} = 0.25 = 25\%$

Think: 20 is one-fourth of 80. One-fourth is 25%.

Twenty is 25% of 80.

EXAMPLE 2

What percent of 64 is 40?

METHOD 1

Think of the unknown percent as a decimal. $? \times 64 = 40$

Divide 40 by 64. $64\overline{)40.000}$ = 0.625

Rewrite the quotient as a percent. $0.625 = 62.5\%$

Forty is 62.5% of 64.

METHOD 2

Use the formula $p = \frac{n}{b}$, where p = the percent, n = the quantity that is a percent of the base quantity, and b = the base quantity.

Substitute 64 for b and 40 for n. $p = \frac{40}{64}$

Divide 40 by 64. $64\overline{)40.000}$ = 0.625

Write p as a percent. $p = 0.625 = 62.5\%$

Forty is 62.5% of 64.

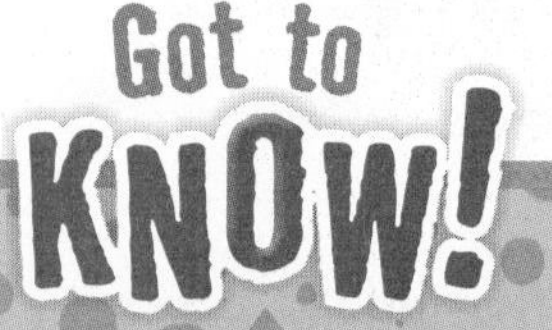

Formula for Finding What Percent One Number Is of Another Number

Use the formula $p = \frac{n}{b}$ to find what percent (p) one number (n) is of another number (b). The numbers you know are the base number and the number that is a certain percent of the base number.

METHOD 3

Use the proportion $\frac{n}{b} = \frac{p}{100}$. Using this method, your answer will be the percent.

Substitute 40 for *n* and 64 for *b*. $\frac{40}{64} = \frac{p}{100}$

Use the Cross Products Property. $40 \times 100 = 64p$

Multiply. $4{,}000 = 64p$

Divide both sides by 64. $\frac{4{,}000}{64} = \frac{64p}{64}$

$62.5 = p$

Forty is 62.5% of 64.

For help writing and solving proportions and using the Cross Products Property, go to *Solving Proportions* (p. 368).

EXAMPLE 3

The star of a basketball team attempted 19 shots. She made 11 of them. What percent of the attempted shots did she make?

Use the proportion $\frac{n}{b} = \frac{p}{100}$ to solve the problem.

Substitute 11 for *n* and 19 for *b*. $\frac{11}{19} = \frac{p}{100}$

Use the Cross Products Property. $11 \times 100 = 19p$

Multiply. $1{,}100 = 19p$

Divide both sides by 19. $\frac{1{,}100}{19} = \frac{19p}{19}$

Round to the nearest whole number. $57.89... = p$

The basketball star made about 58% of her shots.

SEARCH

To see step-by-step videos of these problems, enter the page number into the SWadvantage.com Search Bar.

EXAMPLE 4

Last week, 1,255 people ran in a marathon and 925 people finished the race. What percent of people did not finish the race?

STEP 1 Subtract to find the number of people who did not finish the race.

$1{,}255 - 925 = 330$

STEP 2 Use a proportion to find the percent.

Substitute 330 for *n* and 1,255 for *b*. $\frac{330}{1{,}255} = \frac{p}{100}$

Use the Cross Products Property. $330 \times 100 = 1{,}255p$

Multiply. $33{,}000 = 1{,}255p$

Divide both sides by 1,255. $26.29... = p$

Round to the nearest whole number. $26 \approx p$

About 26% of the people did not finish the race.

Watch Out !

The symbol $\approx$ means "is about" or "is approximately". It is used instead of an equal sign, when the relationship between two values is not exactly equal.

Finding a Number Given a Percent of the Number

Sometimes you need to answer questions such as, "25 is 35% of what number?" You can use the formula in the *Got to Know!* box to help you.

SEARCH

To see step-by-step videos of these problems, enter the page number into the SWadvantage.com Search Bar.

EXAMPLE 1

Thirty is 50% of what number?

Use mental math.

Think: 50% is one-half, so 30 is one-half of what number? $\frac{1}{2} \times 60 = 30$

Thirty is one-half of 60.

Thirty is 50% of 60.

EXAMPLE 2

Eighteen is 24% of what number?

METHOD 1

Rewrite 24% as a decimal. $24\% = 0.24$

Divide 18 by 0.24. $18 \div 0.24 = 75$

CHECK Multiply 24% by 75: $0.24 \times 75 = 18$ ✔

Eighteen is 24% of 75.

METHOD 2

Use the formula $b = \frac{n}{p}$.

Substitute 18 for n and 0.24 for p. $b = \frac{18}{0.24}$

Divide 18 by 0.24. $18 \div 0.24 = 75$

Eighteen is 24% of 75.

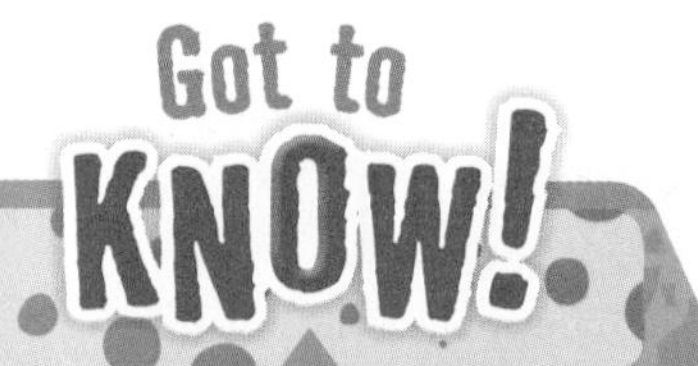

Formula for Finding a Number When Given a Certain Percent of the Number

Use the following formula to find a base number (b) when given another number (n) and the percent (p) the other number is of the base number.

$$b = \frac{n}{p}$$

$$b = \frac{4}{25\%} = \frac{4}{0.25} = 16$$ The number 4 is 25% of the number 16

METHOD 3

Use the proportion $\frac{n}{b} = \frac{p}{100}$.

Substitute 18 for *n* and 24 for *p*.	$\frac{18}{b} = \frac{24}{100}$
Use the Cross Products Property.	$18 \times 100 = 24b$
Multiply.	$1{,}800 = 24b$
Divide both sides by 24.	$\frac{1{,}800}{24} = \frac{24b}{24}$
	$75 = b$

Eighteen is 24% of 75.

Need More HELP

The ratio $\frac{p}{100}$ is equivalent to writing *p*%. You can read the proportion as, "18 is to what number as 24% is to 100%."

For help writing and solving proportions and using the Cross Products Property, go to *Solving Proportions* (p. 370).

EXAMPLE 3

A TV commercial states that 80% of all people surveyed use White & Bright Toothpaste. Later it states that 5,000 of the people surveyed use White & Bright. If both statements are true, how many people were surveyed?

You need to find the base number. Use the proportion $\frac{n}{b} = \frac{p}{100}$ to solve the problem.

Substitute 5,000 for *n* and 80 for *p*.	$\frac{5{,}000}{b} = \frac{80}{100}$
Use the Cross Products Property.	$5{,}000 \times 100 = 80b$
Multiply.	$500{,}000 = 80b$
Divide both sides by 80.	$\frac{500{,}000}{80} = \frac{80b}{80}$
	$6{,}250 = b$

6,250 people were surveyed.

EXAMPLE 4

On a test, Jesse got 30 problems correct and scored 75%. How many problems were on the test?

You need to find the base number. Use the proportion $\frac{n}{b} = \frac{p}{100}$ to solve the problem.

Substitute 30 for *n* and 75 for *p*.	$\frac{30}{b} = \frac{75}{100}$
Use the Cross Products Property.	$30 \times 100 = 75b$
Multiply.	$3{,}000 = 75b$
Divide both sides by 75.	$\frac{3{,}000}{75} = \frac{75b}{75}$
	$40 = b$

There were 40 problems on the test.

Percents < 1% and > 100%

Modeling Percents < 1%

The model shows 1 out of 100 squares shaded, or 1% shaded.

Percents can be less than 1%. Any percent less than the ratio 1 to 100 is less than 1%.

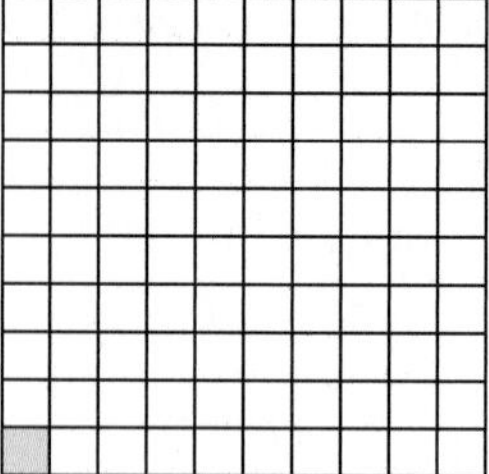

EXAMPLE 1

Use a ten by ten grid to model each percent.

a. $\frac{1}{2}\%$

Shade $\frac{1}{2}$ of 1 of the 100 squares.

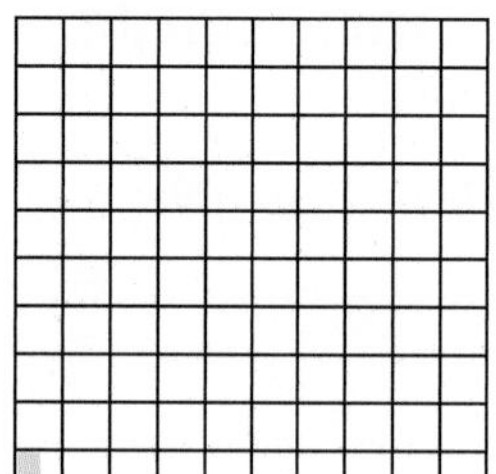

b. $\frac{1}{4}\%$

Shade $\frac{1}{4}$ of 1 of the 100 squares.

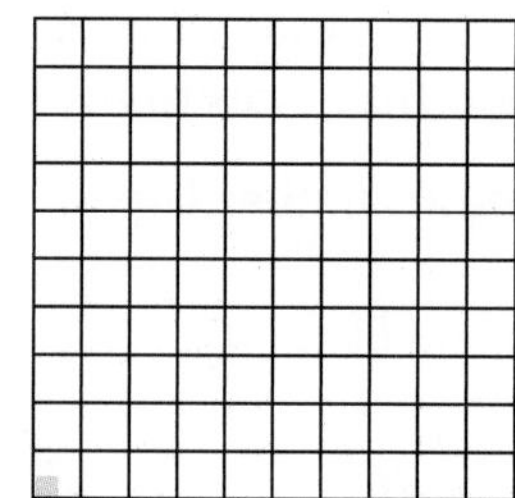

SEARCH

To see step-by-step videos of these problems, enter the page number into the SWadvantage.com Search Bar.

Modeling Percents > 100%

The model shows 100 out of 100 squares shaded, or 100% shaded.

Percents can be greater than 100%. Any percent greater than the ratio 100 to 100 is greater than 100%.

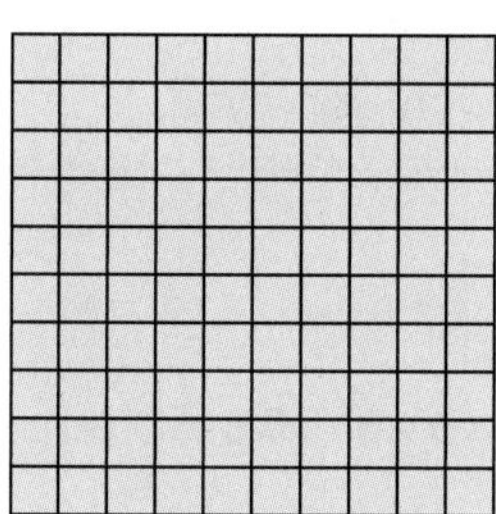

EXAMPLE 2

Use a ten by ten grid to model each percent.

a. 105%

Shade 100 squares on one grid and 5 on another.

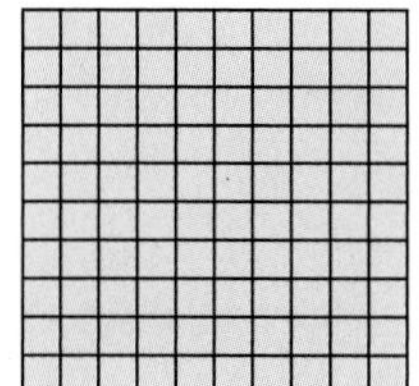
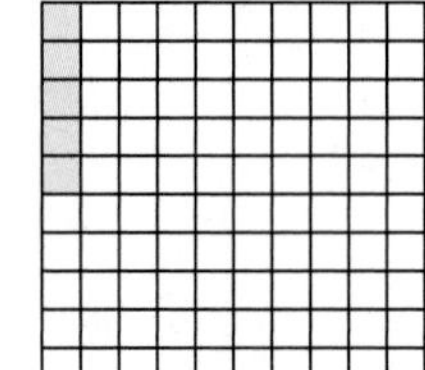

b. 250%

Shade 100 squares on one grid, 100 squares on a second grid, and 50 on a third grid.

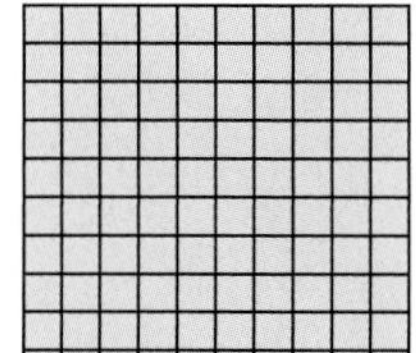
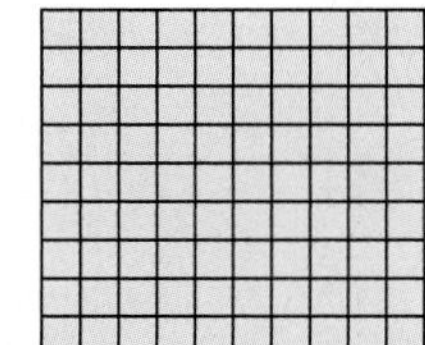
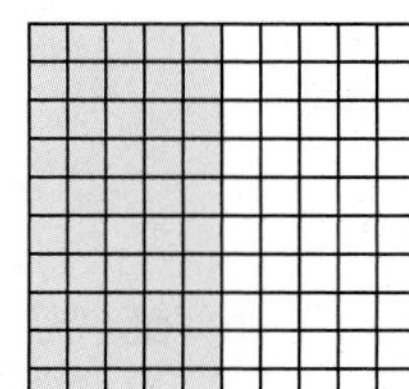

Writing Percents < 1% and > 100% as Decimals

To write a percent that is < 1% or > 100% as a decimal, first write the percent as a fraction with a denominator of 100. Then divide.

Watch Out!

1% is not equal to 1.

$1\% = \frac{1}{100} = 0.01$

$100\% = \frac{100}{100} = 1.0$

EXAMPLE 3

Write each percent as a decimal.

a. 0.5%

METHOD 1

Write as a fraction. $0.5\% = \frac{0.5}{100}$

Divide. $= 0.005$

$0.5\% = 0.005$

METHOD 2

Move the decimal point two places to the left. Drop the % sign. $0.5\% = 0.005$

$0.5\% = 0.005$

b. 185%

METHOD 1

Write as a fraction. $185\% = \frac{185}{100}$

Divide. $= 1.85$

$185\% = 1.85$

METHOD 2

Move the decimal point two places to the left. Drop the % sign. $185\% = 1.85$

$185\% = 1.85$

Writing Percents < 1% as Fractions

To write a percent < 1% as a fraction, first write the percent as a fraction with a denominator of 100. Then rewrite the fraction so the numerator does not contain a decimal point. This is the same as finding an equivalent fraction.

EXAMPLE 4

Write each percent as a fraction.

a. 0.7%

Write as a fraction with a denominator of 100. $0.7\% = \frac{0.7}{100}$

Multiply the numerator and denominator by 10 so the numerator does not contain a decimal point. $= \frac{0.7 \times 10}{100 \times 10}$

Multiply. $= \frac{7}{1{,}000}$

0.7% written as a fraction is $\frac{7}{1{,}000}$.

Watch Out!

When working with percents that are < 1%, you must respect the decimal point. 0.7% is 0.7 hundredths, not 7 hundredths.

b. 0.02%

Write as a fraction with a denominator of 100. $0.02\% = \frac{0.02}{100}$

Multiply the numerator and denominator by 100 so the numerator does not contain a decimal point. $= \frac{0.02 \times 100}{100 \times 10}$

Multiply. $= \frac{2}{10{,}000}$

0.02% written as a fraction is $\frac{2}{10{,}000}$.

Writing Percents > 100% as Fractions

To write a percent > 100% as a fraction, write the percent as a fraction with a denominator of 100. The result will be an improper fraction. Write the improper fraction as a mixed number.

EXAMPLE 5

Write 327% as a fraction.

Write as a fraction with a denominator of 100. $327\% = \frac{327}{100}$

Simplify. $= 3\frac{27}{100}$

327% written as a fraction is $3\frac{27}{100}$.

SEARCH

To see step-by-step videos of these problems, enter the page number into the SWadvantage.com Search Bar.

Writing a Mixed Number as a Percent > 100%

A mixed number is a percent greater than 100% because it has a whole number part and a fraction part. To write a mixed number as a percent, write the mixed number as an improper fraction and divide to express it as a decimal. Then divide the decimal by 100.

For help writing mixed numbers as improper fractions, go to *Improper Fractions and Mixed Numbers* in *Numbers and Operations* (p. 306).

EXAMPLE 6

Write $3\frac{2}{5}$ as a percent.

Write as an improper fraction. Then divide 17 by 5. $3\frac{2}{5} = \frac{17}{5}$

Write 3.4 as a percent. $= 3.4$

Move the decimal point two places to the right. $3.4 = 340\%$

$3\frac{2}{5}$ written as a percent is 340%.

EXAMPLE 7

James bought a baseball card three years ago and paid $5.50 for it. Today, he sold it for 250% of what he paid for it. How much was the sale price?

Multiply the price paid three years ago by 250%.

$5.50 \times 250\% = 5.50 \times 2.50$

$= 13.75$

James sold the card for $13.75.

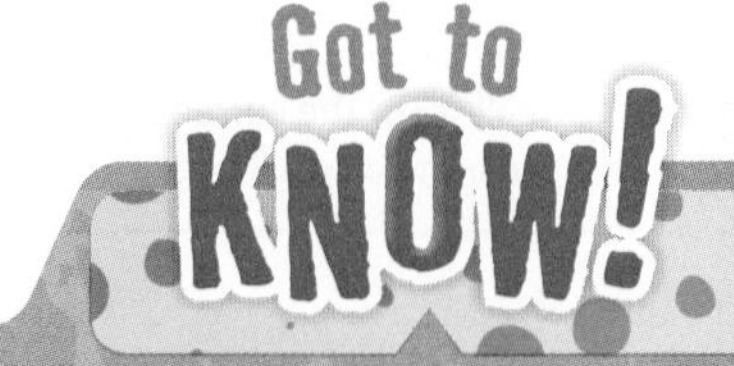

Writing Percents < 1% and > 100% as Fractions and Decimals

To write a percent < 1% or > 100% as a decimal, express it as a fraction with a denominator of 100. Then divide by 100.

To write a percent < 1% as a fraction, first express it as a fraction with a denominator of 100. Then rewrite the fraction so the numerator does not contain a decimal point.

To write a percent > 100% as a fraction, express it as a fraction with a denominator of 100. The result will be an improper fraction. Write the fraction as a mixed number.

To write a mixed number as a percent, express it as an improper fraction and divide to write as a decimal. Then divide the decimal by 100.

Finding a Percent of Increase

For help with repeating decimals, such as $0.041\overline{6}$, go to *Rational Numbers and Number Sets* on page 1446.

A **percent of change** describes how much a quantity changes from an original amount. It is the ratio of the amount of change to the original quantity. If the amount of change is an increase in value, it is a **percent of increase**. You can use the formula shown in the *Got to Know!* box to find a percent of increase.

EXAMPLE 1

Tom learns that the cost of living for a small family a year ago was $288 per week. This year, the cost of living for the same family is $300 per week. What is the percent of increase from a year ago?

Use the percent key on a calculator to check problems that involve percents of increase.

To check the answer in Example 1:

Enter 2 8 8, the original cost of living.

Press +.

Then enter 4 . 2.

Press %.

The calculator display will show the current cost of living.

METHOD 1

Use the formula $p\% = \dfrac{\text{amount of increase}}{\text{original amount}}$.

The *amount of increase* is the current cost of living minus the original cost of living. $p\% = \dfrac{300 - 288}{288}$

Subtract. $= \dfrac{12}{288}$

Divide. $= 0.041\overline{6}$

Write the decimal as a percent. $\approx 4.2\%$

The percent of increase is about 4.2%.

METHOD 2

Write the formula $p\% = \dfrac{\text{amount of increase}}{\text{original amount}}$ as the ratio $\dfrac{p}{100} = \dfrac{\text{amount of increase}}{\text{original amount}}$.

The *amount of increase* is $300 - 288 = 12$. $\dfrac{p}{100} = \dfrac{12}{288}$

Use the Cross Products Property. $288p = 100 \times 12$

Multiply. $288p = 1{,}200$

Divide both sides by 288. $p = \dfrac{1{,}200}{288}$

$\approx 4.2\%$

The percent of increase is about 4.2%.

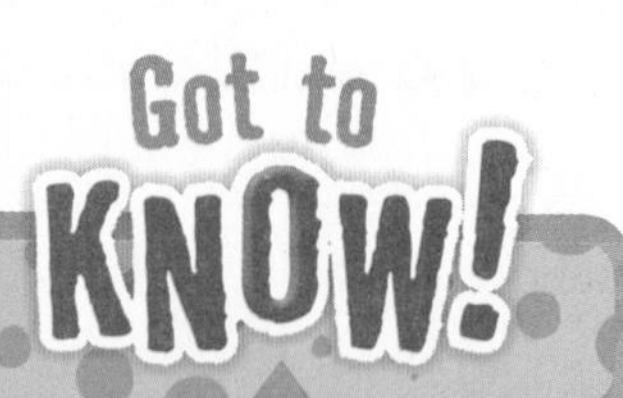

Percent of Increase

Use the following formula to find a **percent of increase** ($p\%$).

$$p\% = \frac{\text{amount of increase}}{\text{original amount}}$$

The **amount of increase** is the new amount − the original amount.

Finding a Percent of Markup

A **markup** is the difference between the price a store pays for an item (wholesale price) and the price a buyer pays for an item (retail price). Because the store marks *up* the price, a markup is an increase, and a percent of markup is a *percent of increase*. Use the formula in the *Got to Know!* box to find a percent of markup.

EXAMPLE 2

An office supply store sells an inkjet printer for $85.99. The store paid $25.50 for the printer. What is the percent of markup on the printer to the nearest whole percent?

METHOD 1

Use the formula $p\% = \frac{\text{amount of markup}}{\text{original cost}}$.

The *amount of markup* is the retail price minus the wholesale price. $p\% = \frac{85.99 - 25.50}{25.50}$

Subtract. $= \frac{60.49}{25.50}$

Divide. ≈ 2.37

Write the decimal as a percent. $\approx 237\%$

The percent of markup is about 237%.

METHOD 2

Write the formula $p\% = \frac{\text{amount of markup}}{\text{original cost}}$ as the ratio $\frac{p}{100} = \frac{\text{amount of markup}}{\text{original cost}}$.

The *amount of markup* is $85.99 - 25.50 = 60.49$. $\frac{p}{100} = \frac{60.49}{25.50}$

Use the Cross Products Property. $25.50p = 100 \times 60.49$

Multiply. $25.50p = 6{,}049$

Divide both sides by 25.50. $\frac{25.50p}{25.50} = \frac{6{,}049}{25.50}$

$\approx 237\%$

The percent of markup is about 237%.

For help with rounding, go to *Rounding Decimals* (p. 224).

SEARCH

To see step-by-step videos of these problems, enter the page number into the SWadvantage.com Search Bar.

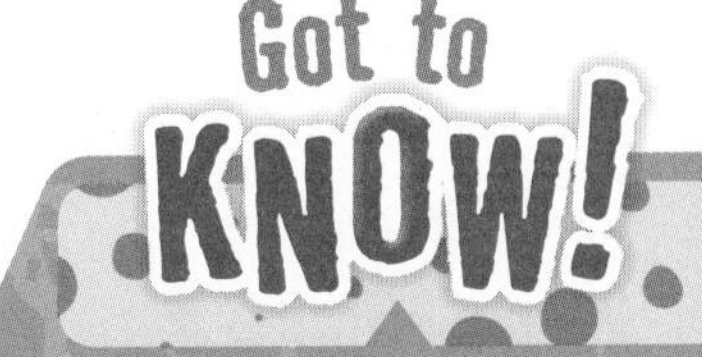

Percent of Markup

A **percent of markup** is a *percent of increase*. Use the following formula to find a percent of markup ($p\%$).

$$p\% = \frac{\text{amount of markup}}{\text{original cost}}$$

The *amount of markup* is selling price minus the price the store paid.

Watch Out !

The denominator is *always* the original amount whether the change is an increase or a decrease. In a problem about a percent decrease, the original amount is the greater quantity.

Try It This Way

Use the percent key on a calculator to check problems that involve percents of decrease.

To check the answer in Example 3:

Enter 6 0 . 4 , the original amount of rainfall.

Press −.

Then enter 7.

Press %.

The calculator display will show the decreased amount of rainfall.

Finding a Percent of Decrease

When an amount of change is a decrease in value, it is a **percent of decrease**. Use the formula shown in the *Got to Know!* box to find a percent of decrease.

EXAMPLE 3

This year, the annual rainfall amount for a city was 56.2 inches. Last year, the annual rainfall amount was 60.4 inches. What was the percent of decrease in rainfall?

METHOD 1

Use the formula $p\% = \frac{\text{amount of decrease}}{\text{original amount}}$.

The *amount of decrease* is the amount last year (60.4) minus the amount this year (56.4). $p\% = \frac{60.4 - 56.2}{60.4}$

Subtract. $= \frac{4.2}{60.4}$

Divide. ≈ 0.07

Write the decimal as a percent. $\approx 7\%$

The percent of decrease was about 7%.

METHOD 2

Write the formula $p\% = \frac{\text{amount of decrease}}{\text{original amount}}$ as the ratio $\frac{p}{100} = \frac{\text{amount of decrease}}{\text{original amount}}$.

The *amount of decrease* is $60.4 - 56.2 = 4.2$. $\frac{p}{100} = \frac{4.2}{60.4}$

Use the Cross Products Property. $60.4p = 100 \times 4.2$

Multiply. $60.4p = 420$

Divide both sides by 60.4. $\frac{60.4p}{60.4} = \frac{420}{60.4}$

$p \approx 7\%$

The percent of decrease was about 7%.

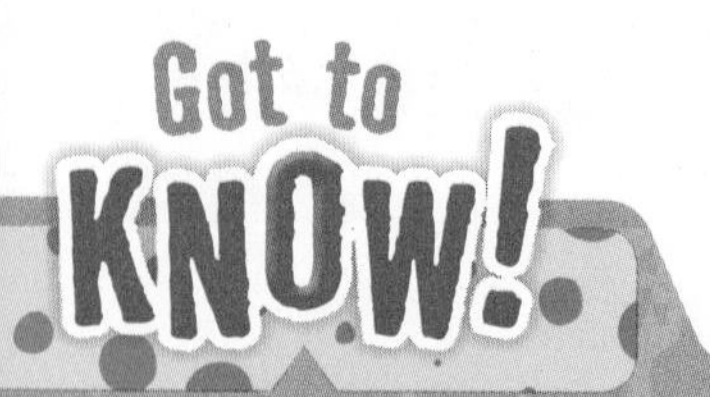

Percent of Decrease

Use the following formula to find a **percent of decrease** (p%).

$$p\% = \frac{\text{amount of decrease}}{\text{original amount}}$$

The **amount of decrease** is the larger amount (original amount) − the smaller amount.

Finding a Percent of Discount

A **discount** is the difference between the original price of an item and the sale price of the item. A discount is a decrease in price, and a percent of discount is a *percent of decrease*. Use the formula in the *Got to Know!* box to find a percent of discount.

EXAMPLE 4

A digital camera that originally sold for $325 is on sale for $250. What is the percent of discount? Round to the nearest whole percent.

METHOD 1

Use the formula $p\% = \frac{\text{amount of discount}}{\text{original cost}}$.

The *amount of discount* is the original price minus the sale price. $p\% = \frac{325 - 250}{325}$

Subtract. $= \frac{75}{325}$

Divide. ≈ 0.23

Write the decimal as a percent. $\approx 23\%$

The percent of discount is about 23%.

METHOD 2

The formula $p\% = \frac{\text{amount of discount}}{\text{original cost}}$ can be written as $\frac{p}{100} = \frac{\text{amount of discount}}{\text{original cost}}$.

The *amount of discount* is $325 - 250 = 75$. $\frac{p}{100} = \frac{75}{325}$

Use the Cross Products Property. $325p = 100 \times 75$

Multiply. $325p = 7{,}500$

Divide both sides by 325. $\frac{325p}{325} = \frac{7{,}500}{325}$

$\approx 23\%$

The percent of discount is about 23%.

SEARCH

To see step-by-step videos of these problems, enter the page number into the SWadvantage.com Search Bar.

Got to KNOW!

Percent of Discount

A **percent of discount** is a *percent of decrease*. Use the following formula to find a percent of discount ($p\%$).

$$p\% = \frac{\text{amount of discount}}{\text{original cost}}$$

The *amount of discount* is the original price minus the sale price.

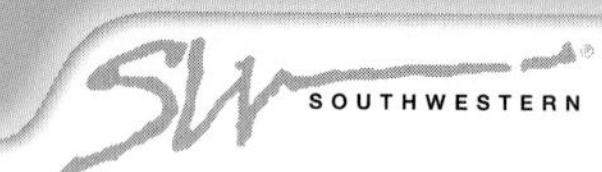

Calculating Simple Interest

Interest is a fee paid for the use of borrowed money. A bank pays interest on some accounts because the bank uses the money to make loans. When the bank loans money, the borrower must pay the bank interest for the use of the borrowed money.

Some savings accounts pay *simple interest*. **Simple interest** is calculated only on the amount that is originally deposited, called the **principal**. The formula used to calculate the simple interest is:

$$\text{interest} = \text{principal} \times \text{rate} \times \text{time}$$
$$i = prt$$

The variable i is the interest earned, the variable p is the principal, the variable r is the annual interest rate (in decimal form), and the variable t is the time (in years).

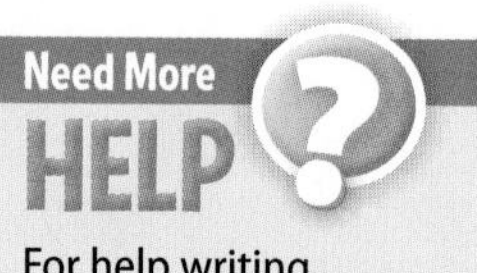

For help writing percents as decimals, go to *Meaning of Percents* (p. 380).

Basil received $500 for his tenth birthday. He put it in a savings account that paid 6% simple interest. If he leaves the money in the bank until his twenty-first birthday, how much interest will Basil earn on the $500?

Use the formula for simple interest.

STEP 1 Determine the value of each of the variables, p, r, and t.

$p = \$500$, the original amount deposited

$r = 0.06$, the rate 6% written in decimal form

$t = 11$ years, the amount of time the money is in the account $(21 - 10 = 11)$

STEP 2 Substitute the known values into the formula and simplify.

Substitute. $i = prt$

Multiply. $= 500 \times 0.06 \times 11$

$= 330$

Basil will earn $330 in interest.

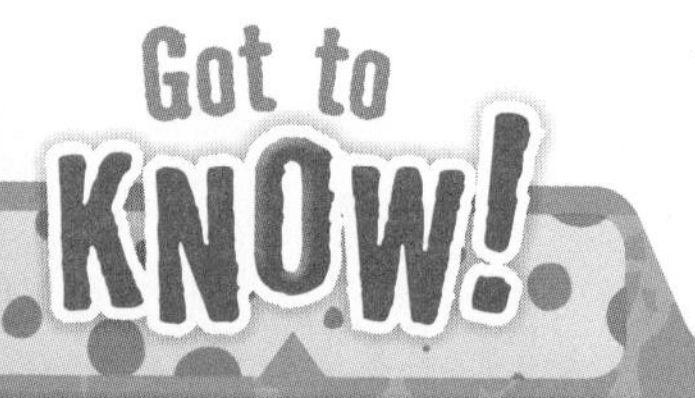

Simple Interest

Simple interest is interest that is earned only on the principal amount invested or borrowed.

The formula for calculating simple interest is

$i = prt$

where i is the interest earned or paid,

p is the principal amount,

r is the interest rate per year, and

t is the time in years.

EXAMPLE 2

Lisa borrowed $800 for 5 years at an annual interest rate of 9%. How much money does Lisa pay back in all?

Use the formula $i = prt$ to find the amount Lisa borrowed.

STEP 1 Determine the value of each of the variables, p, r, and t.

$p = \$800$, the original amount borrowed

$r = 0.09$, the rate 9% written in decimal form

$t = 5$ years, the length of time of the loan

STEP 2 Now substitute the known values into the formula and simplify.

Substitute. $i = prt$

Multiply. $= 800 \times 0.09 \times 5 = 360$

Lisa paid $360 in interest.

STEP 3 Find the total amount she paid back.

Add the amount of the original loan and the interest she paid.

$800 + $360 = $1,160

Lisa paid back $1,160 in all.

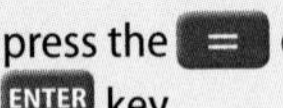

Use a calculator to find the interest. Enter the given values for $p \times r \times t$ and then press the = or ENTER key.

EXAMPLE 3

Big City Bank advertised a simple interest savings account that paid 5.5% interest when at least $15,000 was deposited for 18 months.

a. How much interest would Heiko earn after the 18 months for a deposit of $22,000?

STEP 1 Determine the value of each of the variables, p, r, and t.

$p = \$22{,}000$, the original amount deposited

$r = 0.055$, the rate 5.5% written in decimal form

$t = 18$ months, the amount of time the money is deposited

STEP 2 Express the time in years. Divide 18 months by 12 months per year = 1.5 years.

STEP 3 Substitute the known values into the formula and simplify.

Substitute. $i = prt$

Multiply. $= 22{,}000 \times 0.055 \times 1.5$

$= 1{,}815$

Heiko would earn $1,815 in interest.

b. What is the total amount in Heiko's account after 18 months?

Add the original amount deposited and the interest earned.

$22,000 + $1,815 = $23,815

The total amount in Heiko's account after 18 months is $23,815.

SEARCH

To see step-by-step videos of these problems, enter the page number into the SWadvantage.com Search Bar.

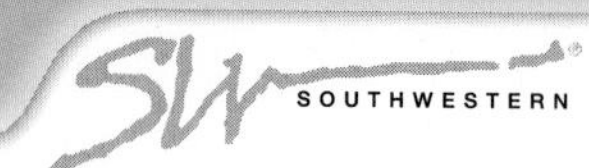

Calculating Compound Interest

For help with simple interest, go to *Simple Interest* on page 398.

Many savings accounts use *compound interest* instead of *simple interest*. The advantage of **compound interest** is that the interest earned is added to the principal, so the principal increases. When you borrow money or charge using a credit card, the interest is usually computed using compound interest. Interest can be compounded using different time periods, which are shown in the *Got to Know!* box at the bottom of the next page.

EXAMPLE 1

Judy put $1,000 in a savings account that offered 6% interest compounded annually. How much money did she have after 3 years?

Use a table to organize the information. Because the time period is annual, the interest is compounded at the end of each year.

METHOD 1

Find the compound interest for each year and add it to the total amount in the savings account at the end of that year.

Year	Principal	Compound Interest	Total
1	$1,000	$1,000 × 0.06 = $60	$1,000 + $60 = $1,060
2	$1,060	$1,060 × 0.06 = $63.60	$1,060 + $63.60 = $1,123.60
3	$1,123.60	$1,123.60 × 0.06 = $67.42	$1,123.60 + $67.42 = $1,191.02

Judy had $1,191.02 after 3 years.

METHOD 2

Find the compound interest and add it to the total amount using only one step. For example, for Year 1 the total amount is: ($1,000 × 1.0) + ($1,000 × 0.06).

For help with The Distributive Property, go to *The Distributive Property* in *Algebra* (Book 2, p. 1410).

Use the Distributive Property to combine the multiplications.

($1,000 × 1.0) + ($1,000 × 0.06)

= $1,000(1.0 + 0.06)

= $1,000(1.06)

For each year, multiply the new principal by 1.06.

Year	Principal	Total
1	$1,000	$1,000(1.06) = $1,060
2	$1,060	$1,060(1.06) = $1,123.60
3	$1,123.60	$1,123.60(1.06) = $1,191.02

Judy had $1,191.02 after 3 years.

EXAMPLE 2

Leo invests $2,500 at 5.5% compounded annually. Juan invests $2,000 at 10% compounded annually. Whose investment has a greater value after 4 years?

Use tables to organize the information. Because the time period is annual, the interest is compounded at the end of each year.

STEP 1 Find the amount of Leo's investment after four years.

Year	Principal	Total
1	$2,500	$2,500(1.055) = $2,637.50
2	$2,637.50	$2,637.50(1.055) = $2,782.56
3	$2,782.56	$2,782.56(1.055) = $2,935.60
4	$2,935.60	$2,935.60(1.055) = $3,097.06

Leo has $3,097.06 after 4 years.

STEP 2 Find the amount of Juan's investment after four years.

Year	Principal	Total
1	$2,000	$2,000(1.10) = $2,200
2	$2,200	$2,200(1.10) = $2,420
3	$2,420	$2,420(1.10) = $2,662
4	$2,662	$2,662(1.10) = $2,928.20

Juan has $2,928.20 after 4 years.

STEP 3 Compare the amounts: $3,097.06 > $2,928.20

Leo's investment has a greater value than Juan's after 4 years.

To see step-by-step videos of these problems, enter the page number into the SWadvantage.com Search Bar.

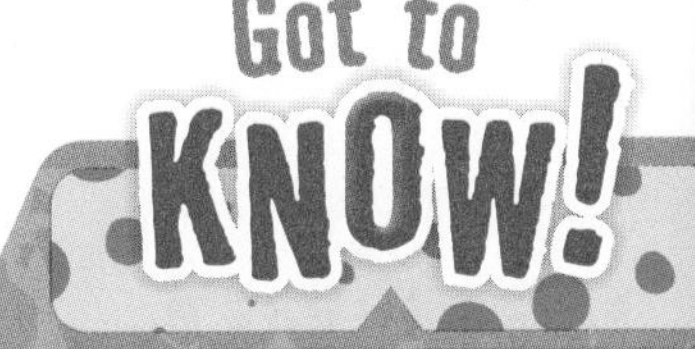

Compounding Periods

Period	Interest is Compounded . . .
Annually	once a year.
Semiannually	twice a year.
Biannually	every two years.
Quarterly	four times a year.
Monthly	twelve times a year.
Daily	every day.

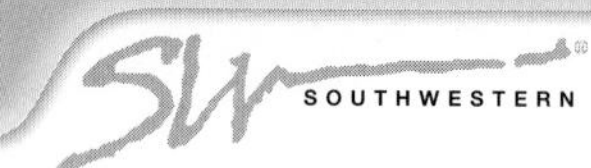

Solving Percent Word Problems

You may find it helpful to follow the steps shown in the *Got to Know!* box below. Example 1, Methods 1 and 2 show a formal application of the steps.

Need More HELP

For help solving word problems, go to *Problem Solving* (p. 446). You will find a four-step problem solving process and strategies for problem solving.

EXAMPLE 1

A shirt that normally sells for $18 is offered at a 15% discount. How much will you have to pay?

METHOD 1

READ Read the problem carefully. Identify what you know and what you need to find out, or need to know.

Know: The shirt sells for $18 and is on sale at 15% off.

Need to Know: The discounted price.

PLAN Find the amount of the discount, and subtract it from the original price.

SOLVE **STEP 1** Multiply $18 by 15% to find the discount.

Express 15% as a decimal: 15% = 0.15

Write the problem in vertical form.

$$\begin{array}{r} 18 \\ \times\ 0.15 \\ \hline 2.7 \end{array}$$

The amount of the discount is $2.70.

STEP 2 Subtract the discount from the original price:

$18.00 − $2.70 = $15.30

CHECK Did I answer the question? Is my answer reasonable?

Use logical reasoning and mental math *to check the discount*. 15% = 10% + 5%. Ten percent of $18 is $1.80, so, 5% is $1.80 ÷ 2 = $0.90. Add $1.80 + $0.90 = $2.70.

Estimate *to check the subtraction:* $2.70 is about $3. Then $18 − $3 is $15, which is about $15.30. The answer is reasonable.

You will pay $15.30 for the shirt.

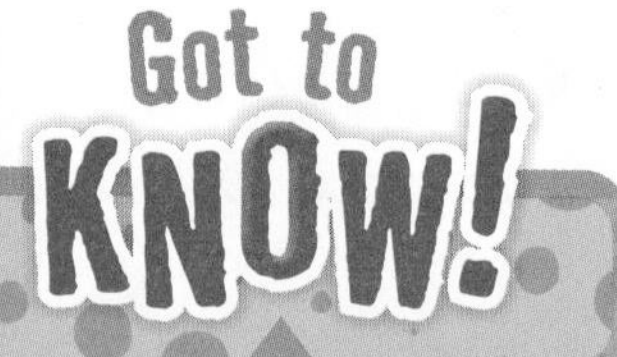

Problem Solving Process

To solve a word problem, you can use this process.

1. **Read** the problem carefully. Identify what you know and what you need to find out.
2. **Plan** how to find the solution.
3. **Solve** the problem using your plan.
4. **Check** your work and ask if your answer makes sense.

METHOD 2

READ Read the problem carefully. Identify what you know and what you need to find out, or need to know.
Know: The shirt sells for $18 and is on sale at 15% off.
Need to Know: The discounted price.

PLAN If the shirt is on sale for 15% off the price, then the sale price is 100% − 15% = 85% of the original price.

SOLVE Find 85% of the original price.
Express 85% as a decimal: 85% = 0.85
Write the problem in vertical form.

$$\begin{array}{r} 18 \\ \times\ 0.85 \\ \hline 15.30 \end{array}$$

CHECK Did I answer the question? Is my answer is correct?
Use logical reasoning and mental math. 85% = 50% + 25% + 10%. 50% of $18 = $9. 25% of $18 = $9 ÷ 2 = $4.50. 10% of $18 = $1.80. *Round to estimate* and add: $9 + $4 + $2 = $15. The answer is reasonable.

You will pay $15.30 for the shirt.

SEARCH

To see step-by-step videos of these problems, enter the page number into the SWadvantage.com Search Bar.

EXAMPLE 2

Ted buys a computer monitor for $580. The sales tax on the purchase is 4.5%. How much does Ted pay for the monitor in all?

READ Know: The monitor costs $580. The sales tax is 4.5%.
Need to Know: Total cost including the sales tax.

PLAN Find the amount of the sales tax and add it to the price of the monitor.

SOLVE Multiply $580 by 4.5%.

Write 4.5% as a decimal. 4.5% = 0.045
Multiply. $580 × 0.045 = $26.10
The amount of the tax is $26.10.
Add the sales tax to the price.

$$\begin{array}{rl} \$580.00 & \text{price} \\ +\ \$26.10 & \text{sales tax} \\ \hline \$606.10 & \text{total cost} \end{array}$$

CHECK Estimate. The monitor costs about $600 and the tax rate is about 5%. Five percent of $600 is $30. So, the estimated total price is $600 + $30 = $630.

It is a little higher than the actual price because both the price and the sales tax rate were increased for the estimate. The answer is reasonable.

Ted paid $606.10 for the monitor.

For help writing percents as decimals, go to *Meaning of Percents* (p. 380).

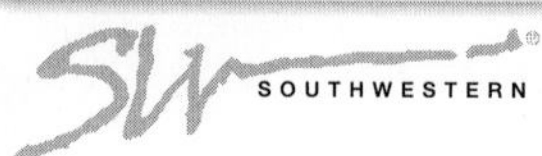

More Word Problems Using Percent

SEARCH

To see step-by-step videos of these problems, enter the page number into the SWadvantage.com Search Bar.

EXAMPLE 3

Carlos earned 112% of the amount he earned last year. Last year he earned $32,000. How much did he earn this year?

READ Know: Amount he earned last year and the percent of that amount he earned this year.

Need to Know: Amount he earned this year.

PLAN This is a percent increase. Multiply the amount he earned last year by 112%.

SOLVE Multiply $32,000 by 112%.

Express 112% as a decimal. $112\% = 1.12$

Multiply.

$$\begin{array}{r} 32{,}000 \\ \times \quad 1.12 \\ \hline 35{,}840 \end{array}$$

CHECK Estimate. 10% of $32,000 = $3,200. $32,000 + 3,200 = $35,200. The actual amount will be more because 12% > 10%, so the answer is reasonable.

Carlos earned $35,840 this year.

EXAMPLE 4

A furniture store sells a sofa for $999.95. The store paid $205.50 for the sofa. What is the percent of markup on the sofa? Round to the nearest whole percent.

READ Know: A store sells a sofa for $999.95 and it cost them $205.50.

Need to Know: The percent of markup on the sofa.

PLAN Use the formula $p\% = \frac{\text{amount of markup}}{\text{original cost}}$ to find the percent of markup.

SOLVE The amount of markup is the selling, or retail, price minus the original cost to the store, or wholesale price. $p\% = \frac{999.95 - 205.50}{205.50}$

Subtract. $= \frac{794.45}{205.50}$

Divide. ≈ 3.87

Write the decimal as a percent. $= 387\%$

CHECK Use logical reasoning and estimate. 387% is about 400% or 4 times the store (wholesale) price of $200. Multiply $200 × 4 = $800 markup. Add $800 (markup) to $200 (wholesale price) = $1,000, which is close to $999.95. The percent markup is reasonable.

The percent of markup is about 387%.

EXAMPLE 5

Samantha borrowed $1,200 from a bank that charges 11.5% simple interest. She paid back the loan in 21 months. How much interest did she pay, and what is the total amount she paid back to the bank?

READ Know: Samantha borrowed $1,200 for 21 months. She paid 11.5% simple interest.

Need to Know: The total amount of interest she paid, and the total amount she paid back to the bank.

PLAN Use the formula $i = prt$ to find the amount of interest paid. Then add the interest paid to the amount borrowed to find the total amount paid.

SOLVE **STEP 1** Determine the value of each of the variables, p, r, and t.
$p = \$1,200$, the amount she borrowed; $r = 0.115$, the rate 11.5% written in decimal form; and $t = 21$ months, the amount of time

Express the time in years.	21 months ÷ 12 months per year = 1.75 years
Substitute into the formula.	$i = prt$
Multiply to simplify.	$= 1{,}200 \times 0.115 \times 1.75$
	$= 241.5$ in interest

STEP 2 Add the amount of interest to the amount of money borrowed. $1,200 + $241.50 = $1,441.50

CHECK Estimate. Round 1,200 to 1,000, 0.115 to 0.10, and 1.75 to 2. Multiply $1{,}000 \times 0.10 \times 2 = 200$. The interest is about $200, which is close to $241.50. Since $1,200 + $400 = $1,600, the answer is reasonable.

Samantha paid $241.50 in interest, and she paid a total of $1,441.50 to the bank.

Watch Out!

The rate, r, in the formula for simple interest is the percent written in decimal form. The time, t, must be expressed in years.

EXAMPLE 6

A school fundraiser earned $9,542. If $5,000 of this money is used to buy new band instruments, what percent of the money earned will be used to buy the instruments?

READ Know: $9,542 raised. $5,000 will be used for band instruments.

Need to Know: What percent of $9,542 is $5,000?

PLAN Write and solve a proportion to find the percent. Use the proportion $\frac{n}{b} = \frac{p}{100}$ to solve the problem.

SOLVE

Substitute 5,000 for n and 9,542 for b.	$\frac{5{,}000}{9{,}542} = \frac{p}{100}$
Use the Cross Products Property.	$5{,}000 \times 100 = 9{,}542p$
Multiply.	$500{,}000 = 9{,}542p$
Divide both sides by 9,642.	$\frac{500{,}000}{9{,}542} = \frac{9{,}542p}{9{,}542}$
Round to the nearest whole number.	$52 \approx p$

CHECK Use logical reasoning. Fifty-two percent is about 50%. $9,542 is about $10,000 and 50% of $10,000 is $5,000. The answer is reasonable.

About 52% of the money earned will be used to buy band instruments.

Need More HELP

For help writing and solving proportions and using the Cross Products Property, go to *Solving Proportions* (p. 368).

Compound Interest and Commissions

EXAMPLE 7

Need More HELP

In Example 7, each year's total is found using the one-step method. You can also use the two-step method found in *Compound Interest* (p. 400).

Lana invests $1,075 at 3.25% compounded annually. Rita invests $1,100 at 2% compounded annually. In what year will Lana's investment have a greater value than Rita's investment?

READ Know: Lana invested $1,075 at 3.25% and Rita invested $1,100 at 2%.

Need to Know: In what year will Lana's investment have a greater value than Rita's?

PLAN Find the interest on both investments and use tables to organize the information.

SOLVE

Lana's Investment

Year	Principal	Total
1	$1,075	$1,075(1.0325) = $1,109.94
2	$1,109.94	$1,109.94(1.0325) = $1,146.01
3	$1,146.01	$1,146.01(1.0325) = $1,183.26

Rita's Investment

Year	Principal	Total
1	$ 1,100	$1,100(1.02) = $1,122
2	$1,122	$1,173(1.02) = $1,144.44
3	$1,144.04	$1,144.04(1.02) = $1,167.33

CHECK Use a calculator to review your multiplication.

At the end of year 2 (or the beginning of year 3), Lana's investment has a greater value.

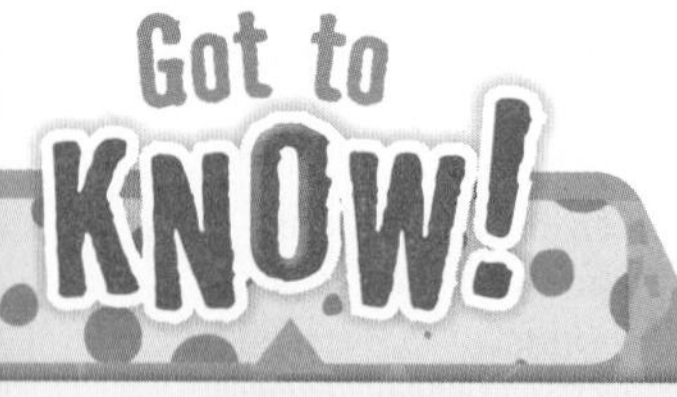

Percent Formulas

To find a **percent of increase**, use $p\% = \frac{\text{amount of increase}}{\text{original amount}}$, where $p\%$ = the percent of increase, and the amount of increase is new amount − the original amount.

To find a **percent of decrease**, use $p\% = \frac{\text{amount of decrease}}{\text{original amount}}$, where ($p\%$) = the percent of decrease, and the *amount of decrease* is the original amount − the new amount.

Simple Interest Formula

To find **simple interest**, use $i = prt$, where i is the interest earned, p is the principal, r is the annual interest rate in decimal form, and t is the time in years.

A **commission** is a payment made to a salesperson that is based on the dollar amount of the sales that person made. It is a percent of a number.

EXAMPLE 8

Marissa earns a salary of $950 per month as a car salesperson. She also earns 1% of the amount of each car she sells. In May, she sold a car for $9,800 and a car for $11,350. How much did she earn in May?

READ Know: She earns $950 each month. She earns a 1% commission on the car sales. She sold a car for $9,800 and a car for $11,350 in May.
Need to Know: The total amount she earned in May.

PLAN Find the commission on the car sales. Add the commission to her salary.

SOLVE

STEP 1 Add to find the total amount of car sales: $9,800 + $11,350 = $21,150
Multiply the amount of car sales by the commission percent.

Express 1% as a decimal. $1\% = 0.01$

Multiply $21,150 by 0.01.

$$\begin{array}{r} 21{,}150 \\ \times \quad 0.01 \\ \hline 211.50 \end{array}$$

The amount of the commission is $211.50.

STEP 2 Add to find the amount she earned in May.
$950 + $211.50 = $1,161.50

CHECK Estimate. She earns about $1,000 each month. In May, she had about $20,000 in car sales. One percent of $20,000 is $200. Add $1,000 + $200 = $1,200, which is close to the answer $1,161.50. The answer is reasonable.

Marissa earned $1,161.50 in May.

To see step-by-step videos of these problems, enter the page number into the SWadvantage.com Search Bar.

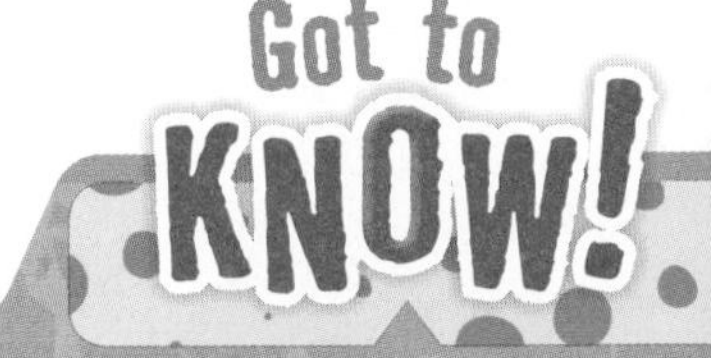

Using a Calculator to Solve or Check a Problem

Calculators can be very helpful in problem solving, but you need to use them with care.

- Always determine in advance whether the calculation you are finding should be greater or less than the greatest number in the problem.
- You may press the wrong key accidentally. Estimate the answer first. Then be certain that the calculator answer is close to the estimate. If it isn't, try again, being careful to press the correct keys.
- If you are using a formula, be certain that you perform the operations in the correct order. Your calculator cannot determine the order for you.

Estimate with Decimals and Fractions

What Came Before?

- Operations with decimals and fractions
- Estimating sums, differences, products, and quotients of whole numbers

What's This About?

- Estimating sums, differences, products, and quotients of decimals and fractions
- Using estimation to predict and check
- Using estimation to solve word problems

Practical Apps

- Repair technicians use estimated products and sums to give potential customers a reasonable price for a repair.
- Carpet companies use estimated room dimensions to give potential customers a price quotation to install new carpeting.

just for FUN!

Serving iced tea won't cost us a thing!

Q: Why not?

A: I estimated the cost per cup to the nearest dollar and it came out to zero!

CONTENTS UPLOAD DOWNLOAD

Numbers and Operations

You can find more practice problems online by visiting:
www.SWadvantage.com

Estimating to Predict or Check

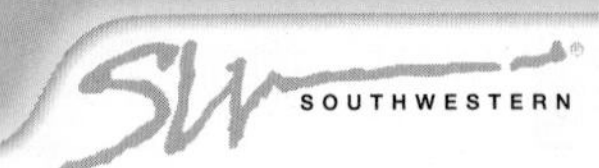

Methods for Estimating

Estimation is most often used in mathematics to predict answers or to check answers. There are different methods that can be used to estimate, as shown in the *Got to Know!* box.

HELP

For help with rounding whole numbers, go to *Round Whole Numbers* in *Foundations of Mathematics* (p. 50).

EXAMPLE 1

Estimate the sum 5,432 + 2,793 + 4,597.

Use rounding. Round each number to the nearest thousand.

$$\begin{array}{rcr} 5{,}432 & \rightarrow & 5{,}000 \\ 2{,}793 & \rightarrow & 3{,}000 \\ +\ 4{,}597 & \rightarrow & 5{,}000 \\ \hline & & 13{,}000 \end{array}$$

The sum is about 13,000.

EXAMPLE 2

Estimate the sum 1,105 + 995 + 1,025.

Use clustering. The values of the numbers cluster at 1,000. Change each number to 1,000.

$$\begin{array}{rcr} 1{,}105 & \rightarrow & 1{,}000 \\ 995 & \rightarrow & 1{,}000 \\ +\ 1{,}025 & \rightarrow & 1{,}000 \\ \hline & & 3{,}000 \end{array}$$

The sum is about 3,000.

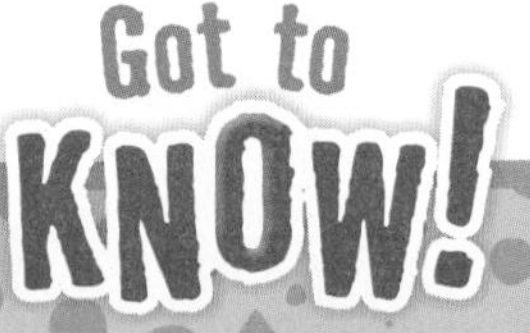

Methods for Estimating

- **Rounding** – Round numbers so that you can use mental math to perform the computation. Sometimes numbers are rounded to a benchmark number rather than to a place value.
- **Clustering** – When all the numbers in a computation have about the same value, round the numbers to that value. This makes it easier to add or multiply the numbers.
- **Compatible Numbers** – Compatible numbers are values that are close to the given numbers used in a problem, but are easier to work with. You can use mental math to solve computations with compatible numbers.
- **Front-end Estimation** – Use only the whole number parts of decimals or mixed numbers to perform a computation.

EXAMPLE 3

a. Estimate the product of 24.02 × 1.95 using compatible numbers and rounding. Then find the actual product.

METHOD 1

Use compatible numbers.

$$\begin{array}{r} 24.02 \\ \times\ 1.95 \\ \hline \end{array} \quad \begin{array}{c} \rightarrow \\ \rightarrow \end{array} \quad \begin{array}{r} 25 \\ \times\ 2 \\ \hline 50 \end{array}$$

The product is about 50.

METHOD 2

Use rounding.

$$\begin{array}{r} 24.02 \\ \times\ 1.95 \\ \hline \end{array} \quad \begin{array}{c} \rightarrow \\ \rightarrow \end{array} \quad \begin{array}{r} 24 \\ \times\ 2 \\ \hline 48 \end{array}$$

The product is about 48.

Use a calculator to find the actual product: 24.02 × 1.95 = 46.839

b. Which method gives the better estimate? Why?

For this problem, rounding gives the better estimate because the factor 24.02 is closer to the rounded value of 24 than to the compatible number 25.

SEARCH

To see step-by-step videos of these problems, enter the page number into the SWadvantage.com Search Bar.

Determining When an Answer Can Be an Estimate

Most of the time, math problems require an exact answer. Sometimes, however, an estimated answer is appropriate.

EXAMPLE 4

For each situation below, decide whether the answer must be exact or if an estimate can be used.

a. Calculating the driving time between two cities

It is almost impossible to calculate the exact driving time between two cities. Driving speed is dependent on the weather, the traffic, and other factors. Driving time can be an estimate.

b. Determining how much money to take to the mall

Unless you know exactly what you are going to purchase and exactly how much everything costs, you need to estimate how much money to take.

c. Calculating the time for a runner in a race

Races are usually timed to an exact measure of time—to the second, or tenth of a second, or hundredth of a second, for example. The time for a runner in a race should be exact.

d. Calculating the amount of sales tax on a purchase

Sales tax is a percent of the cost of an item. The calculation of sales tax should be exact.

Using Estimation to Predict Answers

Estimation is used in mathematics to predict answers. For example, when you are shopping in a supermarket, you can estimate the prices of the items you are buying to determine whether you have enough money to buy them.

SEARCH

To see step-by-step videos of these problems, enter the page number into the SWadvantage.com Search Bar.

EXAMPLE 5

Germaine wants to purchase the items shown on the list below. She has exactly $20 to spend. Is this enough money to buy all of the items on the list?

Item	Cost
Soup	$2.25
Crackers	$3.45
Cookies	$3.29
Cucumbers	$1.25
Peanuts	$5.19
Orange juice	$4.75

Estimate the cost of the items.

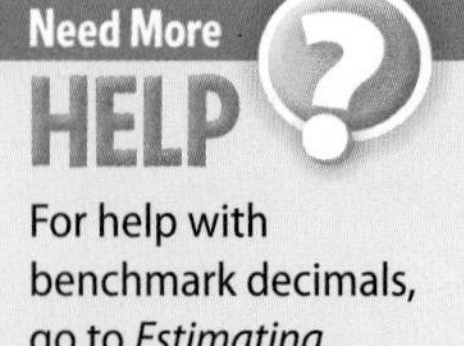

Need More HELP

For help with benchmark decimals, go to *Estimating Decimal Sums and Differences* (p. 414).

STEP 1 Use front-end estimation to add the *whole number parts* of the prices.

$2.25 → $2
3.45 → 3
3.29 → 3
1.25 → 1
5.19 → 5
4.75 → 4
$18

STEP 2 Use the benchmark estimates 0.5 and 1.0 to add the *decimal parts* of the prices.

$0.25 → $0.50
0.45 → 0.50
0.29 → 0.50
0.25 → 0.50
0.19 → 0.50
0.75 → 1.00
$3.50

Each whole number part is less than the actual price, so the exact total is greater than $18.

STEP 3 Add the two estimates: $18 + 3.50 = $21.50.

The estimated sum is about $21.50. Germaine may not have enough money.

Using Estimation to Check Answers

Estimation can also be used to check answers. It is a good way to check computations with decimals, particularly computation on a calculator.

EXAMPLE 6

Find the difference: 0.6974 − 0.0358. Then estimate the difference to check your answer.

Find the difference using a calculator.

$$\begin{array}{r} 0.6974 \\ -0.0358 \\ \hline 0.6616 \end{array}$$

Use rounding to check your answer. Round each number to the nearest hundredth.

$$\begin{array}{rcr} 0.6974 & \rightarrow & 0.7000 \\ -0.0358 & \rightarrow & 0.0400 \\ \hline & & 0.6600 \end{array}$$

The estimate of 0.6600 is close to the actual answer, 0.6616. The answer checks. ✔

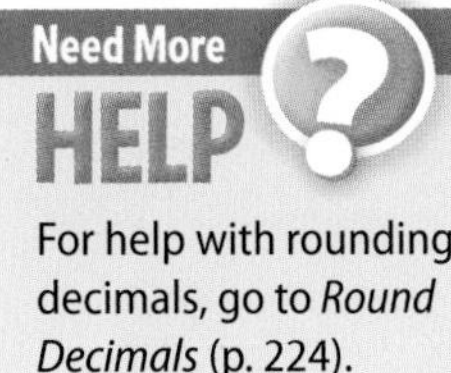

For help with rounding decimals, go to *Round Decimals* (p. 224).

EXAMPLE 7

Harold used his calculator to find this product.

2.9875 × 0.482 = 1.439975

How can he use estimation to see if the product is reasonable?

METHOD 1

Use compatible numbers.

$$\begin{array}{rcr} 2.9875 & \rightarrow & 3.0 \\ \times\ 0.482 & \rightarrow & \times\ 0.5 \\ \hline & & 1.5 \end{array}$$

The estimate of 1.5 is close to the actual answer 1.439975. The answer is reasonable. ✔

METHOD 2

Use rounding. Round each factor to the nearest tenth.

$$\begin{array}{rcr} 2.9875 & \rightarrow & 3.0 \\ \times\ 0.482 & \rightarrow & \times\ 0.5 \\ \hline & & 1.5 \end{array}$$

The estimate of 1.5 is close to the actual answer 1.439975. The answer is reasonable. ✔

Estimating Decimal Sums and Differences Using Rounding

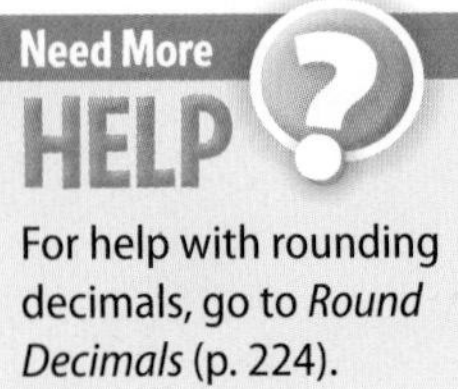

For help with rounding decimals, go to *Round Decimals* (p. 224).

You can use rounding to estimate operations with decimals. You can round to any place value or round to a benchmark number. See the *Got to Know!* box features for methods for estimating with decimal numbers.

EXAMPLE 1

Estimate by rounding to the given place value.

a. Round to the nearest whole number: 6.98 + 7.15 + 11.82

Round each decimal to the nearest whole number.

Then add.

$$\begin{array}{r} 6.98 \\ 7.15 \\ +11.82 \\ \hline \end{array} \begin{array}{c} \rightarrow \\ \rightarrow \\ \rightarrow \\ \\ \end{array} \begin{array}{r} 7 \\ 7 \\ +12 \\ \hline 26 \end{array}$$

The sum is about 26.

b. Round to the nearest tenth: 50.86 − 25.07

Round each decimal to the nearest tenth.

Then subtract.

$$\begin{array}{r} 50.86 \\ -25.07 \\ \hline \end{array} \begin{array}{c} \rightarrow \\ \rightarrow \\ \\ \end{array} \begin{array}{r} 50.9 \\ -25.1 \\ \hline 25.8 \end{array}$$

The difference is about 25.8.

c. Round to the nearest hundredth: 0.0876 + 1.1015

Round each decimal to the nearest hundredth.

Then add.

$$\begin{array}{r} 0.0876 \\ +1.1015 \\ \hline \end{array} \begin{array}{c} \rightarrow \\ \rightarrow \\ \\ \end{array} \begin{array}{r} 0.09 \\ +1.10 \\ \hline 1.19 \end{array}$$

The sum is about 1.19.

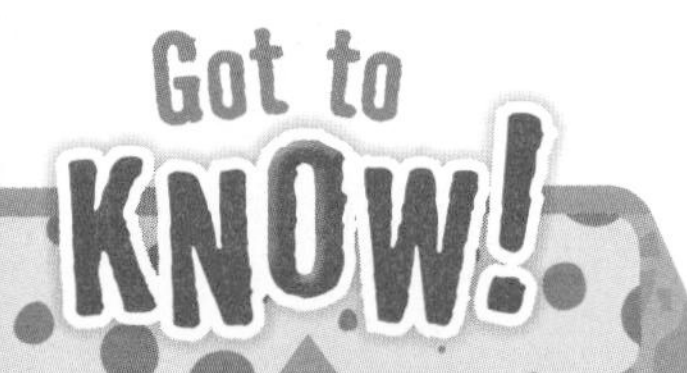

Methods for Estimating with Decimals

- **Rounding** – You can round decimals to any place value to estimate. Choose place values that make it easy for you to use mental math to do the estimation.
- **Compatible Numbers** – Compatible numbers are values that are close to the numbers used in a computation. They make it easier to solve a problem using mental math.
- **Front-end Estimation** – Use the whole number parts of decimals to perform a computation. Then use the decimal parts to achieve a closer estimate.

EXAMPLE 2

The table shows the distance Lance biked (in miles) each day for five days. About how many miles did Lance bike in all?

Day	Monday	Tuesday	Wednesday	Thursday	Friday
Distance (mi)	12.7	15.8	11.2	12.1	15.5

Round each distance to the nearest whole number.

Then add.

$$\begin{array}{rcr} 12.7 & \rightarrow & 13 \\ 15.8 & \rightarrow & 16 \\ 11.2 & \rightarrow & 11 \\ 12.1 & \rightarrow & 12 \\ +15.5 & \rightarrow & +16 \\ \hline & & 68 \end{array}$$

Lance biked about 68 miles in all.

SEARCH

To see step-by-step videos of these problems, enter the page number into the SWadvantage.com Search Bar.

EXAMPLE 3

Use the benchmarks 0, 0.25, 0.5, 0.75, or 1.0 to estimate each answer.

a. 0.2156 + 0.5591 + 0.8095

Round each decimal to the nearest benchmark.

Then add.

$$\begin{array}{rcr} 0.2156 & \rightarrow & 0.25 \\ 0.5591 & \rightarrow & 0.50 \\ +0.8095 & \rightarrow & +0.75 \\ \hline & & 1.50 \end{array}$$

The sum is about 1.5.
A calculator shows that the actual sum is 1.5842, so the estimate is reasonable. ✔

b. 10.923 − 4.012

Round each decimal to the nearest benchmark.

Then subtract.

$$\begin{array}{rcr} 10.923 & \rightarrow & 11.0 \\ -4.012 & \rightarrow & -\ 4.0 \\ \hline & & 7.0 \end{array}$$

The difference is about 7.
A calculator shows that the actual difference is 6.911, so the estimate is reasonable. ✔

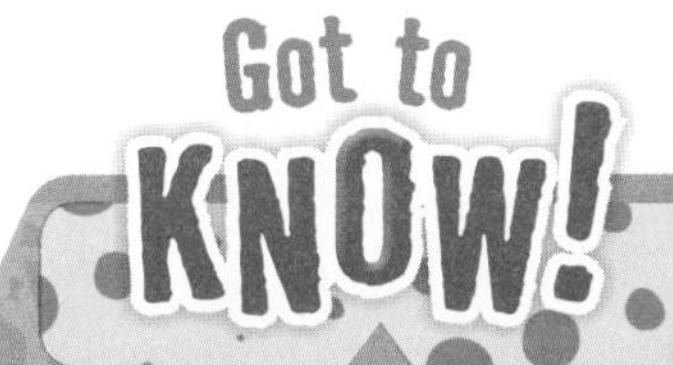

Using a Benchmark to Estimate

Rounding the decimal part of a number to a benchmark instead of a place value sometimes gives you an estimate that is closer to the actual answer. Benchmark decimals are also easy to add or subtract. Use the decimal numbers 0, 0.25, 0.5, 0.75, and 1.0 as benchmarks.

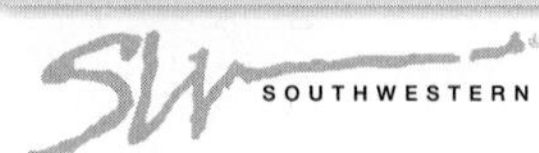

Estimating Decimal Sums and Differences Using Compatible Numbers

Compatible numbers are values that are close to the actual numbers used in a computation. Choose compatible numbers that make it easy to use mental math.

Need More HELP

Remember, compatible numbers are numbers that are very easy to add or subtract mentally. In Example 4(b), you could round to add $6 + 22 + 13 = 41$. Although this estimate is closer to the actual answer than 35 is, the rounded numbers are not as easy to add mentally.

EXAMPLE 4

Estimate by using compatible numbers.

a. 48.92 − 9.75

Use compatible numbers.

Then subtract.

$$\begin{array}{rcr} 48.92 & \rightarrow & 50 \\ -9.75 & \rightarrow & -10 \\ \hline & & 40 \end{array}$$

The difference is about 40.

b. 5.89 + 21.72 + 12.55

Use compatible numbers.

Then add.

$$\begin{array}{rcr} 5.89 & \rightarrow & 5 \\ 21.72 & \rightarrow & 20 \\ +12.55 & \rightarrow & +10 \\ \hline & & 35 \end{array}$$

The sum is about 35.

EXAMPLE 5

The Jefferson family ate dinner at a local restaurant. The restaurant check is shown.

Guest Check **Carla's Restaurant**	
3 Spaghetti Dinners	$14.98
1 Chef's Salad	4.95
1 Hamburger	6.25
5 Iced Teas	5.50

a. Use compatible numbers to estimate about how much money they spent.

$$\begin{array}{rcr} 14.98 & \rightarrow & 15 \\ 4.95 & \rightarrow & 5 \\ 6.25 & \rightarrow & 5 \\ +5.50 & \rightarrow & +5 \\ \hline & & 30 \end{array}$$

The family spent about $30.

b. Use a calculator to see if the estimate is reasonable.

$14.98 + 4.95 + 6.25 + 5.50 = \$31.68$

A calculator shows that the exact sum is $31.68, so the estimate is reasonable. ✔

Estimating Decimal Sums and Differences Using Front-end Estimation

You can estimate decimal sums using front-end estimation. First add only the whole number parts of the decimals. Then look at the decimal parts and use their values to get a better estimate.

EXAMPLE 

Estimate each sum using front-end estimation.

a. 8.95 + 4.52 + 10.41 + 15.89

STEP 1 Add the front-end digits.

$$\begin{array}{r} 8.95 \\ 4.52 \\ 10.41 \\ +15.89 \\ \hline 37 \end{array}$$

The front-end digits have a sum of 37.

STEP 2 Estimate the sum of the decimal parts.

8.95	about 1	
4.52, 10.41	about 1	about 3
+15.89	about 1	

The decimal parts have a sum of about 3.

STEP 3 Add the two estimates. 37 + 3 = 40

The sum is about 40.

b. $15.95 + $3.19 + $21.25 + $12.99

STEP 1 Add the front-end digits.

$$\begin{array}{r} 15.95 \\ 3.19 \\ 21.25 \\ +12.99 \\ \hline 51 \end{array}$$

The front-end digits have a sum of $51.

STEP 2 Estimate the sum of the decimal parts.

15.95	about $1	
3.19, 21.25	about $0.50	about $2.50
+12.99	about $1	

The decimal parts have a sum of about $2.50.

STEP 3 Add the two estimates. $51.00 + $2.50 = $53.50

The sum is about $53.50.

SEARCH

To see step-by-step videos of these problems, enter the page number into the SWadvantage.com Search Bar.

Estimating Decimal Products and Quotients Using Rounding

You can round to any place value to estimate a decimal product or quotient.

For help with rounding decimals, go to *Round Decimals* (p. 224).

EXAMPLE 1

Use rounding to estimate each product.

a. 22.14 × 3.89

Round each decimal to the nearest whole number.

Then multiply.

$$\begin{array}{rcr} 22.14 & \rightarrow & 22 \\ \times\ 3.89 & \rightarrow & \times\ 4 \\ \hline & & 88 \end{array}$$

The product is about 88.

b. 0.048 × 0.059

Round each decimal to the nearest hundredth.

Then multiply.

$$\begin{array}{rcr} 0.048 & \rightarrow & 0.05 \\ \times\ 0.059 & \rightarrow & \times\ 0.06 \\ \hline & & 0.003 \end{array}$$

The product is about 0.003.

c. 2.9375 × 0.0452

Round 2.9375 to the nearest whole number.

Round 0.0452 to the nearest hundredth.

Then multiply.

$$\begin{array}{rcr} 2.9375 & \rightarrow & 3.0 \\ \times\ 0.0452 & \rightarrow & \times\ 0.05 \\ \hline & & 0.15 \end{array}$$

The product is about 0.15.

d. 102.9981 × 0.002178

Round 102.9981 to the nearest hundred.

Round 0.002178 to the nearest thousandth.

Then multiply.

$$\begin{array}{rcr} 102.9981 & \rightarrow & 100 \\ \times\ 0.002178 & \rightarrow & \times\ 0.002 \\ \hline & & 0.200 \end{array}$$

The product is about 0.2.

Methods for Estimating Decimal Products and Quotients

- **Rounding** – You can round decimals to any place value to estimate. Choose place values that make it easy for you to use mental math to do the estimation.
- **Compatible Numbers** – Compatible numbers are values that are close to the numbers used in a computation. They make it easier to solve a problem using mental math.

EXAMPLE 2

Use rounding to estimate each quotient.

a. 98.65 ÷ 3.01

Round each decimal to the nearest whole number. $98.65 \rightarrow 99$, $3.01 \rightarrow 3$

Then divide. $99 \div 3 = 33$

The quotient is about 33.

b. 0.8052 ÷ 0.1896

Round each decimal to the nearest tenth. $0.8052 \rightarrow 0.8$, $0.1896 \rightarrow 0.2$

Then divide. $0.8 \div 0.2 = 4$

The quotient is about 4.

c. 19.891 ÷ 0.0367

Round 19.891 to the nearest whole number. $19.891 \rightarrow 20$

Round 0.0367 to the nearest hundredth. $0.0367 \rightarrow 0.04$

Then divide. $20 \div 0.04 = 500$

The quotient is about 500.

Watch Out !

When the estimated divisor is a decimal number, be certain to place the decimal point correctly in the estimated quotient.

In Example 2(c), the estimate is a whole number divided by a decimal, so the quotient will be greater than the whole number.

Think:

$20 \div 4 = 5$

$20 \div 0.4 = 50$

$20 \div 0.04 = 500$

EXAMPLE 3

A rectangular deck has an area of 95.625 square feet and a length of 12.125 feet. What is the approximate width of the deck?

The formula for finding the area of a rectangle is $A = \ell \times w$, where A is the area, ℓ is the length, and w is the width.

STEP 1 You are given the area (A) and the length (ℓ) of the deck. Substitute the given values into the formula.

Substitute. $A = \ell \times w$

Divide both sides by 12.125 to solve for w. $95.625 = 12.125 \times w$

$$\frac{95.625}{12.125} = w$$

STEP 2 Estimate.

Round each number to the nearest whole number. $\frac{95.625 \rightarrow 96}{12.125 \rightarrow 12} = w$

Then divide. $96 \div 12 = 8$

The width of the deck (w) is about 8 feet.

SEARCH

To see step-by-step videos of these problems, enter the page number into the SWadvantage.com Search Bar.

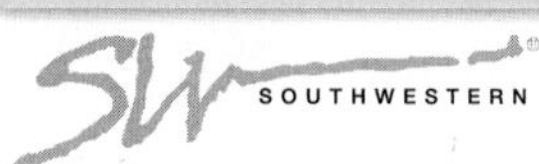

Estimating Decimal Products and Quotients Using Compatible Numbers

Compatible numbers are values that are close to the actual numbers in a problem and that are easy to compute with using mental math. There are many ways to choose the compatible numbers, but it is helpful to think of multiplication and division facts when you choose them.

Need More HELP

There is no one correct way to choose compatible numbers. Example 4(b) shows two different sets of compatible numbers for the same problem. A calculator shows that the exact product is 0.157263, so Method 2 gives a closer estimate. With practice, you can learn to find which numbers will give the closest estimate.

EXAMPLE 4

Use compatible numbers to estimate each product.

a. 42.15 × 5.5

Choose the compatible numbers 40 and 5.

Use mental math to multiply.

The product is about 200.

$$\begin{array}{r} 42.15 \\ \times\ \ 5.5 \\ \hline \end{array} \begin{array}{c} \rightarrow \\ \rightarrow \\ \end{array} \begin{array}{r} 40 \\ \times\ 5 \\ \hline 200 \end{array}$$

b. 0.589 × 0.267

METHOD 1

Choose the compatible numbers 0.6 and 0.2.

Then multiply.

The product is about 0.12.

$$\begin{array}{r} 0.589 \\ \times 0.267 \\ \hline \end{array} \begin{array}{c} \rightarrow \\ \rightarrow \\ \end{array} \begin{array}{r} 0.6 \\ \times 0.2 \\ \hline 0.12 \end{array}$$

METHOD 2

Choose the compatible numbers 0.5 and 0.3.

Then multiply.

The product is about 0.15.

$$\begin{array}{r} 0.589 \\ \times 0.267 \\ \hline \end{array} \begin{array}{c} \rightarrow \\ \rightarrow \\ \end{array} \begin{array}{r} 0.5 \\ \times 0.3 \\ \hline 0.15 \end{array}$$

EXAMPLE 5

Mrs. Gonzales bought 7.24 pounds of tomatoes at \$2.09 per pound and 5.85 pounds of potatoes at \$0.89 per pound. About how much did Mrs. Gonzales spend in all?

STEP 1 Use compatible numbers to estimate the costs.

Tomatoes

$$\begin{array}{r} 7.24 \\ \times \$2.09 \\ \hline \end{array} \begin{array}{c} \rightarrow \\ \rightarrow \\ \end{array} \begin{array}{r} 7 \\ \times 2 \\ \hline \$14 \end{array}$$

Potatoes

$$\begin{array}{r} 5.85 \\ \times \$0.89 \\ \hline \end{array} \begin{array}{c} \rightarrow \\ \rightarrow \\ \end{array} \begin{array}{r} 6 \\ \times 1 \\ \hline \$6 \end{array}$$

STEP 2 Add the amounts. \$14 + \$6 = \$20

Mrs. Gonzales spent about \$20.

EXAMPLE 6

Use compatible numbers to estimate each quotient.

a. 1,595.24 ÷ 39.61

Choose the compatible numbers 1,600 and 40.

$1{,}595.24 \rightarrow 1{,}600$
$39.61 \rightarrow 40$

Use mental math to divide. $1{,}600 \div 40 = 40$

The quotient is about 40.

b. 189.298 ÷ 9.21

METHOD 1

Choose the compatible numbers 180 and 9.

$189.298 \rightarrow 180$
$9.21 \rightarrow 9$

Use mental math to divide. $180 \div 9 = 20$

The quotient is about 20.

METHOD 2

Choose the compatible numbers 200 and 10.

$189.298 \rightarrow 200$
$9.21 \rightarrow 10$

Use mental math to divide. $200 \div 10 = 20$

The quotient is about 20.

Try It This Way

If you are having difficulty choosing a compatible number, try this method.

Underline the greatest whole number digits.

<u>15</u>95.24

<u>3</u>9.61

Think: Do I know a multiplication or division fact that uses numbers close to these numbers?

Yes, $16 \div 4 = 4$. I could divide 1,600 by 40.

EXAMPLE 7

Liam is 187.9 cm tall. His daughter Bonnie is 62.6 cm tall.

a. Estimate how many times taller Liam is than Bonnie.

Choose the compatible numbers 180 and 60.

$187.9 \rightarrow 180$
$62.6 \rightarrow 60$

Use mental math to divide. $180 \div 60 = 3$

Liam is about 3 times taller than Bonnie.

b. Find the exact answer and compare the results.

Use a calculator to find the exact answer. $187.9 \div 62.6 \approx 3.0016$

The estimate of 3 is very close to the exact answer. ✔

SEARCH

To see step-by-step videos of these problems, enter the page number into the SWadvantage.com Search Bar.

Estimating Fraction Sums and Differences Using Benchmarks

You can estimate fraction sums and differences by rounding each fraction to a benchmark. Use the guidelines in the *Got to Know!* box to help you.

EXAMPLE 1

Use benchmarks to estimate each sum or difference.

a. $\frac{5}{9} + \frac{7}{12}$

Round each fraction to a benchmark.

Then add.

$$\begin{array}{rcr} \frac{5}{9} & \rightarrow & \frac{1}{2} \\ +\frac{7}{12} & \rightarrow & +\frac{1}{2} \\ \hline & & 1 \end{array}$$

The sum is about 1.

b. $\frac{9}{13} - \frac{5}{12}$

Round each fraction to a benchmark.

Then subtract.

$$\begin{array}{rcr} \frac{9}{13} & \rightarrow & \frac{3}{4} \\ -\frac{5}{12} & \rightarrow & -\frac{1}{4} \\ \hline & & \frac{1}{2} \end{array}$$

The difference is about $\frac{1}{2}$.

c. $\frac{9}{10} + \frac{1}{12}$

Round each fraction to a benchmark.

Then add.

The sum is about 1.

$$\begin{array}{rcr} \frac{9}{10} & \rightarrow & 1 \\ +\frac{1}{12} & \rightarrow & 0 \\ \hline & & 1 \end{array}$$

You may find it helpful to use a number line to help you see which benchmark to use. Estimate the position of the fraction on the number line. Then decide which benchmark it is closest to.

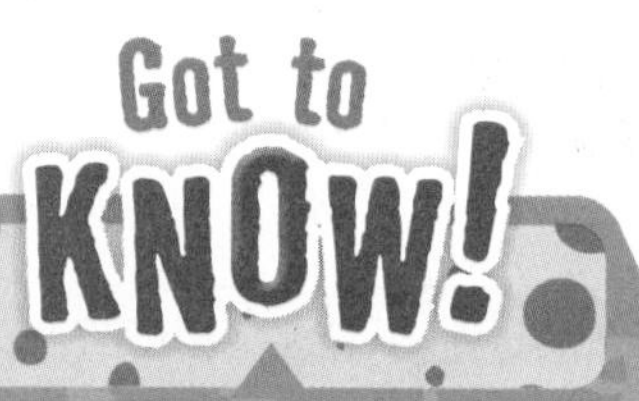

The fraction $\frac{5}{9}$ is closest to $\frac{1}{2}$.

Got to KNOW!

Rounding Fractions Using Benchmarks

Look at the numerator and denominator of the fraction.

If the numerator is . . .	Round to . . .
Much less than one-fourth of the denominator	0
About one-fourth of the denominator	$\frac{1}{4}$
About one-half of the denominator	$\frac{1}{2}$
About three-fourths of the denominator	$\frac{3}{4}$
Much greater than three-fourths of the denominator	1

Estimating Mixed Number Sums and Differences

When estimating sums or differences involving mixed numbers, the best strategy is to estimate by rounding each number in the problem to the nearest whole number. Then find the sum or difference of the whole numbers.

EXAMPLE 2

Use rounding to estimate the sum or difference.

a. $10\frac{2}{5} + 8\frac{1}{9}$

Round each mixed number to the nearest whole number.

$\frac{2}{5}$ is less than $\frac{1}{2}$, so round $10\frac{2}{5}$ to 10.

$\frac{1}{9}$ is less than $\frac{1}{2}$, so round $8\frac{1}{9}$ to 8.

Then add.

$$\begin{array}{rcr} 10\frac{2}{5} & \rightarrow & 10 \\ +\ 8\frac{1}{9} & \rightarrow & +\ 8 \\ \hline & & 18 \end{array}$$

The sum is about 18.

b. $7\frac{4}{7} - 3\frac{11}{24}$

Round each mixed number to the nearest whole number.

$\frac{4}{7}$ is greater than $\frac{1}{2}$, so round $7\frac{4}{7}$ to 8.

$\frac{11}{24}$ is less than $\frac{1}{2}$, so round $3\frac{11}{24}$ to 3.

Then subtract.

$$\begin{array}{rcr} 7\frac{4}{7} & \rightarrow & 8 \\ -\ 3\frac{11}{24} & \rightarrow & -\ 3 \\ \hline & & 5 \end{array}$$

The difference is about 5.

Watch Out!

Make sure you add or subtract the rounded whole numbers, not the whole number parts of the mixed numbers.

SEARCH

To see step-by-step videos of these problems, enter the page number into the SWadvantage.com Search Bar.

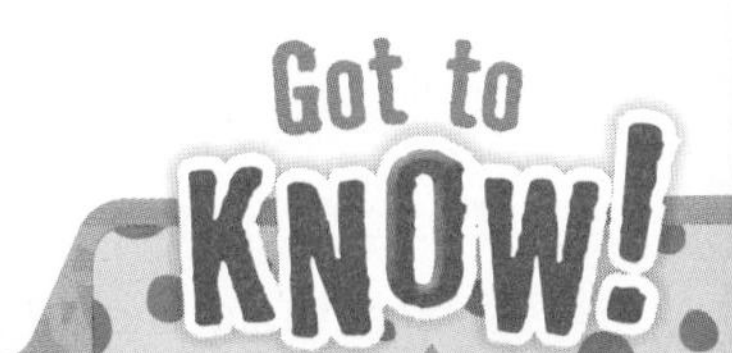

Estimating Fraction Sums and Differences

- When adding two fractions, the answer will be *greater* than either of the fractions in the calculation.
- When subtracting fractions, the answer will be *less* than the greater fraction in the calculation.

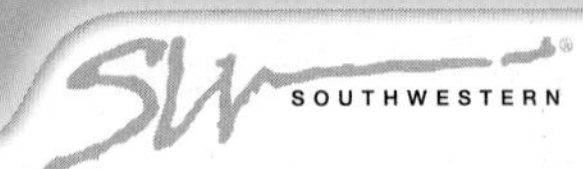

Estimate Fraction Products and Quotients Using Benchmarks

Close estimates for operations with fractions are generally not needed. Often, it is just as easy to compute the actual answer as it is to estimate. However, when you do need to estimate a product or quotient, you can round to a benchmark fraction. Use the guidelines in the *Got to Know!* box to help you.

EXAMPLE 1

Use benchmarks to estimate each product or quotient.

a. $\frac{2}{5} \times \frac{7}{8}$

Round each fraction to a benchmark.

Then multiply.

$\frac{2}{5} \times \frac{7}{8} \rightarrow \frac{1}{2} \times 1 = \frac{1}{2}$

The product is about $\frac{1}{2}$.

b. $\frac{11}{12} \div \frac{2}{9}$

Round each fraction to a benchmark.

Then divide.

$\frac{11}{12} \div \frac{2}{9} \rightarrow 1 \div \frac{1}{4} = 1 \times 4 = 4$

The quotient is about 4.

c. $\frac{4}{9} \times \frac{5}{9}$

Round each fraction to a benchmark.

Then multiply.

$\frac{4}{9} \times \frac{5}{9} \rightarrow \frac{1}{2} \times \frac{1}{2} = \frac{1}{4}$

The product is about $\frac{1}{4}$.

d. $\frac{9}{17} \div \frac{8}{11}$

Round each fraction to a benchmark.

Then divide.

$\frac{9}{17} \div \frac{8}{11} \rightarrow \frac{1}{2} \div \frac{3}{4} = \frac{1}{\cancel{2}_1} \times \frac{\cancel{4}^2}{3} = \frac{2}{3}$

The quotient is about $\frac{2}{3}$.

Need More HELP

For help with dividing fractions, go to *Dividing Fractions by Fractions* (p. 346).

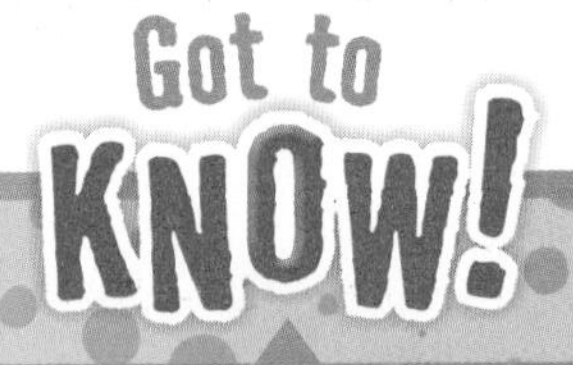

Using Benchmarks to Estimate Fraction Sums and Differences

Look at the numerator and denominator of the fraction.

If the numerator is . . .	Round to . . .
Much less than one-fourth of the denominator	0
About one-fourth of the denominator	$\frac{1}{4}$
About one-half of the denominator	$\frac{1}{2}$
About three-fourths of the denominator	$\frac{3}{4}$
Much greater than three-fourths of the denominator	1

Estimating Mixed Number Products and Quotients Using Compatible Numbers

You can use compatible numbers to estimate mixed number products and quotients. When estimating a quotient, round the divisor to the nearest whole number. Then find a compatible number for the dividend.

EXAMPLE 2

Use compatible numbers to estimate each product.

a. $26\frac{4}{15} \times 4\frac{1}{3}$

Choose the compatible numbers 25 and 4.

Use mental math to multiply.

$$26\frac{4}{15} \rightarrow 25$$
$$\times\ 4\frac{1}{3} \rightarrow \times\ 4 = 100$$

The product is about 100.

b. $14\frac{6}{7} \times 11\frac{4}{9}$

Choose the compatible numbers 15 and 10.

Use mental math to multiply.

$$14\frac{6}{7} \rightarrow 15$$
$$\times\ 11\frac{4}{9} \rightarrow \times\ 10 = 150$$

The product is about 150.

EXAMPLE 3

Use compatible numbers to estimate the quotient of $28\frac{7}{12} \div 2\frac{5}{6}$.

Choose the compatible number 30 for the dividend.

Round the divisor to the nearest whole number.

Round $2\frac{5}{6}$ to 3.

Use mental math to divide.

$$28\frac{7}{12} \rightarrow 30$$
$$\div\ 2\frac{5}{6} \rightarrow \div\ 3 = 10$$

The quotient is about 10.

Watch Out!

Two numbers that are compatible for addition or subtraction may not be compatible for multiplication or division. For Examples 2 and 3, you need to choose numbers you can multiply and divide easily.

Got to KNOW!

Estimated Fraction Sums and Differences

- When estimating the product of two fractions, remember that the product will be *less than* either of the fractions.
- When estimating the quotient of a fraction divided by a fraction, remember that the quotient will be *greater than* the dividend.

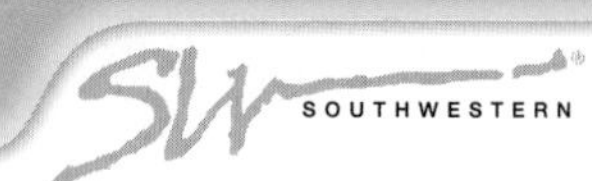

Using Estimation When Checking Word Problems

Some word problems ask you to use estimation to check your answer. Others ask for an estimated answer. When solving either type of problem, you may find it helpful to follow the steps in the *Got to Know!* box below.

Got to KNOW!

Answer the Question Asked

If you state your answer in terms of the question, you will know that you answered the correct question. The question in Example 1 asks, "How many pounds of apples did she buy in all?" The answer states, "Tara bought 7.41 pounds of apples in all."

Need More HELP

For help with estimating to check, go to *Estimating to Predict or Check* (p. 410).

EXAMPLE 1

Tara bought 2.36 pounds of red apples, 3.16 pounds of yellow apples, and 1.89 pounds of green apples. How many pounds of apples did she buy in all? Use estimation to check your answer.

READ Read the problem carefully. Identify what you know and what you need to find out, or need to know.

Know: She bought 2.36 pounds of red apples, 3.16 pounds of yellow, and 1.89 pounds of green.

Need to Know: Total number of pounds in all.

PLAN Add to find the total number of pounds of apples she bought.

SOLVE Write the problem in vertical format and add.

2.36 lb red apples
3.16 lb yellow apples
+ 1.89 lb green apples
7.41 lb in all

CHECK Did I answer the question? Is my answer reasonable?

Estimate the sum. *Round* each decimal to the nearest whole number. Then add.

2.36 → 2
3.16 → 3
+ 1.89 → + 2
7

The estimate is 7, which is close to 7.41. The answer checks. ✔

Tara bought 7.41 pounds of apples in all.

Got to KNOW!

Problem Solving Process

To solve a word problem, you can use this process:

1. **Read** the problem carefully. Identify what you know and what you need to find out.
2. **Plan** how to find the solution.
3. **Solve** the problem using your plan.
4. **Check** your work and ask if your answer makes sense.

The table shows the cost per pound of different kinds of luncheon meats. Alejandro bought 4.92 pounds of turkey. How much did he spend for the turkey? Use estimation to check your answer.

Prices of Luncheon Meat

Luncheon Meat	Price (per lb)
Ham	\$3.89
Bologna	\$2.59
Turkey	\$4.19
Roast Beef	\$5.25
Chicken	\$3.99

READ Read the problem carefully. Identify what you know and what you need to find out, or need to know.

Know: The price per pound of five different luncheon meats. Alejandro bought 4.92 pounds of turkey.

Need to Know: Total amount he spent on the turkey.

PLAN Use the table to find the cost per pound of turkey. Then multiply the cost per pound times the number of pounds he bought.

SOLVE Write the problem in vertical format and multiply. Add zeros for placeholders if it is helpful.

$$\begin{array}{rl} 4.92 & \text{lb} \\ \times\ 4.19 & \text{cost per lb} \\ \hline 4428 & \\ 4920 & \\ 196800 & \\ \hline \end{array}$$

20.6148 = \$20.61

CHECK Did I answer the question? Is my answer reasonable?

Is my answer correct?

Estimate the product. *Round* each decimal to the nearest whole number. Then multiply.

$$\begin{array}{rcr} 4.92 & \rightarrow & 5 \\ \times\ 4.19 & \rightarrow & \times\ 4 \\ \hline & & 20 \end{array}$$

The estimate is \$20, which is close to \$20.61. The answer is reasonable.

Alejandro spent \$20.61 for the turkey.

Need More HELP

For help solving word problems, go to *Problem Solving* (p. 446). You will find a four-step problem solving process and strategies for problem solving.

SEARCH

To see step-by-step videos of these problems, enter the page number into the SWadvantage.com Search Bar.

Need More HELP

For help multiplying decimals, go to *Multiplying Decimals by Decimals* (p. 242).

Using Estimation When Solving Word Problems

SEARCH

To see step-by-step videos of these problems, enter the page number into the SWadvantage.com Search Bar.

EXAMPLE 3

The table shows how much rain fell in a city for each of 5 months.

Monthly Rainfall Totals

Month	March	April	May	June	July
Amount (in.)	$8\frac{1}{2}$	$6\frac{1}{4}$	$11\frac{7}{8}$	5	$4\frac{1}{8}$

a. About how many more inches of rain fell in May than in July?

READ Know: Monthly rainfall totals for March through July.

Need to Know: About how much more rain fell in May than in July.

PLAN The question asks "about how many," so you can estimate the answer. Find the difference between the amount of rainfall in May and the amount of rainfall in June.

SOLVE **STEP 1** Find the amounts of rainfall. May: $11\frac{7}{8}$ in. July: $4\frac{1}{8}$ in.

STEP 2 *Round* each mixed number to the nearest whole number. Then subtract.

Since $\frac{7}{8} > \frac{1}{2}$, round $11\frac{7}{8}$ to 12. $11\frac{7}{8} \rightarrow 12$

Since $\frac{1}{8} < \frac{1}{2}$, round $4\frac{1}{8}$ to 4. $-4\frac{1}{8} \rightarrow -4$

8

CHECK Mentally subtract: $11 - 4 = 7$ and $\frac{7}{8} - \frac{1}{8} = \frac{6}{8}$. $7\frac{6}{8} > 7\frac{1}{2}$, so it is close to 8. ✔

About 8 more inches of rain fell in May than in July.

b. About how many inches of rain fell during the five-month period?

READ Need to Know: An estimate of the total rainfall for the five months.

PLAN Use the benchmarks 0, $\frac{1}{4}$, $\frac{1}{2}$, $\frac{3}{4}$, and 1 to round the numbers. Then add.

SOLVE **STEP 1** Round: $11\frac{7}{8} \rightarrow 12$ $4\frac{1}{8} \rightarrow 4$

STEP 2 Add: $8\frac{1}{2} + 6\frac{1}{4} + 12 + 5 + 4$

$= (8\frac{1}{2} + 12) + (6\frac{1}{4} + 4) + 5$

$= 20\frac{1}{2} + 10\frac{1}{4} + 5 = 35\frac{3}{4}$

CHECK Round each mixed number to the nearest whole number and add.

$9 + 6 + 12 + 5 + 4 =$

$9 + (6 + 4) + 17 =$

$9 + 27 = 36$

36 is close to $35\frac{3}{4}$. ✔

About $35\frac{3}{4}$ inches of rain fell during the five-month period.

Remember, you can reorder addends to make mental addition easier, as shown in the SOLVE and CHECK for part (b).

EXAMPLE 4

A baker has $23\frac{1}{4}$ cups of flour. Each loaf of bread he makes uses $2\frac{3}{4}$ cups of flour. About how many loaves of bread can he make with the flour?

READ Know: The baker has $23\frac{1}{4}$ cups of flour. Each loaf takes $2\frac{3}{4}$ cups.

Need to Know: An estimate of how many loaves of bread he can make.

PLAN Divide the amount of flour by the number of cups needed for each loaf. Use *compatible numbers* to estimate the dividend and the divisor.

SOLVE Choose the compatible numbers 24 and 3.

$23\frac{1}{4} \rightarrow 24 \qquad 2\frac{3}{4} \rightarrow 3$

Use mental math to divide.

$24 \div 3 = 8$

CHECK Use inverse operations. $8 \times 3 = 24$ ✔

The baker can make about 8 loaves of bread.

Try It This Way

Remember, you can use a calculator to check your answer or to see if an estimated answer is reasonable.

For Example 4, express each value as a decimal. Then multiply.

Enter: 23.25

Press: ÷

Enter: 2.75

Press: =

The calculator display will show: 8.45454545, so the estimated answer of 8 is reasonable.

EXAMPLE 5

Jasmine bought a scarf for \$12.95, a hat for \$15.49, gloves for \$19.29, and a purse for \$25.65. About how much did she spend in all?

READ Know: She bought items costing \$12.95, \$15.49, \$19.29, and \$25.65.

Need to Know: What is the total amount she spent?

PLAN Use *front-end estimation* to estimate the sum of the four items she bought.

SOLVE **STEP 1** Add the front-end digits.

$$\begin{array}{r} 12.95 \\ 15.49 \\ 19.29 \\ +25.65 \\ \hline 71 \end{array}$$

The front-end digits have a sum of \$71.

STEP 2 Estimate the sum of the decimal parts.

12.95	about 1	about 2.50
15.49	about 0.50	
19.29	about 1	
+25.65		

The decimal parts have a sum of about \$2.50.

STEP 3 Add the two estimates: $\$71.00 + \$2.50 = \$73.50$

CHECK Round each price to the nearest whole dollar to check: $13 + 15 + 19 + 26 = 73$ ✔

Jasmine spent about \$73.50 in all.

For help with compatible numbers or front-end estimation, go to *Estimating Fraction Products and Quotients* or *Estimating Decimal Sums and Differences* (p. 410).

Patterns

What Came Before?

- Multiples
- Ratios

What's This About?

- Finding patterns in figures and in numbers
- Understanding patterns that grow or shrink
- Predicting how a pattern continues

Practical Apps

- Geneticists look for patterns in DNA sequences to determine whether two people are related.
- Quilters use repeating patterns to make large quilts.

just for FUN!

Q: What's the cheer for patterns?

A: Two, four, six, eight, how do we appreciate?

CONTENTS UPLOAD DOWNLOAD

You can find more practice problems online by visiting:
www.SWadvantage.com

Identifying a Repeating Pattern

A **sequence** is a set of numbers, objects, or shapes that are arranged in a specific order. **Patterns** are sequences that follow a rule. You can identify the rule and use it to predict what comes next in the pattern.

EXAMPLE 1

Identify each pattern.

a.

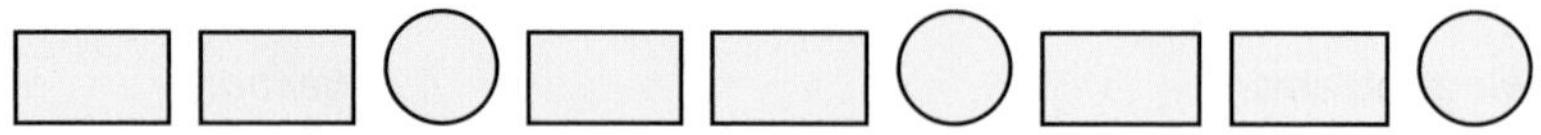

Look for the part of the pattern that repeats.

The pattern is rectangle–rectangle–circle.

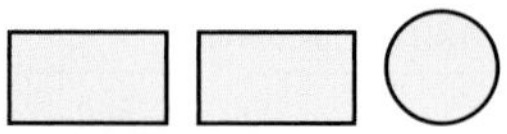

b.

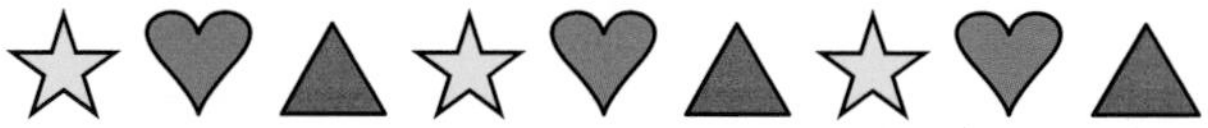

Look for the part of the pattern that repeats.

The pattern is star–heart–triangle.

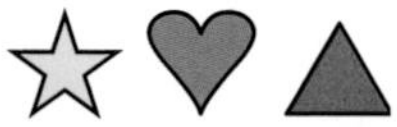

c.

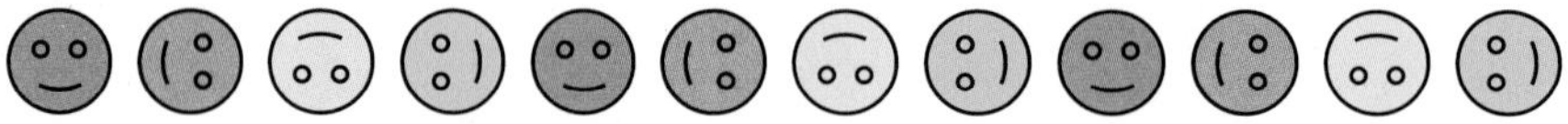

Look for the part of the pattern that repeats.

The pattern is purple–orange–blue–green. Another way to look at the pattern is the position of the face. It rotates 90° clockwise.

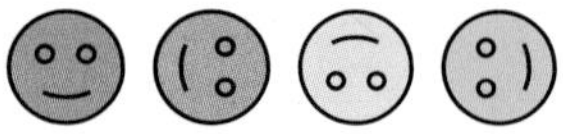

d.

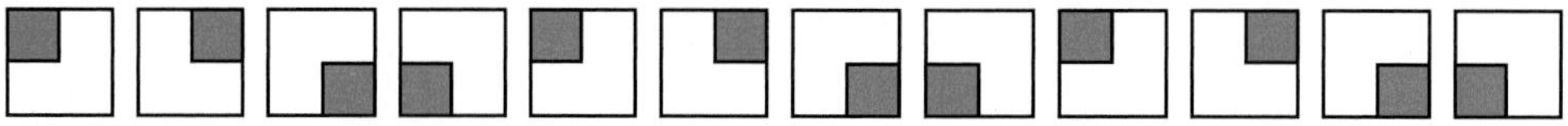

Look for the part of the pattern that repeats.

The pattern is the change in the position of the small blue square, which moves clockwise: upper left–upper right–lower right–lower left.

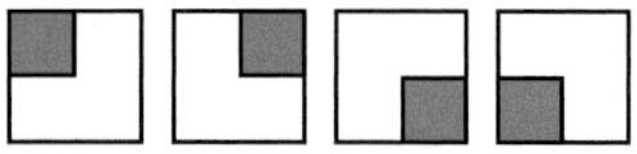

SEARCH

To see step-by-step videos of these problems, enter the page number into the SWadvantage.com Search Bar.

Finding the Next Figure in a Pattern

Each number, object, or shape in a pattern is a **term** of the pattern. When you know the rule for a pattern, you can tell what term comes next.

EXAMPLE 2

Identify the next term in each sequence.

a. 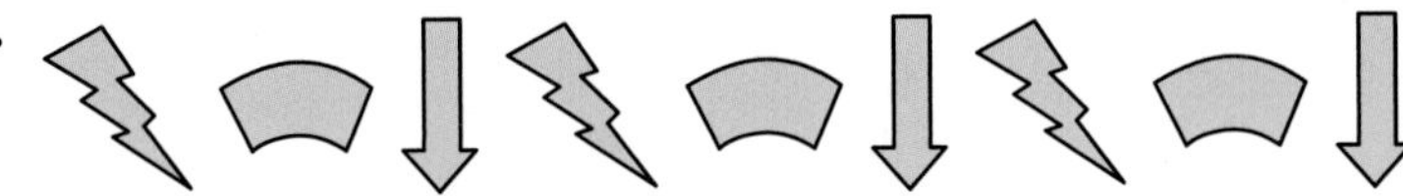

The pattern is these three shapes: 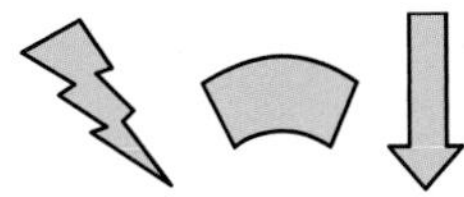

Since the sequence ends with the downward pointing arrow, the next term is: 

b. 

The pattern is these three triangles: 

The pattern repeats three times, so the next term is: 

c.  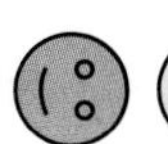

The pattern shows these four shapes: 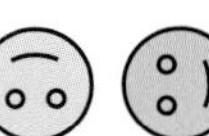

The pattern repeats three times. Then the first two terms of the pattern are shown. This means that the next term is the blue face, not the purple face. 

Watch Out!

In (a) and (b), all the terms in the pattern are repeated. In (c), a part of a sequence is shown.

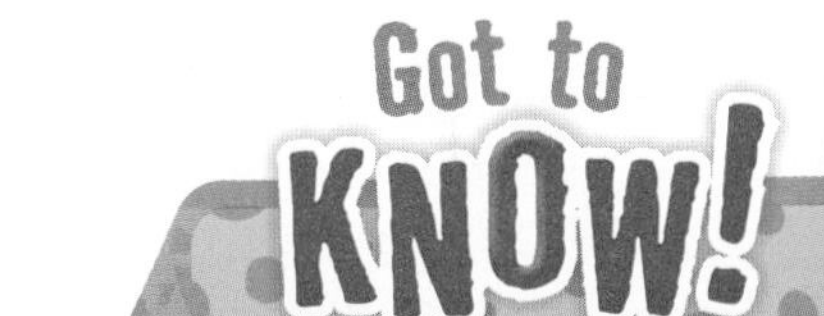

Identifying Patterns

To identify the part of the pattern that repeats, look for changes in shapes, colors, and rotations of the figures in the pattern.

Need More HELP

Remember, a *sequence* is a set of numbers, objects, or shapes that are arranged in a specific order. Each number is a *term* in the sequence. The three dots . . . show that the sequence continues.

Triangular Number Patterns

You can use a diagram to study some number sequences, such as the sequence {1, 3, 6, 9, 10, . . .}. This sequence forms a *triangular number pattern*, and can be represented by a triangular arrangement of dots (or some other shape), as shown below. The first row contains one dot, and each subsequent row contains one more dot than the previous row.

Figure No.	1	2	3	4
	●	● ● ●	● ● ● ● ● ●	● ● ● ● ● ● ● ● ● ●
Dots per Row	1	1, 2	1, 2, 3	1, 2, 3, 4
Total Dots	1	3	6	10

EXAMPLE 1

Determine whether each number pattern is a triangular number pattern.

a.

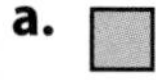
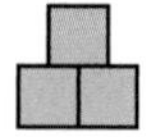
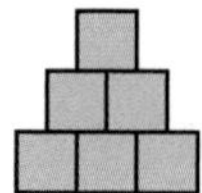
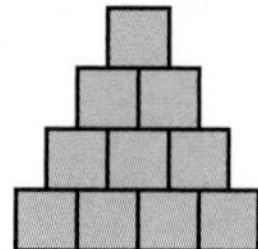

The first figure is made of 1 square. The second figure is made of 3 squares. The third figure is made of 6 squares. The fourth figure is made of 10 squares.

Each row in the figure contains one more square than the previous row.

The pattern is a triangular number pattern.

b.

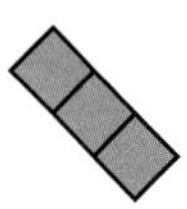
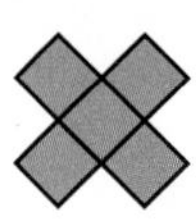
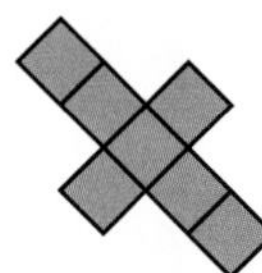

The first figure is made of 1 square. The second figure is made of 3 squares. The third figure is made of 5 squares. The fourth figure is made of 7 squares.

There are no rows that increase by one square.

The figure shows a pattern, but it is not a triangular number pattern.

EXAMPLE 2

The pattern on the right is a triangular number pattern. Draw the next two figures in the pattern.

Think: The right column of the third figure contains 3 cylinders.

The fourth figure will have a column of $3 + 1 = 4$ cylinders on the right side.

The fourth figure is:

Think: The fifth figure will have a column of $4 + 1 = 5$ cylinders on the right.

The fifth figure is:

SEARCH

To see step-by-step videos of these problems, enter the page number into the SWadvantage.com Search Bar.

EXAMPLE 3

The pattern below is a triangular number pattern.

Figure No.	1	2	3	4
Total Dots	1	3	6	10

Describe the arrangement of dots in figures 5 through 8. Then draw the figures.

Figure No.	5	6	7	8
	5 rows; a total of $1 + 2 + 3 + 4 + 5 = 15$ dots.	6 rows; a total of $1 + 2 + 3 + 4 + 5 + 6 =$ 21 dots.	7 rows; a total of $1 + 2 + 3 + 4 + 5 + 6 + 7 =$ 28 dots.	8 rows; a total of $1 + 2 + 3 + 4 + 5 + 6 + 7 + 8 = 36$ dots.

Square Number Patterns

A *square number pattern,* {1, 4, 9, 16, . . .}, can be represented by a square arrangement of dots (or some other shape). The first figure contains one dot, the second figure has 2 rows and 2 columns for a total of 4 dots. Each subsequent figure has one additional row and one additional column. Here is an example.

Got to KNOW!

Triangular number patterns represent the number sequence {1, 3, 6, 10, 15, 21, . . .}. *Square number patterns* represent the number sequence {1, 4, 9, 16, 25, 36, . . .}.

Square Numbers

Figure No.	1	2	3	4
No. of Dots	1	$2 \times 2 = 2^2$	$3 \times 3 = 3^2$	$4 \times 4 = 4^2$
Total Dots	1	4	9	16

EXAMPLE 4

Determine whether each number pattern is a square number pattern.

a.

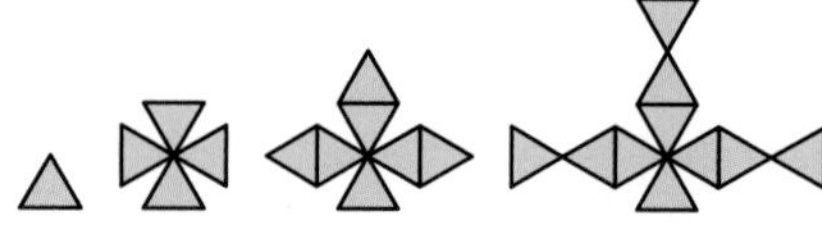

The first figure is made of 1 triangle. The second figure is made of 4 triangles. The third figure is made of 7 triangles. The fourth figure is made of 10 triangles.

The pattern is not a square number pattern.

b.

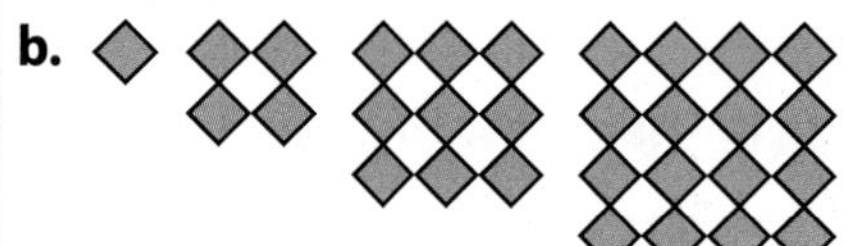

The first figure is made of 1 square. The second figure is made of 2 rows of 2 squares = 4 squares. The third figure is made of 3 rows of 3 squares = 9 squares. The fourth figure is made of 4 rows of 4 squares = 16 squares.

The pattern is a square number pattern.

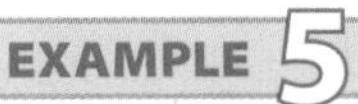

The pattern below is a square number pattern.

Figure No.	1	2	3	4
Total Dots	1	4	9	16

Describe the arrangement of dots in figures 5 through 8. Then draw the figures.

Figure No.	5	6	7	8
	5 dots in each row and column; $5 \times 5 = 5^2 =$ 25 total dots.	6 dots in each row and column; $6 \times 6 = 6^2 =$ 36 total dots.	7 dots in each row and column; $7 \times 7 = 7^2 =$ 49 total dots.	8 dots in each row and column; $8 \times 8 = 8^2 =$ 64 total dots.

SEARCH

To see step-by-step videos of these problems, enter the page number into the SWadvantage.com Search Bar.

Using Pascal's Triangle

Pascal's Triangle, named after the French mathematician Blaise Pascal, is an arrangement of numbers that forms many patterns.

- You can find the *triangular numbers* along this diagonal.
- You can find the *square numbers* along the same diagonal by finding the sum of each adjacent pair of numbers. For example:
  $1 + 3 = 4$
  $3 + 6 = 9$
  $6 + 10 = 16$
  $10 + 15 = 25$,
  and so on.

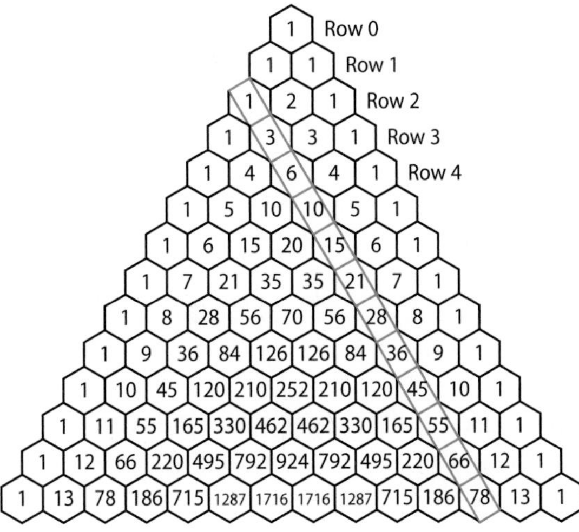

Identifying Growing Patterns

A **number pattern** is a sequence of numbers that follow a certain pattern or rule. Number patterns grow when each subsequent number is greater than the number before it. You can find the rule for a pattern by identifying the constant change between the terms in the pattern.

Some number patterns are **arithmetic**, and grow by adding the same number. Others are **geometric**, and grow by multiplying each subsequent number by a number greater than 1.

Need More HELP

Remember, a *sequence* is a set of numbers, objects, or shapes that are arranged in a specific order. Each number is a *term* in the sequence. The three dots (. . .) show that the sequence continues.

EXAMPLE 1

Find the pattern rule, and tell if the sequence is arithmetic or geometric.

a. 1, 3, 5, 7, 9, . . .

1 3 5 7 9

+2 +2 +2 +2

The pattern rule is "start at 1 and add 2." It is an arithmetic sequence.

b. 1, 2, 4, 8, 16, . . .

1 2 4 8 16

×2 ×2 ×2 ×2

The pattern rule is "start at 1 and multiply by 2." It is a geometric sequence.

c. 4, 8, 12, 16, 20, . . .

4 8 12 16 20

+4 +4 +4 +4

The pattern rule is "start at 4 and add 4." It is an arithmetic sequence.

Watch Out!

The rule must work for every number in the pattern. For example, in Example 1(c), you could have tried the rule "Multiply by 2" since $4 \times 2 = 8$. But this rule does not work for the third term in the pattern, 12, because $8 \times 2 = 16$.

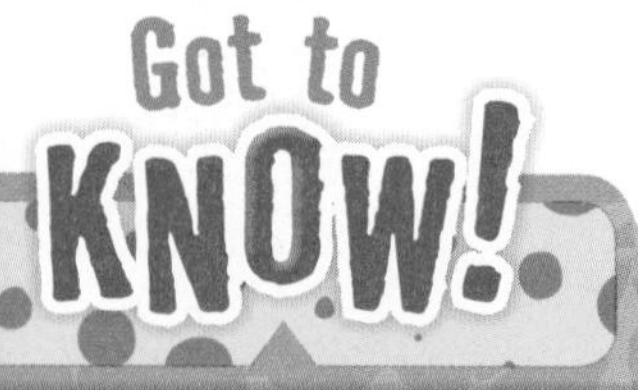

Identifying Growing Patterns

Look for a number that is added to or is used to multiply the previous term in the pattern to find the next term in the pattern. When you think you have found the number, test it with every number in the pattern.

Extending Growing Patterns

When you extend a pattern, you find the next term or terms in the pattern. To find the next number in a growing pattern, first identify the pattern rule, and then apply the rule to the last term.

EXAMPLE 2

Find the next three terms in each pattern.

a. 10, 15, 20, 25, 30, . . .

STEP 1 Find the pattern rule.

Find the number that is added or multiplied to get each subsequent term in the pattern.

10 15 20 25 30

+5 +5 +5 +5

The pattern rule is "start at 10 and add 5."

STEP 2 Find the next three numbers in the pattern.

To find the next three terms, apply the "add 5" rule.

$30 + 5 = 35$ $35 + 5 = 40$ $40 + 5 = 45$

The next three terms in the pattern are: 35, 40, 45.

b. $\frac{1}{4}$, 1, 4, 16, 64, . . .

STEP 1 Find the pattern rule.

Find the number that is added or multiplied to get each subsequent number in the pattern.

$\frac{1}{4}$ 1 4 16 64

×4 ×4 ×4 ×4

The pattern rule is "start at $\frac{1}{4}$ and multiply by 4."

STEP 2 Find the next three terms in the pattern.

To find the next three terms, apply the "multiply by 4" rule.

$64 \times 4 = 256$ $256 \times 4 = 1{,}024$ $1{,}024 \times 4 = 4{,}096$

The next three terms in the pattern are: 256; 1,024; 4,096.

SEARCH

To see step-by-step videos of these problems, enter the page number into the SWadvantage.com Search Bar.

Got to KNOW!

Arithmetic and Geometric Sequences

Arithmetic number sequences grow when the same number is added to each subsequent term in the pattern. For example:

Rule: *Add* 2

1, 3, 5, 7, 9, . . .

Geometric number sequences grow when each subsequent term is multiplied by the same number. For example:

Rule: *Multiply by* 2

1, 2, 4, 8, 16, . . .

You can see that the terms in a geometric sequence grow at a faster rate than the terms in an arithmetic sequence do.

Identifying Shrinking Patterns

Need More HELP

Remember, a *sequence* is a set of numbers, objects, or shapes that are arranged in a specific order. Each number is a *term* in the sequence. The three dots (. . .) show that the sequence continues.

A **number pattern** is a sequence of numbers that follow a certain pattern or rule. Number patterns shrink when each subsequent number is less than the number before it. You can find the rule for a pattern by identifying the constant change between the terms in the pattern.

Some number sequences are **arithmetic**, and shrink by subtracting the same number each time. Other number sequences are **geometric**, and shrink by dividing each subsequent number by the same number.

EXAMPLE 1

Find the pattern rule, and tell if the sequence is arithmetic or geometric.

a. 100, 90, 80, 70, 60, . . .

100 90 80 70 60

−10 −10 −10 −10

The pattern rule is "Start at 100 and subtract 10." It is an arithmetic sequence.

b. 64, 16, 4, 1, $\frac{1}{4}$, . . .

64 16 4 1 $\frac{1}{4}$

÷ 4 ÷ 4 ÷ 4 ÷ 4

The pattern rule is "Start at 64 and divide by 4." It is a geometric sequence.

Need More HELP

The pattern in Example 1(c) includes the negative integers −2 and −7. For help subtracting negative integers, go to *Subtracting Integers* in *Algebra* (Book 2, p. 1392).

c. 13, 8, 3, −2, −7, . . .

13 8 3 −2 −7

−5 −5 −5 −5

The pattern rule is "Start at 13 and subtract 5." It is an arithmetic sequence.

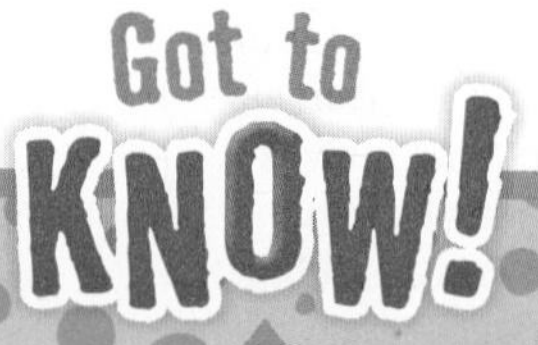

Identifying Shrinking Patterns

Look for a number that is subtracted from or divided by the previous number to find the next number in the pattern. When you think you have found the number, test it with every number in the pattern.

Extending Shrinking Pattern

When you extend a pattern, you find the next term or terms in the pattern. To find the next term in a shrinking pattern, first identify the pattern rule, and then apply the rule to the last term.

EXAMPLE 2

Find the next three numbers in each pattern.

a. 96, 84, 72, 60, 48, . . .

STEP 1 Find the pattern rule.

Find the number that is subtracted or divided to get each subsequent number in the pattern.

96 84 72 60 48

−12 −12 −12 −12

The pattern rule is "Start at 96 and subtract 12."

STEP 2 Find the next three numbers in the pattern.

To find the next three numbers, apply the "Subtract 12" rule.

$48 - 12 = 36 \quad 36 - 12 = 24 \quad 24 - 12 = 12$

The next three terms in the pattern are: 36, 24, 12.

b. 32, 16, 8, 4, 2, . . .

STEP 1 Find the pattern rule.

Find the number that is subtracted or divided to get each subsequent number in the pattern.

32 16 8 4 2

÷ 2 ÷ 2 ÷ 2 ÷ 2

The pattern rule is "Start at 32 and divide by 2."

STEP 2 Find the next three numbers in the pattern.

To find the next three numbers, apply the "Divide by 2" rule.

$2 \div 2 = 1 \quad 1 \div 2 = \frac{1}{2} \quad \frac{1}{2} \div 2 = \frac{1}{4}$

The next three terms in the pattern are: $1, \frac{1}{2}, \frac{1}{4}$.

Got to KNOW!

Arithmetic and Geometric Sequences

Arithmetic number sequences shrink when the same number is subtracted from each subsequent term in the pattern. For example:
Rule: *Subtract 2*
18, 16, 14, 12, 10, . . .

Geometric number sequences shrink as each subsequent term is divided by the same number. For example:
Rule: *Divide by 4*
1,024; 256; 64; 16; . . .

You can see that the terms in a geometric sequence shrink at a faster rate than the terms in an arithmetic sequence do.

Need More HELP

For help with dividing a fraction by a whole number, go to *Dividing Fractions and Whole Numbers* (p. 348).

Patterns with Two Operations

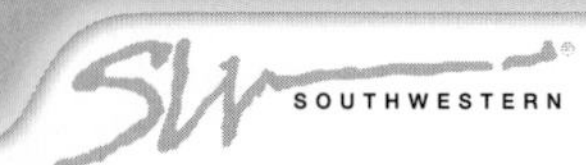

Identifying Patterns with Two Operations

The rule for some number patterns includes more than one operation. When you are finding the rule for a number pattern, it is important to make sure the rule works for the whole pattern.

Need More HELP

Remember, the numbers in a pattern are the *terms* in the pattern. When looking for a pattern, ask yourself, "What operation is performed on this term to get the next term in the pattern?"

EXAMPLE 1

Describe each pattern rule.

a. 12, 24, 26, 52, 54, 108 . . .

Look for a pattern.

You may begin by looking at the first 2 numbers and conclude the rule is "Add 12" or "Multiply by 2." However, when you test this rule for the next term, 26, it does not work.

12 → 24: $+12$, $\times 2$; 24 → ~~26~~: $+12$, $\times 2$

Notice that the second number in the pattern is 2 times the first and the third number is 2 more than the second number.

Try the rule "Multiply 2, add 2."

12 ($\times 2$) 24 ($+2$) 26 ($\times 2$) 52 ($+2$) 54 ($\times 2$) 108

This rule works for all the terms you were given.

The pattern rule is "Multiply by 2, add 2."

SEARCH

To see step-by-step videos of these problems, enter the page number into the SWadvantage.com Search Bar.

b. 128, 64, 68, 34, 38, 19, 23 . . .

Notice that the terms in this pattern decrease and increase. Its rule must include two operations.
The second number in the pattern is one-half the first, and the third number is 4 more than the second number.

Try the rule "Divide by 2, add 4."

128 ($\div 2$) 64 ($+4$) 68 ($\div 2$) 34 ($+4$) 38 ($\div 2$) 19 ($+4$) 23

This rule works for all the terms you were given.

The pattern rule is "Divide by 2, add 4."

Extending Patterns with Two Operations

When you extend a pattern, you find the next term or terms in the pattern. To find the next term in a pattern with two operations, identify and apply the pattern rule.

EXAMPLE 2

Find the next three terms in each pattern.

a. 5, 10, 30, 35, 105, 110, 330 . . .

STEP 1 Find the pattern rule.

Find the operations used to get each subsequent number in the pattern. The pattern is growing, but each term does not increase by the same amount. $10 + 20 = 30$, but $35 + 20 \neq 105$. The rule must include addition and multiplication.

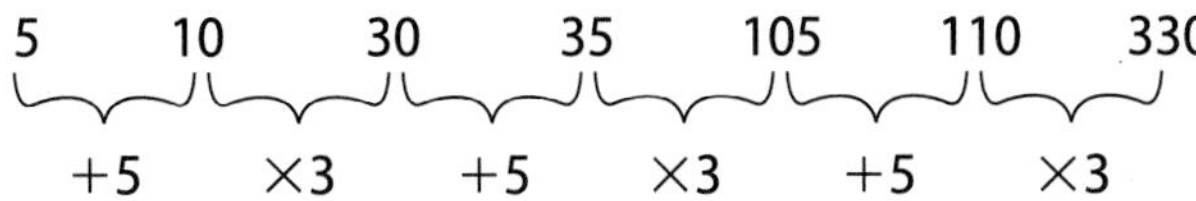

The pattern rule is "Add 5, multiply by 3."

STEP 2 Find the next three numbers in the pattern.

To find the next three numbers, start at 330.

$330 + 5 = 335$ $335 \times 3 = 1{,}005$ $1{,}005 + 5 = 1{,}010$

The next three terms in the pattern are: 335; 1,005; 1,010.

b. 18, 9, 27, 18, 54, 45, 135

STEP 1 Find the pattern rule.

Find the operations used to get each subsequent number in the pattern. Notice that the terms alternately decrease and increase. You know the first operation cannot be "divide by 2" because $27 \div 2 \neq 18$. It must be "subtract 9."

18 9 27 18 54 45 135

−9 ×3 −9 ×3 −9 ×3

The pattern rule is "Subtract 9, multiply by 3."

STEP 2 Find the next three numbers in the pattern.

To find the next three numbers, start at 135.

$135 - 9 = 126$ $126 \times 3 = 378$ $378 - 9 = 369$

The next three terms in the pattern are: 126, 378, 369.

Watch Out !

Remember, the rule must work for every term in the pattern. For patterns with two operations, test each part of the rule on every other number.

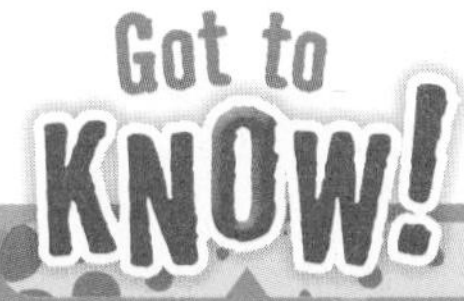

Patterns with Two Operations

Here are two ways to recognize patterns whose rule includes two operations.

- The terms of the pattern both grow and shrink.
- The change between terms is not constant. For example, the change between terms 1 and 2 and between terms 2 and 3 is different.

Solving Word Problems Involving Patterns

You may find it helpful to follow the steps in the *Got to Know!* box below to solve word problems. Examples 1 and 2 show a formal application of the steps.

EXAMPLE 1

Janelle is putting the border shown below around the walls in her bedroom.

What is the next figure in the pattern?

READ Read the problem carefully. Identify what you know and what you need to find out, or need to know.

Know: The figures she has used so far in the pattern.

Need to Know: What figure comes next.

PLAN Identify the pattern and its rule. Then use the rule to find the next figure in the pattern.

SOLVE The pattern is: fish, fish, butterfly.

The pattern repeats three times. Then the first term of the next repeat, a fish, is shown. This means that the next figure will be another fish.

CHECK Is my answer is correct? Complete the fourth repeat of the pattern to check the answer. Circle the given sequence.

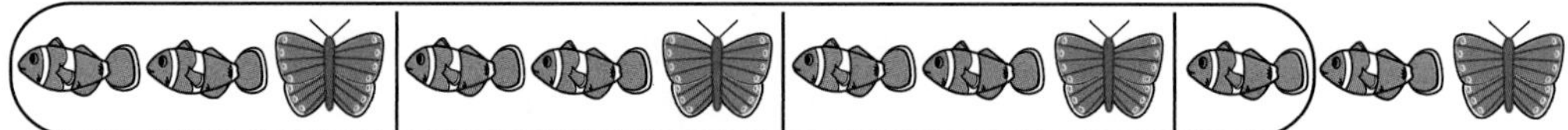

The next figure after the circled sequence is a fish. The answer checks. ✔

Need More HELP

For help solving word problems, go to *Problem Solving* (p. 446). You will find a four-step problem solving process and strategies for problem solving.

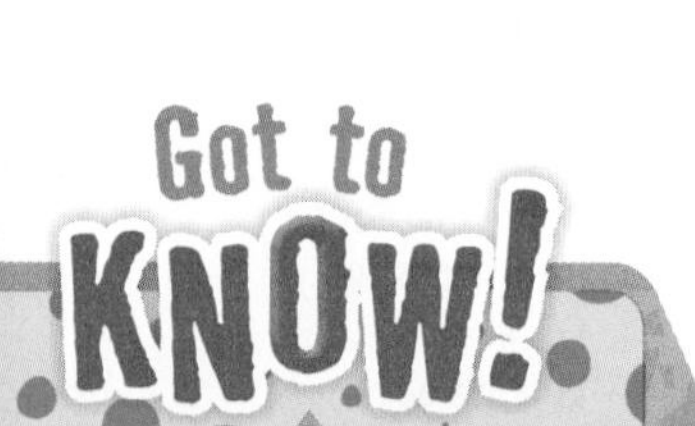

Problem Solving Process

To solve a word problem, you can use this process:

1. **Read** the problem carefully. Identify what you know and what you need to find out.
2. **Plan** how to find the solution.
3. **Solve** the problem using your plan.
4. **Check** your work and ask if your answer makes sense.

EXAMPLE 2

The table shows the noon temperatures for 4 days of the week.

Noon Temperatures

Day	Temperature
Monday	68°
Tuesday	65°
Wednesday	62°
Thursday	59°

If the pattern continues, what will be the noon temperature on Saturday?

READ Read the problem carefully. Identify what you know and what you need to find out, or need to know.

Know: The noon temperatures for Monday, Tuesday, Wednesday, and Thursday.

Need to know: The noon temperature for Saturday, if the pattern continues.

PLAN Use the table to find the pattern rule for the temperatures. Then use the rule to find the temperature for Saturday.

SOLVE The temperatures for the week so far are:

68°, 65°, 62°, 59°

Look for the pattern rule.

68° 65° 62° 59°

−3° −3° −3°

The pattern rule is "Start at 68° and subtract 3°."

To find the temperature for Saturday if the pattern remains the same, subtract 3° two times.

Friday: $59° - 3° = 56°$

Saturday: $56° - 3° = 53°$

If the pattern continues, the noon temperature on Saturday will be 53°.

CHECK Is my answer correct? Use another method to check the answer.

The temperatures are decreasing each day by 3°. Saturday is 2 days after Thursday.

$3° \times 2$ days $= 6°$ $59° - 6° = 53°$

The temperature on Saturday will be 53°. The answer checks. ✔

SEARCH

To see step-by-step videos of these problems, enter the page number into the SWadvantage.com Search Bar.

Problem Solving

What Came Before?

- Operations with whole numbers, fractions, and decimals
- Solving word problems

What's This About?

- The four-step problem-solving process
- Ten strategies for solving problems
- Knowing when to use a particular strategy

Practical Apps

- Project managers use problem-solving strategies to make decisions at every phase of a project.
- Crime scene investigators use strategies such as logical reasoning when looking for evidence at a crime scene.

just for FUN!

Q: What was the carpenter's favorite problem-solving strategy?

A: Make a table.

CONTENTS UPLOAD DOWNLOAD

Numbers and Operations

You can find more practice problems online by visiting:
www.SWadvantage.com

The Problem Solving Process

Being able to solve problems is important in mathematics and in life. To be a good problem solver you need to have a process or plan for solving problems. In this book, you are given a four-step process for solving word problems as outlined below. You can solve word problems using this plan or another plan you know.

The Problem Solving Process		
Step 1	**Read**	Read the problem carefully. You can restate the problem in your own words. Determine what the problem is asking you to find. Identify what you know. This is the information given in the problem. Identify what you need to find out to solve the problem. This is the question asked. You can restate it in your own words.
Step 2	**Plan**	Plan how to find the answer to the question. Think about other similar problems you have solved. Think about how the information you know can help you find the answer. Choose a problem solving strategy.
Step 3	**Solve**	Solve the problem using your plan. As you work, you can revise your plan if you need to. Make sure you write a sentence that states your answer.
Step 4	**Check**	Check your work. Make sure you have answered the question that was asked. Make sure your answer makes sense by using another problem solving strategy to check your work.

Problem Solving Strategies

Here are some problem solving strategies you can use:

Write a Number Sentence – p. 450	Use Logical Reasoning – p. 460
Draw a Diagram – p. 452	Work Backwards – p. 462
Make a Table – p. 454	Solve a Simpler Problem – p. 464
Look for a Pattern – p. 456	Make an Organized List – p. 466
Guess, Check, and Revise – p. 458	Make or Use a Graph – p. 468

Using the Problem Solving Process

EXAMPLE 1

Mario is going on vacation. He packed 2 pairs of pants—a pair of blue jeans and a pair of shorts; 3 shirts—one red, one blue, and one white; and 2 pairs of shoes—flip flops and tennis shoes. How many different outfits can he make consisting of a pair of pants, a shirt, and a pair of shoes?

READ Read the problem carefully. Identify what you know and what you need to find out.

Know: You know the items he packed.

Need to Know: How many outfits he can make.

PLAN Draw a tree diagram to find the number of outfits.

SOLVE

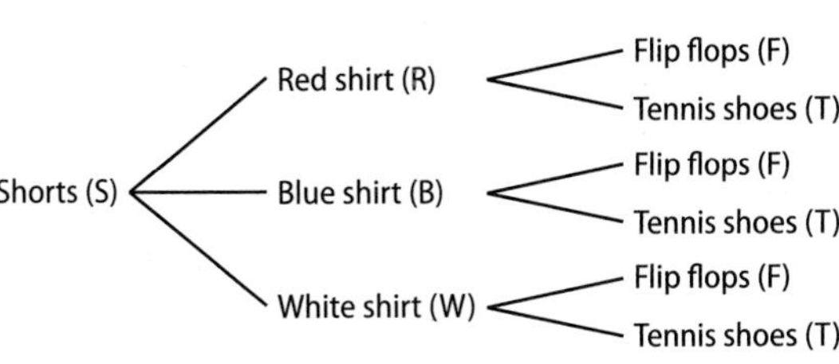

Shorts (S)
Red shirt (R)
Flip flops (F)
Tennis shoes (T)
Blue shirt (B)
Flip flops (F)
Tennis shoes (T)
White shirt (W)
Flip flops (F)
Tennis shoes (T)

Count the number of entries on the right side of the diagram.

Mario can make 12 different outfits with the clothes he packed.

CHECK Make an *organized list* of the outfits. To make the organized list, follow each path on the tree diagram. For example: Jeans (J), Red shirt (R), Flip flops (F) = JRF.

JRF JRT JBF JBT JWF JWT SRF SRT SBF SBT SWF SWT

There are 12 outfits on the organized list. The answer checks. ✔

SEARCH

To see step-by-step videos of these problems, enter the page number into the SWadvantage.com Search Bar.

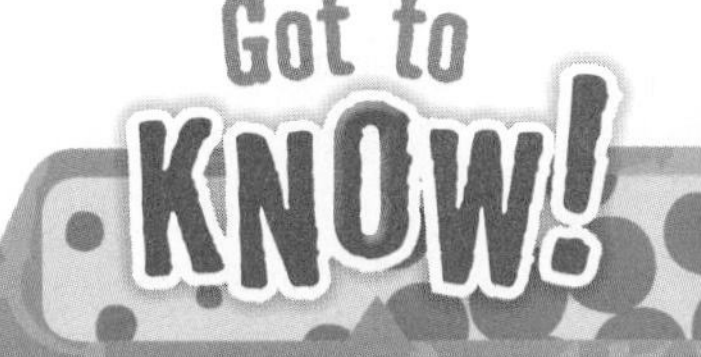

Problem Solving Process

To solve a word problem, you can use this process:

1. **Read** the problem carefully. Identify what you know and what you need to find out.
2. **Plan** how to find the solution.
3. **Solve** the problem using your plan.
4. **Check** your work and ask if your answer makes sense.

Write a Number Sentence

You can use the **write a number sentence** strategy to organize problems where you find the answer by using addition, subtraction, multiplication, or division.

Got to KNOW!

Problem Solving Strategies

Refer to the *Got to Know!* box on page 448 for where to find out more about each strategy. The boldface strategy is featured in this section.

- **Write a Number Sentence**
- Use Logical Reasoning
- Draw a Diagram
- Work Backwards
- Make a Table
- Solve a Simpler Problem
- Look for a Pattern
- Make an Organized List
- Guess, Check, and Revise
- Make or Use a Graph

EXAMPLE 1

Theo works at a local electronics store and earns $7.25 per hour. He also gets paid commission on what he sells. This week he worked 20 hours and earned a commission of $35.50. How much did Theo earn this week?

READ Read the problem carefully.

Identify what you know and what you need to find out.

Know: Theo makes $7.25 per hour.

He worked 20 hours this week.

He also earned a commission of $35.50.

Need to Know: How much he earned this week.

PLAN Use the **write a number sentence** strategy. First write the number sentence in words. Then translate it into numbers.

SOLVE Theo makes $7.25 an hour and worked for 20 hours. He also earned a commission.

Hourly rate × Number of hours worked + Commission = Weekly pay

↓ ↓ ↓ ↓

$7.25 × 20 + $35.50 = Weekly Pay

Multiply first. Then add.

(20 × $7.25) + $35.50

= $145 + $35.50

= $180.50

Theo earned $180.50 this week.

CHECK Is my answer correct? You can use *estimation* to check your answer.

Round $7.25 to $7.00, and use mental math. You know your estimate will be less than the actual answer because you rounded down to $7.00.

20 × 7 = 140

140 + 35.50 = 175.50

$175.50 is close to $180.50.

The answer checks. ✔

Need More HELP

Remember, the order of operations is:

- Parentheses first.
- Then, multiplication and division from left to right.
- Finally, addition and subtraction from left to right.

EXAMPLE 2

A bicycle is on sale for 25% off the regular selling price of $259. What is the sale price of the bicycle?

READ Read the problem carefully.

Identify what you know and what you need to find out.

Know: The bicycle normally sells for $259.

It is on sale at 25% off of the regular price.

Need to Know: The sale price.

PLAN Use the **write a number sentence** strategy. Write the number sentence in words and then translate it into math.

SOLVE

METHOD 1

STEP 1 Find the amount of the discount.

Original price × Discount = Discount amount

↓ ↓ ↓

$259 × 25% = Discount amount

Write 25% as a decimal and multiply. $259 × 0.25 = $64.75

The discount amount is $64.75.

STEP 2 Find the sale price.

Original price − Discount amount = Sale price

↓ ↓ ↓

$259 − $64.75 = Sale price

Subtract. $259 − $64.75 = $194.25

The sale price is $194.25.

METHOD 2

Find the sale price using one number sentence.

Original price − (Original price × Discount amount) = Sale price

↓ ↓ ↓ ↓

$259 − ($259 × 25%) = Sale price

Multiply first, then subtract. $259 − ($259 × 0.25) = $259 − $64.75

= $194.25

The sale price is $194.25.

CHECK Is my answer correct?

Both methods give the same answer, so the answer checks. ✔

SEARCH

To see step-by-step videos of these problems, enter the page number into the SWadvantage.com Search Bar.

For help with writing percents as decimals, go to *Meaning of Percents* (p. 380).

Try It This Way

If you have a calculator with a percent key, you can use it to check your answer.

Enter: 259

Press: −

Enter: 25

Press: %

The display will show the answer.

Draw a Diagram

You can use the **draw a diagram** strategy when problems include figures or objects, and you need to use or find a measurement such as length, distance, or area.

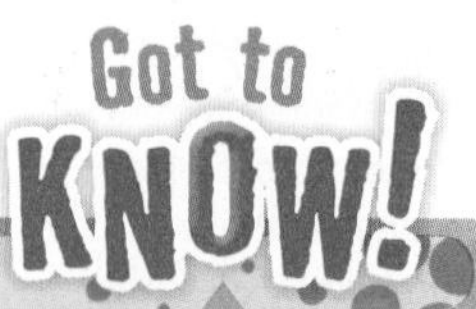

Problem Solving Strategies

Refer to the *Got to Know!* box on page 448 for where to find out more about each strategy. The boldface strategy is featured in this section.

- Write a Number Sentence
- Use Logical Reasoning
- **Draw a Diagram**
- Work Backwards
- Make a Table
- Solve a Simpler Problem
- Look for a Pattern
- Make an Organized List
- Guess, Check, and Revise
- Make or Use a Graph

Need More HELP

Remember, the formula for finding the area of a rectangle is A rectangle = length × width.

EXAMPLE 1

Stan wants to put a walkway around the perimeter of a rectangular pond. The pond is 6 feet long and 3.5 feet wide. The walkway will be 1.5 feet wide on each side of the pond. What is the area of the walkway?

READ Read the problem carefully.

Identify what you know and what you need to find out.

Know: The walkway is around the perimeter of the pond.

The rectangular pond measures 6 ft by 3.5 ft.

The walkway is 1.5 ft wide on *all* sides.

Need to Know: The area of the walkway.

PLAN Use the **draw a diagram** strategy. Draw a diagram of the pond and the walkway. Label the dimensions of the pond. Use the given information to label the entire length and the entire width of the figure. Then find the area of the walkway.

SOLVE Draw a diagram.

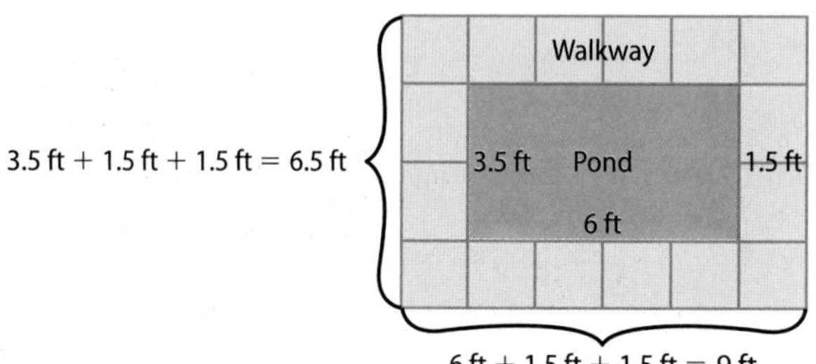

Find the area of the pond: $6 \text{ ft} \times 3.5 \text{ ft} = 21 \text{ ft}^2$

Find the area of the entire figure, including the walkway: $9 \text{ ft} \times 6.5 \text{ ft} = 58.5 \text{ ft}^2$

Subtract to find the area of the walkway: $58.5 \text{ ft}^2 - 21 \text{ ft}^2 = 37.5 \text{ ft}^2$

The area of the walkway is 37.5 ft^2.

CHECK Is my answer correct?

Round the width of the pond to 4 ft and the width of the figure including the border to 7 ft. *Estimate* the area of the pond as $6 \text{ ft} \times 4 \text{ ft} = 24 \text{ ft}^2$ and the area of the entire figure as $9 \text{ ft} \times 7 \text{ ft} = 63 \text{ ft}^2$. Then subtract:

$63 \text{ ft}^2 - 24 \text{ ft}^2 = 39 \text{ ft}^2$, which is close to 37.5 ft^2. The answer checks. ✔

EXAMPLE 2

On field day, the decorations team will place a border of flags along the length of a field. The field is 28 yards long. A flag will be placed every $3\frac{1}{2}$ yards, including one at each end of the field. How many flags are needed?

READ Read the problem carefully.

Identify what you know and what you need to find out.

Know: The length of the field is 28 yards.

A border of flags will be placed along the length of the field.

A flag is to be placed every $3\frac{1}{2}$ yards and at the beginning and the end of the field.

Need to Know: How many flags are needed.

PLAN Use the **draw a diagram** strategy. Use grid paper to model the length of the field and the placement of the flags.

SOLVE Outline 28 squares on the grid paper to model the length of the field. Draw a flag at the beginning, or far left, of the diagram. Then draw a flag every $3\frac{1}{2}$ squares.

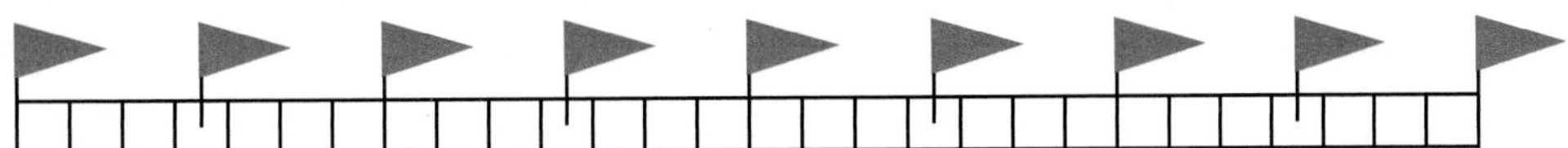

There are 9 flags.

Nine flags are needed to create the border.

CHECK Is my answer correct? Use division to check the answer.

Divide 28 by $3\frac{1}{2}$.

$$28 \div 3\frac{1}{2} = \frac{28}{1} \div \frac{7}{2}$$
$$= \frac{\overset{4}{\cancel{28}}}{1} \times \frac{2}{\underset{1}{\cancel{7}}}$$
$$= 8$$

Eight is the number of $3\frac{1}{2}$ spaces separated by each flag.

8 + the first flag placed = 9 flags. The answer checks. ✔

SEARCH

To see step-by-step videos of these problems, enter the page number into the SWadvantage.com Search Bar.

Need More HELP

For help with dividing whole numbers by mixed numbers, go to *Dividing Mixed Numbers* (p. 352).

Strategy: Make a Table

Make a Table

You can use the make a table strategy to organize data into rows and columns. This strategy is helpful when you need to compare two or more sets of data.

To see step-by-step videos of these problems, enter the page number into the SWadvantage.com Search Bar.

EXAMPLE 1

Ming is buying food for a family reunion. Hamburgers come in packages of 6, buns come in packages of 8, and cheese slices come in packages of 12. How many packs of each item does Ming need to buy to have the same number of hamburgers, buns, and cheese slices?

READ Read the problem carefully. Identify what you know and what you need to find out.

Know: Ming wants to buy an equal number of hamburgers, buns, and cheese slices.
Hamburgers come in packages of 6.
Buns come in packages of 8.
Cheese slices come in packages of 12.

Need to Know: How many packages of each item she needs to buy.

PLAN Use the **make a table** strategy. Use multiples to make a table that lists the total number of items in any given number of packages. Then find the least common multiple on the table.

SOLVE List the multiples of the table.

Number of Packages	1	2	3	4	5	6	7	8
Hamburgers	6	12	18	**24**	30	36	42	48
Buns	8	16	**24**	32	40	48	56	64
Cheese	12	**24**	36	48	60	72	84	96

The least common multiple is 24. Move up to the top of each column to find the number of packages that will give you 24 of each item.

Ming needs to buy 4 packages of hamburgers, 3 packages of buns, and 2 packages of cheese slices.

For help with the least common multiple, go to *Multiples* (p. 288).

CHECK Is my answer is correct? Multiply the number of packages (pkg) by the number of items in each package. Each product should equal 24.

Hamburgers	Buns	Cheese
4 pkg × 6 per pkg = 24 ✓	3 pkg × 8 per pkg = 24 ✓	2 pkg × 12 per pkg = 24 ✓

EXAMPLE 2

Joseph has 20 feet of fencing to enclose a rectangular vegetable garden. He wants the garden to have the greatest area possible. What are the dimensions of the largest garden he can make with the fencing he has?

READ Read the problem carefully. Identify what you know and what you need to find out.

Know: Joe has 20 feet of fencing.
He wants to use it to enclose a rectangular garden.
He wants to make the largest garden possible.

Need to Know: The dimensions of the largest possible garden.

PLAN Use the **make a table** strategy. List the possible lengths and widths for a garden that would have a perimeter of 20 ft. Start with 1 ft $\times$ 9 ft., which would have a perimeter of $1 + 9 + 1 + 9 = 20$ ft., then 2 ft by 8 ft, and so on. Then find each area.

SOLVE Make a table with columns for length, width, and area.

Length (ft)	Width (ft)	Area (ft^2)
1	9	9
2	8	16
3	7	21
4	6	24
5	**5**	**25**
6	4	24
7	3	21

Notice that the areas on the table increase until you get to 6 ft $\times$ 4 ft., where the area begins to decrease.

Go down the Area column to find the greatest area, 25 ft^2.

When the area is 25 ft^2, the length and width are both 5 ft.

The largest garden Joe can make with 20 feet of fencing has the dimensions 5 ft by 5 ft.

CHECK Is my answer correct?

Find the perimeter of the garden to check that it is equal to 20 ft.

5 ft + 5 ft + 5 ft + 5 ft = 20 ft

The answer checks. ✔

Need More HELP

Remember, to find the area of a rectangle, use the formula

$A = \ell \times w$, where A is the area, ℓ is the length, and w is the width.

Got to KNOW!

Problem Solving Strategies

Refer to the *Got to Know!* box on page 448 for where to find out more about each strategy. The boldface strategy is featured in this section.

- Write a Number Sentence
- Use Logical Reasoning
- Draw a Diagram
- Work Backwards
- **Make a Table**
- Solve a Simpler Problem
- Look for a Pattern
- Make an Organized List
- Guess, Check, and Revise
- Make or Use a Graph

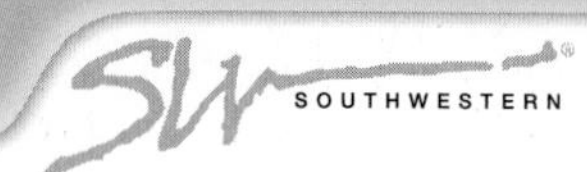

Look for a Pattern

You can use the **look for a pattern** strategy to solve problems that involve patterns of shapes, numbers, and time.

Got to KNOW!

Problem Solving Strategies

Refer to the *Got to Know!* box on page 448 for where to find out more about each strategy. The boldface strategy is featured in this section.

- Write a Number Sentence
- Use Logical Reasoning
- Draw a Diagram
- Work Backwards
- Make a Table
- Solve a Simpler Problem
- **Look for a Pattern**
- Make an Organized List
- Guess, Check, and Revise
- Make or Use a Graph

EXAMPLE 1

Jeff and Germaine are going on a boat tour of the downtown harbor area. The times for the first three tours are shown in the table at the right. If the pattern continues, what time does the fourth boat tour start and end?

Tour	Start	End
1	11:18 A.M.	12:06 P.M.
2	12:22 P.M.	1:10 P.M.
3	1:26 P.M.	2:14 P.M.

READ Read the problem carefully. Identify what you know and what you need to find out.

Know: You know the start time and end time of the first three tours. You know that the next tour does not leave immediately. The table shows that the boat stays at the dock for a short period of time.

Need to Know: What time the fourth boat tour starts and ends.

PLAN Use the **look for a pattern** strategy.

SOLVE Find elapsed times between tours to discover the pattern.

STEP 1 Find the length of the tours by subtracting the end time from the start time.

First Tour: 12:06 P.M. − 11:18 A.M. = 48 min.

Second Tour: 1:10 P.M. − 12:22 A.M. = 48 min.

Third Tour: 2:14 P.M. − 1:26 A.M. = 48 min.

Each tour is 48 minutes.

STEP 2 Find the amount of time the boat stays docked between tours.

First Tour: Returned 12:06 P.M. Second Tour: Departed at 12:22 P.M.

12:22 P.M. − 12:06 P.M. = 16 minutes

Second Tour: Returned at 1:10 P.M. Third Tour: Departed at 1:26 P.M.

1:26 P.M. − 1:10 P.M. = 16 minutes

The boat stays at the dock for 16 minutes.

STEP 3 Use the information from Steps 1 and 2 to find the start and end times for Tour 4.

Think: Start time is 2:14 P.M. + 16 minutes at the dock = 2:30 P.M.

End time is 2:30 P.M. + 48 minutes for the tour = 3:18 P.M.

Tour 4 starts at 2:30 P.M. and ends at 3:18 P.M.

CHECK Is my answer correct? The time between the start of one tour and the start of the next tour is 48 minutes + 16 minutes, which is about 1 hour.

From 1:26 P.M. to 2:26 P.M. is about 1 hour, so 2:30 P.M. is a reasonable answer. ✔

Each tour lasts a little under one hour.

From 2:30 P.M. to 3:15 P.M. is a little less than one hour, so 3:18 P.M. is a reasonable answer. ✔

EXAMPLE 2

Leon is making the pattern below using toothpicks. How many toothpicks will he need for the sixth figure?

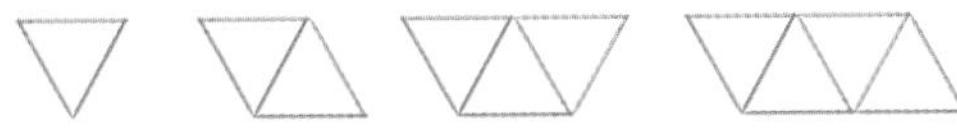

READ Read the problem carefully. Identify what you know and what you need to find out.

Know: Leon is making a pattern of triangles using toothpicks.

The four figures shown use these numbers of toothpicks:

1st figure − 3   2nd figure − 5   3rd figure − 7   4th figure − 9

Need to Know: The number of toothpicks in the 6th figure.

PLAN The problem involves a pattern. Use the **find a pattern** strategy and the **use a table** strategy.

SOLVE Display the information you know in a table.

Figure	1	2	3	4	5	6
Number of Toothpicks	3	5	7	9		

+2 +2 +2

Look for the pattern. For each figure, the number of toothpicks is 2 greater than the figure before. Use this information to extend the pattern.

5th figure = 9 toothpicks + 2 toothpicks = 11 toothpicks

6th figure = 11 toothpicks + 2 toothpicks = 13 toothpicks

Leon will need 13 toothpicks for the sixth figure.

CHECK Draw the fifth and six figures:

Fifth figure

Sixth figure

The sixth figure uses 13 toothpicks. The answer checks. ✔

SEARCH

To see step-by-step videos of these problems, enter the page number into the SWadvantage.com Search Bar.

For help with growing patterns, go to *Growing Patterns* (p. 438).

Strategy: Guess, Check, and Revise

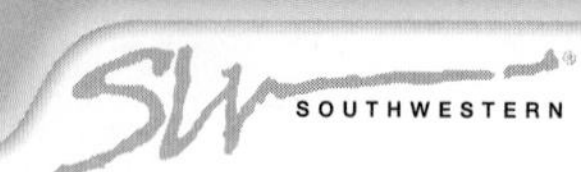

Guess, Check, and Revise

You can use the **guess, check, and revise** strategy when you are not sure how to solve a problem. Use number sense to make your best guess and then check your guess. If it is not correct, guess again. Continue this process until you get the correct answer.

Try It This Way

Another way to solve this problem is to use the *Use Logical Reasoning* strategy. Think: I need to divide 27 into 3 equal parts. Two parts are Carrie's age. One part is her brother's age.

$27 \div 3 = 9$

$2 \times 9 = 18$

Carrie is 18, and her brother is 9.

EXAMPLE 1

Carrie is twice as old as her brother. The sum of their ages is 27. How old are Carrie and her brother?

READ Read the problem carefully. Identify what you know and what you need to find out.

Know: Carrie's age is two times her brother's age.
Carrie's age plus her brother's age is 27.

Need to Know: Each of their ages.

PLAN Use the **guess, check, and revise** strategy. You may want to make a table to keep track of your guesses.

Guess an age for her brother. Then find Carrie's age.

Check if the sum of their ages is 27.

SOLVE Try 7 as your first guess for her brother's age. Then complete the table. If your guess is not correct, make another guess. Use what you learn for each guess to try to make your next guess correct.

Brother's Age	Carrie's Age	Sum of Ages	
7	14	21	21 < 27, 7 is too low.
11	22	33	33 > 27, 11 is too high.
8	16	24	24 < 27, 8 is too low.
10	20	30	30 < 27, 10 is too high.
9	18	27	Correct.

Carrie is 18 and her brother is 9.

CHECK Is my answer correct?

Carrie is 18, which is twice her brother's age of 9.

The sum of their ages is $18 + 9 = 27$.

The answer checks. ✔

To see step-by-step videos of these problems, enter the page number into the SWadvantage.com Search Bar.

EXAMPLE 2

An auditorium has two kinds of seats. Tickets for seats in the lower level cost $8, and tickets for seats in the balcony cost $6. There are twice as many seats in the lower level as in the balcony. When the auditorium is filled, the ticket sales total $5,500. How many of each kind of seat are in the auditorium?

READ Read the problem carefully. Identify what you know and what you need to find out.

Know: Lower level seats sell for $8 each.
Balcony seats sell for $6 each.
There are twice as many lower level seats as balcony seats.
When all the seats are sold, ticket sales total $5,500.

Need to Know: The number of lower level and the number of balcony seats in the auditorium.

PLAN Use the **guess and check** strategy. You may want to use a table to help you keep track of your guesses.

Guess the number of balcony seats and multiply by 2 to find the number of lower level seats. Then find the total sales.

SOLVE Try 400 as your first guess for the number of balcony seats. Then complete the table.

Balcony	Lower Level	Total Ticket Sales	
400	800	$(400 \times \$6) + (800 \times \$8) = \$8{,}800$	Too high
100	200	$(100 \times \$6) + (200 \times \$8) = \$2{,}200$	Too low
300	600	$(300 \times \$6) + (600 \times \$8) = \$6{,}600$	Too high
200	400	$(200 \times \$6) + (400 \times \$8) = \$4{,}400$	Too low
250	500	$(250 \times \$6) + (500 \times \$8) = \$5{,}500$	Correct.

There are 250 seats in the balcony and 500 seats in the lower level.

CHECK Is my answer correct? Check to be certain your answer meets the conditions of the problem.

$250 \times 2 = 500$, so there are 250 balcony seats and 500 lower level seats.

Use compatible numbers and mental math to check your math.

$$\begin{aligned} &(250 \times \$6) + (500 \times \$8) \\ &= (200 \times 6) + (50 \times 6) + (500 \times 8) \\ &= 1{,}200 + 300 + 4{,}000 \\ &= 1{,}500 + 4{,}000 \\ &= 5{,}500 \end{aligned}$$

The answer checks. ✔

Got to KNOW!

Problem Solving Strategies

Refer to the *Got to Know!* box on page 448 for where to find out more about each strategy. The boldface strategy is featured in this section.

- Write a Number Sentence
- Use Logical Reasoning
- Draw a Diagram
- Work Backwards
- Make a Table
- Solve a Simpler Problem
- Look for a Pattern
- Make an Organized List
- **Guess, Check, and Revise**
- Make or Use a Graph

When using the *Guess, Check, and Revise* strategy, your first guess should be a reasonable guess. In Example 2, it would not make sense to choose a very small number, such as 5, or a very large number, such as 10,000, for the first guess.

Use Logical Reasoning

You can use the **use logical reasoning** strategy when you are given clues or facts that lead to the answer. Use the facts to discover the answer.

To see step-by-step videos of these problems, enter the page number into the SWadvantage.com Search Bar.

Problem Solving Strategies

Refer to the *Got to Know!* box on page 448 for where to find out more about each strategy. The boldface strategy is featured in this section.

- Write a Number Sentence
- **Use Logical Reasoning**
- Draw a Diagram
- Work Backwards
- Make a Table
- Solve a Simpler Problem
- Look for a Pattern
- Make an Organized List
- Guess, Check, and Revise
- Make or Use a Graph

EXAMPLE 1

Simon, Moses, and Julian each play one musical instrument—the harp, the violin, or the trumpet. Moses plays the instrument that does not have strings. Julian's brother plays the violin. Match each person with the instrument he plays.

READ Read the problem carefully. Identify what you know and what you need to find out.

Know: Simon, Moses, and Julian all play a different instrument.

The instruments are the harp, the violin, and the trumpet.

The instrument Moses plays does not have strings.

Julian is the brother of the violinist.

Need to Know: Who plays what instrument.

PLAN Use the **use logical reasoning** strategy. Make a table to help you.

SOLVE Make a table with a column for each instrument and a row for each person.

Clue 1: *Moses plays the instrument without strings.* A trumpet does not have strings, so Moses plays the trumpet. Record this information on the table.

You also know that Moses does NOT play the harp or violin, and that Simon and Julian do NOT play the trumpet. Record this information also.

	Harp	Violin	Trumpet
Simon			No
Moses	No	No	Yes
Julian			No

Clue 2: *Julian is the brother of the person who plays the violin.* Since Moses plays the trumpet, Julian's brother is Simon, who plays the violin. Record this information.

You also know that Simon does NOT play the harp, and Julian does NOT play the violin. Record this information also.

	Harp	Violin	Trumpet
Simon	No	Yes	No
Moses	No	No	Yes
Julian		No	No

This leaves the harp, so Julian must play the harp.

Simon plays the violin, Moses plays the trumpet, and Julian plays the harp.

CHECK Is my answer correct? Check that your answer does not conflict with the two given facts in the problem. The answer checks. ✔

EXAMPLE 2

In a class of 28 students, 15 have a dog as a pet, 12 have a cat as a pet, and 5 have both a cat and a dog as a pet. How many students do not have either animal as a pet?

READ Read the problem carefully. Identify what you know and what you need to find out.

Know: 15 students have a dog.

12 students have a cat.

5 students have both a dog and a cat.

Need to Know: How many students do not have a dog or a cat.

PLAN Use the **use logical reasoning** strategy. A Venn diagram can help you.

SOLVE You already know that 5 students have both a dog and a cat.

STEP 1 Find the number of students who have a dog only. Subtract the number of students who have both a cat and a dog (5) from the number of students who have a dog (15).

$15 - 5 = 10$

10 students have a dog only.

STEP 2 Find the number of students who have a cat only. Subtract the number of students who have both a cat and a dog (5) from the number of students who have a cat (12).

$12 - 5 = 7$

7 students have a cat only.

STEP 3 Place this information in a Venn diagram.

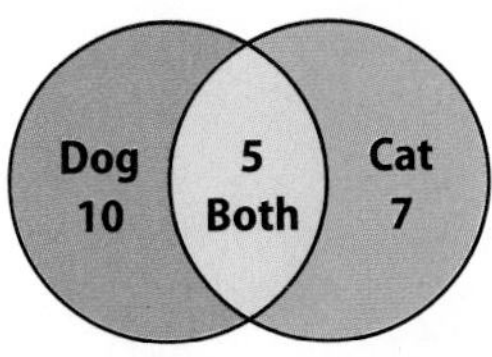

STEP 4 Add the numbers for each section of the Venn diagram to find the total number of students in the class who have either a dog, a cat, or both as a pet.

$10 + 5 + 7 = 22$ students have a dog, a cat, or both

Subtract 22 from the total number of students in the class to find the number of students who have *neither* animal as a pet.

$28 - 22 = 6$

Six students have neither animal as a pet.

CHECK Write and solve a number sentence to see if the answer checks.

28 students − (5 with a dog and cat + 10 with a dog + 7 with a cat)

$= 28 - 22$

$= 6$

The answer checks. ✔

For help with Venn diagrams, go to *Venn Diagrams* in *Probability and Statistics* (Book 2, p. 1288).

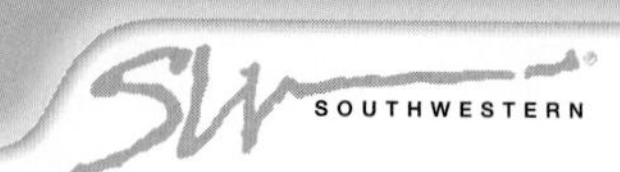

Work Backwards

You can use the **work backwards** strategy when a problem tells you a sequence of events and an ending value, and you need to find the beginning value.

EXAMPLE 1

Marley went to the mall to spend some money she received as a present. First she bought a sweater for $23. Then she spent half of the amount she had left on lunch. Finally she spent $4.50 on a magazine. When she left the mall she had $1.50 left. How much money did she take to the mall?

READ Read the problem carefully. Identify what you know and what you need to find out.

Know: Marley spent $23 for a sweater.
She spent half of the remaining amount for lunch.
Then she spent $4.50 on a magazine.
When she left the mall she had $1.50.

Need to Know: How much money she had to start with.

PLAN Use the **work backwards** strategy. Start with the amount Marley had when she left and work backwards, one step at a time.

SOLVE Marley had $1.50 when she left the mall.

She had $4.50 more before she bought the magazine.	$\$1.50 + \$4.50 = \$6.00$
She had two times that amount before she bought lunch.	$\$6 \times 2 = \$12$
She had $23 more before she bought the sweater.	$\$12 + \$23 = \$35$

Marley took $35 to the mall.

CHECK Is my answer correct? Work forwards to check your answer.

She started with $35. Then she spent $23.	$\$35 - \$23 = \$12$
She spent half of her remaining money on lunch.	$\$12 \div 2 = \$6$
She spent $4.50 on a magazine.	$\$6 - \$4.50 = \$1.50$

The answer checks. ✔

Got to KNOW!

Problem Solving Strategies

Refer to the *Got to Know!* box on page 448 for where to find out more about each strategy. The boldface strategy is featured in this section.

- Write a Number Sentence
- Use Logical Reasoning
- Draw a Diagram
- **Work Backwards**
- Make a Table
- Solve a Simpler Problem
- Look for a Pattern
- Make an Organized List
- Guess, Check, and Revise
- Make or Use a Graph

In Example 2, you will need to work backwards because you are finding an earlier time. For example, an activity is finished at 10:25 A.M. and took 1 hour and 15 minutes. To find what time the activity started, subtract.

Time Finished − Length of Activity = Start Time

10:25 A.M. − 1 hour = 9:25 A.M.

9:25 A.M. − 15 min = 9:10 A.M.

The activity started at 9:10 A.M.

EXAMPLE 2

Sammy surfs the Internet for 45 minutes. After that he walks the dog for 10 minutes. Then he mows the lawn for 20 minutes. Finally he does his homework for 1 hour 15 minutes. He finishes at 7:35 P.M. What time did he begin these activities?

READ Read the problem carefully. Identify what you know and what you need to find out.

Know: Sammy surfs the Internet for 45 minutes.
He walks the dog for 10 minutes.
He mows the lawn for 20 minutes.
He does his homework for 1 hour 15 minutes.
He finished at 7:35 P.M.

Need to Know: What time he began.

PLAN Use the **work backwards** strategy. Start with the time Sammy finished and work backwards, one step at a time.

SOLVE Sammy finished at 7:35 P.M.

	1 hr 15 min before 7:35 P.M. is 6:20 P.M.
20 minutes to do the lawn.	20 min before 6:20 P.M. is 6:00 P.M.
10 minutes to walk the dog.	10 min before 6:00 P.M. is 5:50 P.M.
45 minutes to surf the Internet.	45 min before 5:50 P.M. is 5:05 P.M.

Sammy began the activities at 5:05 P.M.

CHECK Is my answer correct? Work forwards to check your answer.

He starts at 5:05 P.M.

45 minutes to surf the Internet.	45 min after 5:05 P.M. is 5:50 P.M.
10 minutes to walk the dog.	10 min after 5:50 P.M. is 6:00 P.M.
20 minutes to do the lawn.	20 min after 6:00 P.M. is 6:20 P.M.
1 hour 15 minutes for homework.	1 hr 15 min after 6:20 P.M. is 7:35 P.M.

The answer checks. ✔

You could find the total time for the four activities first. Then subtract the total time from the time he finished.

To see step-by-step videos of these problems, enter the page number into the SWadvantage.com Search Bar.

Problem Solving Strategies

Refer to the *Got to Know!* box on page 448 for where to find out more about each strategy. The boldface strategy is featured in this section.

Write a Number Sentence

Use Logical Reasoning

Draw a Diagram

Work Backwards

Make a Table

Solve a Simpler Problem

Look for a Pattern

Make an Organized List

Guess, Check, and Revise

Make or Use a Graph

Solve a Simpler Problem

You can use the **solve a simpler problem** strategy when a problem uses large numbers, has many steps, or uses numbers that are not whole numbers. Use what you learned when you solved the simpler problem to solve the original problem.

EXAMPLE 1

Leona has 15 pairs of shorts and 25 tops. If an outfit consists of one pair of shorts and one top, how many different outfits can she make?

READ Read the problem carefully. Identify what you know and what you need to find out.

Know: Leona has 15 pairs of shorts.
She has 25 tops.
An outfit consists of a pair of shorts and a top.

Need to Know: How many different outfits she can make.

PLAN Use the **solve a simpler problem** strategy. First find the number of outfits she can make with up to 3 pairs of shorts and 3 tops. See if this gives you information that will help you solve the original problem.

SOLVE Carry out the plan and organize the results on a table.

No. of Shorts	No. of Tops	Combinations	No. of Outfits
1	1	S1, T1	$1 \times 1 = 1$
1	2	S1, T1 S1, T2	$1 \times 2 = 2$
2	1	S1, T1 S2, T1	$2 \times 1 = 2$
2	2	S1, T1 S2, T1 S1, T2 S2, T2	$2 \times 2 = 4$
2	3	S1, T1 S2, T1 S1, T2 S2, T2 S1, T3 S2, T3	$2 \times 3 = 6$
3	2	S1, T1 S2, T1 S3, T1 S1, T2 S2, T2 S3, T2	$3 \times 2 = 6$
3	3	S1, T1 S2, T1 S3, T1 S1, T2 S2, T2 S3, T2 S1, T3 S2, T3 S3, T3	$3 \times 3 = 9$

Notice that you can find the number of combinations by multiplying the numbers of each type of clothing item. 15 shorts $\times$ 25 tops $=$ 375 outfits.

Leona can make 375 different outfits.

CHECK Is my answer reasonable? Use logical reasoning to visualize the situation. Suppose you have a horizontal row of 25 squares, each of which represents a top. Below each square are 15 X marks, each of which represents a pair of shorts that Leona could wear with that top. So you have $15 \times 25 = 375$.
The answer is reasonable. ✔

EXAMPLE 2

What is the sum of $10^1 + 10^2 + 10^3 + 10^4 + 10^5 + 10^6 + 10^7 + 10^8 + 10^9 + 10^{10}$?

READ Read the problem carefully. Identify what you know and what you need to find out.

Know: The sum is a large number.

Need to Know: The exact sum of the first 10 powers of ten.

PLAN Use the **solve a simpler problem** strategy. Find the sum of the first four powers of 10. See if this gives you information that will help you solve the original problem.

SOLVE Organize the results on a table.

Power of 10	Value	Sum
10^1	10	10
10^2	100	$10 + 100 = 110$
10^3	1,000	$110 + 1{,}000 = 1{,}110$
10^4	10,000	$1{,}110 + 10{,}000 = 11{,}110$

Notice the following:

- The sum of the first 2 powers of ten is 2 ones followed by a zero.
- The sum of the first 3 powers of ten is 3 ones followed by a zero.
- The sum of the first 4 powers of ten is 4 ones followed by a zero.
- Each sum on the table has one more digit than the exponent of the greatest power of ten in the sum. For example, the sum of $10^1 + 10^2$ is 100. The greatest exponent is 2 and the sum has 3 digits.

So, the sum of the first 10 powers of ten is 10 ones followed by a zero.
$10^1 + 10^2 + 10^3 + 10^4 + 10^5 + 10^6 + 10^7 + 10^8 + 10^9 + 10^{10} = 11{,}111{,}111{,}110$

CHECK Is my answer reasonable?

- The first 10 digits are ones and the last digit is a 0.
- The exponent of the greatest power of 10 is 10, and the number 11,111,111,110 has eleven digits.

The answer is reasonable. ✔

SEARCH
To see step-by-step videos of these problems, enter the page number into the SWadvantage.com Search Bar.

Make an Organized List

You can use the **make an organized list** strategy when there are many different arrangements or ways to organize information. Then analyze the information on the list to solve the problem.

EXAMPLE 1

Maxwell has a bag that contains 1 red, 1 green, 1 blue, and 1 yellow marble. If he takes all four marbles out of the bag, one at a time without looking, how many different orders of removing the marbles are possible?

READ Read the problem carefully. Identify what you know and what you need to find out.

Know: Maxwell has a bag with 4 marbles—1 red, 1 green, 1 blue, and 1 yellow. He takes the marbles out of the bag one at a time.

Need to Know: The number of different orders there are for removing the marbles from the bag.

PLAN Use the **make an organized list** strategy. List all the possible orders for removing the marbles.

SOLVE There are 4 marbles—red (R), green (G), blue (B), or yellow (Y). Once the first marble is chosen, the second marble can be any color except the color of the first marble, and so on. Each list will have the same number of entries.

RGBY	GBYR	BYRG	YRGB
RGYB	GBRY	BYGR	YRBG
RBGY	GYRB	BRYG	YGRB
RBYG	GYBR	BRGY	YGBR
RYGB	GRBY	BGYR	YBRG
RYBG	GRYB	BGRY	YBGR

Count the number of orders.

There are 24 possible orders of removing the marbles from the bag.

CHECK Is my answer correct? Check to make sure that each order is unique and that there are no other possible orders. Here is one way to check.

RGBY The first two colors are the same but the second two are reversed.
RGYB

RBGY The first two colors are the same but the second two are reversed.
RBYG

RYGB The first two colors are the same but the second two are reversed.
RYBG

Use the same method for the other lists.

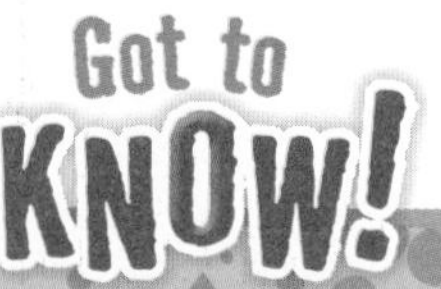

Problem Solving Strategies

Refer to the *Got to Know!* box on page 448 for where to find out more about each strategy. The boldface strategy is featured in this section.

- Write a Number Sentence
- Use Logical Reasoning
- Draw a Diagram
- Work Backwards
- Make a Table
- Solve a Simpler Problem
- Look for a Pattern
- **Make an Organized List**
- Guess, Check, and Revise
- Make or Use a Graph

EXAMPLE 2

Sonia is a contestant on a game show. During her turn, she spins each of the wheels shown at the right. She will win the sum of the two amounts she spins. What is the probability that Sonia will win exactly $500?

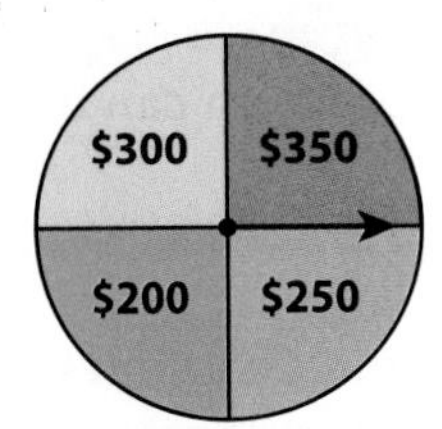

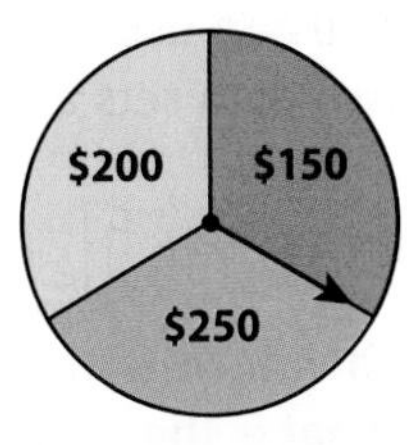

READ Read the problem carefully. Identify what you know and what you need to find out.

Know: Sonia spins each wheel one time during her turn.
She wins the sum of the amounts on the two wheels.

Need to Know: The probability that she will win exactly $500.

PLAN Use the make an organized list strategy. List all the possible arrangements of the two spins. Find the combinations that equal $500.

SOLVE Implement your plan. Start with $300 on the left spinner and pair it with every amount on the right spinner. Then do the same for the remaining amounts on the left spinner—$350, $250, and $200.

Spin 1	Spin 2	Sum
$300	$200	($500)
$300	$150	$450
$300	$250	$550
$350	$200	$550
$350	$150	($500)
$350	$250	$600

Spin 1	Spin 2	Sum
$250	$200	$450
$250	$150	$400
$250	$250	($500)
$200	$200	$400
$200	$150	$350
$200	$250	$450

Circle the sums of $500. There are 3 combinations of spins with a sum of $500.
Count the number of possible combinations of spins. There are 12.

Now find the probability of Sonia winning exactly $500.

$$P(\text{winning \$500}) = \frac{\text{spins with a sum of \$500}}{\text{total number of possible spins}} = \frac{3}{12} = \frac{1}{4} = 25\%$$

The probability of Sonia winning exactly $500 is 25%.

CHECK Is my answer correct? Check to make sure that each arrangement of spins is unique and that there are no other possible arrangements.

SEARCH

To see step-by-step videos of these problems, enter the page number into the SWadvantage.com Search Bar.

Need More HELP

For help with probability, go to *Theoretical Probability* in *Statistics and Probability* (Book 2, p. 1232).

Strategy: Make or Use a Graph

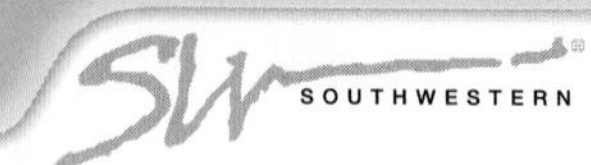

Make or Use a Graph

You can use the **make or use a graph** strategy when there is a relationship between two data sets and the problem can be solved graphically.

For help with line graphs, go to *Line Graphs* in *Foundations of Mathematics* (p. 192) and *Interpreting Line Graphs* in *Algebra* (Book 2, p. 1446).

To see step-by-step videos of these problems, enter the page number into the SWadvantage.com Search Bar.

EXAMPLE 1

The thermometer outside Shannon's window shows the outdoor temperature as 20°C. What is the temperature in degrees Fahrenheit?

READ Read the problem carefully. Identify what you know and what you need to find out.

Know: The outdoor temperature in Celsius is 20°.

Need to Know: The outdoor temperature in degrees Fahrenheit.

PLAN Use the **make or use a graph** strategy. If you can plot two points of a line graph, you can find the value of any other point.

SOLVE Find the coordinates for two points.

First point: You probably already know that 0°C = 32°F, so the first point is (0, 32).

Second point: The equation for converting degrees °F to °C is $F = 1.8C + 32$. Choose a value for C, substitute it into the equation, and solve for F. Choose a value that is easy to compute using mental math. When $C = 10$, $F = 1.8(10) + 32 = 18 + 32 = 50$, so the second point is (10, 50).

Plot the two points and connect them with a line. Extend the line until it goes past 20 on the °F scale.

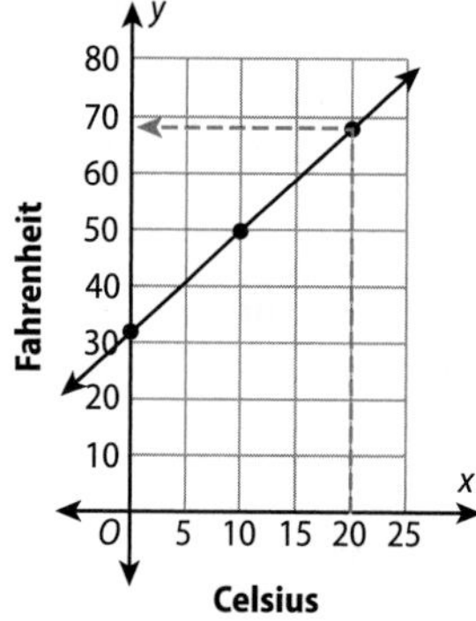

Find 20°C on the x-axis scale. Move up and look to the left to find the corresponding temperature in °F on the y-axis scale.

The temperature 20°C is equal to 68°F.

CHECK Is my answer reasonable? Use estimation. Round 1.8 to 2 in the formula $F = 1.8C + 32$ and use mental math to check. Since I rounded up, the estimate is greater than the actual value.

$F \approx (2 \times 20) + 32 = 72$, which is a little greater than 68. The answer is reasonable.

EXAMPLE 2

Fatima is in a community chorus. She wants to gather information about the ages of the people in the chorus. She took a survey of the ages of the 35 people in the chorus and displayed the information on the stem-and-leaf plot shown.

Find the age of the oldest person in the chorus. Then find the median age.

Ages of Chorus Members

Stem	Leaf
1	6 6 8 8 9
2	5 6 6 7 8
3	0 0 1 2 5 5 5 6
4	0 1 1 1 4 4 5
5	2 3 3 5 9
6	0 2 3
7	1 5

Key: 1 | 6 means 16

READ Read the problem carefully. Identify what you know and what you need to find out.

Know: Fatima took a survey to find the ages of the people in the community chorus.

She made a stem-and-leaf plot to show the data.

Need to Know: The age of the oldest person in the chorus and the median age.

PLAN Use the **make or use a graph** strategy. Use the stem-and-leaf plot to answer the questions.

SOLVE To find the age of the oldest person, find the last (or greatest) value in the plot. The greatest stem is 7. The greatest leaf of the stem is 5.

Ages of Chorus Members

Stem	Leaf
1	6 6 8 8 9
2	5 6 6 7 8
3	0 0 1 2 5 5 5 6
4	0 1 1 1 4 4 5
5	2 3 3 5 9
6	0 2 3
7	1 (5)

Key: 1 | 6 means 16

The oldest person is 75 years old.

The median is the middle number in the set. There are 35 ages, which is an odd number. This means that there are $34 \div 2 = 17$ numbers on either side of the median. The eighteenth age is the median age.

Ages of Chorus Members

Stem	Leaf
1	6 6 8 8 9
2	5 6 6 7 8
3	0 0 1 2 5 5 5 (6)
4	0 1 1 1 4 4 5
5	2 3 3 5 9
6	0 2 3
7	1 5

Key: 1 | 6 means 16

The median age is 36.

CHECK Is my answer correct? Check your answers to make sure you read the graph correctly.

Got to KNOW!

Problem Solving Strategies

Refer to the *Got to Know!* box on page 448 for where to find out more about each strategy. The boldface strategy is featured in this section.

- Write a Number Sentence
- Use Logical Reasoning
- Draw a Diagram
- Work Backwards
- Make a Table
- Solve a Simpler Problem
- Look for a Pattern
- Make an Organized List
- Guess, Check, and Revise
- **Make or Use a Graph**

Need More HELP

For help with stem-and-leaf plots, go to *Stem-and-Leaf Plots* in *Statistics and Probability* (Book 2, p. 1276).

Numbers and Operations

Decimal Place Value

hundreds	tens	ones		tenths	hundredths	thousandths
1	2	3	.	4	5	6

Forms of a Number

Standard form	123.456
Expanded form	100 + 20 + 3 + 0.4 + 0.05 + 0.006
Word form	one hundred twenty-three and four hundred fifty-six thousandths
Short word form	123 and 456 thousandths
Point form	one twenty-three point four five six

Tests for Divisibility

Divisible by	Rule
2	The digit in the ones place is an even digit: 0, 2, 4, 6, or 8.
3	The sum of the digits is divisible by 3.
4	The number formed by the last two digits is divisible by 4.
5	The digit in the ones place is 0 or 5.
6	The number is divisible by both 2 and 3.
8	The number formed by the last three digits is divisible by 8.
9	The sum of the digits is divisible by 9.
10	The digit in the ones place is 0.

Powers of 10

Power of 10	Value	Zeros
10^0	1	0
10^1	10	1
10^2	100	2
10^3	1,000	3
10^4	10,000	4
10^5	100,000	5
10^6	1,000,000	6
10^7	10,000,000	7

Four-Step Problem Solving Plan

Step 1	**Read**	• Read the problem carefully. You can restate the problem in your own words. • Determine what the problem is asking you to find. • Identify what you know. This is the information given in the problem. • Identify what you need to find out to solve the problem. This is the question asked. You can restate it in your own words.
Step 2	**Plan**	• Plan how to find the answer to the question. • Think about other similar problems you have solved. Think about how the information you know can help you find the answer. • Choose a problem solving strategy.
Step 3	**Solve**	• Solve the problem using your plan. As you work, you can revise your plan if you need to. • Make sure you write a sentence that states your answer.
Step 4	**Check**	• Check your work. • Make sure you have answered the question that was asked. • Make sure your answer makes sense by using another problem solving strategy to check your work.

Formulas, Properties, and Theorems

The Fundamental Theorem of Arithmetic	Every positive integer greater than 1 has exactly one set of prime factors (one prime factorization).
Cross Products Property	The cross products of two fractions are the products of the numerator of one fraction and the denominator of the other fraction. If the cross products of two ratios (fractions) are equal, then the ratios form a proportion.
Percent: Find What Number Is a Given Percent of Another Number	$n = p \times b$ number (n) is a given percent (p) of a given base number (b)
Percent: Find What Percent One Number Is of Another Number	$p = \frac{n}{b}$ percent (p) one number (n) is of another number (b)
Percent: Find a Number When Given a Certain Percent of the Number	$b = \frac{n}{p}$ base number (b) when given a number (n) and the percent (p) the number is of the base number
Percent of Increase	$p\% = \frac{\text{amount of increase}}{\text{original amount}}$ amount of increase = new amount − original amount
Percent of Decrease	$p\% = \frac{\text{amount of decrease}}{\text{original amount}}$ amount of decrease = larger amount − the smaller amount
Simple Interest	$I = prt$ where I is the interest earned or paid, p is the principal amount, r is the interest rate per year, t is the time in years

Numbers and Operations

Ways to Check Answers

Addition	Subtraction
• Reverse the addition order. If you added from top to bottom to solve the problem originally, add from the bottom of a column to the top of the column. • Use a calculator to enter the computation. Check the calculator result with your answer. • Use an estimation strategy (*see list below*).	• Reverse the operation. Add the difference (answer) to the subtrahend (number being subtracted). • Use a calculator to enter the computation. Check the calculator result with your answer. • Use an estimation strategy (*see list below*).
Multiplication	**Division**
• Reverse the order of the factors. • Factor the multiplier, and use the factors to multiply. • Use a calculator to enter the computation. Check the calculator result with your answer. • Use an estimation strategy (*see list below*).	• Reverse the operation. Multiply the quotient (answer) by the divisor. • Factor the divisor and divide each factor separately. • Use a calculator to enter the computation. Check the calculator result with your answer. • Use an estimation strategy (*see list below*).

Methods for Estimating

Rounding	• Round numbers so that you can use mental math to perform the computation. • For whole numbers and decimals, add 1 if the digit in the place to the right of the one you're rounding to is greater than or equal to 5. Add 0 if it's less than 5.
Benchmarks	• Rounding to a benchmark instead of a place value sometimes gives you an estimate that is closer to the actual answer. • There are benchmarks for both fractions and decimals.
Compatible Numbers	• Compatible numbers are values that are close to the numbers given in a computation. Choose compatible numbers that make it easy to use mental math. • For division, choose the number for the divisor first. Then find a compatible number for the dividend.
Front-end Estimation	• Use only the whole number parts of decimals or mixed numbers to perform a computation. • You can use the decimal or fraction parts to get a closer estimate.

Benchmarks for Fractions

If the numerator is . . .	Round to . . .
Much less than one-fourth of the denominator	0
About one-fourth of the denominator	$\frac{1}{4}$
About one-half of the denominator	$\frac{1}{2}$
About three-fourths of the denominator	$\frac{3}{4}$
Much greater than three-fourths of the denominator	1

Benchmarks for Decimals

To make addition or subtraction easier, round to ...
0
0.25
0.5
0.75
1

STAY Focused

Fraction-Decimal-Percent Equivalents

Fraction	Decimal	Percent	Fraction	Decimal	Percent
$\frac{1}{100}$	$= 0.01$	$= 1\%$	$\frac{8}{16}, \frac{6}{12}, \frac{5}{10}, \frac{4}{8}, \frac{3}{6}, \frac{2}{4}, \frac{1}{2}$	$= 0.5$	$= 50\%$
$\frac{1}{16}$	$= 0.0625$	$= 6\frac{1}{4}\%$	$\frac{5}{9}$	$= 0.5555...$	$= 55\frac{5}{9}\%$
$\frac{1}{12}$	$= 0.0833...$	$= 8\frac{1}{3}\%$	$\frac{9}{16}$	$= 0.5625$	$= 56\frac{1}{4}\%$
$\frac{1}{10}$	$= 0.1$	$= 10\%$	$\frac{4}{7}$	$= 0.571428...$	$= 57\frac{1}{7}\%$
$\frac{1}{9}$	$= 0.1111...$	$= 11\frac{1}{9}\%$	$\frac{7}{12}$	$= 0.5833...$	$= 58\frac{1}{3}\%$
$\frac{2}{16}, \frac{1}{8}$	$= 0.125$	$= 12\frac{1}{2}\%$	$\frac{10}{16}, \frac{5}{8}$	$= 0.625$	$= 62\frac{1}{2}\%$
$\frac{1}{7}$	$= 0.142857...$	$= 14\frac{2}{7}\%$	$\frac{8}{12}, \frac{6}{9}, \frac{4}{6}, \frac{2}{3}$	$= 0.6666...$	$= 66\frac{2}{3}\%$
$\frac{2}{12}, \frac{1}{6}$	$= 0.1666...$	$= 16\frac{2}{3}\%$	$\frac{11}{16}$	$= 0.6875$	$= 68\frac{3}{4}\%$
$\frac{13}{16}$	$= 0.1875$	$= 18\frac{3}{4}\%$	$\frac{7}{10}$	$= 0.7$	$= 70\%$
$\frac{2}{10}, \frac{1}{5}$	$= 0.2$	$= 20\%$	$\frac{5}{7}$	$= 0.714285...$	$= 71\frac{3}{7}\%$
$\frac{2}{9}$	$= 0.2222...$	$= 22\frac{2}{9}\%$	$\frac{12}{16}, \frac{9}{12}, \frac{6}{8}, \frac{3}{4}$	$= 0.75$	$= 75\%$
$\frac{4}{16}, \frac{3}{12}, \frac{2}{8}, \frac{1}{4}$	$= 0.25$	$= 25\%$	$\frac{7}{9}$	$= 0.7777...$	$= 77\frac{7}{9}\%$
$\frac{2}{7}$	$= 0.285714...$	$= 28\frac{4}{7}\%$	$\frac{8}{10}, \frac{4}{5}$	$= 0.8$	$= 80\%$
$\frac{3}{10}$	$= 0.3$	$= 30\%$	$\frac{13}{16}$	$= 0.8125$	$= 81\frac{1}{4}\%$
$\frac{5}{16}$	$= 0.3125$	$= 31\frac{1}{4}\%$	$\frac{10}{12}, \frac{5}{6}$	$= 0.8333...$	$= 83\frac{1}{3}\%$
$\frac{4}{12}, \frac{3}{9}, \frac{2}{6}, \frac{1}{3}$	$= 0.3333...$	$= 33\frac{1}{3}\%$	$\frac{6}{7}$	$= 0.857142...$	$= 85\frac{5}{7}\%$
$\frac{6}{16}, \frac{3}{8}$	$= 0.375$	$= 37\frac{1}{2}\%$	$\frac{14}{16}, \frac{7}{8}$	$= 0.875$	$= 87\frac{1}{2}\%$
$\frac{4}{10}, \frac{2}{5}$	$= 0.4$	$= 40\%$	$\frac{8}{9}$	$= 0.8888...$	$= 88\frac{8}{9}\%$
$\frac{5}{12}$	$= 0.4166...$	$= 41\frac{2}{3}\%$	$\frac{9}{10}$	$= 0.9$	$= 90\%$
$\frac{3}{7}$	$= 0.428571...$	$= 42\frac{6}{7}\%$	$\frac{11}{12}$	$= 0.9166...$	$= 91\frac{2}{3}\%$
$\frac{7}{16}$	$= 0.4375$	$= 43\frac{3}{4}\%$	$\frac{15}{16}$	$= 0.9375$	$= 93\frac{3}{4}\%$
$\frac{4}{9}$	$= 0.4444...$	$= 44\frac{4}{9}\%$	$\frac{16}{16}, \frac{12}{12}, \frac{10}{10}, \frac{8}{8}, \frac{6}{6}, \frac{4}{4}, \frac{2}{2}$	$= 1.000$	$= 100\%$

Measurement

Architects convert perimeter and area measurements to make scale drawings and models of the buildings that they are designing.

U.S. Customary System

What Came Before?

- Operations with whole numbers, fractions, and decimals
- Ratios, rates, and proportions

What's This About?

- Measuring and adding lengths
- Understanding area, capacity, weight, and temperature measurements
- Converting measurements within one system using a conversion factor

Practical Apps

- Builders use U.S. customary measurements of length, area, and capacity to construct buildings.
- Architects convert measurements to make scale drawings and models.

just for FUN!

FUN FACT: You can measure the height of a horse in feet or in hands!

CONTENTS | UPLOAD | DOWNLOAD

Measurement

You can find more practice problems online by visiting:
www.SWadvantage.com

Measuring U.S. Customary Length

Units of Length in the U.S. Customary System

Length is the distance between two points. In the U.S. customary measurement system, the most commonly used units of length are *inch, foot, yard,* and *mile.* Inches, feet, and yards are often measured using a ruler, yardstick, or tape measure. On most rulers each inch is divided evenly into smaller units.

An **odometer** is an instrument used to measure distances in miles. Today most cars are equipped with a trip meter that can be reset. Drivers use it to record the distance in miles or kilometers (see page 500 for metric measurements) traveled during a trip.

Need More HELP

Each inch on the ruler is divided into fractional parts including half of an inch, quarter of an inch, eighth of an inch, and sixteenth of an inch.

EXAMPLE 1

Find the length of the pencil in inches.

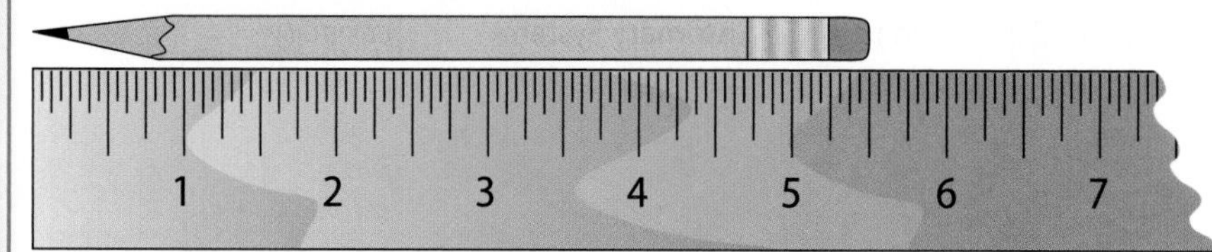

STEP 1 Align the pencil with the beginning of the scale on the ruler. The scale on the ruler does not show zero. Place the pencil so one end is exactly even with the beginning of the scale.

STEP 2 Count the number of whole inches along its length. The pencil measures 5 whole inches.

STEP 3 Count the additional fractional parts of an inch along its length. The pencil measures an additional one-half inch.

The length of the pencil is $5\frac{1}{2}$ inches.

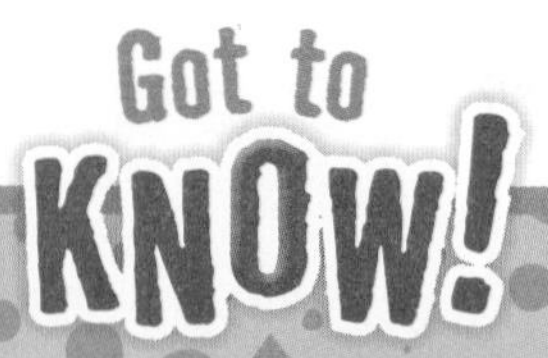

U.S. Customary Units of Length							Unit Abbreviations
1 inch	=	$\frac{1}{12}$ foot	=	$\frac{1}{36}$ yard			in.
12 inches	=	**1 foot**	=	$\frac{1}{3}$ yard			ft
36 inches	=	3 feet	=	**1 yard**			yd
		5,280 feet	=	1,760 yards	=	**1 mile**	mi

Renaming Units of Length

Sometimes lengths are expressed using different units. Often it is easier to work with the lengths if they are expressed using the same unit.

Need More HELP

When you write a unit in a different form, you rename the unit. The directions below mean the same thing.

Rename 5 feet as inches.

Express 5 feet as inches.

Convert 5 feet to inches.

EXAMPLE 2

Which distance is longer, 48 inches or 5 feet?

Use one of the methods below to find the number of inches in 5 feet. Then compare the number of inches to 48 inches.

METHOD 1

Use a chart that renames the units.

feet	1	2	3	4	5
inches	12	24	36	48	60

5 ft = 60 in.

60 > 48

METHOD 2

Multiply to change the larger unit to smaller units.

Think: 5 ft = ? in.

1 ft = 12 in.

Multiply: 5 ft × 12 in. per ft = 60 in.

60 > 48

CHECK Division undoes multiplication. Divide to find the number of feet in 60 inches.

60 in ÷ 12 in. per ft = 5 ft

60 in. = 5 ft ✓

60 > 48 so 5 feet is longer than 48 inches.

SEARCH

To see step-by-step videos of these problems, enter the page number into the SWadvantage.com Search Bar.

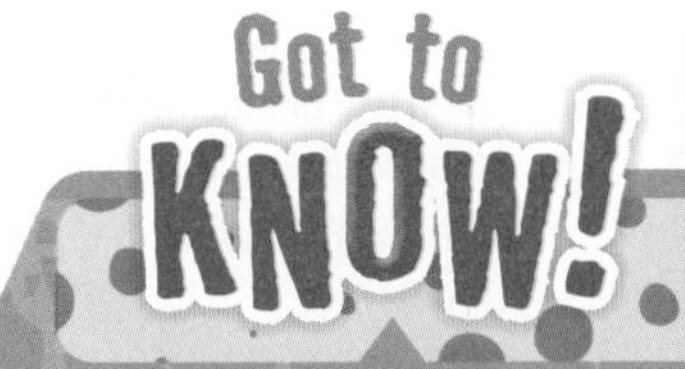

Rules for Renaming Units of Length

Larger unit ⟶ smaller unit You need more of the smaller unit.	Smaller unit ⟶ larger unit You need fewer of the larger unit.
Multiply.	Divide.
20 yd = ? feet	72 in. = ? yd
20 yd × 3 ft per yd = 60 ft	72 in. ÷ 36 in. per yd = 2 yd

Simplifying Units of Length

To simplify a large number of small units, write it as a larger unit plus any remaining small units.

EXAMPLE 3

Simplify 16 inches. Use feet and inches.

STEP 1 Find the number of feet in 16 inches.

Divide: 16 ÷ 12 = 1 R4

STEP 2 Express the measure in feet and inches.

The 1 is 1 foot.
The R4 is the remaining 4 inches.

16 in. = 1 ft 4 in.

Adding Units of Length

Add units of length as you would add any numbers. Sometimes the sum can be simplified.

EXAMPLE 4

a. Add like units, and simplify the answer.

4 in. + 9 in. = ? in.

4 in. + 9 in. = 13 in.

13 > 12, so 13 in. is greater than 1 ft.

Simplify 13 in.
13 in. ÷ 12 in. per ft = 1 R1
13 in. = 1 ft 1 in.

4 in. + 9 in. = 1 ft 1 in.

b. Add mixed units. Simplify the answer.

3 yd 2 ft
+ 5 yd 2 ft

STEP 1	Add the number of feet.	2 ft + 2 ft = 4 ft
STEP 2	Add the number of yards.	3 yd + 5 yd = 8 yd
STEP 3	Simplify the number of feet if it is greater than 3 feet, or a yard.	4 ft ÷ 3 ft per yd = 1 R1, or 1 yd 1 ft
STEP 4	Find the simplified sum.	8 yd + 1 yd 1 ft = 9 yd 1 ft

Try It This Way

You can visualize and then use mental math to solve Example 4(b).

Add each measure mentally.

3 yd 2 ft
+ 5 yd 2 ft
8 yd 4 ft

Think: 3 ft = 1 yd

Think: 4 ft is 3 ft + 1 ft

8 yd + 4 ft

8 yd + 1 yd + 1 ft

9 yd 1 ft

EXAMPLE 5

A length of chain is 6 ft 5 in. long. A second chain is 5 ft 7 in. long. What is the total length of the two chains in feet? What is the total length in yards?

STEP 1 Add the two lengths.

$$\begin{array}{r} 6 \text{ ft } 5 \text{ in.} \\ +\ 5 \text{ ft } 7 \text{ in.} \\ \hline 11 \text{ ft } 12 \text{ in.} \end{array}$$

STEP 2 Simplify the sum.

12 in. = 1 ft

11 ft + 1 ft = 12 ft

The total length of the two chains is 12 feet.

STEP 3 Rename 12 feet as yards.

12 ft = 12 ft ÷ 3 yd per ft = 4 yd

There are 4 yards of chain.

SEARCH

To see step-by-step videos of these problems, enter the page number into the SWadvantage.com Search Bar.

Subtracting Units of Length

Subtract units of length as you would add any numbers. You may need to regroup. Sometimes the difference can be simplified.

EXAMPLE 6

a. Subtract like units.

8 in. − 6 in. = ? in.

8 in. − 6 in. = 2 in.

b. Subtract mixed units.

$$\begin{array}{r} \mathbf{4 \text{ ft } 3 \text{ in.}} \\ \mathbf{-\ 2 \text{ ft } 5 \text{ in.}} \\ \hline \end{array}$$

STEP 1 Regroup.

5 > 3, so you need to regroup.

Rename 4 ft as 3 ft 12 in.

Add the regrouped inches to 3 in.
12 in. + 3 in. = 15 in.

STEP 2 Write the problem with the regrouped inches. Subtract.

$$\begin{array}{r} 3 \text{ ft } 15 \text{ in.} \\ -\ 2 \text{ ft } \ \ 5 \text{ in.} \\ \hline 1 \text{ ft } 10 \text{ in.} \end{array}$$

Watch Out

When you regroup units of U.S. customary measure, you do not regroup groups of 10. You use the number of units used to rename. 1 yd regroups to 36 in. or 3 ft, and 1 ft regroups to 12 in.

Area in the U.S. Customary System

Area is the size of the surface of a flat figure or shape. Area is measured in square units.

Area of cover = 66 in.^{2}

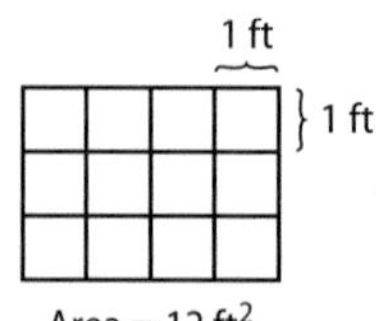

Area = 12 ft^2

The units used to measure area are based on units of length. The most common U.S. customary units of area are *square inches, square feet, square yards,* and *square miles.* A unit used for large areas is the **acre**, which is 4,840 square yards.

EXAMPLE 1

Find the area of this figure.

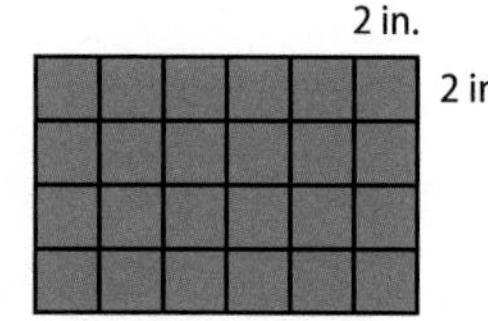

Multiply to find the number of squares.

Think: There are 6 squares in each row.

There are 4 squares in each column.

Multiply: $6 \times 4 = 24$ squares. There are 24 small squares.

Think: Each side of a square is 2 in., so the area of one small square is 4 sq in.

Multiply: 4 sq in. per square $\times$ 24 squares = 96 sq in.

The area of the figure is 96 square inches.

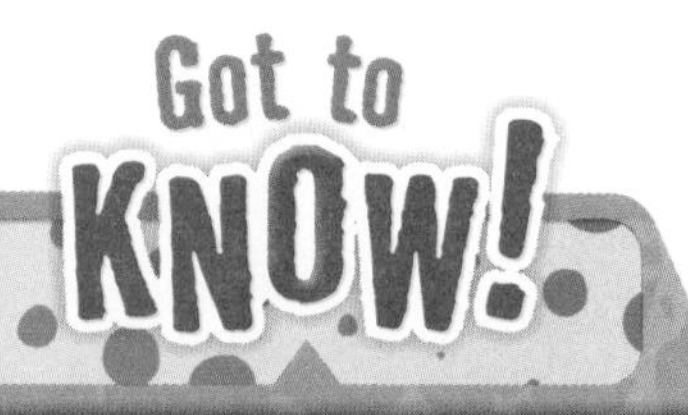

Number the squares in the bottom row: 1–6

Number the squares on the left from top to bottom: 1–4

Multiply the largest number in each sequence: $6 \times 4 = 24$

This is the total number of small squares.

Got to KNOW!

Units of Area

Units	Abbreviations	
square inch	sq in.	in.^{2}
square foot	sq ft	ft^2
square yard	sq yd	yd^2
square mile	sq mi	mi^2
acre	Not abbreviated	

Using a Grid to Find Area

You can place a drawing of a shape on a grid to help determine its area.

EXAMPLE 2

Lin has a square piece of carpet that measures 4 feet on each side. She draws it on a grid. She uses the carpet to make two identical triangular rugs. How many square feet are in each rug?

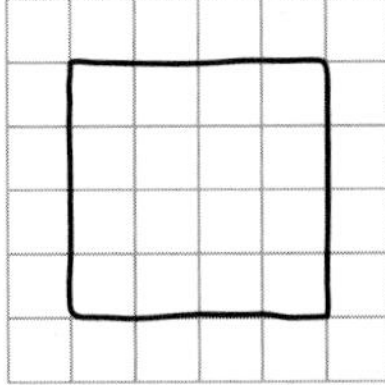

METHOD 1

Find the total number of square feet in the drawing. $4\text{ ft} \times 4\text{ ft} = 16\text{ ft}^2$

Divide the total number of square feet by 2. $16\text{ ft}^2 \div 2 = 8\text{ ft}^2$

There are 8 square feet in each triangular rug.

METHOD 2

Draw a diagonal to divide the drawing in half. Then shade one half of the drawing.

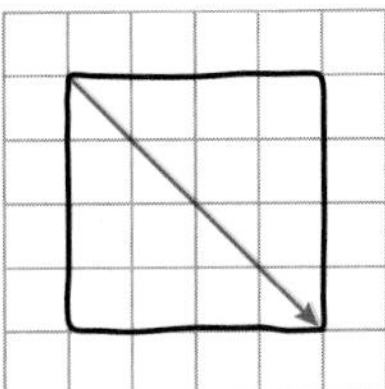

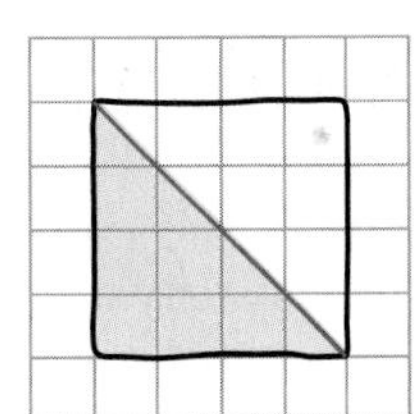

Count the number of whole square feet shaded in the picture. 6 whole squares

Count the number of half square feet shaded in the picture. 4 half squares

Add the two figures. 6 whole squares + 4 half squares = 8 whole squares

There are 8 square feet in each triangular rug.

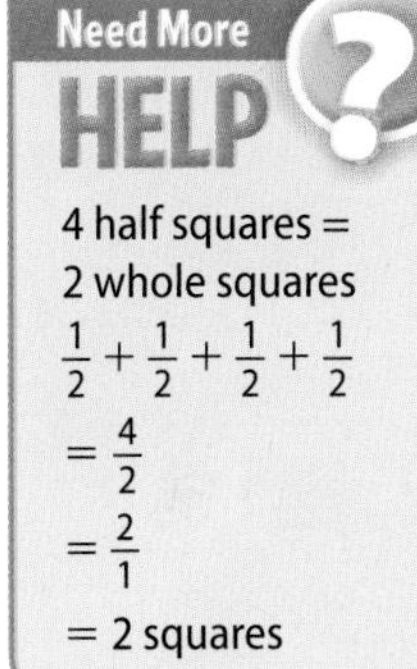

4 half squares = 2 whole squares

$\frac{1}{2} + \frac{1}{2} + \frac{1}{2} + \frac{1}{2}$

$= \frac{4}{2}$

$= \frac{2}{1}$

= 2 squares

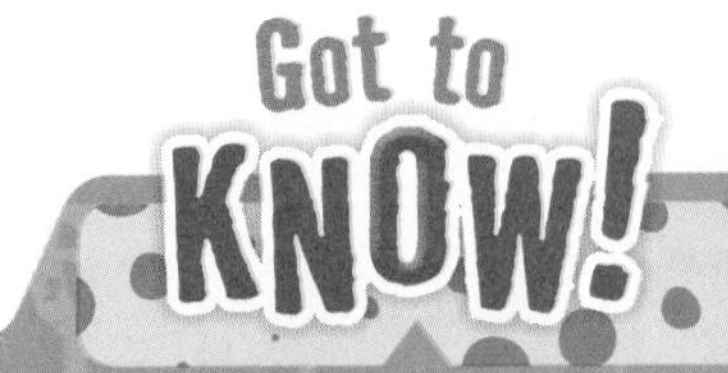

Rules for Using Units of Area

Unit Size	Comparison	When to Use	Example
square inches (in.^{2})		smaller areas	sheet of paper
square feet (ft^2)	1 sq ft = 144 in.^{2}	larger areas	size of a room
square yards (yd^2)	1 sq yd = 9 ft^2	larger areas	size of a playground
acre	1 acre = 4,840 yd^2	larger areas	size of a park
square miles (mi^2)	1 sq mi = 640 acres	very large areas	size of a city

Measuring Capacity in the U.S. Customary System

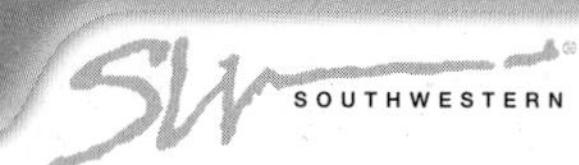

Units of Capacity

Watch Out !

Capacity is not the same as volume. *Volume* is the amount of space an object takes up and is measured in cubic units. For example, a *bushel* is a U.S. customary unit of dry volume and is equal to 2,152.42 cubic inches.

Capacity is the measure of the maximum amount of a liquid (or some other substance) a container can hold. The most common U.S. customary units of capacity are *fluid ounce, cup, pint, quart,* and *gallon.*

You are probably familiar with the sizes of milk containers seen in a grocery store.

EXAMPLE 1

Which is a more reasonable measure of the capacity of a large glass—1 pint or 1 gallon?

METHOD 1

The capacity of a large glass is most likely greater than 1 cup. Compare the number of fluid ounces in 1 cup, 1 pint, and 1 gallon.

1 c = 8 fl oz   1 pt = 16 fl oz   1 gal = 128 fl oz

Because 1 pint is 2 cups, it is a more reasonable measure of the capacity of a large glass.

METHOD 2

Think about the sizes of milk containers. A gallon container of milk contains more than one glass of milk. It is not a reasonable measure of the capacity of a large glass.

A pint of milk is a more reasonable choice.

U.S. Customary Units of Capacity										Unit Abbreviations
1 fluid ounce	=	$\frac{1}{8}$ cup								fl oz
8 fluid ounces	=	**1 cup**	=	$\frac{1}{2}$ pint						c
16 fluid ounces	=	2 cups	=	**1 pint**	=	$\frac{1}{2}$ quart				pt
32 fluid ounces	=	4 cups	=	2 pints	=	**1 quart**	=	$\frac{1}{4}$ gal		qt
128 fluid ounces	=	16 cups	=	8 pints	=	4 quarts	=	**1 gallon**		gal

Renaming Units of Capacity

Sometimes a problem includes measures that use different units of capacity. You may need to *rename* some of the measures. When you **rename** a measure, you express the same quantity using a different unit of measure.

EXAMPLE 2

A recipe uses 3 pints of water. How many cups of water does the recipe use?

METHOD 1

Use a chart that renames the units.

pints	1	2	3	4	5
cups	2	4	6	8	10

3 pt = 6 c

The recipe uses 6 cups of water.

METHOD 2

Multiply to change larger unit to smaller units.

Think: 3 pt = ? c

1 pt = 2 c

Multiply: 3 pt × 2 c per pt = 6 c

The recipe uses 6 cups of water.

CHECK Division undoes multiplication. Divide to find the number of pints in 2 cups.

6 c ÷ 2 c per pt = 3 pt

6 c = 3 pt ✔

SEARCH

To see step-by-step videos of these problems, enter the page number into the SWadvantage.com Search Bar.

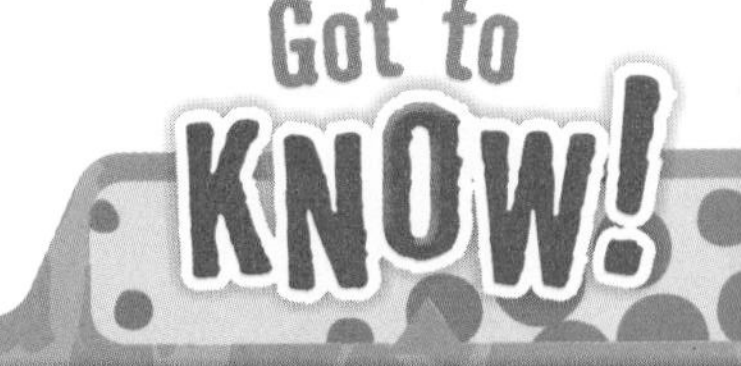

Rules for Renaming Units of Capacity

Larger unit → smaller unit	Smaller unit → larger unit
You need more of the smaller unit.	You need fewer of the larger unit.
Multiply. 4 gal = ? qt 4 gal × 4 qt per gal = 16 qt	Divide. 48 fl oz = ? c 48 fl oz ÷ 8 fl oz per c = 6 c

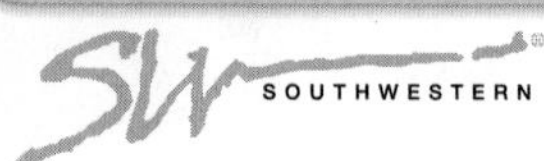

Simplifying Units of Capacity

To simplify a large number of small units, write the units as a larger unit plus any remaining small units.

Need More HELP

When you simplify units, you rename them in their simplest form. For example, 7 pints can be renamed as quarts and pints.

7 pt = 6 pt + 1 pt

↓ 3 qt ↓ 1 pt

EXAMPLE 3

Simplify 9 pints. Use quarts and pints.

STEP 1 Find the number of quarts in 9 pints.

Divide: 9 pt ÷ 2 pt per qt = 4 R1

STEP 2 Express the measure in quarts and pints.

Divide: 9 pt ÷ 2 pt per qt = 4 R1

The 4 is 4 quarts.

The R1 is the remaining 1 pint.

9 pt = 4 qt 1 pt

Adding Units of Capacity

Add units of capacity as you would add any numbers. Sometimes the sum can be simplified.

EXAMPLE 4

a. Add like units.

3 qt + 2 qt = ? qt

3 qt + 2 qt = 5 qt

4 qt = 1 gal, so 5 qt $>$ 1 gal.

Simplify the answer: 5 qt ÷ 4 qt per gal = 1 R1

5 qt = 1 gal 1 qt

b. Add mixed units.

4 c 4 fl oz
+ 6 c 4 fl oz

STEP 1 Add the number of fluid ounces.	4 fl oz + 4 fl oz = 8 fl oz
STEP 2 Simplify the number of fluid ounces.	8 fl oz = 1 c
STEP 3 Add the number of cups.	4 c + 6 c = 10 c
STEP 4 Find the sum.	10 c + 1 c = 11 c

Subtracting Units of Capacity

Subtract units of capacity as you would add any numbers. You may need to regroup.

EXAMPLE 5

a. Subtract like units.

4 qt − 3 qt = ? qt

4 qt − 3 qt = 1 qt

b. Subtract mixed units.

$$\begin{array}{r} \textbf{6 gal 1 qt} \\ \underline{-\ \textbf{4 gal 3 qt}} \end{array}$$

STEP 1 Subtract quarts first.

3 > 1, so you need to regroup.

Rename 6 gal as 5 gal 4 qt.

Add: 4 qt + 1 qt = 5 qt

STEP 2 Subtract.

$$\begin{array}{r} \text{5 gal 5 qt} \\ \underline{-\ \text{4 gal 3 qt}} \\ \text{1 gal 2 qt} \end{array}$$

Try It This Way

You can visualize and then use mental math to solve Example 5(b).

$$\begin{array}{r} \text{6 gal 1 qt} \\ \underline{-\ \text{4 gal 3 qt}} \end{array}$$

Think: I need more quarts, and 1 gal = 4 qt.

Visualize:

6 gal 1 qt =

5 gal + 4 qt + 1 qt

Subtract mentally.

5 gal − 4 gal = 1 gal

5 qt − 3 qt = 2 qt

The answer is 1 gal 2 qt.

EXAMPLE 6

A can of frozen orange juice contains 8 fluid ounces. The directions say to mix with 3 cups of water. How many fluid ounces of orange juice will this make?

STEP 1 Add.

$$\begin{array}{r} \text{8 fl oz} \\ \underline{+\ \text{3 c}\qquad} \\ \text{3 c 8 fl oz} \end{array}$$

STEP 2 Rename 3 cups as fluid ounces.

3 c × 8 fl oz per cup = 24 fl oz

STEP 3 Add.

8 fl oz + 24 fl oz = 32 fl oz

It will make 32 fluid ounces of orange juice.

SEARCH

To see step-by-step videos of these problems, enter the page number into the SWadvantage.com Search Bar.

Measuring Weight in the U.S. Customary System

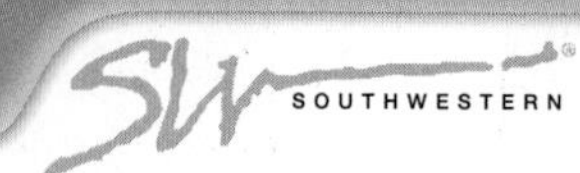

Units of Weight in the U.S. Customary System

SEARCH

To see step-by-step videos of these problems, enter the page number into the SWadvantage.com Search Bar.

Weight is the measure of how heavy an object is. Sometimes weight is confused with *mass,* a measure of the amount of matter in an object. A good way to tell the difference between weight and mass is to remember that gravity affects weight but not mass. As shown at the right, your weight would change if you were standing on the moon, but your body size, or mass, would remain the same.

Need More HELP

There is more than one type of ton. In North America, 1 t = 2,000 lb and is sometimes called a *short ton.*

Great Britain uses the *long ton,* which is equal to 2,240 lb.

A *metric ton* = 2,200 lb.

The most common U.S. customary units of weight are: *ounce, pound,* and *ton.* The illustration below shows some common objects and their approximate weights.

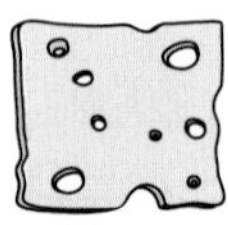

About 1 ounce

About 1 pound

About 1 ton

Refer to the *Got to Know!* box to see how the units are related.

EXAMPLE 1

Which is the most reasonable measure of weight for a bag of apples—5 ounces, 5 pounds, or 5 tons?

Think: The weight of a single apple is probably equal to that of several slices of cheese.

At the grocery store, apples are sold by the pound.

A small car weighs about 1 ton.

The most reasonable measure of weight for a bag of apples is 5 pounds.

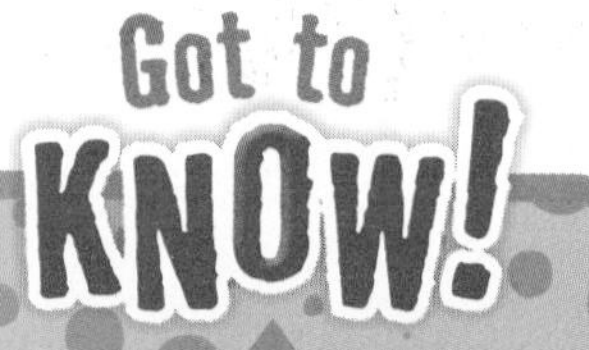

U.S. Customary Units of Weight					Unit Abbreviations
1 ounce	=	$\frac{1}{16}$ pound			oz
16 ounces	=	**1 pound**			lb
		2,000 pounds	=	**1 ton**	t

Renaming Units of Weight

Sometimes a problem includes different units of weight. To solve the problem or compare the weights, you may need to *rename* some of them. When you **rename** a measure, you express the same quantity using a different unit of measure.

EXAMPLE 2

How many ounces are in 4 pounds?

METHOD 1

Use a chart that renames the units.

pounds	1	2	3	4	5
ounces	16	32	48	64	80

4 lb = 64 oz

METHOD 2

Multiply to change larger units to smaller units.

Think: 4 lb = ? oz

1 lb = 16 oz

Multiply: 4 lb × 16 oz per lb = 64 oz

4 lb = 64 oz

CHECK Division undoes multiplication. Divide to find the number of pounds in 64 ounces.

64 oz ÷ 16 oz per lb = 4 lb

64 oz = 4 lb ✔

Ways to REMEMBER

Think of the weights of items that are familiar to you. For example, a bird weighs a few ounces, flour comes in 1-, 5-, and 10-pound bags, and a truck weighs several tons. This will help you remember when to use the different units of weight.

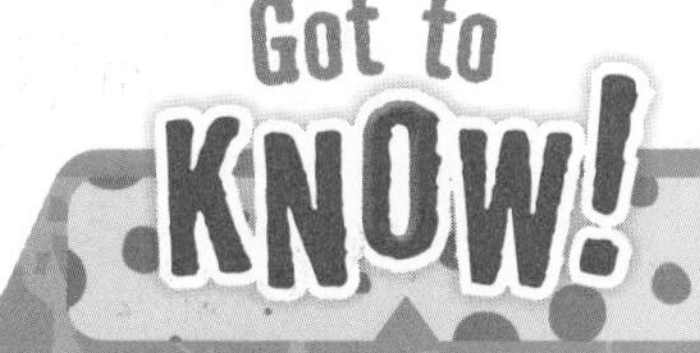

Rules for Renaming Units of Weight

Larger unit → smaller unit	Smaller unit → larger unit
You need more of the smaller unit.	You need fewer of the larger unit.
Multiply.	Divide.
3.5 lb = ? oz	12,000 lb = ? t
3.5 × 16 oz per lb = 56 oz	12,000 lb ÷ 2,000 lb per t = 6 t

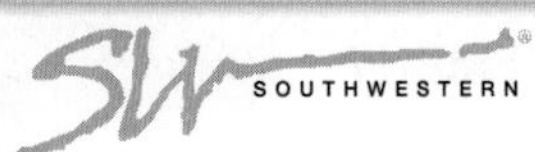

Simplifying Units of Weight

To simplify a large number of small units, write the units as a larger unit plus any remaining small units.

EXAMPLE 3

Simplify 8,500 pounds. Use tons and pounds.

STEP 1 Find the number of tons in 8,500 pounds.

Divide: 8,500 ÷ 2,000 lb per t = 4 R500

STEP 2 Express the measure in tons and pounds.

The 4 is 4 tons.

The R500 is the remaining pounds.

8,500 lb = 4 t 500 lb

SEARCH

To see step-by-step videos of these problems, enter the page number into the SWadvantage.com Search Bar.

Adding Units of Weight

Add units of weight as you would add any numbers. Sometimes the sum can be simplified.

EXAMPLE 4

a. Add like units.

8 oz + 12 oz = ? oz

8 oz + 12 oz = 20 oz

16 oz = 1 lb, so 20 oz > 1 lb.

Simplify the answer: 20 oz ÷ 16 oz per lb = 1 R4

20 oz = 1 lb 4 oz

b. Add mixed units.

$$\begin{array}{r} \textbf{12 lb} \ \ \textbf{7 oz} \\ + \ \textbf{7 lb 10 oz} \\ \hline \end{array}$$

STEP 1 Add the number of ounces. 7 oz + 10 oz = 17 oz

STEP 2 Simplify the number of ounces. 17 oz ÷ 16 oz per lb = 1 lb 1 oz

STEP 3 Add the number of pounds. 12 lb + 7 lb = 19 lb

STEP 4 Find the sum. 19 lb + 1 lb 1 oz = 20 lb 1 oz

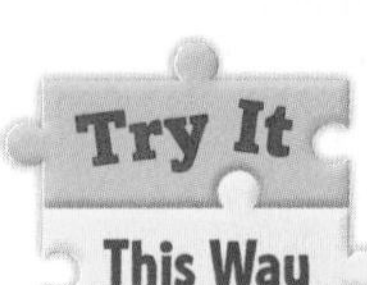

Try It This Way

You can use two colors of counters to model the addition. Use the red counters for pounds and yellow counters for ounces.

Place 12 red counters and 7 yellow counters on your desk.

Now add 7 more red counters and 10 more yellow counters.

You now have 19 red counters and 17 yellow counters.

Because 16 oz = 1 lb, you can exchange 16 yellow counters for 1 red counter.

That leaves you with 20 red counters and 1 yellow counter, which represent 20 lb 1 oz.

Subtracting Units of Weight

Units of weight can be subtracted. Sometimes units need to be renamed before the subtraction can occur.

EXAMPLE 5

a. Subtract like units.

14 t − 5 t = ? t

14 t − 5 t = 9 t

b. Subtract mixed units.

	21 lb 8 oz
−	**5 lb 15 oz**

STEP 1 Subtract ounces first. Because 15 > 8, you need to regroup.

STEP 2 Rename 21 lb 8 oz.
21 lb 8 oz = 20 lb + 16 oz + 8 oz = 20 lb 24 oz

STEP 3 Subtract using the renamed units.

	20 lb 24 oz
−	5 lb 15 oz
	15 lb 9 oz

Try It This Way

For Example 5(b), use one color of counters to represent 21 pounds and another color to represent 8 ounces.

Exchange 1 pound counter for 16 ounce counters so you have 20 lb 24 oz.

Now take away 5 lb 15 oz.

That leaves you with 15 lb 9 oz.

EXAMPLE 6

Maria bought three boxes of cereal weighing $1\frac{1}{2}$ lb, 32 oz, and 18 oz. How many pounds of cereal did Maria buy?

STEP 1 Rename $1\frac{1}{2}$ lb as ounces.

1 lb (16 oz) + $\frac{1}{2}$ lb (8 oz) = 24 oz

STEP 2 Add: 24 oz + 32 oz + 18 oz = 74 oz

STEP 3 Rename 74 oz as pounds and ounces.
74 oz ÷ 16 oz per lb = 4 R10
So, 4 is the number of pounds. R10 is the number of ounces.

Maria bought 4 pounds 10 ounces of cereal.

What Is Dimensional Analysis?

Need More HELP

To write conversion factors, you need to know equivalent units.

For help with equivalent units, see topics on length, capacity, and weight in the U.S. customary system (pp. 478, 482, 484).

Dimensional analysis is a method of converting from one unit to another within a system of measurement, using a *conversion factor.* A **conversion factor** is a ratio of equal quantities.

For example, 1 ft = 12 in. The conversion factor for converting inches to feet is the ratio $\frac{1 \text{ ft}}{12 \text{ in.}} = \frac{1}{12}$. To convert 60 inches to feet, multiply by $\frac{1}{12}$.

$$60 \times \frac{1}{12} = \frac{60}{12} = 5 \qquad 60 \text{ in.} = 5 \text{ ft}$$

EXAMPLE 1

a. Write the conversion factor for changing yards to inches.

Write the number of inches in 1 yard. 36 in. = 1 yd

Compare inches to yards. $\frac{36 \text{ in.}}{1 \text{ yd}}$

The conversion factor for yards to inches is $\frac{36 \text{ in.}}{1 \text{ yd}} = \frac{36}{1}$.

b. Convert 14 yards to inches.

Multiply 14 yards by the conversion factor. $14 \text{ yd} \times \frac{36}{1} = 504$

14 yards is equal to 504 inches.

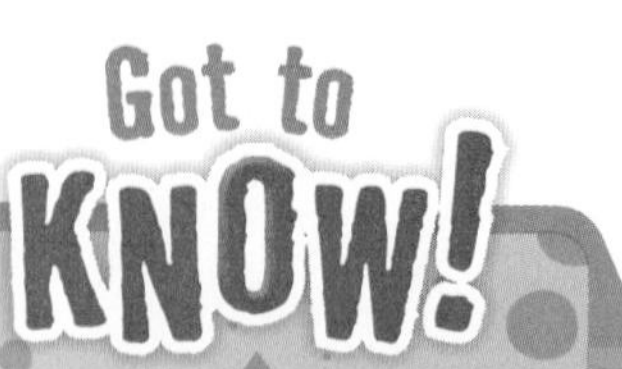

One-Step Conversions

The unit that is being changed is the denominator of the conversion factor.

Conversion: feet to inches — inches to feet

Conversion factor: $\frac{12 \text{ in.}}{1 \text{ ft}} = \frac{12}{1}$ — $\frac{1 \text{ ft}}{12 \text{ in.}} = \frac{1}{12}$

Larger unit → Smaller unit

The conversion factor is a whole number because you need more of the smaller unit.

Smaller unit → Larger unit

The conversion is a fraction because you need fewer of the larger unit.

Using Dimensional Analysis

To convert units using dimensional analysis, first find the conversion factor. Then multiply the units you want to change by the conversion factor.

To visualize the conversion more easily,

- write the unit you are changing as a fraction and
- then cross out the name of the unit you are converting from.

For Example 2, write:

54 yd = ? ft

$\frac{54 \not{yd}}{1} \times \frac{3 \text{ ft}}{1 \not{yd}} = 162 \text{ ft}$

EXAMPLE 2

Use dimensional analysis to convert 54 yards to feet.

Think: 3 ft = 1 yd. You are converting yards. Use yards as the denominator.

The conversion factor is $\frac{3 \text{ ft}}{1 \text{ yd}}$.

Multiply: $54 \text{ yd} \times \frac{3 \text{ ft}}{1 \text{ yd}} = 162 \text{ ft}$

54 yards converts to 162 feet.

EXAMPLE 3

Use dimensional analysis to convert 3 pounds to ounces.

Think: 16 oz = 1 lb. You are converting pounds. Use pounds as the denominator.

The conversion factor is $\frac{16 \text{ oz}}{1 \text{ lb}}$.

Multiply: $3 \text{ lb} \times \frac{16 \text{ oz}}{1 \text{ lb}} = 48 \text{ oz}$

3 pounds converts to 48 oz.

EXAMPLE 4

A carton contains 60 fluid ounces of orange juice. How many cups of orange juice are in the carton?

Think: 1 c = 8 oz.

The conversion factor is $\frac{1 \text{ c}}{8 \text{ fl oz}}$.

Multiply: $60 \text{ fl oz} \times \frac{1 \text{ c}}{8 \text{ fl oz}} = 7.5 \text{ or } 7\frac{1}{2} \text{ c}$

There are $7\frac{1}{2}$ cups of orange juice in the carton.

SEARCH

To see step-by-step videos of these problems, enter the page number into the SWadvantage.com Search Bar.

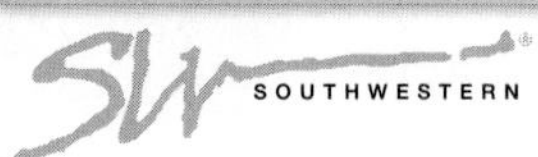

Solving Problems Using Dimensional Analysis

Use dimensional analysis when you need to compare rates. In these problems, the conversion factor:

- must include the unit needed for the answer, and
- must cancel the original unit so only the unit you need is left.

Sometimes you will need to make more than one conversion.

A unit rate (or unit price) is the price of one unit. For example, \$1.29 per gallon is a unit price.

For help with unit rates, go to *Writing Rates* in *Numbers and Operations* (p. 366).

EXAMPLE 5

Darla sees the following prices for milk at the grocery store.

Brand of Milk	A	B
Cost	\$2.59 for 64 fl oz	\$4.89 for 1 gal

Which brand has the lower unit price—Brand A or Brand B?

Consider the relationship between the given units. Suppose you know the following.

128 fluid ounces = 16 cups = 8 pints = 4 quarts = 1 gallon

Find the unit price for Brand A in gallons.

STEP 1 Find the conversion factor to change fluid ounces to gallons.

1 gallon = 128 fl oz The conversion factor is $\frac{1 \text{ gal}}{128 \text{ fl oz}}$.

STEP 2 Convert 64 fluid ounces to gallons. (You can cancel the measures "fl oz" just as you can cancel numbers that are in a numerator and a denominator.)

$$\frac{64 \cancel{\text{fl oz}}}{1} \times \frac{1 \text{ gal}}{128 \cancel{\text{fl oz}}} = 0.5 \text{ gal}$$

STEP 3 Find the unit price for Brand A.

$$\frac{\$2.59 \text{ per gal}}{0.5 \text{ gal}} = \$5.18 \text{ per gal}$$

STEP 4 Compare this price of Brand A to the price of Brand B.

\$5.18 per gal > \$4.89 per gal

Brand B has the lower unit price.

EXAMPLE 6

Ana rode her bike at a rate of 6 miles per hour. Imani rode her bike at a rate of 352 feet per minute. Which girl rode at a faster rate?

Notice that, in this problem, the two rates do not share a common unit. You need to decide which rate to change.

Try converting Imani's rate, 352 feet per minute, to miles per hour.

$$\frac{352 \text{ ft}}{1 \text{ min}} = \frac{? \text{ mi}}{? \text{ hr}}$$

This will be a two-step conversion.

STEP 1 First convert 352 feet per minute to feet per hour.

1 hour = 60 minutes

You want an answer that does not include minutes. Use $\frac{60 \text{ min}}{1 \text{ hr}}$ as the conversion factor so you cancel the minutes.

$$\frac{352 \text{ ft}}{1 \cancel{\text{min}}} \times \frac{60 \cancel{\text{min}}}{1 \text{ hr}} = \frac{21{,}120 \text{ ft}}{1 \text{ hr}}$$

352 feet per minute = 21,120 feet per hour.

STEP 2 Next convert 21,120 feet per hour to miles per hour.

1 mile = 5,280 feet

You want an answer that does not include feet. Use $\frac{1 \text{ mi}}{5{,}280 \text{ ft}}$ as the conversion factor so you can cancel the feet.

$$\frac{21{,}120 \cancel{\text{ft}}}{1 \text{ hr}} \times \frac{1 \text{ mi}}{5{,}280 \cancel{\text{ft}}} = \frac{4 \text{ mi}}{1 \text{ hr}}$$

21,120 feet per hour = 4 miles per hour

Imani's rate is $\frac{4 \text{ mi}}{1 \text{ hr}}$.

STEP 3 Compare the two rates.

Ana's Rate		Imani's Rate
$\frac{6 \text{ mi}}{1 \text{ hr}}$	$>$	$\frac{4 \text{ mi}}{1 \text{ hr}}$

Ana rode her bike at a faster rate.

SEARCH

To see step-by-step videos of these problems, enter the page number into the SWadvantage.com Search Bar.

Temperature in the U.S. Customary System

Temperature describes how hot or cold a substance is. It is measured with a thermometer in a unit called a **degree**. In the U.S. customary system, temperature is measured on the **Fahrenheit scale** and is expressed in **degrees Fahrenheit (°F)**.

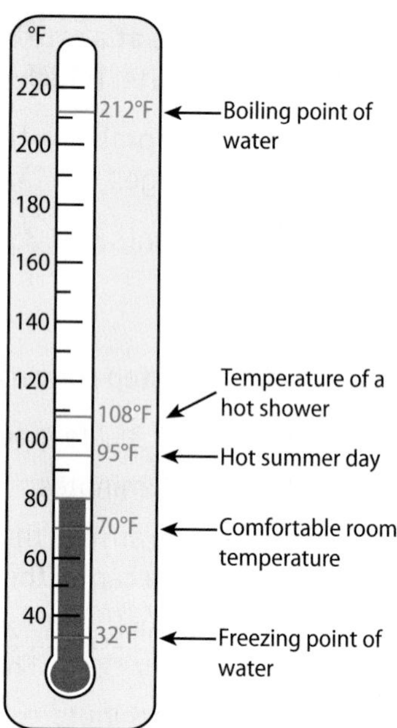

Look at the thermometer on the right. It shows some benchmark temperatures. These benchmarks will help you understand what different temperatures mean.

U.S. Customary System – Temperature

Basic unit:	1°F
Freezing Point:	32°F
Boiling Point:	212°F

EXAMPLE 1

What is the temperature shown on the thermometer?

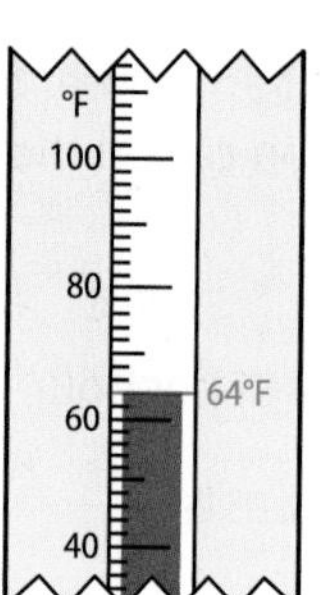

STEP 1 Determine the scale of the thermometer.

The scale is in degrees Fahrenheit.
There are 10 intervals between 60°F and 80°F.

$80° - 60° = 20°$ $\quad$ $20° \div 10 \text{ intervals} = 2°$

Each interval represents 2°.

STEP 2 Locate the height of the red temperature line.
It is between 60°F and 70°F.

STEP 3 Count the number of 2° intervals from 60° to the top of the red column.

There are 2 interval lines.

STEP 4 Multiply to find the value of the two interval lines.

$2 \text{ interval lines} \times 2° \text{ per line} = 4°$

STEP 5 Add the product to 60°.

$60° + 4° = 64°$

The temperature is 64°F.

Watch Out!

The scales on thermometers vary. To understand the scale, you need to know the number of intervals between each labeled number.

Solving Problems

You can add or subtract degrees to solve problems.

EXAMPLE 2

The temperature was 58°F at 7:00 A.M. The temperature rose 12°F by 10:00 A.M. What was the temperature at 10:00 A.M.?

When temperatures rise, use addition.

Write the problem. 58°F + 12°F = ?

Add the degrees. 58°F + 12°F = 70°F

Write the total. 70°F

The temperature at 10:00 A.M. was 70°F.

EXAMPLE 3

The temperature at 8:00 P.M. was 40°F. By midnight, the temperature had dropped 9°F. What was the temperature at midnight?

When temperatures drop, use subtraction.

Write the problem. 40°F − 9°F = ?

Subtract the degrees. 40°F − 9°F = 31°F

Write the total. 31°F

The temperature at midnight was 31°F.

SEARCH

To see step-by-step videos of these problems, enter the page number into the SWadvantage.com Search Bar.

EXAMPLE 4

What is the change in temperature from Thermometer 1 to Thermometer 2?

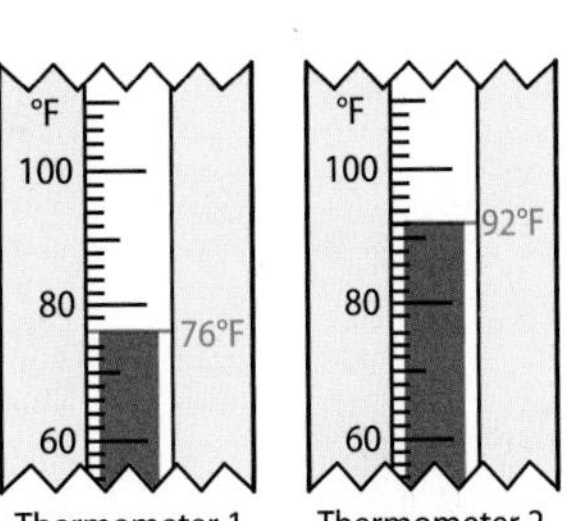

Read the temperature on Thermometer 1. 76°F

Read the temperature on Thermometer 2. 92°F

Subtract the lower temperature from the higher. 92°F − 76°F = 16°F

The change in temperature is an increase of 16°F.

Metric System

What Came Before?

- U.S. Customary length, capacity, weight, and temperature measurements
- Converting U.S. Customary measurements

What's This About?

- Measuring and adding metric lengths
- Metric area, capacity, mass, and temperature measurements
- Using a conversion factor to convert between U.S. customary and metric measurements

Practical Apps

- Weights and measures inspectors assure that measurement claims are accurate and meet established standards.
- Scientists in all fields of science use metric units to describe measures such as wavelengths, the mass of cells, and vast distances.

just for FUN!

FARMER: I'd like 10 yards of chicken wire.

CLERK: We've gone metric, and sell it by meters now, not yards.

FARMER: OK, I'd like 10 meters of chicken wire.

CLERK: Do you want the half-inch or the quarter-inch holes?

CONTENTS | UPLOAD | DOWNLOAD | *Measurement*

You can find more practice problems online by visiting:
www.SWadvantage.com

Measuring Length in the Metric System

You may see metric measures referenced as SI. This abbreviation stands for the International System of Units (*Système Internationale*), the modern version of the metric system.

Units of Length in the Metric System

Length is the distance between two points. In the metric system, the most commonly used units of length are **millimeter**, **centimeter**, **meter**, and **kilometer**.

The prefixes to the basic metric unit, the *meter,* tell the value of each unit. The prefixes extend to very large and very small numbers. The units of length in the metric system are related through powers of ten. Each unit of measure is ten times greater than the next smaller unit of measure.

EXAMPLE 1

Find the length of the paper clip in centimeters.

There are 10 increments on the scale between the numbers. These smaller units are tenths of a centimeter, or millimeters.

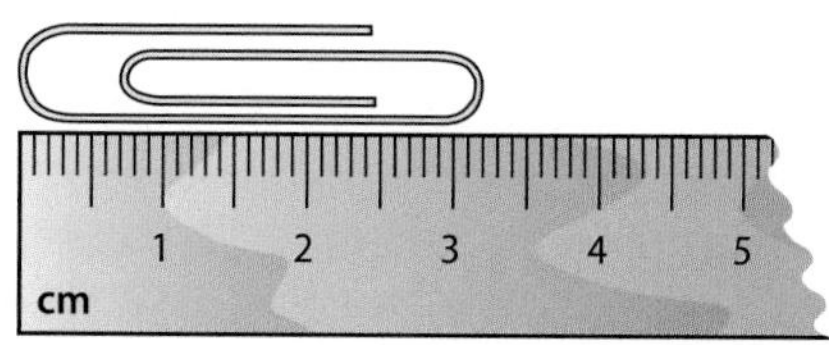

STEP 1 Left align the paper clip at the beginning of the scale on the ruler.

STEP 2 Count the number of whole centimeters covered by the paper clip.
3 centimeters

STEP 3 Count the number of millimeters covered by the paper clip.
2 millimeters

The length of the paper clip is 3.2 centimeters.

Got to KNOW!

Metric Units of Length (Abbreviations)

1 millimeter (mm)	=	$\frac{1}{10}$ centimeter	=	$\frac{1}{1,000}$ meter		
10 millimeters	=	**1 centimeter (cm)**	=	$\frac{1}{100}$ meter		
1,000 millimeters	=	100 centimeters	=	**1 meter (m)**	=	$\frac{1}{1,000}$ kilometer
				1,000 meters	=	**1 kilometer (km)**

Renaming Units of Length

Sometimes lengths are expressed using different units. Often it is easier to work with the lengths if they are expressed using the same unit.

EXAMPLE 2

How many centimeters are in 7 meters?

METHOD 1

Use a chart that renames the units.

Meters	1	2	3	4	5	6	7
Centimeters	100	200	300	400	500	600	700

There are 700 centimeters in 7 meters.

METHOD 2

Multiply to change larger units to smaller units.

Think: 7 m = ? cm

1 m = 100 cm

Multiply: 7 m × 100 cm per m = 700 cm

CHECK Division undoes multiplication. Divide to check the answer.

700 cm ÷ 100 cm per m = 7 m

700 cm = 7 m ✔

SEARCH

To see step-by-step videos of these problems, enter the page number into the SWadvantage.com Search Bar.

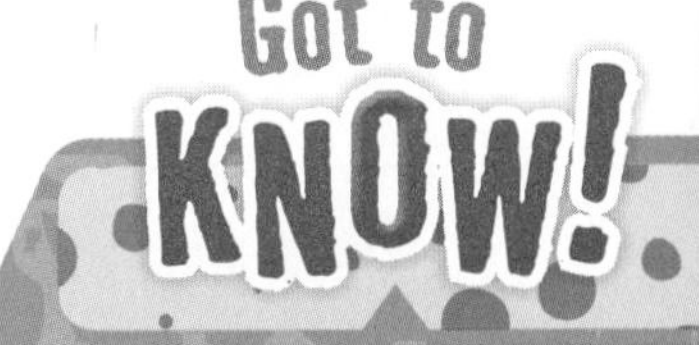

Renaming Metric Units of Length

Larger unit → smaller unit

You need more units. Multiply.

Kilometers	→ Meters
5 km	× 1,000 = 5,000 m
Centimeters	**→ Millimeters**
5 cm	× 10 = 50 mm

Smaller unit → larger unit

You need fewer units. Divide.

Centimeters	→ Meters
500 cm	÷ 100 = 5 m
Millimeters	**→ Meters**
5 mm	÷ 1,000 = 0.005 m

Simplifying Units of Length

To simplify a large number of small units, write it as a larger unit plus any remaining small units. Metric values are written as decimals because of the unit relationships to ten.

EXAMPLE 3

Simplify 755 millimeters.

a. Express as centimeters and millimeters.

10 mm = 1 cm
Divide by 10.

STEP 1 755 ÷ 10 cm = 75.5 cm

STEP 2 Express 0.5 cm as mm.
0.5 cm × 10 cm per mm = 5 mm

755 mm = 75 cm 5 mm

b. Express using a decimal.

$\frac{755 \text{ mm}}{10 \text{ mm per cm}} = 75.5 \text{ cm}$

755 mm = 75.5 cm

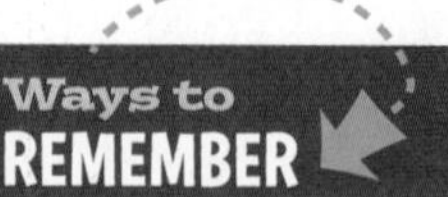

Each metric unit has the root word, "meter." The prefix shows the size of the unit when compared to a meter. Knowing the meanings of the prefixes will help you remember their values.

Kilo- means 1,000.

Centi- means 100th.

Milli- means thousandth.

Adding Units of Length

Add units of length as you would add any numbers. Simplify the sum.

a. Add like units.

645 m + 813 m = ? m

STEP 1 645 m + 813 m = 1,458 m

STEP 2 1,458 > 1,000, so 1,458 is greater than 1 meter.

STEP 3 Simplify the answer.
1,458 ÷ 1,000 m per km
= 1.458 km (1 km 458 m)

The simplified sum is 1 km 458 m.

b. Add mixed units.

3 cm 4 mm
+ 11 cm 8 mm

STEP 1 Add the number of millimeters.
4 mm + 8 mm = 12 mm

STEP 2 Add the number of centimeters.
3 cm + 11 cm = 14 cm

STEP 3 Simplify the millimeters.
12 mm ÷ 10 cm per mm =
1.2 cm (1 cm 2 mm)

STEP 4 Write the sum.
14 cm + 1 cm 2 mm = 15 cm 2 mm

The simplified sum is 15 cm 2 mm.

Subtracting Units of Length

Subtract units of length as you would subtract any numbers. You may need to rename units before you can subtract. Simplify the sum.

EXAMPLE 5

a. Subtract like units.

15 km − 6 km = ? km

15 km − 6 km = 9 km

b. Subtract mixed units.

$$\begin{array}{r} \textbf{17 m 5 cm} \\ \underline{-\ \textbf{6 m 9 cm}} \end{array}$$

STEP 1 Subtract centimeters first. Since 9 cannot be subtracted from 5, you must regroup.

STEP 2 Rename 17 m as 16 m 100 cm so you can subtract.

17 m 5 cm = 16 m 100 cm + 5 cm = 16 m 105 cm

STEP 3 Subtract using the renamed value.

$$\begin{array}{rrr} & \text{16 m} & \text{105 cm} \\ - & \text{6 m} & \text{9 cm} \\ \hline & \text{10 m} & \text{96 cm} \end{array}$$

The difference is 10 m 96 cm.

SEARCH

To see step-by-step videos of these problems, enter the page number into the SWadvantage.com Search Bar.

EXAMPLE 6

Emma jumped 2 meters 3 centimeters at the track meet. Tanya jumped 1 meter 8 centimeters. What is the difference in meters in the lengths of their jumps?

STEP 1 Write the subtraction problem.

$$\begin{array}{r} \text{2 m 3 cm} \\ \underline{-\ \text{1 m 8 cm}} \end{array}$$

STEP 2 Subtract centimeters first. Since 8 > 3, rename 2 m 3 cm as 1 m 103 cm.

STEP 3 Subtract using the renamed value.

$$\begin{array}{rrr} & \text{1 m} & \text{103 cm} \\ - & \text{1 m} & \text{8 cm} \\ \hline & & \text{95 cm} \end{array}$$

STEP 4 Write the answer in meters.

95 cm ÷ 100 cm per m = 0.95 m

The difference in the lengths of their jumps is 0.95 meters.

Measuring Area in the Metric System

Units of Area

Area is the size of the surface of a flat figure or shape. Area is measured in square units. The basic metric unit for measuring area is the **square meter**.

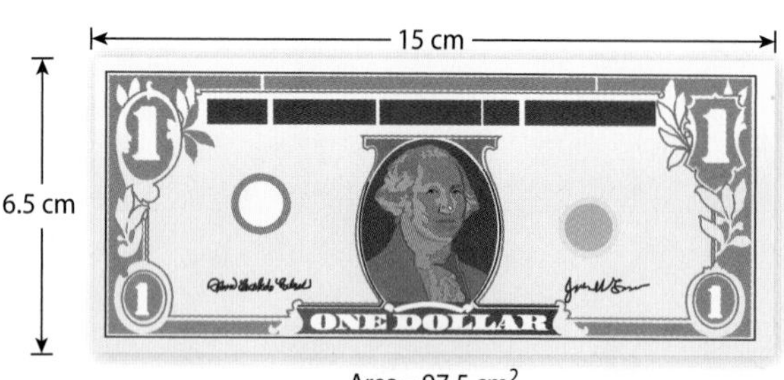

Area= 97.5 cm^2

1.5 m

1.0 m

Area= 1.5 m^2

The metric units used to measure area are based on metric units of length. The most common metric units of area are *square millimeters, square centimeters, square meters,* and *square kilometers.*

EXAMPLE 1

Find the area of the figure below. The area of each square is 1 sq m.

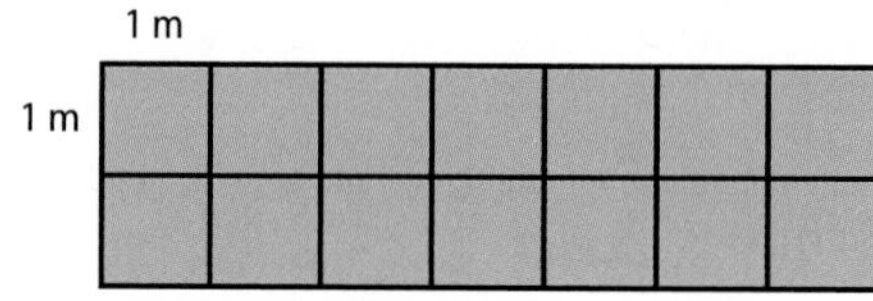

Think: There are 2 squares in each row.
There are 6 squares in each column.

Multiply: $2 \times 6 = 12$ squares. There are 12 small squares.

Think: The area of each small square is 1 sq m.

Multiply: 1 sq m per square $\times$ 12 squares $=$ 12 sq m

The area is 12 m^2.

SEARCH

To see step-by-step videos of these problems, enter the page number into the SWadvantage.com Search Bar.

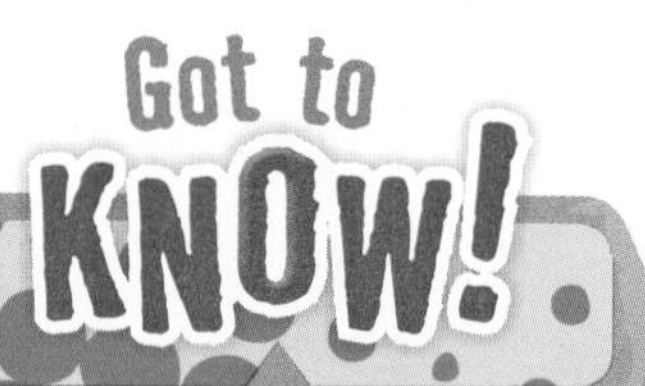

Metric Units of Area (Abbreviations)

Metric Units of Area	Abbreviations	
square millimeter	sq mm	mm^2
square centimeter	sq cm	cm^2
square meter	sq m	m^2
square kilometer	sq km	km^2

Using a Grid to Find Area

You can place a drawing of a shape on a grid to help determine its area.

EXAMPLE 2

Each square on a grid represents 1 square centimeter. Carlos drew and shaded a shape on a grid. The shape covers half the grid. What is the area of the shape Carlos drew?

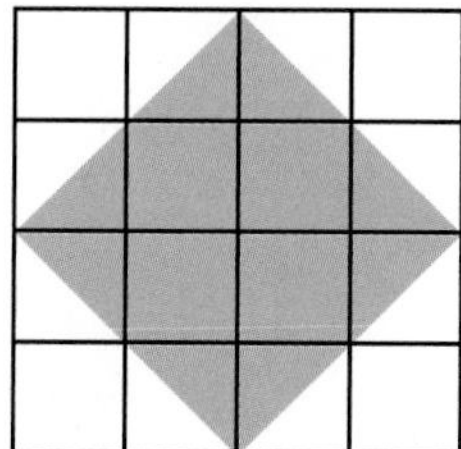

METHOD 1

Count the number of whole square centimeters shaded. 4

Count the number of half square centimeters shaded. 8

Add: 4 whole squares + 8 half squares $= 4 + \frac{8}{2} = 4 + 4 = 8$

The area of the shape Carlos drew is 8 cm^2.

METHOD 2

Count the total number of squares on the grid. 16

The shape covers half the grid. Divide by 2. $16 \div 2 = 8$

There are 8 squares shaded.

The area of the shape Carlos drew is 8 cm^2.

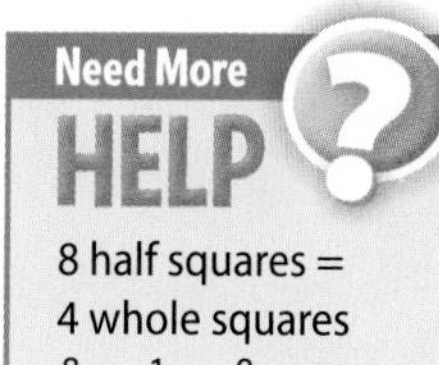

8 half squares =
4 whole squares
$\frac{8}{1} \times \frac{1}{2} = \frac{8}{2} = 4$

Got to KNOW!

Rules for Using Units of Area

Unit Size	Comparison	When to Use	Example
square millimeters (mm^2)	1 sq mm = 0.01 sq cm	very small areas	the face of a dime
square centimeters (cm^2)	1 sq cm = 100 mm^2	small areas	the size of an index card
square meters (m^2)	1 sq m = 10,000 cm^2	larger areas	the size of a classroom
square kilometers (km^2)	1 sq km = 1,000,000 m^2	very large areas	the size of a city

Measuring Capacity in the Metric System

To help you remember metric capacity, think about how bottled water and sodas are packaged. They are usually available in 1-, 2-, or 3-liter bottles.

Units of Capacity

Capacity is the measure of the maximum amount of a liquid (or some other substance) a container can hold. The basic unit of capacity in the metric system is the **liter**.

The most common metric units of capacity are the *milliliter* and *liter.* However, other units include *centiliter* and *kiloliter.* All units of capacity in the metric system are related through powers of ten.

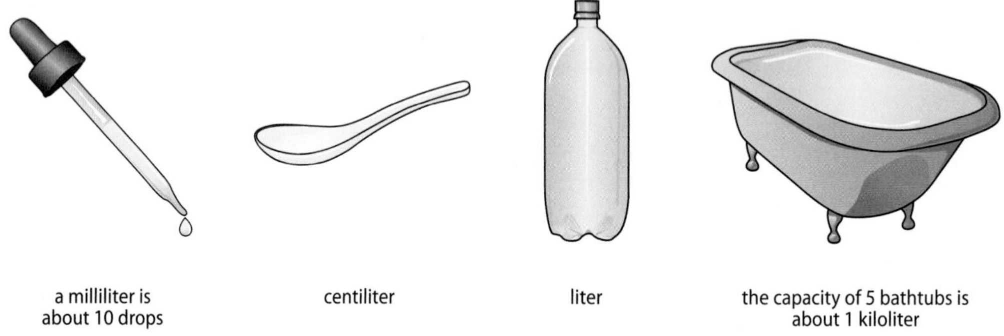

a milliliter is about 10 drops | centiliter | liter | the capacity of 5 bathtubs is about 1 kiloliter

EXAMPLE 1

Ben has a beaker with water in it.

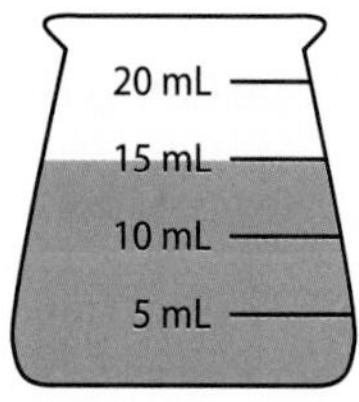

a. How many milliliters of water are in the beaker?

The water is level with the mark for 15 mL.

There are 15 mL of water in the beaker.

b. How many liters of water are in the beaker?

Convert milliliters to liters.

1,000 milliliters = 1 liter

15 mL ÷ 1,000 L per mL = 0.015 L

There is 0.015 L of water in the beaker.

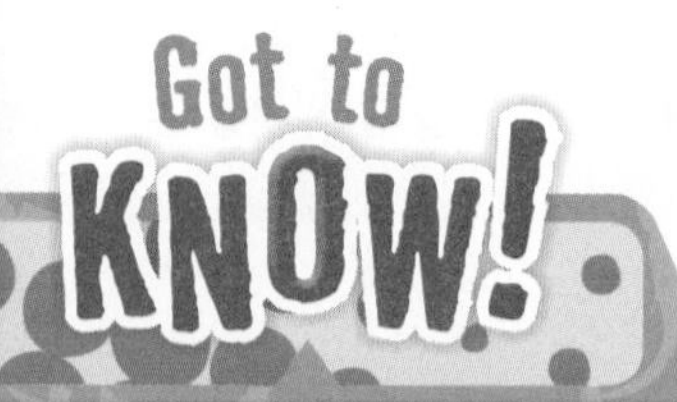

Metric Units of Capacity (Abbreviations)

1 milliliter (mL)	=	0.1 centiliter	=	0.001 liter		
10 milliliters	=	**1 centiliter (cL)**	=	0.01 liter		
1,000 milliliters	=	100 centiliters	=	**1 liter (L)**	=	0.001 kiloliter
				1,000 liters	=	**1 kiloliter (kL)**

Renaming Units of Capacity

Sometimes it is easier to work with different capacities if the same types of units are used.

EXAMPLE 2

Carmen bought a 3-liter bottle of lemonade for her party. Her cups are measured in milliliters. How many milliliters of lemonade does she have?

METHOD 1

A chart can be used to help rename the units.

Liters	1	2	3	4	5
Milliliters	1,000	2,000	3,000	4,000	5,000

3 L = 3,000 milliliters

Carmen has 3,000 milliliters of lemonade.

METHOD 2

Multiplication can be used to change larger units to smaller units.

Think: 3 L = _?_ mL 1 L = 1,000 mL

Multiply. 3 L × 1,000 mL per L = 3,000 mL

Carmen has 3,000 milliliters of lemonade.

CHECK Division can be used to change smaller units to larger units.

How many liters are in 3,000 mL?

Think: 3,000 mL = _?_ L 1,000 mL = 1 L

Divide. 3,000 mL ÷ 1,000 mL per L = 3 L

3,000 mL = 3 L ✔

To see step-by-step videos of these problems, enter the page number into the SWadvantage.com Search Bar.

When multiplying or dividing by 1,000, you move the decimal point 3 places to the right or 3 places to the left.

Example:

3.000 × 1,000 = 3,000

2,735.0 ÷ 1,000 = 2.735

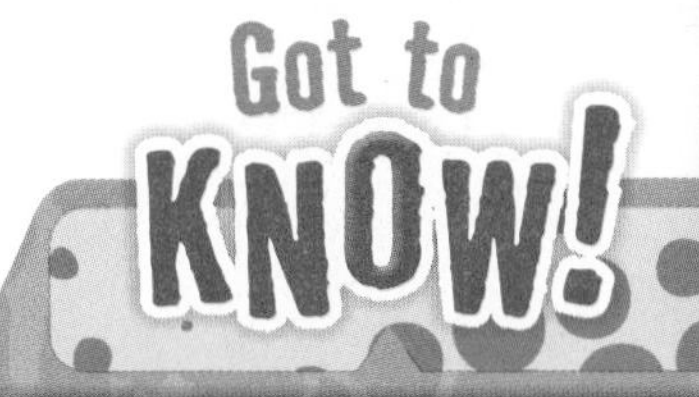

Renaming Metric Units of Capacity

Larger unit → smaller unit

You need more units. Multiply.

Kiloliters	→ Liters
8 kL	× 1,000 = 8,000 L
Centiliters	**→ Milliliters**
8 cL	× 10 = 80 mL

Smaller unit → larger unit

You need fewer units. Divide.

Centiliters	→ Liters
800 cL	÷ 100 = 8 L
Milliliters	→ Liters
8 mL	÷ 1,000 = 0.008 L

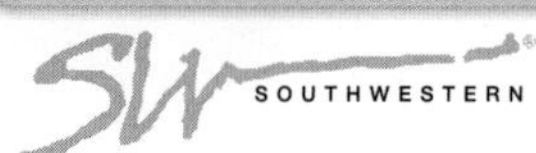

Simplifying Units of Capacity

To simplify a large number of small units, write the units as a larger unit plus any remaining small units. In metric measures you can also express the simplified answer as a decimal.

Need More HELP

For help with multiplying and dividing by powers of 10, go to *Multiply and Divide by 10, 100, etc.* in *Foundations of Mathematics* (p. 94).

EXAMPLE 3

Simplify 4,250 liters. Express as a decimal and as a mixed unit.

Think. $1{,}000 \text{ L} = 1 \text{ kL}$

Divide. $4{,}250 \text{ L} \div 1{,}000 \text{ kL per L} = 4.25 \text{ kL}$

Rename. $0.25 \text{ kL} \times 1{,}000 \text{ kL per L} = 250 \text{ L}$

Add. $4 \text{ kL} + 250 \text{ L} = 4 \text{ kL } 250 \text{ L}$

4,250 liters = 4,250 L = 4 kL 250 L

Adding Units of Capacity

Add units of capacity as you would add any numbers. Sometimes the sum can be simplified.

SEARCH

To see step-by-step videos of these problems, enter the page number into the SWadvantage.com Search Bar.

EXAMPLE 4

a. Add like units. Express the answer as a decimal in simplest form.

314 mL + 768 mL = ? mL

STEP 1 Add. 314 mL + 768 mL = 1,082 mL

STEP 2 1,000 mL = 1 L. Since 1,082 mL > 1,000 mL, you can simplify the sum.

STEP 3 Simplify.
1,082 mL ÷ 1,000 mL per L = 1.082 L

314 mL + 768 mL = 1.082 L

b. Add mixed units. Express the sum as a mixed unit.

7 cL 9 mL + 14 cL 5 mL = ? cL ? mL

STEP 1 Add: 7 cL 9 mL + 14 cL 5 mL = 21 cL 14 mL

STEP 2 1 cL = 10 mL. Since 14 > 10, regroup 14 mL as 1 cL 4 mL.

STEP 3 Write the simplified sum:

$$\begin{aligned} 21 \text{ cL } 14 \text{ mL} &= 21 \text{ cL} + 1 \text{ cL} + 4 \text{ mL} \\ &= 22 \text{ cL} + 4 \text{ mL} \end{aligned}$$

The sum is 22 cL 4 mL.

Subtracting Units of Capacity

Subtract units of capacity as you would subtract any numbers. You may need to regroup.

EXAMPLE 5

a. Subtract like units.

9 mL − 5 mL = ? mL

19 mL − 5 mL = 14 mL

b. Subtract mixed units.

$$\begin{array}{r} \textbf{8 L 293 mL} \\ \underline{-\ \textbf{3 L 772 mL}} \end{array}$$

STEP 1 Subtract milliliters first. 772 > 293, so 8 L must be renamed.

STEP 2 Rename 8 L as 7 L 1,000 mL.

STEP 3 Add the renamed units and subtract.

8 L 293 mL = 7 L 1,000 mL + 293 mL =

$$\begin{array}{rr} 7\text{ L} & 1{,}293\text{ mL} \\ -\ 3\text{ L} & 772\text{ mL} \\ \hline 4\text{ L} & 521\text{ mL} \end{array}$$

The difference is 4 L 521 mL.

EXAMPLE 6

A water cooler was filled with 3 liters of water. Now there are 750 mL of water in the water cooler. How many liters of water were used? Express the answer in decimal form.

STEP 1 Write the problem.

$$\begin{array}{rr} 3\text{ L} & 0\text{ mL} \\ - & 750\text{ mL} \\ \hline \end{array}$$

STEP 2 Rename 3 L as 2 L 1,000 mL and subtract.

$$\begin{array}{rr} 2\text{ L} & 1{,}000\text{ mL} \\ - & 750\text{ mL} \\ \hline 2\text{ L} & 250\text{ mL} \end{array}$$

STEP 3 Rename 2 L 250 mL as liters.

$2\text{ L }250\text{ mL} = 2\frac{250}{1{,}000}\text{ L} = 2.25\text{ L}.$

2.25 liters of water were used.

Ways to REMEMBER

Use this sentence to remember the metric system in order.

King **H**enry **D**oesn't **U**sually **D**rink **C**old **M**ilk

Kilo-

Hecto-

Deca-

Units (m, L, g)

Deci-

Centi-

Milli-

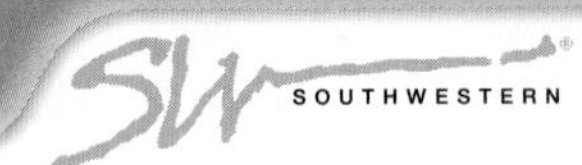

Units of Mass in the Metric System

Mass is the measure of the amount of matter in an object. Unlike weight, a U.S. customary unit of measurement, mass is not affected by gravity. If you were standing on the moon, your mass (body size) would not change, but you would weigh less. Mass is measured in the metric system using the base unit, **gram**.

The most common metric units of mass are the *milligram, gram, kilogram,* and *metric ton.*

The pictures below will help you to understand the size of each unit of mass.

Ways to REMEMBER

One way to remember the meaning of *mass* is to think, "Mass is the amount of matter in an object." Both words start with *ma-*.

about 1 milligram | about 1 gram | about 1 kilogram | about 1 metric ton

EXAMPLE 1

Which is the most reasonable measure of mass for a penny—3 milligrams, 3 grams, or 3 kilograms?

Think: A paper clip has a mass of about 1 gram.

The mass of a penny is much greater than the mass of a paper clip, so 3 mg is not reasonable.

Think: A textbook has a mass of about 1 kg.

It would probably take more than 300 pennies to make 1 kilogram, so 3 kg is not reasonable.

The most reasonable measure of mass for a penny is 3 grams.

Metric Units of Mass (Abbreviations)

1 milligram (mg) = 0.001 gram

1,000 milligrams = **1 gram (g)**

1,000 grams = **1 kilogram (kg)** = 0.001 metric ton

1,000 kilograms = **1 metric ton (t)**

Renaming Units of Mass

Sometimes a problem includes different units of mass. To solve the problem or compare the masses, you may need to *rename* some of them. When you rename a measure, you express the same quantity using a different unit of measure.

EXAMPLE 2

How many grams are in 5 kilograms?

METHOD 1

Use a chart that renames the units.

Kilograms	1	2	3	4	5
Grams	1,000	2,000	3,000	4,000	5,000

5 kg = 5,000 g

METHOD 2

Multiply to change larger units to smaller units.

Think: 5 kg = ? g

1 kg = 1,000 g

Multiply: 5 kg × 1,000 g per kg = 5,000 g

5 kg = 5,000 g

Check the answer.

Division undoes multiplication. Divide to find the number of grams in 5 kilograms.

5,000 g ÷ 1,000 g per kg = 5 kg

5,000 g = 5 kg ✔

SEARCH

To see step-by-step videos of these problems, enter the page number into the SWadvantage.com Search Bar.

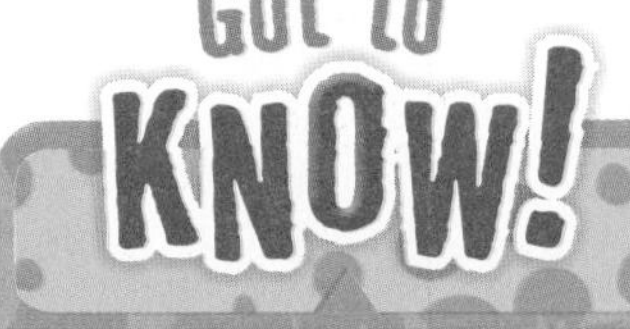

Rules for Renaming Units of Mass

Larger unit ⟶ smaller unit

You need more of the smaller unit. Multiply.

Kilograms	⟶ Grams
6 kg	× 1,000 = 6,000 g
Grams	**⟶ Milligrams**
5 g	× 1,000 = 5,000 mg

Smaller unit ⟶ larger unit

You need fewer of the larger unit. Divide.

Grams	⟶ Kilograms
8,000 g	÷ 1,000 = 8 kg
Milligrams	**⟶ Grams**
800 mg	÷ 1,000 = 0.8 g

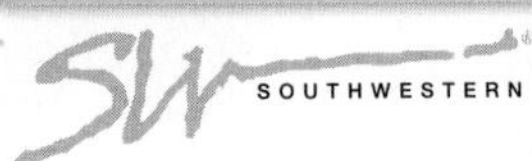

Simplifying Units of Mass

To simplify a large number of small units, write the units as a larger unit plus any remaining small units. In metric measures you can also express the simplified answer as a decimal.

EXAMPLE 3

Simplify 1,500 milligrams.

a. Express in grams and milligrams.

STEP 1 Find the number of grams and milligrams in 1,500 milligrams.

Divide: 1,500 mg ÷ 1,000 mg per g = 1 R500

STEP 2 Express the measure in grams and milligrams.

The 1 is 1 gram.

The R500 is the remaining 500 milligrams.

1,500 mg = 1 g 500 mg

b. Express as a decimal.

1,500 mg ÷ 1,000 g per mg = 1.5 g

1,500 mg = 1.5 g

Need More HELP

To understand why 1 g 500 mg = 1.5 g, write 1 g 500 mg as a fraction. Then simplify and express as a decimal.

$1\text{ g }\frac{500}{1{,}000}\text{ g} =$

$1\text{ g }\frac{1}{2}\text{ g} =$

1.5 g

Adding Units of Mass

Add units of mass as you would add any numbers. Simplify the sum.

EXAMPLE 4

a. Add like units.
407 kg + 862 kg = ? t

407 kg + 862 kg = 1,269 kg

1 t = 1,000 kg, so 1,269 kg > 1 t.

Simplify the answer: 1,269 kg ÷ 1,000 kg per t = 1.269 t

407 kg + 862 kg = 1.269 t

b. Add mixed units.

$$\begin{array}{r} \textbf{321 kg 593 g} \\ \underline{\textbf{+ 187 kg 547 g}} \end{array}$$

STEP 1 Find the sums of the grams and kilograms. 508 kg 1,140 g

STEP 2 Simplify the number of grams. 1,140 g ÷ 1,000 per kg = 1 kg 140 g

STEP 3 Simplify the sum. 508 kg + (1 kg 140 g) = 509 kg 140 g

Subtracting Units of Mass

Units of mass can be subtracted. Sometimes units need to be renamed before the subtraction can occur.

EXAMPLE 5

a. Subtract like units.

765 g − 574 g = ? g

765 g − 574 g = 191 g

b. Subtract mixed units.

$$\begin{array}{r} \textbf{338 g 490 mg} \\ -\ \textbf{94 g 682 mg} \\ \hline \end{array}$$

STEP 1 Subtract milligrams first.

490 mg < 682 mg, so you need to regroup.

STEP 2 Rename 338 g 490 mg.

338 g 490 mg = 337 g + (1,000 mg + 490 mg) = 337 g + 1,490 mg

STEP 3 Subtract using the renamed units.

$$\begin{array}{rr} 337 \text{ g} & 1{,}490 \text{ mg} \\ -\ 94 \text{ g} & 682 \text{ mg} \\ \hline 243 \text{ g} & 808 \text{ mg} \end{array}$$

SEARCH

To see step-by-step videos of these problems, enter the page number into the SWadvantage.com Search Bar.

EXAMPLE 6

Paul's dog has a mass of 12,250 grams. Tia's cat has a mass of 17.5 kilograms.

a. Whose pet has a larger mass?

You need like units. Rename 12,250 grams.

12,250 ÷ 1,000 g per kg = 12.250 kg

Compare the two masses: 17.5 kg > 12.250 kg

Tia's cat has a greater mass than Paul's dog.

b. How much greater is the mass?

Subtract.

$$\begin{array}{r} 17.500 \text{ kg} \\ -\ 12.250 \text{ kg} \\ \hline 5.250 \text{ kg} \end{array}$$

The cat's mass is 5.250 kg greater than the mass of the dog.

Converting Between U.S. Customary and Metric Measures

Need More HELP

Remember, when writing a conversion factor, use the unit that is being changed as the denominator.

For more help with conversion factors, go to *Dimensional Analysis* on page 492.

Measurements can be expressed in the U.S. customary system or in the metric system. You need to use a *conversion factor* to convert between the two systems. In these conversions, it does not matter if you are going from small units to large or large units to small. The conversion factor allows for the difference in unit size.

However, due to differences in the two systems, all conversions between the U.S. customary and metric measures give approximate measures.

One meter is approximately equal to ($\approx$) 1.09 yards. The conversion factor for changing meters to yards is $\frac{1.09 \text{ yd}}{1 \text{ m}}$.

When you multiply by the conversion factor, the unit that you are converting from cancels out. The unit you are converting to remains.

$2 \cancel{\text{m}} \times \frac{1.09 \text{ yd}}{1 \cancel{\text{m}}} \approx 2 \times 1.09 \text{ yd} = 2.18 \text{ yd}$

$2 \text{ m} \approx 2.18 \text{ yd}$

EXAMPLE 1

8 miles = ? kilometers

STEP 1 Write the conversion factor. Use 1 mile $\approx$ 1.61 kilometers.

Conversion factor: $\frac{1.61 \text{ km}}{1 \text{ mi}}$

STEP 2 Use the conversion factor to convert miles to kilometers.

$\frac{8 \cancel{\text{mi}}}{1} \times \frac{1.61 \text{ km}}{1 \cancel{\text{mi}}} \approx 12.88 \text{ km}$

8 miles $\approx$ 12.88 kilometers

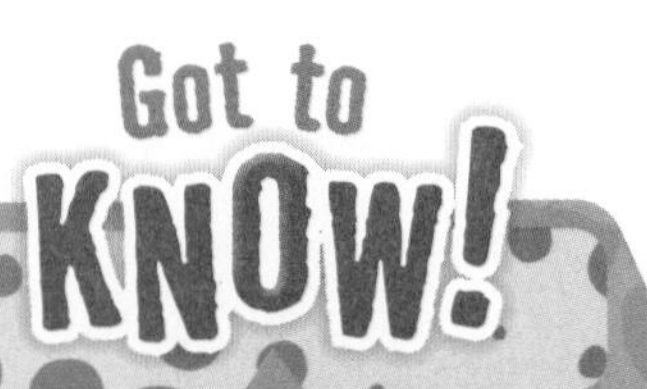

U.S. Customary and Metric Equivalents—Length

U.S. Customary to Metric	Metric to U.S. Customary
1 in. $\approx$ 2.54 cm	1 mm $\approx$ 0.04 in.
1 ft $\approx$ 30.48 cm	1 cm $\approx$ 0.39 in.
1 yd $\approx$ 91.44 cm	1 m $\approx$ 3.28 ft $\approx$ 1.09 yd
1 mi $\approx$ 1.61 km	1 km $\approx$ 0.62 mi

Converting Capacity

To convert units of capacity, first write a conversion factor. Then multiply the units you want to change by the conversion factor.

EXAMPLE 2

7 liters = ? fluid ounces

STEP 1 Write the conversion factor. Use 1 liter ≈ 33.8 fluid ounces.

Conversion factor: $\frac{33.8 \text{ fl oz}}{1 \text{ L}}$

STEP 2 Use the conversion factor to convert liters to fluid ounces.

$\frac{7\cancel{L}}{1} \times \frac{33.8 \text{ fl oz}}{1\cancel{L}} \approx 7 \times 33.8 \text{ fl oz} \approx 236.6 \text{ fl oz}$

7 liters ≈ 236.6 fluid ounces

EXAMPLE 3

12 cups = ? liters

STEP 1 Write the conversion factor. Use 1 cup ≈ 236.6 mL.

Conversion factor: $\frac{236.6 \text{ mL}}{1 \text{ c}}$

STEP 2 Use the conversion factor to convert cups to milliliters.

$\frac{12\cancel{c}}{1} \times \frac{236.6 \text{ mL}}{1\cancel{c}} \approx 12 \times 236.6 \approx 2{,}839.2 \text{ mL}$

STEP 3 Convert 2,839.2 milliliters to liters. Use 1 L ≈ 1,000 mL.

2,839.2 mL ÷ 1,000 mL per L ≈ 2.8391 L

12 cups ≈ 2.8392 liters

SEARCH

To see step-by-step videos of these problems, enter the page number into the SWadvantage.com Search Bar.

Watch Out!

In Example 3, Step 3, you do not need to find a conversion factor because 1,000 is a power of 10. Divide 2,839.2 by 1,000 by moving the decimal point three places to the left.

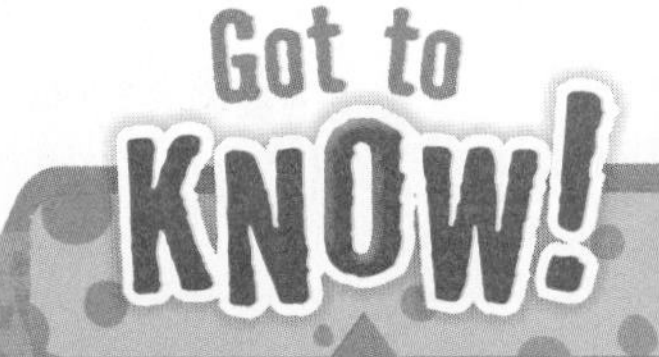

U.S. Customary and Metric Equivalents—Capacity

U.S. Customary to Metric	Metric to U.S. Customary
1 fl oz ≈ 29.6 mL	1 mL ≈ 0.03 fl oz
1 cup ≈ 236.6 mL	1 cL = 0.34 fl oz
1 pt ≈ 473.2 mL	1 L ≈ 33.8 fl oz ≈ 1.06 qt
1 qt ≈ 0.95 L	1 kL ≈ 264.2 gal
1 gal ≈ 3.79 L	

Converting Mass and Weight

To convert units of weight and mass, first write a conversion factor. Then multiply the units you want to change by the conversion factor.

EXAMPLE 4

A doctor needs to calculate how many milligrams of a certain medicine to give to a patient. The dosage is calculated based on the mass of the person taking it. If the patient weighs 125 lb, what is the patient's mass in kilograms?

STEP 1 Write the conversion factor. Use 1 pound $\approx$ 0.45 kilograms.

Conversion factor: $\frac{0.45 \text{ kg}}{1 \text{ lb}}$

STEP 2 Use the conversion factor to convert pounds to kilograms.

$$\frac{125 \cancel{\text{lb}}}{1} \times \frac{0.45 \text{ kg}}{1 \cancel{\text{lb}}} \approx 125 \times 0.45 \text{ kg} \approx 56.25 \text{ kg}$$

The patient's mass is approximately equal to 56.25 kilograms.

EXAMPLE 5

A boulder has a mass of 2.5 metric tons. How many pounds does the boulder weigh?

STEP 1 Write the conversion factor. Use 1 metric ton $\approx$ 2,205 pounds.

Conversion factor: $\frac{2{,}205 \text{ lb}}{1\text{t}}$

STEP 2 Use the conversion factor to convert metric tons to pounds.

$$\frac{2.5 \cancel{\text{t}}}{1} \times \frac{2{,}205 \text{ lb}}{1 \cancel{\text{t}}} \approx 2.5 \times 2{,}205 \text{ lb} \approx 5{,}512.5 \text{ lb}$$

The boulder weighs approximately 5,512.5 pounds.

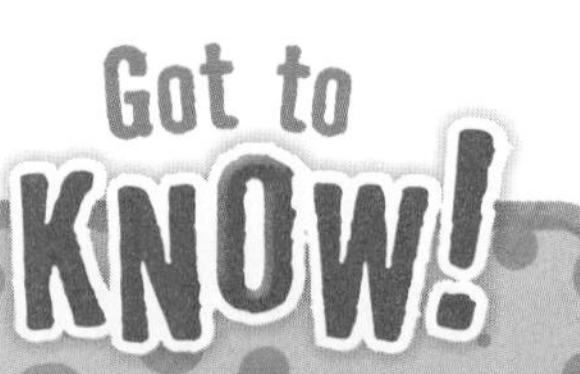

U.S. Customary and Metric Equivalents—Weight and Mass

U.S. Customary to Metric	Metric to U.S. Customary
1 oz $\approx$ 28.35 g	1 mg $\approx$ 0.000035 oz
1 lb $\approx$ 0.45 kg	1 g $\approx$ 0.0353 oz
1 short ton $\approx$ 907.2 kg $\approx$ 0.91 metric ton	1 kg $\approx$ 35.27 oz $\approx$ 2.2 b
	1 metric ton $\approx$ 2,205 lb $\approx$ 1.1 short ton

Solving Problems with Unit Conversions

Remember, when solving problems that require a conversion between U.S. customary and metric systems, the answer is almost always an approximate measure. You may need to round the estimate up or down to answer the question.

EXAMPLE 6

Anita needs to buy enough energy drink to fill a 5-gallon cooler completely. The brand of energy drink that she buys is sold only in 1-liter bottles. How many bottles of energy drink should she buy?

Before you can answer this question, you need to know the number of liters in 5 gallons.

STEP 1 Write a conversion factor for gallons to liters. Use 1 gallon $\approx$ 3.79 liters.

Conversion factor: $\frac{3.79 \text{ L}}{1 \text{ gal}}$

STEP 2 Use the conversion factor to convert 5 gallons to liters.

$$\frac{5 \cancel{\text{gal}}}{1} \times \frac{3.79 \text{ L}}{1 \cancel{\text{gal}}} \approx 5 \times 3.79 \text{ L} \approx 18.95 \text{ L}$$

5 gal $\approx$ 18.95 L

STEP 3 Compare the quantities.

18 1-L bottles $<$ 18.95 L $<$ 19 1-L bottles

Since the capacity of the cooler is 18.95 L, Anita should buy 19 bottles if she wants to fill the cooler completely.

> **SEARCH**
> To see step-by-step videos of these problems, enter the page number into the SWadvantage.com Search Bar.

EXAMPLE 7

Hector has 23 meters of rope. He needs 76 feet of rope to mark off a section of a parking lot. Does he have enough rope?

STEP 1 Write a conversion factor for meters to feet. Use 1 meter $\approx$ 3.28 feet.

Conversion factor: $\frac{3.28 \text{ ft}}{1 \text{ m}}$

STEP 2 Use the conversion factor to convert meters to feet.

$$\frac{23 \cancel{\text{m}}}{1} \times \frac{3.28 \text{ ft}}{1 \cancel{\text{m}}} \approx 75.44 \text{ ft}$$

The length of Hector's rope is 75.44 feet.

Since 75.44 feet $<$ 76 feet, Hector does not have enough rope.

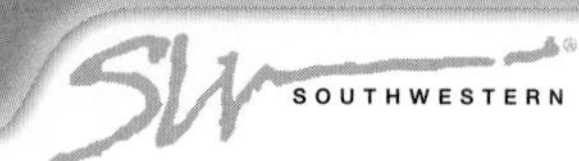

Units of Temperature in the Metric System

Temperature describes how hot or cold a substance is. It is measured with a thermometer in a unit called a **degree**. In the metric system, temperature is measured on the **Celsius scale** and is expressed in **degrees Celsius (°C)**.

The thermometer on the right shows some benchmark metric temperatures. These benchmarks will help you understand what different temperatures on the Celsius scale mean.

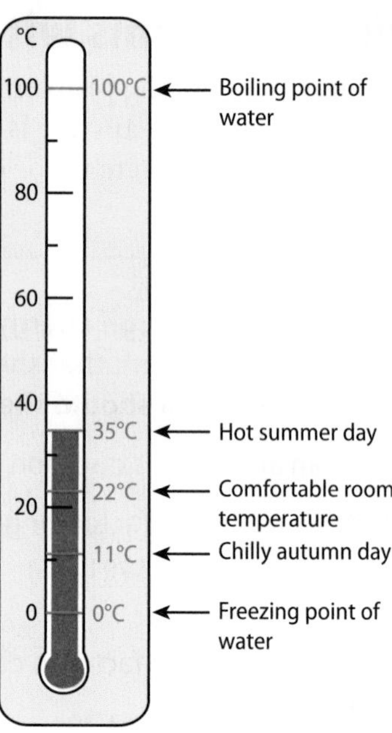

EXAMPLE 1

What is the temperature shown on the thermometer?

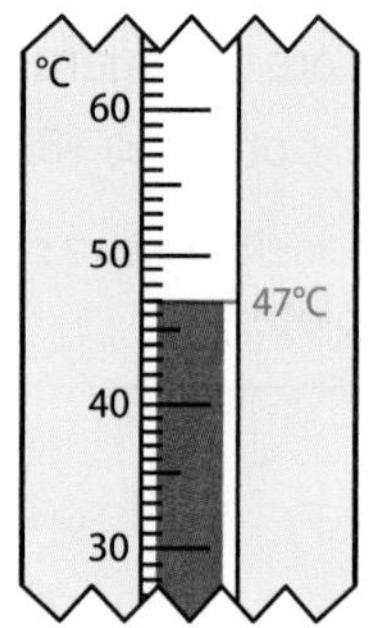

STEP 1 Determine the height of the temperature line.
It is between 40°C and 50°C.

STEP 2 Count the number of intervals between 40° and 50°.
There are 10 intervals.

STEP 3 Determine how many degrees are in each interval.
Each interval represents 1°.

STEP 4 Count the number of degrees above the 40°.
7 degrees

STEP 5 Add: 40°C + 7°C = 47°C

The temperature shown on the thermometer is 47°C.

Watch Out !

The scales on thermometers vary. To understand the scale, you need to know the number of intervals between each labeled number.

Got to KNOW!

Metric System—Temperature

Basic unit:	1°C
Freezing point of water:	0°C
Boiling point of water:	100°C

Solve Problems by Adding or Subtracting Temperatures

Degrees can be added or subtracted.

EXAMPLE 2

The temperature in Toronto was 15°C at 8:00 A.M. The temperature rose 8°C by 11:00 A.M. What was the temperature at 11:00 A.M.?

When temperatures rise, addition is used.

Write the problem. 15°C + 8°C = ? °C

Add the degrees. 15°C + 8°C = 23°C

The temperature at 11:00 A.M. was 23°C.

SEARCH

To see step-by-step videos of these problems, enter the page number into the SWadvantage.com Search Bar.

EXAMPLE 3

The temperature in St. Louis at 8:30 P.M. was 27°C. By midnight, the temperature had dropped 12°C. What was the temperature at midnight?

When temperatures drop, subtraction is used.

Write the problem. 27°C − 12°C = ? °C

Subtract the degrees. 27°C − 12°C = 15°C

The temperature at midnight was 15°C.

EXAMPLE 4

What is the change in temperature from Thermometer 1 to Thermometer 2?

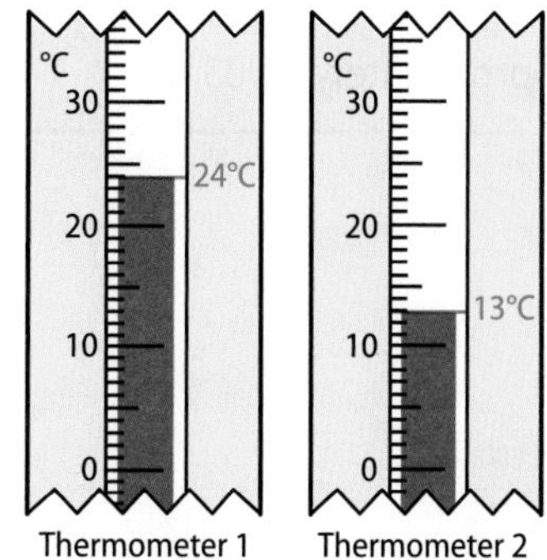

Read the temperature on Thermometer 1. 24°C

Read the temperature on Thermometer 2. 13°C

Subtract the lower temperature from the higher. 24°C − 13°C = 11°C

The change in temperature is a decrease of 11°C.

Place an index card above the two thermometers and level with the temperature on Thermometer 1. Count down the scale to the height of the temperature line on Thermometer 2. You will count down 11 degrees.

Converting Between the Fahrenheit and Celsius Scales

On the Celsius scale, the freezing point of water is 0° and the boiling point is 100°. On the Fahrenheit scale, water freezes at 32° and boils at 212°, a difference of 180°. You can use these facts to see the relationship between the degrees Celsius (°C) and degrees Fahrenheit (°F).

$\frac{100}{180} = \frac{100 \div 20}{180 \div 20} = \frac{5}{9}$, therefore 1°F is $\frac{5}{9}$ of 1°C.

There may be times when you need to convert between the Fahrenheit and the Celsius temperature scales. Formulas are used to change from one type of temperature measurement to another.

Try It This Way

To visualize the difference, look at the graphic below.

0°C 100°C

← 100 degrees →

32°F 212°F

← 180 degrees →

To fit 180 degrees in the same space as 100 degrees, the degrees must be smaller.

Converting Fahrenheit to Celsius

To change from °F to °C, use this formula: $C = \frac{5}{9}(F - 32)$

EXAMPLE 1

The melting point of copper is 1,981°F. What is the melting point of copper in °C?

Write the formula. $C = \frac{5}{9}(F - 32)$

Substitute 1,981 for *F*. $C = \frac{5}{9}(1{,}981 - 32)$

Simplify. $C = \frac{5}{9}(1{,}949)$

$= \frac{9{,}745}{9}$

$= 1{,}082.777...$

$\approx 1{,}083$

The melting point of copper is approximately 1,083°C.

SEARCH

To see step-by-step videos of these problems, enter the page number into the SWadvantage.com Search Bar.

Got to KNOW!

Temperature Conversion Formulas

Fahrenheit to Celsius	Celsius to Fahrenheit
$C = \frac{5}{9}(F - 32)$	$F = \frac{9}{5}C + 32$ or $F = 1.8C + 32$

Converting Celsius to Fahrenheit

To change from °C to °F, use this formula: $F = \frac{9}{5}C + 32$ or $F = 1.8C + 32$

Need More **HELP**

The reason the second formula also works is because $\frac{9}{5} = 1.8$.

EXAMPLE 2

The melting point of gold is 1,063°C. What is the melting point of gold in °F?

Write the formula. $F = \frac{9}{5}C + 32$

Substitute 1,063 for *C*. $F = \frac{9 \times 1{,}063}{5} + 32$

Simplify. $F = \frac{9{,}567}{5} + 32$

$= 1{,}913.4 + 32$

$= 1{,}945.4$

The melting point of gold is 1,945.4°F.

EXAMPLE 3

The average high temperature in Barrow, Alaska, in July is 7°C. What is the temperature in degrees Fahrenheit?

Use the Celsius-to-Fahrenheit formula. $F = 1.8C + 32$

Substitute 7 for *C*. $F = 1.8(7) + 32$

$F = 12.6 + 32$

Simplify. $= 44.6$

≈ 45

The average high temperature in Barrow, Alaska, in July is about 45°F.

Ways to **REMEMBER**

The difference between the freezing points in Celsius and Fahrenheit is 32°.

So, to change from Fahrenheit to Celsius, use the formula that subtracts 32°.

To change from Celsius to Fahrenheit, use the formula that adds 32°.

EXAMPLE 4

Which is hotter, 75°F or 57°C?

Convert 57°C to degrees Fahrenheit. $F = 1.8C + 32$

Substitute 57 for *C*. $F = 1.8(57) + 32$

Simplify. $= 102.6 + 32$

$= 134.6 \approx 135$

Compare. $135 > 75$

57°C is hotter than 75°F.

Perimeter and Area

What Came Before?

- Measuring length and area
- Identifying polygons and shapes in a plane

What's This About?

- Finding the perimeter and area of triangles and rectangles
- Finding the circumference and area of circles
- Finding the perimeter and area of composite figures

Practical Apps

- Architects design buildings that satisfy area and perimeter requirements so that their plans will be approved.
- Mall administrators use square footage and store location to determine the amount of rent to charge for a given space.

just for FUN!

Q: What do you get when you divide the circumference of the sun by its diameter?

A: Pi in the sky.

CONTENTS UPLOAD DOWNLOAD

Measurement

You can find more practice problems online by visiting:
www.SWadvantage.com

Perimeter

Finding Perimeter by Adding

Perimeter is the distance around a closed plane figure (polygon). To find the perimeter of any polygon, add the lengths of all the sides.

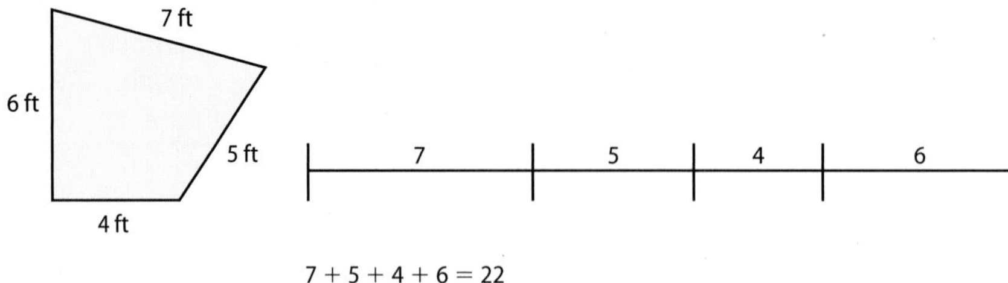

7 + 5 + 4 + 6 = 22

The perimeter is 22 feet.

Ways to REMEMBER

The word per*im*eter has the small word "rim" in the middle. A rim is the outside edge of an object or shape. Remembering the "rim" in *perimeter* can remind you of the meaning of perimeter.

Watch Out !

The perimeter of a figure is a length. Express the measure of a perimeter using a number *and* a unit of length.

EXAMPLE 1

Find the perimeter of the polygon at the right.

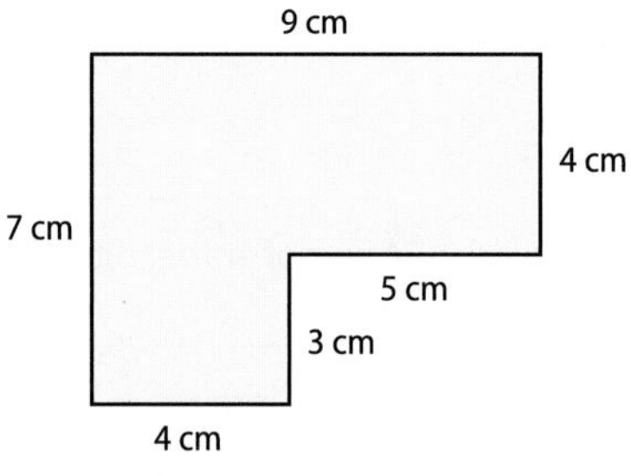

Add the lengths of the six sides.

9 + 4 + 5 + 3 + 4 + 7 = 32

Include the unit of length in the answer.

The perimeter of the polygon is 32 cm.

EXAMPLE 2

Every day Mrs. Lee walks the entire distance around Triangle Park. Use the figure to find this distance.

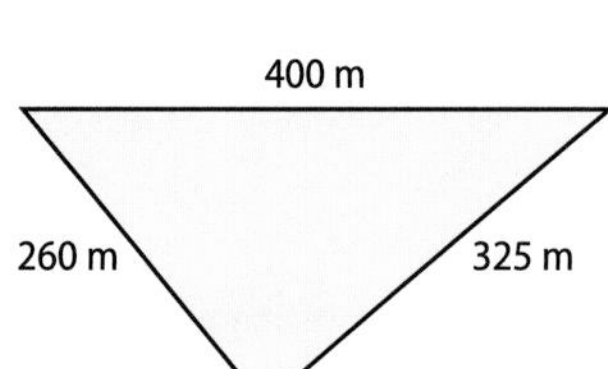

The distance around the park is the perimeter of a triangle.

Add the lengths of the three sides.

400 + 325 + 260 = 985

Include the unit of length in the answer.

The distance Mrs. Lee walks around the park is 985 meters.

Perimeter of Regular Polygons

A **regular polygon** is a polygon with equal length sides and equal measure angles. Five regular polygons are shown below.

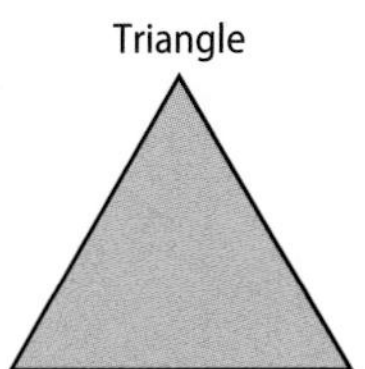

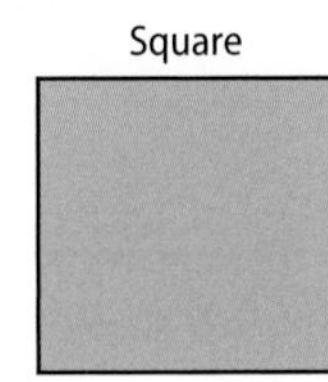

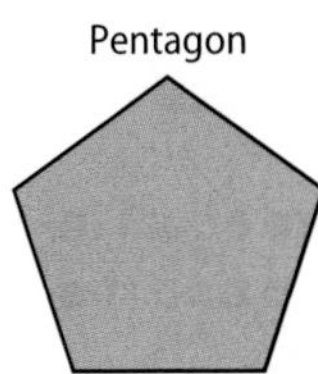

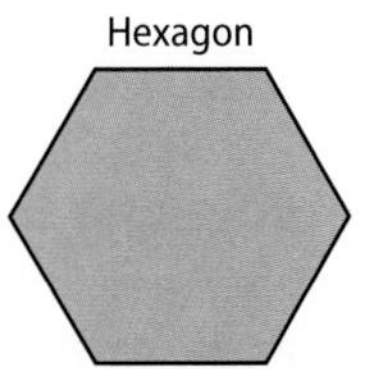

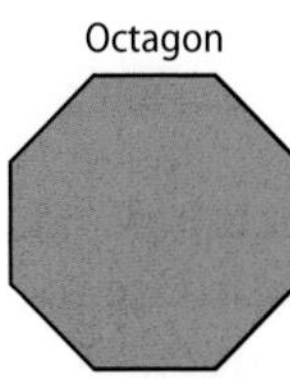

To find the perimeter of a regular polygon, multiply the length of one side by the number of sides.

EXAMPLE 3

Find the perimeter of the figure.

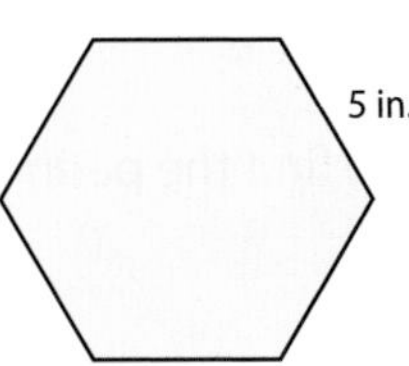

The figure has 6 sides.

Each side is 5 in. in length.

The perimeter is 5 in. $\times$ 6 $=$ 30 in.

The perimeter of this regular polygon is 30 in.

EXAMPLE 4

David wants to sew trim around a square rug that has 12-ft sides. How much trim will he need?

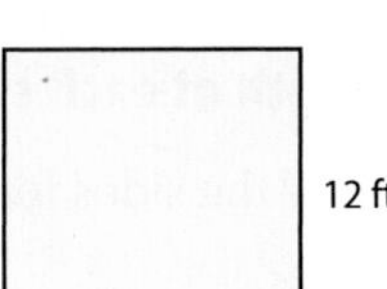

A square has 4 sides that are equal in length.

Each side is 12 ft long.

The perimeter is 12 ft $\times$ 4 $=$ 48 ft.

David will need 48 feet of trim.

EXAMPLE 5

A regular pentagon has sides that measure 8 centimeters. What is the perimeter of the pentagon?

A regular pentagon has 5 sides that are equal in length.

Each side measures 8 cm in length.

The perimeter is 8 cm $\times$ 5 $=$ 40 cm.

Try It This Way

You may find it helpful to number the sides of a figure to be sure you count them correctly.

1 2 3 4 5 6

SEARCH

To see step-by-step videos of these problems, enter the page number into the SWadvantage.com Search Bar.

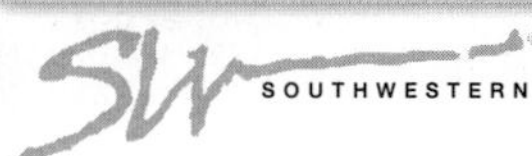

Finding Perimeter Using a Formula

A **formula** is an equation that shows a relationship. In geometry, you often use a formula to find a measure.

Need More HELP

Several standard abbreviations are used in geometry. They include:
P = perimeter
b = base
h = height
s = side

EXAMPLE 6

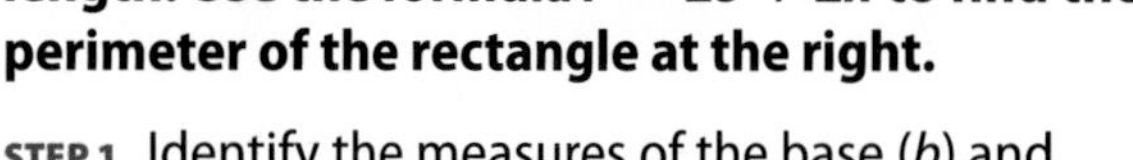

A rectangle has opposite sides that are equal in length. Use the formula $P = 2b + 2h$ to find the perimeter of the rectangle at the right.

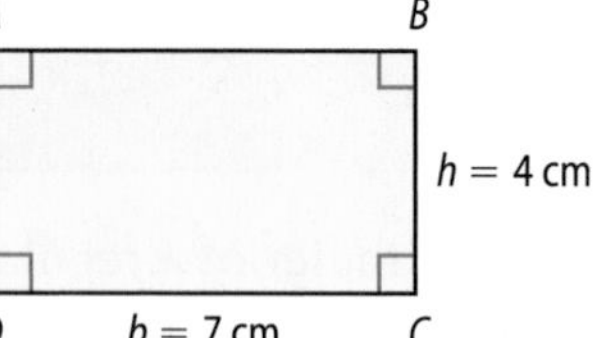

STEP 1 Identify the measures of the base (b) and height (h) of the rectangle.

$b = 7$ cm $\qquad h = 4$ cm

STEP 2 Substitute the values into the formula.

$P = 2(7) + 2(4)$

STEP 3 Multiply and add to find the perimeter.

$P = 14 + 8$
$= 22$

The perimeter of the rectangle is 22 cm.

EXAMPLE 7

Find the perimeter of a regular triangle with sides 9 m long. Use the formula $P = 3s$, in which s is the length of each side.

STEP 1 Substitute the length of the sides for s in the formula.

$P = 3(9)$

STEP 2 Multiply to find the perimeter.

$P = 27$

The perimeter of the triangle is 27 m.

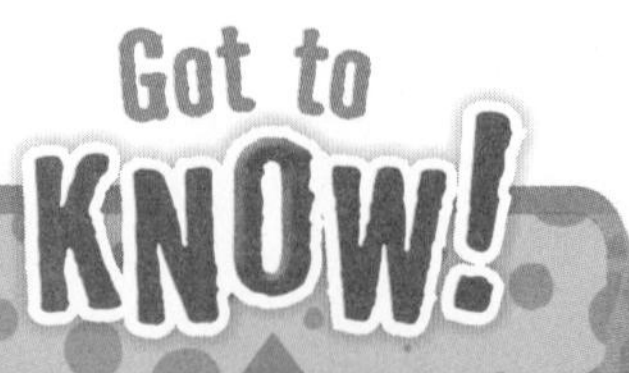

Perimeter of Polygons

Perimeter is the distance around a closed plane figure (polygon).

Regular polygons have equal length sides and equal measure angles.

Finding the perimeter of a regular polygon: Use the formula, where n = the number of sides and s = the length of each side.

$$P = ns$$

When given a *perimeter formula*: Substitute what you know into the formula. Then simplify to find the missing value.

Finding the Length of a Side

If you know the perimeter of a figure and the length of every side but one, you can find the missing side length. If the figure is a regular polygon, you can find the length of each side.

EXAMPLE 8

A regular octagon has a perimeter of 16 feet. What is the length of one side? Use $P = 8s$.

Think: You know that the perimeter of the octagon is 16 feet.

Substitute: What you know into the formula.

$$P = 8s$$

$$16 = 8s$$

Simplify: Divide both sides by 8.

$$\frac{\cancel{16}^{2}}{\cancel{8}} = \frac{\cancel{8}s}{\cancel{8}}$$

$$2 = s$$

The length of one side is 2 feet.

SEARCH

To see step-by-step videos of these problems, enter the page number into the SWadvantage.com Search Bar.

EXAMPLE 9

The diagram of a field does not show the length of one of the sides. If the perimeter of the field is 35 yards, what is the length of the missing side?

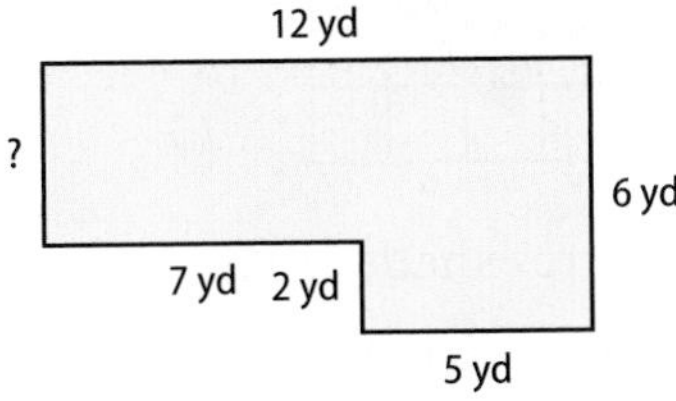

Think: The diagram shows the lengths of every side except one: 12 yd, 6 yd, 5 yd, 2 yd, and 7 yd.

You are given the perimeter, 35 yd.

Find: P − total length of known sides = length of missing side

Substitute and simplify:

$35 - (12 + 6 + 5 + 2 + 7) =$ length of missing side

$35 - 32 = 3$

The length of the missing side is 3 yd.

Estimating Area

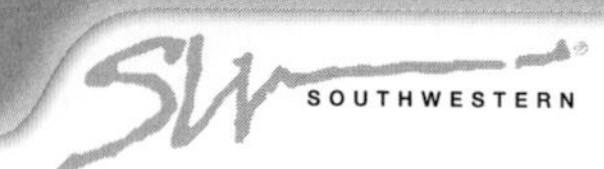

Area

The **area** of a plane, or 2-dimensional figure, is the number of square units needed to cover the surface of the figure. The standard unit of measure is a square, which is one unit per side. The units used to express area include *square inch*, *square centimeter*, *square yard*, *square meter*, and *square mile.*

For example, the shaded area on the grid below has an area of 9 square centimeters. You can also write this as 9 sq cm or 9 cm^2.

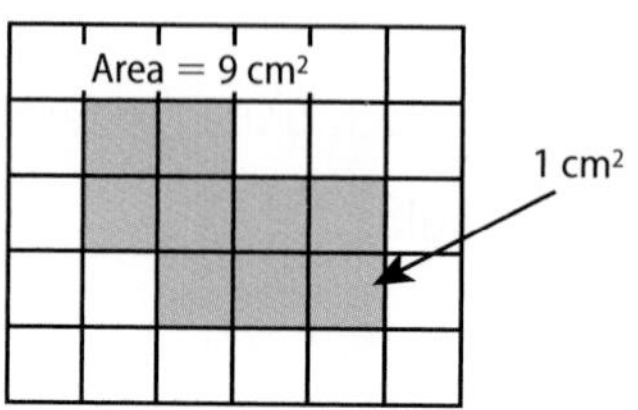

Estimating Area

Sometimes the surface of a figure is not an exact number of square units. In this case, you can estimate the area by

- determining the number of square units that are completely covered,
- then estimating the remaining number of square units.

You can use this method to find the area of the shaded figure on the grid below.

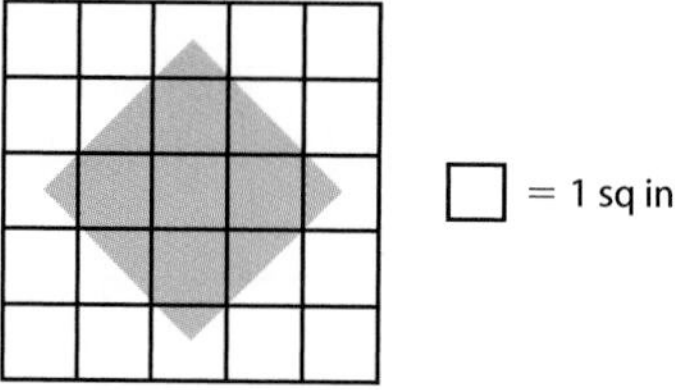

- The figure shows 5 whole squares shaded. This is 5 square units.
- There are 4 squares that are half shaded: This is $4 \div 2 = 2$ square units.
- There are 4 squares that are less than half shaded. This area is about 1 square unit.
- 5 + 2 + "about 1" = about 8 squares

The estimated area of the figure is about 8 square units.

You may find it helpful to trace each square unit and partial unit of the area in question. Tracing helps to identify the parts of the area.

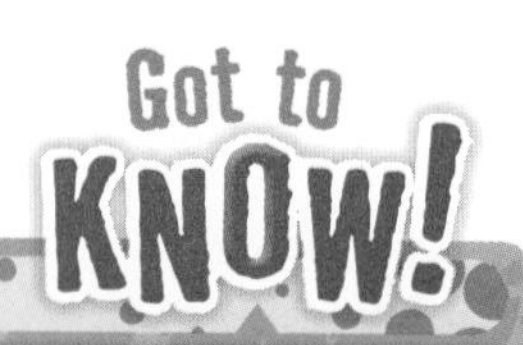

Estimating Area

1. Count the number of whole squares on a figure.
2. Look at the partial squares. Use logical reasoning to find about how many whole squares they represent.
3. Add to estimate the area.

EXAMPLE 1

Estimate the area of the figure on the grid.

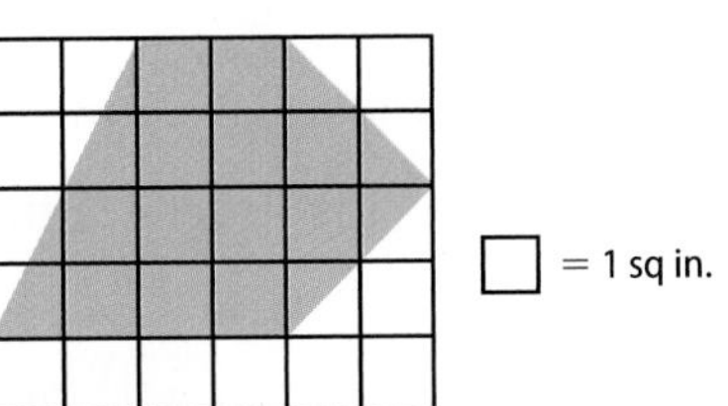

□ = 1 sq in.

STEP 1 Count the number of whole squares in the figure.

12 whole squares

STEP 2 Count the number of half squares in the figure.

4 half squares = 2 whole squares

STEP 3 Count any partial squares in the figure.

2 partial squares that are almost completely shaded + 2 partial squares that are barely shaded = about 2 whole squares

STEP 4 Find the total number of squares inside the figure.

12 + 2 + about 2 = about 14

The estimated area of the figure is about 14 $in.^2$.

Need More HELP

For help with units used to express area, go to *Area in the U.S. Customary System* and *Area in the Metric System* (pp. 482, 504).

EXAMPLE 2

Estimate the total number of square feet in the five diamond patterns.

□ = 4 sq ft

STEP 1 Find the number of whole squares.

0 whole squares

STEP 2 Find the number of half squares.

Think: The 4 outer diamonds are each made of 4 half squares.

$4 \times 4 = 16$ half squares

$16 \div 2 = 8$ whole squares

STEP 3 Count any other partial squares.

Think: The center diamond covers almost 2 whole squares.

It also covers a small part of 4 other squares.

It looks as though if you put these pieces together there would be about 2 whole squares.

STEP 4 Estimate the total area of the diamond patterns.

0 + 8 + about 2 = about 10.

The key says that each square = 4 sq ft.

$10 \times 4 = 40$

The estimated number of square feet in the diamond patterns is about 40 square feet.

SEARCH

To see step-by-step videos of these problems, enter the page number into the SWadvantage.com Search Bar.

Watch Out!

Area grids often include a key. It is important to read the key because 1 square may represent more than 1 square unit.

Area of a Rectangle

Need More HELP

Another way to define *area* is: The size of the region enclosed by a plane figure.

The **area** of a rectangle is the number of square units needed to cover the inside of the rectangle. You can find the area of a rectangle by

- counting the square units needed to cover it or
- by multiplying its length times its width.

1	2	3	4
5	6	7	8

1 m, 1 m

4 m, 2 m

1	2	3	4
5	6	7	8

Area = 8 m^2

The **length** of a rectangle is its longer dimension, or measure. The **width** of a rectangle is its shorter dimension. You can use the formula below to find the area of any rectangle.

$$\text{Area} = \text{length} \times \text{width}$$
$$A = \ell \times w$$
$$A = \ell w$$

Square units commonly used to measure area include: *square inch*, *square centimeter*, *square yard*, *square meter*, and *square mile*.

Watch Out!

Area is measured in square units and is the amount of space on the surface of a shape.

Perimeter is measured in units of length and is the distance around the outside edge of a shape.

EXAMPLE 1

Find the area of the rectangle below.

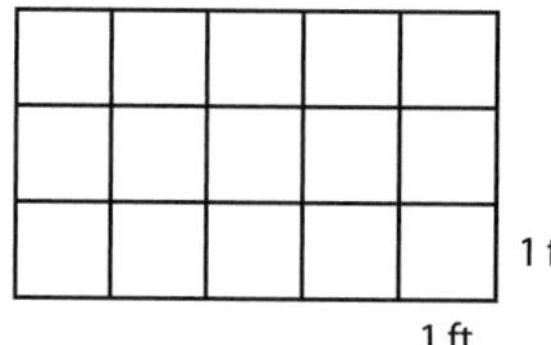

METHOD 1

Count the number of square units in the rectangle. 15

Include the unit. 15 ft^2

METHOD 2

Use the formula: $A = \ell \times w$

Count to find the length and width of the rectangle. length = 5 ft, width 3 ft

Substitute the values into the formula and simplify: $A = 5\text{ ft} \times 3\text{ ft}$

$A = 15\text{ ft}^2$

The area of the rectangle is 15 square feet.

EXAMPLE 2

A U.S. football field is 100 yd long and 55 yd wide. What is the area of a football field?

Think: The problem gives the measure of the length and the width of the football field. The area formula is $A = \ell \times w$.

Substitute the given length and width into the area formula.

$A = 100 \text{ yd} \times 55 \text{ yd}$

Multiply: $A = 5{,}500 \text{ yd}^2$

The area of the football field is 5,500 yd^2.

Got to KNOW!

Length and Width

The *length* of a rectangle is the measure of the longer side. The *width* is the measure of the shorter side.

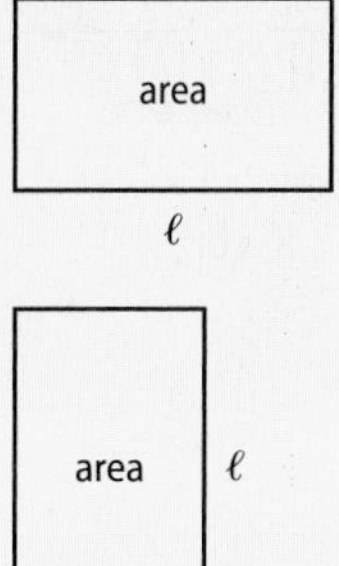

Because a rectangle has four 90° angles, any of its sides is also a height of the rectangle. Your may see a problem that gives a rectangle's *base* and *height*. In these cases, use the formula: Area = base × height, which can be written as $A = b \times h$ or $A = bh$.

EXAMPLE 3

Find the area of the rectangle shown.

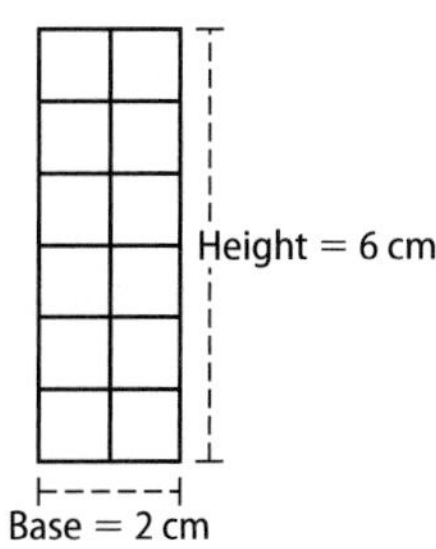

STEP 1 Find the given measures: base = 2 cm, height = 6 cm

STEP 2 Substitute the measures into the area formula.
$A = b \times h$
$A = 2 \text{ cm} \times 6 \text{ cm}$

STEP 3 Multiply to find the area: $A = 12 \text{ cm}^2$

The area of the rectangle is 12 cm^2.

EXAMPLE 4

A rectangle has a 7 in. base and a 4 in. height. What is the area of the rectangle?

Think: You know the base equals 7 in. and the height equals 4 in.

Substitute the measures into the area formula: $A = \ell w$.
$A = 7 \text{ in.} \times 4 \text{ in.}$

Multiply: $A = 28 \text{ in}^2$.

The area of the rectangle is 28 in^2.

SEARCH

To see step-by-step videos of these problems, enter the page number into the SWadvantage.com Search Bar.

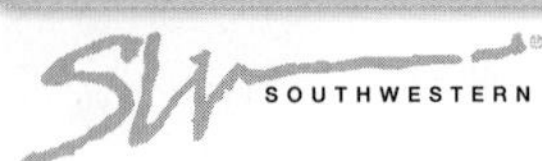

Area of a Square

A **square** is a special rectangle with four sides of equal length. You can find the area of a square using the formula $A = \ell w$. Since the sides of a square are equal in length, you can also use the formula:

A square $= s \times s$, or
$A = s^2$, where s is the length of the sides of the square.

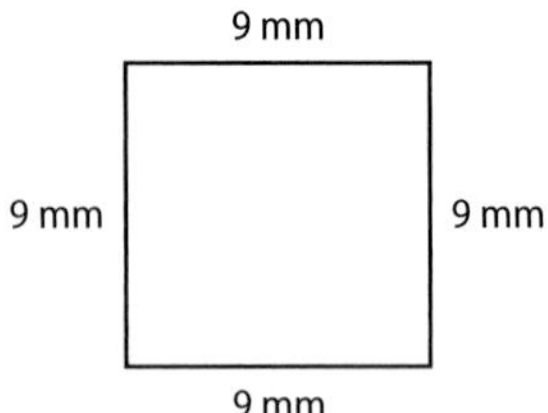

The area of the square above is $A = 9^2$, or 81 square millimeters.

EXAMPLE 5

Find the area of the square.

s = 5 m

STEP 1 Substitute the given side length for s into the area formula.
$A = s^2$
$= 5^2$

STEP 2 Simplify.
$A = 5 \times 5$
$= 25$

STEP 3 State the area using the correct unit: 25 m^2

The area of the square is 25 m^2.

Watch Out!

Remember, $s^2 = s \times s$, not $2 \times s$ or $2s$.

EXAMPLE 6

A square field has a fence that measures 4 km per side. What is the area of the field?

Think: The problem gives the length of one side of the square field. The area formula for a square is $A = s^2$.

Substitute the given side length into the area formula.
$A = 4^2$

Simplify: $A = 4 \times 4$
$= 16$

The area of the field is 16 km^2.

SEARCH

To see step-by-step videos of these problems, enter the page number into the SWadvantage.com Search Bar.

Got to KNOW!

Area Formulas for Rectangles and Squares

Rectangle	$A = \ell \times w$	$A = \ell w$	$A = b \times h$	$A = bh$
Square	$A = s \times s$	$A = s^2$		

Area of a Parallelogram

A **parallelogram** is a four-sided figure with both pairs of opposite sides parallel and equal in length. Unlike a rectangle, the angles of a parallelogram do not have to be 90° angles.

The shape of a parallelogram can be rearranged to form a rectangle. As shown below, a triangle is cut off the rectangle, flipped, and repositioned to make the parallelogram.

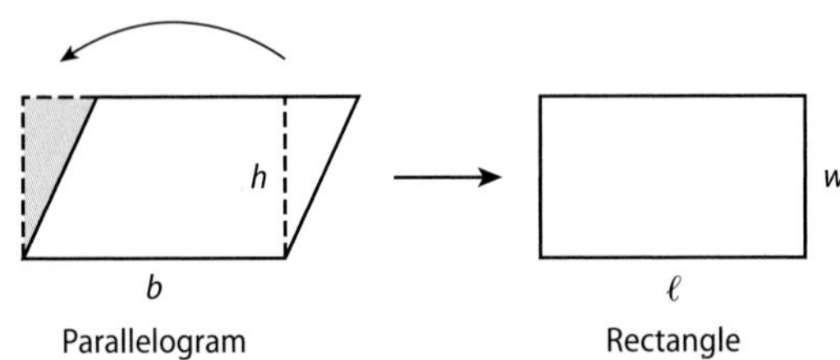

Since the area did not change when the figure became a parallelogram, you can use the formula $A = b \times h$ to find the area of the parallelogram.

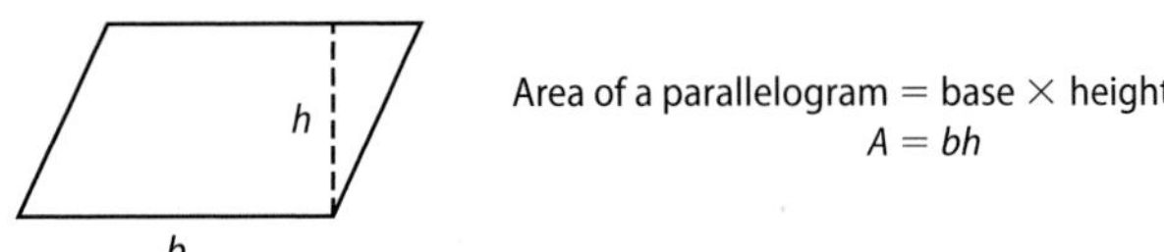

EXAMPLE 7

Find the area of the parallelogram shown below.

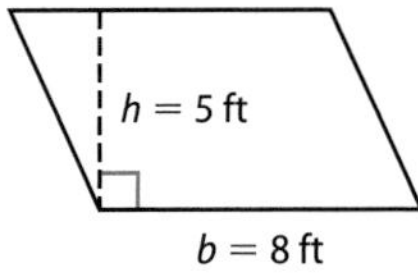

STEP 1 Substitute the given measures into the area formula.

$A = b \times h$

$A = 8 \times 5$

STEP 2 Simplify.

$A = 40$

STEP 3 State the area using the correct unit: 40 ft^2

The area of the parallelogram is 40 ft^2.

Need More HELP

For more about the relationship between parallelograms, rectangles, and squares, go to *Classifying Quadrilaterals* in *Foundations of Mathematics* (p. 158).

Watch Out!

The *height* of a parallelogram always forms a right angle with the base that it adjoins. The height is not necessarily the measure of one of the sides. So you must use the formula $A = bh$.

Area of a Parallelogram

EXAMPLE 8

A parallelogram has a 6 m base and a 12 m height. What is the area of the parallelogram?

Think: The problem gives the length of the base and the height.
The area formula for a parallelogram is: $A = bh$.

Substitute the given base and height measures into the area formula.

$A = 6 \times 12$

Simplify: $A = 72$

The area of the parallelogram is 72 m^2.

Need More HELP

When you substitute given measures into a formula and simplify, it is not necessary to write the unit of measure. You do need to include the correct unit of measure in the final answer.

In Example 8, the final answer is not 72. It is 72 m^2.

EXAMPLE 9

The parallelogram shown has a height equal to the base. What is the area of the parallelogram?

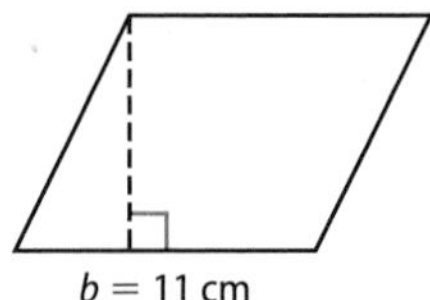

STEP 1 Substitute the given measures into the area formula.

$A = b \times h$

$A = 11 \times 11$

STEP 2 Simplify.

$A = 121$

STEP 3 State the area using the correct unit: $A = 121$ cm^2.

The area of the parallelogram is 121 cm^2.

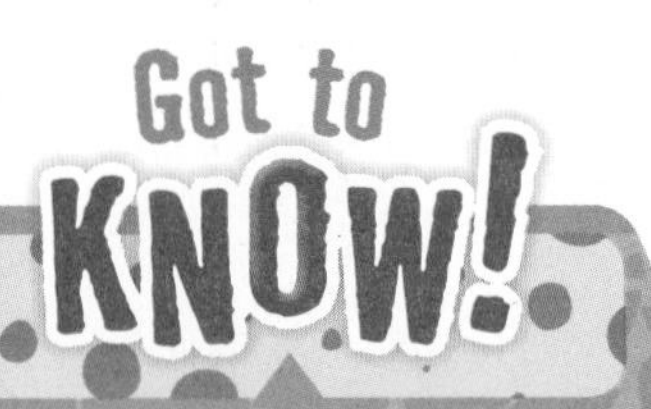

Area Formulas for Rectangles and Parallelograms

Rectangle	$A = \ell \times w$	$A = \ell w$	$A = b \times h$	$A = bh$
Square	$A = s \times s$	$A = s^2$		
Parallelogram	$A = b \times h$	$A = bh$		

EXAMPLE 10

A parallelogram has a height that is 2 in. less than the base. The base measures 14 in. What is the area of the parallelogram?

Think: The problem gives the measure of the base.
It tells you that the height is 2 inches shorter.
You know the area formula is $A = bh$.

Subtract: Height is equal to: 14 in. $-$2 in. = 12 in.

Substitute the measures into the area formula.

$A = 14 \times 12$

Simplify: $A = 168$

The area of the parallelogram is 168 in^2.

SEARCH

To see step-by-step videos of these problems, enter the page number into the SWadvantage.com Search Bar.

EXAMPLE 11

The area of the parallelogram shown is 56 km^2. What is the height of the parallelogram?

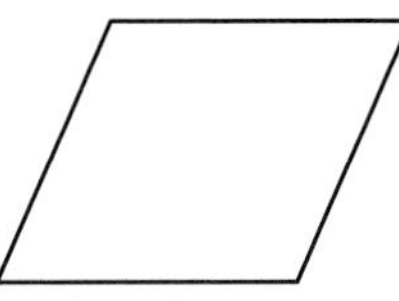

STEP 1 Substitute the given measures into the area formula.

$A = b \times h$

$56 = 8 \times h$

STEP 2 Simplify. Divide both sides by 8.

$$\frac{56}{8} = \frac{8 \times h}{8}$$

$7 = h$

STEP 3 State the height using the correct unit: $h = 7$ km.

The height of the parallelogram is 7 km.

Watch Out !

The height of a parallelogram always forms a right angle with the base that it adjoins. So for a parallelogram, you *cannot* just multiply its length and width. You must use the formula $A = bh$.

EXAMPLE 12

Daisha plants a square garden with a side that measures 3 meters. Anton's garden is a parallelogram with a 2 m height and a 4 m base. Who has the larger garden?

STEP 1 Find the area of Daisha's garden. Use $A = s^2$. $A = 3^2 = 9$ m^2

STEP 2 Find the area of Anton's garden. Use $A = b \times h$. $A = 4 \times 2 = 8$ m^2

STEP 3 Compare the areas. Daisha, 9 m^2 > Anton, 8 m^2

Daisha has the larger garden.

Areas of Triangles

Remember, a *rectangle* is a special type of *parallelogram*. To prove the formula is true, draw a triangle within a rectangle, as shown below. Shade two triangles and cut them off. When you place the shaded triangles on their corresponding unshaded triangles, you will see that they are equal in area to the large triangle.

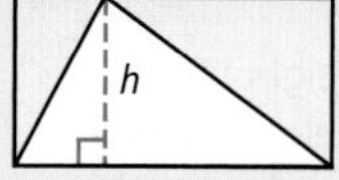

Deriving the Area Formula

The formula for finding the area of a triangle is related to the formula for finding the area of a parallelogram. Look at the diagram below. The line drawn from one vertex of a parallelogram to the opposite vertex divides it in half. The triangles formed have the same area.

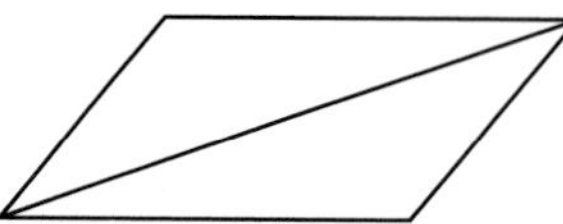

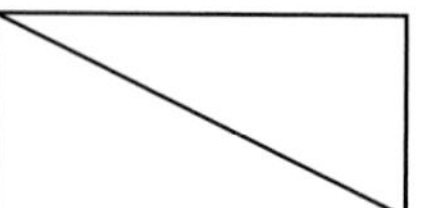

Therefore, the formula for the area of a triangle is one-half that for a parallelogram.

A parallelogram $= b \times h$, or bh $\quad$ A triangle $= \frac{1}{2} \times b \times h$, or $\frac{1}{2}bh$

EXAMPLE 1

Find the area of the triangle shown.
Use $A = \frac{1}{2}bh$.

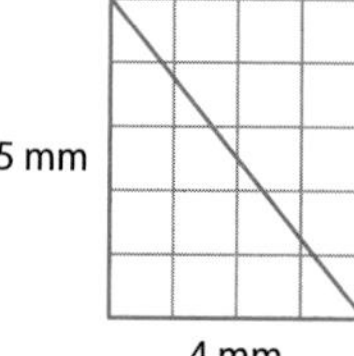

STEP 1 Substitute the measures given in the figure into the area formula.

$$A = \frac{1}{2}bh$$
$$= \frac{1}{2}(4 \times 5)$$

STEP 2 Simplify.

$$A = \frac{1}{2}(20)$$
$$= 10$$

STEP 3 Express the area using the correct unit: $A = 10 \text{ mm}^2$

The area of the triangle is 10 mm^2.

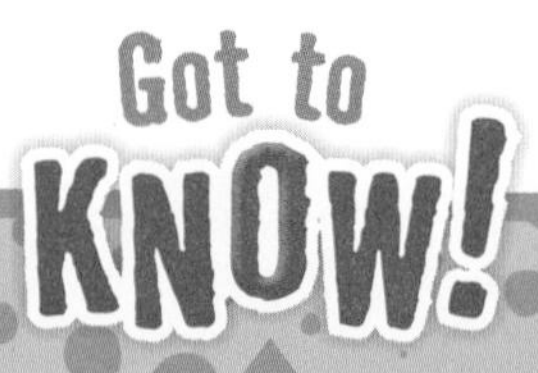

Area Formulas

When a parallelogram is divided into two equal pieces, the two triangles formed each have an area that is one-half the area of the parallelogram.

Parallelogram	$A = b \times h$	$A = bh$
Triangle	$A = \frac{1}{2} \times b \times h$	$A = \frac{1}{2}bh$

Area of a Right Triangle

The base and height of a **right triangle** meet to form a right angle. The area formula for a right triangle is $A = \frac{1}{2}bh$.

EXAMPLE 2

Find the area of the right triangle. Use $A = \frac{1}{2}bh$.

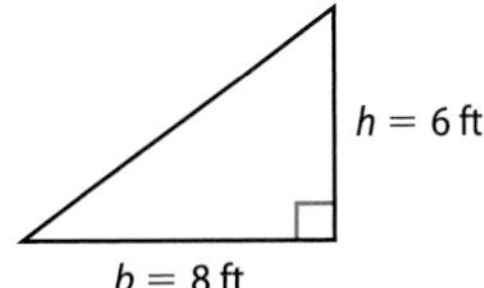

Think: The figure shows the base and the height of the triangle.

The area formula is $A = \frac{1}{2}bh$.

Substitute the given base and height into the area formula.

$$A = \frac{1}{2}(8 \text{ ft} \times 6 \text{ ft})$$

Simplify: $A = \frac{1}{2}(48)$

$= 24$

The area of the right triangle is 24 ft^2.

Need More HELP

For help with simplifying an equation, go to *Order of Operations* in *Algebra* (Book 2, p. 1418).

Area of Acute Triangles

The **height** of a triangle, also called the **altitude of a triangle**, is the perpendicular distance from the vertex to the base opposite the vertex. In an *acute triangle* and an *obtuse triangle*, the height is *not* a side of the triangle as it is in a right triangle. In fact, when you draw the height of an obtuse triangle, it lies outside of the triangle.

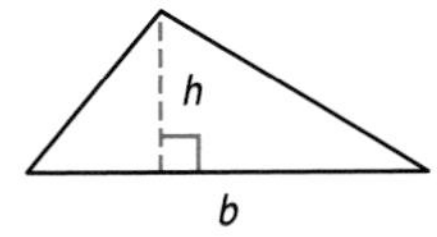

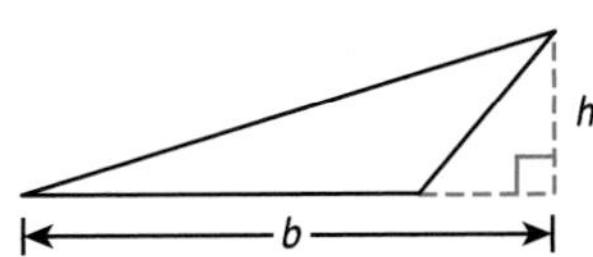

EXAMPLE 3

Find the area of the triangle shown at right. Use $A = \frac{1}{2}bh$.

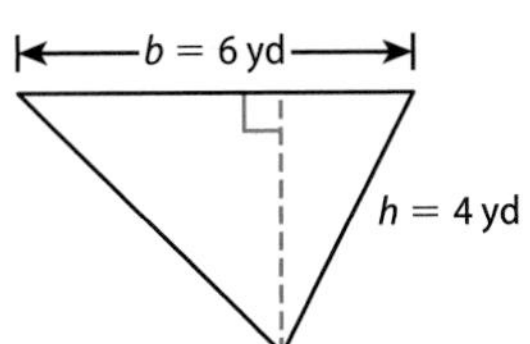

Substitute into the area formula.

$$A = \frac{1}{2}(6 \text{ ft} \times 4 \text{ ft})$$

Simplify: $A = \frac{1}{2}(24) = 12$

The area of the triangle is 12 yd^2.

SEARCH

To see step-by-step videos of these problems, enter the page number into the SWadvantage.com Search Bar.

Area of Obtuse Triangles

Watch Out!

Do not confuse a side measurement for the height in a triangle. You can use a side measurement as the height only when two sides form a right angle.

Find the area of the triangle shown at right. Use $A = \frac{1}{2}bh$.

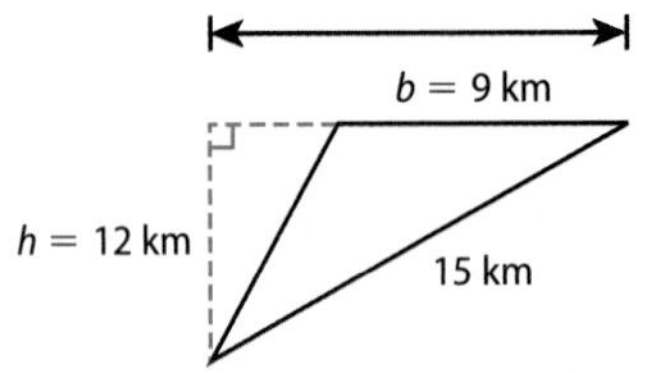

STEP 1 Substitute into the area formula.

$$A = \frac{1}{2}(9 \text{ km} \times 12 \text{ km})$$

STEP 2 Simplify: $A = \frac{1}{2}(108) = 54$

STEP 3 State the area using the correct unit: 54 km^2

The area of the triangle is 54 km^2.

Area of an Equilateral Triangle

An **equilateral triangle** has three sides of equal length and three angles of equal measure. If you are given the height of an equilateral triangle, you can use the usual area formula. Note, however, the height may not be given as a whole number.

If you know only the length of one side, you can use a special formula for the area of an equilateral triangle: $A = \frac{s^2\sqrt{3}}{4}$. The area is often expressed using a square root.

EXAMPLE 5

Need More HELP

Remember, when you know only a side measure, the problem may say that you can leave a square root in the answer. If you need to simplify the answer completely, use a calculator. Use the word about or *approximately* if you round the answer.

Find the area of the equilateral triangle. Use $A = \frac{s^2\sqrt{3}}{4}$.

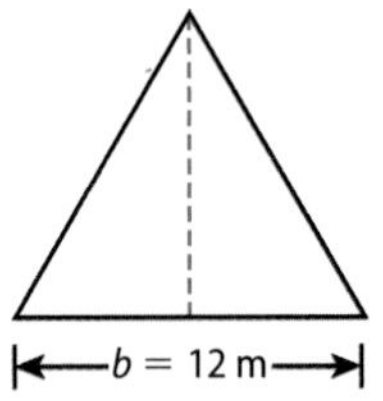

STEP 1 The measure of the sides is 12 meters.
Substitute: 12 into the area formula.

$$A = \frac{12^2\sqrt{3}}{4}$$

STEP 2 Simplify: $12^2 = 144$. $144 \div 4 = 36$.

$$A = \frac{144\sqrt{3}}{4} = A = 36\sqrt{3}$$

The area of the equilateral triangle is $36\sqrt{3}$ m^2.

You can use a calculator to simplify the answer further. Press [3], and then the square root key, [√]. Next, press [×], enter [3] [6], and press [=]. The product has many decimal places. Round it to 62.35. The area of the triangle in Example 5 is about 62.35 square meters.

Problem Solving Using Areas of Triangles

To solve problems that involve the area of a triangle, look at the given information and apply the correct formula.

EXAMPLE 6

An isosceles triangle has sides that measure 50 mm, 50 mm, and 80 mm. The perpendicular height from the longest side to the opposite vertex measures 30 mm. What is the area of the triangle?

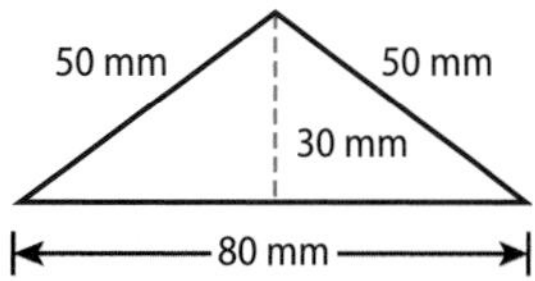

Think: The longest side of the triangle measures 80 mm.

The perpendicular height from this side to the vertex opposite it measures 30 mm.

Substitute values in the formula $A = \frac{1}{2}bh$.

$$A = \frac{1}{2}(80 \text{ mm} \times 30 \text{ mm})$$

Simplify: $A = \frac{1}{2}(2{,}400)$

$= 1{,}200$

The area of the triangle is 1,200 mm^2.

Got to KNOW!

Area of an Equilateral Triangle

- If you know the measure of a base and height, use the formula $A = \frac{1}{2}bh$.
- If you know only the measure of a side, use the formula $A = \frac{s^2\sqrt{3}}{4}$.

EXAMPLE 7

Keisha has a triangular kite that is 6 ft wide and has an area of 21 ft^2. How tall is the kite?

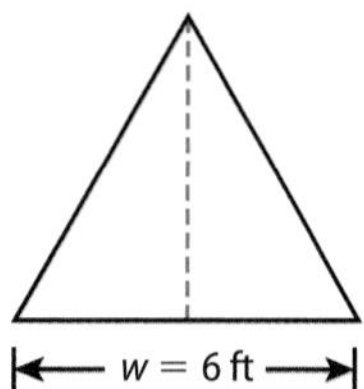

To answer the question, find the height of the kite.

Think: You have this information: base = 6 ft, area = 21 ft^2.

Use the formula $A = \frac{1}{2}bh$.

Substitute known values in the formula. $21 \text{ ft}^2 = \frac{1}{2}(6 \text{ ft} \times h)$

Simplify: $21 = \frac{1}{2}(6 \times h)$

$21 = \frac{1}{2}6h$ Simplify inside the parentheses.

$21 = 3h$ Multiply $6h$ by one-half.

$\frac{^7\cancel{21}}{\cancel{3}} = \frac{\cancel{3}h}{\cancel{3}}$ Divide each side by 3.

$7 = h$

Keisha's kite is 7 ft tall.

SEARCH

To see step-by-step videos of these problems, enter the page number into the SWadvantage.com Search Bar.

Areas of Trapezoids

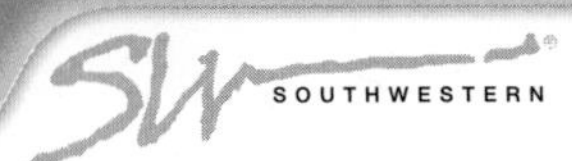

Deriving the Area Formula

A **trapezoid** is a four-sided polygon that has exactly one set of parallel sides. The parallel sides are called the **bases**, b_1 and b_2.

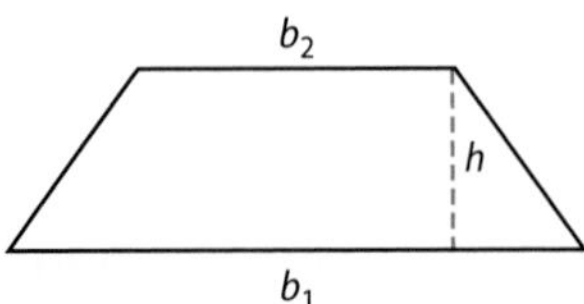

You may find the relationship easier to understand by using paper models. Trace a paper trapezoid and cut it out. Then tape the two halves together to make the parallelogram.

The formula for the area of a trapezoid is related to the formula for the area of a parallelogram. Look at the diagram below. Suppose a trapezoid identical to the trapezoid on the left is rotated and pasted onto the right. Now you have a parallelogram that has 2 × the area of the trapezoid.

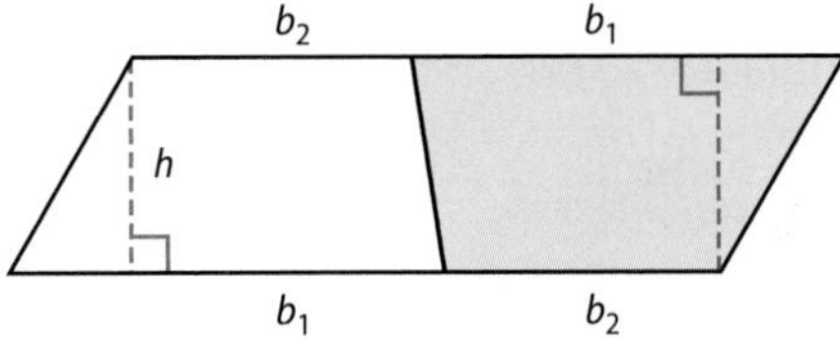

The area of a parallelogram is equal to base × height. In this case, the base is $b_1 + b_2$, so the area formula can be written as: A parallelogram $= \left(b_1 + b_2\right) \times h$.

To find the area of one-half of the parallelogram (one trapezoid), multiply by one-half. A trapezoid $= \frac{1}{2}\left(b_1 + b_2\right) \times h$

You can also write it as: A trapezoid $= \frac{1}{2}h\left(b_1 + b_2\right)$.

Look at the trapezoid on the right.

$b_1 = 10$ ft
$b_2 = 4$ ft
$h = 3$ ft

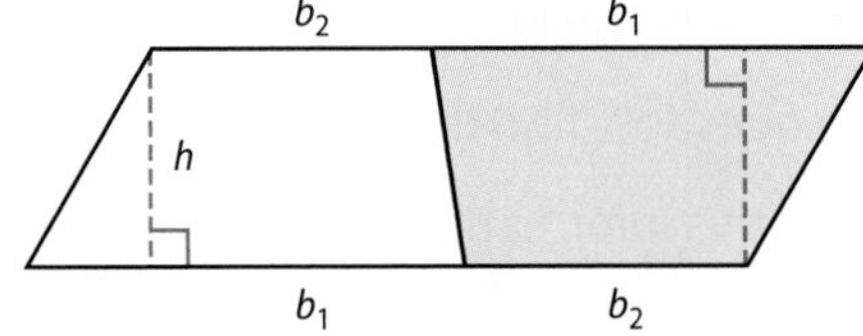

For help with simplifying an equation, go to *Order of Operations* in *Algebra* (Book 2, p. 1418).

To find the area of this trapezoid, substitute the values given on the figure into the area formula. Then follow the order of operations to simplify.

$$\textit{Area}\text{ of trapezoid} = \frac{1}{2}h\left(b_1 + b_2\right)$$

$$\text{Add within the parentheses: } = \frac{1}{2}3(10 + 4)$$

$$\text{Multiply: } = \frac{1}{2}3(14)$$

$$\text{Multiply: } = \frac{1}{2}(42)$$

$$= 21$$

The area of the trapezoid is 21 square feet.

Finding Areas of Trapezoids

EXAMPLE 1

The two triangles shown are combined to form a trapezoid. What is the total area of the trapezoid?

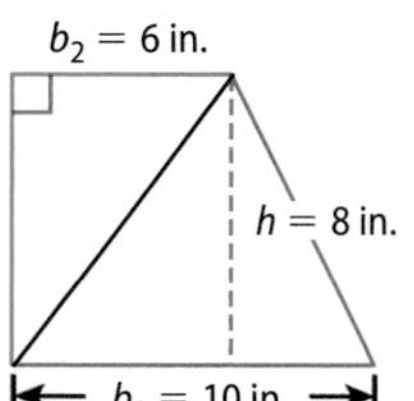

METHOD 1

Use the formula for the area of a triangle:
$A = \frac{1}{2}bh$.

STEP 1 To find the area of the smaller triangle, substitute 6 in. and 8 in. into the formula.

$A = \frac{1}{2}(6 \text{ in.} \times 8 \text{ in.})$

STEP 2 Simplify to find the area of the smaller triangle.

$A = \frac{1}{2}(48) = 24$

The area of the smaller triangle is 24 in.^{2}

STEP 3 To find the area of the larger triangle, substitute 10 in. and 8 in. into the formula.

$A = \frac{1}{2}(10 \text{ in.} \times 8 \text{ in.})$

STEP 4 Simplify to find the area of the larger triangle.

$A = \frac{1}{2}(80) = 40$

The area of the larger triangle is 40 in.^{2}

STEP 5 Add the two areas.
$24 + 40 = 64$

The area of the trapezoid is 64 in.^{2}

METHOD 2

Use the formula for the area of a trapezoid: $A = \frac{1}{2}h(b_1 + b_2)$.

Think: You know measures of the bases and the height of the trapezoid.
6 in. = base_1 10 in. = base_2 8 in. = height

Substitute these values into the formula for the area of a trapezoid:

$$A = \frac{1}{2}h(b_1 + b_2)$$
$$= \frac{1}{2}(8 \text{ in.})(6 \text{ in.} + 10 \text{ in.})$$

Simplify: $A = \frac{1}{2}(8)(16) = \frac{1}{2}(128) = 64$

The area of the trapezoid is 64 in.^{2}

You can also use your calculator to simplify or check your answer. You still need to add the bases first. Then, using 0.5 for one-half, enter [.] [5], press [×], enter [8], press [×], enter [1] [6], and press [=]. The calculator display will show 64.

Got to KNOW!

Area of a Trapezoid

$A = \frac{1}{2}h(b_1 + b_2)$

Either the top or the bottom base can be b_1 or b_2.

SEARCH

To see step-by-step videos of these problems, enter the page number into the SWadvantage.com Search Bar.

Watch Out!

Be certain you substitute the three values correctly for the variables h, b_1, and b_2.

The two bases are added. Then the height is multiplied by their sum.

Finding Areas of Trapezoids

EXAMPLE 2

Find the area of the trapezoid.
Use $A = \frac{1}{2}h(b_1 + b_2)$.

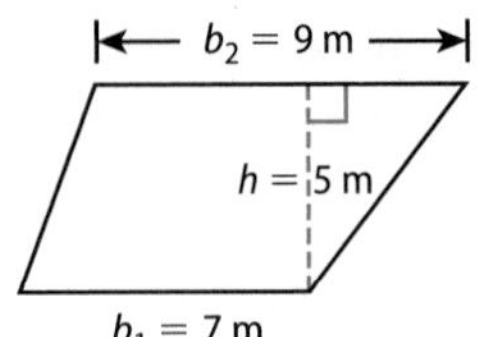

SEARCH

To see step-by-step videos of these problems, enter the page number into the SWadvantage.com Search Bar.

STEP 1 To find the area of the trapezoid, substitute the given measures for the bases and the height into the area formula.

$$A = \frac{1}{2}(5 \text{ m})(7 \text{ m} + 9 \text{ m})$$

STEP 2 Simplify.

$$A = \frac{1}{2}(5)(16)$$

$$= \frac{1}{2}(80) = 40$$

The area of the trapezoid is 40 m^2.

Finding Other Missing Measures

EXAMPLE 3

The town recreational area is shaped as shown on the right. The total area is 1,200 m^2. The missing side, s, is b_1. Use $A = \frac{1}{2}h(b_1 + b_2)$ to find the measure of the missing side.

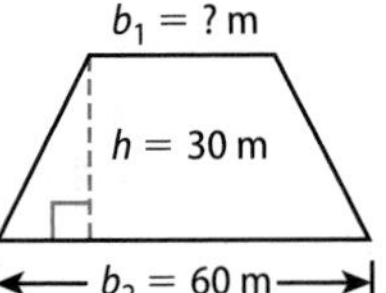

Think: You know that:

$A = 1{,}200 \text{ m}^2$ $h = 30$ m
$b_1 = s$ $b_2 = 60$ m

Substitute what you know into the formula for the area of a trapezoid:

$$A = \frac{1}{2}h(b_1 + b_2)$$

$$1{,}200 \text{ m} = \frac{1}{2}(30)(s + 60)$$

Evaluate the expression:

Divide 30 by 2.	$1{,}200 = 15(s + 60)$
Multiply s and 60 by 15.	$1{,}200 = 15s + 900$
Subtract 900 from each side of the equation.	$300 = 15s$
Divide both sides by 15.	$20 = s$

The missing side length is 20 m.

Watch Out !

You cannot simplify within the parentheses first because they contain the unknown value s.

Other Ways to Find the Area of a Trapezoid

EXAMPLE 4

A regular trapezoid has two equal sides. Cesar found the area of the regular trapezoid below by dividing it into a rectangle and 2 triangles with base 4 cm. Find the area using Cesar's method.

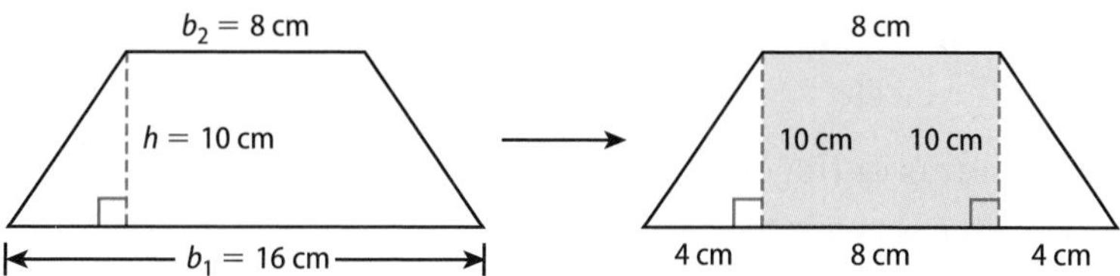

Think: The base of each triangle = 4 cm. The height = 10 cm.
The base of the rectangle = 8 cm. The height = 10 cm.
Area of the trapezoid = Area of the rectangle + 2 × the area of one triangle.

Substitute and simplify.

A rectangle $= bh$
$= 8 \text{ cm} \times 10 \text{ cm}$
$= 80 \text{ cm}^2$

A triangle $= \frac{1}{2}bh$
$= \frac{1}{2}(4 \times 10)$
$= \frac{1}{2}(40)$
$= 20 \text{ cm}^2$

Solve the problem.

Area of the trapezoid = Area of the rectangle + 2 × the area of one triangle
$A = 80 + 2(20)$
$= 80 + 40$
$= 120 \text{ cm}^2$

The area of the trapezoid is 120 cm^2.

EXAMPLE 5

Ella drew a blue line to divide the trapezoid below into two triangles. Explain how she can find the area of the trapezoid *without* using the formula $A = \frac{1}{2}h(b_1 + b_2)$.

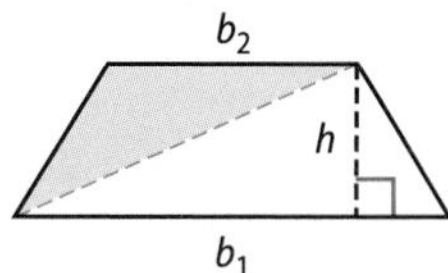

The trapezoid is made up of the smaller, shaded triangle and the larger, unshaded one. Ella can use the formula for the area of a triangle to find the areas of both of these triangles. Then she can add the areas to find the area of the trapezoid.

Circumference

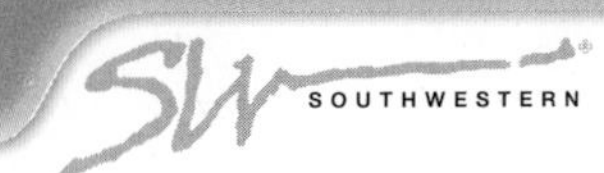

What Is Circumference?

The **circumference** of a circle is the distance around the circle. To find the circumference of a circle, you need to know the measure of either the *radius* or the *diameter* of the circle.

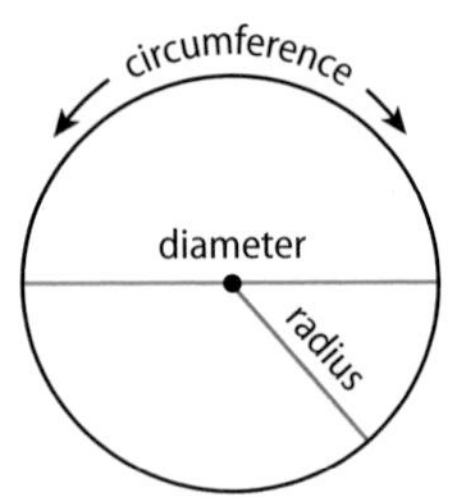

The **radius** is a line segment from the center of the circle to any point on the circle. The **diameter** is a line segment that passes through the center of a circle and connects any two points on the circle.

The length of the radius of the circle is half the length of the diameter: $r = \frac{d}{2}$. The length of the diameter is twice the length of the radius: $d = 2r$.

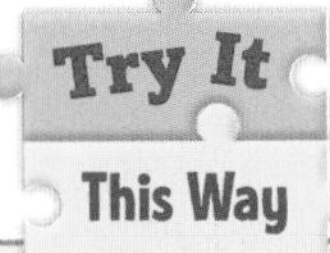

Got to KNOW!

Approximation of π

The values for pi are approximate. As soon as you substitute a value for pi into a formula, you must use the symbol $\approx$, which means, "is approximately equal to."

Finding the Circumference of a Circle

The ratio of the circumference of a circle to its diameter is the irrational number pi (π). The value of pi is an irrational number a little greater than 3. Two approximate values used for pi are $\frac{22}{7}$ and 3.14.

The formula for the circumference of a circle is

$C = \pi d$ or $C = 2\pi r$,

where C = circumference, d = diameter, and r = radius.

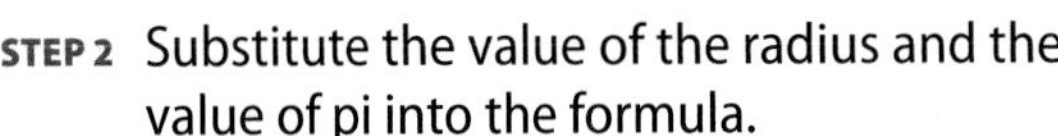

EXAMPLE 1

Find the circumference of circle *M*. Use 3.14 for π.

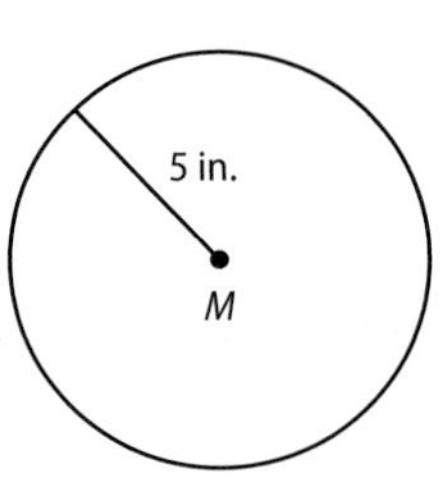

METHOD 1

Use the formula $C = 2\pi r$.

STEP 1 The radius of the circle is 5 in.

STEP 2 Substitute the value of the radius and the value of pi into the formula.

$$C = 2\pi r$$
$$\approx (2)(3.14)(5)$$
$$\approx 31.4$$

The circumference of the circle is approximately 31.4 in.

Try It This Way

Use a calculator to multiply the factors. You can also reorder the factors and multiply mentally: $(2)(5)(3.14) = (10)(3.14) = 31.4$.

METHOD 2

Use the formula $C = \pi d$.

STEP 1 Use $d = 2r$ to find the diameter.

$$d = 2(5)$$
$$= 10$$

The diameter of the circle is 10 in.

STEP 2 Substitute the value of the diameter and the value of pi into the formula.

$$C = \pi d$$
$$\approx (3.14)(10)$$
$$\approx 31.4$$

The circumference of the circle is approximately 31.4 in.

SEARCH

To see step-by-step videos of these problems, enter the page number into the SWadvantage.com Search Bar.

EXAMPLE 2

Find the circumference of the circle on the right. Use $\frac{22}{7}$ for π.

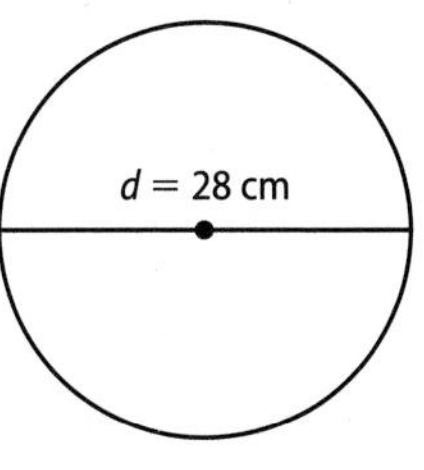

Since you are given the diameter, use $C = \pi d$.

$$C = \pi d$$
$$\approx \frac{22}{7}(28)$$
$$\approx \frac{22}{\cancel{7}} \times \frac{\cancel{28}^{4}}{1}$$
$$\approx 22 \times 4$$
$$\approx 88$$

The circumference of the circle is approximately 88 cm.

EXAMPLE 3

Find the circumference of a circle with a radius of 9 inches. Use 3.14 for π.

Since you are given the radius, use $C = 2\pi r$.

	$C = 2\pi r$
Substitute 3.14 for π and 9 for r.	$\approx (2)(3.14)(9)$
Multiply.	$\approx (6.28)(9)$
	≈ 56.52

The circumference of the circle is approximately 56.52 in.

Try It This Way

Use your calculator to multiply (2)(3.14)(9). If you don't have a calculator, try this method.

Mentally multiply:

$2 \times 3.14 = 6.28$

Think: 9 is 1 less than 10.

$6.28 \times 10 = 62.8$
$62.8 - 6.28 = 56.52$

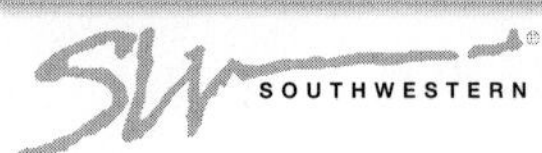

Choosing a Formula and a Value for Pi

When finding the circumference, first analyze the given information. Then decide which formula and which value of pi will give values that are easy to work with.

Here are two general rules. There may be exceptions, so always analyze each problem carefully.

- Choose the fractional value for pi, $\frac{22}{7}$, when working with dimensions that are multiples of 7.
- Choose the decimal value for pi, 3.14, when working with dimensions that are in decimal form.

SEARCH

To see step-by-step videos of these problems, enter the page number into the SWadvantage.com Search Bar.

EXAMPLE 4

Find the circumference of the circle. Decide which formula and value for π to use.

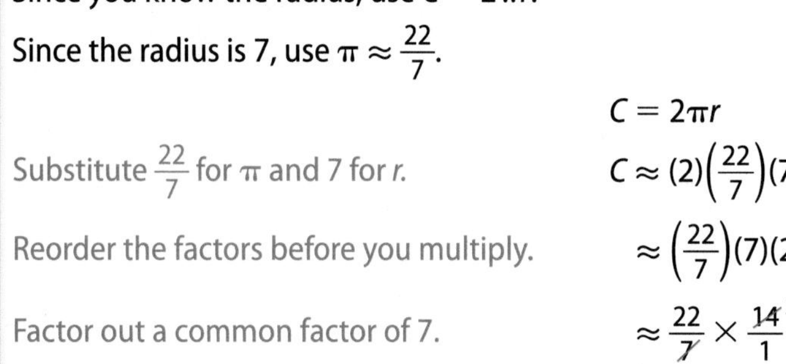

Think: The radius of the circle is 7 yd.

$2 \times 7 = 14$, and $14 \div 7 = 2$.

Since you know the radius, use $C = 2\pi r$.

Since the radius is 7, use $\pi \approx \frac{22}{7}$.

	$C = 2\pi r$
Substitute $\frac{22}{7}$ for π and 7 for r.	$C \approx (2)\left(\frac{22}{7}\right)(7)$
Reorder the factors before you multiply.	$\approx \left(\frac{22}{7}\right)(7)(2)$
Factor out a common factor of 7.	$\approx \frac{22}{\cancel{7}} \times \frac{\cancel{14}^{2}}{1}$
Multiply.	$\approx 22 \times 2$
	≈ 44

The circumference of the circle is 44 yd.

EXAMPLE 5

The radius of a bike tire is 13 in. What is the circumference of the tire?

Think: 13 is not a multiple of 7. Use 3.14, not $\frac{22}{7}$, for the value of pi.

Since you are given the radius, use $C = 2\pi r$.

$C = 2\pi r$

$\approx (2)(3.14)(13)$

≈ 81.64

The circumference of the bike tire is about 81.64 in.

Finding the Radius or the Diameter

EXAMPLE 6

The circumference of a circle is 12.56 m.

a. What is the approximate diameter of the circle?

Find the diameter. Substitute the given value into the formula $C = \pi d$.

$$C = \pi d$$

Use 3.14 for π. $\quad 12.56 \approx (3.14)(d)$

Divide both sides by 3.14. $\quad \frac{12.56}{3.14} \approx \frac{(3.14)(d)}{3.14}$

$$4 \approx d$$

$C = 12.56$ m

$d = ?$

The diameter is about 4 meters.

b. What is the approximate radius of the circle?

The radius of a circle is one half its diameter: $4 \div 2 = 2$

The radius is about 2 m.

Remember, you can use your calculator to divide decimal numbers. If you need more help dividing decimals, go to *Dividing Decimals by Decimals* in *Numbers and Operations* (p. 254).

EXAMPLE 7

The circumference of a circular herb garden is 15.7 feet. What is its radius?

You could use the formula $C = 2\pi r$, but it may be easier to find the diameter and divide by 2.

STEP 1 Substitute the value of the circumference into the formula $C = \pi d$.

$$C = \pi d$$

Use 3.14 for π. $\quad 15.7 \approx (3.14)(d)$

Divide both sides by 3.14. $\quad \frac{15.7}{3.14} \approx \frac{(3.14)(d)}{3.14}$

$$5 \approx d$$

STEP 2 Divide the diameter by 2.

$5 \div 2 = 2.5$

The radius of the herb garden is about 2.5 ft.

Got to KNOW!

Circumference of a Circle

The **circumference** is the distance around a circle.

You can use either of the following formulas to find the circumference (C) of a circle.

$C = \pi d \qquad C = 2\pi r$

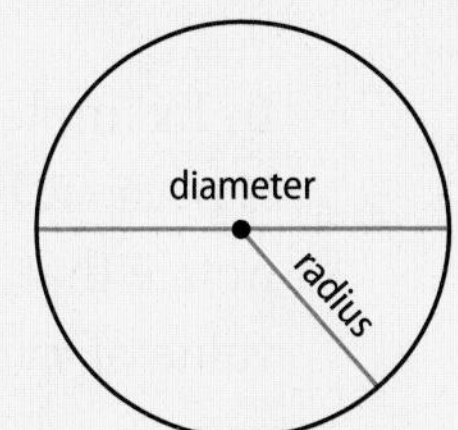

diameter (d) $\quad d = r \times 2$

radius (r) $\quad r = \frac{d}{2}$

Areas of Circles

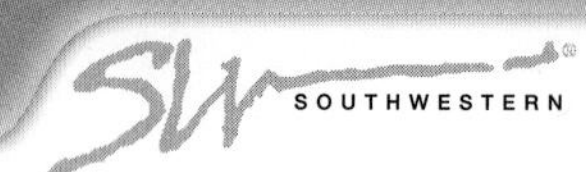

Finding the Area of a Circle

Remember, the *radius* of a circle is a line segment from the center of the circle to the edge. The *diameter* of a circle is a line segment that passes through the center of the circle and has both end points on the circle.

The **area of a circle** is the number of square units needed to cover the circle.

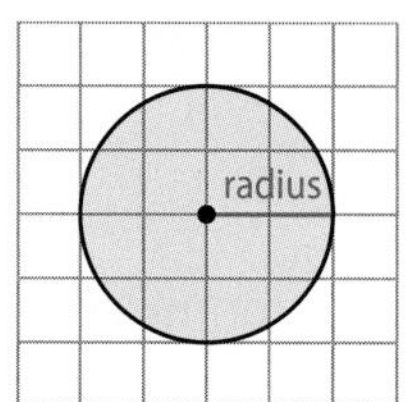

The area of this circle is shaded blue. If you count the shaded squares, you will see that the area is about 12 square units.

The formula for the area of a circle is:

$A = \pi r^2$; where A = area and r = radius

To find the area of any circle, substitute the values for the radius and for pi into the formula. Remember, the diameter of a circle is two times the radius. If you know the diameter of a circle, divide by two to find the radius.

The value of pi (π) is an irrational number a little greater than 3. Two approximate values used for pi are $\frac{22}{7}$ and 3.14. Because these values are approximate, when you substitute them into a formula, you must use the symbol $\approx$, which means "is approximately equal to."

Watch Out!

In the area formula, πr^2 means $\pi \times r \times r$. You never square the value of pi.

EXAMPLE 1

Find the area of a circle with a radius that measure 4 centimeters (cm).

METHOD 1 **Use 3.14 for π.**

STEP 1 Substitute the given values into the area formula.

$A = \pi r^2$

$\approx (3.14)(4^2)$

STEP 2 Multiply to find the area.

$A \approx (3.14)(4)(4)$

≈ 50.24

The area of the circle is about 50.24 sq cm.

METHOD 2 **Use $\frac{22}{7}$ for π.**

STEP 1 Substitute the given values into the area formula.

$A = \pi r^2$

$\approx \left(\frac{22}{7}\right)(4^2)$

STEP 2 Multiply to find the area.

$\approx \frac{22}{7} \times \frac{16}{1}$

$\approx \frac{352}{7}$

≈ 50.29

The area of the circle is about 50.29 sq cm.

In Example 1, notice that the two values for π give slightly different answers. This is because both values are approximate and they are not equal. In Method 2 Step 2, notice that 16 is not divisible by 7. For this problem, 3.14 is a better choice for the value of π. The fraction $\frac{22}{7}$ is the best choice when the radius is a multiple of 7.

EXAMPLE 2

Find the area of the circle.

Use $\frac{22}{7}$ for π.

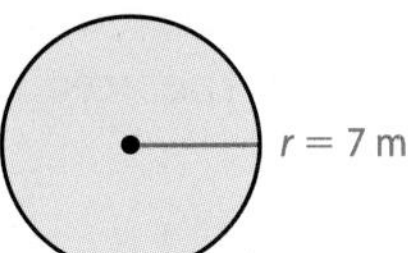

STEP 1 Substitute the values of the radius and of π into the area formula.

$$A = \pi r^2$$
$$\approx \left(\frac{22}{7}\right)(7^2)$$

STEP 2 Multiply to find the area.

$$A \approx \frac{22}{7}(49)$$
$$\approx \frac{22}{\cancel{7}^{1}} \times \frac{\cancel{49}^{7}}{1}$$
$$\approx 154$$

The area of the circle is about 154 sq m.

Need More HELP

For help with multiplying fractions, go to *Multiplying Fractions by Fractions* in *Numbers and Operations* (p. 334).

EXAMPLE 3

Find the area of the circle.

Use 3.14 for π.

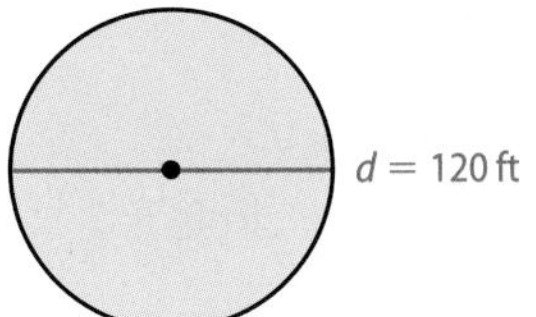

Think: The diameter is 120 feet, so the radius is $120 \div 2 = 60$.

Substitute the values into the area formula.

$$A = \pi r^2$$
$$\approx (3.14)(60)(60)$$
$$\approx (3.14)(3{,}600)$$
$$\approx 11{,}304$$

The area of the circle is about 11,304 sq ft.

SEARCH

To see step-by-step videos of these problems, enter the page number into the SWadvantage.com Search Bar.

Got to KNOW!

Area of a Circle

The **area** of a circle is the number of square units needed to cover the circle. Like all areas, it is expressed in square units.

The formula for finding the area of a circle is:

$$A = \pi r^2$$

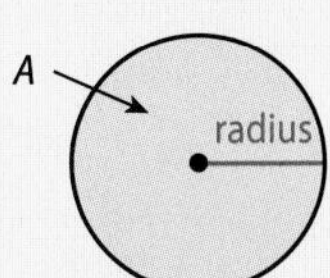

$A = \pi r^2$, where r is the radius of the circle

Finding the Radius of a Circle

Sometimes you are given the area of a circle and need to find the radius. In these cases, substitute the value of the area into the formula and solve for the radius (r).

EXAMPLE 4

The approximate area of a circular crater on the moon is 113 square miles. What is the approximate length of the diameter of the crater?

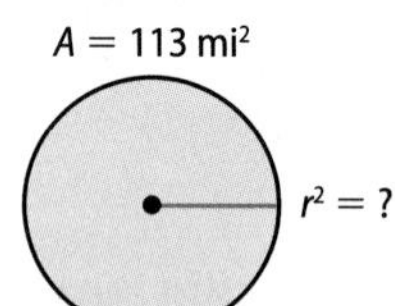

STEP 1 Find the radius of the crater. Use 3.14 for π.

	$A = \pi r^2$
Substitute 113 for A and 3.14 for π.	$113 \approx (3.14)(r^2)$
Divide both sides by 3.14.	$\frac{113}{3.14} \approx \frac{(3.14)(r^2)}{3.14}$
	$\frac{113}{3.14} \approx r^2$
Divide.	$35.99 \approx r^2$
Round 35.99 to 36.	$36 \approx r^2$
Find the square root of 36.	$\sqrt{36} \approx r$
Think: $6 \times 6 = 36$.	$6 \approx r$

The radius is about 6 miles.

STEP 2 Think: The diameter of a circle is $2 \times$ the radius.

$6 \times 2 = 12$

The diameter of the crater is about 12 miles.

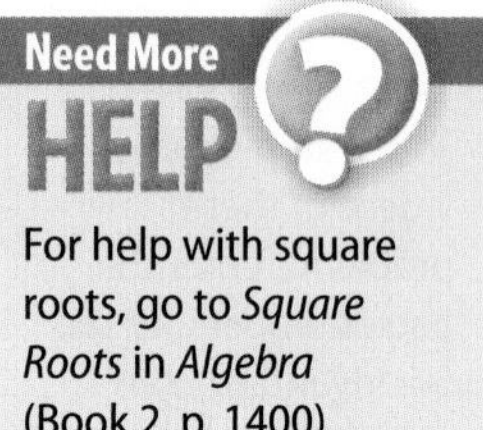

For help with square roots, go to *Square Roots* in *Algebra* (Book 2, p. 1400).

Solving Problems Using the Area Formula

The first Ferris wheel was built for the 1893 World's Fair in Chicago. It had a diameter of 250 feet. What was the area of the first Ferris wheel rounded to the nearest thousand?

Think: The diameter is 250 feet, so the radius is
$250 \div 2 = 125$ feet.

Use the area formula. Since 125 is not a factor or 7, use 3.14 for the value of π.

	$A = \pi r^2$
Substitute 3.14 for π and 125 for r.	$\approx (3.14)(125)(125)$
Multiply.	$\approx 49{,}062.5$
Round to the nearest thousand.	$\approx 49{,}000$

The area rounded to the nearest foot is 49,000 sq ft.

EXAMPLE 6

Mr. Brown uses a circular water sprinkler to water his garden. The sprinkler sprays a distance of 14 ft in all directions. What is the approximate area that the sprinkler will water?

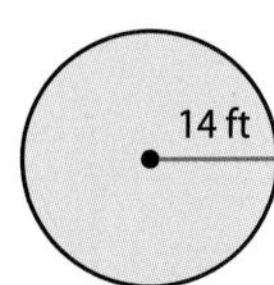

Use the given radius and the formula. Since 14 is a factor or 7, use $\frac{22}{7}$ for the value of π.

$A = \pi r^2$

Substitute $\frac{22}{7}$ for π and 14 for r. $\approx \frac{22}{\not{7}^{1}} \times \frac{\not{196}^{28}}{1}$

Divide by 7 to simplify. $\approx 22 \times 28$

Multiply. ≈ 616

The sprinkler will water approximately 616 sq ft of the garden.

SEARCH

To see step-by-step videos of these problems, enter the page number into the SWadvantage.com Search Bar.

EXAMPLE 7

The diameter of the cup (hole) on a golf course green is 4.25 inches. What is the area of the ground covered by the cup rounded to the nearest tenth?

Think: The diameter is 4.25 inches, so the radius is
$4.25 \div 2 = 2.125$ inches.

Use the area formula. Since 2.125 is not a factor or 7, use 3.14 for the value of π.

$A = \pi r^2$

Substitute 3.14 for π and 2.125 for r. $\approx (3.14)(2.125)(2.125)$

Multiply. ≈ 14.179

Round to the nearest tenth. ≈ 14.2

The area of ground covered by the cup is about 14.2 sq in.

Composite Figures

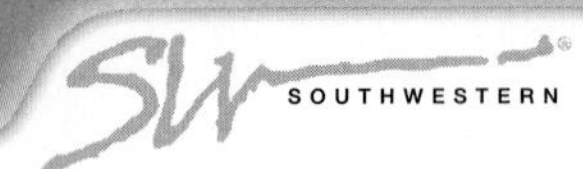

What Is a Composite Figure?

You may see composite figures referred to as *complex figures*.

A **composite figure** is a figure that is made up of two or more smaller polygons or circles. Another way to think about a composite figure is that it can be divided into smaller polygons. One way to divide the figure below is into a trapezoid and a square. You could also divide it into a triangle sitting on a rectangle.

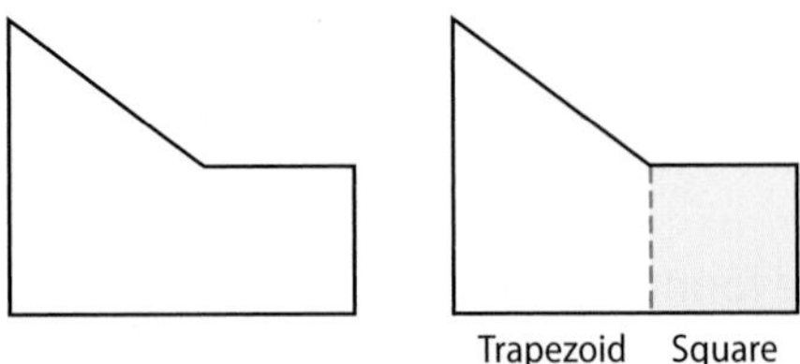

Finding the Perimeter of a Composite Figure

To find the perimeter of a composite figure, add the lengths of all of the sides.

Watch Out !

It's easy to omit a side measure. Count the number of sides on the figure. Then list the measures in order going clockwise. Before you add, count the number of addends. It should be the same as the number of sides on the figure.

EXAMPLE 1

Find the perimeter of the composite figure on the right.

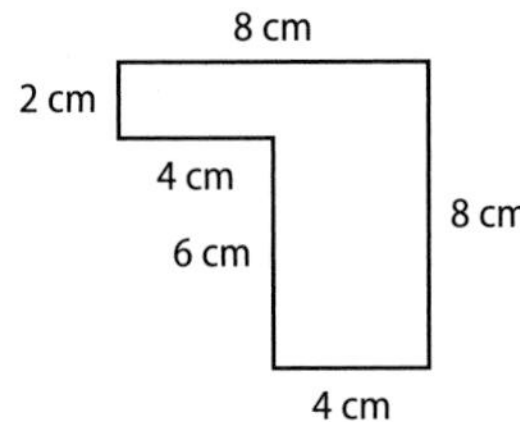

Find the sum of the six sides.

$P = 2 + 8 + 8 + 4 + 6 + 4$

$= 32$

The perimeter of the composite figure is 32 cm.

EXAMPLE 2

Find the perimeter of the composite figure at right.

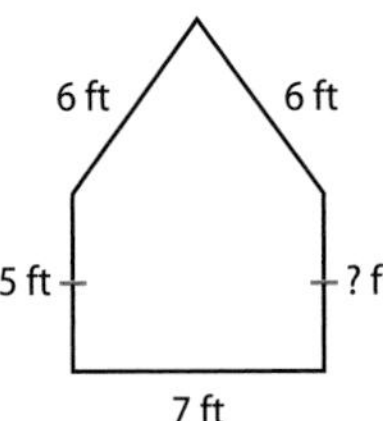

Think: You know the lengths of 4 of the sides. The tick marks tell you that the side opposite the 5-foot side is also 5 ft.

Add: List the measures starting from the left side and going clockwise.

$P = 5 + 6 + 6 + 5 + 7$

$= 29$

The perimeter of the composite figure is 29 ft.

Finding the Area of a Composite Figure

To find the area of a composite figure, divide the figure into smaller polygons whose areas you can find. Most figures can be divided in more than one way. Always use the combination that will help you to find the perimeter or the area of the figure in the simplest manner.

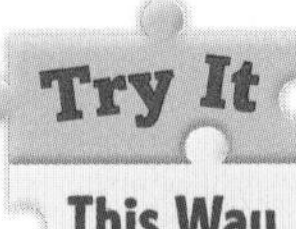

You may find it helpful to shade one of the polygons formed.

EXAMPLE 3

Find the area of the figure at the right.

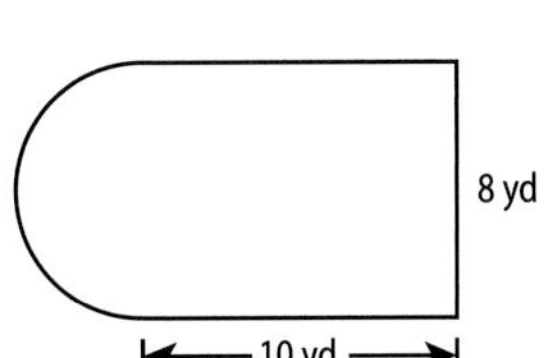

STEP 1 Divide the figure into a rectangle and a semicircle.

STEP 2 Find the area of the rectangle.

$A = b \times h$

$= 10 \times 8$

$= 80 \text{ yd}^2$

STEP 3 Find the area of the semicircle with diameter 8 yd.

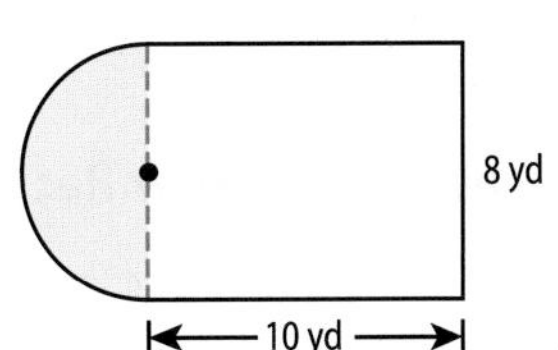

First, find the area of a circle with radius $= 8 \div 2 = 4$ yd.

$A = \pi r^2$

$\approx (3.14)(4^2)$

$\approx (3.14)(4)(4)$

$\approx 50.24 \text{ yd}^2$

The area of a semicircle is one half the area of a circle with the same radius. The area of the semicircle is $50.24 \div 2 = 25.12 \text{ yd}^2$.

STEP 4 Add the two areas: $80 + 25.12 = 105.12$

The area of the figure is about 105.12 yd^2.

SEARCH

To see step-by-step videos of these problems, enter the page number into the SWadvantage.com Search Bar.

Remember, you may see the area formula for a rectangle written as $A = bh$.

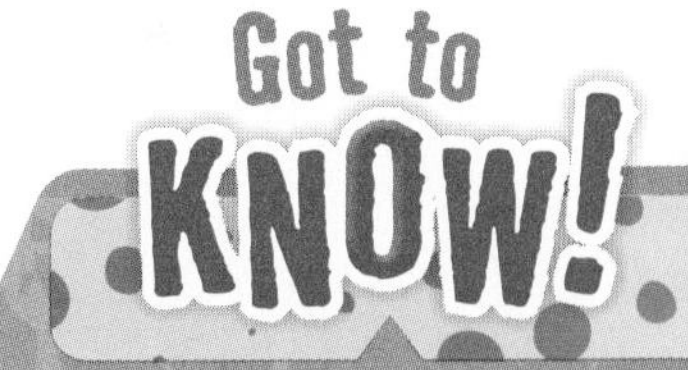

Formulas for Perimeters and Areas

Figure	Perimeter Formula	Area Formula
Triangle	$P = s_1 + s_2 + s_3$	$A = \frac{1}{2}bh$
Square	$P = 4s$	$A = s^2$
Rectangle	$P = 2\ell + 2w$ or $2(\ell + w)$	$A = \ell \times w$
Parallelogram	$P = 2(s_1 + s_2)$	$A = b \times h$
Circle	$C = \pi d$ or $C = 2\pi r$	$A = \pi r^2$
Trapezoid	$P = s_1 + s_2 + s_3 + s_4$	$A = \frac{1}{2}h(b_1 + b_2)$

Finding Perimeters and Areas

EXAMPLE 4

SEARCH

To see step-by-step videos of these problems, enter the page number into the SWadvantage.com Search Bar.

Find the area of the composite figure below.

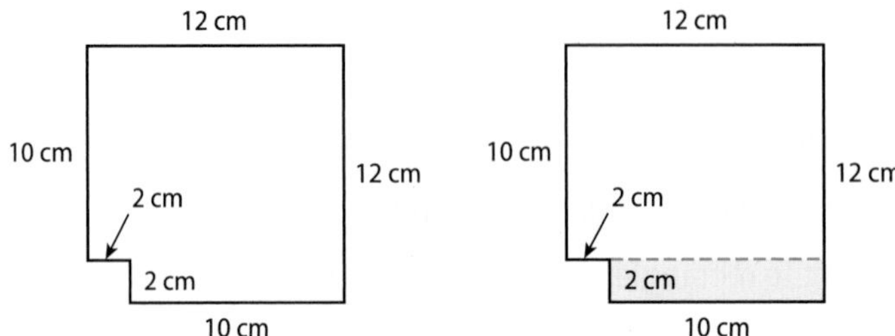

METHOD 1

The figure is made up of a large rectangle and a smaller rectangle. Find the area of both figures.

Area of the Larger Rectangle

$A = \ell \times w$, where $\ell = 12$ and $w = 10$
$= 12 \times 10$
$= 120$

The area of the large rectangle is 120 sq cm.

Area of Smaller Rectangle

$A = \ell \times w$, where $\ell = 10$ and $w = 2$
$= 10 \times 2$
$= 20$

The area of the small rectangle is 20 sq cm.

The total area of the figure is 120 sq cm + 20 sq cm = 140 sq cm.

METHOD 2

You could extend the figure so it is a square and find the area of this square. Then subtract the area of the extension, the small square in the bottom left corner.

Area of Large Square

$A = s^2$ where $s = 12$
$= 12 \times 12$
$= 144$

The area of the large square is 144 sq cm.

Area of Small Square

$A = s^2$, where $s = 2$
$= 2 \times 2$
$= 4$

The area of the small square is 4 sq cm.

The total area of the figure is 144 sq cm − 4 sq cm = 140 sq cm.

The two methods give the same area.

EXAMPLE 5

A nature center has a large meeting room with a screened in porch on one side. The porch is connected to a smaller storage room.

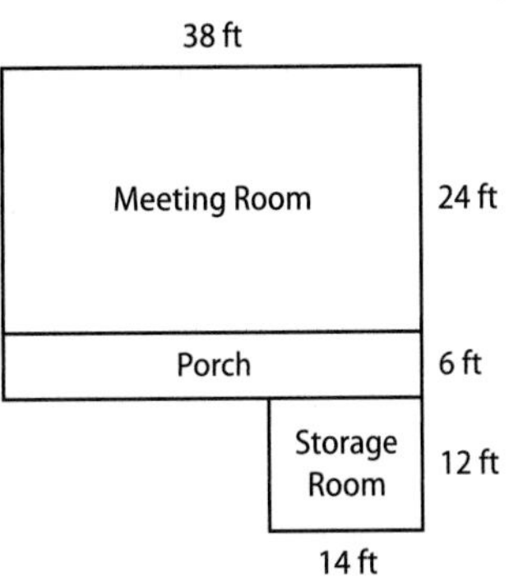

a. What is the perimeter of the entire structure?

The structure is made up of 6 lengths. Start at the top and go clockwise.

1. The length of the top side is 38 ft.
2. The length of the right side is 24 ft + 6 ft + 12 ft = 42 ft.
3. The length of the bottom right side is 14 ft.
4. The length of the left side of the storage room is 12 ft.
5. The length of the bottom left side is not given. However, when you examine the figure you can see that its length is the length of the meeting room minus the length of the storage room, which is 38 ft − 14 ft = 24 ft.
6. The length of the left side is not given. However, the figure shows that this length is equal to the width of the porch plus the width of the meeting room, which is 6 ft + 24 ft = 30 ft.

Add the 6 lengths: 38 + 42 + 14 + 12 + 24 + 30 = 160

The perimeter of the entire structure is 160 feet.

b. What is the area of the entire structure?

Decide how to divide the figure. One way is shown below.

Area 1 Find the area of the rectangle formed by the meeting room and the porch. The length is 38 ft. The width is 24 ft + 6 ft = 30 ft.

$A = \ell w$
$= 38 \times 30$
$= 1{,}140$ sq ft

Area 2 Find the area of the storage room.

$A = \ell w$
$= 14 \times 12$
$= 168$ sq ft

Add the two areas: 1,140 + 168 = 1,308 sq ft

The area of the entire structure is 1,308 sq ft.

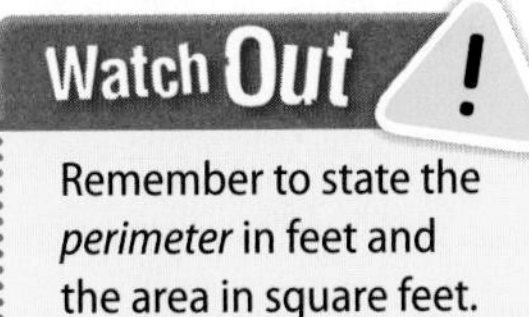

Remember to state the *perimeter* in feet and the area in square feet.

Use the strategy *Make Ten* to add the six lengths. Then use your calculator to check your addition.

Surface Area and Volume

What Came Before?

- Analyzing solid figures
- Finding perimeter, circumference and area of plane figures

What's This About?

- Finding the surface area of solid figures
- Finding the volume of solid figures
- Finding the surface area and volume of composite solid figures

Practical Apps

- Solar energy engineers and technicians calculate how much solar panel surface area is needed to generate given amounts of electricity.
- Geologists in the petroleum industry calculate the volumes of underground stores of oil and other substances such as natural gas.

just for FUN!

Q: What's the surface area of this boom box?

A: I can't hear you. Can you turn down the volume?

CONTENTS UPLOAD DOWNLOAD

Measurement

You can find more practice problems online by visiting:
www.SWadvantage.com

Surface Area of Prisms

What Is Surface Area?

For help finding area, go to page 482.

For help with nets, go to *Nets* in *Geometry* (p. 694).

The **surface area** of a prism is the total area of its faces. You can see the faces better if you unfold the prism into a **net**, or 2-dimensional representation of a solid object. The net of the rectangular prism shown below clearly shows its 6 faces.

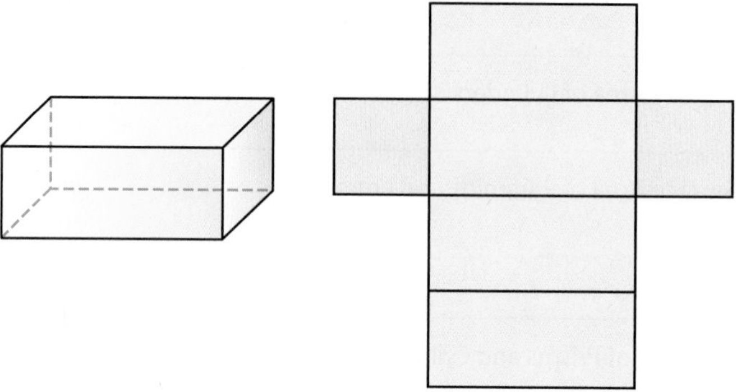

To find the surface area of a prism, find the area of each face and add to find the total area. Refer to the *Got to Know!* box for area formulas for basic polygons.

Finding Surface Area of Rectangular Prisms

SEARCH

To see step-by-step videos of these problems, enter the page number into the SWadvantage.com Search Bar.

EXAMPLE 1

Find the surface area of the prism below.

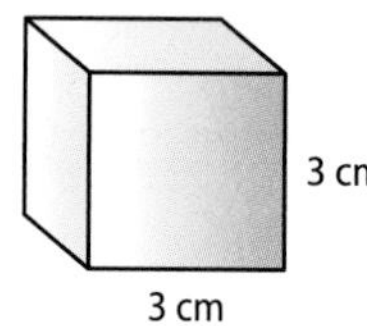

Think: The prism is a cube.
It has 6 identical square faces that measure 3 cm per side.

STEP 1 Find the area of each face.

Use the area formula for a square. $A = s^2$

Substitute 3 cm for s. $= (3\text{ cm})^2$

$= 9\text{ cm}^2$

The area of each face is 9 cm^2.

STEP 2 Multiply the area by 6 because there are 6 faces.

$SA = 6 \times 9\text{ cm}^2 = 54\text{ cm}^2$

The surface area of the prism is 54 cm^2.

EXAMPLE 2

Find the surface area of the rectangular prism shown on the right.

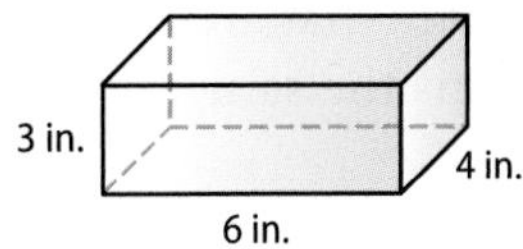

Think: If the prism were cut apart and flattened out, it would look like this net.

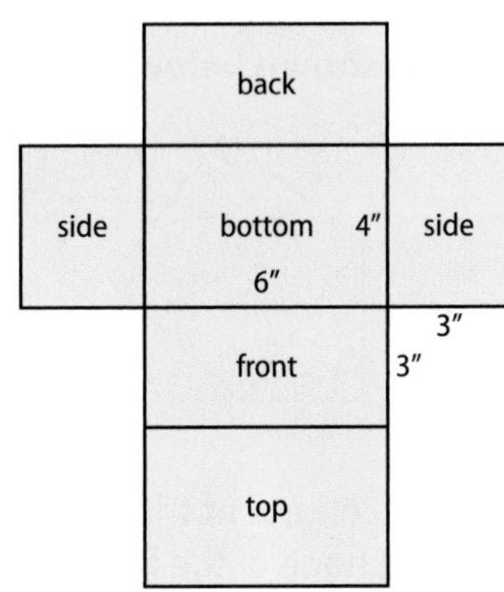

The rectangular prism has 6 faces. Find the area of each face.

- The bottom and the top faces have the same dimensions: 6″ by 4″
- The front and the back faces have the same dimensions: 6″ by 3″
- The faces on each side (the bases) have the same dimensions: 4″ by 3″

STEP 1

Find the area of the bottom and the top.

$$A = bh = 6(4) = 24 \text{ in.}^2$$

The area of the bottom and the top is $24 \text{ in.}^2 \times 2 = 48 \text{ in.}^2$.

STEP 2

Find the area of the front and the back.

$$A = bh = 6(3) = 18 \text{ in.}^2$$

The area of the front and the back is $18 \text{ in.}^2 \times 2 = 36 \text{ in.}^2$.

STEP 3

Find the area of the two sides.

$$A = bh = 3(4) = 12 \text{ in.}^2$$

The area of the two sides is $12 \text{ in.}^2 \times 2 = 24 \text{ in.}^2$.

STEP 4 Add to find the total surface area. $48 \text{ in.}^2 + 36 \text{ in.}^2 + 24 \text{ in.}^2 = 108 \text{ in.}^2$

The surface area of the prism is 108 in.^2.

This Way

You may find it helpful to color in pairs of faces that have the same area.

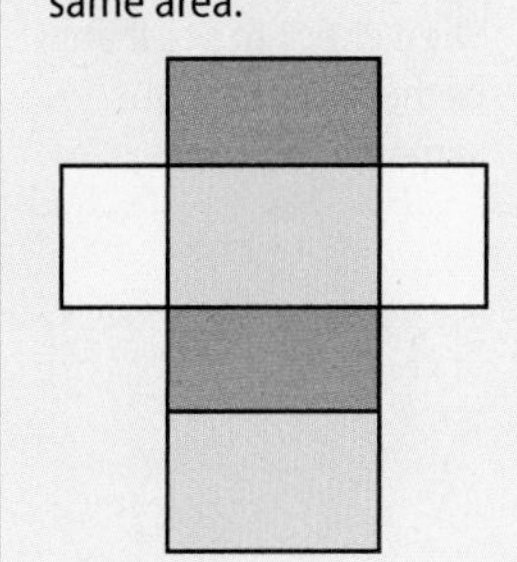

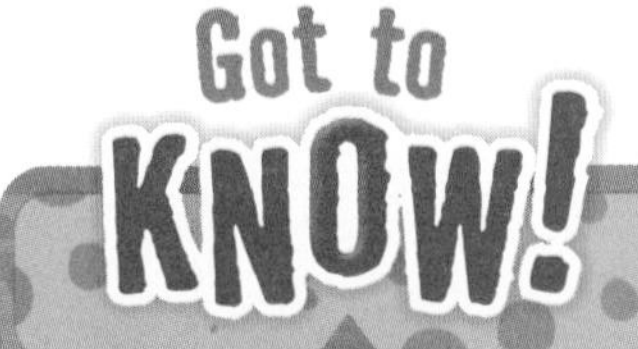

Area Formulas for Polygons

Triangle	Square	Rectangle
$A = \frac{1}{2}bh$	$A = s^2$	$A = \ell w$ or $A = bh$

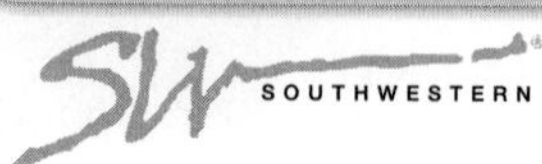

Finding Surface Area of Triangular Prisms

Not all prisms have bases that are rectangles or squares. But the method for finding the surface area remains the same: find the area of each face and add to find the total area.

Identify the two bases of the prism and shade them. Count the number of sides on the base. There will be this number of rectangular faces. List the dimensions of each rectangular face. Then check to see if any of the faces have the same dimensions.

EXAMPLE 3

Find the area of the triangular prism shown below.

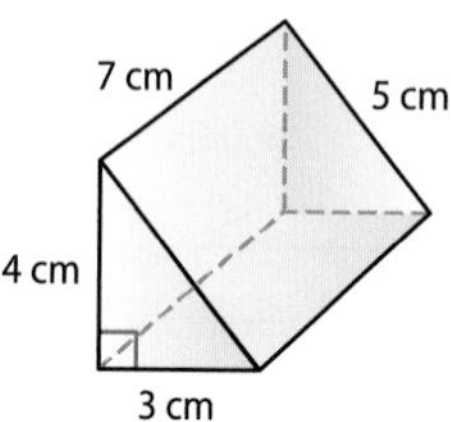

Think: The prism has two bases that are congruent triangles with $b = 3$ cm and $h = 4$ cm. It has three rectangular faces, but none of the faces have the same dimensions. Find the area of each face.

STEP 1 Find the area of each triangular base.

Substitute 3 cm for b and 4 cm for h.

$$A = \frac{1}{2}bh$$
$$= \frac{1}{2}(3 \text{ cm} \times 4 \text{ cm}) = 6 \text{ cm}^2$$

There are two triangular bases. $2(6 \text{ cm}^2) = 12 \text{ cm}^2$

STEP 2 Find the area of the front (slanted) rectangular face.

Substitute 7 cm for b and 5 cm for h.

$$A = bh$$
$$= 7 \text{ cm} \times 5 \text{ cm} = 35 \text{ cm}^2$$

STEP 3 Find the area of the back rectangular face.

Substitute 7 cm for b and 4 cm for h.

$$A = bh$$
$$= 7 \text{ cm} \times 4 \text{ cm} = 28 \text{ cm}^2$$

STEP 4 Find the area of the bottom rectangular face.

Substitute 7 cm for b and 3 cm for h.

$$A = bh$$
$$= 7 \text{ cm} \times 3 \text{ cm} = 21 \text{ cm}^2$$

STEP 5 Add to find the total surface area (SA).

$$SA = 12 \text{ cm}^2 + 35 \text{ cm}^2 + 28 \text{ cm}^2 + 21 \text{ cm}^2 = 96 \text{ cm}^2$$

The surface area of the triangular prism is 96 cm^2.

Solving Problems with Prisms

The method used for finding surface area can be applied when solving real-world problems involving prisms.

EXAMPLE 4

Ana wants to wrap a present in the box shown below.

a. What is the surface area of the box?

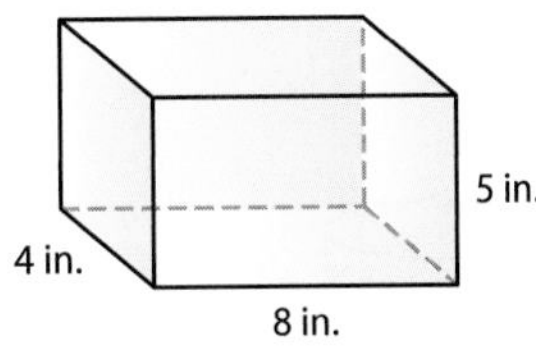

STEP 1 Find the area of the two ends of the box.

$A = bh$
$= 4 \text{ in.} \times 5 \text{ in.} = 20 \text{ in.}^2$
$2 \times 20 \text{ in.}^2 = 40 \text{ in.}^2$

STEP 2 Find the area of the two sides.

$A = bh$
$= 8 \text{ in.} \times 5 \text{ in.} = 40 \text{ in.}^2$
$2 \times 40 \text{ in.}^2 = 80 \text{ in.}^2$

STEP 3 Find the area of top and the bottom.

$A = bh$
$= 8 \text{ in.} \times 4 \text{ in.} = 32 \text{ in.}^2$
$2 \times 32 \text{ in.}^2 = 64 \text{ in.}^2$

STEP 4 Add the areas of the faces.

$SA = 40 \text{ in.}^2 + 80 \text{ in.}^2 + 64 \text{ in.}^2 = 184 \text{ in.}^2$

The surface area of the box is 184 in.^{2}.

b. Ana has 216 in.^{2} of wrapping paper that is 12 in. wide. Is this enough paper?

Think: She has 216 in.^{2} of wrapping paper that is 12 inches wide. This means that the length of the paper is $\frac{216 \text{ in.}^2}{12 \text{ in.}} = 18$ in. Look at the box sitting on the paper.

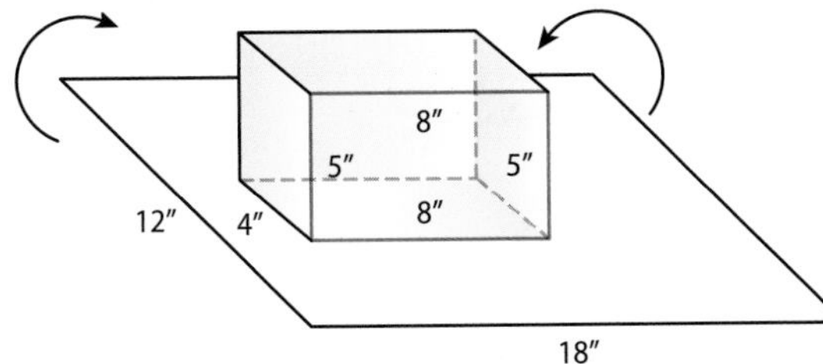

The 18″ length must fold around these sides: 5″ + 8″ + 5″ + 8″ = 26″.

If she turns the box the other direction, the paper must go around 4″ + 8″ + 4″ + 8″ = 24″.

Since 18″ < 24″ < 26″, Ana does not have enough wrapping paper to cover her present.

SEARCH

To see step-by-step videos of these problems, enter the page number into the SWadvantage.com Search Bar.

Watch Out !

Just because 216 in.^{2} > 184 in.^{2}, it does not mean that she has enough wrapping paper. You have to consider the dimensions of the paper and the box.

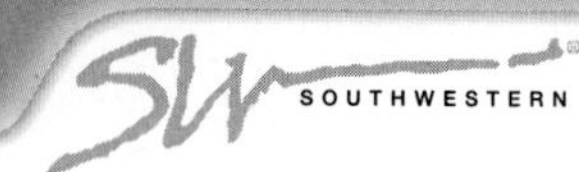

Surface Area of a Cylinder

Need More HELP

Sometimes the figure shown is not proportional to the given measures. In the figure in Example 1, the diameter is 6 ft and the height is 25 feet. This means that the actual cylinder is about 4 times taller than it is wide.

The **surface area** of a cylinder is the sum of the areas of its two circular bases and its curved side, which is called the **lateral surface**. A net of a cylinder shows that, when unrolled and flattened, the lateral surface is a rectangle. Notice that

- the height of the lateral surface is the height of the cylinder, and
- the base of the lateral surface is equal to the circumference of the circular bases.

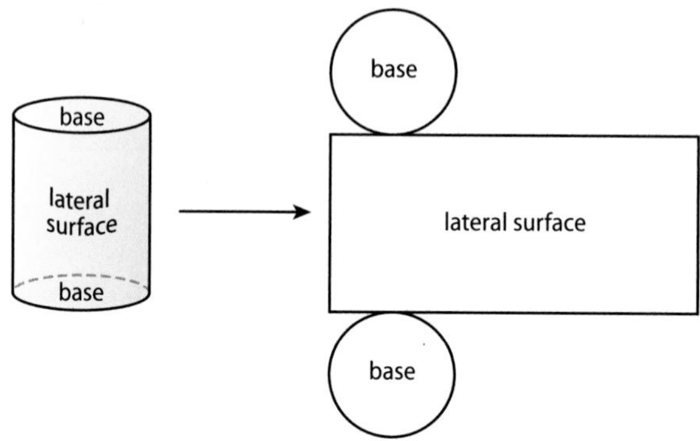

Watch Out!

The formula for the surface area of a cylinder requires you to use the irrational number π. As soon as you substitute 3.14 for π, use the "is approximately equal to" sign: $\approx$.

To find the surface area of a cylinder, use the formula for the area of a circle to find the area of the two congruent bases. Use the formula for the area of a rectangle to find the area of its curved side (lateral surface). Then add to find the total area.

EXAMPLE 1

Find the surface area of the cylinder shown to the right. Use 3.14 for π.

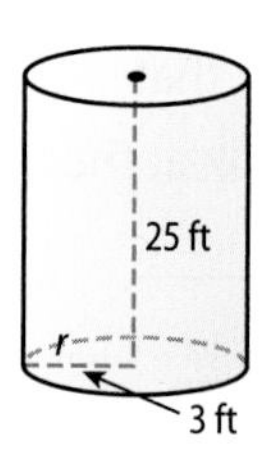

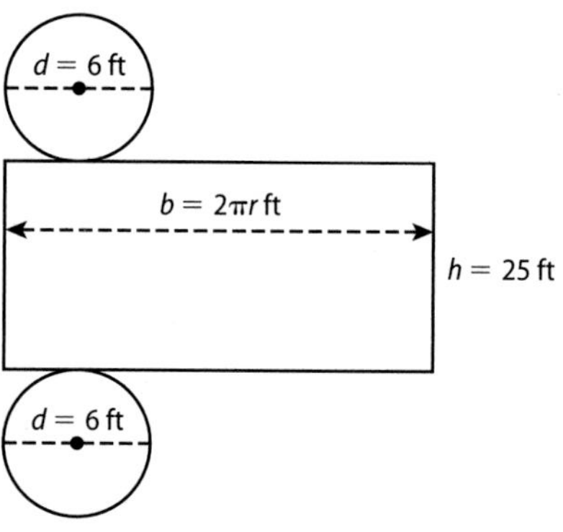

STEP 1 Find the area of the 2 circular bases. The radius $r = 3$ ft.

$A = 2\pi r^2$
$\approx (2)(3.14)(3)(3)$
$\approx 56.52\text{ ft}^2$

STEP 2 Find the lateral surface area. The base b is the circumference of the circular base. The height $h = 25$ ft.

$A = (b)(h)$
$= (2\pi r)(h)$
$\approx (2)(3.14)(3)(25)$
$\approx 471\text{ ft}^2$

STEP 3 Add to find the total surface area. $SA = 56.52 + 471 \approx 527.52$

The dimensions are in feet, so the surface area of the cylinder is approximately 527.52 ft^2.

Got to KNOW!

Area Formulas for Polygons

Area of a circle:
$A = \pi r^2$

Area of a rectangle:
$A = bh$, or
$A = \ell w$

Circumference:
$C = 2\pi r$

Deriving a Surface Area Formula

All cylinders consist of two parallel congruent circular bases and a curved lateral surface. For this reason, there is a surface area formula that can be used for all cylinders. The steps for deriving the formula are shown below.

$SA = (2 \times \text{area of base}) + (\text{area of lateral surface})$

$= (2 \times \text{area of base}) + (\text{length of side} \times \text{height of side})$

$= (2 \times \text{area of base}) + (\text{circumference of base} \times \text{height of cylinder})$

$= (2 \times \pi r^2) \qquad + (2\pi r \times h)$

Thus the formula is $SA = 2\pi r^2 + 2\pi rh$, where r is the radius of the cylinder and h is its height.

Because the formula includes the irrational number pi, the calculated surface area of a cylinder is always an approximate value. When applying the formula, you can find the answer in terms of pi, and then substitute for pi, as shown in Example 2.

Try It This Way

In the *SA* formula, if you factor $2\pi r$ from each term, you get $2\pi r(r + h)$.

EXAMPLE 2

Find the surface area of the cylinder shown below. Use the formula $SA = 2\pi r^2 + 2\pi rh$. Use $\frac{22}{7}$ for π.

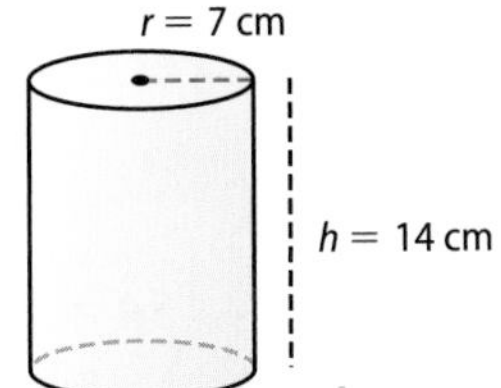

Think: I know these values: $r = 7$ cm and $h = 14$ cm.
I can substitute them into the *SA* formula and simplify.

$SA = 2\pi r^2 + 2\pi rh$

$= 2\pi(7)^2 + 2\pi(7)(14)$

$= 2\pi 49 + 2\pi 98$

$= 98\pi + 196\pi$

$= 294\pi$

Think: The answer is in terms of pi. Substitute a value for π and simplify.

$SA = \frac{\cancel{294}^{42}}{1} \times \frac{22}{\cancel{7}^{1}}$

$= 924$

The dimensions are in cm, so the surface area of the cylinder is approximately 924 cm^2.

SEARCH 

To see step-by-step videos of these problems, enter the page number into the SWadvantage.com Search Bar.

Try It This Way

To help you see the numbers in the formula better, do not include the unit of measure until you state the answer.

Finding Surface Area

EXAMPLE 3

Use the net of the cylinder to find its surface area.

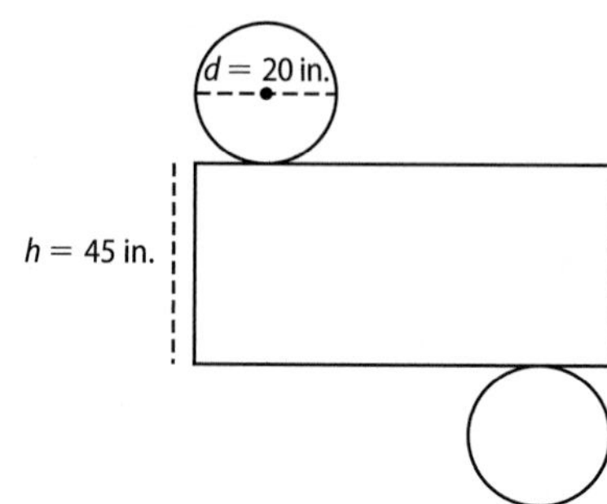

SEARCH

To see step-by-step videos of these problems, enter the page number into the SWadvantage.com Search Bar.

METHOD 1

Find the area for each part of the net, and then find the total surface area.

STEP 1 Find the area of the circular bases.

Substitute 20 ÷ 2 or 10 for r.

$$A = 2\pi r^2$$
$$= 2\pi(10)^2$$
$$= 2\pi 100$$
$$= 200\pi$$

STEP 2 Find the lateral surface area.

Substitute 10 for r and 45 for h.

$$A = 2\pi rh$$
$$= 2\pi(10)(45)$$
$$= \pi 900$$

STEP 3 Find the total surface area.
Use 3.14 for pi.

$$SA = 200\pi + \pi 900$$
$$= \pi 1{,}100$$
$$\approx (3.14)(1{,}100)$$
$$\approx 3{,}454$$

METHOD 2

Find the surface area using the formula $SA = 2\pi r^2 + 2\pi rh$.

STEP 1 Substitute the given values into the formula.

Substitute 10 for r and 45 for h.

Simplify.

$$SA = 2\pi r^2 + 2\pi rh$$
$$= 2\pi(10)^2 + 2\pi(10)(45)$$
$$= 2\pi 100 + 2\pi 450$$
$$= 200\pi + 900\pi$$
$$= 1{,}100\pi$$

STEP 2 Substitute 3.14 for π.

$$SA \approx 1{,}100(3.14)$$
$$\approx 3{,}454$$

The dimensions are given in inches, so the surface area of the cylinder shown by its net is approximately 3,454 in.^{2}

Solving Problems with Cylinders

The methods used for finding the surface area of a cylinder can be applied when solving real-world problems.

EXAMPLE 4

Joan will use a cardboard mailing tube 15 inches long and 4 inches in diameter in an art project. She plans to cover it with glitter. The information on the package of glitter reads, "Will cover 350 square inches with a medium coat of glitter or 200 square inches with a heavy coat of glitter." Is one package of glitter enough?

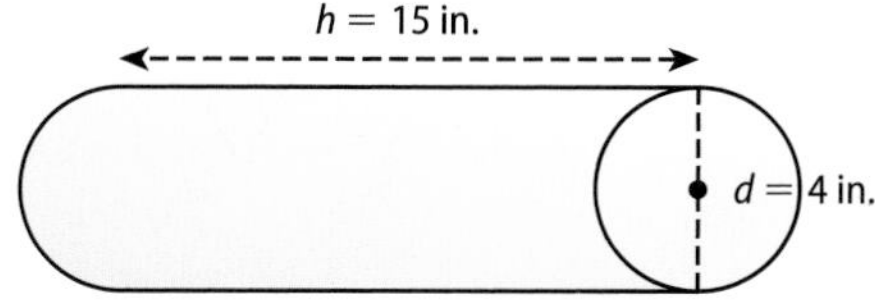

Think: Use the area formula and substitute the given values to find the surface area of the mailing tube.

Formula: $A = 2\pi r^2 + 2\pi rh$
Given values: $h = 15$ in.; $d = 4$ in., so $r = 2$ in.

	$SA = 2\pi r^2 + 2\pi rh$
Substitute the values into the formula.	$= 2\pi(2)^2 + 2\pi(2)(15)$
Clear the exponent; multiply.	$= 2\pi 4 + 2\pi 30$
Multiply.	$= 8\pi + 60\pi$
Add to find the total surface area.	$= 68\pi$
Substitute 3.14 for π.	$\approx 68(3.14)$
Multiply.	≈ 213.63

The dimensions are given in inches, so the *SA* of the tube is approximately 213.63 in.^{2}.

350 sq in. > 214 sq in. > 200 sq in.

medium coat of glitter → heavy coat of glitter

One package of glitter should permit Joan to cover the mailing tube with a medium coat of glitter.

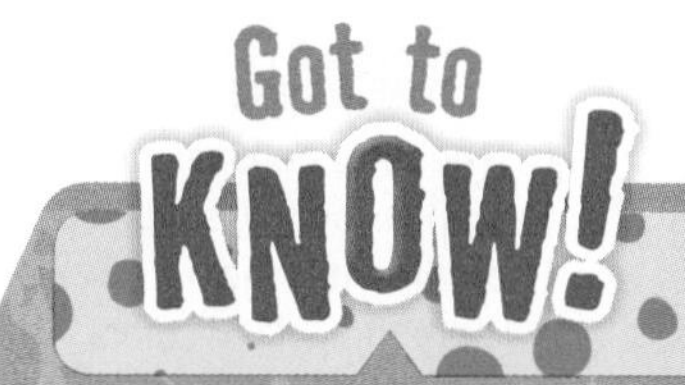

Surface Area of a Cylinder

Use the formula *SA* of a cylinder $= 2\pi r^2 + 2\pi rh$.

You can substitute a value for π

- when you substitute for the other values, or
- after you have found the answer in terms of π.

Surface Area of Pyramids and Cones

A polygon has a *height*, which is the perpendicular distance from the base to the opposite side. A pyramid and a cone also have a *height*, but it is the shortest distance from the center of a base to the apex.

Surface Area of a Pyramid

A **pyramid** is a solid figure with triangular faces and one base that is a polygon. The **surface area** of a pyramid is the sum of the areas of its base and its faces. If you unfold a pyramid into a **net**, or 2-dimensional representation of a solid figure, you can clearly see its base and triangular faces. Notice that the *slant height* of the pyramid is the height of the triangular face.

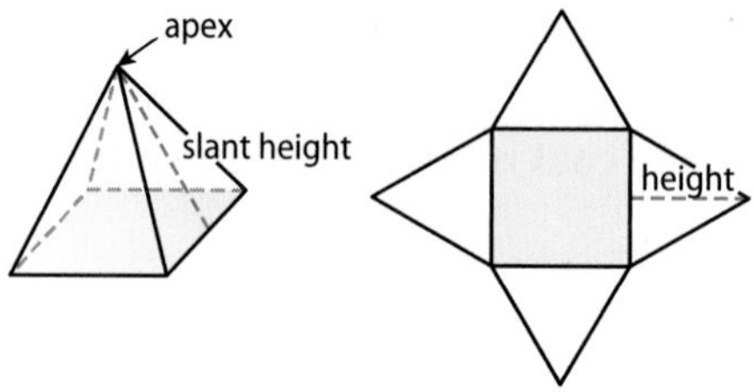

Finding the Surface Area

To find the surface area of a pyramid, find the area of the base and the area of the triangular sides. Then add to find the total area. Refer to the *Got to Know!* box to review area formulas.

SEARCH

To see step-by-step videos of these problems, enter the page number into the SWadvantage.com Search Bar.

EXAMPLE 1

Find the surface area of the square pyramid.

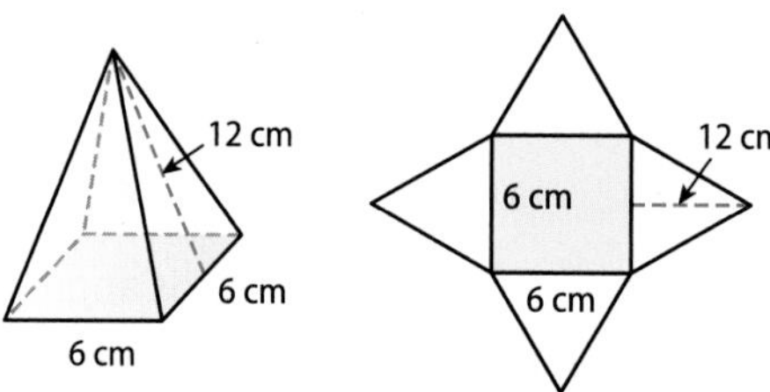

Think: The pyramid has a square base that measures 6 cm per side. Its sides are four congruent triangles with base $b = 6$ cm and height $h = 12$ cm.

STEP 1 Find the area of the square base.

$$A = s^2 \text{ and } s = 6$$
$$= (6)^2$$
$$= 36$$

The area of the base is 36 cm².

STEP 2 Find the area of the triangular faces.

$$A = \frac{1}{2}bh$$
$$= \frac{1}{2}(6)(12)$$
$$= 36$$

The area of the 4 triangular faces is $4(36 \text{ cm}^2) = 144 \text{ cm}^2$.

STEP 3 Add the areas of the faces and base. $SA = 144 + 36 = 180$

The surface area of the square pyramid is 180 cm².

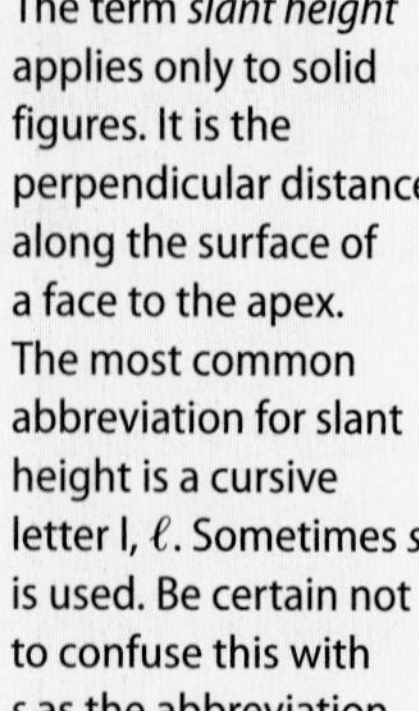

Watch Out!

The term *slant height* applies only to solid figures. It is the perpendicular distance along the surface of a face to the apex. The most common abbreviation for slant height is a cursive letter l, ℓ. Sometimes s is used. Be certain not to confuse this with s as the abbreviation for side.

A pyramid is named according to the type of polygon that forms its base. A square pyramid has a square base and a triangular pyramid has a triangle base. The surface area formula will change according to the shape of the base.

SA = (area of base) + (area of triangular face $\times$ number of faces)

EXAMPLE 2

Find the surface area of the triangular pyramid with $b = 8$ in. and $h = 5$ in. Since the base is a triangle, use the formula

$$SA = \frac{1}{2}bh + (\frac{1}{2}bh \times 3).$$

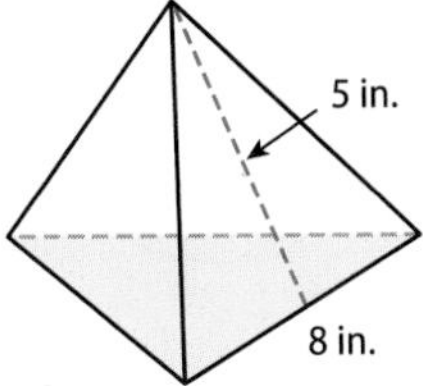

Think: I know the values for the triangles: $b = 8$ in. and $h = 5$ in.
I can substitute them into the given SA formula and simplify.

$$SA = \frac{1}{2}bh + \left(\frac{1}{2}bh \times 3\right)$$
$$= \frac{1}{2}(8)(5) + \left(\frac{1}{2}\right)(8)(5)(3)$$
$$= \frac{1}{2}(40) + \frac{1}{2}(120)$$
$$= 20 + 60 = 80$$

The dimensions are in inches, so the surface area of the triangular pyramid is 80 in.^{2}.

Got to KNOW!

Area Formulas for Polygons

Triangle: $A = \frac{1}{2}bh$

Square: $A = s^2$

Rectangle: $A = \ell w$ or $A = bh$

EXAMPLE 3

Terry made a model pyramid for a history project. Its base is a 12-cm square. The height of each triangular side is 10 cm. How much construction paper did Terry use to make the model? Use $SA = bh + \left(\frac{1}{2}bh \times 4\right)$.

Substitute the given values into the formula and simplify.

Substitute the values into the formula.	$SA = bh + \left(\frac{1}{2}bh \times 4\right)$
Multiple the numbers in parentheses.	$= (12)(10) + \frac{1}{2}(12)(10)(4)$
Multiply 480 by one half, and add.	$= 120 + \frac{1}{2}(480)$
	$= 120 + 240 = 360$

The measures are in cm, so the surface area of the pyramid is 360 cm^2.

Terry used 360 cm^2 of construction paper to make the model pyramid.

Watch Out !

The pyramid in Example 3 is a square pyramid, so the SA formula changes:

- the first part changes to bh because the base is a square, a type of rectangle, and
- the second part changes to $\times$ 4 because there are four triangular faces.

Surface Area of a Cone

Need More HELP

Remember, the *apex* of a cone is the pointed top. It is sometimes called the *vertex*.

A **cone** is a solid figure that has a base that is a circle and a curved surface (*lateral surface*) that tapers to a point at the top. The *surface area* of a cone is the sum of the area of the base and the curved surface. If you unfold the cone to form its *net*, you can see a 2-dimensional representation of its curved lateral surface and its circular base. The lateral surface is a section of a circle.

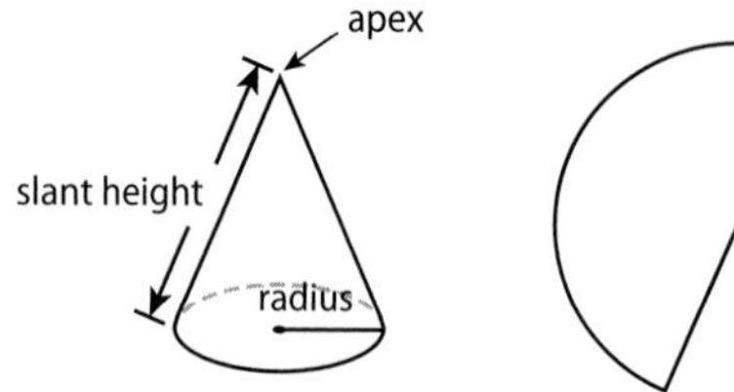

Finding the Surface Area

Watch Out!

Because the formula includes the irrational number pi, the calculated surface area is an approximate value.

To find the surface area of a cone, find the area of the circular base and the area of the curved surface. Then add the areas together. The area formula for each part of a cone is the same for all cones. So, the formula for the surface area of any cone is always the same.

$$SA = (\text{area of circular base}) + (\text{area of lateral surface})$$
$$= (\pi r^2) + (\pi r\ell)$$

Look closely at the part of the formula of the area of the lateral surface, $\pi r\ell$. The area of the lateral surface is found by multiplying pi $\times$ the radius of the base $\times$ the slant height of the cone.

EXAMPLE 4

Find the surface area of the cone to the right. Use 3.14 for π.

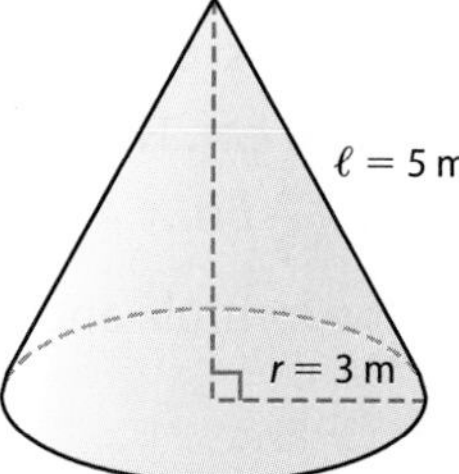

STEP 1 Find the area of the circular base. Use the formula for the area of a circle: $A = \pi r^2$.

$A = \pi r^2$

$A \approx 3.14(3)^2$

$\approx 3.14(9)$

≈ 28.26

STEP 2 Find the area of the lateral surface.

$A = \pi r\ell$

$\approx 3.14(3)(5)$

≈ 47.10

STEP 3 Add the two areas.

$SA \approx 28.26 + 47.25$

≈ 75.36

Since the measures are in meters, the SA of the cone is approximately 75 m^2.

EXAMPLE 5

Find the surface area of a cone with $r = 14$ ft, $\ell = 21$ ft, and $\pi = \frac{22}{7}$. Use the formula $SA = \pi r^2 + \pi r\ell$.

Substitute the values into the formula and simplify.

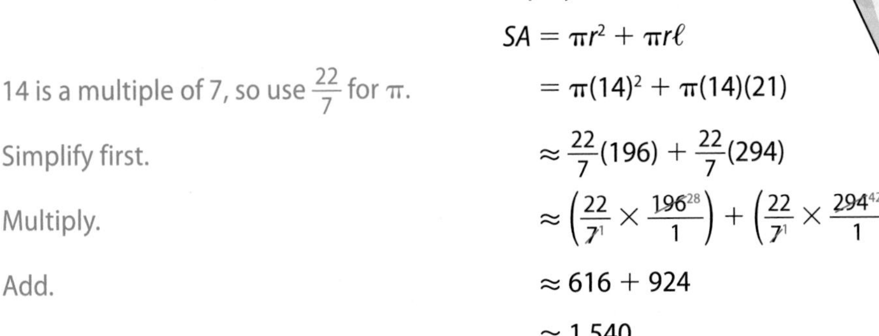

$$SA = \pi r^2 + \pi r\ell$$

14 is a multiple of 7, so use $\frac{22}{7}$ for π. $\quad = \pi(14)^2 + \pi(14)(21)$

Simplify first. $\quad \approx \frac{22}{7}(196) + \frac{22}{7}(294)$

Multiply. $\quad \approx \left(\frac{22}{7^1} \times \frac{196^{28}}{1}\right) + \left(\frac{22}{7^1} \times \frac{294^{42}}{1}\right)$

Add. $\quad \approx 616 + 924$

$\approx 1{,}540$

Since the measures are given in feet, the surface area of the cone is about 1,540 ft^2.

SEARCH

To see step-by-step videos of these problems, enter the page number into the SWadvantage.com Search Bar.

EXAMPLE 6

The radius of a party hat is 3 inches and the slanted side of the hat is 8 inches. How much decorative paper does it take to make a hat?

Use $SA = \pi r^2 + \pi rs$ and $\pi = 3.14$.

Think: The slanted side of the hat is the slant height. Substitute the given values into the formula and simplify.

$$SA = \pi r^2 + \pi rs$$
$$\approx 3.14(3)^2 + 3.14(3)(8)$$
$$\approx 3.14(9) + 3.14(24)$$
$$\approx 28.26 + 75.36$$
$$\approx 103.62$$

It will take at least 104 in.^{2} of decorative paper to make a hat.

Remember, slant height is sometimes abbreviated as s. Since there are no sides in this problem, using s for slant height is not confusing.

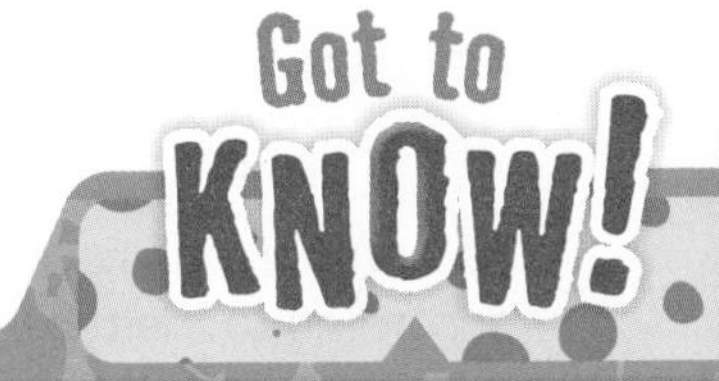

Surface Area of a Cone

The formula for the surface area of a cone is the same for all cones.

SA = (area of circular base) + (lateral surface area), or

$(\pi r^2) + (\pi r\ell)$, where ℓ = the slant height.

You may also see the formula written with s = the slant height.

Volumes of Prisms and Cylinders

Finding the Volume of a Prism

A **prism** is a geometric solid with two congruent, parallel faces called **bases**. The other faces of a prism are rectangles. The **volume** of a prism is the space the prism occupies. A prism has three dimensions—length, width, and height—so its volume is measured in cubic units.

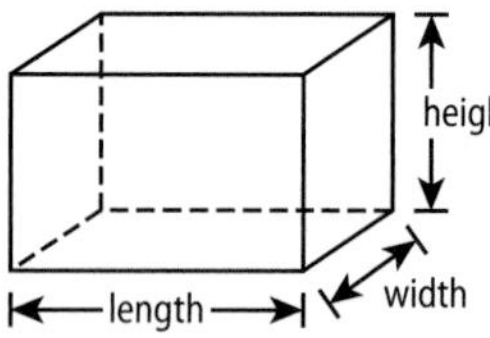

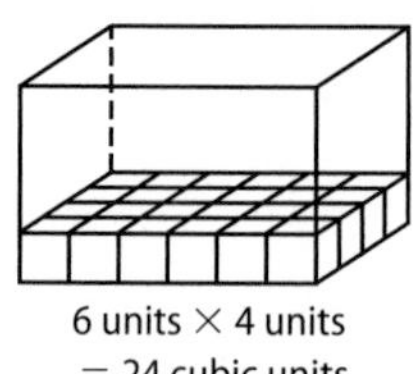

6 units × 4 units
= 24 cubic units

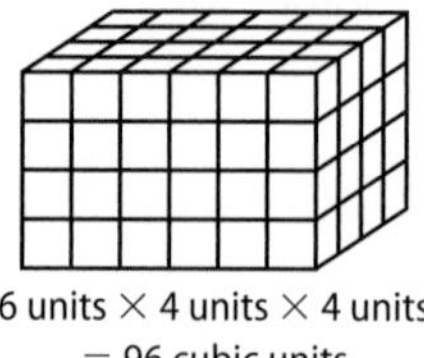

6 units × 4 units × 4 units
= 96 cubic units

In the rectangular prism above, four layers of 24 cubes, or 96 cubes, fit inside of it. So its volume is 96 cubic units. You can find the volume without using cubes by multiplying *length* × *width* × *height:* $6 \times 4 \times 4 = 96$ cubic units. Since the *length* times the *width* gives the *area of the base,* the formula for finding the volume of a prism is:

V of a prism = area of the base (B) times the height (h)
$V = Bh$

This formula works for all prisms. However, not all prisms are rectangular prisms. The formula used to find the area of the base (B) will vary. Refer to the *Got to Know!* box to see the area formula for specific types of prisms.

Got to KNOW!

Express Volume in Cubic Units

Volume is measured in cubic units. The answer to a volume problem should always state the unit.

For example, if you calculate $V = 12$ and the given information is in meters, you must state the volume in one of the following ways:

12 cubic meters

12 m^3

12 cu m

Formulas for the Volume of a Prism

$V = Bh$, where B = the area of the base of the prism and h = the height of the prism.

Remember, prisms are named by the shape of their bases. So the formula for B varies according to the type of prism.

Prism	Volume Formula
Rectangular	$V = B \times h$, where $B = \ell \times w$
Square	$V = B \times h$, where $B = s^2$
Triangular	$V = B \times h$, where $B = \frac{1}{2}bh$

In the formula for the *area of a triangular prism,* the h refers to two different heights. In $\frac{1}{2}(bh)$, the h is the height of the triangular base. The h in $B \times h$ is the height of the prism.

EXAMPLE 1

Find the volume of the prism on the right.

The prism is a triangular prism because its base is a triangle. Use the formula for the volume of a triangular prism.

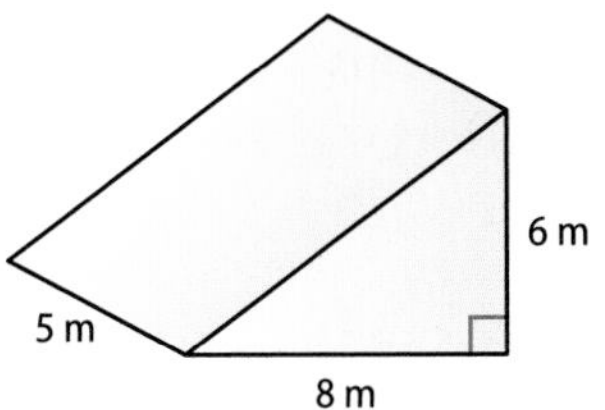

Write the formula. $V = B \times h$

$= \left(\frac{1}{2}bh\right) \times h$

Substitute the values given. $V = \frac{1}{2}(8 \times 6) \times 5$

Multiply. $= \frac{1}{2}(48) \times 5$

$= 24 \times 5$

$= 120$

Since the measures are in meters, the volume of the triangular prism is 120 cubic meters. You can also write this as 120 m^3.

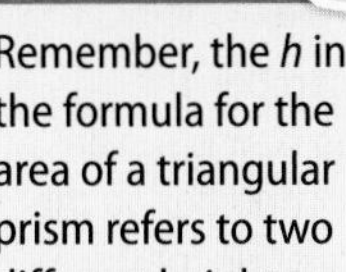

Remember, the *h* in the formula for the area of a triangular prism refers to two different heights.

SEARCH

To see step-by-step videos of these problems, enter the page number into the SWadvantage.com Search Bar.

EXAMPLE 2

The box on the right can hold 20 CD cases. Each case measures 0.5 cm × 13 cm × 14 cm. What is the volume of the box?

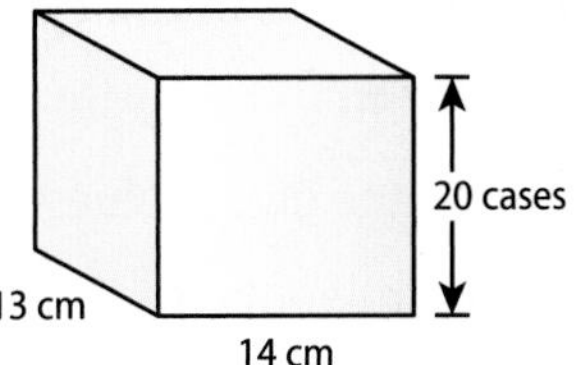

Think: The length and the width of the box are given. The height of the box is 20 times the height of a CD case.

STEP 1 Find the height of the box. $h = 20 \times \text{height of CD case}$

$= 20 \times 0.5$

$= 10$

STEP 2 Find the volume of the box. $V = Bh$

$= 13 \times 14 \times 10$

$= 1{,}820$

Since the measures are in centimeters, the volume of the box is 1,820 cm^3.

Try It This Way

Draw a cube like the one shown. If you draw 19 horizontal lines across one face, you would represent the 20 CD cases inside of the box. The height of each case is 0.5 cm, so the height of the box is 20×0.5 cm.

Finding the Volume of a Cylinder

A **cylinder** is a geometric solid with two circular bases and one curved lateral surface. The **volume** of a cylinder is the space it occupies. A cylinder has three dimensions—length, width, and height—so its volume is measured in cubic units.

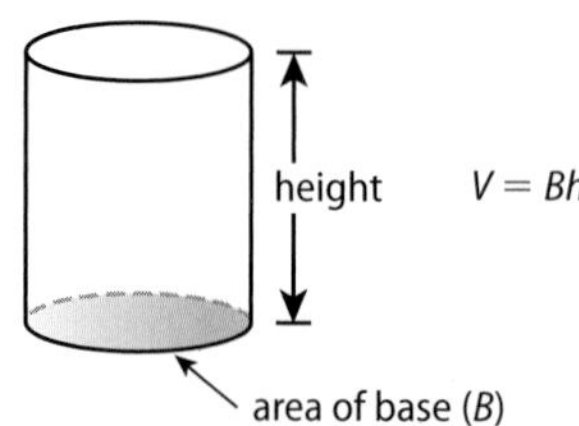

All cylinders have a circular base. To find the area of the base, use the formula for the area of a circle, πr^2. So the formula for finding the volume of a cylinder is:

V of a cylinder = area of the base (B) times the height (h)
$V = Bh$
$V = \pi r^2 h$

Need More HELP

Remember, the value of π is not an exact number, so the calculation for the volume of a cylinder will always be an approximation. As soon as you substitute a value for π into the formula, you must use the symbol for "approximately equal to," which is $\approx$.

EXAMPLE 3

Find the volume of the cylinder to the right. Use $\frac{22}{7}$ for π.

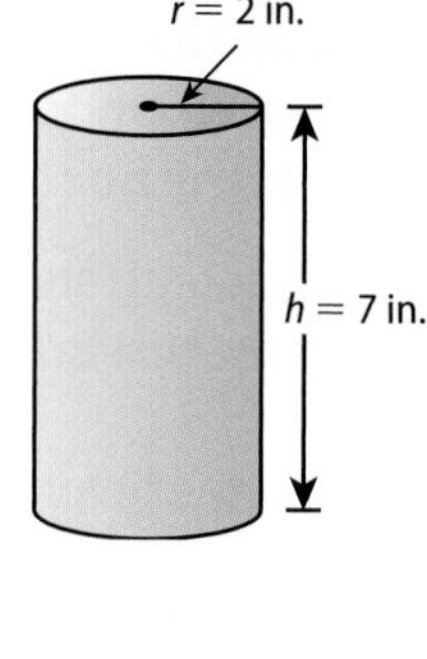

Substitute the given values into the formula.	$V = \pi r^2 h$
Simplify the exponent.	$\approx \left(\frac{22}{7}\right)(2^2)(7)$
Reorder the factors and simplify.	$\approx \left(\frac{22}{7}\right)(4)(7)$
Multiply.	$\approx \frac{22}{\cancel{7}_1} \cdot \frac{\cancel{7}^1}{1} \cdot \frac{4}{1}$
	≈ 88

Since the measures are in inches, the volume of the cylinder is approximately 88 in.^{3}.

Got to KNOW!

Volume of a Cylinder

The formula for the volume of a cylinder is the area of the base times the height.

$V = Bh$, where B = the area of the circular base

$V = \pi r^2 h$

EXAMPLE 4

Find the volume of the cylinder to the right. Use 3.14 for π. Round the volume to the nearest cubic centimeter.

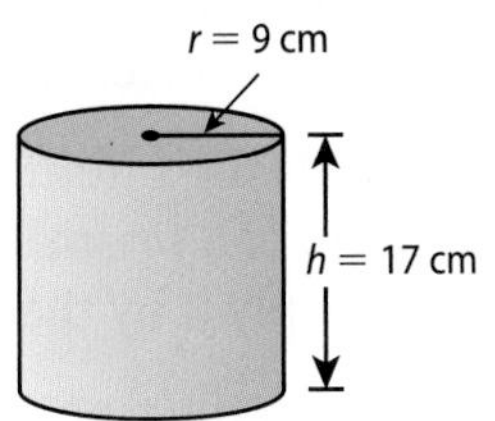

Substitute the values into the formula.	$V = \pi r^2 h$
Simplify the exponent.	$\approx (3.14)(9^2)(17)$
Multiply.	$\approx (3.14)(81)(17)$
Round.	$\approx 4{,}323.78$
	$\approx 4{,}324$

Since the measures are in centimeters, the volume of the cylinder is approximately 4,324 cm^3.

Try It This Way

You can substitute a value for π first, as shown in Examples 4 and 5, or you can substitute the value last. For Example 4, the alternate calculation would be:

$V = \pi r^2 h$
$= \pi(9^2)(17)$
$= \pi(81)(17)$
$= \pi(1{,}377)$
$\approx 3.14(1{,}377)$
$\approx 4{,}323.78$

EXAMPLE 5

The tank in a rainwater collection system has a diameter of 8.8 feet and a height of 12 feet. What is the volume of the tank to the nearest cubic foot?

Think: The radius of the tank is one-half of its diameter. This means that $r = 8.8 \div 2 = 4.4$, and $r^2 = 4.4 \times 4.4 = 19.36$, which is not divisible by 7, so I should use 3.14 for π.

Substitute the values into the formula.	$V = \pi r^2 h$
Multiply.	$\approx (3.14)(19.36)(12)$
Round.	≈ 729.48
	≈ 729

Since the measures are given in feet, the volume of the tank is approximately 729 ft^3.

EXAMPLE 6

Which container has the greater volume? Use 3.14 for π.

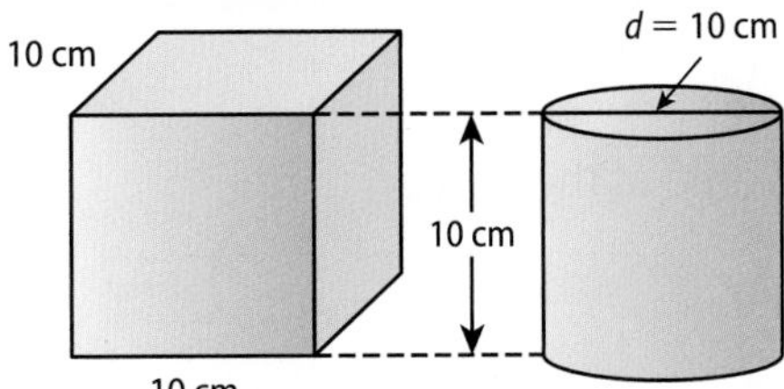

Substitute the given values into the correct formula and solve for V. The radius of the cylinder is: $10 \div 2 = 5$

Volume of the Cube	**Volume of the Cylinder**
$V = Bh$	$V = Bh$
$= (s^2)(h)$	$= \pi r^2 h$
$= (10^2)(10)$	$\approx (3.14)(5^2)(10)$
$= (100)(10)$	$\approx (3.14)(25)(10)$
$= 1{,}000$	≈ 785

The volume of the cube is 1,000 cm^3, and the volume of the cylinder is 785 cm^3, so the cube has the greater volume.

SEARCH

To see step-by-step videos of these problems, enter the page number into the SWadvantage.com Search Bar.

Volumes of Pyramids and Cones

Finding the Volume of a Pyramid

A **pyramid** is a geometric solid with one base that is a polygon and triangular faces that meet at a vertex. Pyramids are named for the shape of their bases.

The formula for finding the volume of a pyramid is related to the formula for finding the volume of a prism. To find the volume of a prism, first find the area of the base B. Then multiply it by the height of the prism.

The figure to the right shows a pyramid inside a prism. The figures have the same base measures and the same height.

The pyramid does not fill the prism completely. In fact, its volume is one-third the volume of the prism.

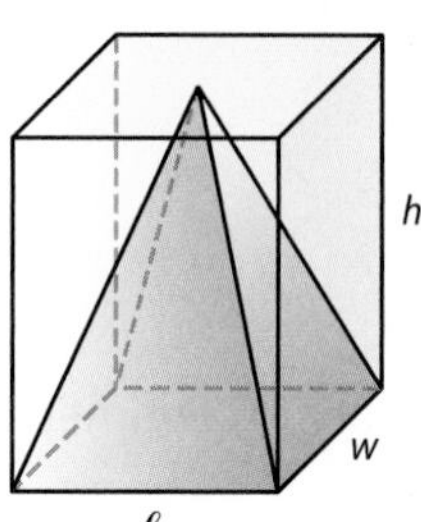

So the volume formula for a pyramid is one-third that of a prism, where B = the area of the base.

$$V \text{ prism} = Bh$$

$$V \text{ of a pyramid} = \frac{1}{3}Bh$$

Not all pyramids have the same shaped base. Refer to the *Got to Know!* box to review formulas for the volume of a pyramid.

Volume Formulas for Pyramids

V of a pyramid $= \frac{1}{3}Bh$, where B = area of the base.

Pyramid	Volume Formula
Square	$V = \frac{1}{3}(s^2)(h)$
Rectangular	$V = \frac{1}{3}(\ell \times w)(h)$ or $\frac{1}{3}(B \times h)(h)$
Triangular	$V = \frac{1}{3}\left(\frac{1}{2}Bh\right)(h)$

In the formula for the *area of a triangular pyramid*, the h refers to two different heights. In $\frac{1}{2}(Bh)$, the h is the height of the triangular base. The *other* h is the height of the pyramid.

EXAMPLE 1

Find the volume of the pyramid to the right.

Use the formula for the volume of a pyramid. $V = \frac{1}{3}Bh$

Substitute ℓw for B. $V = \frac{1}{3}\ell wh$

Substitute for ℓ, w, and h. $= \frac{1}{3}(8)(3)(4)$

Multiply to simplify. $= \frac{1}{3}(24)(4)$

$= \frac{1}{\cancel{3}_1} \cdot \frac{\cancel{96}^{32}}{1}$

$= 32$

The volume of the rectangular pyramid is 32 m³.

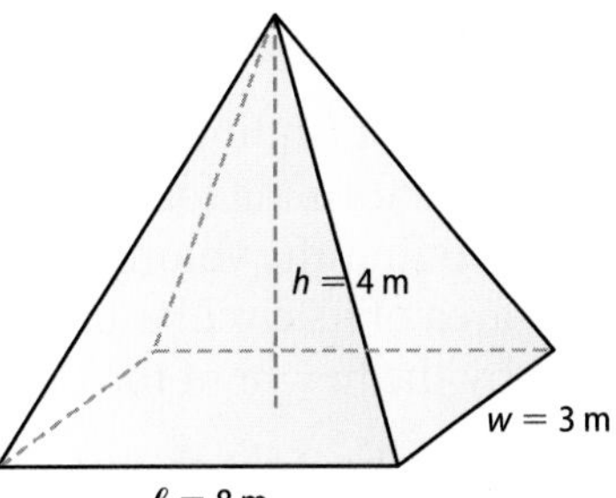

EXAMPLE 2

An artist designed an outdoor sculpture that includes a glass pyramid. The pyramid is 120 ft tall and has a square base with a 64-ft perimeter. What is the volume of the pyramid?

Think: I can divide the perimeter by 4 to find the length of one side of the base.

Find the length of the sides of the base. $s = \text{perimeter} \div 4$

Substitute 64 for p. $= 64 \div 4$

$= 16$ ft

Use the volume formula. $V = \frac{1}{3}Bh$, where $B = s^2$.

Substitute 16 for s and 120 for h. $= \frac{1}{3}(16)(16)(120)$

Multiply to simplify. $= \frac{1}{\cancel{3}_1} \cdot \frac{256}{1} \cdot \frac{\cancel{120}^{40}}{1}$

$= 256 \cdot 40$

$= 10{,}240$

The volume of the sculpture is 10,240 ft³.

Got to KNOW!

Express Volume in Cubic Units

Volume is the amount of space a solid object occupies. A solid object has three dimensions—*length*, *width*, and *height*—and is measured in cubic units.

If you calculate $V = 15$ and the given information is in feet, you must state the volume in one of the following ways.

15 cubic feet

15 ft³

15 cu ft

SEARCH

To see step-by-step videos of these problems, enter the page number into the SWadvantage.com Search Bar.

Finding the Volume of a Cone

A **cone** is a geometric solid figure with one base that is a circle and a curved surface that tapers to a point called the *vertex*.

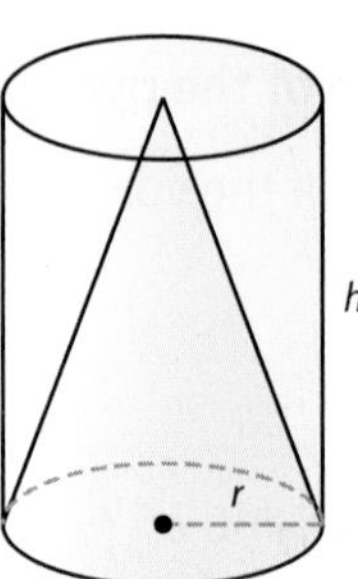

The formula for finding the volume of a cone is related to the formula for finding the volume of a cylinder. To find the volume of a cylinder, first find the area of its circular base B. Then multiply the area by the height of the cylinder.

The figure to the right shows a cone inside of a cylinder. Their bases and their heights are congruent. The cone does not fill the cylinder completely. In fact, its volume is one-third the volume of the cylinder.

So the volume formula for a cone is one-third that of a cylinder. Since B is the area of the circular base, you can substitute the formula for the area of a circle for B.

$$V \text{ cylinder} = Bh$$
$$= (\pi r^2)(h)$$
$$V \text{ of a cone} = \frac{1}{3}Bh$$
$$= \frac{1}{3}(\pi r^2)(h)$$

Watch Out!

Any value substituted for π is an approximate value, so the volume of a cone will always be an approximation. Be sure to use the symbol $\approx$ as soon as you replace π with a value, such as 3.14.

SEARCH

To see step-by-step videos of these problems, enter the page number into the SWadvantage.com Search Bar.

EXAMPLE 3

Find the volume of the cone to the right. Use 3.14 for π.

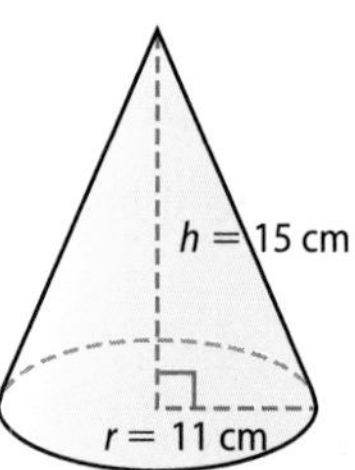

Use the formula $V = \frac{1}{3}Bh$, where B = the area of the circular base. Substitute for π last.

Find the area of the base in terms of π. $B = \pi r^2$

Substitute 11 for *r*. $= \pi(11^2)$

$= \pi(121)$

Use the volume formula. $V = \frac{1}{3}Bh$

Substitute the known values. $= \frac{1}{\cancel{3}_1} \cdot \frac{\pi}{1} \cdot \frac{121}{1} \cdot \frac{\cancel{15}^5}{1}$

Multiply to simplify. $= 605\pi$

Substitute for π. $\approx 605(3.14)$

$\approx 1{,}899.7$

The volume of the cone is approximately 1,899.7 cm^3.

EXAMPLE 4

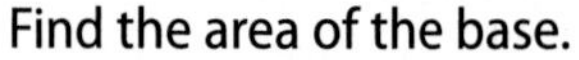

Find the volume of the paper cup. Use $\frac{22}{7}$ for π.

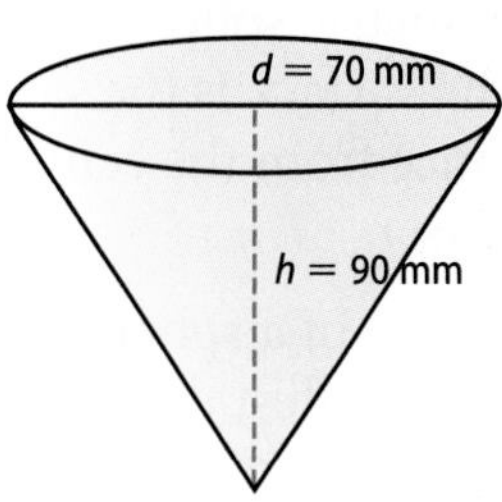

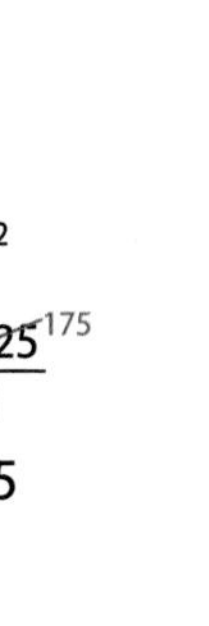

Use the formula $V = \frac{1}{3}Bh$.

Think: $B = \pi r^2$ but the diameter is given. Divide the diameter by 2 to find the radius.
70 mm ÷ 2 = 35mm, so $r = 35$.

Find the area of the base.	$B = \pi r^2$
Substitute for r and π.	$B = \frac{22}{7} \cdot 35^2$
Multiply and simplify.	$= \frac{22}{\cancel{7}_1} \cdot \frac{\cancel{1225}^{175}}{1}$
	$= 22 \cdot 175$
	$= 3{,}850$
Use the volume formula.	$V = \frac{1}{3}Bh,$
Substitute the known values.	$= \frac{1}{\cancel{3}_1} \cdot \frac{3{,}850}{1} \cdot \frac{\cancel{90}^{30}}{1}$
Multiply to simplify.	$= 115{,}500$

The volume of the paper cup is approximately 115,500 mm^3.

Try It This Way

Use a calculator to do the multiplications or to check your answer. Use 3.14 for π. The calculation is long, so you may want to do it in parts. To solve or check Example 4:

Enter

Then press ×.
Enter 3 5.
Then press ×.
Enter 3 5.
Then press ENTER.

The display will show the area of the base:

3846.5

Press ×.
Enter 9 0.
Then press ÷.
Enter 3.
Then press ENTER.

The display will show the volume:

115395

The volume is slightly different from the volume shown in Exercise 4 because you used 3.14 for π.

EXAMPLE 5

Which figure has the greater volume, the square pyramid or the cone? Use 3.14 for π.

Think: The volume formula for both figures is $V = \frac{1}{3}Bh$.

This means that the figure with the greater value for B will have the greater volume. Find the area of each base.

Square Pyramid	Cone
$B = s^2$	$B = \pi r^2$
$= 4^2$	$\approx (3.14)(2^2)$
$= 16$ sq in.	$\approx (3.14)(4)$
	≈ 12.56 sq in.

Since $16 > 12.56$, then $\frac{1}{3}(16)(6) > \frac{1}{3}(12.56)(6)$.

The volume of the pyramid is greater than the volume of the cone.

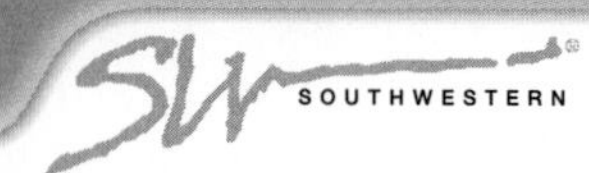

Finding the Surface Area of a Sphere

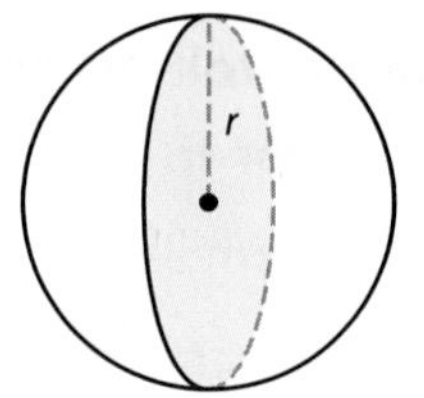

A **sphere** is a geometric solid with a smooth curved surface. Every point on the surface is the same distance from the center. This distance from the center of the circle to its surface is its radius, *r*.

The surface area (*SA*) of a sphere is equal to the lateral surface area of the smallest cylinder that can contain the sphere. You can demonstrate this by placing a sphere on a piece of paper with a *length equal to the diameter of the sphere* and *a width equal to the circumference of the sphere.* If you could wrap the paper around the sphere with no overlaps, it would completely cover the sphere.

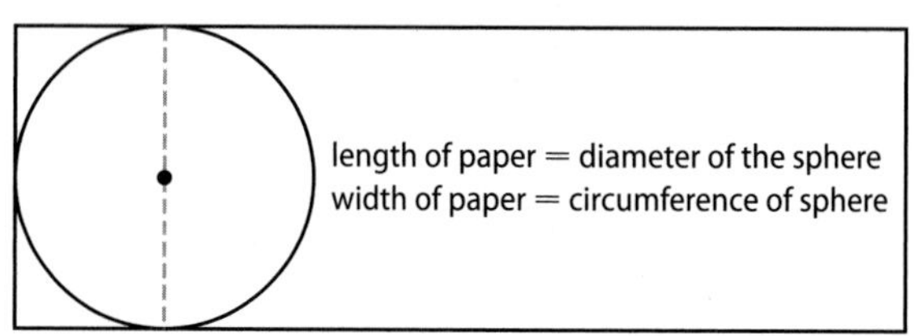

As you can see, you can find the surface area of a sphere using the formula for the area of the rectangular paper: length × width.

length (diameter of sphere) × width (circumference of sphere)
$(2r) \times (2\pi r)$

To find the surface area of a sphere, use the formula: $SA = 4\pi r^2$.

Remember, *surface area* is measured using square units because area has two dimensions.

To see step-by-step videos of these problems, enter the page number into the SWadvantage.com Search Bar.

EXAMPLE 1

Find the surface area of the sphere at the right to the nearest square inch. Use 3.14 for π.

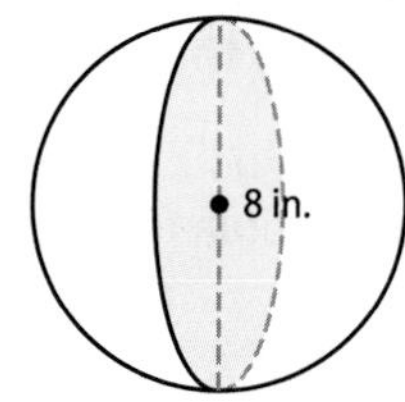

Think: If $d = 8$ in., then $r = 8 \div 2 = 4$ in.

Substitute the known values into the formula.	$SA = 4\pi r^2$
Clear the exponent.	$\approx 4(3.14)(4^2)$
Multiply to simplify.	$\approx (4)(3.14)(16)$
	≈ 200.96
Round.	≈ 201

The units are in inches, so surface area of the sphere is approximately 201 in.^{2}.

EXAMPLE 2

A decorator wants to cover a concrete sphere with spray glitter paint. The paint can says it will cover 2,200 square centimeters. How many cans of paint will the decorator need? Use $\frac{22}{7}$ for π.

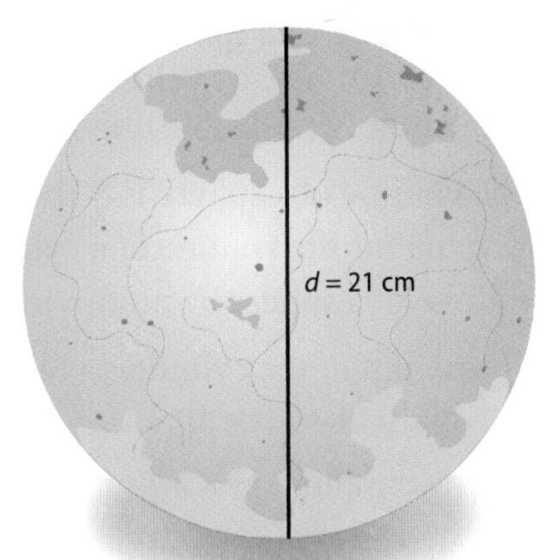

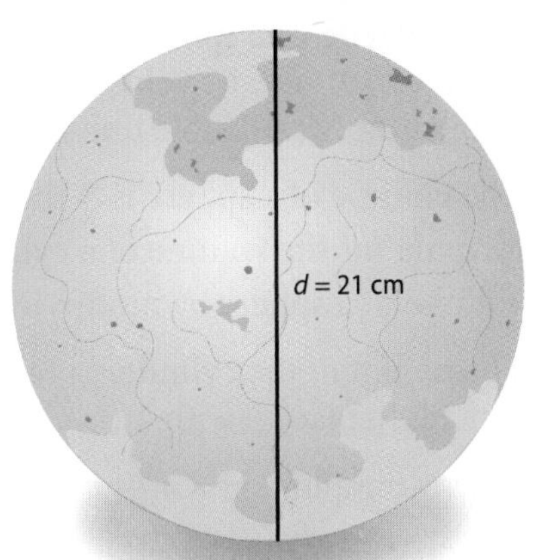

Think: I need to find the surface area of the sphere. If $d = 21$ cm, then $r = \frac{21}{2}$ cm. I can substitute for π last.

Substitute the value for r into the formula.	$SA = 4\pi r^2$
Clear the exponent.	$= 4\pi\left(\frac{21}{2}\right)^2$
Multiply to simplify.	$= \frac{\overset{1}{\cancel{4}}}{1}\pi\left(\frac{21}{\underset{1}{\cancel{2}}}\right)\left(\frac{21}{\underset{1}{\cancel{2}}}\right)$
Substitute for π.	$= \pi\left(\frac{441}{1}\right)$
	$\approx \left(\frac{22}{\underset{1}{\cancel{7}}}\right)\left(\frac{\overset{63}{\cancel{441}}}{1}\right)$
	$\approx (22)(63)$
	$\approx 1{,}386$

The surface area of the sphere is 1,386 cm^2. Since $1{,}386 < 2{,}200$, one can of spray glitter paint should be enough.

EXAMPLE 3

A sphere is inscribed in a cube with sides of 8 cm. What is the surface area of the sphere?

Think: When a figure is *inscribed* in another figure, it fits exactly. The sphere and the cube have the same height and width. The radius of the sphere is half the length of the side of the cube: $8 \div 2 = 4$ cm.

8 cm

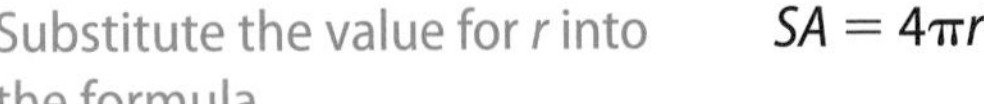
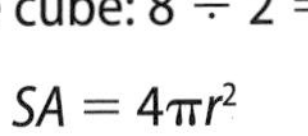

Substitute the value for r into the formula.	$SA = 4\pi r^2$
Clear the exponent.	$= 4\pi(4)(4)$
Multiply.	$= 4\pi(16)$
Substitute 3.14 for π.	$\approx \pi(64)$
Multiply.	$\approx (3.14)(64)$
	≈ 200.96

The surface area of the sphere is approximately 200.96 cm^2.

Got to KNOW!

Surface Area of a Sphere

$SA = 4\pi r^2$

Try It This Way

You can use a calculator to find the surface area, but you should use 3.14 for π and 10.5 for r. The calculation for Example 2 is:
$SA = (4)(3.14)(10.5)^2$.

Enter: 4
Press: ×
Enter: 3.14
Press: ×
Enter: 10.5
Press: ×
Enter: 10.5
Press: ENTER

The calculator display will show: 1384.74

The SA is slightly different from the SA shown in Example 2 because you used 3.14 for π.

Finding the Volume of a Sphere

The **volume** of a sphere is the amount of space it occupies. Even though a sphere has a curved surface, its volume is measured in cubic units. You can think of the volume as the number of cubic units needed to fill the sphere.

The volume of a sphere is $\frac{2}{3}$ the volume of a cylinder that has the same height. The formula for the volume of a cylinder is $V = \pi r^2 h$. You can find the formula for the volume of a sphere by modifying the formula for the volume of a cylinder.

The height of the cylinder is the diameter of the sphere. Replace h with $2r$.	$V = \frac{2}{3}(\pi r^2 h)$
STEP 1 Simplify: $r^2 \times r = r^3$. Reorder the factors.	$V = \frac{2}{3}(\pi r^2 2r)$
STEP 2 Simplify: $\frac{2}{3}(2) = \frac{4}{3}$	$V = \frac{2}{3}(2\pi r^3)$
Formula for the volume of a sphere.	$V = \frac{4}{3}\pi r^3$

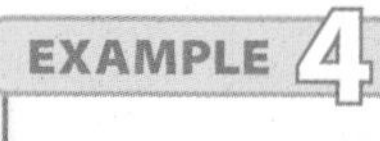

Use the formula to find the volume of the sphere to the right to the nearest cm³. Use 3.14 for π.

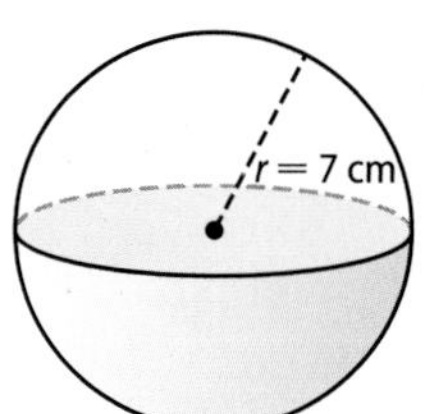

Substitute the known values into the formula.	$V = \frac{4}{3}\pi r^3$
Clear the exponent.	$\approx \frac{4}{3}(3.14)(7)^3$
Multiply to simplify.	$\approx \frac{4}{3}(3.14)(343)$
Divide to simplify.	$\approx \frac{4{,}308.08}{3}$
Round to the nearest whole centimeter.	$\approx 1{,}436.0266$
	$\approx 1{,}436$

The volume of the sphere is approximately 1,436 cm³.

Need More HELP

For help with exponents, go to *Exponents* in *Algebra* (Book 2, p. 1396).

EXAMPLE 5

The radius of the golf ball shown to the right is 21 mm. What is the volume? Use $\frac{22}{7}$ for π.

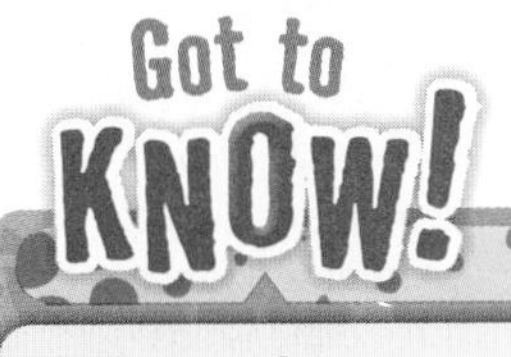

Volume of a Sphere

$V = \frac{4}{3}\pi r^3$

Substitute the given values into the formula.	$V = \frac{4}{3}\pi r^3$
Clear the exponent. Simplify.	$\approx \left(\frac{4}{3}\right)\left(\frac{22}{7}\right)(21)^3$
Multiply.	$\approx \left(\frac{4}{\cancel{3}_1}\right)\left(\frac{22}{\cancel{7}_1}\right)\left(\frac{\overset{441}{\cancel{\overset{1323}{\cancel{9{,}261}}}}}{1}\right)$
	$\approx 38{,}808 \text{ mm}^3$

The volume of a golf ball is approximately 38,808 mm^3.

EXAMPLE 6

The sphere has a diameter of 3.4 inches.

a. What is its volume in terms of π, rounded to the nearest tenth?

Think: If $d = 3.4$ in., then $r = 3.4 \div 2 = 1.7$ in.

Substitute the value of r into the formula.	$V = \frac{4}{3}\pi r^3$
Clear the exponent. Simplify.	$= \frac{4}{3}(\pi)(1.7)^3$
Multiply.	$= \left(\frac{4}{3}\right)(\pi)(4.913)$
Round.	$= (\pi)6.55066\ldots$
	$= 6.55\pi$

The volume of the sphere in terms of π, rounded to the nearest tenth is 6.6π in.^{3}.

b. What is the approximate volume rounded to the nearest cubic inch? Use 3.14 for π.

Substitute 3.14 for π.	$V = 6.55\pi \text{ in.}^3$
Simplify.	$\approx (6.55)(3.14)$
Round.	≈ 20.567
	≈ 21

The volume of the sphere, rounded to the nearest cubic inch, is about 21 in.^{3}.

The phrase "in terms of π" means that you leave π in the answer.

SEARCH

To see step-by-step videos of these problems, enter the page number into the SWadvantage.com Search Bar.

Need More HELP

Remember, a solid geometric figure has three dimensions—length, width, and height—and is sometimes referred to as a 3-D, 3-dimensional, or three-dimensional figure.

For help finding the surface area of various solid figures, go to *Surface Area* (pp. 558, 562, 566, 578).

What Is a 3-D Composite Figure?

A **3-D composite** is a figure made up of two or more smaller solid figures, such as prisms, cubes, pyramids, cylinders, cones, and spheres. The composite figure on the left below is composed of a rectangular prism and a square pyramid.

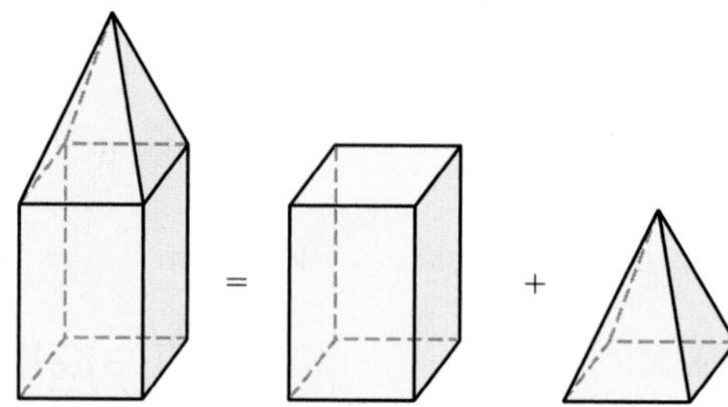

Finding the Surface Area of a Composite Figure

The surface area (*SA*) of a composite 3-D figure is made up of polygons and/or curved surfaces. To find the surface area of a composite figure, follow these steps:

- First identify the smaller figures that compose the larger figure.
- Then find the area of each *external* surface of the larger figure.
- Finally, add the areas of the external surfaces to find the total surface area.

Refer to the *Got to Know!* box to review area formulas.

EXAMPLE 1

Find the surface area of the composite figure shown on the right.

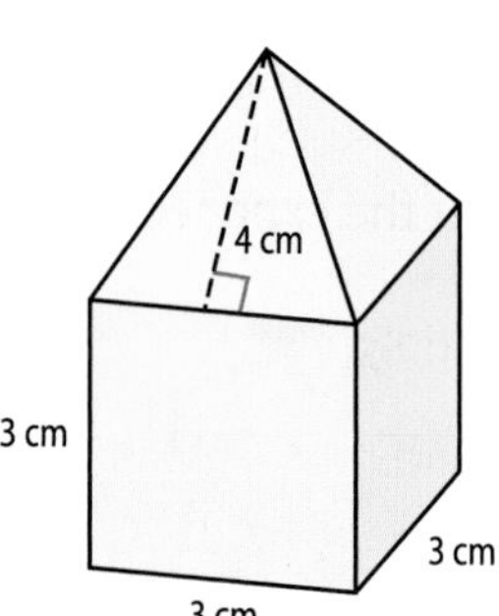

STEP 1 Identify the smaller figures that compose the figure. This figure is composed of a cube with a square pyramid sitting on top of it. The base of the pyramid is congruent to the sides of the cube.

STEP 2 The external surface of the composite figure is made up of:

- 5 congruent squares (4 sides and the bottom of the cube) and
- 4 congruent triangles (4 sides of the pyramid).

A square $= s^2$
$= 3^2$
$= 9 \text{ cm}^2$

A triangle $= \frac{1}{2}bh$
$= \frac{1}{2}(3 \times 4)$
$= 6 \text{ cm}^2$

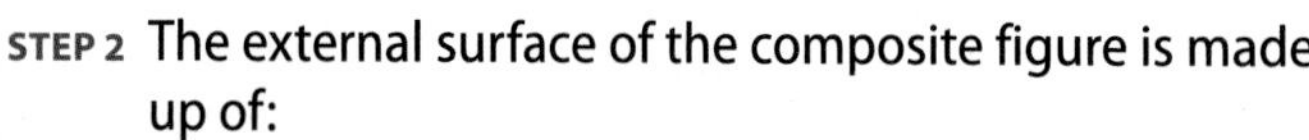
$9 \text{ cm}^2 \times 5$ squares $= 45 \text{ cm}^2$ $6 \text{ cm}^2 \times 4$ triangles $= 24 \text{ cm}^2$

STEP 3 Add to find the total surface area.

$45 \text{ cm}^2 + 24 \text{ cm}^2 = 69 \text{ cm}^2$

The surface area of the composite figure is 69 cm².

Watch Out!

The sides of the smaller figures that join to form the composite figure are *not* included in the surface area. In Example 1, the top surface of the cube and the base of the pyramid join and are not on the surface of the composite figure. Do not include them in the total surface area.

EXAMPLE 2

The figure on the right is made from large wooden blocks. Find the figure's surface area.

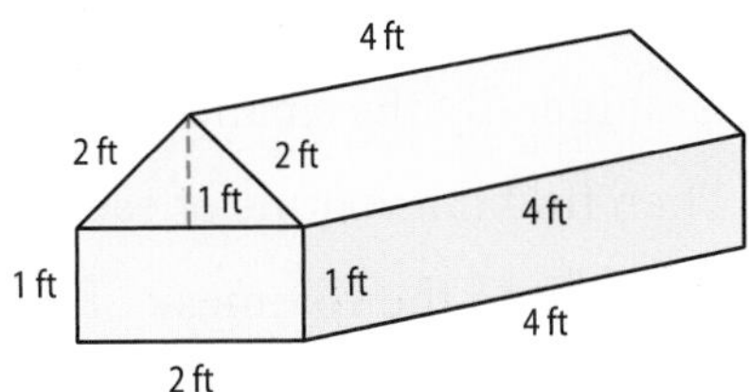

STEP 1 The house is made from a triangular prism and a rectangular prism. The sides of the triangular prism are congruent to the top and the bottom of the rectangular prism because they all measure 2 ft by 4 ft.

STEP 2 The external surface of the composite figure is made up of:

- 2 congruent triangles (bases of the triangular prism)
- 3 congruent rectangles (2 sides of the triangular prism + the bottom of the rectangular prism)
- 2 congruent rectangles (bases of the rectangular prism)
- 2 congruent rectangles (1×4 sides of the rectangular prism)

A triangle base $= \frac{1}{2}bh$

$= \frac{1}{2}(2 \times 1) = 1 \text{ ft}^2$

$1 \text{ ft}^2 \times 2$ triangles $= 2 \text{ ft}^2$

A rectangle side $= bh$

$= 2 \times 4 = 8 \text{ ft}^2$

$8 \text{ ft}^2 \times 3$ rectangles $= 24 \text{ ft}^2$

A rectangle base $= bh$

$= 2 \times 1 = 2 \text{ ft}^2$

$2 \text{ ft}^2 \times 2$ rectangles $= 4 \text{ ft}^2$

A rectangle side $= bh$

$= 1 \times 4 = 4 \text{ ft}^2$

$4 \text{ ft}^2 \times 2$ rectangles $= 8 \text{ ft}^2$

STEP 3 Add to find the total surface area: $2 \text{ ft}^2 + 24 \text{ ft}^2 + 4 \text{ ft}^2 + 8 \text{ ft}^2 = 38 \text{ ft}^2$

The surface area of the figure is 38 ft^2.

EXAMPLE 3

Find the surface area of this figure. Round your answer to the nearest whole number. Use 3.14 for π.

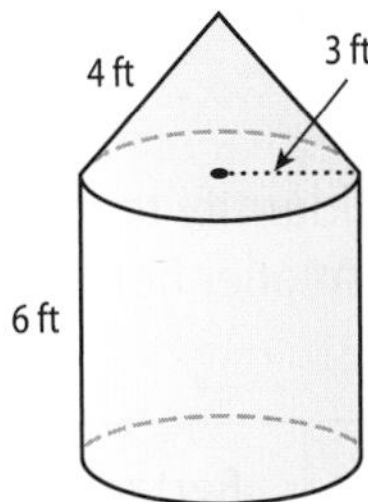

STEP 1 The figure is composed of a cylinder and a cone.

STEP 2 The SA is made up of the lateral surface area of the cylinder, 1 base of the cylinder, and the lateral surface area of the cone.

Cylinder		Cone
Lateral SA	A of One Base	Lateral SA
$= (2\pi r)(h)$	$= \pi r^2$	$(\pi r\ell)$, where ℓ = slant height of cone
$\approx (2 \times 3.14 \times 3)(6)$	$\approx 3.14 \times 3^2$	$\approx 3.14 \times 3 \times 4$
$\approx 113.04 \text{ ft}^2$	$\approx 28.26 \text{ ft}^2$	$\approx 37.68 \text{ ft}^2$

STEP 3 Add the three areas: $113 \text{ ft}^2 + 28 \text{ ft}^2 + 38 \text{ ft}^2 = 179 \text{ ft}^2$

The surface area of the composite figure is approximately 179 ft^2.

Got to KNOW!

Surface Area of 3-D Composite Figures

To find the surface area:

- Identify the smaller figures that compose the larger one.
- Find the area of each external surface.
- Add to find the total surface area.

Use area formulas to find the area of the individual surfaces:

Triangle $A = \frac{1}{2}bh$

Square $A = s^2$

Rectangle $A = \ell w$ or bh

Circle $A = \pi r^2$

Sphere $SA = 4\pi r^2$

Hemisphere $SA = 2\pi r^2$

Cylinder Lateral $SA = (2\pi r)(h)$

Cone Lateral $SA = (\pi r\ell)$, where ℓ = slant height of the cone.

SEARCH

To see step-by-step videos of these problems, enter the page number into the SWadvantage.com Search Bar.

Finding the Volume of a 3-D Composite Figure

To find the volume of a 3-D composite figure:

- First identify the smaller figures that compose the larger figure.
- Then find the volume of each of the smaller figures.
- Finally, add the volumes to find the volume of the composite figure.

Refer to the *Got to Know!* box to review volume formulas.

Need More HELP

Remember, volume is the space inside a figure and is measured in cubic units, such as ft^3 or m^3.

You can write the measure in three ways:

For example:
6 cubic feet

6 cu ft

6 ft^3

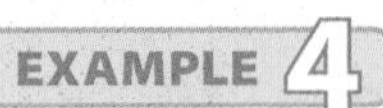

EXAMPLE 4

Find the volume of the composite figure shown on the right.

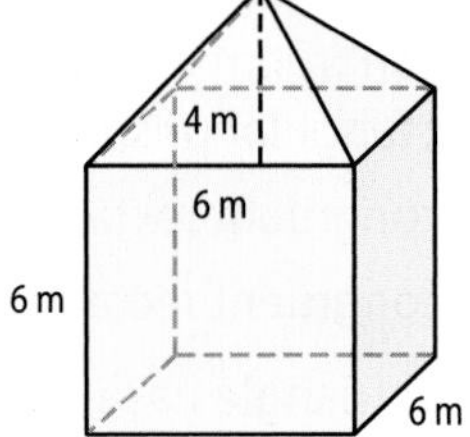

STEP 1 The composite figure is made up of a square prism and a square pyramid.

STEP 2 Find the volume of each smaller figure.

Square Prism

$V = Bh$, where $B = s^2$

$= 6^2 \times 6$

$= 216 \text{ m}^3$

Square Pyramid

$V = \frac{1}{3}(s^2)(h)$

$= \frac{1}{3}(6^2)(4)$

$= \frac{1}{3}(144)$

$= 48 \text{ m}^3$

STEP 3 Find the sum of the volumes: $216 \text{ m}^3 + 48 \text{ m}^3 = 264 \text{ m}^3$

The volume of the composite figure is 264 m^3.

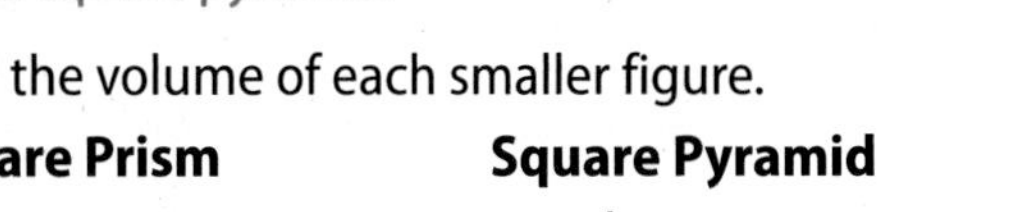

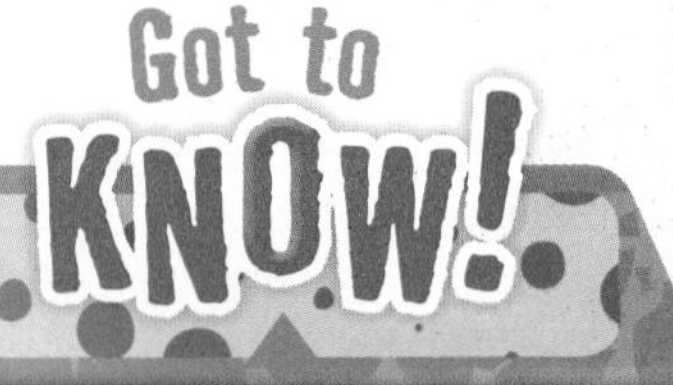

Volume of 3-D Composite Figures

To find the volume of a composite figure, identify the smaller figures that compose the larger one. Then find the volume of each smaller figure. Finally, add to find the total volume. Use volume formulas below.

Triangular Prism	$V = \left(\frac{1}{2}bh\right) \times h$	**Rectangular Pyramid**	$V = \frac{1}{3}(\ell w)(h)$
Square Prism	$V = Bh$, where $B = s^2$	**Cone**	$V = \frac{1}{3}Bh$, where $B = \pi r^2$
Rectangular Prism	$V = Bh$, where $B = \ell w$	**Cylinder**	$V = Bh$, where $B = \pi r^2$
Triangular Pyramid	$V = Bh$, where $B = \frac{1}{2}bh$	**Sphere**	$V = \frac{4}{3}\pi r^3$
Square Pyramid	$V = \frac{1}{3}(s^2)(h)$	**Hemisphere**	$V = \left(\frac{4}{3}\pi r^3\right) \div 2$

EXAMPLE 5

A farmer stores grain in the two silos shown to the right. Which silo can store more grain? Use 3.14 for π.

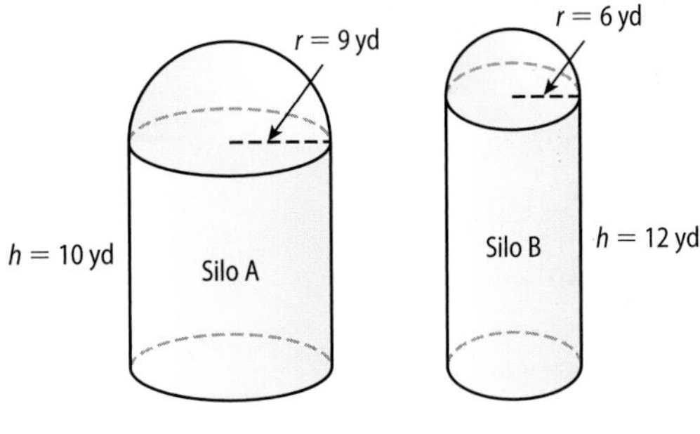

Find the volume of each silo. Then compare their volumes. The silo with the greater volume can store more grain.

Think: Each silo is composed of a cylinder and a half sphere (hemisphere). Find the volume of each smaller figure to the nearest whole number. Then add to find the volume of the composite figure.

Silo A

Volume of the cylinder

$V = \pi r^2 h$

$\approx 3.14(9^2)(10)$

$\approx 2{,}543 \text{ yd}^3$

Volume of the hemisphere

$V = \left(\frac{4}{3}\pi r^3\right) \div 2$

$\approx \left(\frac{4}{3}\right)(3.14)(9^3) \div 2$

$\approx \frac{9156.24}{3} \div 2$

$\approx 3052.08 \div 2$

$\approx 1{,}526 \text{ yd}^3$

V of Silo A:

$2{,}543 \text{ yd}^3 + 1{,}526 \text{ yd}^3 = 4{,}069 \text{ yd}^3$

Silo B

Volume of the cylinder

$V = \pi r^2 h$

$\approx 3.14(6^2)(12)$

$\approx 1{,}356 \text{ yd}^3$

Volume of the hemisphere

$V = \left(\frac{4}{3}\pi r^3\right) \div 2$

$\approx \left(\frac{4}{3}\right)(3.14)(6^3) \div 2$

$\approx \frac{2712.96}{3} \div 2$

$\approx 904.32 \div 2$

$\approx 452 \text{ yd}^3$

V of Silo B:

$1{,}356 \text{ yd}^3 + 452 \text{ yd}^3 = 1{,}808 \text{ yd}^3$

Compare the volumes.

$4{,}069 \text{ yd}^3 > 1{,}808 \text{ yd}^3$

Silo A has a greater volume than Silo B, so it can store more grain.

Need More HELP

For help finding the volume of solid figures, go to *Volumes of Prisms and Cylinders*, *Volume of Pyramids and Cones*, and *Surface Area and Volume of Spheres* (pp. 570, 574, 578).

SEARCH

To see step-by-step videos of these problems, enter the page number into the SWadvantage.com Search Bar.

Scientific Notation

What Came Before?

- Exponents and powers of 10
- Operations with decimals

What's This About?

- Converting between scientific notation and standard notation
- Multiplying and dividing numbers in scientific notation
- Significant digits

Practical Apps

- Computer programmers use scientific notation for calculations with large and small numbers.
- Astronomers use scientific notation to describe vast distances in space.

just for FUN!

Q: Why did the zero in 4,520 look sad?

A: Because it was feeling insignificant.

CONTENTS UPLOAD DOWNLOAD

You can find more practice problems online by visiting:
www.SWadvantage.com

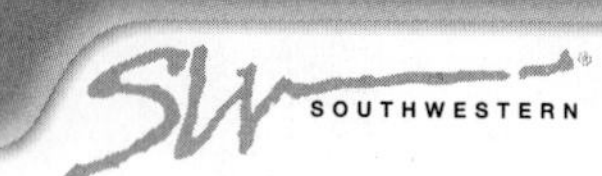

What Is Scientific Notation?

For help with exponents and powers of 10, go to *Exponents,* p. 294.

For help with multiplying or dividing by a power of 10, go to *Multiplying and Dividing by 10, 100, etc.* in *Foundations of Mathematics,* p. 94.

Scientific notation is a system of expressing very large or very small numbers as the product of a decimal and a power of 10. Numbers written in scientific notation are made up of two parts: a **coefficient** and a **power of 10**.

$$2.4 \times 10^5$$

↑ coefficient ↑ power of 10

- The *coefficient* is a decimal number greater than 1 but less than 10. It always contains one non-zero digit to the left of the decimal point. The coefficient is sometimes called the *mantissa.*
- The *power of 10* has a base (10) and an exponent. The exponent tells how many times the coefficient is multiplied by 10. For the number above, 2.4 is multiplied by 10 five times: $2.4 \times 10^5 = 2.4 \times 100{,}000 = 240{,}000$.

Writing Very Large Numbers in Scientific Notation

To express a large number in scientific notation, follow these steps:

- Find the coefficient by moving the decimal point *to the left* until there is one non-zero digit to the left of the decimal point. — 3,610,000. → 3.610000 (6 5 4 3 2 1)
- Count the number of places you moved the decimal point. — 6 places
- Use 6 as the exponent for the power of 10. — 3.61×10^6

3,610,000 expressed in scientific notation is 3.61×10^6.

EXAMPLE 1

Write 75,400,000 in scientific notation.

STEP 1 Move the decimal point *to the left* until there is one non-zero digit to the left of the decimal point.
75,400,000. → 7.5400000

STEP 2 Count the number of places that the decimal point moved.
The decimal point moved 7 places.

STEP 3 Use 7 as the exponent for the power of 10.
Multiply the decimal number by the power of 10.
7.54×10^7

75,400,000 in scientific notation is 7.54×10^7.

SEARCH

To see step-by-step videos of these problems, enter the page number into the SWadvantage.com Search Bar.

EXAMPLE 2

Express both distances in scientific notation.

a. The distance between Earth and the moon is approximately 385,000 km.

STEP 1 Move the decimal point to the left until there is one non-zero digit to the left of the decimal point.
385,000. → 3.85000

STEP 2 Count the number of places that the decimal point moved.
The decimal point moved 5 places.

STEP 3 Use 5 as the exponent for the power of 10.
Multiply the decimal number by the power of 10.
3.85×10^5

The distance between Earth and the moon is approximately 3.85×10^5 km.

b. The distance between Earth and the sun is approximately 150,000,000 km.

STEP 1 Move the decimal point to the left until there is one non-zero digit to the left of the decimal point.
150,000,000. → 1.50000000

STEP 2 Count the number of places that the decimal point moved.
The decimal point moved 8 places.

STEP 3 Use 8 as the exponent for the power of 10.
Multiply the decimal number by the power of 10.
1.5×10^8

The distance between Earth and the sun is approximately 1.5×10^8 km.

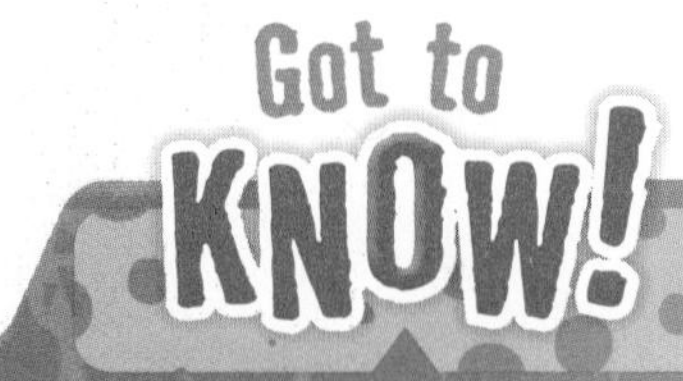

Writing Large Numbers in Scientific Notation

You can use scientific notation to express a number greater than 1 as the product of a decimal number (coefficient) and a positive power of 10.

To go from *standard form to scientific notation*:

- Move the decimal point *to the left* until there is one non-zero digit to the left of the decimal point.

  37,800,000. → 3.7800000 The decimal point moved 7 places. There is one non-zero digit (3) to the left of the decimal point.

- Use the number of places the decimal point moved as the exponent in the power of 10.

  $37{,}800{,}000 = 3.78 \times 10^7$

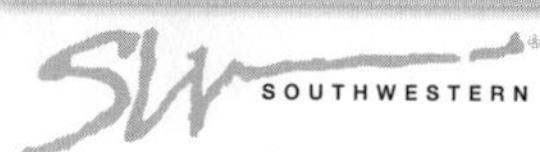

Writing Very Small Numbers in Scientific Notation

Very small numbers, such as 0.0000000013, are often expressed in scientific notation. Express them as the product of the coefficient and a *negative* power of ten. The negative exponent tells how many times the decimal coefficient is multiplied by $\frac{1}{10}$ (0.1).

- To find the coefficient, move the decimal point *to the right* until there is one non-zero digit to the left of the decimal point. — 0.000000001.3 → 1.3 (1 2 3 4 5 6 7 8 9)
- Count the number of places you moved the decimal point. — The decimal point moved 9 places to the right.
- The power on the 10 is −9. — 1.3×10^{-9}

0.0000000013 expressed in scientific notation is 1.3×10^{-9}.

Watch Out!

Negative exponents do not mean that the number is negative.

$10^{-3} = \frac{1}{10} \times \frac{1}{10} \times \frac{1}{10}$
$= \frac{1}{1{,}000}$.

EXAMPLE 3

Write 0.00000925 in scientific notation.

Think: The number has a value less than 1, so the exponent is negative.

STEP 1 Move the decimal point *to the right* until there is one non-zero digit to the left of the decimal point.
0.000009.25 → 9.25

STEP 2 Count the number of places that the decimal point moved. The decimal point moved 6 places.

STEP 3 The power on the 10 is −6. Multiply the decimal number by the power of 10.
9.25×10^{-6}

0.00000925 expressed in scientific notation is 9.25×10^{-6}.

SEARCH

To see step-by-step videos of these problems, enter the page number into the SWadvantage.com Search Bar.

EXAMPLE 4

The mass of a small grain of sand is about 0.00000000035 kg. Express this weight in scientific notation.

STEP 1 Move the decimal point to the right until there is one non-zero digit to the left of the decimal point.
0.0000000003.5 → 3.5

STEP 2 Count the number of places that the decimal point moved. The decimal point moved 10 places.

STEP 3 The power on the 10 is −10. Multiply the decimal number by the power of 10.
3.5×10^{-10}

The mass of a small grain of sand is about 3.5×10^{-10} kg.

Scientific Notation and Calculators

On a calculator display, the letter E means "times the power of 10." For example, 5.012E12 $= 5.012 \times 10^{12}$ and 5.012E-12 $= 5.012 \times 10^{-12}$.

EXAMPLE 5

Visible light has a wavelength range from about 0.00000075 meters to 0.0000004 meters. Express the range of the wavelengths in scientific notation.

STEP 1 For each number, move the decimal point to the right until there is one non-zero digit to the left of the decimal point.

0.0000007.5 → 7.5

0.0000004. → 4.0

When a decimal point is included with a whole number, a zero is usually placed to the right of the decimal point.

STEP 2 Count the number of places that the decimal point moved.

In both numbers, the decimal point moved 7 places to the right.

STEP 3 The power on the 10 is −7. Multiply the decimal number by the negative power of 10.

7.5×10^{-7} [7.5E-7] 4.0×10^{-7} [4E-7]

Visible light has a wavelength range from about 7.5×10^{-7} meters to 4.0×10^{-7} meters.

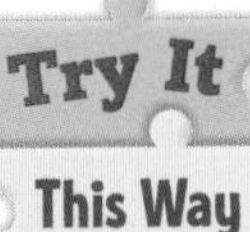

Try It This Way

If you have a calculator with a MODE button, you can change the mode to SCI to work with scientific notation. The exact steps to follow vary depending on what brand of calculator you are using.

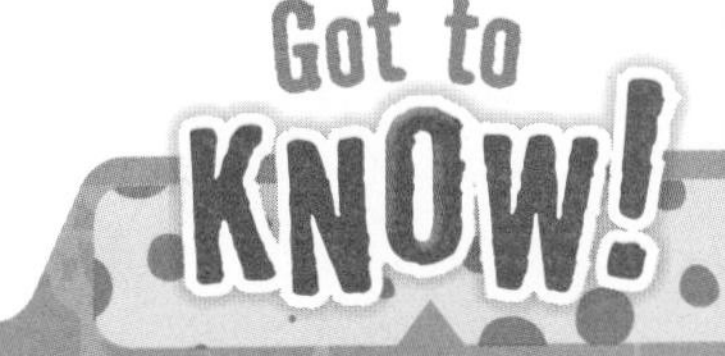

Writing Numbers Less Than 1 in Scientific Notation

You can express a number less than 1 as the product of a decimal number (coefficient) and a *negative* power of 10.

To go from *standard form to scientific notation*:

- Move the decimal point *to the right* until there is one non-zero digit to the left of the decimal point.

  0.0000003.78 → 3.78 The decimal point moved 7 places to the right. There is one non-zero digit (3) to the left of the decimal point.

- Use the number of places the decimal point moved as the exponent in the power of 10. Because the decimal point moved to the right, the power is negative.

  $0.000000378 = 3.78 \times 10^{-7}$

Converting to Standard Notation

To answer the question, "What is scientific notation?" go to *Writing in Scientific Notation*, p. 588.

For help with multiplying or dividing by a power of 10, go to *Multiplying and Dividing by 10, 100, etc.* in *Foundations of Mathematics*, p. 94.

Scientific Notation to Standard Form: Values > 1

A number written in scientific notation is expressed as *the product of a decimal coefficient and a power of 10.* The number below is written in scientific notation.

$$9.7 \times 10^3$$

coefficient ↑ (9.7)   power of 10 ↑ (10^3)

To convert a number in scientific notation to standard form, multiply the coefficient by the power of 10.

$$\begin{aligned} 9.7 \times 10^3 &= 9.7 \times 10 \times 10 \times 10 \\ &= 9.7 \times 1{,}000 \\ &= 9{,}700 \end{aligned}$$

You do not actually need to do the multiplication shown above. You can use the rules for multiplying by a power of 10, as shown below.

- Identify the exponent. The exponent is 3. — 9.7×10^3
- Move the decimal point in the coefficient *to the right* the number of places indicated by the exponent. — 9.7 → 9.700. (1 2 3)
- Fill in the empty places with zeros. — 9,700.

EXAMPLE 1

Express each number in standard notation.

a. 7.61×10^5

Think: The exponent of the power of 10 is 5. I need to multiply 7.61 by 10 five times.

Multiply: Follow the rules for multiplying by a power of 10. Move the decimal point 5 places to the right.

7.61 → 7.16000. → 761,000

The number 7.61×10^5 in standard notation is 761,000.

b. 1.88×10^6

STEP 1 Identify the exponent.

1.88×10^6 The exponent is 6.

STEP 2 Move the decimal point 6 places to the right and add zeros.

1.88 → 1880000.

STEP 3 Insert zeros to express the number in standard form.

1,880,000

The number 1.88×10^6 in standard notation is 1,880,000.

In Example 1(b), use the method shown in part (a). When moving the decimal point in a number, draw in the circular arrows with each move. Go back and place a zero in each loop so you will have the correct number of zeros in the answer.

EXAMPLE 2

The distance between the sun and the planet Mars is about 2.28×10^8 km. What is the distance in standard form?

STEP 1 Identify the exponent.

2.28×10^8 The exponent is 8.

STEP 2 Move the decimal point 8 places to the right and add zeros.

2.28 → 2.28000000.

STEP 3 Insert zeros to express the number in standard form.

228,000,000

The distance between the sun and Mars is about 228,000,000 km.

If you have a scientific calculator with an EE or EXP button, you can use it to convert from scientific notation to standard form (decimal notation.) Read the instructions for the calculator you are using.

EXAMPLE 3

The distance between Earth and the moon varies. At one point during a lunar month, this distance was about 3.98×10^5 km. Use multiplication to find this distance in standard form.

Think: $3.98 \times 10^5 =$
$3.98 \times 10 \times 10 \times 10 \times 10 \times 10 =$
$3.98 \times 100{,}000 =$
398,000

CHECK The exponent is 5. Move the decimal point 5 places to the right.
3.98000. ✔

The distance in standard form is about 398,000 km.

SEARCH

To see step-by-step videos of these problems, enter the page number into the SWadvantage.com Search Bar.

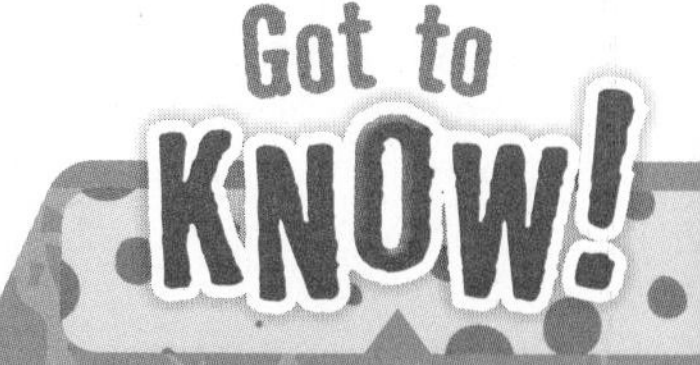

Scientific Notation to Standard Form

Follow these steps to change scientific form to standard form.

Numbers > 1	Numbers < 1
6.45×10^6 • Identify the exponent. The exponent is 6. • Move the decimal point in the coefficient *to the right* the number of places indicated by the exponent, filling the empty places with zeros. 6.450000. 1 2 3 4 5 6 $6.45 \times 10^6 = 6{,}450{,}000$	4.3×10^{-4} • Identify the exponent. The exponent is −4. • Move the decimal point in the coefficient *to the left* the number of places indicated by the exponent, filling the empty places with zeros. .0004.3 4 3 2 1 $4.3 \times 10^{-4} = 0.00043$

Scientific Notation to Standard Form: Values < 1

Numbers with a value less than 1 expressed in scientific notation have a negative exponent. The exponent tells how many times the decimal coefficient is multiplied by one-tenth.

$$\underset{\text{coefficient}}{9.7} \times \underset{\text{power of 10}}{10^{-3}}$$

Remember, a decimal number with a value less than 1 is written with a zero to the left of the decimal point.

To convert the number in scientific notation to standard form, multiply the coefficient by the power of 10.

$$\begin{aligned} 9.7 \times 10^{-3} &= 9.7 \times 0.1 \times 0.1 \times 0.1 \\ &= 9.7 \times 0.001 \\ &= 0.0097 \end{aligned}$$

Just as with positive powers of 10, you do not actually need to do the multiplication. Follow these steps to convert from scientific notation to standard notation.

- Identify the exponent. The exponent is −3. — 9.7×10^{-3}
- Move the decimal point in the coefficient *to the left* the number of places indicated by the exponent. — 9.7 → 0.009.7 (3 2 1)
- Fill in missing places with zeros. — 0.0097

The number 9.7×10^{-3} in standard notation is 0.0097.

SEARCH

To see step-by-step videos of these problems, enter the page number into the SWadvantage.com Search Bar.

EXAMPLE 4

Express 4.5×10^{-5} in standard notation.

METHOD 1

Think: 4.5 is multiplied by 10^{-5}.
Multiply by 0.1 five times.

Multiply: $4.5 \times 0.1 \times 0.1 \times 0.1 \times 0.1 \times 0.1$
$= 4.5 \times 0.00001$
$= 0.000045$

METHOD 2

- Identify the exponent.
  The exponent is −5.
- Move the decimal point 5 places to the left and insert zeros.
  .00004.5
- Insert zeros to write the number in standard form.
  0.000045

The number 4.5×10^{-5} written in standard notation is 0.000045.

Comparing and Ordering Numbers

When comparing and ordering numbers expressed in scientific notation, compare the values of the exponents first.

If the *exponents are the same*, then compare the values of the coefficients. The number with the greater coefficient has the greater value.

$9.1 \times 10^8 > 8.3 \times 10^8$

If the *exponents are different*,

- the number with the *greater positive exponent* has the *greater value* because it is multiplied by 10 more times.

  $8.3 \times 10^8 > 8.3 \times 10^7$

- the number with the *greater negative exponent* has the *lesser value* because it is multiplied by one-tenth more times.

  $4.6 \times 10^{-7} < 4.6 \times 10^{-6}$

When some numbers are written in scientific notation and others in standard notation, they must all be expressed in standard notation or all in scientific notation before they can be compared and ordered.

Remember, in 5.2×10^3, 5.2 is multiplied by 10 three times.
In 5.2×10^{-3}, 5.2 is multiplied by 0.1 three times.

Order the numbers from least to greatest.

9.3×10^3 103,000 2,900,000 7.54×10^{-4} 8.532×10^5 0.990

METHOD 1

STEP 1 Express the three numbers in scientific notation in standard notation.

$9.3 \times 10^3 = 9{,}300$ $7.54 \times 10^{-4} = 0.000754$ $8.532 \times 10^5 = 853{,}200$

STEP 2 Then use place value to order the numbers.

$0.000754 > 0.990 > 9{,}300 > 103{,}000 > 853{,}200 > 2{,}900{,}000$

METHOD 2

STEP 1 Express the three numbers in standard notation in scientific notation.

$103{,}000 = 1.03 \times 10^5$ $2{,}900{,}000 = 2.9 \times 10^6$ $0.990 = 9.9 \times 10^{-1}$

STEP 2 Only two numbers have the same exponent. Compare their coefficients.

$1.03 < 8.532$, so $1.03 \times 10^5 < 8.532 \times 10^5$.

STEP 3 Compare the exponents to order the other numbers.

$7.54 \times 10^{-4} > 9.9 \times 10^{-1} > 9.3 \times 10^3 > 1.03 \times 10^5 > 8.532 \times 10^5 > 2.9 \times 10^6$

Both sets of numbers are ordered from least to greatest.

Try It This Way

When comparing numbers, you may find it easier if you write the numbers in a vertical format and insert placeholder zeros as needed.

0.0000754
0.99
9,300.0
103,000.0
853,200.0
2,900,000.0

7.540×10^{-4}
9.900×10^{-1}
9.300×10^3
1.030×10^5
8.532×10^5
2.900×10^6

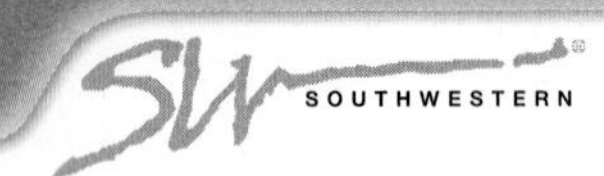

Multiplying Numbers with Scientific Notation

SEARCH

To see step-by-step videos of these problems, enter the page number into the SWadvantage.com Search Bar.

Remember that a number in scientific notation is expressed as the product of a decimal coefficient and a power of ten.

$$(2.4 \times 10^4) \times (8.9 \times 10^3)$$

To multiply numbers written in scientific notation, use the steps shown below.

STEP 1 Use the properties of numbers to reorder the factors.
$(2.4)(10^4)(8.9)(10^3) = (2.4 \times 8.9) \times (10^4 \times 10^3)$

STEP 2 Simplify: $(21.36) \times (10^4 \times 10^3)$

Multiply the coefficients.	$(21.36) \times (10^7)$
Multiply the powers of 10 by *adding* the exponents.	21.36×10^7

Need More HELP

For help with expressing numbers in scientific notation, go to pp. 588–591.

STEP 3 Express the product in scientific notation.

Move the decimal point *to the left* until there is one non-zero digit to the left of the decimal point. Then increase the value of the exponent by the number of places you moved the decimal point.

$$21.36 \times 10^7 = 2.136 \times 10^8$$

$21.36 \times 10^7 = 2.136 \times 10^8$

EXAMPLE 1

Multiply $(4.6 \times 10^3) \times (5.3 \times 10^5)$.

STEP 1 Reorder the factors.
$(4.6 \times 5.3) \times (10^3 \times 10^5)$

STEP 2 Simplify.

Multiply the coefficients.	$24.38 \times (10^3 \times 10^5)$
Multiply the powers of 10.	24.38×10^8

STEP 4 Write the product in scientific notation.
$24.38 \times 10^8 = 2.438 \times 10^9$

$(4.6 \times 10^3) \times (5.3 \times 10^5) = 2.438 \times 10^9$

Watch Out!

Remember, to multiply powers of 10, you *add* the values of the exponents. Do not multiply them.

Got to KNOW!

Multiplying Numbers in Scientific Notation

- Use the properties of numbers to reorder the factors.
- Multiply the coefficients.
- Multiply the powers of 10 by adding the exponents.
- Express the product in scientific notation.

Expressing the Product in Scientific Notation

When the exponent is positive, it is easy to remember to increase the value of the exponent the same number of places that you moved the decimal point. It can be a little confusing when the exponent is negative. For example:

$$(3.2 \times 10^4) \times (4.3 \times 10^{-6}) = 13.76 \times 10^{-2}$$

When you move the decimal point to the left one place, 13.76 becomes 1.376. But watch out! The exponent does not become negative 3. Look at this situation as another multiplication problem.

$$13.76 \times 10^{-2} = (1.376 \times 10^1)(10^{-2}) = (1.376)(10^1)(10^{-2}) \text{ Add the exponents.}$$
$$= (1.376)(10^{-1})$$

You *increase the value of the exponent* in this situation. Remember that -1 is greater than -2. You can multiply to see that the values are equivalent.

$$13.76 \times 10^{-2} = 1.3.76 \times 0.1 \times 0.1 = 0.0376$$
$$1.376 \times 10^{-1} = 1.376 \times 0.1 = 0.0376$$

For help adding positive and negative numbers (integers), go to *Adding Integers* in *Algebra*, Book 2, p. 1390.

Find the product of $(3.25 \times 10^6) \times (6.2 \times 10^{-8})$.

STEP 1 Reorder the factors.
$(3.25 \times 6.2) \times (10^6 \times 10^{-8})$

STEP 2 Simplify.

Multiply the coefficients. $20.15 \times (10^6 \times 10^{-8})$

Multiply the powers of 10. 20.15×10^{-2}

STEP 3 Write the product in scientific notation.
$20.15 \times 10^{-2} = 2.015 \times 10^{-1}$

$(3.25 \times 10^6) \times (6.2 \times 10^{-8}) = 2.015 \times 10^{-1}$

EXAMPLE 3

The mass of one oxygen atom is approximately 2.68×10^{-26} kg. A container can hold 5.44×10^{30} oxygen atoms. What is the total mass of oxygen that the container can hold?

Express the quantity as a multiplication expression.	$(2.68 \times 10^{-26}) \times (5.44 \times 10^{30})$
Rearrange the factors.	$(2.68 \times 5.44) \times (10^{-26} \times 10^{30})$
Multiply the coefficients.	$2.68 \times 5.44 = 14.58$
Add the exponents.	$10^{-26} \times 10^{30} = 10^{-26+30} = 10^4$
Write the product in scientific notation.	$14.58 \times 10^4 = 1.458 \times 10^5$

The container can hold approximately 1.458×10^5 kg of oxygen.

Try It This Way

Use the EE key on a scientific calculator to check your answer. You can also find the product using a graphing calculator. Refer to the instruction manual for specific instructions for the calculator you are using.

Dividing with Scientific Notation

Dividing Numbers Written with Scientific Notation

Remember that a number in scientific notation is expressed as the product of a decimal coefficient and a power of ten.

$$(3.2 \times 10^9) \div (6.4 \times 10^5)$$

To divide numbers written in scientific notation, such as the ones above, follow the steps shown below. Notice that when dividing, you subtract the values of the exponents.

STEP 1 Write the problem in fractional form.

$$\frac{3.2 \times 10^9}{6.4 \times 10^5} = \left(\frac{3.2}{6.4}\right)\left(\frac{10^9}{10^5}\right)$$

STEP 2 Simplify $\left(\frac{3.2}{6.4}\right)\left(\frac{10^9}{10^5}\right)$.

Divide the coefficients. $(0.50)\left(\frac{10^9}{10^5}\right)$

Divide the powers of 10 by subtracting the exponents. $(0.50)(10^{9-5}) = (0.50)(10^4)$

STEP 3 Write the quotient in scientific notation. Remember, there must be one non-zero digit to the left of the decimal point. Because you move the decimal point one place to the right, the value of the exponent decreases by 1.

$0.5.0 \times 10^4 = 5.0 \times 10^3$

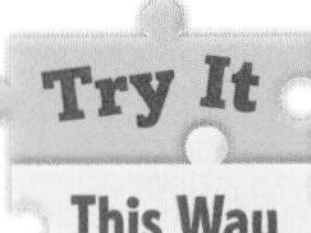

Use the EE key on a scientific calculator to divide numbers expressed in scientific notation. You can also find the product using a graphing calculator. Refer to the instruction manual for specific instructions for the calculator you are using.

EXAMPLE 1

Divide: $(1.8 \times 10^7) \div (4.5 \times 10^5)$

STEP 1 You can write the problem in fractional form or reordered as shown below.

$(1.8 \div 4.5) \div (10^7 \div 10^5)$

STEP 2 Simplify.

Divide the coefficients. $0.40 \times (10^7 \div 10^5)$

Divide the powers of 10. 0.40×10^2

STEP 3 Write the product in scientific notation.

$0.4.0 \times 10^2 = 4.0 \times 10^1$

$(1.8 \times 10^7) \div (4.5 \times 10^5) = 4.0 \times 10^1$

Dividing Numbers in Scientific Notation

- Write the problem in fractional form.
- Divide the coefficients.
- Divide the powers of 10 by subtracting the exponents.
- Express the product in scientific notation.

EXAMPLE 2

Divide: $(1.23 \times 10^{-10}) \div (2.4 \times 10^{6})$

STEP 1 You can write the problem in fractional form or reordered as shown below.
$(1.23 \div 2.4) \times (10^{-10} \div 10^{6})$

STEP 2 Simplify.
Divide the coefficients. $(0.5125) \times (10^{-10} \div 10^{6})$
Divide the powers of 10. $0.5125 \times 10^{-10-(6)} = 0.5125 \times 10^{-16}$

STEP 3 Write the product in scientific notation.
Think: $0.5125 = 5.125 \times 10^{-1}$
$(5.125 \times 10^{-1}) \times 10^{-16} = (5.125) \times (10^{-1}) \times (10^{-16})$
$= 5.125 \times 10^{-1+(-16)}$

$(1.23 \times 10^{-10}) \div (2.4 \times 10^{6}) = 5.125 \times 10^{-17}$

For help subtracting positive and negative numbers (integers), go to *Subtracting Integers* in *Algebra*, Book 2, p. 1392.

EXAMPLE 3

Divide: $(7.35 \times 10^{-3}) \div (9.323 \times 10^{-7})$

STEP 1 You can write the problem in fractional form or reordered as shown below.
$(7.35 \div 9.323) \times (10^{-3} \div 10^{-7})$

STEP 2 Simplify.
Divide the coefficients. $\approx 0.788 \times (10^{-3} \div 10^{-7})$
Divide the powers of 10. $\approx 0.788 \times 10^{-3-(-7)} \approx 0.788 \times 10^{4}$

STEP 3 Write the product in scientific notation.
$0.788 \times 10^{4} = 7.88 \times 10^{3}$

$(7.35 \div 9.323) \times (10^{-3} \div 10^{-7} = 7.88 \times 10^{3}$

SEARCH

To see step-by-step videos of these problems, enter the page number into the SWadvantage.com Search Bar.

EXAMPLE 4

The average distance between Earth and the moon is about 2.39×10^{5} miles. If a rocket could travel at the speed of light, 1.86×10^{5} mi/sec, approximately how many seconds would it take to reach the moon?

Think: This is a rate problem. Since distance = rate × time, time = distance ÷ rate.

Write a division expression.	$(2.39 \times 10^{5}) \div (1.86 \times 10^{5})$
Reorder.	$(2.39 \div 1.86) \times (10^{5} \div 10^{5})$
Divide the coefficients.	$2.39 \div 1.86 \approx 1.28$
Subtract the exponents.	$10^{5} \div 10^{5} = 10^{0}$
Write the quotient.	1.28×10^{0}

There is only one non-zero digit to the left of the decimal point so the quotient is in scientific notation.

If a rocket could travel at the speed of light, it would take approximately 1.28 seconds to reach the moon.

Significant Digits

Significant digits are the digits in a number that represent an actual measurement.

- All non-zero digits in a number are significant.
- Some zeros in a number are significant.

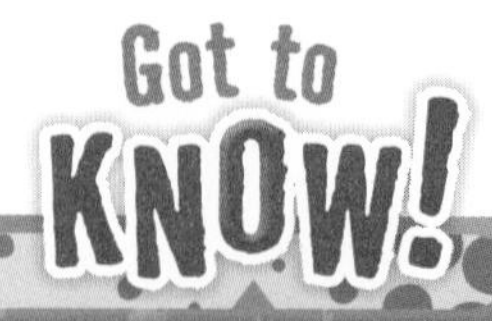

Significant Digits

Significant digits are the digits in a number that represent actual measurements.

- All non-zero digits in a number are significant.
- Some zeros in a number are significant.

Not Significant and Significant Zeros

Decimal Numbers Between 0 and 1	*Not Significant:* Zeros to the left of *all* the non-zero digits *Significant:* All other zeros in the number, including zeros between two significant digits and *trailing* zeros to the right of the number	0.085403 0.0854030
Positive Integers	*Not Significant:* Zeros to the right of *all* the non-zero digits *Significant:* Zeros between two significant digits	804,200 804,200
Decimal Numbers Greater Than 1	*Significant:* All zeros are significant.	5,087,00.40 804,200.0 4,925.0

The two zeros on the right in 804,200 are sometimes called *ambiguous*. They may represent a measure, or the number may be a rounded number. However, when counting significant figures, they must be counted as not significant.

To see step-by-step videos of these problems, enter the page number into the SWadvantage.com Search Bar.

EXAMPLE 1

Classify the digits in each number as significant or not significant. Support your choices.

a. 2,304

The non-zero digits 2, 3, and 4 are significant because all non-zero digits are significant.

The 0 is significant because it is between two significant digits.

b. 0.03200

The digits 3 and 2 are significant because all non-zero digits are significant.

The zeros to the *right* of 2 are significant because they are trailing zeros.

The zeros to the *left* of 3 are *not* significant because they are to the left of all the non-zero digits.

c. 42,960

The digits 4, 2, 9, and 6 are significant because all non-zero digits are significant.

The zero to the *right* of 6 is *not* significant because it is to the right of all the non-zero digits.

d. 3,046.0760

All of the digits are significant because the number is a decimal number greater than 1.

Operations and Significant Digits

Often you need to perform a calculation with numbers that do not have the same number of significant digits. Use the rules below to find the answers.

Products and Quotients	Sums and Differences
The product or quotient of two measurements should contain only as many *significant digits* as there are in the measurement with the lesser number of significant digits.	The sum or difference of two measurements should contain only as many *decimal places* (not significant digits) as there are in the measurement with the lesser number of decimal places.

EXAMPLE 2

Multiply: 15.034 × 0.72

15.034	×	0.72	=	10.82448	⟶	round to 11
5 significant digits		2 significant digits		7 significant digits		2 significant digits

The product is approximately 11.

Watch Out!

When you round the product in Example 2, remember, the zero in 10.8 is significant so this number has 3 significant digits.

EXAMPLE 3

Divide: 0.55125 ÷ 0.25

0.55125	÷	0.25	=	2.205	⟶	round to 2.2
5 significant digits		2 significant digits		4 significant digits		2 significant digits

The quotient is approximately 2.2.

Watch Out!

The rules for addition and subtraction are different from the rules for multiplication and division.

EXAMPLE 4

Add: 24.6 + 28.058

$$\begin{array}{r} 24.6 \\ +\ 28.058 \\ \hline 52.658 \end{array}$$

1 decimal place
3 decimal places

Round 52.658 to 1 decimal place.
52.658 rounds to 52.7.

The sum is about 52.7.

EXAMPLE 5

Subtract: 0.7086 − 0.034

$$\begin{array}{r} 0.7086 \\ -\ 0.034 \\ \hline 0.6746 \end{array}$$

4 decimal places
3 decimal places

Round 0.6746 to 3 decimal places.
0.6746 rounds to 0.675.

The difference is about 0.675.

Try It This Way

You can draw a vertical line to help you see the number of decimal places in an addition or subtraction problem.

$$\begin{array}{r|l} 4.57 & 8 \\ +\ 0.34 & \\ \hline 4.91 & 8 = 4.92 \end{array}$$

Precision in Measurement

The **precision of a measurement** is the smallest possible unit that is measured. It is related to the unit of the measurement used and the number of significant digits in the measurement. The measuring tool you use dictates how precise your measure can be. Look at the ruler and pencil below.

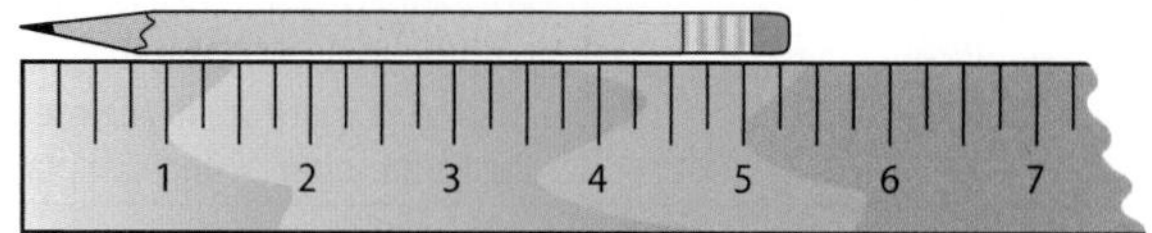

The increments on the scale are in fourths of an inch, so the ruler can measure to only one-quarter of an inch. Since the pencil is longer than $5\frac{1}{4}$ in. but less than $5\frac{1}{2}$ (or $5\frac{2}{4}$) in., your measurement will be accurate to only the nearest $\frac{1}{4}$ in.

The smaller the unit used to measure an object, the greater the accuracy of the measurement. Suppose you measured the pencil with three rulers that have the following scales.

Scale Increments	one-quarter inch	one-eighth inch	one-sixteenth inch
Pencil Measure	$5\frac{1}{4}$ in.	$5\frac{3}{8}$ in.	$5\frac{5}{16}$ in.

The most accurate measure of the pencil is $5\frac{5}{16}$ in.

Need More HELP

Sometimes the terms *precision* and *accuracy* are used to mean the same thing. In other contexts, precision and accuracy are two separate concepts. *Accuracy* refers to how closely a measured value agrees with the correct value. *Precision* refers to how closely a series of individual measurements of a value agree with each other.

EXAMPLE 6

Choose the more precise measurement. Support your answer.

a. 6 cm or 6 m

A centimeter is smaller than a meter, so 6 cm is more precise.

b. Donnie has a bathroom scale that measures in pounds and a kitchen scale that measure in ounces.

The kitchen scale is more precise because ounces are smaller than pounds.

SEARCH

To see step-by-step videos of these problems, enter the page number into the SWadvantage.com Search Bar.

EXAMPLE 7

Choose the more precise measurement. Support your answer.

a. 0.458 kL or 0.45 kL

0.458 kL; the units are the same, but 0.458 kL contains more significant digits.

b. 3.2 grams or 3.25 grams

3.25 grams; the units are the same but the number 3.25 contains more significant digits.

EXAMPLE 8

Three students measured the mass of a bag of pattern blocks and got the following measurements.

Angel: 1.1 kg **Connie: 1.0 kg** **Beker: 1.13 kg**

Whose measurement is the most precise? Why?

All of the measurements are in kilograms. Beker's is the most precise because it has the most significant digits, 3.

EXAMPLE 9

Dana needs to measure out one-fourth teaspoon of baking powder. She has a tablespoon, a teaspoon, and a half-teaspoon measuring spoon. Which measuring spoon is the best choice if she wants to measure the baking powder as precisely as possible? Explain your reasoning.

Of the three measuring spoons given, the one-half teaspoon will measure the smallest quantity of a substance. She can use it and estimate when it is half full.

The one-half teaspoon measure is the best choice.

Got to KNOW!

Precision in Measurement

- The smaller the unit, the more precise the measurement is.
- When the units are the same, the greater the number of significant digits in the measurement, the more precise the measure is.

Greatest Possible Error

The greatest possible error in a measurement is equal to one half of the smallest measurement in the unit. It is expressed as $\pm$ 0.5 [name of unit] and is read as, "plus or minus one-half [name of unit]."

EXAMPLE 10

What is the greatest possible error for a measurement of 3.6 kilograms?

Think: The unit is kilograms (kg). The smallest measurement in the unit is to one-tenth of a kg, or 0.1 kg.

$0.5 \times 0.1 \text{ kg} = 0.05 \text{ kg}$

The greatest possible error for the measurement 3.6 kg is $\pm$ 0.05 kg.

EXAMPLE 11

What is the greatest possible error for a measurement of 25 inches?

Think: The unit is inches. The smallest measurement in the unit is one inch.

$\frac{1}{2} \times 1 \text{ in.} = \frac{1}{2} \text{ in.}$

The greatest possible error for the measurement 25 inches is $\pm \frac{1}{2}$ inch.

Measurement

U.S. Customary System	Metric System
Length	
1 mile (mi) = 1,760 yards = 5,280 feet **1 yard (yd)** = 3 feet = 36 inches **1 foot (ft)** = 12 inches $\frac{1}{36}$ yard = $\frac{1}{12}$ foot = **1 inch (in.)**	**1 kilometer (km)** = 1,000 m 0.001 km = **1 meter (m)** = 100 cm = 1,000 mm 0.01 m = **1 centimeter (cm)** = 10 mm 0.001 m = 0.1 cm = **1 millimeter (mm)**
Area	
1 square mile (mi²) = 640 acres **1 acre (a)** = 4,840 yd^2 **1 square yard (yd²)** = 9 ft^2 **1 square foot (ft²)** = 144 $in.^2$ $\frac{1}{144}$ ft^2 = **1 square inch (in.²)**	**1 square kilometer (km²)** = 1,000,000 m^2 **1 square meter (m²)** = 10,000 cm^2 **1 square centimeter (cm²)** = 100 mm^2 0.01 cm^2 = **1 square millimeter (mm²)**
Volume	
1 cubic yard (yd³) = 27 ft^3 **1 cubic foot (ft³)** = 1,728 $in.^3$ $\frac{1}{1,728}$ ft^3 = **1 cubic inch (in.³)**	**1 cubic meter (m³)** = 1,000,000 cm^3 **1 cubic centimeter (cm³)** = 1,000 mm^3 0.001 cm^3 = **1 cubic millimeter (mm³)**
Capacity (Liquid)	
1 gallon (gal) = 4 qt = 8 pt = 16 c = 128 fl oz **1 quart (qt)** = 2 pt = 4 c = 32 fl oz **1 pint (pt)** = 2 c = 16 fl oz **1 cup (c)** = 8 fl oz $\frac{1}{8}$ cup = **1 fluid ounce (fl oz)**	**1 kiloliter (kL)** = 1,000 L 0.001 kL = **1 liter (L)** = 100 cL = 1,000 mL 0.01 L = **1 centiliter (cL)** = 10 mL 0.001 L = 0.1 cL = **1 milliliter (mL)**
Weight	**Mass**
1 ton (t) = 2,000 pounds **1 pound (lb)** = 16 ounces $\frac{1}{16}$ pound = **1 ounce (oz)**	**1 metric ton (t)** = 1,000 kg 0.001 t = **1 kilogram (kg)** = 1,000 g 0.001 kg = **1 gram (g)** = 100 cg = 1,000 mg 0.01 g = **1 centigram (cg)** = 10 mg 0.001 g = 0.1 cg = **1 milligram (mg)**
Temperature 	
32°F = freezing point of water 98.6°F = normal body temperature 212°F = boiling point of water $F = \frac{9}{5}C + 32$ or $F = 1.8C + 32$	0°C = freezing point of water 37°C = normal body temperature 100°C = boiling point of water $C = \frac{5}{9}(F - 32)$

Time

60 seconds (s) = **1 minute (min)**	365 days = **1 year (yr)**
60 minutes = **1 hour (h)**	52 weeks (approx.) = 1 year
24 hours = **1 day (d)**	12 months = 1 year
7 days = **1 week (wk)**	10 years = 1 decade
4 weeks (approx.) = **1 month (mo)**	100 years = 1 century

Equivalents

1 acre = 43,560 square feet = 4,840 square yards
1 bushel (U.S.) = 2,150.42 cubic inches
= 32 quarts
1 cord = 128 cubic feet
1 cubic centimeter = 0.061 cubic inch
1 cubic foot = 7.481 gallons = 1,728 cubic inches
1 cubic inch = 0.554 fluid ounce
= 16.387 cubic centimeters
1 cubic meter = 1.308 cubic yards
1 cubic yard = 0.765 cubic meter = 27 cubic feet
1 cup = 8 fluid ounces = 0.5 liquid pint
1 gallon (U.S.) = 231 cubic inches
= 128 U.S. fluid ounces
= 4 liquid quarts
1 liter = 1.057 liquid quarts
1 meter = 39.37 inches = 1.094 yards
1 micron = 0.001 millimeter = 0.00003937 inch
1 mile, nautical = 1.852 kilometers
= 1.151 statute miles
= 6,076.1155 feet
1 milliliter = 0.061 cubic inch
1 pint, dry = 33.600 cubic inches = 0.551 liter
1 pint, liquid = 28.875 inches = 0.473 liter
= 2 cups = 16 fluid ounces
1 pound, avoirdupois = 7,000 grains = 16 ounces
= 453.59237 grams
1 quart, dry (U.S.) = 67.201 cubic inches
= 1.101 liters
1 quart, liquid (U.S.) = 57.75 cubic inches
= 0.946 liter
= 2 pints = 32 fluid ounces
1 square foot = 929 square centimeters
= 144 square inches
1 square inch = 6.45 square centimeters
1 square kilometer = 0.386 square miles
= 247.105 acres
1 square meter = 1.196 square yards
= 10.764 square feet
1 square mile = 640 acres
1 square yard = 0.836 square meter
= 9 square feet
= 1,296 square inches
1 tablespoon = 3 teaspoons = 0.5 fluid ounce
1 ton, metric = 2,204.623 pounds
= 1.102 net tons
1 ton, net or short = 2,000 pounds
= 0.907 metric ton
1 yard = 0.9144 meter = 3 feet = 36 inches

Conversions

To Convert	Into	Multiply By
angstroms	microns	0.0001
centimeters	feet	0.03281
centimeters	inches	0.3937
cubic cm	cubic inches	0.06102
cubic feet	cubic meters	0.02832
days	seconds	86,400.0
degrees (angle)	radians	0.01745
fathoms	feet	6.0
feet	centimeters	30.48
feet	meters	0.3048
feet/min.	cm/sec.	0.5080
feet/sec.	knots	0.5921
feet/sec.	statute mi./hr.	0.6818
furlongs/hr.	statute mi./hr.	0.125
furlongs	feet	660.0
gallons (liq.)	liters	3.785
gal. of water	pounds of water	8.3453
grams	oz. (avoirdupois)	0.03527
grams	pounds	0.002205
hours	days	0.04167
hours	weeks	0.005952
inches	centimeters	2.540
kilograms	pounds	2.205
kilometers	feet	3,280.8
kilometers	mi. (statute)	0.6214
knots	feet/hr.	6080.0
knots	nautical mi./hr.	1.0
knots	statute mi./hr.	1.151
liters	gallons (liq.)	0.2642
liters	pints (liq.)	2.113
meters	feet	3.281
meters	mi. (nautical)	0.0005396
meters	mi. (statute)	0.0006214
microns	meters	0.000001
mi. (nautical)	feet	6,076.115
mi. (statute)	feet	5,280.0
mi. (nautical)	kilometers	1.852
mi. (statute)	kilometers	1.609
mi. (nautical)	mi. (statute)	1.1508
mi. (statute)	mi. (nautical)	0.8684
mi. (statute)/hr.	feet/min.	88.0
millimeters	inches	0.03937
oz. (avoirdupois)	grams	28.3495
oz. (avoirdupois)	lb. (avoirdupois)	0.0625
pints (liq.)	gallons (liq.)	0.125
pints (liq.)	quarts (liq.)	0.5
lb. (avoirdupois)	kilograms	0.4536

Measurement

Two-Dimensional Figures

	Perimeter	Area	
Triangle	$P = s_1 + s_2 + s_3$	$A = \frac{1}{2}bh$ Equilateral: $A = \frac{s^2}{4}\sqrt{3}$	h b
Rectangle	$P = 2\ell + 2w$ or $P = 2(\ell + w)$	$A = \ell w$ or $A = bh$	w ℓ
Square	$P = 4s$	$A = s^2$	s
Parallelogram	$P = 2\ell + 2w$ or $P = 2(\ell + w)$	$A = bh$	h b
Regular Polygon	$P = ns$	$A = \frac{1}{2}ap$	s s a
Circle	$C = \pi d$ or $C = 2\pi r$	$A = \pi r^2$	diameter radius
Trapezoid	$P = s_1 + s_2 + s_3 + s_4$	$A = \frac{1}{2}h(b_1 + b_2)$	b_2 h b_1
Kite	$P = 2s_1 + 2s_2$	$A = \frac{1}{2}d_1d_2$	D d_1 X C A d_2 B

Three-Dimensional Figures

	Surface Area	Volume	
Cube	$SA = 6e^2$	$V = e^3$	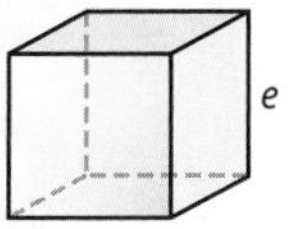 e
Rectangular Prism	$SA = Ph + 2B$	$V = \ell wh$	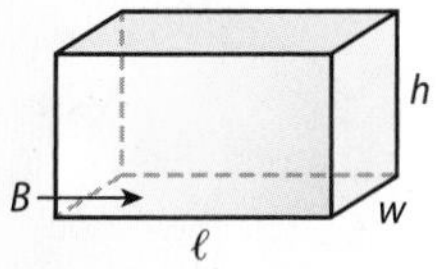 h, B, w, ℓ
Prism	$SA = Ph + 2B$	$V = Bh$	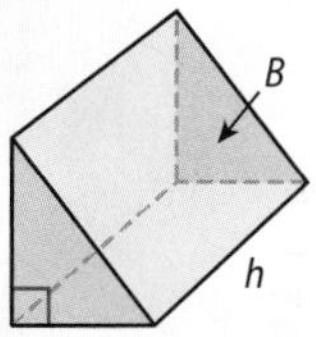 B, h
Right Cylinder	$SA = 2\pi rh + 2\pi r^2$ or $SA = 2\pi r(h + r)$	$V = \pi r^2 h$	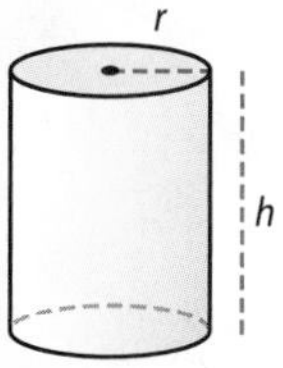 r, h
Pyramid	$SA = \frac{1}{2}P\ell + B$	$V = \frac{1}{3}Bh$	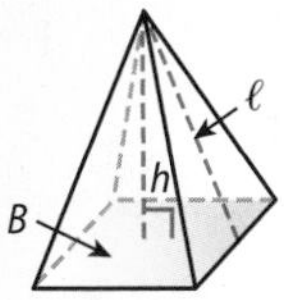 ℓ, h, B
Right Cone	$SA = \pi r\ell + \pi r^2$ or $SA = \pi r(\ell + r)$	$V = \frac{1}{3}\pi r^2 h$	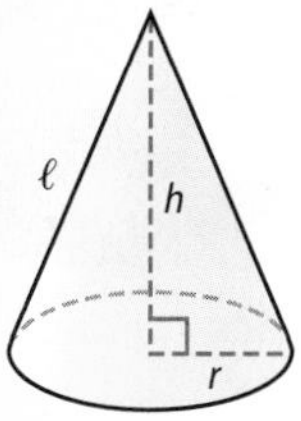 ℓ, h, r
Sphere	$SA = 4\pi r^2$	$V = \frac{4}{3}\pi r^3$	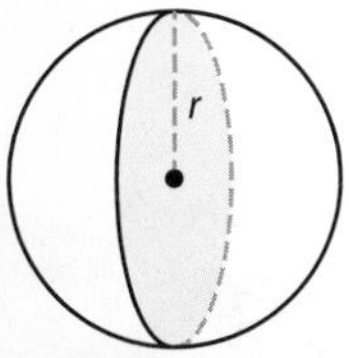 r

Geometry

Landscape artists use congruent figures when designing gardens to make them more visually appealing.

Reasoning and Proof

What Came Before?

- Congruent, complementary, supplementary, and vertical angles
- Parallel and perpendicular lines

What's This About?

- Using *if-then* statements
- Deductive and inductive reasoning
- Theorems about angles, congruence and parallel lines

Practical Apps

- Logic and deductive reasoning is used by lawyers to prove their cases.
- Parallel lines are used in the manufacturing of windows and in the architectural design of buildings.

Just for FUN!

Q: What is a geometry gymnast's favorite Olympic event?

A: The parallel bars.

CONTENTS UPLOAD DOWNLOAD

Geometry

You can find more practice problems online by visiting: **www.SWadvantage.com**

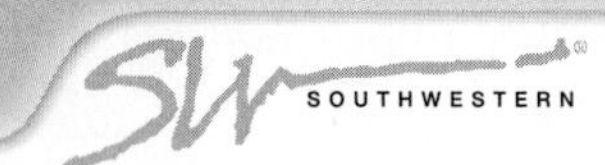

Parts of a Conditional Statement

A **conditional statement** is a statement of the form *if p, then q*. You can write this symbolically as $p \rightarrow q$, which is read "if p, then q" or "p implies q." Every conditional contains two parts. The part that follows *if* is the **hypothesis**. The part that follows *then* is the **conclusion**.

If p, then q.

↑ ↑

p: hypothesis q: conclusion

The Venn diagram to the right is a visual representation of the conditional *If p, then q*. The diagram shows that if a point lies in the area labeled p, then it must also lie in the area labeled q.

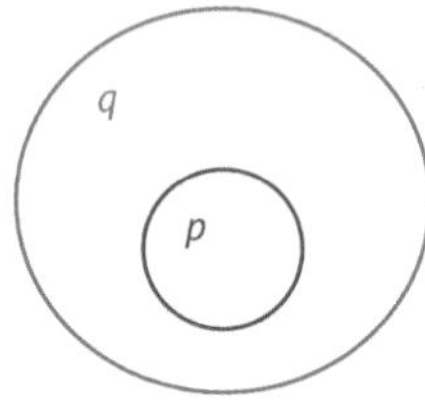

EXAMPLE 1

Identify the hypothesis and conclusion of this conditional statement:

If a number is an integer, then the number is a rational number.

Hypothesis: A number is an integer.

Conclusion: The number is a rational number.

You can rewrite some statements as conditionals. To begin, identify the hypothesis. To do this, find the part of the statement that must be true in order for the other part to be true.

EXAMPLE 2

Write each sentence in *if-then* form.

a. Any number that is a multiple of 6 is also a multiple of 3.

STEP 1 Identify the hypothesis.
Hypothesis: A number is a multiple of 6.

STEP 2 Identify the conclusion.
Conclusion: The number is a multiple of 3.

STEP 3 Write the sentence in *if-then* form.
If a number is a multiple of 6, then it is a multiple of 3.

b. The temperature goes down whenever the sun goes down.

STEP 1 Identify the hypothesis.
Hypothesis: The sun goes down.

STEP 2 Identify the conclusion.
Conclusion: The temperature goes down.

STEP 3 Write the sentence in *if-then* form.
If the sun goes down, then the temperature goes down.

To see step-by-step videos of these problems, enter the page number into the SWadvantage.com Search Bar.

Truth Value

Every conditional statement is either true or false. This is the **truth value** of the statement. The only time a conditional is false is when the hypothesis is true and the conclusion is false. An example that shows that the hypothesis is true and the conclusion is false is a **counterexample**. To prove a conditional false, you need only one counterexample.

EXAMPLE 3

Find the truth value of each statement. If the statement is false, give a counterexample.

a. If a number is a perfect square, then it is even.

The statement is false.

The number 9 is a counterexample: 9 is a perfect square and 9 is not even.

b. If a board is more than one yard wide, then it is more than one foot wide.

The statement is true.

c. If a triangle has four sides, then a square has five sides.

The hypothesis is *"a triangle has four sides."* The hypothesis is false.

Therefore, the conditional is true (even though we know squares have four sides. It's like saying, "If cars can fly, then hippos can skateboard." A false hypothesis generates a true conditional in Geometry—just not necessarily in the real-life sense of "true.")

EXAMPLE 4

Find the truth value of the statement below. Then draw a Venn diagram to illustrate the conditional statement.

If a polygon is a rhombus, then it is a quadrilateral.

The statement is true.

The hypothesis is *"a polygon is a rhombus."* Put "rhombus" in the inner circle of the Venn diagram.

Put the conclusion "quadrilateral" in the outer circle.

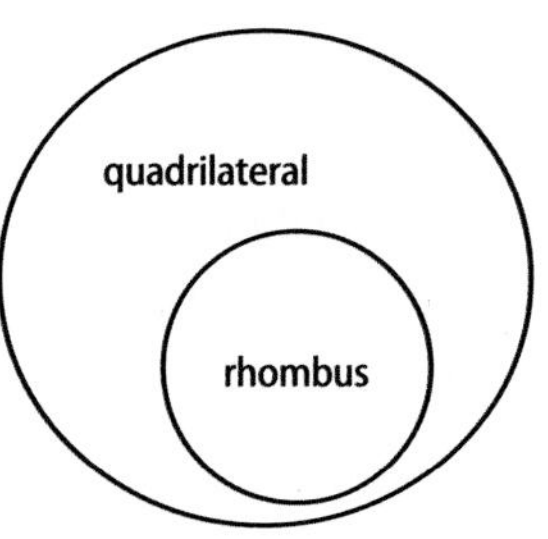

Truth Table for $p \rightarrow q$

Hypothesis p	Conclusion q	Conditional $p \rightarrow q$
T	T	T
T	F	F
F	T	T
F	F	T

Negation, Inverse, and Converse

The **negation** of a statement has the opposite truth value. You can write the negation of statement p symbolically as $\sim p$, which is read "not p." If p is true, $\sim p$ is false, and if p is false, $\sim p$ is true.

EXAMPLE 5

Write the negation of this statement:

The measure of an acute angle is less than 90.

METHOD 1

The measure of an acute angle is not less than 90.

METHOD 2

The measure of an acute angle is greater than or equal to 90.

The **inverse** of a conditional statement negates the hypothesis and the conclusion. The **converse** of a conditional statement switches the hypothesis and conclusion.

Statement:	If p, then q.	$p \rightarrow q$
Inverse:	If not p, then not q.	$\sim p \rightarrow \sim q$
Converse:	If q, then p.	$q \rightarrow p$

EXAMPLE 6

Write the converse and inverse of each true statement. Give the truth value of each.

a. If a polygon is a triangle, then the polygon has at least three sides.

Converse: If a polygon has at least three sides, then the polygon is a triangle.

False; a quadrilateral has at least 3 sides.

Inverse: If a polygon is not a triangle, then the polygon does not have at least three sides.

False; a quadrilateral is not a triangle.

b. If a number is a factor of 12, then the number is a factor of 48.

Converse: If a number is a factor of 48, then the number is a factor of 12.

False; 16 is a factor of 48 but not of 12.

Inverse: If a number is not a factor of 12, then the number is not a factor of 48.

False; 16 is not a factor of 12 but it is a factor of 48.

Watch Out !

Assuming a conditional is logically equivalent to its converse or inverse is a common error.

Contrapositive

The contrapositive of a conditional statement switches and negates the hypothesis and conclusion.

Statement:	If p, then q.	$p \rightarrow q$
Contrapositive:	If not q, then not p.	$\sim q \rightarrow \sim p$

Logically equivalent statements always have the same truth value. As you saw in Example 6, a conditional and its converse can have different truth values. On the other hand, a statement and its contrapositive are always logically equivalent.

When you want to determine whether a conditional is true or false, you can look at the original statement or its contrapositive. Sometimes one is easier to read than the other.

EXAMPLE 7

Write the contrapositive of each statement. Then find the truth value of the contrapositive.

a. If a number is a multiple of 4, then the number is even.

Contrapositive: If a number is not even, then it is not a multiple of 4.

The original statement is true, so its contrapositive is true.

b. If a package weighs less than one pound, then the package weighs less than one ounce.

Contrapositive: If a package does not weigh less than one ounce, then the package does not weigh less than one pound.

A package that weighs 10 ounces is a counterexample. The statement is false.

c. If tomorrow is Thursday, then today is Wednesday.

Contrapositive: If today is not Wednesday, then tomorrow is not Thursday.

The original statement is true, so its contrapositive is true.

SEARCH

To see step-by-step videos of these problems, enter the page number into the SWadvantage.com Search Bar.

GOT TO KNOW!

Converse, Inverse, and Contrapositive Statements

Statement	In Words	In Symbols
Conditonal	If p, then q.	$p \rightarrow q$
Contrapositive	If not q, then not p.	$\sim q \rightarrow \sim p$
Converse	If q, then p.	$q \rightarrow p$
Inverse	If not p, then not q.	$\sim p \rightarrow \sim q$

Biconditionals

Parts of a Biconditional Statement

A conditional statement and its converse are not always logically equivalent. When they are, you can combine them to form a statement called a *biconditional*. A **biconditional statement** is a statement of the form *p if and only if q*, which is just a shorter way to say *if p, then q AND if q, then p*. You can write this symbolically as $p \leftrightarrow q$.

EXAMPLE 1

Write the converse of each true conditional statement. If the converse is true, combine the conditionals to form a biconditional.

a. If tomorrow is October 1, then today is September 30.

Converse: If today is September 30, then tomorrow is October 1. This is true.

Biconditional: Tomorrow is October 1 if and only if today is September 30.

b. If $12 - x = 3$, then $x = 9$.

Converse: If $x = 9$, then $12 - x = 3$. This is true.

Biconditional: $12 - x = 3$ if and only if $x = 9$.

EXAMPLE 2

Write the two conditionals that make up each biconditional.

a. You can vote in the election if and only if you are at least 18 years old.

Conditional: If you can vote in the election, then you are at least 18 years old.

Converse: If you are at least 18 years old, then you can vote in the election.

b. The jigsaw puzzle is solved if and only if every piece is in the correct position.

Conditional: If the jigsaw puzzle is solved, then every piece of the puzzle is in the correct position.

Converse: If every piece of the puzzle is in the correct position, then the jigsaw puzzle is solved.

GOT TO KNOW!

Truth Table for $p \leftrightarrow q$

p	q	$p \rightarrow q$	$q \rightarrow p$	$p \leftrightarrow q$
T	T	T	T	T
T	F	F	T	F
F	T	T	F	F
F	F	T	T	T

Biconditionals and Definitions

A biconditional statement *p if and only if q* is true when *p* and *q* have the same truth value.

EXAMPLE 3

Write the two conditionals that form each biconditional. Find the truth value of the biconditional.

a. A whole number is composite if and only if it has a factor other than 1 and itself.

Conditional: If a whole number is composite, then it has a factor other than 1 and itself. This is true.

Converse: If a whole number has a factor other than 1 and itself, then it is composite. This is true.

Both the conditional and its converse are true, so the biconditional is true.

b. $x^2 = 25$ if and only if $x = 5$.

Conditional: If $x^2 = 25$, then $x = 5$. This is false because x could equal -5.

Converse: If $x = 5$, then $x^2 = 25$. This is true.

Because the conditional and its converse do not have the same truth value, the biconditional is false.

Watch Out!

Example 3(a) shows that the biconditional $p \leftrightarrow q$ is true when both p and q are true.

But a biconditional $p \leftrightarrow q$ is also true when both p and q are false.

Definitions are some of the most powerful tools used in mathematical proofs. Every mathematical definition is reversible and therefore can be written as a biconditonal.

EXAMPLE 4

Write this definition as a biconditional.

Definition: Every even number is divisible by two.

STEP 1 Write the conditional.
If a number is even, then it is divisible by two.

STEP 2 Write the converse.
If a number is divisible by two, then it is even.

STEP 3 If both conditionals are true, then you can write the definition as a biconditional.
A number is even if and only if it is divisible by two.

SEARCH

To see step-by-step videos of these problems, enter the page number into the SWadvantage.com Search Bar.

EXAMPLE 5

Is this a good definition? Explain.

A square is a polygon with four congruent sides.

Test the definition to see if it is reversible.

Conditional: If a polygon is a square, then it has four congruent sides; true.

Converse: If a polygon has four congruent sides, then it is a square; false. The polygon could be a rhombus without any right angles.

This is not a good definition because it is not reversible.

Using the Law of Detachment

People often use examples to support a proposal and show that it is true in specific cases. But in order to show that a proposal is *always* true, you must prove it. When you use properties, rules, definitions, theorems, given facts, and the laws of logic to arrive at a conclusion, you are using **deductive reasoning**.

One law of deductive reasoning is the **Law of Detachment**.

Law of Detachment
If a conditional statement is true and its hypothesis is true, then the conclusion is true.

SEARCH

To see step-by-step videos of these problems, enter the page number into the SWadvantage.com Search Bar.

EXAMPLE 1

Assume the given statements are true. Use the Law of Detachment to draw a valid conclusion.

Given: If Mark mows at least three lawns this weekend, then he can afford to go on the school trip.
Mark mows four lawns this weekend.

Identify the hypothesis.	Mark mows at least three lawns this weekend.
Identify the conclusion.	He can afford to go on the school trip.

Because the conditional and its hypothesis are both true, the Law of Detachment says the conclusion must be true. You can conclude that Mark can afford to go on the school trip.

You can also use a Venn diagram to help you reason logically.

EXAMPLE 2

Assume the following statements are true. What can you conclude?

All dragons are ferocious.
Fluffy is a dragon.

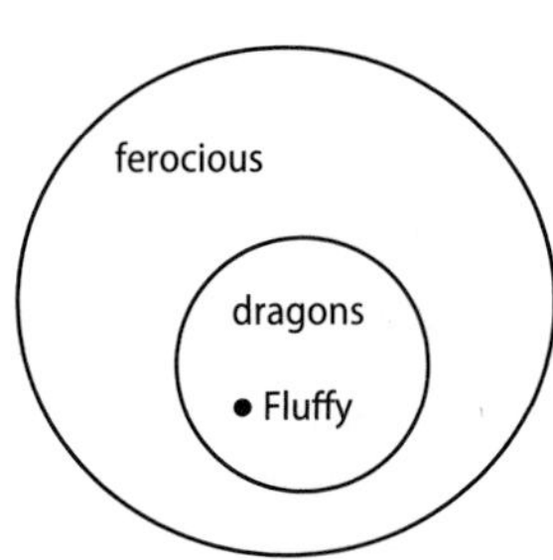

All the points in the "dragons" circle are inside the "ferocious" circle. Since Fluffy is in the "dragons" circle, Fluffy is also in the "ferocious" circle. You can conclude that Fluffy is ferocious.

Using the Law of Syllogism

Another important law of deductive reasoning is the **Law of Syllogism**.

Law of Syllogism
If $p \rightarrow q$ is true and $q \rightarrow r$ is true, then $p \rightarrow r$ must be true.

EXAMPLE 3

The given statements are true. Use the Law of Syllogism to draw a valid conclusion.

**Given: If the sum of the digits in a number is divisible by 9, then the number is divisible by 9.
If a number is divisible by 9, then the number is divisible by 3.**

STEP 1 Assign p, q, and r as follows:

p: The sum of the digits in a number is divisible by 9.
q: The number is divisible by 9.
r: The number is divisible by 3.

STEP 2 Rewrite the given statements symbolically.

$p \rightarrow q$
$q \rightarrow r$

Now it is easy to see that q is the conclusion of the first conditional as well as the hypothesis of the second conditional. You can use the Law of Syllogism to conclude that $p \rightarrow r$: If the sum of the digits in a number is divisible by 9, then the number is divisible by 3.

EXAMPLE 4

Use the Law of Detachment and the Law of Syllogism to draw a conclusion from the given statements.

**Given: (1) If the perimeter of a square is 20 cm, then one side is 5 cm long.
(2) If one side of a square is 5 cm long, then the area is 25 cm^2.
(3) The perimeter of a square is 20 cm.**

METHOD 1

Use the Law of Detachment first.

You can use statements (1) and (3) and the Law of Detachment to conclude that one side of the square is 5 cm long.

Then you can use this result, statement (2), and the Law of Detachment to conclude that the area of the square is 25 cm^2.

METHOD 2

Use the Law of Syllogism first.

You can use statements (1) and (2) and the Law of Syllogism to conclude that if the perimeter of a square is 20 cm, then the area of the square is 25 cm^2.

Now you can use this conditional, statement (3), and the Law of Detachment to conclude that the area of the square is 25 cm^2.

GOT TO KNOW!

Law of Detachment

If $p \rightarrow q$ is true and p is true, then q is true.

Law of Syllogism

If $p \rightarrow q$ is true and $q \rightarrow r$ is true, then $p \rightarrow r$ is true.

Inductive Reasoning

Patterns and Conjectures

When you use **inductive reasoning** you make a conclusion, also called a **conjecture**, based on observations. This process often involves finding a pattern. Unlike deductive reasoning, you cannot use inductive reasoning to prove something. The conjecture that you make as a result of inductive reasoning may or may not be true.

EXAMPLE 1

Describe each pattern. Use the pattern to guess the next term in the pattern.

a. February, April, June, . . .

This is a list of every other month beginning with February. The next term is August.

b. 1, 4, 9, 16, . . .

$1 = 1^2$ $4 = 2^2$ $9 = 3^2$ $16 = 4^2$

The numbers are the squares of consecutive integers. The next term is 5^2, or 25.

c.

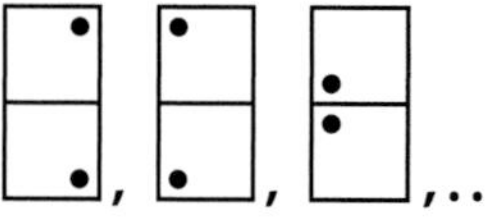

In each figure, the dot in the top half moves counterclockwise to the next corner, and the dot in the bottom half moves clockwise. The next term is:

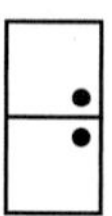

Not every conjecture made using inductive reasoning is true. You can prove a conjecture false by finding just one counterexample.

EXAMPLE 2

Dolores looks at the equations below, sees a pattern, and makes the conjecture that every multiple of 5 ends in 5. Prove that this conjecture is false.

$1(5) = 5$ $3(5) = 15$ $5(5) = 25$ $7(5) = 35$

A counterexample is the number 20. It is a multiple of 5 and does not end in 5.

Types of Reasoning

Deductive Reasoning	Inductive Reasoning
• Uses properties, rules, definitions, theorems, given facts, and the laws of logic to arrive at a conclusion. • The conclusion must be true if the hypotheses are true.	• Uses observations and patterns. • The conclusion is not necessarily true.

EXAMPLE 3

Use inductive reasoning to form a conjecture.

a. The sum of an even integer and an odd integer

STEP 1 Find examples. $2 + 3 = 5$ $6 + 1 = 7$ $4 + 3 = 7$ $8 + 5 = 13$
$4 + 5 = 9$ $8 + 3 = 11$ $10 + 5 = 15$ $2 + 7 = 9$

STEP 2 Look for a pattern.
All the sums are odd.

STEP 3 Form a conjecture.
The sum of an even integer and an odd integer is an odd integer.

b. The product of a positive integer and a negative integer

STEP 1 Find examples. $2(-3) = -6$ $2(-4) = -8$ $2(-5) = -10$
$3(-3) = -9$ $3(-5) = -15$ $3(-6) = -18$
$4(-10) = -40$ $4(-15) = -60$ $4(-17) = -68$

STEP 2 Look for a pattern.
All the products are negative.

STEP 3 Form a conjecture.
The product of a positive integer and a negative integer is a negative integer.

c. The number of sides of a polygon and the number of triangles formed by drawing all the diagonals from one vertex of the polygon

STEP 1 Find examples.

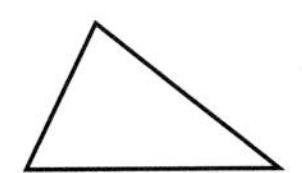
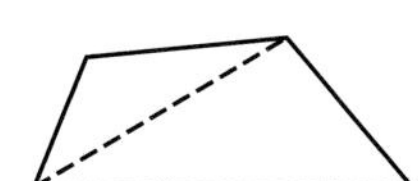
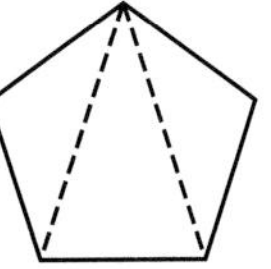
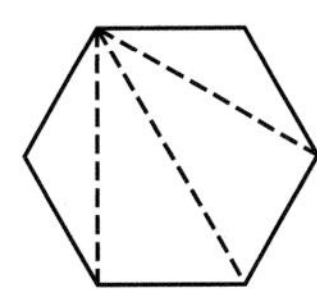

STEP 2 Make a table and look for a pattern.

Number of Sides	3	4	5	6
Number of Triangles	1	2	3	4

Each number in the second row is two less than the corresponding number in the first row.

STEP 3 Form a conjecture.
The number of triangles formed when you draw all the diagonals from one vertex of a polygon is two less than the number of sides.

SEARCH 

To see step-by-step videos of these problems, enter the page number into the SWadvantage.com Search Bar.

Need More HELP

Remember: A vertex is the point where two sides of a polygon intersect.

EXAMPLE 4

Make a conjecture about the sum of the first *n* positive even integers.

Find the sum for $n = 3$. $2 + 4 + 6 = 12 = 3(4)$

Find the sum for $n = 4$. $2 + 4 + 6 + 8 = 20 = 4(5)$

Find the sum for $n = 5$. $2 + 4 + 6 + 8 + 10 = 30 = 5(6)$

Find the sum for $n = 6$. $2 + 4 + 6 + 8 + 10 + 12 = 42 = 6(7)$

In each case, the sum equals the product of n and $n + 1$.

Conjecture: The sum of the first n positive even integers is $n(n + 1)$.

Properties of Congruence

Congruence

Congruent (≅) figures have the exact same shape and size. **Congruent segments** have equal lengths. **Congruent** angles have equal measures. Corresponding sides and corresponding angles of congruent polygons are congruent.

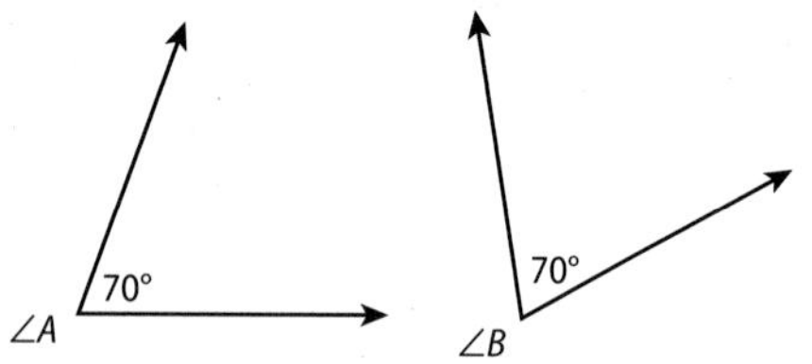

$m\angle A = m\angle B$ if and only if $\angle A \cong \angle B$

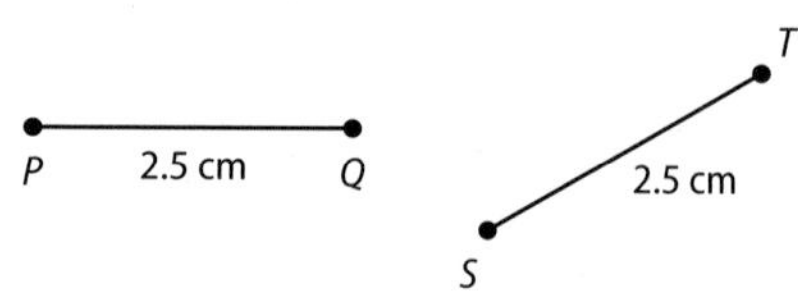

$PQ = ST$ if and only if $\overline{PQ} \cong \overline{ST}$

You can mark segments and angles alike to indicate that they are congruent. The markings in the figures at the right show that:

$\angle B \cong \angle Y$ $\overline{AB} \cong \overline{XY}$ $\overline{BC} \cong \overline{YZ}$

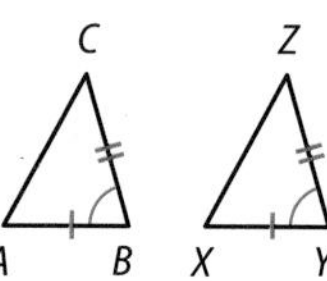

EXAMPLE 1

Complete the congruence statements for the given segments and angles.

$AB = 3$ $m\angle 1 = 35°$ $CD = 6$ $m\angle 3 = 35°$ $HI = 5$

$m\angle 2 = 50°$ $DE = 5$ $m\angle 4 = 40°$ $JK = 3$ $m\angle 5 = 50°$

a. $\overline{AB} \cong$?

$AB = JK$, so $\overline{AB} \cong \overline{JK}$.

b. $\angle 5 \cong$?

$m\angle 5 = m\angle 2$, so $\angle 5 \cong \angle 2$.

c. $\overline{HI} \cong$?

$HI = DE$, so $\overline{HI} \cong \overline{DE}$.

GOT TO KNOW!

Congruence Properties

Property	Segments	Angles
Reflexive	$\overline{AB} \cong \overline{AB}$	$\angle X \cong \angle X$
Symmetric	If $\overline{AB} \cong \overline{CD}$, then $\overline{CD} \cong \overline{AB}$.	If $\angle X \cong \angle Y$, then $\angle Y \cong \angle X$.
Transitive	If $\overline{AB} \cong \overline{CD}$ and $\overline{CD} \cong \overline{EF}$, then $\overline{AB} \cong \overline{EF}$.	If $\angle X \cong \angle Y$ and $\angle Y \cong \angle Z$, then $\angle X \cong \angle Z$.

The properties of congruence in geometry are very much like the properties of equality for real numbers. Though they may seem simple, you will find them extremely useful in proofs.

EXAMPLE 2

Name the property of equality or congruence that justifies each statement.

a. If $\angle CDE \cong \angle GHI$, then $\angle GHI \cong \angle CDE$.

Symmetric Property of Congruence

b. If $m\angle P = m\angle Q$ and $m\angle Q = 120°$, then $m\angle P = 120°$.

Transitive Property of Equality

c. $\overline{MN} \cong \overline{NM}$

Reflexive Property of Congruence

SEARCH

To see step-by-step videos of these problems, enter the page number into the SWadvantage.com Search Bar.

EXAMPLE 3

Given: $\angle 1 \cong \angle 2$, $\angle 2 \cong \angle 3$, $m\angle 1 = (3x + 5)°$, and $m\angle 3 = 65°$. Find the value of x.

STEP 1 Use the Transitive Property.

If $\angle 1 \cong \angle 2$ and $\angle 2 \cong \angle 3$, then $\angle 1 \cong \angle 3$.

STEP 2 Use the definition of congruent angles.

If $\angle 1 \cong \angle 3$, then $m\angle 1 = m\angle 3$.

STEP 3 Substitute for $m\angle 1$ and $m\angle 3$.

$3x + 5 = 65$

STEP 4 Solve for x.

$$3x + 5 = 65$$
$$3x = 60$$
$$x = 20$$

Need More HELP

For help with solving equations, go to *Two-Step Equations* in *Algebra* (Book 2, p. 1464).

EXAMPLE 4

Find the perimeter of polygon *ABCDE*.

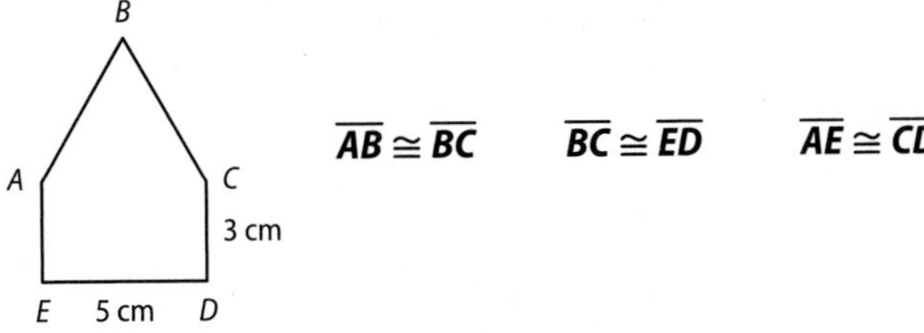

$\overline{AB} \cong \overline{BC}$ $\overline{BC} \cong \overline{ED}$ $\overline{AE} \cong \overline{CD}$

$\overline{AB} \cong \overline{BC}$ and $\overline{BC} \cong \overline{ED}$, so $\overline{AB} \cong \overline{ED}$ and $AB = ED = 5$.

$\overline{BC} \cong \overline{ED}$, so $BC = ED = 5$.

$\overline{AE} \cong \overline{CD}$, so $AE = CD = 3$.

$$\text{perimeter} = AB + BC + CD + ED + AE$$
$$= 5 + 5 + 3 + 5 + 3$$
$$= 21 \text{ cm}$$

The perimeter of polygon *ABCDE* is 21 cm.

Proving Angles Congruent

Classifying Angles

You can classify angles by their measures. The measure of a **right angle** is 90°. The measure of a **straight angle** is 180°. The measure of an **acute angle** is greater than 0° and less than 90°. The measure of an **obtuse angle** is greater than 90° and less than 180°.

EXAMPLE 1

State whether each angle appears to be acute, right, obtuse, or straight.

A B F E D

a. $\angle FEB$

Look for the right angle symbol. $\angle FEB$ is a right angle.

b. $\angle F$

$\angle F$ appears to be acute.

c. $\angle A$

$\angle A$ appears to be obtuse.

d. $\angle FED$

Points *D, E,* and *F* are collinear, so $\angle FED$ is a straight angle.

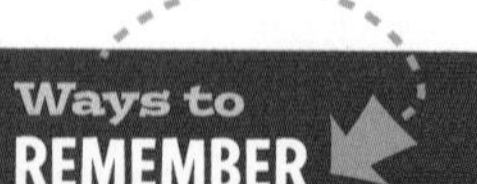

To remember what an acute angle looks like, think of the capital letter *A*, as in *Acute*. The angle at the top of the letter A is acute.

Angle Addition Postulate

A **postulate** is a statement that is accepted as true without being proven. Postulates are one of the basic tools used in proofs. Here is a basic postulate about angles.

Angle Addition Postulate

If point *M* is in the interior of $\angle JKL$, then $m\angle JKM + m\angle MKL = m\angle JKL$.

J M K L

GOT TO KNOW!

Types of Angles

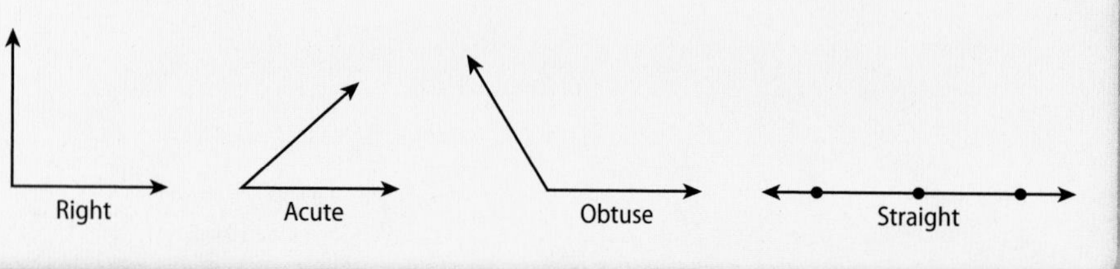

EXAMPLE 2

Find each angle measure.

a. $m\angle LMO$

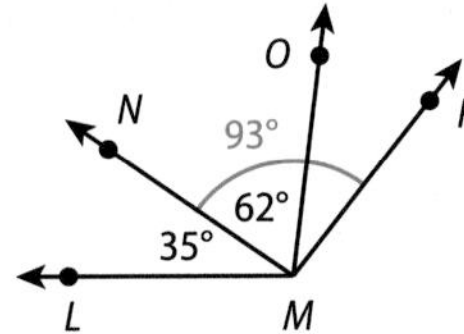

Use the Angle Addition Postulate. $m\angle LMO = m\angle LMN + m\angle NMO$

Substitute the given angle measures. $= 35° + 62°$

$= 97°$

$m\angle LMO = 97°$

b. $m\angle OMP$

Use the Angle Addition Postulate. $m\angle NMP = m\angle NMO + m\angle OMP$

Substitute the given angle measures. $93° = 62° + m\angle OMP$

Subtract 62 from both sides. $31° = m\angle OMP$

$m\angle OMP = 31°$

SEARCH

To see step-by-step videos of these problems, enter the page number into the SWadvantage.com Search Bar.

Identifying Angle Pairs

Two angles are **complementary** if the sum of their measures is 90°. Two angles are **supplementary** if the sum of their measures is 180°. Two angles that have the same vertex and share a side but have no common interior points are called **adjacent angles**. If two angles are adjacent and their exterior sides lie on a straight line, then the angles form a **linear pair**.

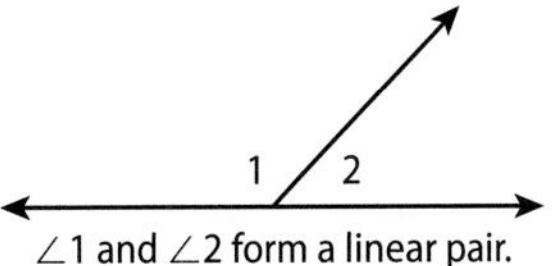

∠1 and ∠2 form a linear pair.

Watch Out!

Complementary angles and supplementary angles do not have to be adjacent angles.

EXAMPLE 3

Use the diagram to name the angle pairs.

a. complementary angles

∠*XVY* and ∠*YVW*

b. supplementary angles

∠*UVX* and ∠*XVW*, ∠*UVY* and ∠*YVW*

c. adjacent angles

∠*UVX* and ∠*XVW*, ∠*UVY* and ∠*YVW*, ∠*UVX* and ∠*XVY*

d. linear pairs

∠*UVX* and ∠*XVW*, ∠*UVY* and ∠*YVW*

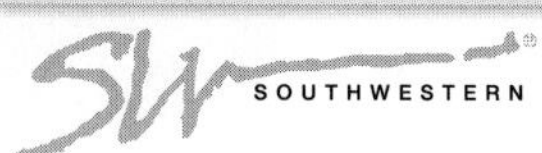

Theorems about Angle Pairs

A **theorem** is a statement that can be proven through deductive reasoning. This theorem states that a linear pair of angles is always supplementary.

Linear Pair Theorem
If two angles form a linear pair, then they are supplementary.

When you prove a theorem, you must justify every statement with a definition, property, postulate, or previously proved theorem.

A **paragraph proof** uses complete sentences to explain and justify each step, eventually reaching the desired conclusion.

SEARCH

To see step-by-step videos of these problems, enter the page number into the SWadvantage.com Search Bar.

EXAMPLE 4

Write a paragraph proof.

Given: $\angle 1$ is supplementary to $\angle 3$.
$\angle 2$ is supplementary to $\angle 3$.
Prove: $\angle 1 \cong \angle 2$

$\angle 1$ and $\angle 3$ are supplementary.

By definition, $m\angle 1 + m\angle 3 = 180°$. Similarly, $m\angle 2 + m\angle 3 = 180°$.

Substituting, you get $m\angle 1 + m\angle 3 = m\angle 2 + m\angle 3$. The Subtraction Property of Equality lets you subtract $m\angle 3$ from both sides.

So, $m\angle 1 = m\angle 2$ and $\angle 1 \cong \angle 2$.

This proves the Congruent Supplements Theorem. The proof of the Congruent Complements Theorem is similar.

Congruent Supplements Theorem
If two angles are supplementary to the same angle (or to congruent angles), then the angles are congruent.
Congruent Complements Theorem
If two angles are complementary to the same angle (or to congruent angles), then the angles are congruent.

EXAMPLE 5

$\angle CBD$ and $\angle EFG$ are supplementary. Find the value of x.

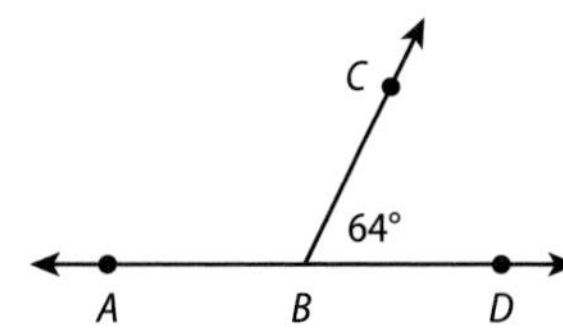

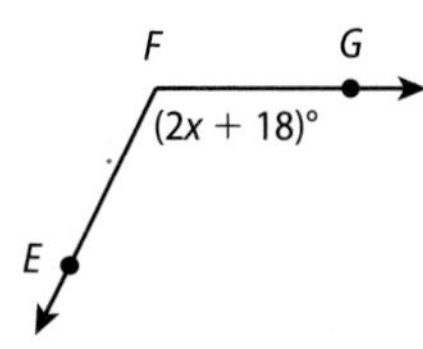

Use the Linear Pair Theorem and the Congruent Supplements Theorem.

$\angle ABC$ and $\angle CBD$ form a linear pair.	$m\angle ABC + m\angle CBD = 180$
Substitute 64 for $m\angle CBD$.	$m\angle ABC + 64 = 180$
	$m\angle ABC = 116°$
Supplements of the same angle are congruent.	$m\angle ABC = m\angle EFG$
Substitute.	$116 = 2x + 18$
Solve the equation for x.	$98 = 2x$
	$x = 49$

Vertical Angles

Vertical angles are the pairs of non-adjacent angles formed when two lines intersect.

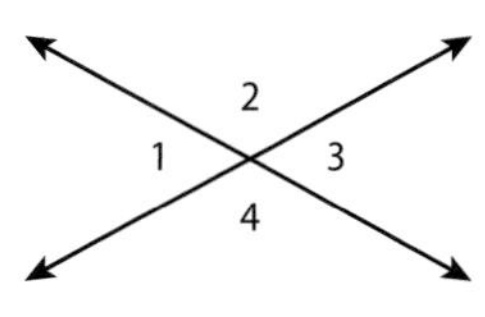

$\angle 1$ and $\angle 3$ are vertical angles.

$\angle 2$ and $\angle 4$ are vertical angles.

Vertical angles have a very special property.

Watch Out !

Vertical angles are not always in a vertical position relative to each other. They are always opposite each other across their common *vertex*.

Vertical Angles Theorem

Vertical angles are congruent.
$\angle 1 \cong \angle 3$ and $\angle 2 \cong \angle 4$

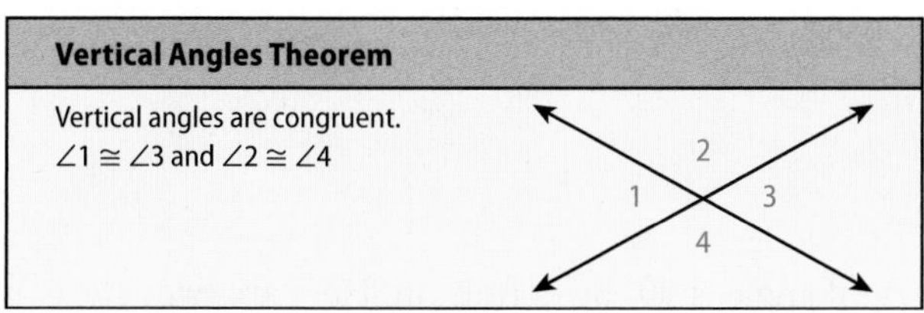

Proof of the Vertical Angle Theorem

Given: $\angle 1$ and $\angle 3$ are vertical angles.
Prove: $\angle 1 \cong \angle 3$

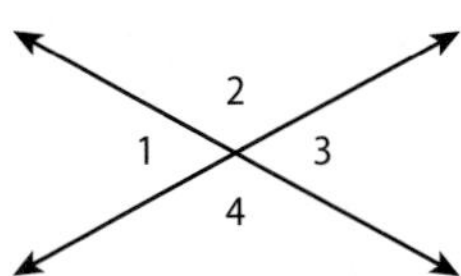

$\angle 1$ and $\angle 2$ form a linear pair. By the Linear Pair Theorem, $\angle 1$ and $\angle 2$ are supplementary. Similarly, $\angle 2$ and $\angle 3$ are supplementary. Since $\angle 1$ and $\angle 3$ are both supplementary to $\angle 2$, $\angle 1 \cong \angle 3$ by the Congruent Supplements Theorem.

Using the Vertical Angles Theorem

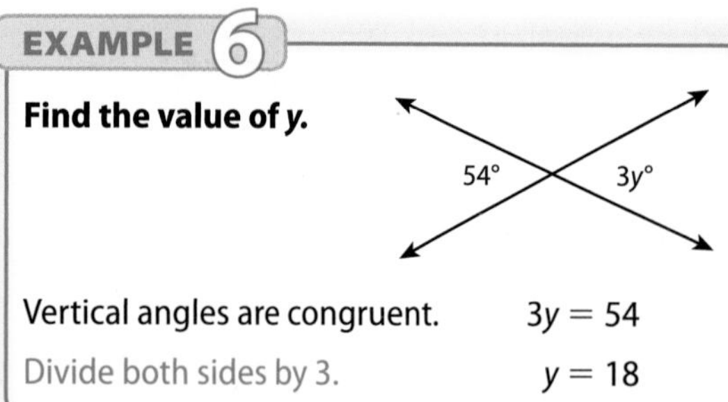

EXAMPLE 6

Find the value of *y*.

Vertical angles are congruent.	$3y = 54$
Divide both sides by 3.	$y = 18$

SEARCH

To see step-by-step videos of these problems, enter the page number into the SWadvantage.com Search Bar.

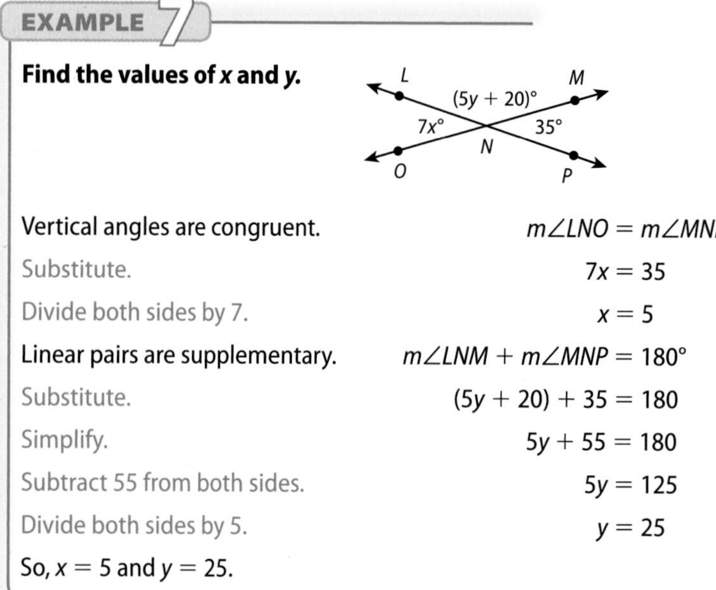

EXAMPLE 7

Find the values of *x* and *y*.

Vertical angles are congruent.	$m\angle LNO = m\angle MNP$
Substitute.	$7x = 35$
Divide both sides by 7.	$x = 5$
Linear pairs are supplementary.	$m\angle LNM + m\angle MNP = 180°$
Substitute.	$(5y + 20) + 35 = 180$
Simplify.	$5y + 55 = 180$
Subtract 55 from both sides.	$5y = 125$
Divide both sides by 5.	$y = 25$

So, $x = 5$ and $y = 25$.

Right Angles

You already know that the measure of a right angle is 90° by definition. Here are two theorems that tell you more about right angles.

Right Angle Congruence Theorem
All right angles are congruent.
Theorem
If two angles are congruent and supplementary, then each angle is a right angle.

EXAMPLE 8

Prove the Right Angle Congruence Theorem.

Given: $\angle 1$ and $\angle 2$ are right angles.
Prove: $\angle 1 \cong \angle 2$

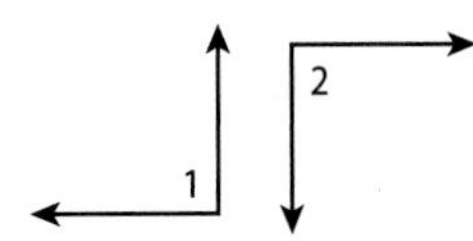

By definition of a right angle, $m\angle 1 = 90°$ and $m\angle 2 = 90°$.
By the Transitive Property of Equality, $m\angle 1 = m\angle 2$, or $\angle 1 \cong \angle 2$.

EXAMPLE 9

Given: $\angle 1$ and $\angle 2$ are congruent and supplementary.
Prove: $\angle 1$ and $\angle 2$ are right angles.

By definition of supplementary angles, $m\angle 1 + m\angle 2 = 180°$.
By definition of congruent angles, $m\angle 1 = m\angle 2$.
Using substitution and algebra, $m\angle 1 + m\angle 1 = 180°$.

$$2(m\angle 1) = 180°$$
$$m\angle 1 = 90°$$

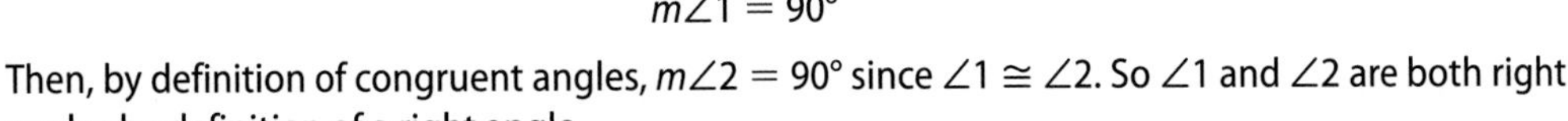
Then, by definition of congruent angles, $m\angle 2 = 90°$ since $\angle 1 \cong \angle 2$. So $\angle 1$ and $\angle 2$ are both right angles by definition of a right angle.

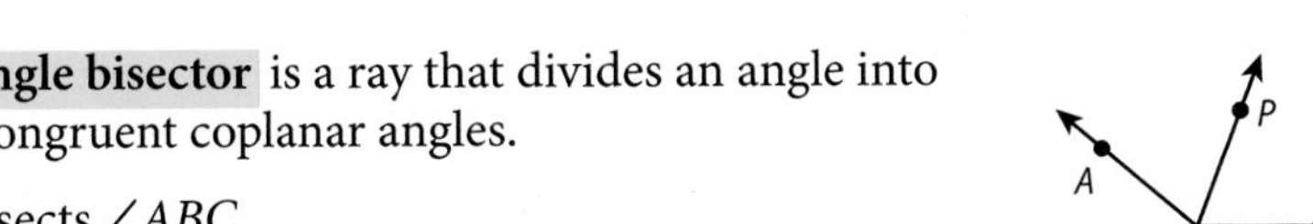
An **angle bisector** is a ray that divides an angle into two congruent coplanar angles.

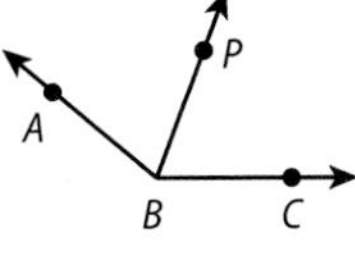

$\overrightarrow{BP}$ bisects $\angle ABC$.
$\angle ABP \cong \angle CBP$
$m\angle ABP = m\angle CBP = \frac{1}{2}m\angle ABC$.

EXAMPLE 10

$\overrightarrow{EG}$ bisects $\angle DEF$ and $m\angle DEF = 150°$. Find the values of x and y.

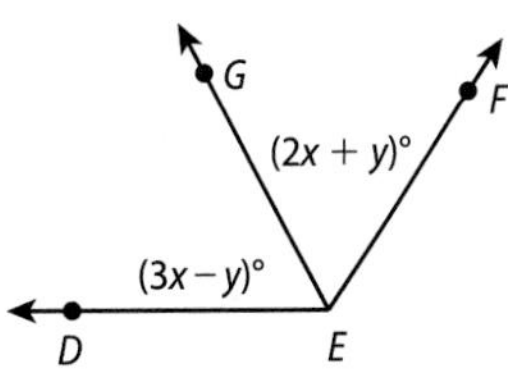

Write and solve two equations in two variables.

Use the Angle Addition Postulate.	$m\angle DEG + m\angle GEF = m\angle DEF$
Substitute.	$(3x - y) + (2x + y) = 150$
Simplify.	$5x = 150$
Divide both sides by 5.	$x = 30$
Use the definition of an angle bisector.	$m\angle DEG = m\angle GEF$
Substitute.	$3x - y = 2x + y$
Substitute 30 for x.	$3(30) - y = 2(30) + y$
Simplify.	$90 - y = 60 + y$
Solve for y.	$30 = 2y$
	$y = 15$

So, $x = 30$ and $y = 15$.

Need More HELP

For a review on solving systems of equations, go to *Solving a System by Substitution* in *Algebra* (Book 2, p. 1568).

Theorems About Parallel Lines

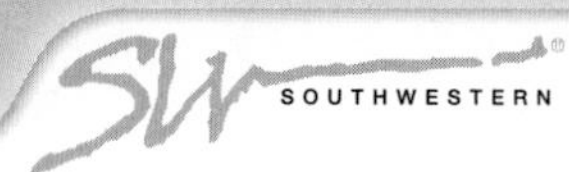

Watch Out!

Two segments that do not intersect are not necessarily parallel. To be parallel, they must be parts of parallel lines.

Properties of Parallel Lines

Lines that do not intersect are either *parallel* or *skew*. Coplanar lines that do not intersect are **parallel**. Non-coplanar lines that do not intersect are **skew**. Diagrams use solid red arrowheads to denote lines that are parallel.

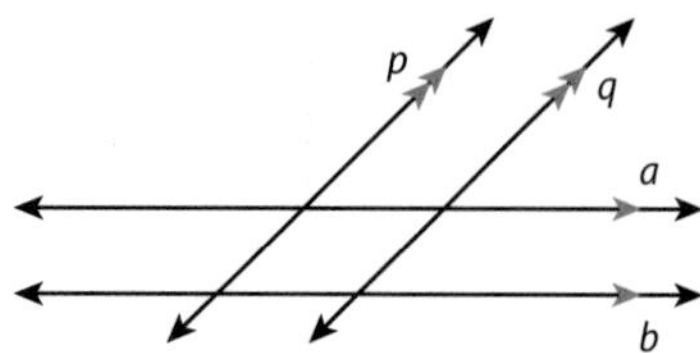

Line a is parallel to line b ($a \parallel b$) and line p is parallel to line q.

A **transversal** is a line that intersects two or more coplanar lines at different points. When a transversal intersects parallel lines, the pairs of angles formed have special names.

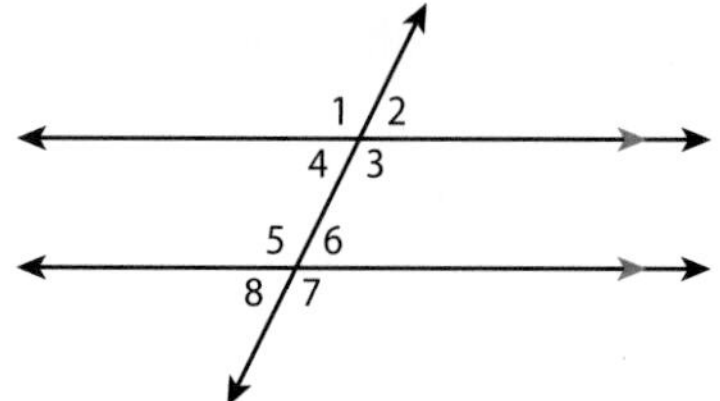

Corresponding angles lie in corresponding positions on the same side of a transversal.

$\angle 1$ and $\angle 5$ $\angle 4$ and $\angle 8$ $\angle 2$ and $\angle 6$ $\angle 3$ and $\angle 7$

Alternate interior angles lie between the parallel lines on opposite sides of a transversal.

$\angle 4$ and $\angle 6$ $\angle 3$ and $\angle 5$

Same-side interior angles lie between the parallel lines on the same side of a transversal.

$\angle 3$ and $\angle 6$ $\angle 4$ and $\angle 5$

Alternate exterior angles lie outside the parallel lines on opposite sides of a transversal.

$\angle 1$ and $\angle 7$ $\angle 2$ and $\angle 8$

Corresponding Angles Postulate
If two parallel lines are cut by a transversal, then corresponding angles are congruent.

GOT TO KNOW!

Parallel Postulate

Given a line and a point not on the line, there is exactly one line through the point parallel to the line.

EXAMPLE 1

Find the value of x if $m\angle 1 = (10x + 16)°$ and $m\angle 2 = (13x - 8)°$.

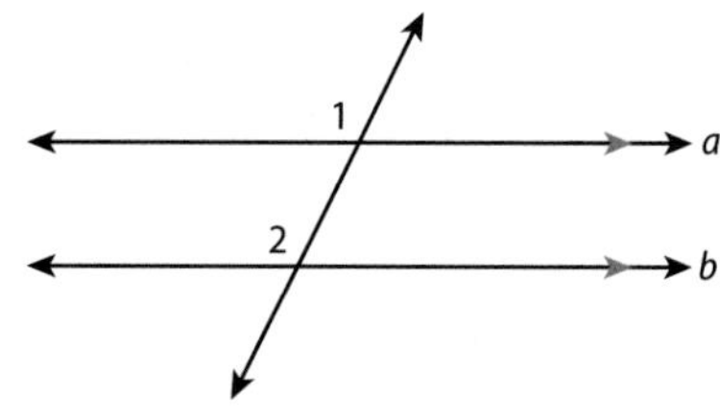

The diagram shows that $a \parallel b$.

Corresponding angles are congruent.	$13x - 8 = 10x + 16$
Subtract $10x$ from both sides.	$3x - 8 = 16$
Add 8 to both sides.	$3x = 24$
Divide both sides by 3.	$x = 8$

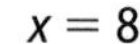

You can use the Corresponding Angles Postulate to prove other theorems about pairs of angles formed when a transversal cuts parallel lines.

Alternate Interior Angles Theorem
If two parallel lines are cut by a transversal, then alternate interior angles are congruent.

Alternate Exterior Angles Theorem
If two parallel lines are cut by a transversal, then alternate exterior angles are congruent.

In a **two-column proof** you organize the steps of a proof and their justifications in separate columns. The first step generally states the given information. Here is a two-column proof of the Alternate Exterior Angles theorem.

EXAMPLE 2

Given: $\overleftrightarrow{AB} \parallel \overleftrightarrow{CD}$
Prove: $\angle 1 \cong \angle 3$

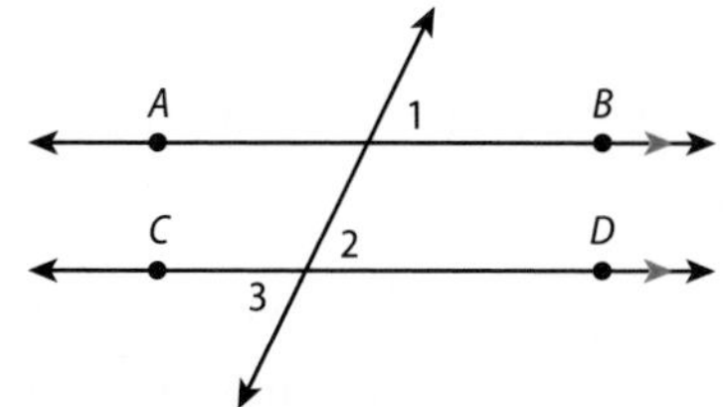

Statements	Reasons
1. $\overleftrightarrow{AB} \parallel \overleftrightarrow{CD}$	1. Given
2. $\angle 1 \cong \angle 2$	2. If two $\parallel$ lines are cut by a transversal, then corr. $\angle$s are $\cong$.
3. $\angle 2 \cong \angle 3$	3. Vertical angles are $\cong$.
4. $\angle 1 \cong \angle 3$	4. Transitive Property of $\cong$

SEARCH

To see step-by-step videos of these problems, enter the page number into the SWadvantage.com Search Bar.

The proof of the Alternate Interior Angles theorem is very similar.

EXAMPLE 3

Find $m\angle GDE$.

Alternate interior $\angle$s are $\cong$.	$3x - 30 = 2x + 20$
Add 30 to both sides.	$3x = 2x + 50$
Subtract $2x$ from both sides.	$x = 50$
Substitute 50 for x.	$m\angle GDE = (3x - 30)°$
	$= 3(50) - 30$
	$= 120$

$m\angle GDE = 120°$

Same-Side Interior Angles

Every pair of angles formed by parallel lines and a transversal is either congruent or supplementary. The next theorem involves pairs of angles that lie on the same side of a transversal and between two parallel lines. The proof of this theorem is in Example 4.

Same-Side Interior Angles Theorem
If two parallel lines are cut by a transversal, then same-side interior angles are supplementary.

Watch Out !

When a transversal intersects two parallel lines, all the acute angles are congruent and all the obtuse angles are congruent. Every acute angle is supplementary to every obtuse angle.

EXAMPLE 4

Prove the Same-Side Interior Angles Theorem.

Given: $\ell \parallel m$

Prove: $\angle 2$ **and** $\angle 3$ **are supplementary.**

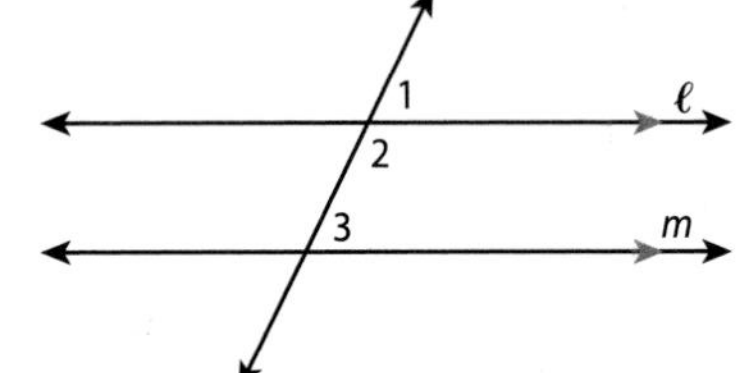

Statements	Reasons
1. $\ell \parallel m$	1. Given
2. $m\angle 1 + m\angle 2 = 180°$	2. If two angles form a linear pair, then they are supplementary.
3. $m\angle 1 = m\angle 3$	3. If two $\parallel$ lines are cut by a transversal, then corr. $\angle$s are $\cong$.
4. $m\angle 3 + m\angle 2 = 180°$	4. Substitution
5. $\angle 2$ and $\angle 3$ are supplementary.	5. Definition of supplementary angles

EXAMPLE 5

Find the values of *a* and *b*.

$a + 2b + 110 = 180$

$a + 2b = 70$ **(1)**

$a - 2b + 150 = 180$

$a - 2b = 30$ **(2)**

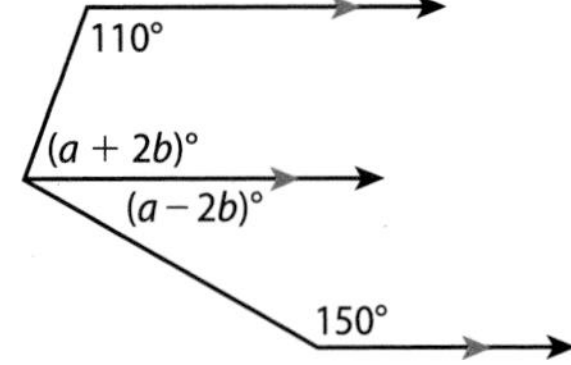

METHOD 1

Add Equations **(1)** and **(2)**.

$a + 2b = 70$

$a - 2b = 30$

$2a = 100$, so $a = 50$

Substitute into Equation **(1)**.

$50 + 2b = 70$

$2b = 20$, so $b = 10$

METHOD 2

Solve Equation **(2)** for *a*, then substitute into Equation **(1)**.

$a = 30 + 2b$

$(30 + 2b) + 2b = 70$ **(1)**

$4b = 40$, so $b = 10$

$a + 2b = 70$ **(1)**

$a + 2(10) = 70$, so $a = 50$

Need More HELP

For help with solving systems of equations, go to *Solving a System by Substitution* and *Solving a System by Addition or Subtraction* in *Algebra* (Book 2, pp. 1568, 1572).

Sometimes the converse of a conditional is true. In particular, the converse of the Corresponding Angles Postulate is true.

Converse of the Corresponding Angles Postulate
If two lines are cut by a transversal and corresponding angles are congruent, then the lines are parallel.

You can use this postulate to prove the following theorem.

Theorem
In a plane, if two lines are perpendicular to the same line, then they are parallel.

Watch Out !

Is this theorem still true if you remove the words "in a plane"? No, the lines could be perpendicular, but they could also be skew.

EXAMPLE 6

Given: Lines p and q are coplanar, $p \perp t$, and $q \perp t$.
Prove: $p \parallel q$

Statements	Reasons
1. $p \perp t$	1. Given
2. $\angle 1$ is a right angle.	2. $\perp$ lines form right $\perp$s.
3. $q \perp t$	3. Given
4. $\angle 2$ is a right angle.	4. $\perp$ lines form right $\angle$s.
5. $\angle 1 \cong \angle 2$	5. Right $\angle$s are $\cong$.
6. $p \parallel q$	6. If two lines are cut by a trans. and corr. $\angle$s are $\cong$, then the lines are $\parallel$.

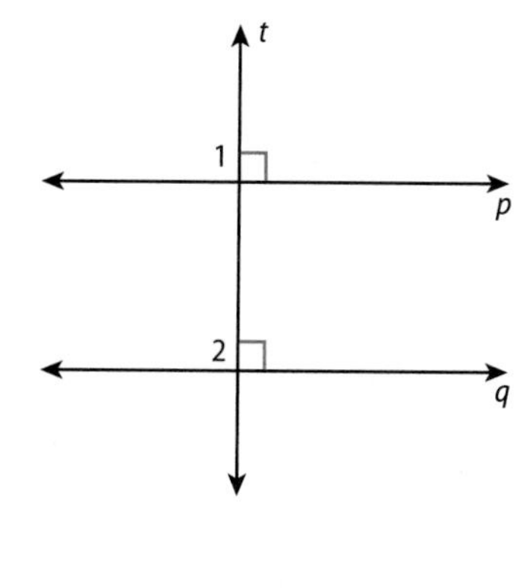

EXAMPLE 7

Find the value of x that makes $\overleftrightarrow{DE} \parallel \overleftrightarrow{CF}$.

$\overleftrightarrow{DE} \parallel \overleftrightarrow{CF}$ if $\angle ABE \cong \angle BGF$.

STEP 1 Find $m\angle ABE$.

$\angle ABD$ and $\angle ABE$ form a linear pair, so they are supplementary.

$m\angle ABD + m\angle ABE = 180°$

$149° + m\angle ABE = 180°$

$m\angle ABE = 31°$

STEP 2 Write an equation about $m\angle ABE$ and $m\angle BGF$.

$\overleftrightarrow{DE} \parallel \overleftrightarrow{CF}$ if $\angle ABE \cong \angle BGF$, so $m\angle ABE = m\angle BGF$.

$31° = (3x + 1)°$

$3x = 30$

$x = 10$

SEARCH

To see step-by-step videos of these problems, enter the page number into the SWadvantage.com Search Bar.

Proving Lines Parallel

The converses of three theorems introduced earlier in this lesson are also true.

Converse of the Alternate Interior Angles Theorem
If two lines are cut by a transversal and alternate interior angles are congruent, then the lines are parallel.

Converse of the Alternate Exterior Angles Theorem
If two lines are cut by a transversal and alternate exterior angles are congruent, then the lines are parallel.

Converse of the Same-Side Interior Angles Theorem
If two lines are cut by a transversal and same-side interior angles are supplementary, then the lines are parallel.

SEARCH

To see step-by-step videos of these problems, enter the page number into the SWadvantage.com Search Bar.

EXAMPLE 8

Prove the Converse of the Alternate Interior Angles Theorem.

Given: $\angle 1 \cong \angle 2$
Prove: $\ell \parallel m$

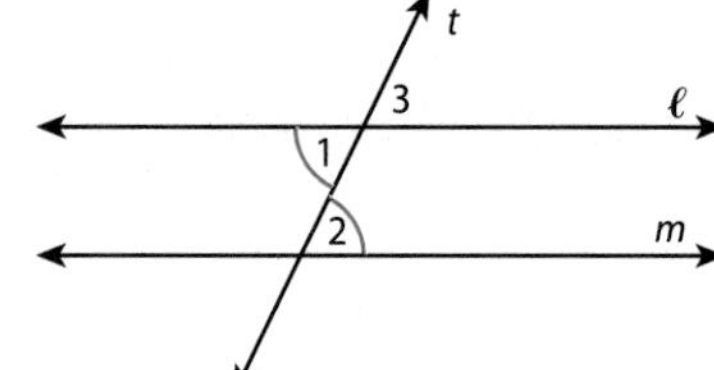

Statements	Reasons
1. $\angle 1 \cong \angle 2$	1. Given
2. $\angle 1 \cong \angle 3$	2. Vertical $\angle$s are $\cong$.
3. $\angle 2 \cong \angle 3$	3. Substitution
4. $\ell \parallel m$	4. If two lines are cut by a trans. and corr. $\angle$s are $\cong$, the lines are $\parallel$.

The proof of the Converse of the Alternate Exterior Angles Theorem is very similar.

EXAMPLE 9

Prove the Converse of the Same-Side Interior Angles Theorem.

Given: $\angle 4$ and $\angle 5$ are supplementary.
Prove: $a \parallel b$

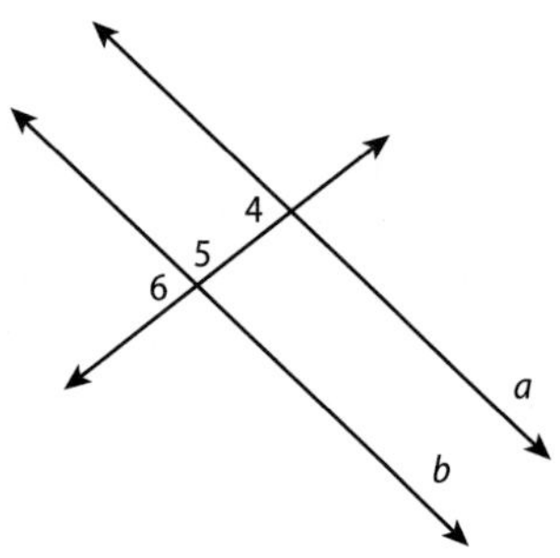

Statements	Reasons
1. $\angle 4$ and $\angle 5$ are supplementary.	1. Given
2. $\angle 5$ and $\angle 6$ are supplementary.	2. If two angles form a linear pair, then they are supplementary.
3. $\angle 4 \cong \angle 6$	3. Two $\angle$s supplementary to the same $\angle$ are $\cong$.
4. $a \parallel b$	4. If two lines are cut by a trans. and corr. $\angle$s are $\cong$, the lines are $\parallel$.

EXAMPLE 10

In the figure, $m\angle 1 = (5x + 14)°$ and $m\angle 2 = (8x - 3)°$. Find the value of x that makes $p \parallel r$.

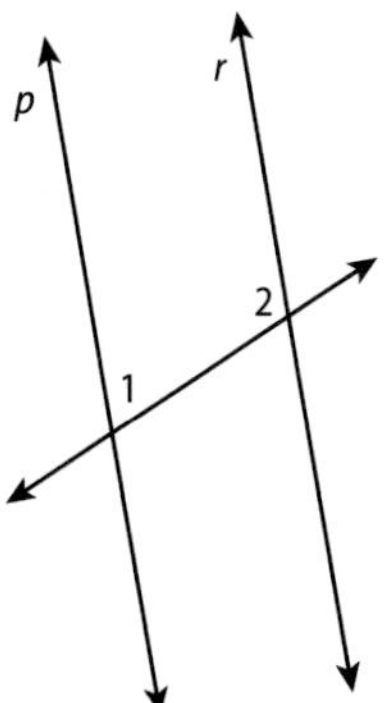

$\angle 1$ and $\angle 2$ are same-side interior angles.

$p \parallel r$ if $\angle 1$ and $\angle 2$ are supplementary.	$m\angle 1 + m\angle 2 = 180°$
Substitute.	$5x + 14 + 8x - 3 = 180$
Simplify.	$13x + 11 = 180$
Subtract 11 from both sides.	$13x = 169$
Divide both sides by 13.	$x = 13$

EXAMPLE 11

In the figure, $m\angle 2 = (6x - 9)°$ and $m\angle 8 = (-2x + 39)°$. Find the value of x that makes $m \parallel n$.

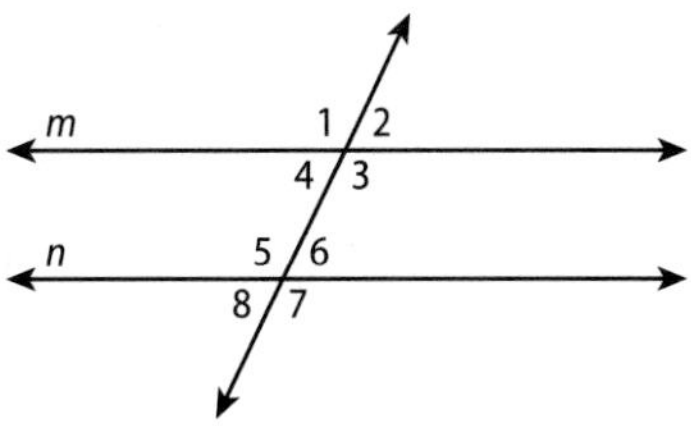

$\angle 2$ and $\angle 8$ are alternate exterior angles.

$m \parallel n$ if $\angle 2$ and $\angle 8$ are congruent.	$m\angle 2 = m\angle 8$
Substitute.	$6x - 9 = -2x + 39$
Add $2x$ to both sides.	$8x - 9 = 39$
Add 9 to both sides.	$8x = 48$
Divide both sides by 8.	$x = 6$

GOT TO KNOW!

Ways to Prove Lines Parallel

Show that:

- CORRESPONDING ANGLES are CONGRUENT.
- ALTERNATE INTERIOR ANGLES are CONGRUENT.
- ALTERNATE EXTERIOR ANGLES are CONGRUENT.
- SAME-SIDE INTERIOR ANGLES are SUPPLEMENTARY.
- Two lines are coplanar and are perpendicular to the same line.

Quadrilaterals

What Came Before?

- Classifying quadrilaterals
- Theorems about parallel lines and congruence

What's This About?

- The properties of parallelograms
- The study of special quadrilaterals
- Proving figures to be parallelograms and other special quadrilaterals

Practical Apps

- The Romans used Golden Rectangles to build the Parthenon.
- Artists use the properties of quadrilaterals in sectioning their paintings.

Just for FUN!

Q: Why is the obtuse angle always upset?

A: Because he's never right.

CONTENTS UPLOAD DOWNLOAD

Geometry

You can find more practice problems online by visiting:
www.SWadvantage.com

Properties of Parallelograms

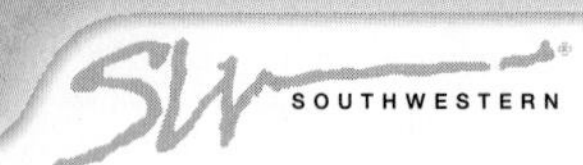

Opposite Sides of a Parallelogram

You know that a quadrilateral is a polygon with four sides. A **parallelogram** is a quadrilateral in which both pairs of opposite sides are parallel.

Need More HELP

To review parallelograms, go to *Classifying Quadrilaterals* in *Foundations of Mathematics* (p. 158).

EXAMPLE 1

Is the polygon a parallelogram? Explain.

a.

This quadrilateral has only one pair of parallel opposite sides, not two. It is not a parallelogram.

b.

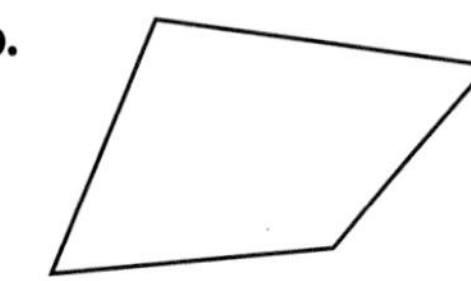

This quadrilateral does not have any parallel sides. It is not a parallelogram.

c.

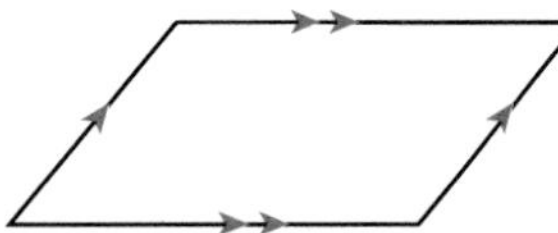

This quadrilateral has two pairs of parallel opposite sides. It is a parallelogram.

d.

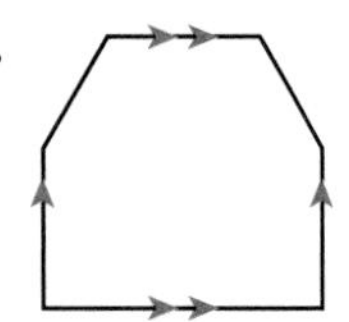

This polygon has two pairs of parallel opposite sides, but it is not a quadrilateral, so it is not a parallelogram.

SEARCH

To see step-by-step videos of these problems, enter the page number into the SWadvantage.com Search Bar.

Several other properties follow from the definition of a parallelogram. One of these is that opposite sides are congruent.

GOT TO KNOW!

Sides of a Parallelogram

Opposite sides are parallel.

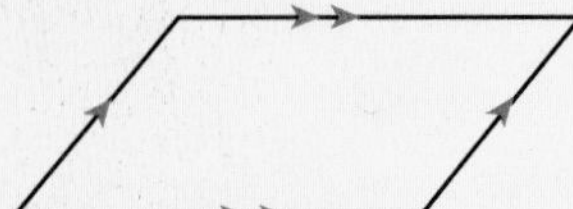

Opposite sides are congruent.

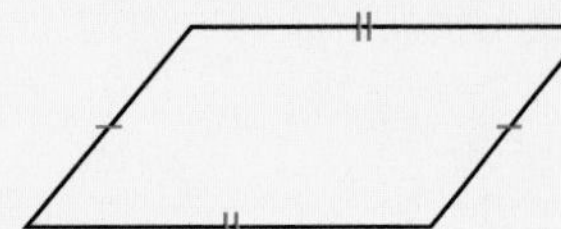

EXAMPLE 2

Prove that opposite angles of a parallelogram are congruent.

Given: *ABCD* is a parallelogram. $\overline{AC}$ is a diagonal.

Prove: $\overline{AB} \cong \overline{CD}$ and $\overline{BC} \cong \overline{AD}$.

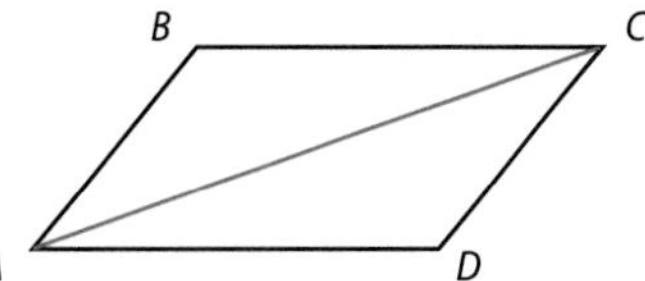

By definition of a parallelogram, $\overline{AB} \parallel \overline{CD}$. If two parallel lines are cut by a transversal, then alternate interior angles are congruent. So $\angle BAC \cong \angle DCA$ and $\angle BCA \cong \angle DAC$.

$AC = AC$ by the Reflexive Property, so $\triangle ABC \cong \triangle CDA$ by Angle-Side-Angle (ASA).

Since corresponding parts of congruent triangles are congruent, it follows that $\overline{AB} \cong \overline{CD}$ and $\overline{BC} \cong \overline{AD}$.

Try It This Way

Draw a parallelogram. Cut along a diagonal. Match up the triangles. Which sides of the parallelogram are congruent? Which angles are congruent?

EXAMPLE 3

In parallelogram *DEFG*, $\overline{DE}$ is twice as long as $\overline{GD}$. Find the perimeter of the parallelogram.

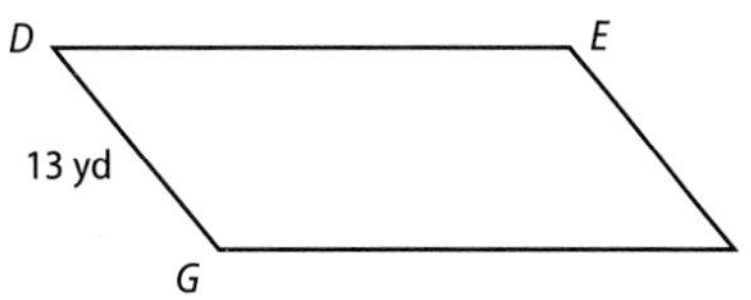

$\overline{EF} \cong \overline{GD}$, so $\overline{EF}$ is 13 yards long.

$\overline{DE}$ is twice the length of $\overline{GD}$, so $\overline{DE}$ is $2 \times 13 = 26$ yards long.

$\overline{GF} \cong \overline{DE}$, so $\overline{GF}$ is 26 yards long.

$$\begin{aligned} \text{perimeter} &= DE + EF + FG + GD \\ &= 26 + 13 + 26 + 13 \\ &= 78 \end{aligned}$$

The perimeter is 78 yd.

EXAMPLE 4

***ABCD* is a parallelogram. Find its perimeter.**

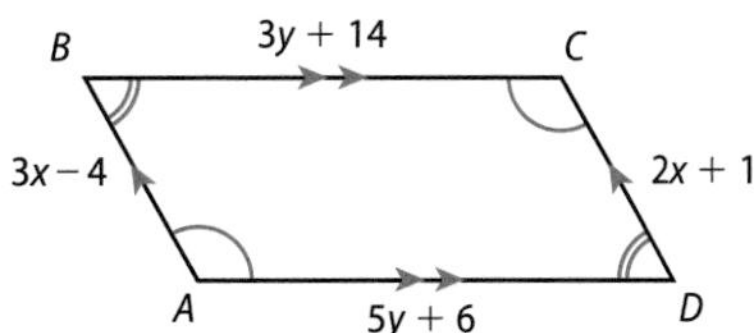

STEP 1 Write two equations. Use the fact that the opposite sides are congruent.

$3x - 4 = 2x + 1$ and $3y + 14 = 5y + 6$

STEP 2 Solve both equations.

$x = 5$ and $y = 4$

STEP 3 Substitute to find the lengths of the sides.

$AB = 3x - 4 = 3(5) - 4 = 11$

$CD = 2x + 1 = 2(5) + 1 = 11$

$BC = 3y + 14 = 3(4) + 14 = 26$

$AD = 5y + 6 = 5(4) + 6 = 26$

STEP 4 Find the perimeter.

$$\begin{aligned} \text{perimeter} &= AB + BC + CD + AD \\ &= 11 + 26 + 11 + 26 = 74 \end{aligned}$$

The perimeter of parallelogram *ABCD* is 74 units.

Need More HELP

For a review of finding the perimeter, go to *Perimeter* in *Measurement* (p. 524).

Angles of a Parallelogram

The angles in a parallelogram have two important properties. The first is that opposite angles are congruent.

EXAMPLE 5

Prove that opposite angles of a parallelogram are congruent.

Given: *PQRS* is a parallelogram.

Prove: $\angle P \cong \angle R$ and $\angle Q \cong \angle S$

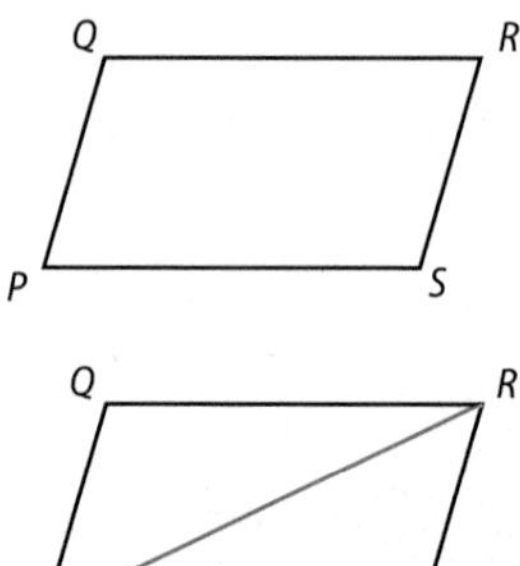

In Example 2 you saw that when you drew the diagonal of a parallelogram two congruent triangles were formed. If you draw $\overline{PR}$, you can prove that $\triangle PQR \cong \triangle RSP$ and therefore $\angle Q \cong \angle S$ by CPCTC. Similarly, if you draw $\overline{QS}$, you can prove that $\angle P \cong \angle R$.

EXAMPLE 6

***ABCD* is a parallelogram. Find the value of *x*.**

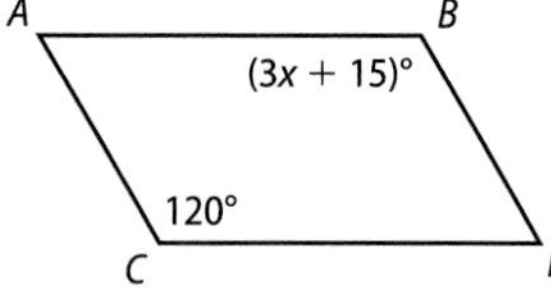

Opposite angles are congruent, so $3x + 15 = 120$.

Solve for *x*. $3x = 105$

$x = 35$

Watch Out!

Do not confuse opposite angles with consecutive angles, which are angles that share a side.

The second property of angles in a parallelogram is that consecutive angles are supplementary. This makes sense when you realize that consecutive angles are same-side interior angles between parallel lines.

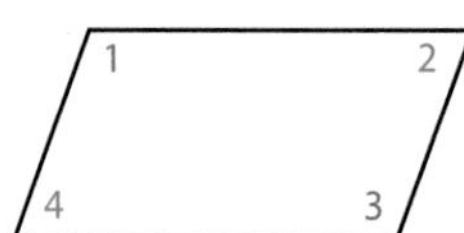

supplementary pairs: $\angle 1$ and $\angle 2$, $\angle 2$ and $\angle 3$, $\angle 3$ and $\angle 4$, $\angle 4$ and $\angle 1$

***EFGH* is a parallelogram. What can you conclude?**

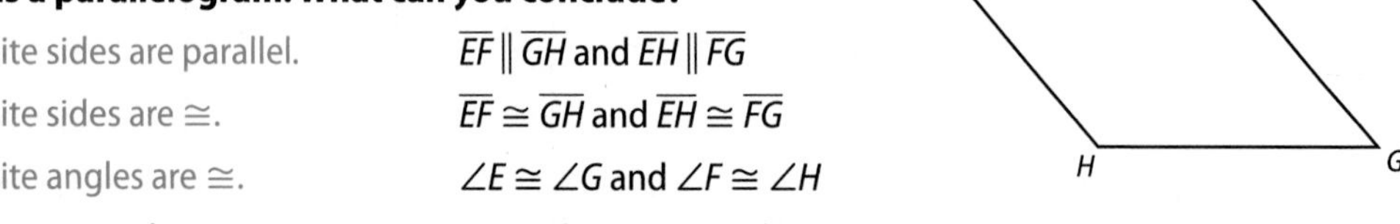

Opposite sides are parallel.	$\overline{EF} \parallel \overline{GH}$ and $\overline{EH} \parallel \overline{FG}$
Opposite sides are $\cong$.	$\overline{EF} \cong \overline{GH}$ and $\overline{EH} \cong \overline{FG}$
Opposite angles are $\cong$.	$\angle E \cong \angle G$ and $\angle F \cong \angle H$
Consecutive angles are supplementary.	$\angle E$ and $\angle F$ are supplementary. $\angle F$ and $\angle G$ are supplementary.
$\angle G$ and $\angle H$ are supplementary.	$\angle H$ and $\angle E$ are supplementary.

E F H G

EXAMPLE 8

Find the missing angle measures in parallelogram *JKLM*.

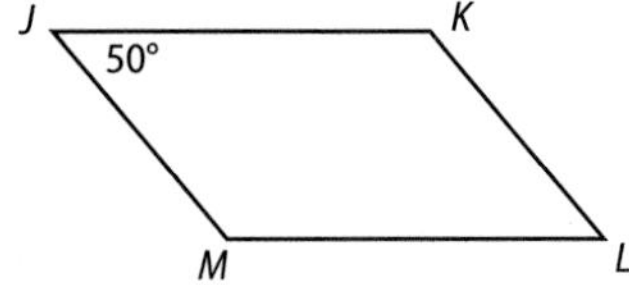

METHOD 1

$\angle J$ and $\angle K$ are supplementary, so $50° + m\angle K = 180°$.

$$m\angle K = 130°$$

$\angle K$ and $\angle L$ are supplementary, so $130° + m\angle L = 180°$.

$$m\angle L = 50°$$

$\angle L$ and $\angle M$ are supplementary, so $50° + m\angle M = 180°$.

$$m\angle M = 130°$$

METHOD 2

Opposite $\angle$s are congruent. $\angle L \cong \angle J$, so $m\angle L = 50°$.

Consecutive $\angle$s are supplementary. $\angle K$ and $\angle L$ are supplementary, so $m\angle K + 50° = 180°$.

$$m\angle K = 130°$$

Opposite $\angle$s are congruent. $\angle K \cong \angle M$, so $m\angle M = 130°$.

SEARCH

To see step-by-step videos of these problems, enter the page number into the SWadvantage.com Search Bar.

EXAMPLE 9

Find the values of *x*, *y*, and *z* in parallelogram *PQRS*.

P, Q, R, S; angles $5y°$, $3x°$, $4z°$, $2z°$

STEP 1 Write an equation that uses like terms only.

Consecutive $\angle$s are supplementary. $4z + 2z = 180$

STEP 2 Solve the equation.

Combine like terms. $6z = 180$

Divide both sides by 6. $z = 30$

STEP 3 Write equations to find the values of the other variables.

Opposite angles are congruent. $3x = 2z$ $5y = 4z$

STEP 4 Substitute for z and simplify.

$3x = 2(30)$ $5y = 4(30)$

$3x = 60$ $5y = 120$

STEP 5 Solve for x and y.

Divide by 3, and divide by 5. $x = 20$ $y = 24$

So, $x = 20$, $y = 24$, and $z = 30$.

GOT TO KNOW!

Angles in a Parallelogram

Opposite angles are congruent.

$\angle 1 \cong \angle 3$

$\angle 2 \cong \angle 4$

Consecutive angles are supplementary.

$\angle 1$ and $\angle 2$ $\angle 3$ and $\angle 4$

$\angle 2$ and $\angle 3$ $\angle 4$ and $\angle 1$

SOUTHWESTERN

Diagonals of a Parallelogram

The diagonals of a parallelogram bisect each other.

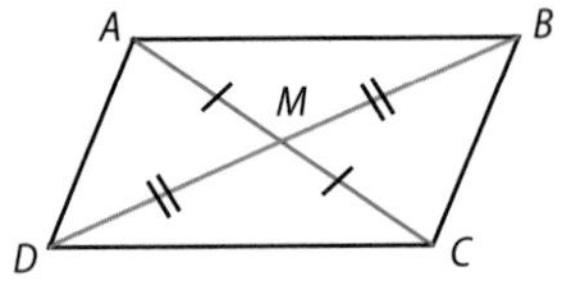

$\overline{AM} \cong \overline{CM}$ $\quad$ $\overline{BM} \cong \overline{DM}$

Sometimes you can use this property to find unknown lengths in a parallelogram.

EXAMPLE 10

In parallelogram *KLMN*, *KO* = 6 and *LN* = 20. Find *OM*, *KM*, *NO*, and *LO*.

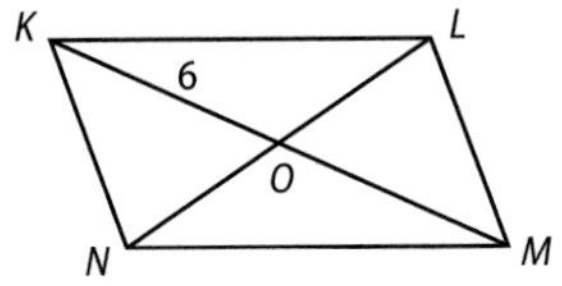

The diagonals of a parallelogram bisect each other, so $KO = OM = \frac{1}{2}KM$. Therefore, $OM = 6$ and $KM = 12$.

Similarly, $NO = LO = \frac{1}{2}LN$. Since $LN = 20$, $NO = 10$ and $LO = 10$.

SEARCH

To see step-by-step videos of these problems, enter the page number into the SWadvantage.com Search Bar.

EXAMPLE 11

***QRST* is a parallelogram. Find *QS* and *RT*.**

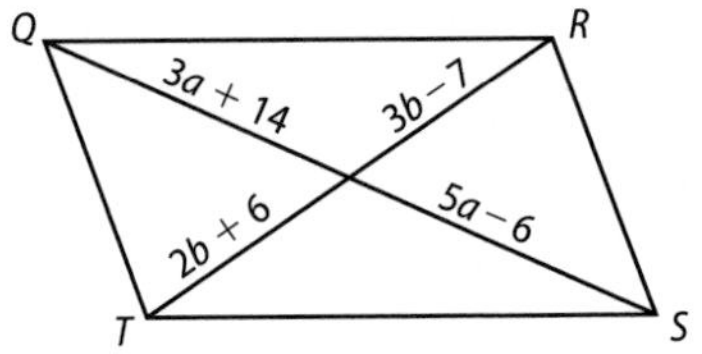

STEP 1 Use the fact that the diagonals of a parallelogram bisect each other to write two equations. Then solve the equations.

(1) $5a - 6 = 3a + 14$
$2a = 20$
$a = 10$

(2) $3b - 7 = 2b + 6$
$b = 13$

STEP 2 Substitute for a and b.

$QS = (5a - 6) + (3a + 14)$
$= 5(10) - 6 + 3(10) + 14$
$= 88$

$RT = (3b - 7) + (2b + 6)$
$= 3(13) - 7 + 2(13) + 6$
$= 64$

$QS = 88$, $RT = 64$

GOT TO KNOW!

Diagonals of a Parallelogram

The diagonals of a parallelogram bisect each other.

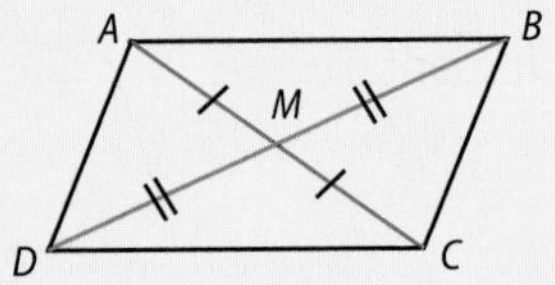

EXAMPLE 12

***ABCD* is a parallelogram. Find the values of *a*, *b*, *c*, and *d*.**

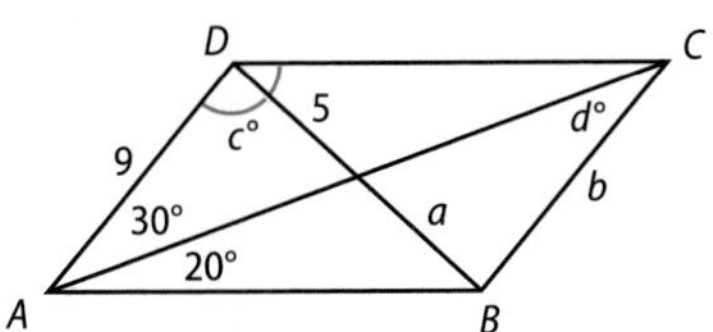

Diagonals bisect each other.	$a = 5$
Opposite sides are congruent.	$b = 9$
Consecutive ∠s are supplementary.	$(30° + 20°) + c° = 180°$
	$c = 130$
Alternate interior ∠s are congruent.	$\angle ACB \cong \angle DAC$, so $d = 30$.

So, $a = 5$, $b = 9$, $c = 130$, and $d = 30$.

Watch Out !

Read carefully what is given so you know how to answer.

In the figure, the label for the angle measure is $c°$. The value of c is only a number, 130, because the degree symbol is given.

If the figure showed just c for the angle measure, your answer would be 130°.

EXAMPLE 13

A parallelogram has vertices at *O*(0, 0), *P*(2, 3), *Q*(3, 2), and *R*. Find three possible sets of coordinates for vertex *R*.

There are three cases to consider. Draw a sketch for each possibility. Then use slope and the fact that opposite sides are parallel to locate *R*.

Case 1 Consider parallelogram *OPQR*.

Case 2 Consider parallelogram *OQPR*.

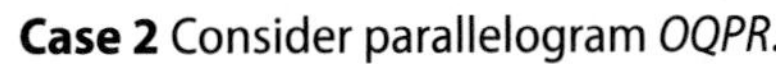

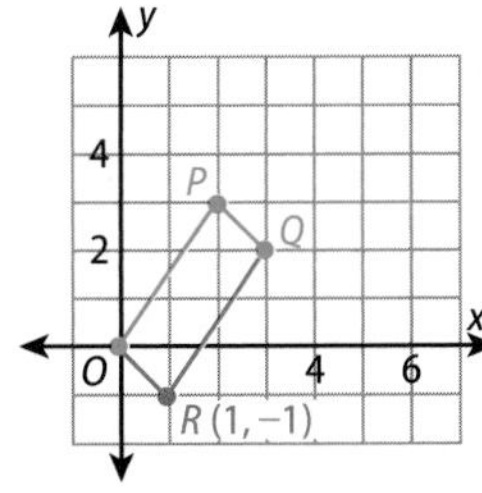

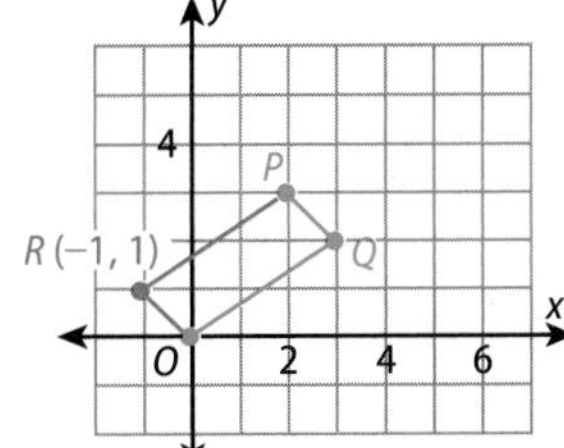

Case 3 Consider parallelogram *OQRP*.

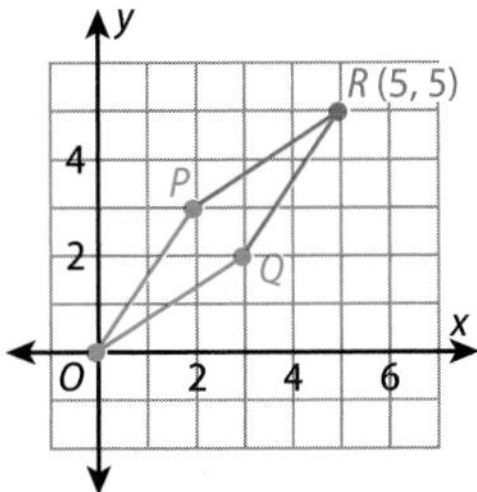

The three possible sets of coordinates for vertex *R* are (1, −1), (−1, 1), and (5, 5).

Need More HELP

For help with slope, go to *Rate of Change and Slope* in *Algebra* (Book 2, p. 1536).

Using Sides

There are three ways to use the sides of a quadrilateral to prove that the quadrilateral is a parallelogram. The first uses the definition of a parallelogram.

If both pairs of opposite sides of a quadrilateral are parallel, then the quadrilateral is a parallelogram.

ABCD is a parallelogram.

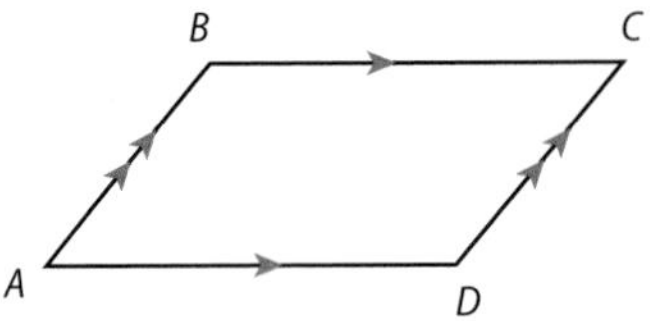

SEARCH

To see step-by-step videos of these problems, enter the page number into the SWadvantage.com Search Bar.

GOT TO KNOW!

Proving Triangles Congruent

Triangles are congruent if:

SSS: three sides of one triangle are congruent to the corresponding three sides of another triangle.

SAS: two sides and the included angle of one triangle are congruent to the corresponding sides and included angle of another triangle.

ASA: two angles and the included side of one triangle are congruent to the corresponding angles and included side of another triangle.

CPCTC: **C**orresponding **P**arts of **C**ongruent **T**riangles are **C**ongruent.

EXAMPLE 1

Given: $\angle 2 \cong \angle 3$ and $\angle 5 \cong \angle 8$
Prove: *ABCD* is a parallelogram.

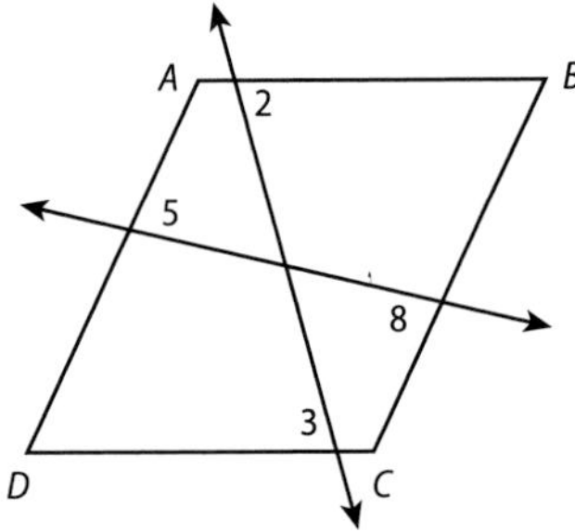

$\angle 2$ and $\angle 3$ are congruent alternate interior angles formed by the transversal that cuts $\overline{AB}$ and $\overline{CD}$, so $\overline{AB} \parallel \overline{CD}$. $\angle 5$ and $\angle 8$ are congruent alternate interior angles formed by the transversal that cuts $\overline{AD}$ and $\overline{BC}$, so $\overline{AD} \parallel \overline{BC}$. Both pairs of opposite sides are parallel, so *ABCD* is a parallelogram by definition of a parallelogram.

The second way to prove that a quadrilateral is a parallelogram is to show that both pairs of opposite sides are congruent.

Theorem
If both pairs of opposite sides of a quadrilateral are congruent, then the quadrilateral is a parallelogram.

PROOF

Given: $\overline{HI} \cong \overline{JK}$ and $\overline{HK} \cong \overline{JI}$

Prove: *HIJK* is a parallelogram.

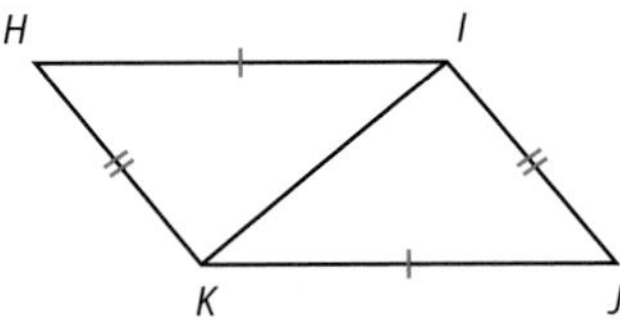

Statements	Reasons
1. $\overline{HI} \cong \overline{JK}$, $\overline{HK} \cong \overline{JI}$	1. Given
2. $\overline{KI} \cong \overline{IK}$	2. Reflexive property of congruency
3. $\triangle IHK \cong \triangle KJI$	3. SSS
4. $\angle HIK \cong \angle JKI$, $\angle HKI \cong \angle JIK$	4. CPCTC
5. $\overline{HI} \parallel \overline{JK}$, $\overline{HK} \parallel \overline{JI}$	5. If two lines are cut by a transversal and alternate interior $\angle$s are $\cong$, then the lines are $\parallel$.
6. *HIJK* is a parallelogram.	6. Definition of a parallelogram

EXAMPLE 2

Given: *WXYZ* is a parallelogram, $\angle 1 \cong \angle 2$.
Prove: *AXBZ* is a parallelogram.

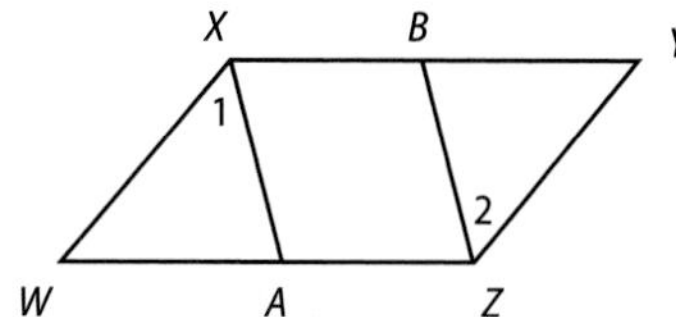

Statements	Reasons
1. *WXYZ* is a parallelogram; $\angle 1 \cong \angle 2$	1. Given
2. $\angle W \cong \angle Y$	2. Opposite $\angle$s of a parallelogram are $\cong$.
3. $WX = YZ$	3. Opposite sides of a parallelogram are $\cong$.
4. $\triangle WXA \cong \triangle YZB$	4. ASA
5. $AX = BZ$	5. CPCTC
6. $WZ = XY$	6. Opposite sides of a parallelogram are $\cong$.
7. $WA = YB$	7. CPCTC
8. $AZ = XB$	8. Subtraction property of =
9. *AXBZ* is a parallelogram.	9. If both pairs of opposite sides of a quadrilateral are $\cong$, then the quadrilateral is a parallelogram.

Need More HELP

For help with proving triangles congruent, go to *Using SSS and SAS* and *Using ASA and AAS* on pages 768 and 772.

The third method requires information about only one pair of sides.

Theorem
If two sides of a quadrilateral are both congruent and parallel, then the quadrilateral is a parallelogram.

Watch Out!

Is this theorem still true if you take out the word *both*? No.

PROOF

Given: $\overline{LM} \cong \overline{NO}$ and $\overline{LM} \parallel \overline{NO}$

Prove: *LMNO* is a parallelogram.

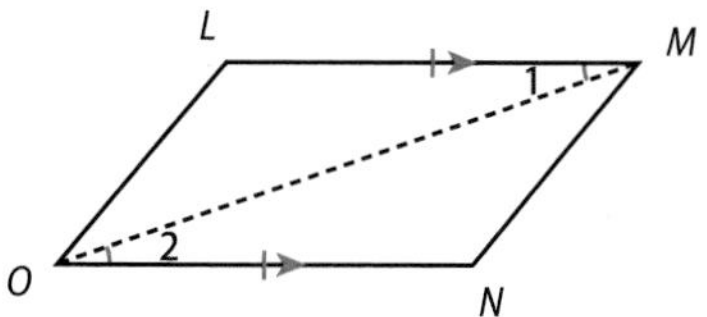

Statements	Reasons
1. $\overline{LM} \cong \overline{NO}$, and $\overline{LM} \parallel \overline{NO}$	1. Given
2. $\angle 1 \cong \angle 2$	2. If two $\parallel$ lines are cut by a transversal, then alternate interior $\angle$s are $\cong$.
3. $\overline{OM} \cong \overline{MO}$	3. Reflexive property of $\cong$
4. $\triangle LMO \cong \triangle NOM$	4. SAS
5. $\overline{LO} \cong \overline{NM}$	5. CPCTC
6. *LMNO* is a parallelogram.	6. If both pairs of opposite sides of a quadrilateral are $\cong$, the quadrilateral is a parallelogram.

GOT TO KNOW!

Using Sides to Prove a Quadrilateral Is a Parallelogram

- Show that both pairs of opposite sides are parallel.
- Show that both pairs of opposite sides are congruent.
- Show that two sides are both congruent and parallel.

Two More Ways

Showing that both pairs of opposite angles in a quadrilateral are congruent is sufficient to prove that a quadrilateral is a parallelogram.

Theorem
If both pairs of opposite angles of a quadrilateral are congruent, then the quadrilateral is a parallelogram.

Need More HELP

Remember! The sum of the measures of the angles of a quadrilateral is 360°.

PROOF

Given: $\angle 1 \cong \angle 3$ **and** $\angle 2 \cong \angle 4$

Prove: ***WXYZ*** **is a parallelogram.**

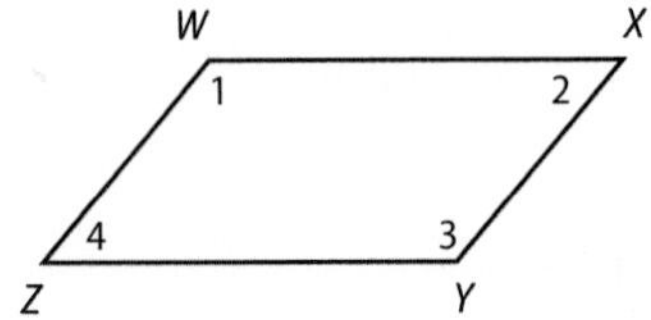

Statements	Reasons
1. $m\angle 1 = m\angle 3$ and $m\angle 2 = m\angle 4$	1. Given
2. $m\angle 1 + m\angle 2 + m\angle 3 + m\angle 4 = 360°$	2. Sum of measures of ∠s of a quad. is 360°.
3. $m\angle 1 + m\angle 2 + m\angle 1 + m\angle 2 = 360°$	3. Substitution
4. $2(m\angle 1 + m\angle 2) = 360°$	4. Distributive property
5. $m\angle 1 + m\angle 2 = 180°$	5. Division property of =
6. $m\angle 1 + m\angle 4 = 180°$	6. Substitution
7. $\overline{WX} \parallel \overline{ZY}, \overline{WZ} \parallel \overline{XY}$	7. If two lines are cut by a transversal so that same-side int. ∠s are supp., then the lines are ‖.
8. *WXYZ* is a parallelogram.	8. Definition of a parallelogram

EXAMPLE 3

Given: $\angle 1 \cong \angle 3, \angle F \cong \angle C$

Prove: ***BCEF*** **is a parallelogram.**

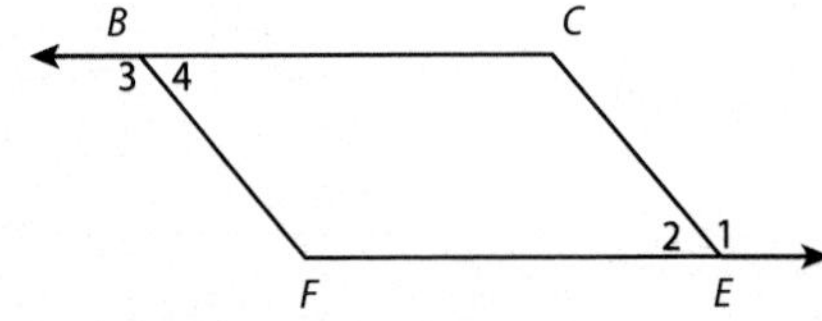

SEARCH

To see step-by-step videos of these problems, enter the page number into the SWadvantage.com Search Bar.

Statements	Reasons
1. ∠1 and ∠2 are supplementary; ∠3 and ∠4 are supplementary.	1. If two angles form a linear pair, then they are supplementary.
2. $\angle 1 \cong \angle 3$	2. Given
3. $\angle 2 \cong \angle 4$	3. Supplements of ≅ ∠s are ≅.
4. $\angle F \cong \angle C$	4. Given
5. *BCEF* is a parallelogram.	5. If both pairs of opposite ∠s of a quadrilateral are ≅, then the quadrilateral is a parallelogram.

If you can show the diagonals of a quadrilateral bisect each other, then you can prove the quadrilateral is a parallelogram.

Theorem
If the diagonals of a quadrilateral bisect each other, then the quadrilateral is a parallelogram.

PROOF

Given: $\overline{RT}$ and $\overline{SU}$ bisect each other.

Prove: *RSTU* is a parallelogram.

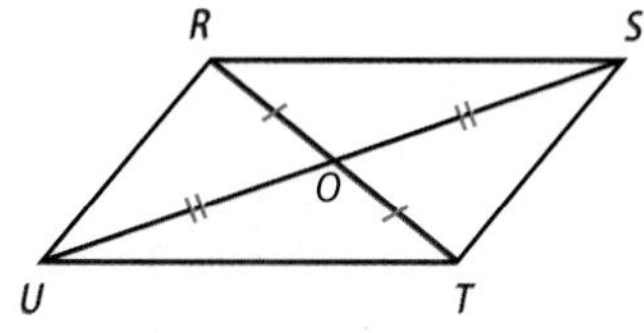

Statements	Reasons
1. $\overline{RT}$ and $\overline{SU}$ bisect each other.	1. Given
2. $\overline{RO} \cong \overline{TO}, \overline{UO} \cong \overline{SO}$	2. Definition of bisect
3. $\angle ROS \cong \angle TOU$	3. Vertical $\angle$s are $\cong$.
4. $\triangle ROS \cong \triangle TOU$	4. SAS
5. $\angle RSO \cong \angle TUO, RS = TU$	5. CPCTC
6. $\overline{RS} \parallel \overline{TU}$	6. If two lines are cut by a transversal so that alternate interior $\angle$s are $\cong$, then the lines are $\parallel$.
7. *RSTU* is a parallelogram.	7. If two sides of a quadrilateral are both $\cong$ and $\parallel$, then the quadrilateral is a parallelogram.

Try It This Way

Before you read the proof of this theorem, write your own proof. There is more than one way to prove this theorem.

EXAMPLE 4

Find the values of *x* and *y* for which *ABCD* must be a parallelogram.

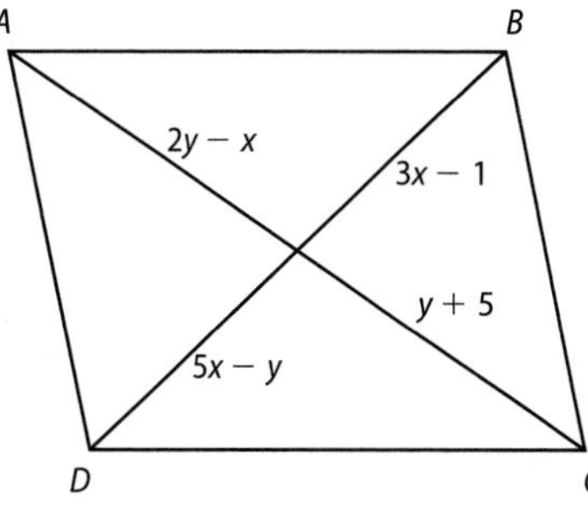

For *ABCD* to be a parallelogram, the diagonals must bisect each other. So,

$2y - x = y + 5$ and $5x - y = 3x - 1$

$y = x + 5$ $\quad$ $2x = y - 1$

Substitute $x + 5$ for y. $\quad$ $2x = (x + 5) - 1$

$x = 4$

Substitute 4 for x in first equation. $\quad$ $2y - x = y + 5$

$2y - 4 = y + 5$

$y = 9$

$x = 4$ and $y = 9$

GOT TO KNOW!

Ways to Prove a Quadrilateral Is a Parallelogram

- Show that both pairs of opposite sides are parallel.
- Show that both pairs of opposite sides are congruent.
- Show that two sides are both congruent and parallel.
- Show that opposite angles are congruent.
- Show that the diagonals bisect each other.

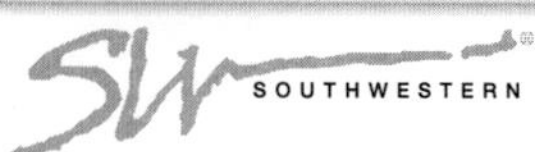

Putting It All Together

EXAMPLE 5

Can you use the given information to prove that *WXYZ* is a parallelogram? If *yes*, state the definition or theorem you would use.

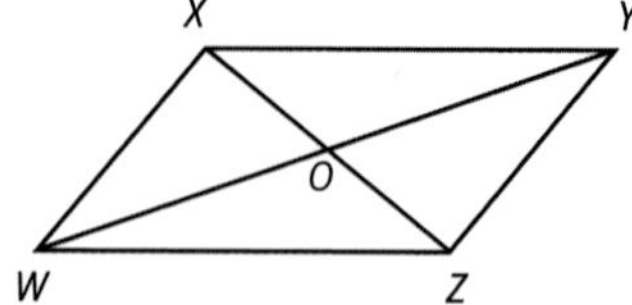

SEARCH

To see step-by-step videos of these problems, enter the page number into the SWadvantage.com Search Bar.

a. $\overline{WX} \parallel \overline{YZ}, \overline{XY} \parallel \overline{WZ}$

Yes; if both pairs of opposite sides of a quadrilateral are parallel, then the quadrilateral is a parallelogram by definition of a parallelogram.

b. $WO = YO, ZO = XO$

Yes; if the diagonals of a quadrilateral bisect each other, then the quadrilateral is a parallelogram.

c. $WX = ZY, \overline{WZ} \parallel \overline{XY}$

No.

d. $\angle ZWX \cong \angle XYZ, \angle WZY \cong \angle YXW$

Yes; if both pairs of opposite angles of a quadrilateral are congruent, then the quadrilateral is a parallelogram.

e. $WX = ZY, \overline{WX} \parallel \overline{YZ}$

Yes; if two sides of a quadrilateral are both congruent and parallel, then the quadrilateral is a parallelogram.

e. $WO = ZO, XO = YO$

No.

f. $WX = ZY, WZ = XY$

Yes; if both pairs of opposite sides of a quadrilateral are congruent, then the quadrilateral is a parallelogram.

g. ***O* is the midpoint of $\overline{XZ}$; *O* is the midpoint of $\overline{WY}$.**

Yes; if the diagonals of a quadrilateral bisect each other, then the quadrilateral is a parallelogram.

h. $\overline{WX} \parallel \overline{YZ}, \angle WZX \cong \angle YXZ$

Yes; if both pairs of opposite sides of a quadrilateral are parallel, then the quadrilateral is a parallelogram by definition of a parallelogram.

i. $WY = XZ$

No.

j. $WO = OY = OX, WY = ZX$

Yes; if the diagonals of a quadrilateral bisect each other, then the quadrilateral is a parallelogram.

EXAMPLE 6

The vertices of *ABCD* are *A*(−2, 5), *B*(4, 3), *C*(6, −2), and *D*(0, 0). Show that *ABCD* is a parallelogram.

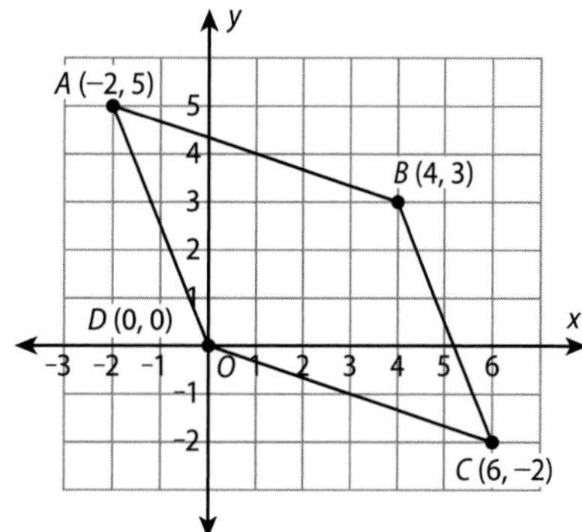

METHOD 1

Show that opposite sides are parallel.

STEP 1 Find the slope of each side.

Slope of $\overline{AB} = \dfrac{5-3}{-2-4} = -\dfrac{2}{6}$

Slope of $\overline{DC} = \dfrac{0-(-2)}{0-6} = -\dfrac{2}{6}$

Slope of $\overline{AD} = \dfrac{5-0}{-2-0} = -\dfrac{5}{2}$

Slope of $\overline{BC} = \dfrac{-2-3}{6-4} = -\dfrac{5}{2}$

STEP 2 Compare slopes of opposite sides.

Slope of $\overline{AB} = -\dfrac{2}{6}$ = slope of $\overline{DC}$

Slope of $\overline{AD} = -\dfrac{5}{2}$ = slope of $\overline{BC}$

Sides with the same slope are parallel, so $\overline{AB} \parallel \overline{DC}$ and $\overline{AD} \parallel \overline{BC}$. Since both pairs of opposite sides are parallel, *ABCD* is a parallelogram.

METHOD 2

Show that opposite sides are congruent.

STEP 1 Find the length of each side, using the distance formula.

$AB = \sqrt{(-2-4)^2 + (5-3)^2} = \sqrt{40}$

$DC = \sqrt{(0-6)^2 + [0-(-2)]^2} = \sqrt{40}$

$AD = \sqrt{(-2-0)^2 + (5-0)^2} = \sqrt{29}$

$BC = \sqrt{(4-6)^2 + [3-(-2)]^2} = \sqrt{29}$

STEP 2 Compare the lengths of opposite sides.

$AB = \sqrt{40} = DC \qquad AD = \sqrt{29} = BC$

Since both pairs of opposite sides are congruent, *ABCD* is a parallelogram.

METHOD 3

Show that one pair of opposite sides is both parallel and congruent.

In Methods 1 and 2, you showed that $\overline{AB} \parallel \overline{DC}$ and $\overline{AB} \cong \overline{DC}$. Since one pair of opposite sides is both parallel and congruent, *ABCD* is a parallelogram.

Need More HELP

For a review of the distance formula, go to *Distance Formula* on page 818.

For a reminder of what properties all parallelograms have, go to *Properties of Parallelograms* on page 638.

Rectangles

A **rectangle** is a parallelogram with four right angles.

RECT is a rectangle.

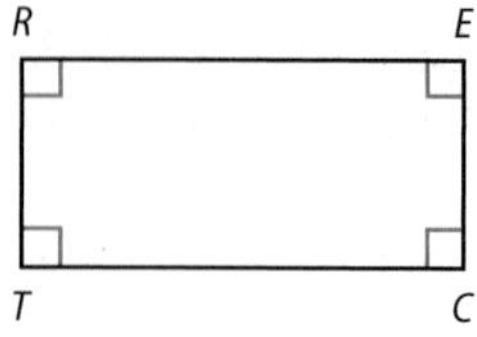

Since a rectangle is a parallelogram, it has all of the properties of a parallelogram. In addition, it has special properties of its own.

Theorem
The diagonals of a rectangle are congruent.

PROOF

Given: *ABCD* is a rectangle.

Prove: $\overline{AC} \cong \overline{BD}$

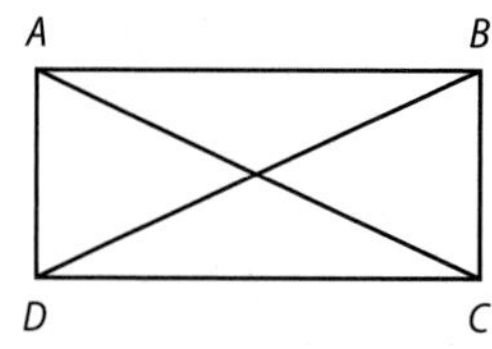

Statements	Reasons
1. *ABCD* is a rectangle.	1. Given
2. $\overline{AD} \cong \overline{BC}$	2. Opposite sides of a parallelogram are ≅.
3. $\angle ADC$ and $\angle BCD$ are right ∠s.	3. Definition of a rectangle
4. $\angle ADC \cong \angle BCD$	4. All right ∠s are ≅.
5. $\overline{CD} \cong \overline{DC}$	5. Reflexive property of ≅
6. $\triangle ADC \cong \triangle BCD$	6. SAS
7. $\overline{AC} \cong \overline{BD}$	7. CPCTC

EXAMPLE 1

***QRST* is a rectangle with $RT = 13$ and $TS = 11$.**

a. Find *QR*.

Opposite sides of a parallelogram are ≅. $QR = TS = 11$

b. Find *QX*.

Diagonals of a rectangle are ≅. $QS = RT = 13$

Diags. of a parallelogram bisect each other. $QX = \frac{1}{2}QS$

Substitute for *QS* and simplify. $QX = \frac{1}{2}(13) = 6.5$

c. Find *RS*.

Use the Pythagorean Theorem. $TS^2 + RS^2 = RT^2$

Substitute. $11^2 + RS^2 = 13^2$

Solve. $RS^2 = 169 - 121$

$RS = \sqrt{48} = 4\sqrt{3}$

For help with the Pythagorean Theorem, go to *Pythagorean Theorem* in *Triangles and Polygons* on page 678.

Theorem
If a parallelogram has one right angle, then it is a rectangle.

PROOF

Given: *WXYZ* is a parallelogram and $\angle Y$ is a right angle.

Prove: *WXYZ* is a rectangle.

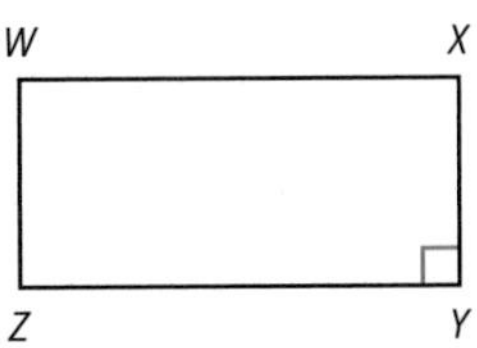

If $\angle Y$ is a right angle, then $\angle W$ is a right angle because opposite angles of a parallelogram are congruent.

If $\angle Y$ is a right angle, then $\angle X$ must be a right angle because consecutive angles of a parallelogram are supplementary.

If $\angle X$ is a right angle, then $\angle Z$ is a right angle because opposite angles of a parallelogram are congruent.

WXYZ is a parallelogram with four right angles, so it is a rectangle by definition.

EXAMPLE 2

***HIJK* is a parallelogram, $m\angle HJI = 58°$, $m\angle KJH = 32°$, and $KO = 8.2$. Find *HJ*.**

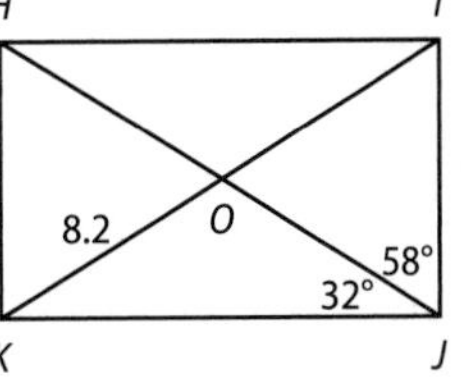

Angle Addition Postulate	$m\angle KJI = m\angle KJH + m\angle HJI$
Substitute.	$m\angle KJI = 32° + 58°$
Simplify.	$m\angle KJI = 90°$

Since $\angle KJI$ is a right angle, *HIJK* is a rectangle.

Diags. of a parallelogram bisect each other.	$KI = 2(KO)$
Substitute for *KO*.	$KI = 2(8.2)$
Simplify.	$KI = 16.4$
Diags. of a rectangle are congruent.	$HJ = KI$
Substitute.	$HJ = 16.4$

SEARCH

To see step-by-step videos of these problems, enter the page number into the SWadvantage.com Search Bar.

GOT TO KNOW!

Properties of Rectangles

All the angles are right angles.

The diagonals are congruent.

All the properties of parallelograms apply:

- Opposite sides are parallel.
- Opposite sides are congruent.
- Opposite angles are congruent.
- The diagonals bisect each other.
- Consecutive angles are supplementary.

Rhombuses

A **rhombus** is a parallelogram with four congruent sides.

RMBS is a rhombus.

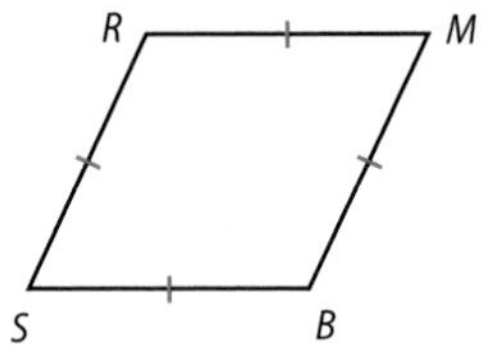

In addition to all of the properties of a parallelogram, a rhombus has several other properties.

Try It This Way

Draw a rhombus and cut it along the diagonals to form four triangles. What do you notice about the triangles? What does this tell you about the diagonals of a rhombus?

Theorem
The diagonals of a rhombus are perpendicular. 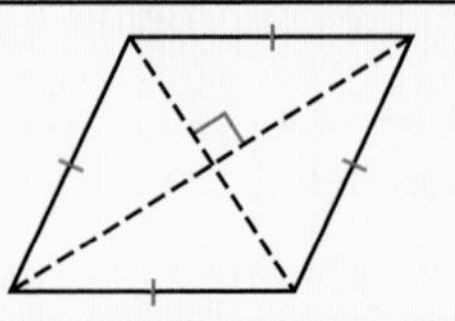

PROOF

Given: *ABCD* is a rhombus.

Prove: $\overline{AC} \perp \overline{BD}$

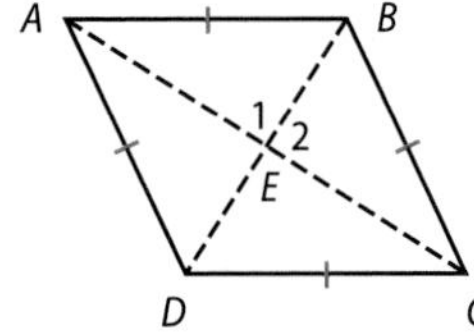

Statements	Reasons
1. *ABCD* is a rhombus.	1. Given
2. $\overline{AB} \cong \overline{BC}$	2. Definition of a rhombus
3. $\overline{AE} \cong \overline{CE}$	3. Diagonals of a parallelogram bisect each other.
4. $\overline{BE} \cong \overline{BE}$	4. Reflexive property of congruency
5. $\triangle ABE \cong \triangle CBE$	5. SSS
6. $\angle 1 \cong \angle 2$	6. CPCTC
7. $\angle 1$ and $\angle 2$ are supplementary.	7. Two $\angle$s that form a linear pair are supplementary.
8. $\angle 1$ and $\angle 2$ are right angles.	8. If 2 $\angle$s are $\cong$ and supp., then each $\angle$ is a rt. $\angle$.
9. $\overline{AC} \perp \overline{BD}$	9. Definition of $\perp$ lines

The diagonals of a rhombus have another property.

Theorem
The diagonals of a rhombus bisect the angles of the rhombus. 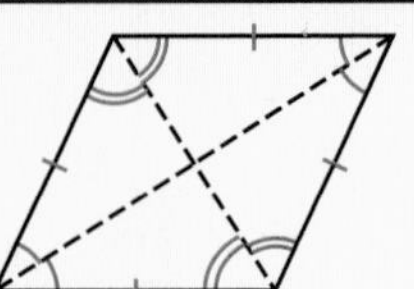

EXAMPLE 3

WXYZ is a rhombus with $m\angle WXY = 110°$.

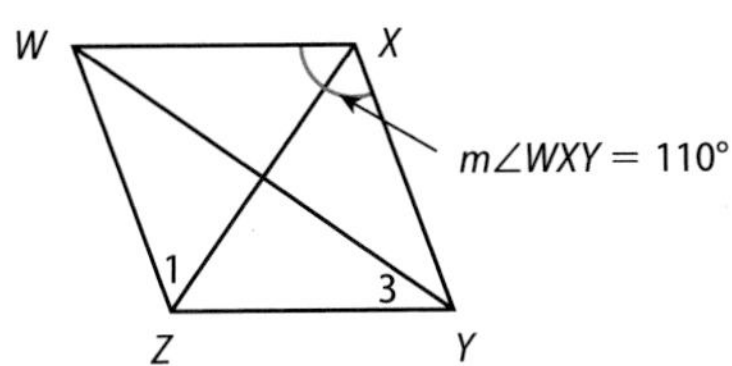

a. Find $m\angle 1$.

The diagonals of a rhombus bisect its angles.	$m\angle 1 = \frac{1}{2} m\angle WZY$
Opposite $\angle$s of a parallelogram are $\cong$.	$m\angle WZY = m\angle WXY$
Substitute.	$m\angle 1 = \frac{1}{2} \cdot 110°$
	$m\angle 1 = 55°$

b. Find $m\angle 3$.

Consec. $\angle$s of a parallelogram are supp.	$m\angle WZY + m\angle ZYX = 180°$
Substitute.	$110° + m\angle ZYX = 180°$
Subtraction Property of =	$m\angle ZYX = 70°$
The diagonals of a rhombus bisect its angles.	$m\angle 3 = \frac{1}{2} m\angle ZYX$
Substitute.	$m\angle 3 = \frac{1}{2} \cdot 70°$
	$m\angle 3 = 35°$

SEARCH

To see step-by-step videos of these problems, enter the page number into the SWadvantage.com Search Bar.

EXAMPLE 4

KLMN is a rhombus with $m\angle KON = (5x + 8)°$ and $m\angle OLM = (2x - 2)°$. Find $m\angle KLM$.

K L O N M

STEP 1 Find the value of x.

Diags. of a rhombus are $\perp$.	$m\angle KON = 90°$
Substitute for $m\angle KON$.	$5x + 8 = 90$
Solve.	$5x = 82$
	$x = 16.4$

STEP 2 Find $m\angle OLM$.

$m\angle OLM = (2x - 2)°$

$m\angle OLM = 2(16.4) - 2$

$m\angle OLM = 30.8°$

STEP 3 Find $m\angle KLM$.

Diags. bisect opp. $\angle$s.	$m\angle KLM = 2(m\angle OLM)$
Substitute for $m\angle OLM$.	$m\angle KLM = 2(30.8)$
	$m\angle KLM = 61.6°$

GOT TO KNOW!

Properties of Rhombuses

All the sides are congruent. The diagonals are perpendicular. The diagonals bisect the angles.

Squares

A square is a parallelogram with four right angles and four congruent sides.

SQRE is a square.

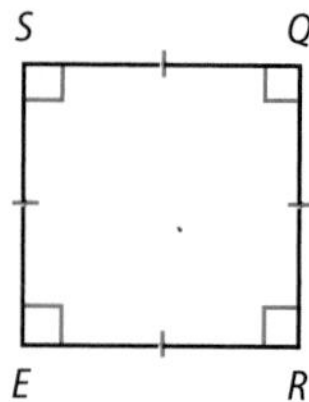

So by definition, a square is also a rectangle and a rhombus. This is illustrated in the Venn diagram below.

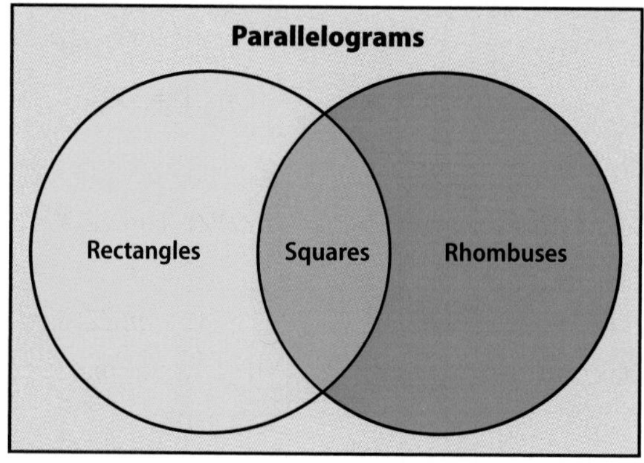

Therefore, a square has all of the properties of a rectangle and a rhombus, in addition to all the properties of a parallelogram.

GOT TO KNOW!

Properties of Squares

All the properties of parallelograms apply.

All the properties of rectangles apply.

All the properties of rhombuses apply.

Watch Out!

A square has the properties of both a rectangle and a rhombus, but a rectangle and a rhombus do not necessarily have the properties of a square.

EXAMPLE 5

Determine whether each statement is always, sometimes, or never true.

a. A square is a rectangle.

Always true; all squares are rectangles.

b. A parallelogram is a square.

Sometimes true; if a parallelogram has four right angles and four congruent sides, then it is a square.

c. A square is a parallelogram.

Always true; all squares are parallelograms.

d. A square is not a rhombus.

Never true; all squares are rhombuses.

e. A rhombus is a rectangle.

Sometimes true; if a rhombus is a square, then it is also a rectangle.

EXAMPLE 6

***ABCD* is a square. Find *AC* given $m\angle AEB = (3x + 15)°$ and $BD = 2x$.**

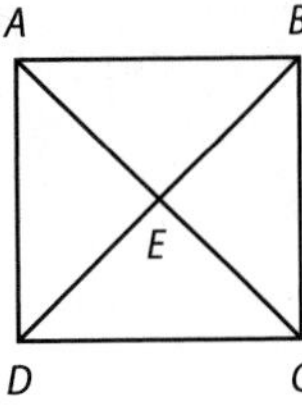

STEP 1 Find the value of x.

Diags. of a square are ⊥.	$m\angle AEB = 90°$
Substitute.	$3x + 15 = 90$
Solve for x.	$3x = 75$
	$x = 25$

STEP 2 Find AC.

Diags. of a square are ≅.	$AC = BD$
Substitute.	$BD = 2x = 2(25) = 50$
	$AC = 50$

SEARCH

To see step-by-step videos of these problems, enter the page number into the SWadvantage.com Search Bar.

EXAMPLE 7

***PQRS* is a square with $QM = 6$. Find the area of *PQRS*.**

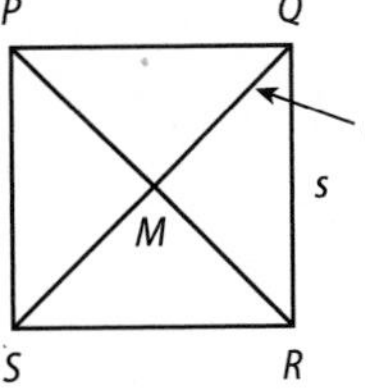

METHOD 1

The diagonals of a square divide it into four congruent isosceles right triangles. Find the area of one triangle, and multiply it by 4.

Triangle area formula $\qquad$ area of triangle $= \frac{1}{2} \times$ base $\times$ height

The base and height of each triangle is 6.

Substitute. $\qquad$ area of triangle $= \frac{1}{2}(6)(6)$

area of triangle $= 18$

Area of square = 4(area of triangle) = area of $PQRS = 4(18) = 72$

The area of *PQRS* is 72 square units.

METHOD 2

Find the length of one side of the square, then square that length to find the area.

Each side s of the square is the hypotenuse of a right triangle with legs of length 6.

Pythagorean Theorem	$s^2 = 6^2 + 6^2$
Solve for the side length s.	$s^2 = 72$
	$s = \sqrt{72}$
	area of $PQRS = s^2$
	area of $PQRS = \left(\sqrt{72}\right)^2 = 72$

The area of *PQRS* is 72 square units.

Need More HELP

For help with finding area, go to *Perimeter and Area* in *Measurement* (starting on p. 522).

Properties of Trapezoids and Kites

SOUTHWESTERN

Watch Out !

The bases and the base angles are not always on the top and bottom.

Trapezoids

A **trapezoid** is a quadrilateral with exactly one pair of parallel sides. The parallel sides are **bases**, and the other two sides are **legs**. Each pair of angles that lie on the same base are called **base angles**.

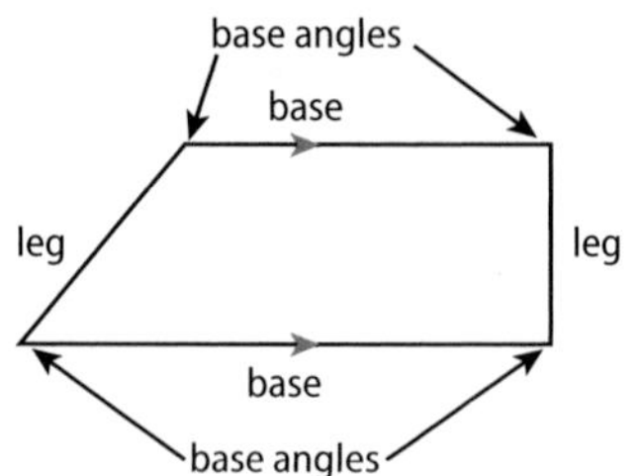

EXAMPLE 1

Find the measures of the missing angles in trapezoid *ABCD*.

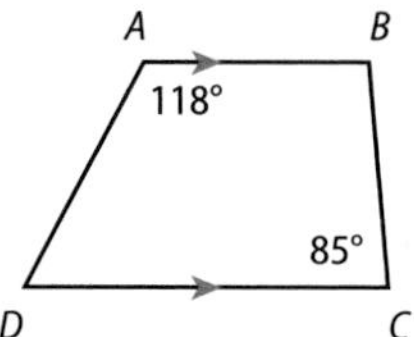

Same-side interior angles are supp.	$m\angle A + m\angle D = 180°$	$m\angle B + m\angle C = 180°$
Substitute.	$118° + m\angle D = 180°$	$m\angle B + 85° = 180°$
Solve.	$m\angle D = 62°$	$m\angle B = 95°$

The **midsegment of a trapezoid** is the segment whose endpoints are the midpoints of the legs.

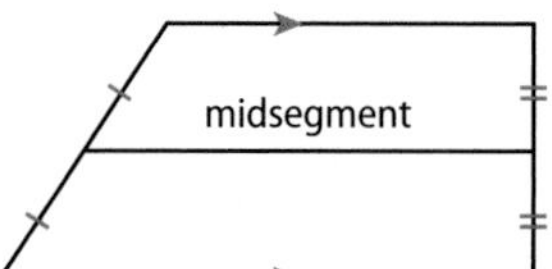

EXAMPLE 2

Identify the bases, legs, and midsegment of trapezoid *QRST*.

$\overline{QR}$ and $\overline{ST}$ are parallel, so they are bases.

$\overline{QT}$ and $\overline{RS}$ are not parallel, so they are legs.

The endpoints of $\overline{UV}$ are the midpoints of $\overline{QT}$ and $\overline{RS}$, so it is the midsegment.

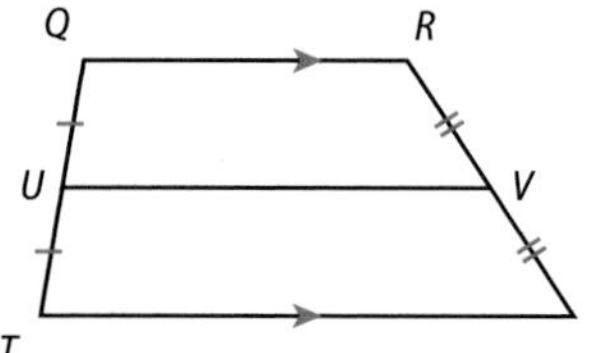

GOT TO KNOW!

Properties of Trapezoids

The bases are parallel.

The midsegment is parallel to bases.

The length of the midsegment is the mean of the base lengths.

Trapezoid Midsegment Theorem

The midsegment of a trapezoid is parallel to each of the bases, and its length is half the sum of the lengths of the bases.

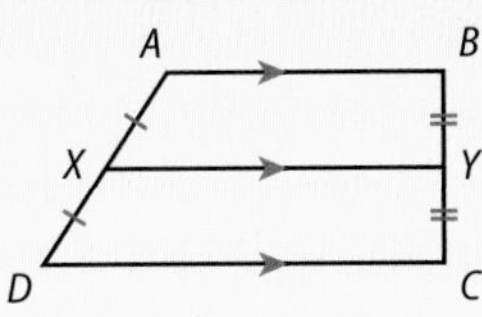

$\overline{XY} \parallel \overline{AB}$ and
$\overline{XY} \parallel \overline{DC}$
$XY = \frac{1}{2}(AB + DC)$

EXAMPLE 3

$\overline{MN}$ is the midsegment of trapezoid *GHIJ*.

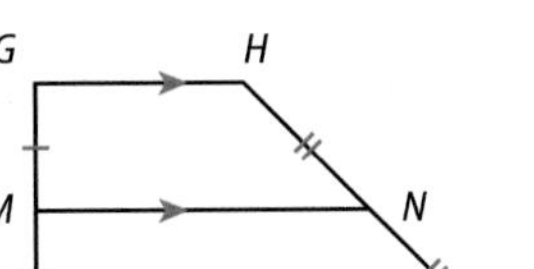

a. $GH = 13$ and $JI = 29$; find MN.

Trapezoid midsegment theorem $\quad MN = \frac{GH + JI}{2}$

Substitute. $\quad MN = \frac{13 + 29}{2}$

Simplify. $\quad MN = 21$

b. $JI = 18$ and $MN = 14$; find GH.

Trapezoid midsegment theorem $\quad MN = \frac{GH + JI}{2}$

Substitute. $\quad 14 = \frac{GH + 18}{2}$

Multiply both sides by 2. $\quad 28 = GH + 18$

Subtract 18 from both sides. $\quad GH = 10$

c. $MJ = 5$ and $NI = 6$; find GM and HN.

M and N are the midpoints of $\overline{GJ}$ and $\overline{HI}$ by definition of a midsegment.

$GM = MJ = 5$ and $HN = NI = 6$

SEARCH

To see step-by-step videos of these problems, enter the page number into the SWadvantage.com Search Bar.

EXAMPLE 4

Find the length of the midsegment.

STEP 1 Find the value of x.

Trapezoid midsegment theorem $\quad x + 12 = \frac{(3x + 5) + (x + 9)}{2}$

Simplify. $\quad x + 12 = \frac{4x + 14}{2}$

$x + 12 = 2x + 7$

Solve. $\quad x = 5$

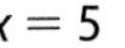

STEP 2 Find the length of the midsegment.

Evaluate the expression $x + 12$ for $x = 5$. $\quad 5 + 12 = 17$

The length of the midsegment is 17.

Isosceles Trapezoids

An **isosceles trapezoid** has congruent legs.

TRAP is an isosceles trapezoid.

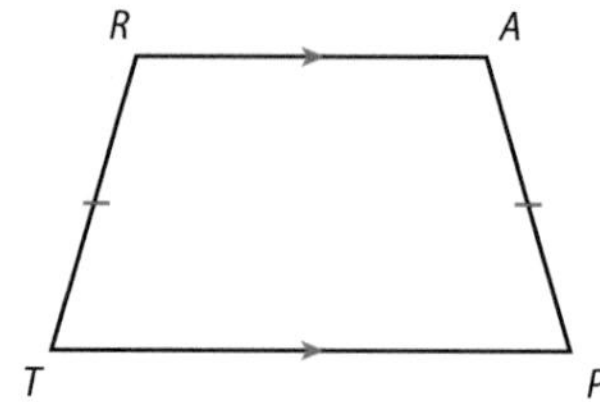

Theorem
The base angles of an isosceles trapezoid are congruent. $\angle T \cong \angle P$ and $\angle R \cong \angle A$

For more information about the properties of isosceles triangles, go to *Isosceles and Equilateral Triangles* in *Congruence* on page 784.

PROOF

Given: ***TRAP*** **is an isosceles trapezoid with** $\overline{RA} \parallel \overline{TP}$ **and** $\overline{TR} \cong \overline{PA}$**.**

Prove: $\angle T \cong \angle P$

Start by drawing $\overline{AE} \parallel \overline{RT}$.

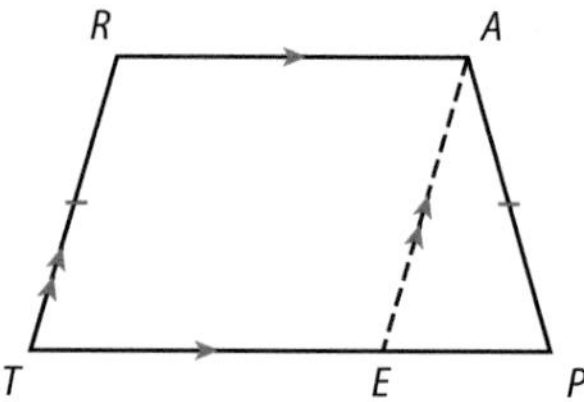

Statements	Reasons
1. $\overline{RA} \parallel \overline{TP}$ and $\overline{TR} \cong \overline{PA}$; $\overline{AE} \parallel \overline{RT}$	1. Given
2. *TRAE* is a parallelogram.	2. Definition of a parallelogram
3. $TR = AE$	3. Opposite sides of a parallelogram are $\cong$.
4. $\angle AEP \cong \angle P$	4. Base $\angle$s of an isosceles triangle are $\cong$.
5. $\angle T \cong \angle AEP$	5. If two lines are $\parallel$, then corres. $\angle$s are $\cong$.
6. $\angle T \cong \angle P$	6. Transitive property of congruence

EXAMPLE 5

EFGH **is an isosceles trapezoid and** $m\angle H = 54°$**.**
Find the measures of the other three angles.

Base $\angle$s of isosceles trap. are $\cong$. $\quad m\angle G = m\angle H$

$m\angle G = 54°$

Same-side interior $\angle$s are supp. $\quad m\angle E + m\angle H = 180°$

$m\angle E + 54° = 180°$

$m\angle E = 126°$

Base $\angle$s of isosceles trap. are $\cong$. $\quad m\angle F = m\angle E$

$m\angle F = 126°$

To see step-by-step videos of these problems, enter the page number into the SWadvantage.com Search Bar.

Notice that opposite angles of an isosceles trapezoid are supplementary.

Theorem
The diagonals of an isosceles trapezoid are congruent.

PROOF

Given: *WXYZ* is an isosceles trapezoid with $\overline{WZ} \cong \overline{YX}$.

Prove: $\overline{WY} \cong \overline{XZ}$

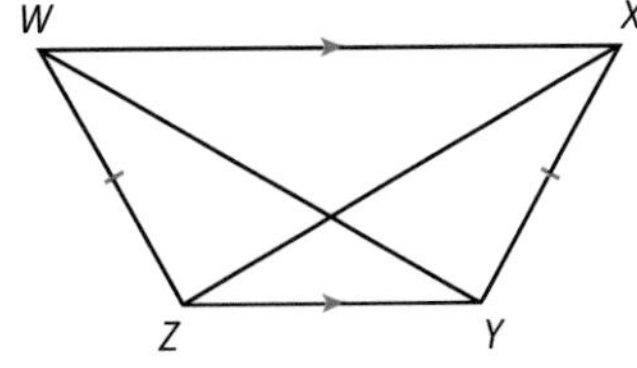

Statements	Reasons
1. *WXYZ* is an isosceles trapezoid with $\overline{WZ} \cong \overline{YX}$	1. Given
2. $\overline{YZ} \cong \overline{ZY}$	2. Reflexive property of congruency
3. $\angle WZY \cong \angle XYZ$	3. Base ∠s of isosceles trapezoid are congruent.
4. $\triangle WZY \cong \triangle XYZ$	4. SAS
5. $\overline{WY} \cong \overline{XZ}$	5. CPCTC

Try It This Way

"Pull apart" overlapping triangles *WZY* and *XYZ*. Draw them separately and mark the congruent parts.

EXAMPLE 6

***HIJK* is an isosceles trapezoid. Find *IO* if *HJ* = 17.6 and *KO* = 11.8.**

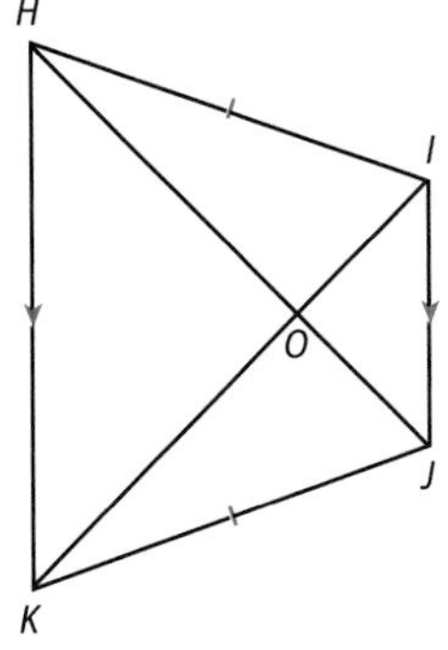

Diags. of isosceles trap. are ≅.	$KI = HJ$
Substitute for *HJ*.	$KI = 17.6$
Segment addition postulate	$IO + KO = KI$
Substitute.	$IO + 11.8 = 17.6$
Solve.	$IO = 5.8$

Need More HELP

For help solving two equations with two variables, go to *Solving a System by Substitution* in *Algebra* (Book 2, p. 1568).

EXAMPLE 7

***LMNO* is an isosceles trapezoid. *LO* = 2*y* − 3, *MN* = *x* + *y*, *LN* = 5*x*, and *OM* = *y* + 5. Find the values of *x* and *y*.**

The legs of an isosceles trapezoid are ≅.	$2y - 3 = x + y$
Solve for *y*.	$y = x + 3$
The diagonals of an isosceles trapezoid are ≅.	$5x = y + 5$
Solve for *y*.	$y = 5x - 5$
Substitute.	$x + 3 = 5x - 5$
Solve for *x*.	$4x = 8, x = 2$
Substitute to find the value of *y*.	$y = x + 3 = 2 + 3 = 5$

GOT TO KNOW!

Properties of Isosceles Trapezoids

The legs are congruent.

The base angles are congruent.

The diagonals are congruent.

All the properties of trapezoids apply.

Kites

A **kite** is a quadrilateral with exactly two pairs of congruent, consecutive sides.

KITE is a kite.

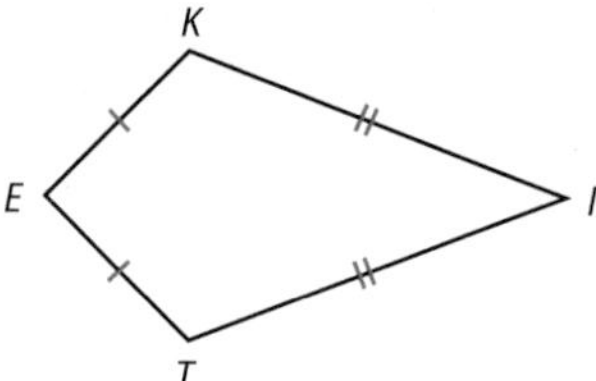

Watch Out !

Opposite sides of a kite are not congruent. If they were, it would be a parallelogram!

EXAMPLE 8

The perimeter of kite *WXYZ* is 27.6 and *WX* = 8.5. Find *XY*.

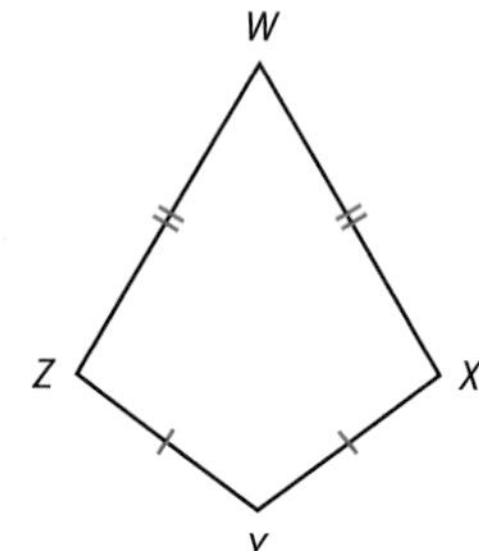

Given	$WX = WZ$ and $XY = YZ$
Given	$WZ + WX + XY + YZ = 27.6$
Substitute.	$2WX + 2XY = 27.6$
Substitute 8.5 for *WX*.	$2(8.5) + 2XY = 27.6$
Solve for *XY*.	$17 + 2XY = 27.6$
	$2XY = 10.6$
	$XY = 5.3$

Theorem
If a quadrilateral is a kite, then exactly one pair of opposite angles is congruent.

PROOF

Given: *HIJK* is a kite with $\overline{HI} \cong \overline{HK}$ and $\overline{IJ} \cong \overline{KJ}$.

Prove: $\angle I \cong \angle K$

It is given that $\overline{HI} \cong \overline{HK}$ and $\overline{IJ} \cong \overline{KJ}$. $\overline{HJ} \cong \overline{HJ}$ by the Reflexive property of congruence, so $\triangle HIJ \cong \triangle HKJ$ by SSS. By CPCTC, $\angle I \cong \angle K$.

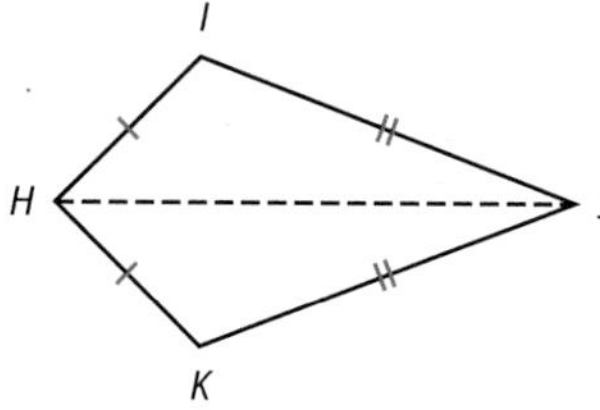

EXAMPLE 9

In kite *QRST*, $m\angle Q = 38°$ and $m\angle S = 81°$. Find $m\angle T$.

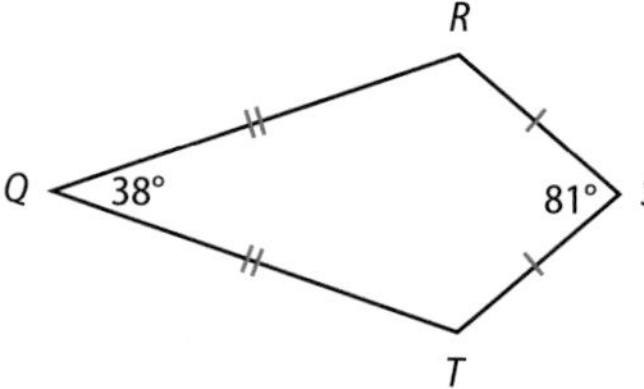

Sum of measures of ∠s in a quad. is 360°.	$m\angle Q + m\angle R + m\angle S + m\angle T = 360°$
Substitute.	$38° + 81° + m\angle R + m\angle T = 360°$
Simplify.	$m\angle R + m\angle T = 241°$
One pair of opp. ∠s of kite is ≅.	$m\angle R = m\angle T$
Substitute.	$2(m\angle T) = 241°$
Solve.	$m\angle T = 120.5°$

SEARCH

To see step-by-step videos of these problems, enter the page number into the SWadvantage.com Search Bar.

Theorem
The diagonals of a kite are perpendicular.

PROOF

Given: $ABCD$ is a kite with $\overline{AB} \cong \overline{AD}$ and $\overline{CB} \cong \overline{CD}$.

Prove: $\overline{AC} \perp \overline{BD}$

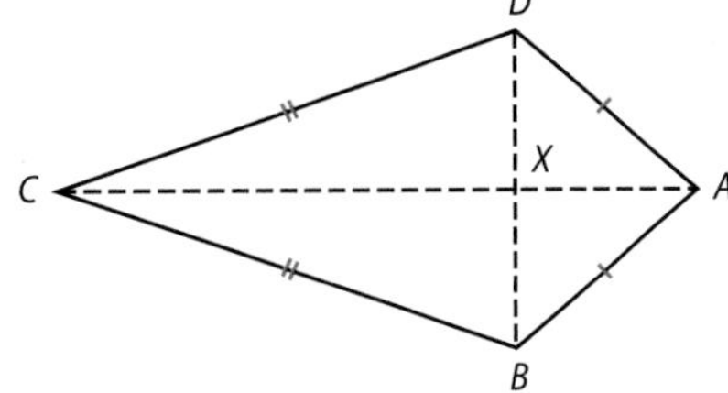

Statements	Reasons
1. $\overline{AB} \cong \overline{AD}, \overline{CB} \cong \overline{CD}$	1. Given
2. $\overline{AC} \cong \overline{AC}$	2. Reflexive property of congruency
3. $\triangle ABC \cong \triangle ADC$	3. SSS
4. $\angle BAC \cong \angle DAC$	4. CPCTC
5. $\overline{AX} \cong \overline{AX}$	5. Reflexive property of congruency
6. $\triangle ABX \cong \triangle ADX$	6. SAS
7. $\angle AXB \cong \angle AXD$	7. CPCTC
8. $\angle AXB$ and $\angle AXD$ are supplementary.	8. If 2 $\angle$s form a linear pair, then they are supplementary.
9. $\angle AXB$ and $\angle AXD$ are right angles.	9. If two $\angle$s are $\cong$ and supplementary, each $\angle$ is a rt. $\angle$.
10. $\overline{AC} \perp \overline{BD}$	10. Definition of $\perp$ lines

EXAMPLE 10

In kite $JKLM$, $m\angle OJK = 46°$ and $m\angle OLK = 32°$. Find $m\angle JKL$.

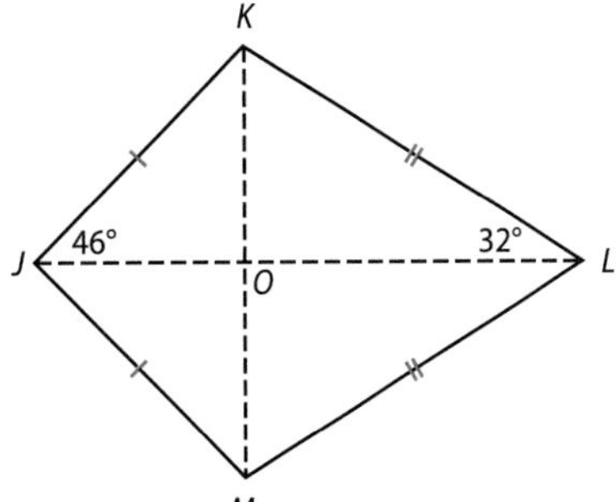

Diagonals of kite are $\perp$. $m\angle KOJ = m\angle KOL = 90°$

Triangle angle-sum theorem $m\angle KOJ + m\angle OJK + m\angle JKO = 180°$
$m\angle KOL + m\angle OLK + m\angle LKO = 180°$

Substitute. $90° + 46° + m\angle JKO = 180°$
$90° + 32° + m\angle LKO = 180°$

Solve. $m\angle JKO = 44°$
$m\angle LKO = 58°$

Angle addition postulate $m\angle JKL = m\angle JKO + m\angle LKO$

Substitute. $m\angle JKL = 44° + 58°$

Solve. $m\angle JKL = 102°$

GOT TO KNOW!

Properties of Kites

Two pairs of consecutive sides are congruent.

Exactly one pair of opposite angles is congruent.

The diagonals are perpendicular.

Triangles and Polygons

What Came Before?

- Theorems and properties of quadrilaterals and parallelograms
- Proving angles congruent and properties of congruence

What's This About?

- Theorems about the side lengths and angle measures of a triangle
- Finding the measures of a right triangle when other measures are known
- Regular polygons

Practical Apps

- Carpenters regularly use a 3-4-5 right triangle to confirm that walls are perpendicular.
- The pattern on a soccer ball is made from regular pentagons and regular hexagons.

just for FUN!

Q: What kind of triangle has no right angle?

A: A wrong triangle. No, wait . . . a *left* triangle!

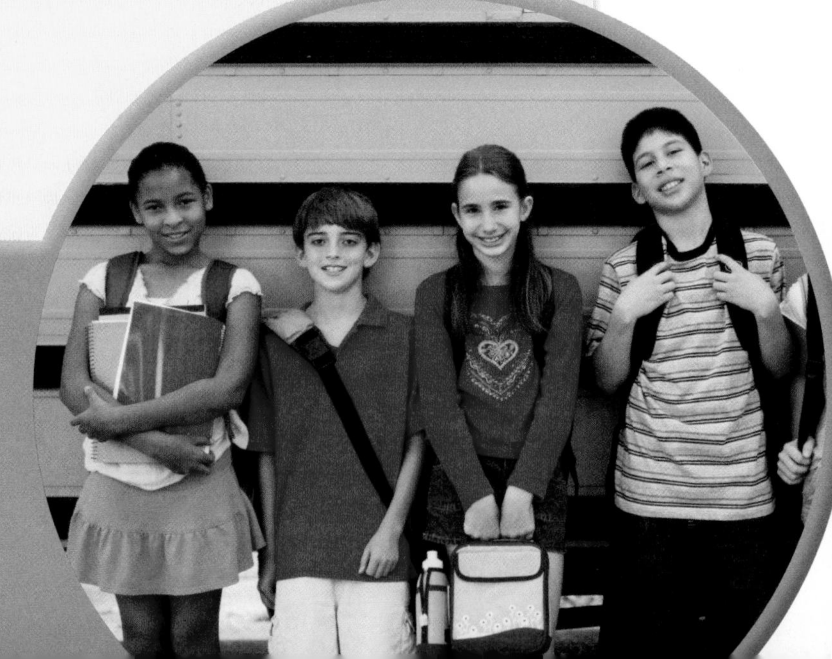

CONTENTS UPLOAD DOWNLOAD *Geometry*

You can find more practice problems online by visiting:
www.SWadvantage.com

Inequalities in One Triangle

There are two inequalities that relate the angles and the sides of a triangle.

Theorem		
If one side of a triangle is longer than another side, then the angle opposite the longer side is larger than the angle opposite the shorter side.	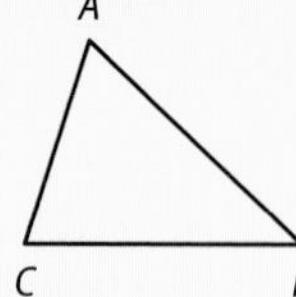	If $AB > AC$, then $m\angle C > m\angle B$.

EXAMPLE 1

Order the angles from smallest to largest.

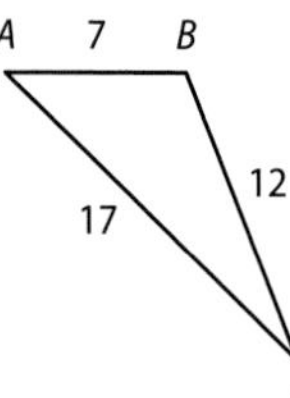

The smallest angle, $\angle C$, is opposite the shortest side, $\overline{AB}$.

The largest angle, $\angle B$, is opposite the longest side, $\overline{AC}$.

From smallest to largest, the angles are $\angle C$, $\angle A$, $\angle B$.

Theorem		
If one angle of a triangle is larger than another angle, then the side opposite the larger angle is longer than the side opposite the smaller angle.	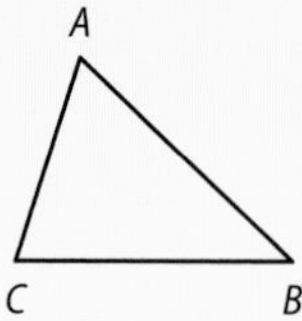	If $m\angle A > m\angle C$, then $BC > AB$.

EXAMPLE 2

Name the longest segment in each diagram.

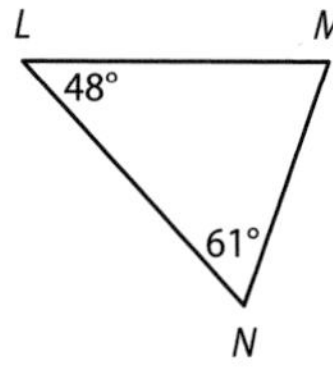

a. **STEP 1** Find $m\angle M$.

$48 + 61 + m\angle M = 180$; $m\angle M = 71°$

STEP 2 Identify the longest side of the triangle.

The longest side lies opposite the largest angle. $\angle M$ is the largest angle, so $\overline{LN}$ is the longest side.

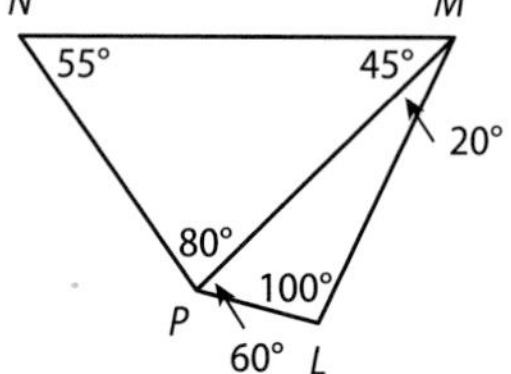

b. **STEP 1** Order the sides in $\triangle MNP$.

$MN > MP > NP$

STEP 2 Order the sides in $\triangle PLM$.

$MP > LM > PL$

STEP 3 Compare the inequalities.

The longest side of $\triangle PLM$ is $\overline{MP}$, but $MN > MP$, so $\overline{MN}$ is the longest segment.

Watch Out!

When a figure is made up of more than one triangle, the longest segment in the figure may not be opposite the largest angle.

This inequality involves the lengths of the three sides of a triangle.

Triangle Inequality Theorem	
The sum of the lengths of any two sides of a triangle is always greater than the length of the third side.	$a + b > c$ $b + c > a$ $a + c > b$

Try It This Way

Here is another way to state the **Triangle Inequality Theorem:**

The shortest distance between two points is along a straight line.

EXAMPLE 3

Determine whether each list could represent side lengths of a triangle.

a. 5, 8, 15

$5 + 8 = 13, 13 \not> 15$

The sum of two side lengths is not greater than the third, so these cannot be the sides of a triangle.

b. 11, 12, 19

$11 + 12 = 23$ $\quad$ $11 + 19 = 30$ $\quad$ $12 + 19 = 31$

$23 > 19$ $\quad$ $30 > 12$ $\quad$ $31 > 11$

The sum of the lengths of any two sides is always greater than the third, so these can be the sides of a triangle.

c. 18, 12, 6

$12 + 6 = 18$

The sum of two side lengths is equal to but not greater than the third, so these cannot be the sides of a triangle.

EXAMPLE 4

Francisco is building a triangular frame. Two sides are 8 in. and 12 in. long. What are possible lengths for the third side?

Use the Triangle Inequality Theorem to write three inequalities.

$x + 8 > 12 \rightarrow x > 4$

$x + 12 > 8 \rightarrow x > -4$

This is always true because x represents a positive length.

$8 + 12 > x \rightarrow 20 > x$

Combine the inequalities: $4 < x < 20$

The third side must be longer than 4 in. and shorter than 20 in.

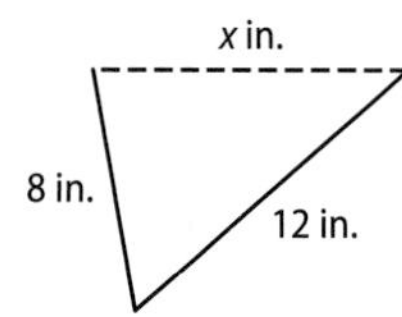

SEARCH

To see step-by-step videos of these problems, enter the page number into the SWadvantage.com Search Bar.

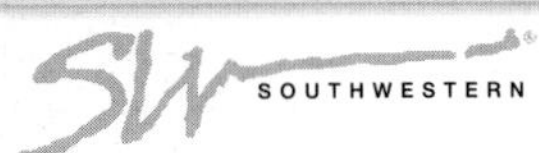

Inequalities in Two Triangles

There are also inequalities that relate the sides and angles of two triangles to each other.

Hinge Theorem

If two sides of one triangle are congruent to two sides of another triangle, but their included angles are not congruent, then the side opposite the larger included angle is longer than the side opposite the smaller included angle.

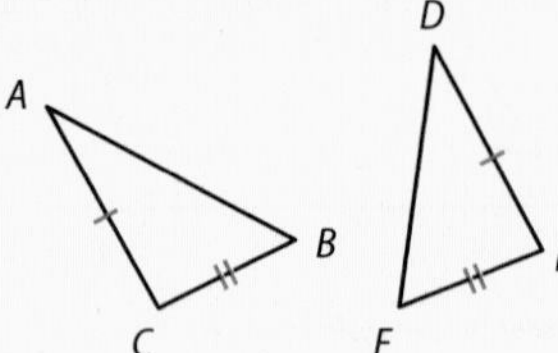

If $m\angle C > m\angle E$, then $AB > DF$.

EXAMPLE 5

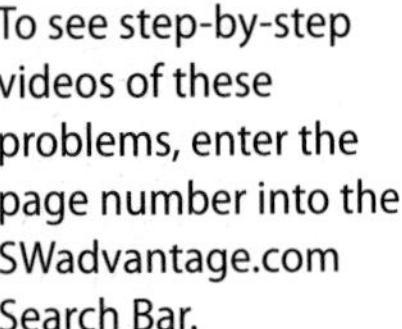

SEARCH

To see step-by-step videos of these problems, enter the page number into the SWadvantage.com Search Bar.

a. Which side is longer, $\overline{JK}$ or $\overline{PR}$?

The triangles have two pairs of congruent sides, so compare the included angles: $m\angle Q > m\angle L$. $\overline{PR}$ is opposite $\angle Q$, so $\overline{PR}$ is longer than $\overline{JK}$.

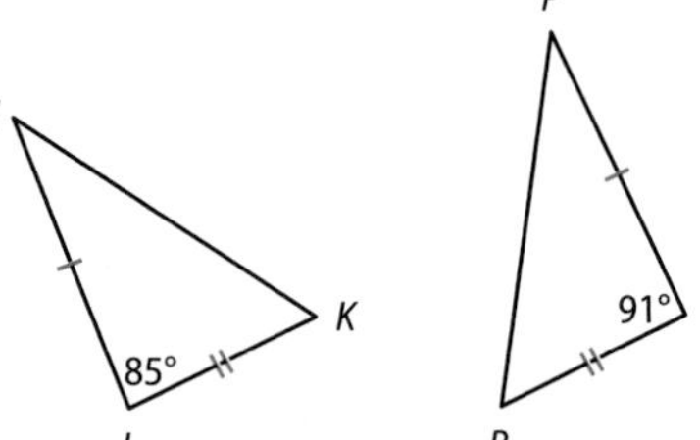

b. Which side is longer, $\overline{DC}$ or $\overline{DE}$?

The triangles have two pairs of congruent sides, so compare the included angles: $m\angle CBD > m\angle EBD$. $\overline{DC}$ is opposite $\angle CBD$, so $\overline{DC}$ is longer than $\overline{DE}$.

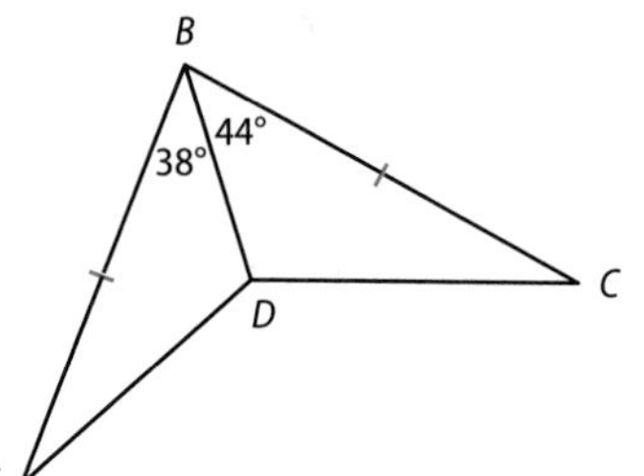

c. Which side is shorter, $\overline{JG}$ or $\overline{HI}$?

The triangles have two pairs of congruent sides, so compare the included angles: $m\angle HGI < m\angle GIJ$. $\overline{HI}$ is opposite $\angle HGI$, so $\overline{HI}$ is shorter than $\overline{JG}$.

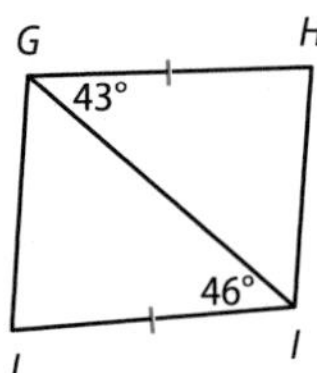

Converse of Hinge Theorem

If two sides of one triangle are congruent to two sides of another triangle, but the third sides are not congruent, then the angle opposite the longer side is larger than the angle opposite the shorter side.

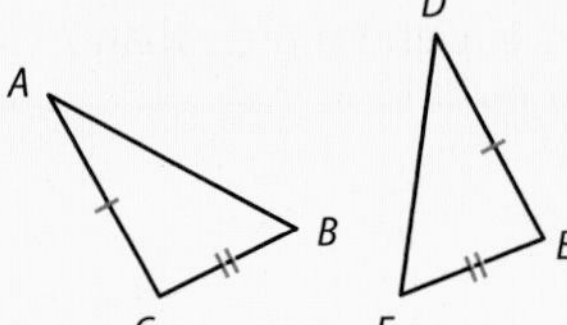

If $AB > DF$, then $m\angle C > m\angle E$.

EXAMPLE 6

a. Which angle is larger, $\angle EDF$ or $\angle GDF$?

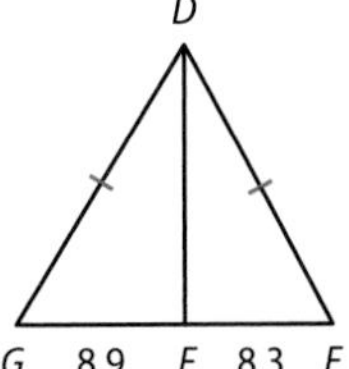

The triangles have two pairs of congruent sides, so compare the non-congruent sides: $GF > EF$. $\angle GDF$ is opposite $\overline{GF}$, so $\angle GDF$ is larger than $\angle EDF$.

b. Which angle is smaller, $\angle STR$ or $\angle UTR$?

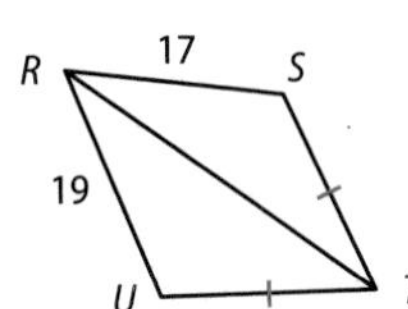

The triangles have two pairs of congruent sides, so compare the non-congruent sides: $SR < UR$. $\angle STR$ is opposite $\overline{SR}$, so $\angle STR$ is smaller than $\angle UTR$.

EXAMPLE 7

Find the range of values for x.

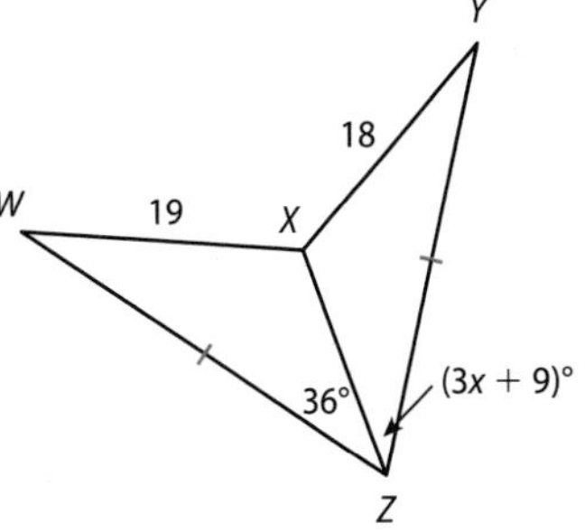

STEP 1 Compare $\angle XZY$ and $\angle XZW$.

The triangles have two pairs of congruent sides, so compare the non-congruent sides: $XY < WX$. $\angle XZY$ is opposite $\overline{XY}$, so $m\angle XZY < m\angle XZW$.

STEP 2 Write and solve an inequality based on your conclusion about the angle measures.

$m\angle XZY < m\angle XZW$

$3x + 9 < 36, x < 9$

STEP 3 $m\angle XZY$ must be positive. Write and solve a second inequality.

$3x + 9 > 0, x > -3$

STEP 4 Combine the inequalities: $-3 < x < 9$

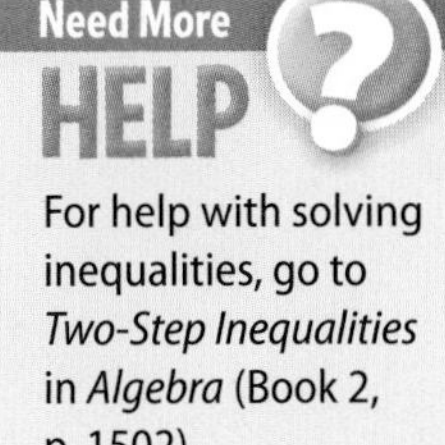

For help with solving inequalities, go to *Two-Step Inequalities* in *Algebra* (Book 2, p. 1502).

GOT TO KNOW!

Inequalities in One and Two Triangles

In $\triangle ABC$, if $AB > BC$, then $m\angle C > m\angle A$.
If $m\angle C > m\angle A$, then $AB > BC$.

The sum of the lengths of any two sides of a triangle is greater than the length of the third side.

If two sides of one triangle are congruent to two sides of another triangle, but their included angles are not congruent, then the side opposite the larger included angle is longer than the side opposite the smaller included angle.

If two sides of one triangle are congruent to two sides of another triangle, but the third sides are not congruent, then the angle opposite the longer side is larger than the angle opposite the shorter side.

Triangle Angle-Sum Theorem

Angles of a Triangle

Regardless of the triangle, the sum of the angle measures is 180°. You will find this theorem very useful.

Triangle Angle-Sum Theorem

The sum of the angle measures of a triangle is 180°.

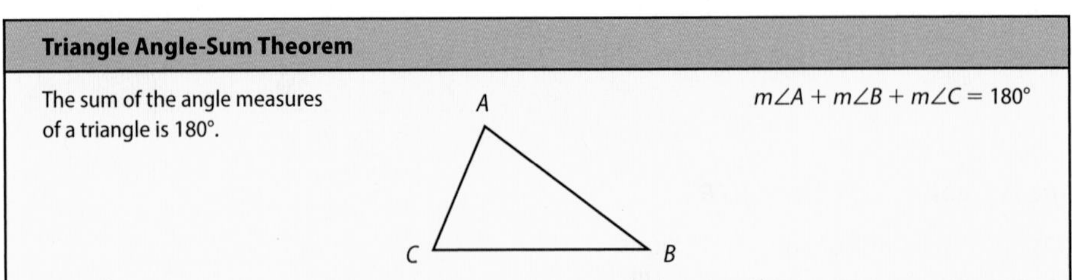

$m\angle A + m\angle B + m\angle C = 180°$

Draw and cut out a paper triangle. Number the angles. Then tear off the corners and rearrange them to form a straight angle.

PROOF

Given: $\triangle ABC$ **with line** $\ell \parallel \overline{BC}$

Prove: $m\angle 1 + m\angle 2 + m\angle 3 = 180°$

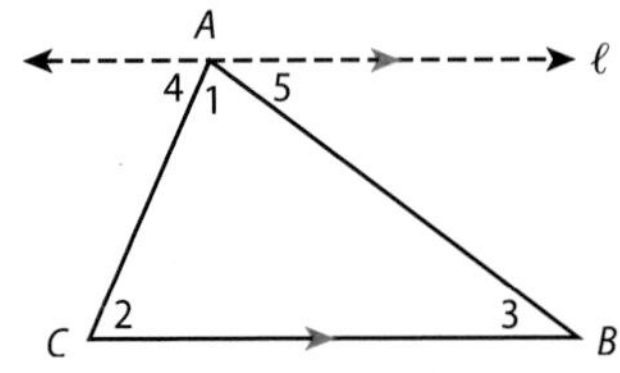

Statements	Reasons
1. $\ell \parallel \overline{BC}$	1. Given
2. $m\angle 4 = m\angle 2, m\angle 5 = m\angle 3$	2. If two $\parallel$ lines are cut by a trans., alt. int. $\angle$s are $\cong$.
3. $m\angle 1 + m\angle 4 + m\angle 5 = 180°$	3. Def. straight angle, Angle Addition Postulate
4. $m\angle 1 + m\angle 2 + m\angle 3 = 180°$	4. Substitution

EXAMPLE 1

Find $m\angle F$.

$m\angle E + m\angle F + m\angle G = 180°$

$63° + m\angle F + 52° = 180°$

$m\angle F = 65°$

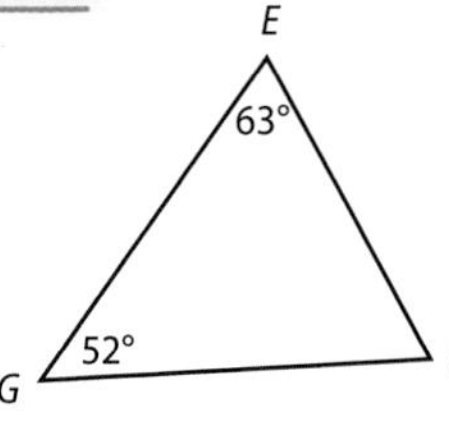

SEARCH

To see step-by-step videos of these problems, enter the page number into the SWadvantage.com Search Bar.

EXAMPLE 2

Find the measure of each angle in $\triangle QRS$.

Triangle Angle-Sum Theorem $\quad m\angle Q + m\angle R + m\angle S = 180°$

Substitute. $\quad (4x + 6) + (5x - 10) + (7x + 8) = 180$

Combine like terms. $\quad 16x + 4 = 180$

Solve for x. $\quad 16x = 176$

$x = 11$

Substitute 11 for x. $\quad m\angle Q = 4(11) + 6 = 50°$

$m\angle R = 5(11) - 10 = 45°$

$m\angle S = 7(11) + 8 = 85°$

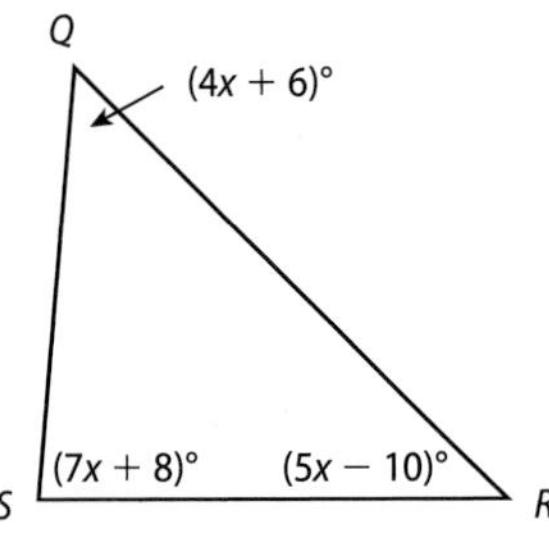

A **corollary** is a statement whose proof follows directly from another theorem.

Corollary
The acute angles of a right triangle are complementary.

PROOF

Given: $\angle Q$ is a right angle.

Prove: $\angle R$ and $\angle S$ are complementary.

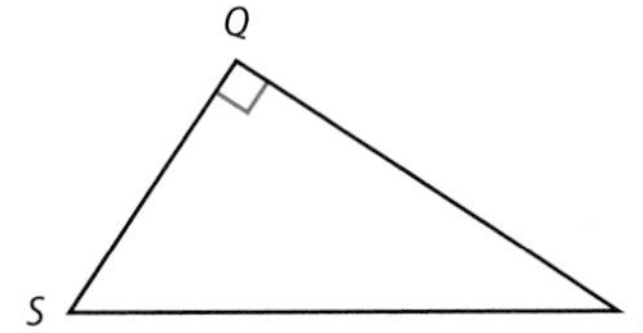

Statements	Reasons
1. $\angle Q$ is a right angle.	1. Given
2. $m\angle Q = 90°$	2. Definition of right $\angle$
3. $m\angle Q + m\angle R + m\angle S = 180°$	3. Sum of measures of $\angle$s in a triangle is 180°.
4. $90° + m\angle R + m\angle S = 180°$	4. Substitution
5. $m\angle R + m\angle S = 90°$	5. Subtraction Property of Equality
6. $\angle R$ and $\angle S$ are complementary.	6. Definition of complementary $\angle$s

All the angles of an **equiangular triangle** are congruent.

Corollary
The measure of each angle of an equiangular triangle is 60°.

PROOF

Given: $\triangle XYZ$ is equiangular.

Prove: $m\angle X = m\angle Y = m\angle Z = 60°$

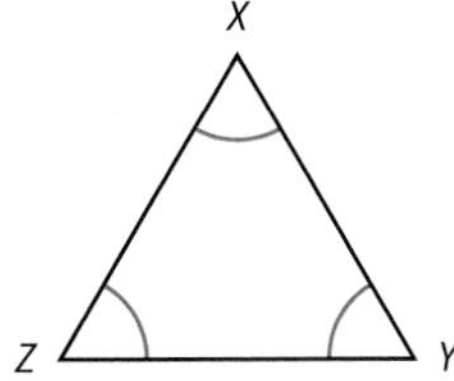

Statements	Reasons
1. $\triangle XYZ$ is equiangular.	1. Given
2. $m\angle X = m\angle Y = m\angle Z$	2. Definition of an equiangular triangle
3. $m\angle X + m\angle Y + m\angle Z = 180°$	3. Sum of measures of $\angle$s in a triangle is 180°.
4. $3(m\angle X) = 180°$	4. Substitution
5. $m\angle X = 60°$	5. Division Property of Equality
6. $m\angle X = m\angle Y = m\angle Z = 60°$	6. Substitution

Watch Out!

This is only true for right triangles.

GOT TO KNOW!

Triangle Angle Relationships

The sum of the angle measures of a triangle is 180°.

The acute angles of a right triangle are complementary.

The measure of each angle of an equiangular triangle is 60°.

Exterior Angle Theorem

Two consecutive sides of a polygon determine an **interior angle** of the polygon. An **exterior angle** is formed when you extend one side of a polygon. Each exterior angle of a triangle has two **remote interior angles**. They are the two interior angles that are not adjacent to the exterior angle.

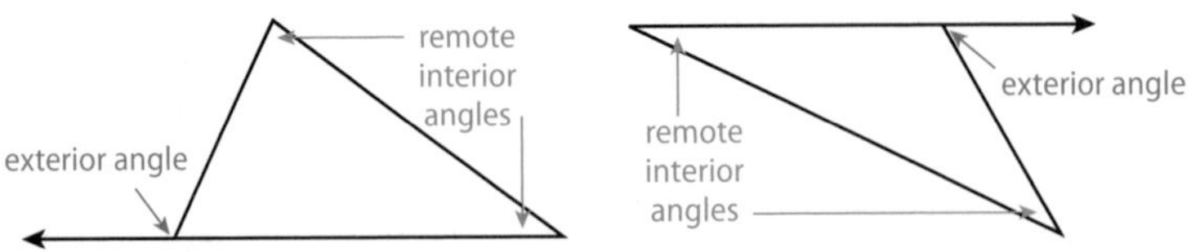

Try It This Way

Copy the diagram. Cut out the two remote interior angles and superimpose them on the exterior angle. What do you notice?

Exterior Angle Theorem
The measure of an exterior angle of a triangle equals the sum of the measures of its remote interior angles.

PROOF

Given: $\triangle LMN$ **with exterior** $\angle 4$

Prove: $m\angle 1 + m\angle 2 = m\angle 4$

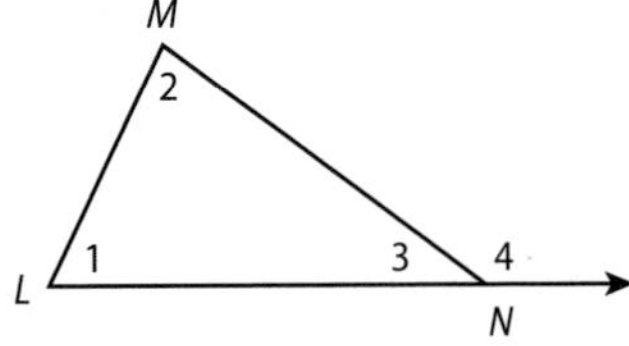

Statements	Reasons
1. $m\angle 1 + m\angle 2 + m\angle 3 = 180°$	1. Sum of measures of $\angle$s in a triangle is 180°.
2. $m\angle 3 + m\angle 4 = 180°$	2. If 2 $\angle$s form a linear pair, then they are supp.
3. $m\angle 1 + m\angle 2 + m\angle 3 = m\angle 3 + m\angle 4$	3. Substitution
4. $m\angle 1 + m\angle 2 = m\angle 4$	4. Subtraction Property of Equality

EXAMPLE 3

SEARCH

To see step-by-step videos of these problems, enter the page number into the SWadvantage.com Search Bar.

Find the indicated angle measures.

a. $m\angle 1$ **and** $m\angle 2$

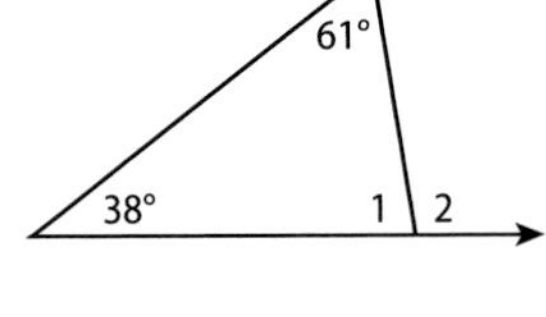

Triangle Angle-Sum Theorem $\quad m\angle 1 + 61° + 38° = 180°$

$m\angle 1 = 81°$

Exterior Angle Theorem $\quad m\angle 2 = 61° + 38°$

$m\angle 2 = 99°$

$m\angle 1 = 81°$ and $m\angle 2 = 99°$

b. $m\angle 3$ **and** $m\angle 4$

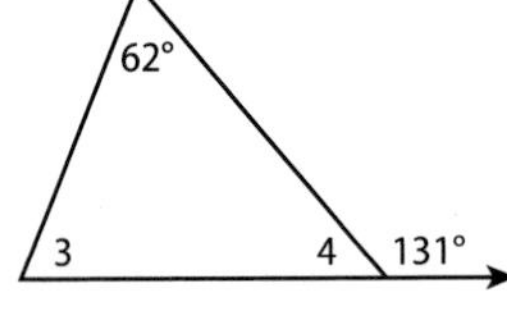

Exterior Angle Theorem $\quad m\angle 3 + 62° = 131°$

$m\angle 3 = 69°$

Triangle Angle-Sum Theorem $\quad 62° + m\angle 3 + m\angle 4 = 180°$

Substitute for $m\angle 3$. $\quad 62° + 69° + m\angle 4 = 180°$

Subtract. $\quad m\angle 4 = 49°$

$m\angle 3 = 69°$ and $m\angle 4 = 49°$

EXAMPLE 4

Draw a triangle that satisfies the given conditions. If no triangle is possible, write *not possible*.

a. A triangle with two obtuse exterior angles

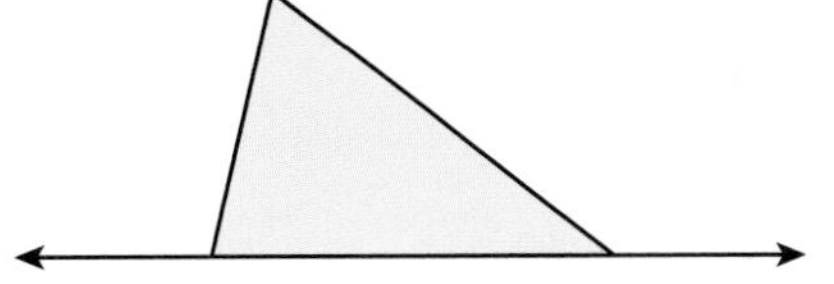

b. An obtuse equiangular triangle

Each angle of an equiangular triangle is 60°.
Not possible.

GOT TO KNOW!

Exterior Angle Theorem

The measure of an exterior angle of a triangle equals the sum of the measures of its remote interior angles.

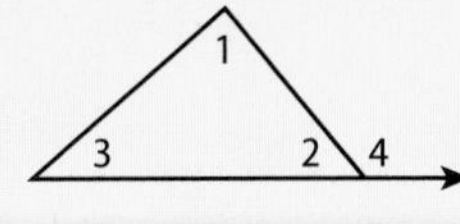

EXAMPLE 5

Find the values of the variables.

a.

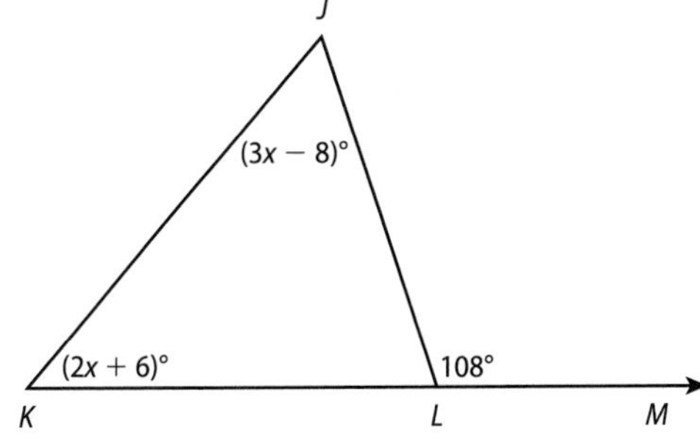

Exterior Angle Theorem	$(3x - 8) + (2x + 6) = 108$
Combine like terms.	$5x - 2 = 108$
Solve for x.	$5x = 110$
	$x = 22$

b.

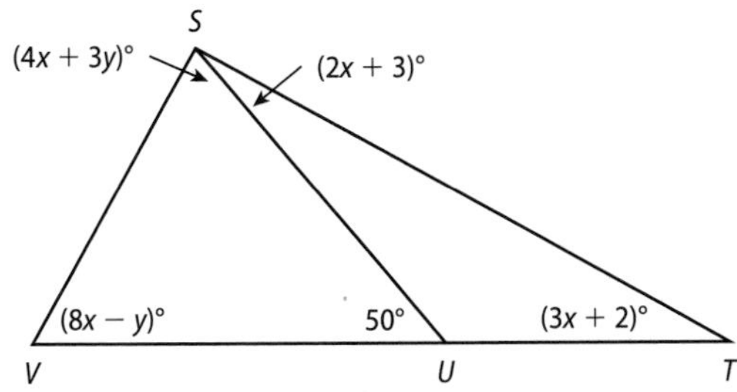

Exterior Angle Theorem	$(2x + 3) + (3x + 2) = 50$
Combine like terms.	$5x + 5 = 50$
Solve for x.	$x = 9$
Triangle Angle-Sum Theorem	$50 + (8x - y) + (4x + 3y) = 180$
Combine like terms.	$50 + 12x + 2y = 180$
Substitute for x.	$50 + 12(9) + 2y = 180$
Solve for y.	$158 + 2y = 180$
	$2y = 22$
	$y = 11$

Angles of a Polygon

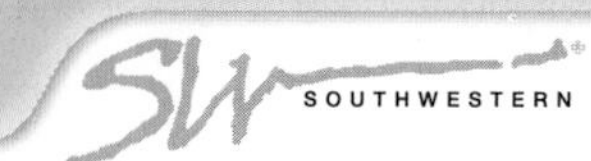

Interior Angles

By the Triangle Angle-Sum Theorem, the sum of the measures of the interior angles of a triangle is 180°.

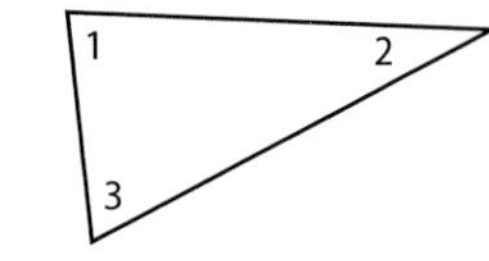

$$m\angle 1 + m\angle 2 + m\angle 3 = 180°$$

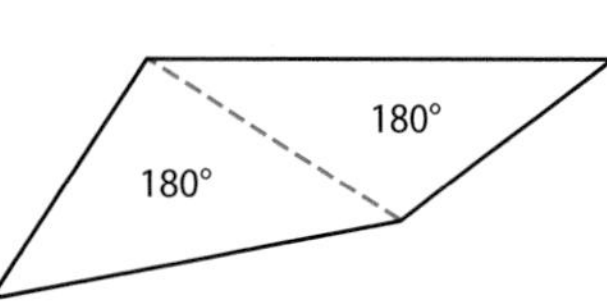

You can divide a quadrilateral into two triangles that do not overlap. So the sum of the measures of the interior angles of a quadrilateral is $180° + 180° = 360°$.

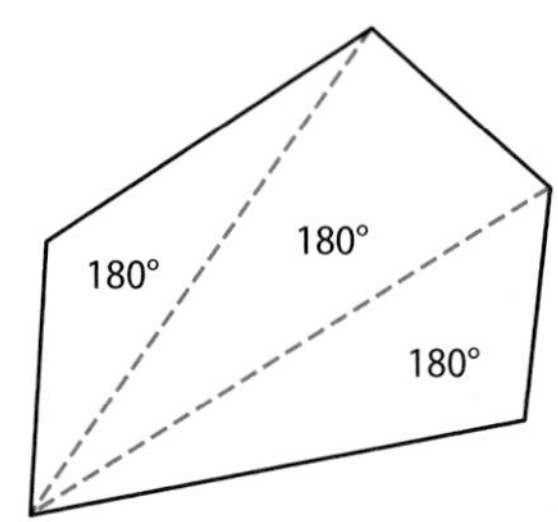

You can divide a pentagon into three non-overlapping triangles. So the sum of the measures of the interior angles of a pentagon is $3(180°) = 540°$.

Polygon	# of Sides	# of Triangles	Interior Angle Sum
Triangle	3	1	$(3 - 2)180° = 180°$
Quadrilateral	4	2	$(4 - 2)180° = 360°$
Pentagon	5	3	$(5 - 2)180° = 540°$
n-gon	n	$n - 2$	$(n - 2)180°$

As you can see, the number of non-overlapping triangles that can be drawn in a polygon is 2 less than the number of sides.

Polygon Interior Angle-Sum Theorem
The sum of the measures of the interior angles of a convex polygon with n sides is $(n - 2)180°$.

Watch Out!

Can you see why the *Triangle Angle-Sum Theorem* is a special case of the *Polygon Interior Angle-Sum Theorem?*

EXAMPLE 1

The sum of the measures of the angles of a polygon is 1080°. What kind of polygon is it?

$$(n - 2)180° = 1080°$$
$$n - 2 = \frac{1080}{180}$$
$$n - 2 = 6$$
$$n = 8$$

The polygon has 8 sides, so the polygon is an octagon.

EXAMPLE 2

Find the sum of the interior angle measures of each polygon.

a. heptagon (7 sides)

$(7 - 2)180° = 900°$

b. 13-gon

$(13 - 2)180° = 1,980°$

Try It This Way

Sometimes it is easiest to count the number of vertices to find the number of sides.

EXAMPLE 3

A hexagon has two right angles and four congruent angles. Find the measure of one of the congruent angles.

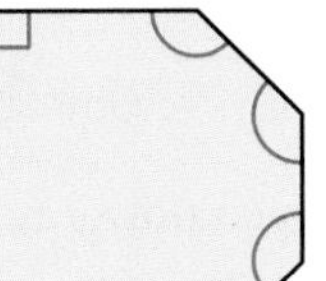

Let x = measure of one congruent angle.

STEP 1 Write an equation for the sum of the angle measures.

$(6 - 2)180 = 2(90) + 4x$

STEP 2 Solve the equation.

$720 = 180 + 4x$

$4x = 540$

$x = 135$

Each of the congruent angles measures 135°.

SEARCH

To see step-by-step videos of these problems, enter the page number into the SWadvantage.com Search Bar.

EXAMPLE 4

Find the measures of the indicated angles.

a. $\angle 1$

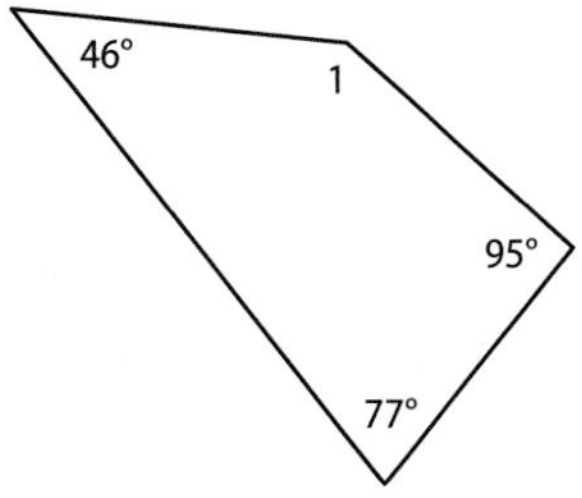
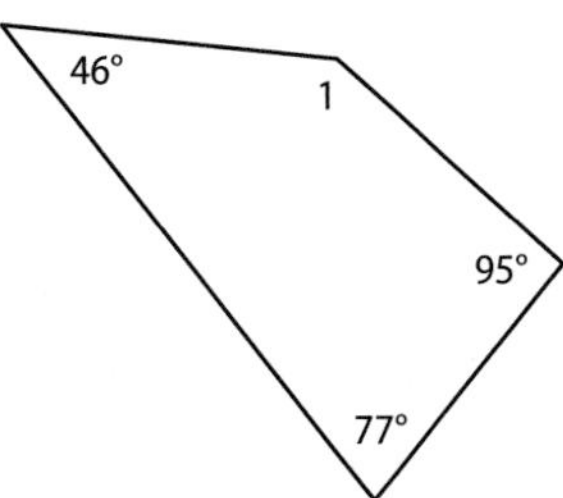

Use the Polygon Interior Angle-Sum Theorem for $n = 4$.

$m\angle 1 + 95° + 77° + 46° = (4 - 2)180°$

$m\angle 1 + 218° = 360°$

$m\angle 1 = 142°$

b. $\angle 2$ **and** $\angle 3$

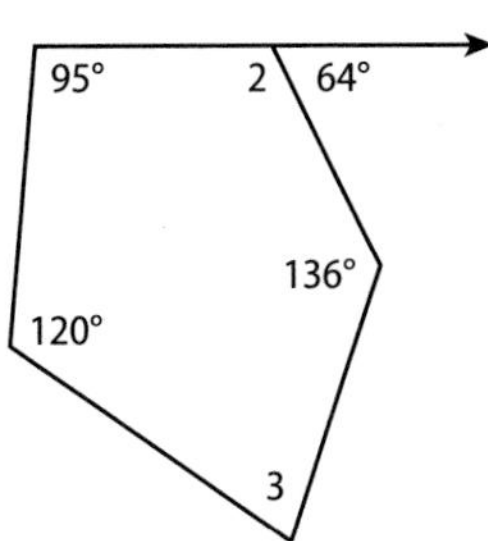

STEP 1 Use the Linear Pair Theorem to find $m\angle 2$.

$m\angle 2 + 64° = 180°$

$m\angle 2 = 116°$

STEP 2 Use the Polygon Interior Angle-Sum Theorem for $n = 5$ and the results of STEP 1 to find $m\angle 3$.

$95° + 120° + m\angle 3 + 136° + 116° = (5 - 2)180°$

$467° + m\angle 3 = 540°$

$m\angle 3 = 53°$

Exterior Angles

Here are some polygons with one exterior angle drawn at each vertex.

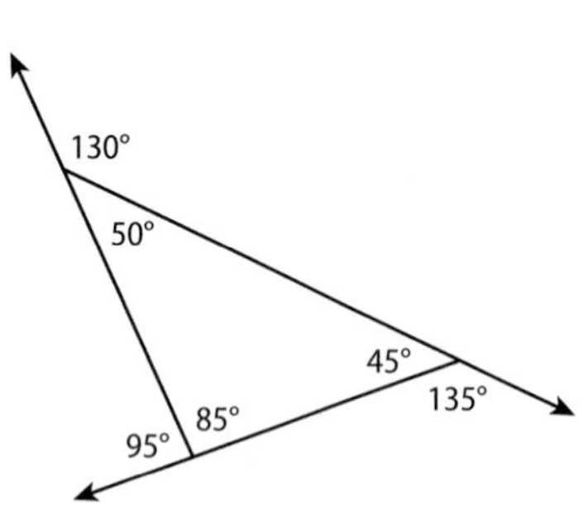

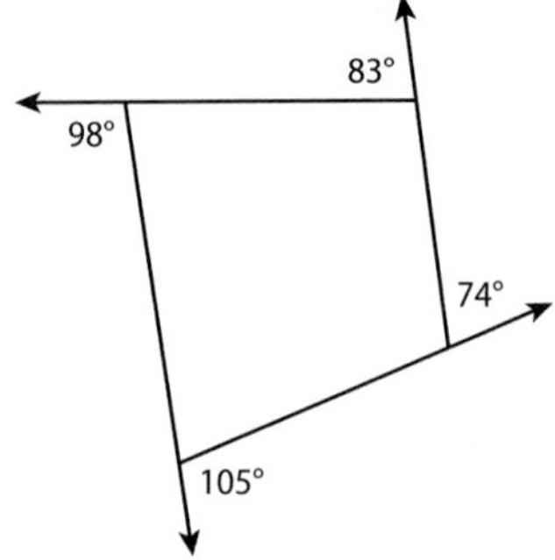

$130° + 135° + 95° = 360°$

$98° + 105° + 74° + 83° = 360°$

Notice that in each polygon, the sum of the measures of the exterior angles is 360°.

Polygon Exterior Angle-Sum Theorem
The sum of the measures of the exterior angles of a convex polygon is 360°.

You can show that this is true using algebra.

Consider what happens if you draw an exterior angle at each vertex of a polygon with n sides. In the figure:

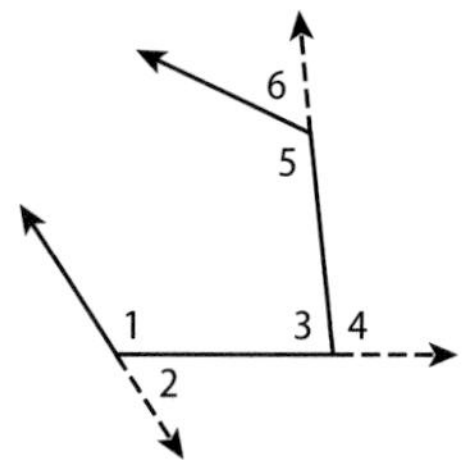

$m\angle 1 + m\angle 2 = 180°$

$m\angle 3 + m\angle 4 = 180°$

$m\angle 5 + m\angle 6 = 180°$, and so on.

A polygon with n sides has n vertices. The sum of the measures of all the interior and exterior angles, one at each vertex, is $180n$. The sum of the measures of the interior angles is $(n - 2)180$. Therefore,

$180n = \text{interior angle sum} + \text{exterior angle sum}$

$180n = (n - 2)180 + \text{exterior angle sum}$

$180n = 180n - 360 + \text{exterior angle sum}$

$360° = \text{exterior angle sum}$

SEARCH

To see step-by-step videos of these problems, enter the page number into the SWadvantage.com Search Bar.

EXAMPLE 5

The measure of each exterior angle of a polygon is 20°. How many sides does the polygon have?

Let n = number of sides. $20n = 360$

$n = 18$

The polygon has 18 sides.

EXAMPLE 6

Find $m\angle ABC$ and $m\angle BDE$.

STEP 1 Find the value of x.

$$82 + 27 + 90 + 53 + (12x - 5) + (16x + 1) = 360$$
$$248 + 28x = 360$$
$$28x = 112$$
$$x = 4$$

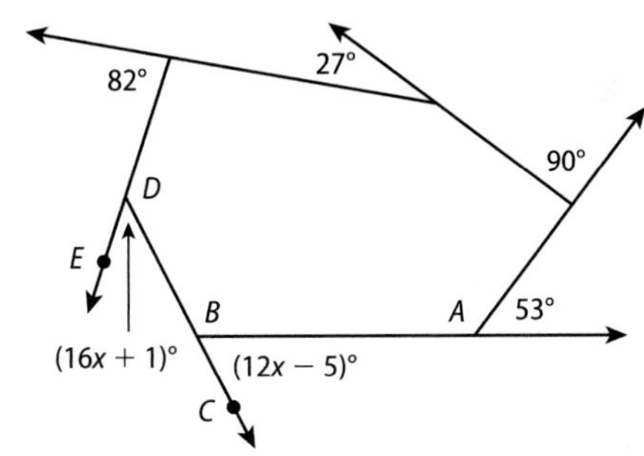

STEP 2 Substitute to find $m\angle ABC$ and $m\angle BDE$.

$$m\angle ABC = 12x - 5$$
$$= 12(4) - 5$$
$$= 43$$
$$m\angle BDE = 16x + 1$$
$$= 16(4) + 1$$
$$= 65$$

So $m\angle ABC = 43°$ and $m\angle BDE = 65°$.

Need More HELP

For a review of the special names of polygons, go to *Polygons* in *Analyzing Shapes in a Plane* (p. 152).

EXAMPLE 7

The sum of the measures of the interior angles of a polygon is twice the sum of the measures of the exterior angles. What kind of polygon is this?

Let n = number of sides of the polygon. Write an equation.

The sum of measures of interior angles is twice the sum of the measures of the exterior angles.

↓ ↓ ↓

$$(n - 2)180 = 2(360)$$

$$180n - 360 = 720$$
$$180n = 1080$$
$$n = 6$$

The polygon has 6 sides, so it is a hexagon.

GOT TO KNOW!

Polygon Angle-Sum Theorems

In a convex n-gon:

- The sum of the measures of the interior angles is $(n - 2)180°$.
- The sum of the measures of the exterior angles is 360°.

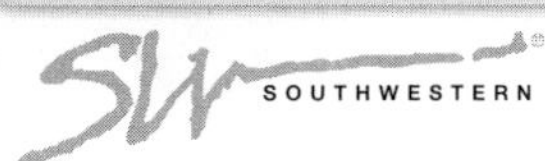

Regular Polygons

An **equilateral polygon** has congruent sides. An **equiangular polygon** has congruent angles. A **regular polygon** is equilateral and equiangular.

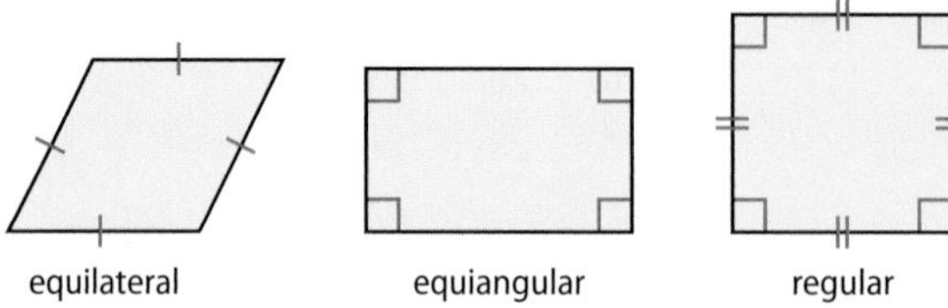

In a regular polygon, all the exterior angles are congruent. Since the sum of the measures of the exterior angles is 360°, the measure of each exterior angle of a regular n-gon is $\frac{360°}{n}$.

EXAMPLE 8

Find the measure of one exterior angle of each regular polygon.

a. nonagon

$\frac{360°}{9} = 40°$

b. 15-gon

$\frac{360°}{15} = 24°$

EXAMPLE 9

Watch Out !

If your calculations show that the measure of an interior angle is 180° or more, you have made an error.

Find the measure of an interior angle and an exterior angle of a regular 20-gon.

METHOD 1

Find the measure of an interior angle first.

interior angle sum	$(20 - 2)180° = 3240°$
one interior angle	$\frac{3240°}{20} = 162°$
adjacent exterior angle	$180° - 162° = 18°$

METHOD 2

Find the measure of an exterior angle first.

exterior angle sum	$360°$
one exterior angle	$\frac{360°}{20} = 18°$
adjacent interior angle	$180° - 18° = 162°$

EXAMPLE 10

The polygon is regular. Find the value of the variable.

a. the value of x

STEP 1 Find the measure of an exterior angle.

A hexagon has 6 sides. $\frac{360°}{6} = 60°$

STEP 2 Solve for x.

$8x + 4 = 60$

$8x = 56$

$x = 7$

b. the value of y

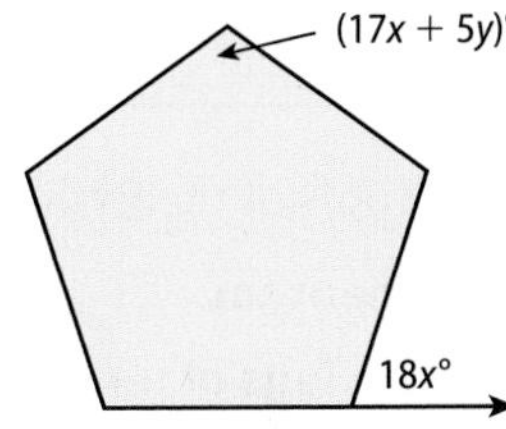

STEP 1 Find the measure of an exterior angle.

A pentagon has 5 sides. $\frac{360°}{5} = 72°$

STEP 2 Solve for x.

$18x = 72$

$x = 4$

STEP 3 Find the measure of an interior angle.

$180° - 72° = 108°$

STEP 4 Substitute for x and solve for y.

$17x + 5y = 108$

$17(4) + 5y = 108$

$68 + 5y = 108$

$5y = 40$

$y = 8$

SEARCH

To see step-by-step videos of these problems, enter the page number into the SWadvantage.com Search Bar.

EXAMPLE 11

Find the number of sides of each regular polygon described.

a. The measure of each exterior angle is 14.4°.

Let n = number of sides.

Sum of measures of ext. ∠s is 360°. $14.4n = 360$

$n = 25$

b. The measure of each interior angle is five times the measure of each exterior angle.

Let x = measure of an exterior angle. Then $5x$ = measure of an interior angle.

An int. ∠ and ext. ∠ are supplementary. $5x + x = 180$

Solve for x to find the measure of one exterior angle. $x = 30$

Let n = number of sides.

Sum of measures of ext. ∠s is 360°. $30n = 360$

$n = 12$

Pythagorean Theorem

The Pythagorean Theorem

One of the most famous and most widely used theorems of geometry is the Pythagorean Theorem. Pythagoras was a Greek mathematician and philosopher who was born around 540 B.C. and who is credited with the first proof of this theorem.

In a right triangle, the **hypotenuse** is the side opposite the right angle and is the longest side. The **legs** are the two shorter sides that form the right angle.

Pythagorean Theorem

The sum of the squares of the lengths of the legs of a right triangle equals the square of the length of the hypotenuse.

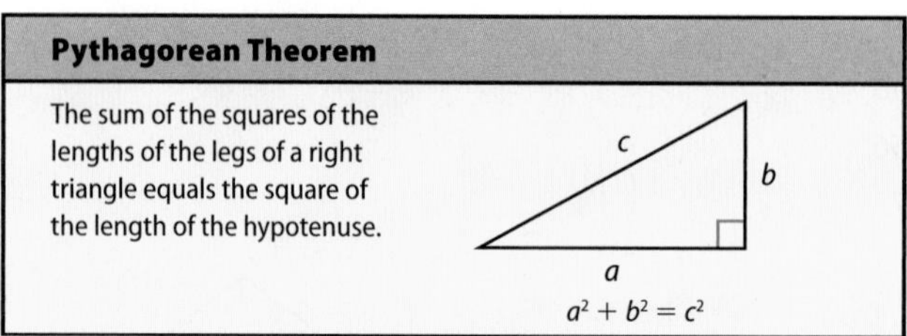

There are now over 300 proofs of the Pythagorean Theorem. The following proof uses area.

PROOF of Pythagorean Theorem

Given: a right triangle with legs of lengths *a* and *b* and hypotenuse of length *c*

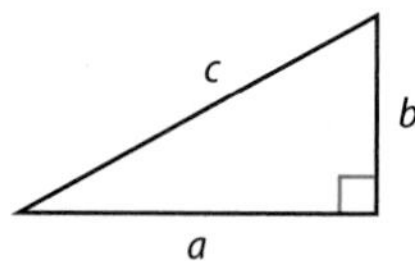

Prove: $a^2 + b^2 = c^2$

The figure shows four congruent right triangles. They determine two squares. Each side of the **larger** square has length c. Each side of the **smaller** square has length $a - b$. The area of the larger square equals the sum of the areas of the four triangles plus the area of the smaller square.

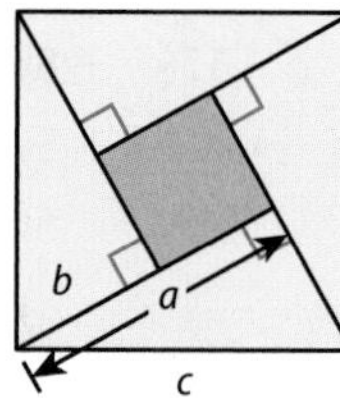

area of larger square		4 × area of triangle		area of smaller square
c^2	$=$	$4 \times \left(\frac{1}{2}ab\right)$	$+$	$(a - b)^2$
c^2	$=$	$2ab$	$+$	$a^2 - 2ab + b^2$

$c^2 = a^2 + b^2$

EXAMPLE 1

Find the length of the hypotenuse of a right triangle with legs of lengths 5 and 12.

Let c = length of the hypotenuse.

$c^2 = a^2 + b^2$

$c^2 = 5^2 + 12^2$

$c^2 = 25 + 144$

$c^2 = 169$

$c = 13$

SEARCH

To see step-by-step videos of these problems, enter the page number into the SWadvantage.com Search Bar.

EXAMPLE 2

Find the value of the variable. Leave your answer in simplified radical form.

a. value of *c*

Use the Pythagorean Theorem.	$c^2 = 6^2 + 10^2$
Simplify.	$c^2 = 36 + 100$
Solve.	$c^2 = 136$
	$c = \sqrt{136}$
Simplify the radical.	$c = \sqrt{4 \cdot 34} = \sqrt{4} \cdot \sqrt{34}$
	$c = 2\sqrt{34}$

b. value of *y*

Use the Pythagorean Theorem.	$8^2 + y^2 = 12^2$
Simplify.	$64 + y^2 = 144$
Solve.	$y^2 = 80$
Simplify the radical.	$y = \sqrt{80} = \sqrt{16 \cdot 5}$
	$y = 4\sqrt{5}$

c. value of *x*

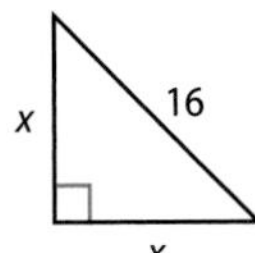

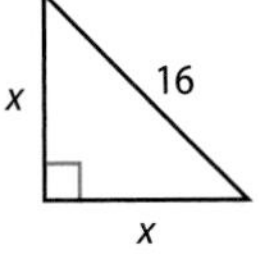

Use the Pythagorean Theorem.	$x^2 + x^2 = 16^2$
Simplify.	$2x^2 = 256$
Solve.	$x^2 = 128$
Simplify the radical.	$x = \sqrt{128} = \sqrt{64 \cdot 2}$
	$x = 8\sqrt{2}$

d. value of *z*

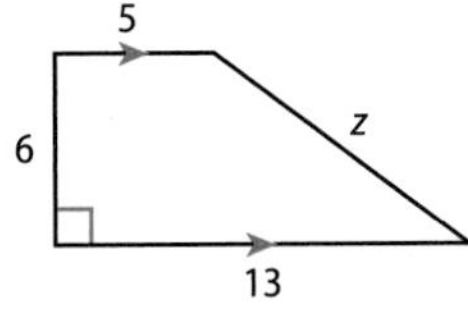

STEP 1 The figure is a trapezoid. Draw an altitude as shown, forming a 6-by-5 rectangle and a right triangle.

STEP 2 Find the lengths of the legs of the right triangle. The legs are 6 and $13 - 5 = 8$.

STEP 3 Use the Pythagorean Theorem.

$$6^2 + 8^2 = z^2$$
$$36 + 64 = z^2$$
$$100 = z^2$$
$$z = 10$$

For help with simplifying radicals, go to *Square Roots* in *Algebra* (Book 2, p. 1400).

GOT TO KNOW!

Pythagorean Theorem

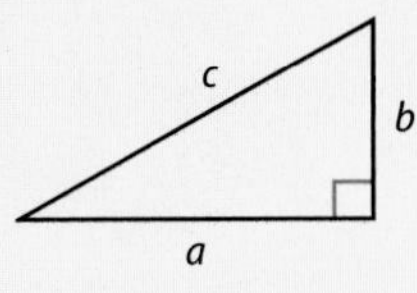

$a^2 + b^2 = c^2$

SOUTHWESTERN

Applying the Pythagorean Theorem

Try It This Way

Use a calculator to find the value of $\sqrt{20.25}$.

EXAMPLE 3

Find the perimeter of $\triangle ABC$.

The perimeter of $\triangle ABC = AB + BC + AC$.

STEP 1 Find AC.

Use right $\triangle ADB$ to find AD.

$$6^2 + AD^2 = 7.5^2$$
$$36 + AD^2 = 56.25$$
$$AD^2 = 20.25$$
$$AD = \sqrt{20.25} = 4.5$$

$AC = AD + DC$

$$AC = 4.5 + 8 = 12.5$$

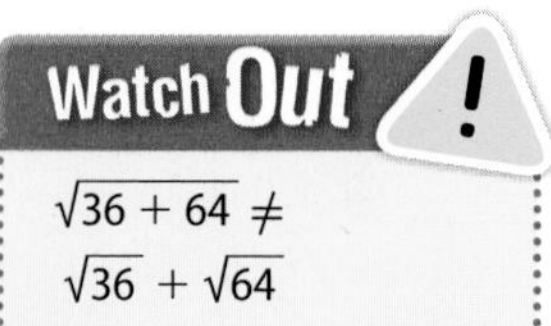

$\sqrt{36 + 64} \neq$
$\sqrt{36} + \sqrt{64}$

STEP 2 Use right $\triangle BDC$ to find BC.

$$BC^2 = 6^2 + 8^2$$
$$BC^2 = 36 + 64 = 100$$
$$BC = \sqrt{100}$$
$$BC = 10$$

STEP 3 Find the perimeter of $\triangle ABC$.

$$\text{perimeter} = AB + BC + AC$$
$$= 7.5 + 10 + 12.5 = 30$$

The perimeter of $\triangle ABC$ is 30 units.

EXAMPLE 4

To see step-by-step videos of these problems, enter the page number into the SWadvantage.com Search Bar.

Dhara rides her bike 5 km east, 4 km north, then 3 km east and 6 km north. How much shorter would her ride be if she rode her bike in a straight line from beginning to end?

STEP 1 Draw a diagram.

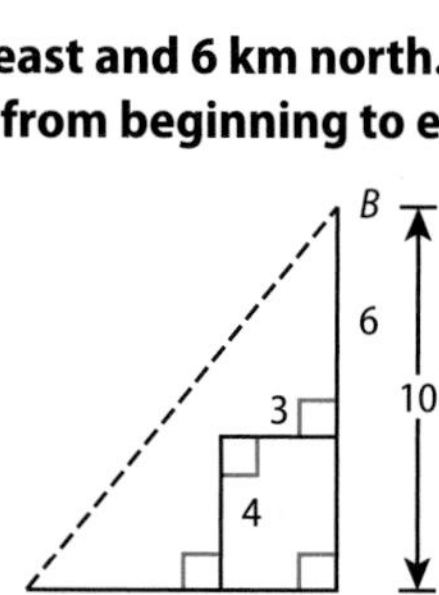

STEP 2 Find AB, the distance along a straight line.

$\overline{AB}$ is the hypotenuse of a right triangle with legs 8 and 10, so use the Pythagorean Theorem.

$$AB^2 = 8^2 + 10^2$$
$$AB^2 = 164$$
$$AB = \sqrt{164} \approx 12.8 \text{ km}$$

STEP 3 Find the total distance Dhara rode her bike.

total distance = 5 km + 4 km + 3 km + 6 km = 18 km

STEP 4 Find the difference.

18 km − 12.8 km = 5.2 km

Dhara's ride would be 5.2 km shorter.

Pythagorean Triples

Three whole numbers that satisfy the Pythagorean Theorem form a **Pythagorean triple**. For example, the numbers 3, 4, 5 form a Pythagorean triple because $3^2 + 4^2 = 5^2$.

Watch Out !

The term *Pythagorean triples* refers only to positive integers, not every group of three numbers that satisfies the Pythagorean Theorem.

EXAMPLE 5

Do the numbers form a Pythagorean triple? Explain.

a. 5, 12, 13

$5^2 + 12^2 \stackrel{?}{=} 13^2$

$25 + 144 = 169$ ✔

Yes, the numbers form a Pythagorean triple. They are whole numbers and they satisfy the Pythagorean Theorem.

b. 0.3, 0.4, 0.5

$0.3^2 + 0.4^2 \stackrel{?}{=} 0.5^2$

$0.09 + 0.16 = 0.25$ ✔

No, the numbers do not form a Pythagorean triple. They satisfy the Pythagorean Theorem, but they are not whole numbers.

Any multiple of a Pythagorean triple is also a Pythagorean triple. For example, because 5, 12, 13 is a Pythagorean triple, it follows that 10, 24, 26 is also a Pythagorean triple. You can use this fact to simplify some right triangle problems.

EXAMPLE 6

Find *AB*.

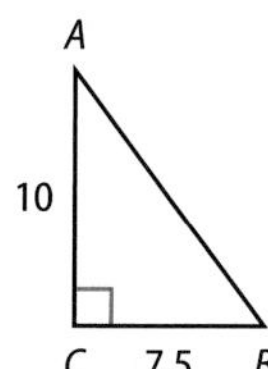

METHOD 1

Use the Pythagorean Theorem.

$\left(7\frac{1}{2}\right)^2 + 10^2 = AB^2$

$\frac{225}{4} + 100 = AB^2$

$\frac{625}{4} = AB^2$

$AB = \sqrt{\frac{625}{4}} = \frac{25}{2} = 12\frac{1}{2}$

METHOD 2

Notice that $7.5 = 3(2.5)$ and $10 = 4(2.5)$.

So, $(7.5, 10, AB)$ belongs to the $(3, 4, 5)$ family.

Therefore, $AB = 5(2.5) = 12.5$.

GOT TO KNOW!

Common Pythagorean Triples and Their Multiples

3, 4, 5	5, 12, 13	8, 15, 17	7, 24, 25
6, 8, 10	10, 24, 26	16, 30, 34	14, 48, 50
9, 12, 15	15, 36, 39		

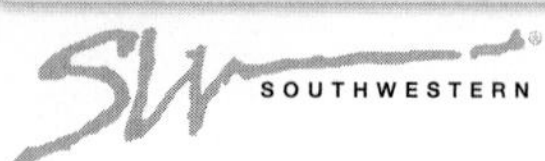

Classifying Triangles

You use side lengths to classify a triangle as right, acute, or obtuse. You can use the converse of the Pythagorean Theorem to determine if given side lengths form a right triangle.

Converse of the Pythagorean Theorem
If the sum of the squares of the lengths of two sides of a triangle is equal to the square of the length of the third side, then the triangle is a right triangle.

The next theorem is an extension of the Converse of the Pythagorean Theorem.

Pythagorean Inequality Theorem

Given: a, b, and c are the side lengths of a triangle with c the length of the longest side

If $c^2 < a^2 + b^2$, then $\triangle ABC$ is acute.

If $c^2 > a^2 + b^2$, then $\triangle ABC$ is obtuse.

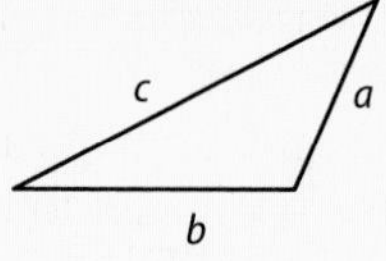

EXAMPLE 7

Classify the triangle with the given side lengths. If no triangle is possible, write *not possible*.

Watch Out!

When you compare c^2 to $a^2 + b^2$, always substitute the greatest value for c.

a. 5, 8, 9

Compare c^2 to $a^2 + b^2$. Always substitute the greatest number for c.

$9^2 \stackrel{?}{=} 5^2 + 8^2$

$81 \stackrel{?}{=} 25 + 64$

$81 < 89$

The triangle is acute.

b. 9, 12, 17

$17^2 \stackrel{?}{=} 9^2 + 12^2$

$289 \stackrel{?}{=} 81 + 144$

$289 > 225$

The triangle is obtuse.

c. 13, 5, 25

Use the Triangle Inequality Theorem.

$13 + 5 \not> 25$

Not possible

d. 30, 40, 50

$50^2 \stackrel{?}{=} 30^2 + 40^2$

$2500 = 900 + 1600$

The triangle is a right triangle.

For a review of the Triangle Inequality Theorem, go to *Triangle Inequalities* in *Triangles and Polygons* on page 664.

EXAMPLE 8

Shauna wants to determine if the table leg she is repairing is perpendicular to the top of the table. She measures from the bottom of the 3.2-ft leg to a point 1.2 ft from the end of the table. The tape measure reads 3.5 ft. What type of angle does the leg form with the table top?

The tape measure, the leg, and the table top form a triangle. The longest side is 3.5 ft.

$3.5^2 \; [\stackrel{?}{=}] \; 3.2^2 + 1.2^2$

$12.25 \; [\stackrel{?}{=}] \; 10.24 + 1.44$

$12.25 > 11.68$

The angle is obtuse.

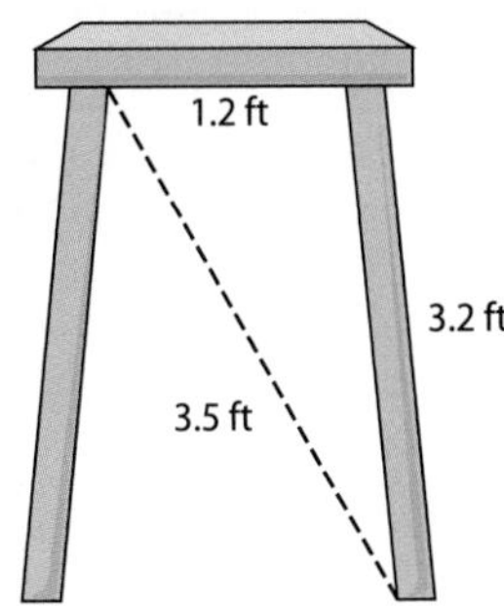

SEARCH

To see step-by-step videos of these problems, enter the page number into the SWadvantage.com Search Bar.

EXAMPLE 9

Builders sometimes use a rope with 13 knots spaced at 1-ft intervals to determine whether a wall is perpendicular to the floor. Why does this work?

The builder puts a 3-ft length along a wall and a 4-ft length along the floor.

If possible, he or she then connects the first and thirteenth knot.

If the first and last knot meet exactly, then the three lengths form a 3-4-5 triangle.

The angle between the 3-ft side and the 4-ft side must be a right angle by the Converse of the Pythagorean Theorem.

If the knots do not meet, or if there is overlap, then the angle is not a right angle.

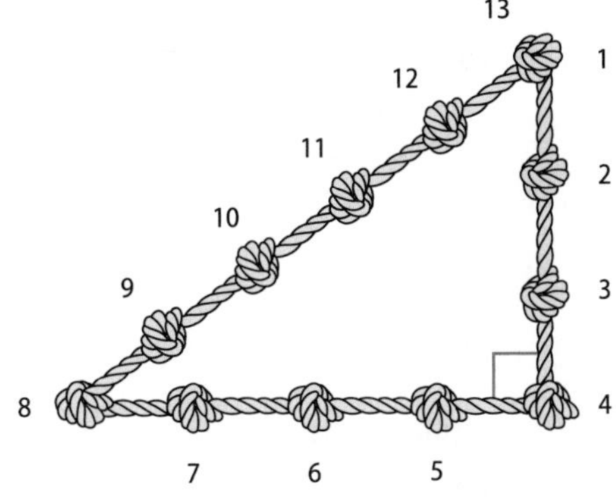

GOT TO KNOW!

Types of Triangles and Their Side Lengths

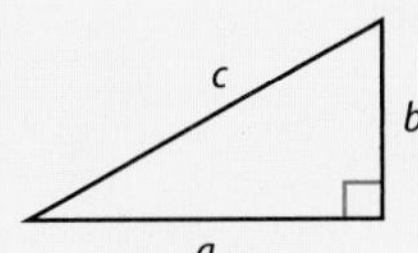

right triangle

$c^2 = a^2 + b^2$

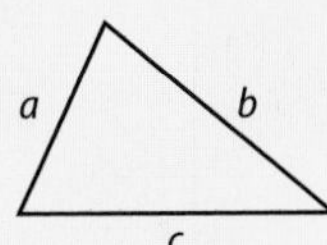

acute triangle

$c^2 < a^2 + b^2$

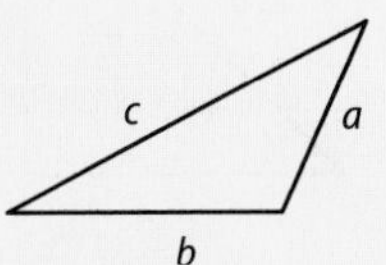

obtuse triangle

$c^2 > a^2 + b^2$

Special Right Triangles

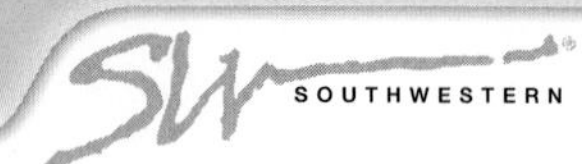

45°–45°–90° Triangles

Base angles of an isosceles triangle are congruent. The acute angles of a right triangle are complementary. Therefore, the base angles of an isosceles right triangle both measure 45°. Another name for an isosceles right triangle is a **45°–45°–90° triangle**.

45°–45°–90° Triangle Theorem

In a 45°–45°–90° triangle, the length of the hypotenuse is $\sqrt{2}$ times the length of a leg.

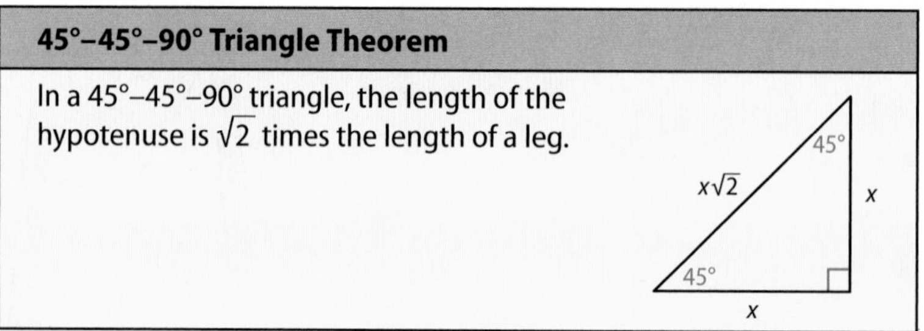

PROOF

Given: $\triangle ABC$ is a 45°–45°–90° triangle.
Prove: $AB = AC\sqrt{2}$

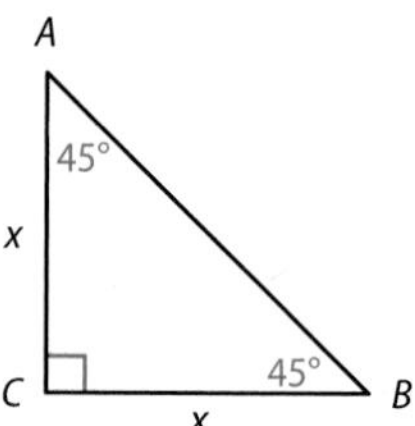

Let $AC = x$. Then $BC = x$ because the triangle is isosceles. By the Pythagorean Theorem:

$$AB^2 = x^2 + x^2$$
$$AB^2 = 2x^2$$
$$AB = \sqrt{2x^2}$$
$$AB = x\sqrt{2}$$
$$AB = AC\sqrt{2}$$

GOT TO KNOW!

45°–45°–90° Triangle Theorem

In a 45°–45°–90° triangle, the length of the hypotenuse is $\sqrt{2}$ times the length of a leg.

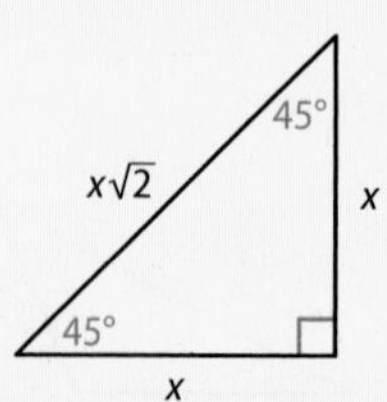

EXAMPLE 1

***PQRS* is a square. Find the value of *x*.**

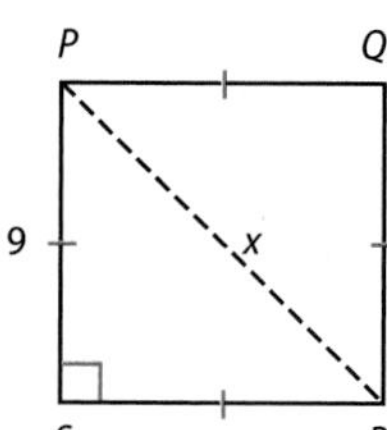

A diagonal of a square divides it into two congruent 45°–45°–90° triangles.

hypotenuse = $\sqrt{2}$ · leg

$$x = 9\sqrt{2}$$

CHECK Use the Pythagorean Theorem to verify that your answer is correct.

Pythagorean Theorem	$PS^2 + SR^2 = PR^2$
Substitute.	$9^2 + 9^2 \stackrel{?}{=} (9\sqrt{2})^2$
Simplify.	$81 + 81 \stackrel{?}{=} (81)(2)$
	$162 = 162$ ✔

EXAMPLE 2

Find the value of *x* in each triangle.

a.

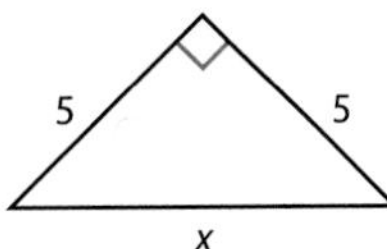

This is a 45°–45°–90° triangle.

hypotenuse $= \sqrt{2} \cdot$ leg

$x = 5\sqrt{2}$

b.

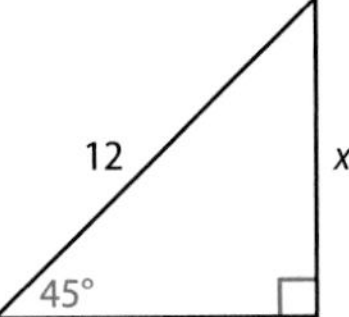

hypotenuse $= \sqrt{2} \cdot$ leg $\qquad 12 = x\sqrt{2}$

Divide both sides by $\sqrt{2}$. $\qquad \frac{12}{\sqrt{2}} = x$

Simplify the radical. $\qquad \frac{12\sqrt{2}}{2} = x$

$x = 6\sqrt{2}$

c.

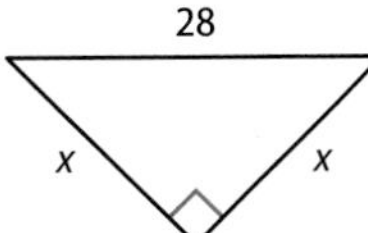

hypotenuse $= \sqrt{2} \cdot$ leg $\qquad 28 = x\sqrt{2}$

Divide both sides by $\sqrt{2}$. $\qquad \frac{28}{\sqrt{2}} = x$

Simplify the radical. $\qquad \frac{28\sqrt{2}}{2} = x$

$x = 14\sqrt{2}$

d.

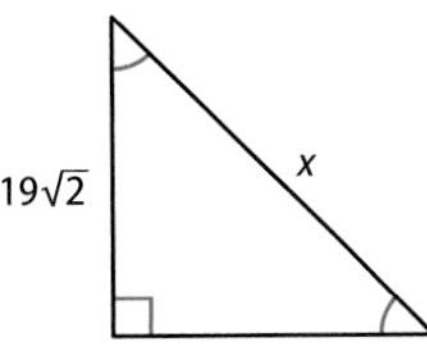

hypotenuse $= \sqrt{2} \cdot$ leg $\qquad x = (19\sqrt{2})(\sqrt{2})$

Simplify. $\qquad x = 19 \cdot 2$

$x = 38$

SEARCH

To see step-by-step videos of these problems, enter the page number into the SWadvantage.com Search Bar.

Need More HELP

For help with rationalizing the denominator, go to *Dividing Rational Expressions* in *Advanced Algebra* (Book 2, p. 1962).

30°–60°–90° Triangles

There is a special relationship between the lengths of the sides of a 30°–60°–90° triangle.

Watch Out!

You will use the properties of 45°–45°–90° and 30°–60°–90° triangles often. Memorize them.

30°–60°–90° Triangle Theorem

In a 30°–60°–90° triangle, the hypotenuse is twice the length of the shorter leg. The longer leg is $\sqrt{3}$ times the length of the shorter leg.

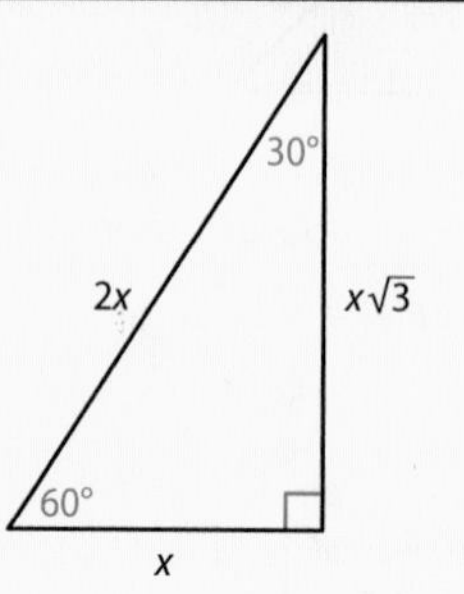

The bisector of an angle in an equilateral triangle divides the triangle into two congruent 30°–60°–90° triangles.

PROOF

Given: $\triangle PQR$ is equilateral; $\overline{QM}$ bisects $\angle PQR$.

Prove: $PQ = 2PM$ and $QM = PM\sqrt{3}$

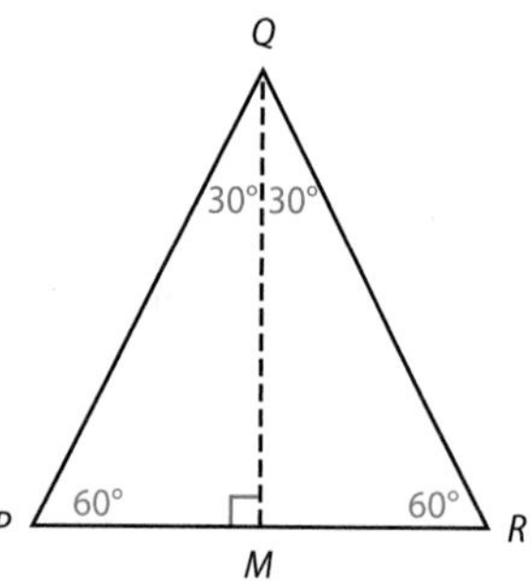

$\overline{QM}$ divides $\triangle PQR$ into two congruent 30°–60°–90° triangles, and $PR = 2PM = PQ$. By the Pythagorean Theorem:

$$PM^2 + QM^2 = PQ^2$$
$$PM^2 + QM^2 = (2PM)^2$$
$$PM^2 + QM^2 = 4PM^2$$
$$QM^2 = 3PM^2$$
$$QM = PM\sqrt{3}$$

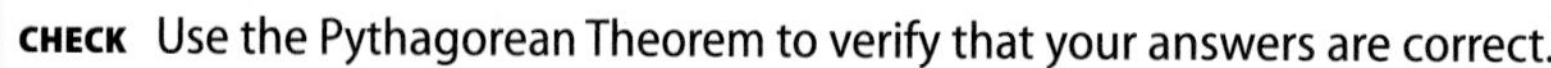

EXAMPLE 3

Find the values of *x* and *y*.

You are given the length of the shorter leg.

STEP 1 Find *x*, the length of the longer leg.

longer leg = shorter leg • $\sqrt{3}$ $\quad x = 8\sqrt{3}$

STEP 2 Find *y*, the length of the hypotenuse.

hypotenuse = 2 • shorter leg $\quad y = 2(8) = 16$

CHECK Use the Pythagorean Theorem to verify that your answers are correct.

Pythagorean Theorem	$8^2 + x^2 = y^2$
Substitute.	$8^2 + (8\sqrt{3})^2 \stackrel{?}{=} 16^2$
Simplify.	$64 + 64(3) \stackrel{?}{=} 256$
	$64 + 192 \stackrel{?}{=} 256$
	$256 = 256$ ✔

SEARCH

To see step-by-step videos of these problems, enter the page number into the SWadvantage.com Search Bar.

EXAMPLE 4

Find the values of the variables.

a.

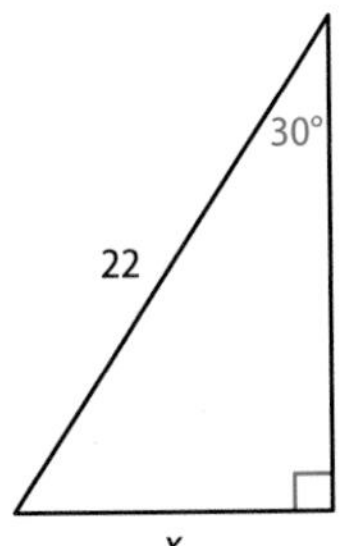

You are given the length of the hypotenuse.

STEP 1 Find the length of the shorter leg.

hypotenuse = 2 • shorter leg $22 = 2x$

$x = 11$

STEP 2 Find the length of the longer leg.

longer leg = shorter leg • $\sqrt{3}$ $y = 11\sqrt{3}$

$x = 11; y = 11\sqrt{3}$

b.

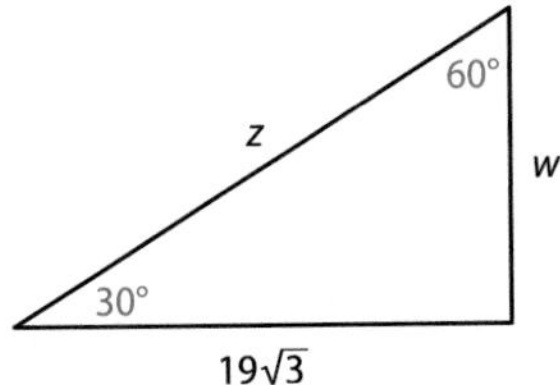

You are given the length of the longer leg.

STEP 1 Find the length of the shorter leg.

longer leg = shorter leg • $\sqrt{3}$ $19\sqrt{3} = w\sqrt{3}$

Divide both sides by $\sqrt{3}$. $w = 19$

STEP 2 Find the length of the hypotenuse.

hypotenuse = 2 • shorter leg $z = 2(19) = 38$

$w = 19; z = 38$

c.

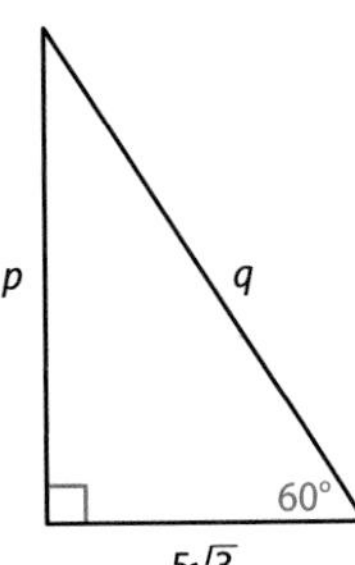

You are given the length of the shorter leg.

STEP 1 Find the length of the longer leg.

longer leg = shorter leg • $\sqrt{3}$ $p = 5\sqrt{3} \cdot \sqrt{3}$

Simplify. $p = 5(3) = 15$

STEP 2 Find the length of the hypotenuse.

hypotenuse = 2 • shorter leg $q = 2(5\sqrt{3}) = 10\sqrt{3}$

$p = 15; q = 10\sqrt{3}$

Need More HELP

Remember! The shortest side of a triangle is opposite the smallest angle.

More Practice with Special Triangles

EXAMPLE 5

Watch Out!

When in doubt, you can always check your answer by using the Pythagorean Theorem.

a. Find the value of *x*.

This is a 45°–45°–90° triangle.

hypotenuse = $\sqrt{2}$ • leg $\quad 3x^2 = x\sqrt{2}$

Divide both sides by *x*. $\quad 3x = \sqrt{2}$

Divide both sides by 3. $\quad x = \frac{\sqrt{2}}{3}$

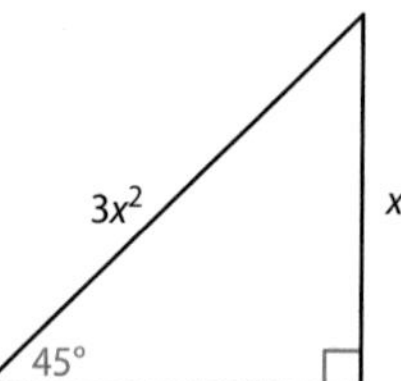

b. Find the value of *y*.

This is a 30°–60°–90° triangle. You are given the length of the hypotenuse.

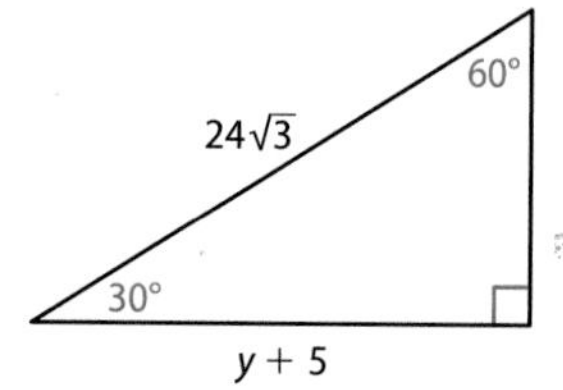

STEP 1 Find the length of the shorter leg.

hypotenuse = 2 • shorter leg $\quad 24\sqrt{3} = 2 \cdot \text{shorter leg}$

Divide both sides by 2. $\quad \text{shorter leg} = 12\sqrt{3}$

STEP 2 Find the length of the longer leg.

longer leg = shorter leg • $\sqrt{3}$

$$y + 5 = 12\sqrt{3}\,(\sqrt{3})$$
$$y + 5 = 12(3)$$
$$y = 31$$

GOT TO KNOW!

30°–60°–90° Triangle Theorem

In a 30°–60°–90° triangle, the hypotenuse is twice the length of the shorter leg. The longer leg is $\sqrt{3}$ times the length of the shorter leg.

30°
2x
$x\sqrt{3}$
60°
x

c. Find the value of *z*.

STEP 1 Find *AC*.

$\overline{AC}$ is the hypotenuse of a 30°–60°–90° triangle. The length of the shorter leg is 4, so $AC = 2(4) = 8$.

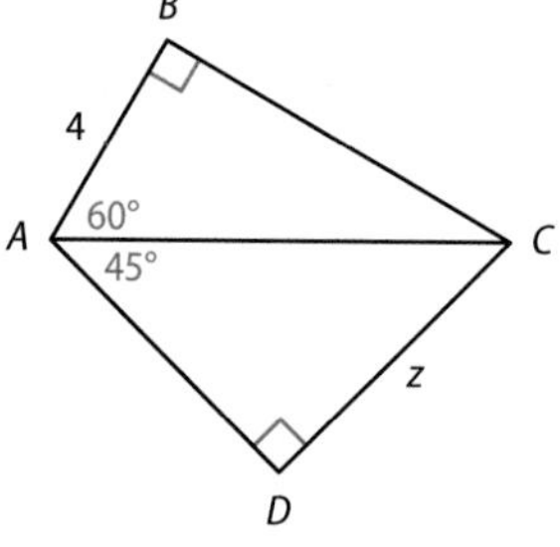

STEP 2 Find the value of *z*.

$\triangle ACD$ is a 45°–45°–90° triangle with a hypotenuse of 8. The variable *z* represents the length of a leg.

hypotenuse = $\sqrt{2}$ • leg $\quad 8 = z\sqrt{2}$

Divide both sides by $\sqrt{2}$. $\quad z = \frac{8}{\sqrt{2}}$

Simplify the radical. $\quad z = \frac{8}{\sqrt{2}} \cdot \frac{\sqrt{2}}{\sqrt{2}} = \frac{8\sqrt{2}}{2}$

$$z = 4\sqrt{2}$$

EXAMPLE 6

Find the perimeter and area of $\triangle ABC$.

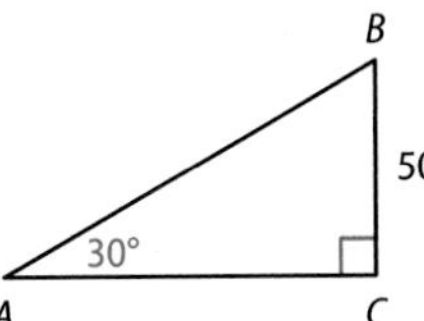

Use the 30°–60°–90° Triangle Theorem to find the lengths of the other sides.

hypotenuse = 2 • shorter leg $\quad AB = 2(50) = 100$

longer leg = shorter leg • $\sqrt{3}$ $\quad AC = 50\sqrt{3}$

$$\begin{aligned} \text{perimeter} &= AC + BC + AB \\ &= 50\sqrt{3} + 50 + 100 \\ &= 150 + 50\sqrt{3} \end{aligned}$$

$$\text{area} = \frac{1}{2} \cdot 50 \cdot 50\sqrt{3} = 1{,}250\sqrt{3}$$

Need More HELP

The area of a triangle is one-half the base times the height.

EXAMPLE 7

Find the area of square *PQRS*.

METHOD 1

Use the Pythagorean Theorem.

$$x^2 + x^2 = 15^2$$
$$2x^2 = 225$$
$$x^2 = 112.5$$

The area of square *PQRS* is 112.5 cm^2.

METHOD 2

Use the 45°–45°–90° Triangle Theorem.

hypotenuse = 2 • shorter leg $\quad 15 = x\sqrt{2}$

Divide both sides by $\sqrt{2}$. $\quad x = \frac{15}{\sqrt{2}}$

Calculate the area. $\quad x^2 = \left(\frac{15}{\sqrt{2}}\right)^2 = \frac{225}{2} = 112.5$

The area of square *PQRS* is 112.5 cm^2.

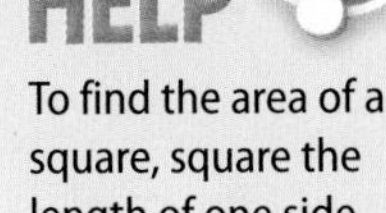

Need More HELP

To find the area of a square, square the length of one side.

EXAMPLE 8

Find *AD*.

STEP 1 Use the 30°–60°–90° Triangle Theorem in $\triangle ABC$ to find *AB*.

longer leg = shorter leg • $\sqrt{3}$ $\quad AB = 12\sqrt{3}$

STEP 2 Use the 30°–60°–90° Triangle Theorem in $\triangle ABD$ to find *BD*, then *AD*.

$$BD = \frac{1}{2}AB = 6\sqrt{3}$$
$$AD = BD\sqrt{3} = 6\sqrt{3} \cdot \sqrt{3} = 6 \cdot 3$$
$$AD = 18$$

SEARCH

To see step-by-step videos of these problems, enter the page number into the SWadvantage.com Search Bar.

Area of a Regular Polygon

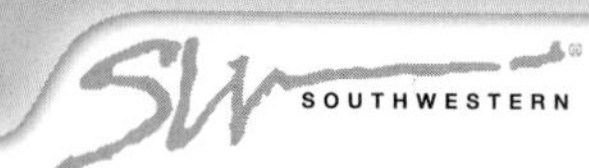

Finding the Area of a Regular Polygon

Watch Out ! The radius is always longer than the apothem.

The **center** of a regular polygon is the center of the circumscribed circle. The endpoints of a **radius** of a regular polygon are the center and a vertex of the polygon. The sides of a **central angle** of a regular polygon are two radii. The measure of a central angle of a polygon with n sides is $\frac{360°}{n}$. The **apothem a** is the distance from the center to a side.

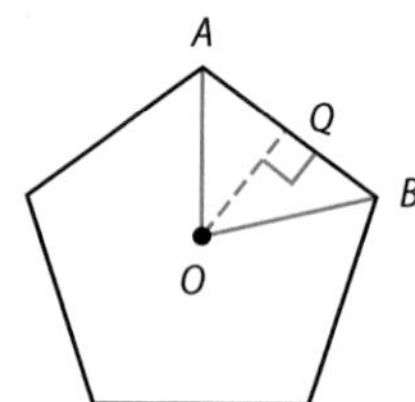

O is the center of the regular pentagon.
$\angle AOB$ is a central angle.
$\overline{AO}$ is a radius.
$\overline{OQ}$ is an apothem.
$m\angle AOB = \frac{360°}{5} = 72°$

Watch Out ! The area of the polygon is A, and the apothem is a.

When you draw all the radii of a regular n-gon, n congruent isosceles triangles are formed. The area of each triangle is $\frac{1}{2}as$. So the area A of the polygon is $\frac{1}{2}asn$. But $sn =$ the perimeter p, so:

$$A = \frac{1}{2}ap$$

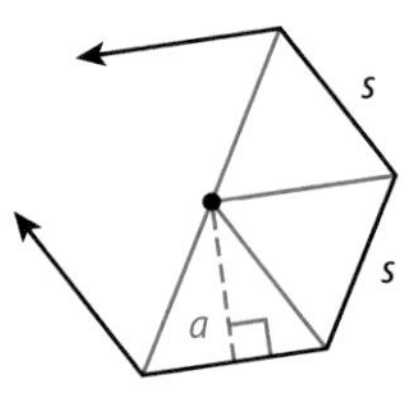

EXAMPLE 1

Find the area of an equilateral triangle with a side length of 8 ft.

The measure of a central angle $= \frac{360°}{3} = 120°$.

The apothem is the shorter leg of a $30°-60°-90°$ triangle.

$a = \frac{4}{\sqrt{3}} = \frac{4\sqrt{3}}{3}$ ft

$p = 8 + 8 + 8 = 24$ ft

$A = \frac{1}{2}ap = \frac{1}{2}\left(\frac{4\sqrt{3}}{3}\right)24$

area $= 16\sqrt{3}$ ft^2

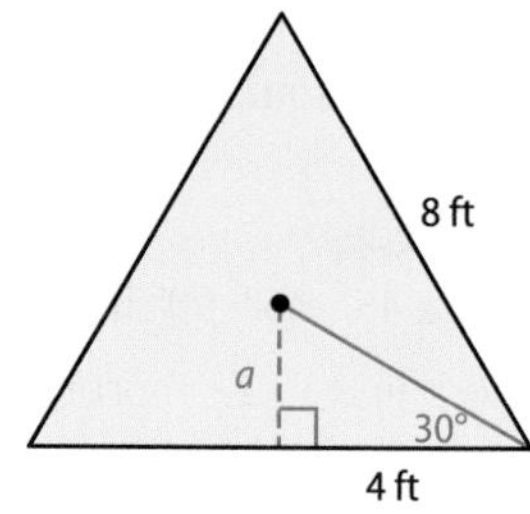

The segment associated with the apothem of a regular polygon bisects a side of the polygon.

EXAMPLE 2

Find the area of a regular hexagon with a perimeter of 84 m.

The length of each side is $\frac{84}{6} = 14$ m. The measure of a central angle $= 60°$.

The apothem is the longer leg of a $30°–60°–90°$ triangle.

$a = 7\sqrt{3}$ m

$A = \frac{1}{2}ap = \frac{1}{2}(7\sqrt{3})84$

area $= 294\sqrt{3}$ m^2

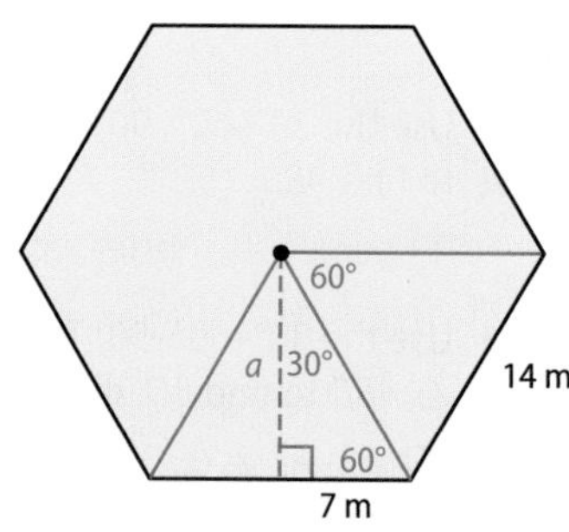

Need More HELP? For help with 30°–60°–90° triangles, go to *Special Right Triangles* (p. 684).

EXAMPLE 3

Find the area of a square with a radius of 22 cm.

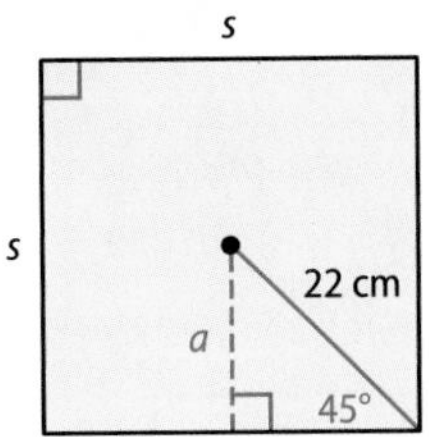

METHOD 1

Use the formula $A = \frac{1}{2}ap$.

The apothem is a leg of a 45°–45°–90° triangle.

$a = \frac{22}{\sqrt{2}} = 11\sqrt{2}$ cm

Find the length of a side.

$s = 2(11\sqrt{2}) = 22\sqrt{2}$ cm

Find the perimeter.

$p = 4(22\sqrt{2}) = 88\sqrt{2}$ cm

$A = \frac{1}{2}ap = \frac{1}{2}(11\sqrt{2})(88\sqrt{2}) = \frac{1}{2}(11)(88)2$

area $= 968$ cm^2

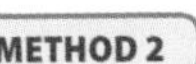

METHOD 2

Use the formula $A = s^2$, where $s =$ the length of one side.

Find the length of a side.

$s = 2(11\sqrt{2}) = 22\sqrt{2}$ cm

$A = s^2 = (22\sqrt{2})^2 = 22^2(2)$

area $= 968$ cm^2

SEARCH

To see step-by-step videos of these problems, enter the page number into the SWadvantage.com Search Bar.

EXAMPLE 4

Find the area of a regular pentagon with a side length of 7 yd.

The measure of a central angle is $\frac{360°}{5} = 72°$.

Use trigonometry to find the apothem.

$\tan 36° = \frac{3.5}{a}$, $a = \frac{3.5}{\tan 36°} \approx 4.8$ yd

$p = 35$ yd

$A = \frac{1}{2}ap \approx \frac{1}{2}(4.8)35 \approx 84$ yd^2

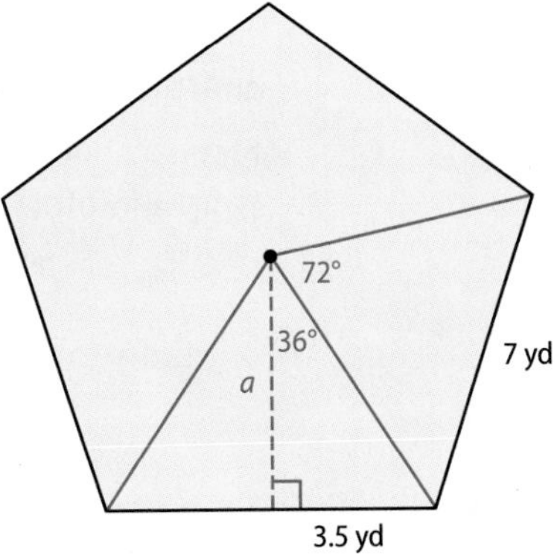

Need More HELP

For help with using trigonometry, go to *Trigonometric Ratios* in *Trigonometry* (p. 902).

GOT TO KNOW!

Area of a Regular Polygon

The area A of a regular polygon with apothem a and perimeter p is $A = \frac{1}{2}ap$.

Spatial Reasoning

What Came Before?

- Classifying solid figures
- Perimeter, circumference, and area of polygons

What's This About?

- Drawing three-dimensional figures in different ways
- Finding the lateral area of pyramids and cones
- Rotating plane figures to form solid figures

Practical Apps

- Holographers rotate figures to form three-dimensional images.
- Nets are folded to form cardboard boxes, soccer balls and other shapes.

just for FUN!

Q: What do you get when you crush an angle?

A: A rect-angle.

CONTENTS UPLOAD DOWNLOAD *Geometry*

You can find more practice problems online by visiting:
www.SWadvantage.com

Identifying and Drawing Nets

Have you ever cut down one corner of a cardboard box, unfolded it, and laid it out flat? If so, you have created a *net* for a rectangular prism.

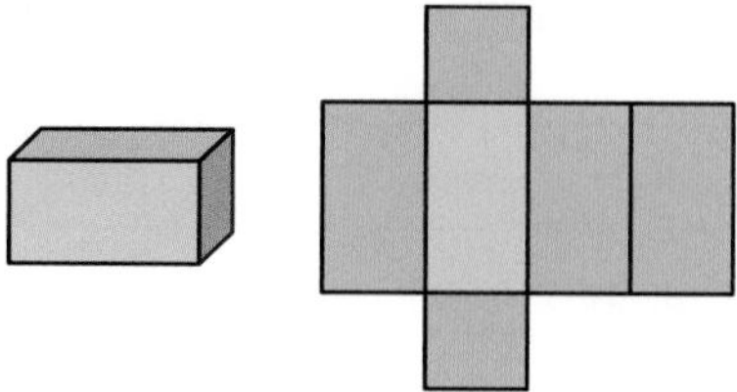

A **net** is a two-dimensional diagram that you can fold to form a three-dimensional figure.

Copy the diagram onto graph paper. Cut it out and try to fold it into a cube.

EXAMPLE 1

Determine whether each diagram is a net for a cube.

a. 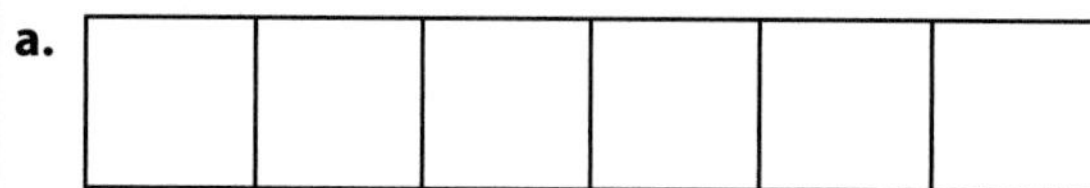

STEP 1 Determine whether the diagram shows all of the surfaces of a cube. A cube has six faces that are congruent squares. This diagram does show all of the surfaces, so it could be a net for a cube.

STEP 2 Determine whether the diagram can be folded to form a cube. To do this, you can actually fold it, as shown below.

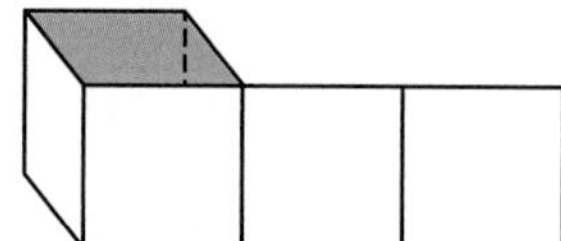

The bases of the cube are open, so the diagram is not a net for a cube.

b. 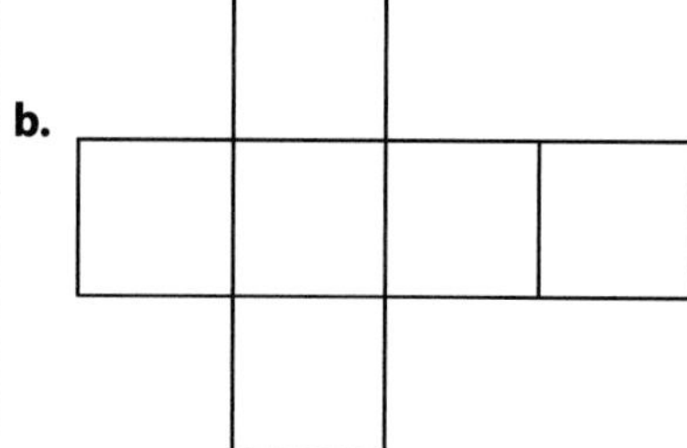

STEP 1 Determine whether the diagram shows all of the surfaces of a cube. A cube has six faces that are congruent squares. This diagram does show all of the surfaces, so it could be a net for a cube.

STEP 2 Determine whether the diagram can be folded to form a cube. To do this, copy the diagram above, cut it out, and try to fold it to form a cube. The row of four squares forms the lateral faces of a cube, much as in the folded diagram in part (a) of Example 1. You can fold the two remaining squares to form the bases of a cube.

You can fold the diagram to form a cube, so it is a net for a cube.

EXAMPLE 2

Draw a net for a right hexagonal prism.

A right hexagonal prism has two bases that are congruent hexagons and six lateral faces that are congruent rectangles.

STEP 1 Draw one hexagonal base.

STEP 2 Draw a row of six congruent rectangles. The width of each rectangle must equal the width of a side of the hexagon.

STEP 3 Draw the other hexagonal base. Attach one side of this base to the bottom of one of the rectangles.

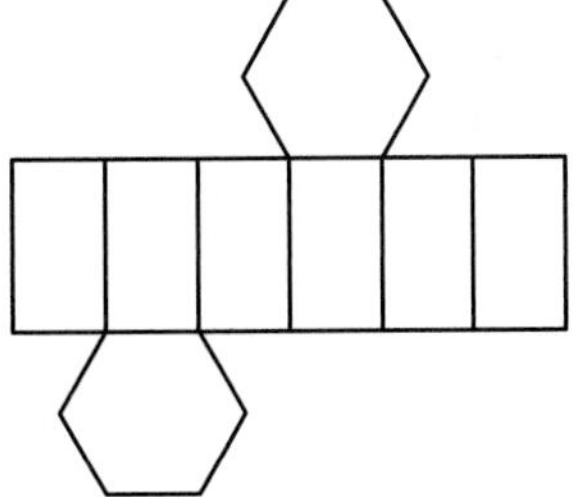

Watch Out !

You can draw more than one net for a given solid.

So far, we have considered only nets whose faces are polygons. You can also draw nets for three-dimensional figures with faces that are circles.

EXAMPLE 3

Match each net with the figure it represents.

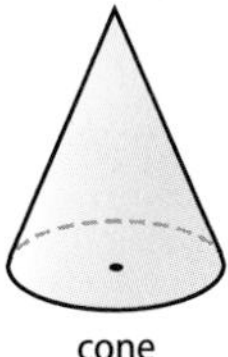
cone

triangular prism

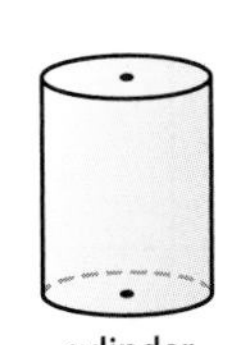
cylinder

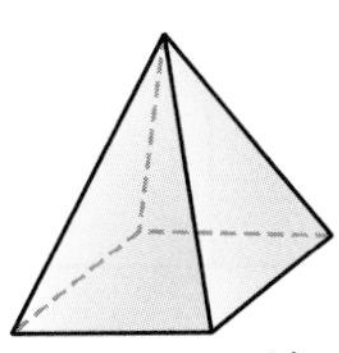
square pyramid

a.

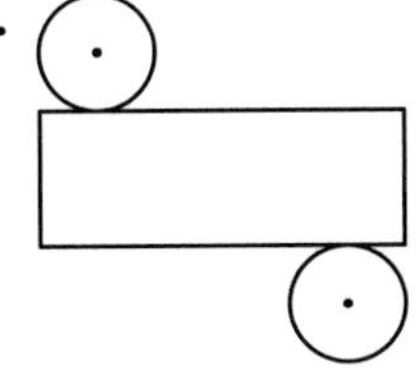

This is a net for a cylinder.

b.

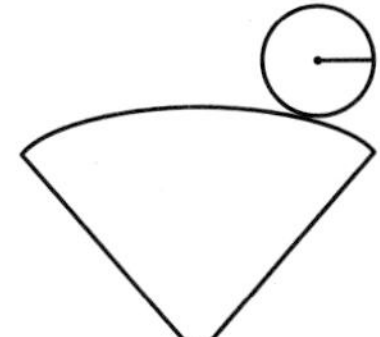

This is a net for a cone.

c.

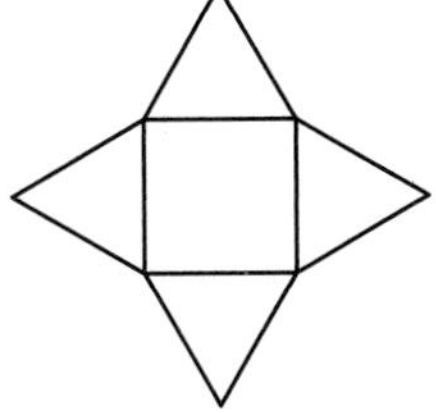

This is a net for a square pyramid.

d.

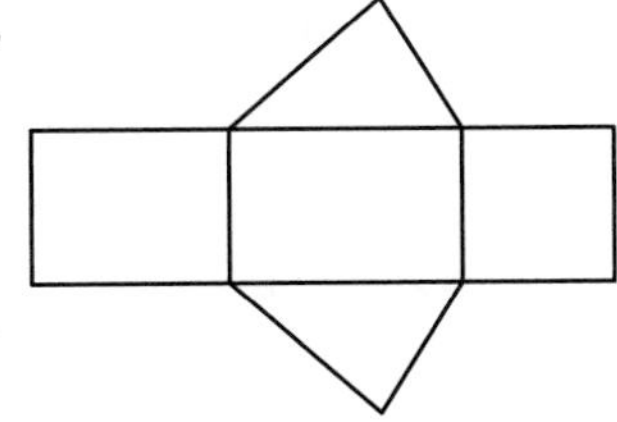

This is a net for a triangular prism.

SEARCH

To see step-by-step videos of these problems, enter the page number into the SWadvantage.com Search Bar.

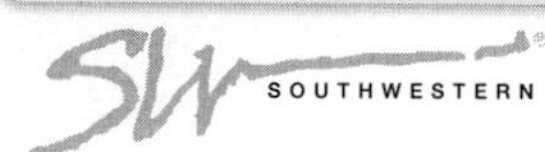

Nets and Surface Area

Because nets are two-dimensional representations of three-dimensional figures, they are extremely useful for visualizing all of the surfaces of a solid. This makes nets good tools for finding surface area.

EXAMPLE 4

The bases of a right triangular prism are equilateral triangles with a perimeter of 36 cm. The lateral edges of the prism are 15 cm long. Draw the net. Then use the net to find the total surface area of the prism. Round your answer to the nearest square centimeter.

STEP 1 Draw a net of the triangular prism. Each base is an equilateral triangle with a perimeter of 36 cm, so each side of the triangle is 12 cm. The lateral faces of the prism are congruent rectangles 12 cm wide and 15 cm long.

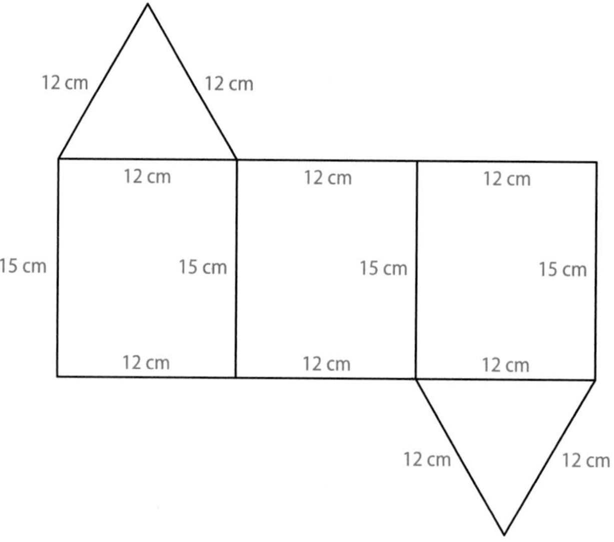

STEP 2 Find the area of one triangular base. Use the formula for the area A of an equilateral triangle with sides $s = 12$ cm.

Substitute. $A = \frac{s^2\sqrt{3}}{4} = \frac{12^2\sqrt{3}}{4} = \frac{144\sqrt{3}}{4}$

$A = 36\sqrt{3}\text{ cm}^2$

STEP 3 Find the area of one rectangular face.

Use the formula for the area of a rectangle. area = length • width

Substitute the values from the figure in the formula. $= 15 \cdot 12$

Multiply. area = 180 cm^2

STEP 4 Find the total surface area of the figure by adding the areas of the bases and the lateral faces. This prism has two bases and three lateral faces.

Add the areas. surface area $= 2(36\sqrt{3}) + 3(180)$

Multiply. $= 72\sqrt{3} + 540$

Use a calculator. $\approx 665\text{ cm}^2$

The surface area of the triangular prism is about 665 cm^2.

SEARCH

To see step-by-step videos of these problems, enter the page number into the SWadvantage.com Search Bar.

Need More HELP

For help with the area of equilateral triangles, go to *Areas of Triangles* in *Measurement* (p. 536).

GOT TO KNOW!

Nets and Surface Area

A **net** is a two-dimensional diagram that you can fold to form a three-dimensional figure.

The **surface area** of a solid is the sum of the areas of all the faces.

EXAMPLE 5

Name the solid whose net is shown. Then find its surface area.

The solid is a square pyramid. The lateral faces are four congruent triangles.

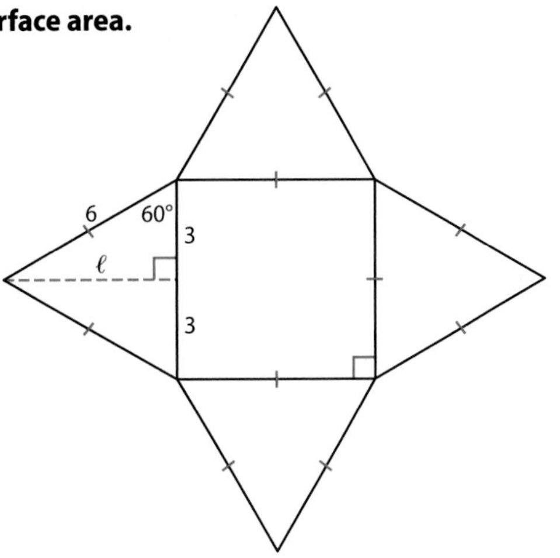

METHOD 1

Use the net to find the surface area.

STEP 1 Use the 30°-60°-90° Triangle Theorem to find the height ℓ of each triangle.

longer leg = shorter leg • $\sqrt{3}$

$\ell = 3\sqrt{3}$

STEP 2 Find the area of one triangle.

area $= \frac{1}{2} \cdot$ base • height

area $= \frac{1}{2} \cdot 6 \cdot 3\sqrt{3}$

area of one triangle $= 9\sqrt{3}$

STEP 3 Find the area of the square base.

area $= 6^2$

area of square base = 36

STEP 4 Add the areas of the four triangles and the square base.

surface area $= 4(9\sqrt{3}) + 36$

surface area $= 36\sqrt{3} + 36$

METHOD 2

Use the formula for the surface area of a pyramid, $SA = B + \frac{1}{2}p\ell$.

STEP 1 Draw the prism and label the known lengths.

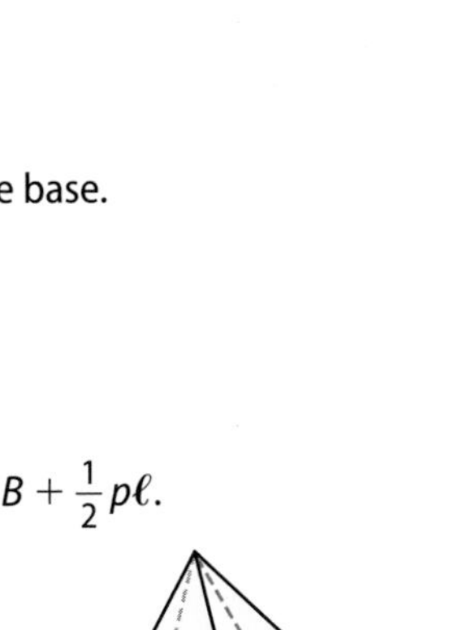

STEP 2 Find p, the perimeter of the square base.

$p = 4(6)$

$p = 24$

STEP 3 Find B, the area of the square base.

$B = 6^2$

$B = 36$

STEP 4 Substitute into the formula for the surface area of a pyramid.

$SA = B + \frac{1}{2}p\ell = 36 + \frac{1}{2}(24)3\sqrt{3}$

$SA = 36 + 36\sqrt{3}$

The surface area is $(36 + 36\sqrt{3})$ square units.

Need More HELP

For help with the 30°-60°-90° Triangle Theorem, go to *Special Right Triangles* in *Triangles and Polygons* (p. 684).

GOT TO KNOW!

Surface Area of a Pyramid

The formula for the surface area SA of a regular pyramid is $SA = B + \frac{1}{2}p\ell$, where B is the area of the base, p is the perimeter of the base, and ℓ is the slant height of the pyramid.

Creating Isometric Drawings

You live in three-dimensional space. This means that every object you encounter, even something as thin as a page in this book, has length, width, and depth. Artists and engineers draw two-dimensional models of three-dimensional objects. Artists use shading and perspective to accomplish this. Geometry uses a few different methods.

The first of these methods is **isometric drawings**. An isometric drawing shows three sides of a figure, using triangular isometric dot paper, also called a *triangular lattice*. The dots are vertices of equilateral triangles. Each 60° angle on the dot paper represents a right angle of a three-dimensional figure.

You can use isometric drawings to represent figures constructed from congruent cubes.

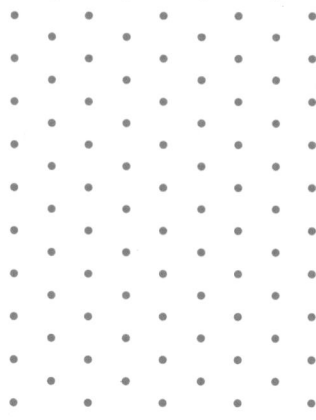

Isometric dot paper

If you are having difficulty visualizing the corner view of a figure constructed from cubes, use actual cubes to build it.

Lou is arranging cubes to form the letters in his name. Use isometric dot paper to draw the letter "L."

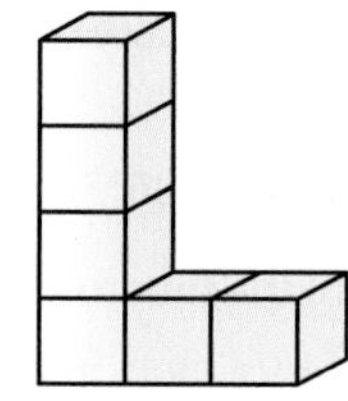

STEP 1 Draw the front.

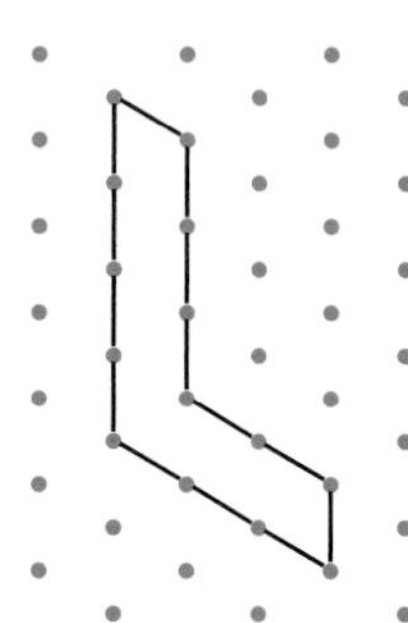

STEP 2 Draw the back.

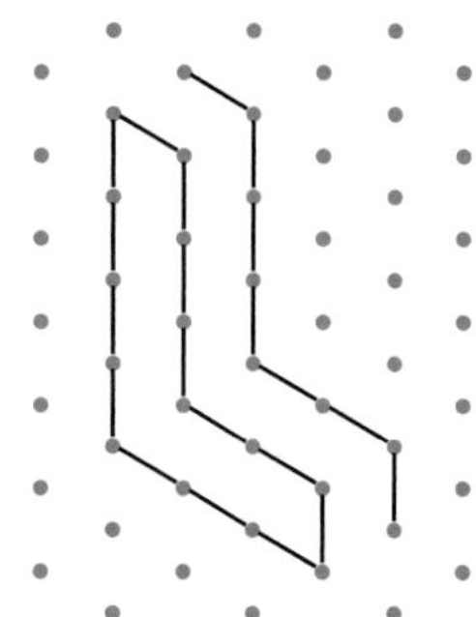

STEP 3 Connect corresponding vertices.

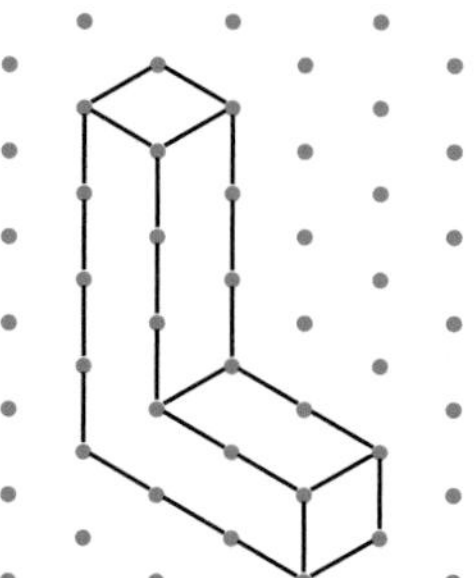

You can use isometric drawings to represent other three-dimensional figures.

EXAMPLE 2

Use isometric dot paper to draw a rectangular prism 5 units high, 4 units long, and 3 units wide.

STEP 1 Draw the top of the figure, a 3 × 4 rectangle.

STEP 2 Draw vertical segments from each of the three "front" vertices of the top. Each segment is 5 units long.

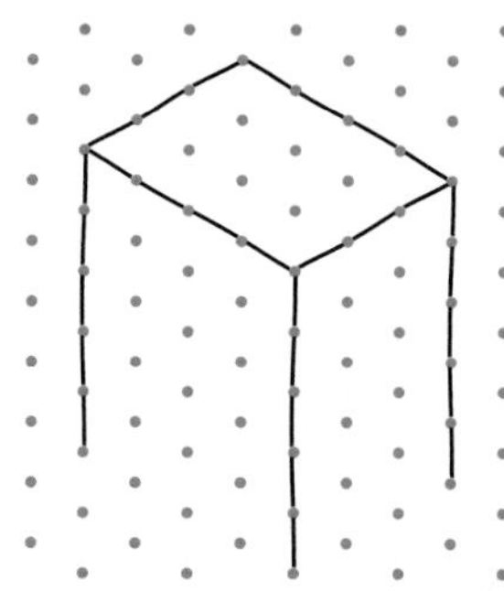

STEP 3 Draw the two visible edges of the bottom. Notice that the segments you just drew are parallel to the edges of the top.

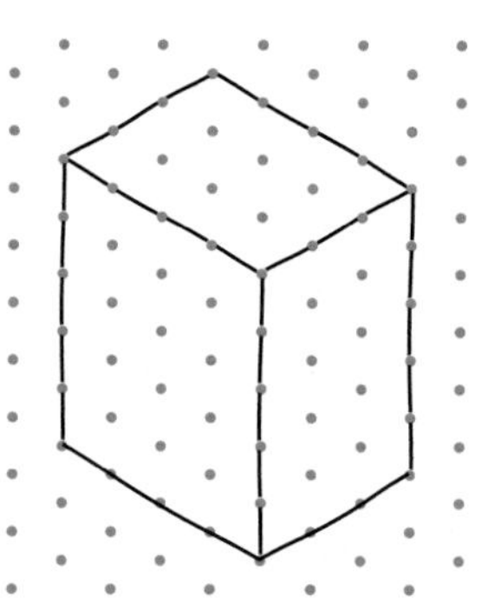

EXAMPLE 3

Use isometric dot paper to draw the solid with the given net.

STEP 1 Identify the solid.

The solid is a 2 × 2 × 2 cube.

STEP 2 Draw the cube.

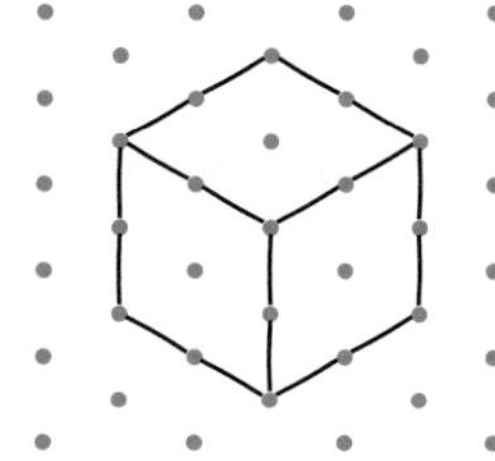

SEARCH

To see step-by-step videos of these problems, enter the page number into the SWadvantage.com Search Bar.

Need More HELP

For a review of nets, go to *Nets* in *Spatial Reasoning*, p. 694.

Using Isometric Drawings

Since isometric drawings represent three-dimensional figures, you can use them to determine properties of those figures. One thing to keep in mind when using isometric drawings is that the drawings do not show all the faces. Some faces are hidden from view.

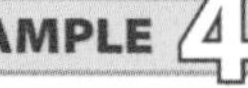

Determine the numbers of faces, edges, and vertices of each solid.

a.

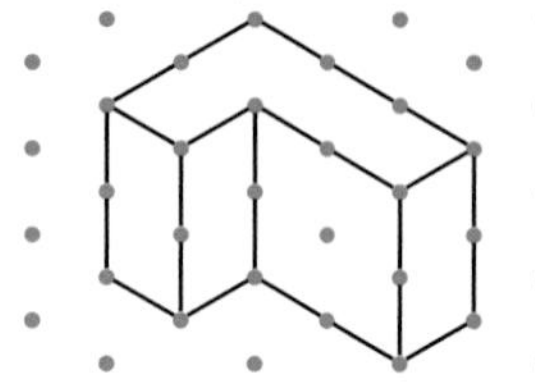

STEP 1 Count the faces. Five faces are visible in the drawing. Three faces are hidden from view: the back right, the back left, and the bottom.

The figure has 8 faces.

STEP 2 Count the edges. There are 15 visible edges. In addition, there are 3 edges hidden from view: 1 vertical edge where the right back and left back faces intersect, and 2 edges of the bottom base.

The figure has 18 edges.

STEP 3 Count the vertices. There are 11 visible vertices. In addition, there is 1 hidden vertex at the rear of the figure.

The figure has 12 vertices.

b.

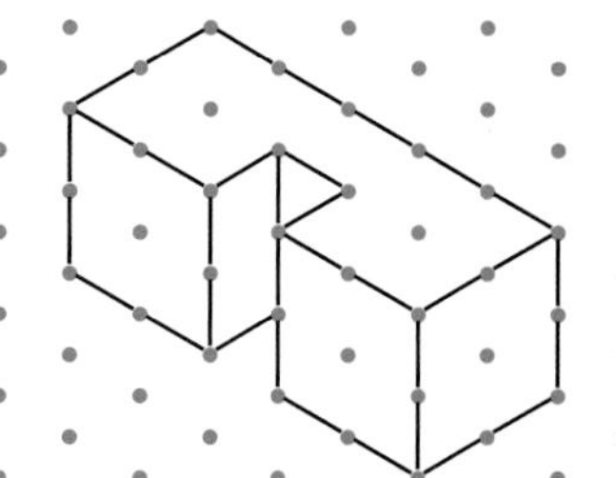

STEP 1 Count the faces. Including one face that is partially obscured, there are six visible faces. Four faces are hidden from view: one side of the indentation, the back right, the back left, and the bottom.

The figure has 10 faces.

STEP 2 Count the edges. Including 1 edge that is partially hidden, there are 18 visible edges. In addition, 6 edges are hidden from view: 3 edges in the indentation and 3 edges at the back of the figure.

The figure has 24 edges.

STEP 3 Count the vertices. There are 13 visible vertices. In addition, 3 vertices are hidden from view: 2 in the indentation and 1 in the back corner.

The figure has 16 vertices.

Try It This Way

If you are having difficulty visualizing the hidden edges, copy the figure and draw the hidden edges with a colored pencil.

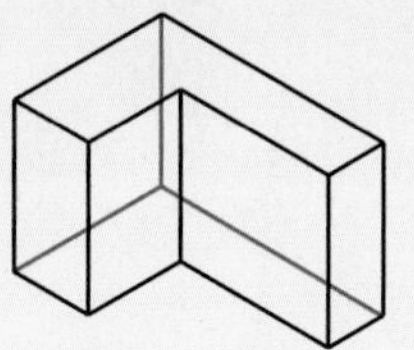

GOT TO KNOW!

Isometric Dot Paper

An isometric drawing uses triangular isometric dot paper. The dots are vertices of equilateral triangles. Each 60° angle on the dot paper represents a right angle of a three-dimensional figure.

Isometric drawings can also help you calculate the surface area and volume of geometric solids. In this lesson, you can assume that a segment joining two dots has a length of 1 unit.

EXAMPLE 5

Find the total surface area and volume of each figure.

a.

STEP 1 Find the total surface area (*SA*).

The figure is a rectangular prism. The formula for its surface area is

$SA = 2(\ell w + \ell h + wh)$, where ℓ is the length, w is the width, and h is the height.

Substitute values from the figure.

$SA = 2[(6 \cdot 4) + (6 \cdot 3) + (4 \cdot 3)]$

Simplify.

$= 2(24 + 18 + 12)$

$SA = 108$

The total surface area is 108 square units.

STEP 2 Find the volume (*V*).

Use the volume formula. $V = \ell \cdot w \cdot h = 6 \cdot 4 \cdot 3 = 72$

The volume is 72 cubic units.

b.

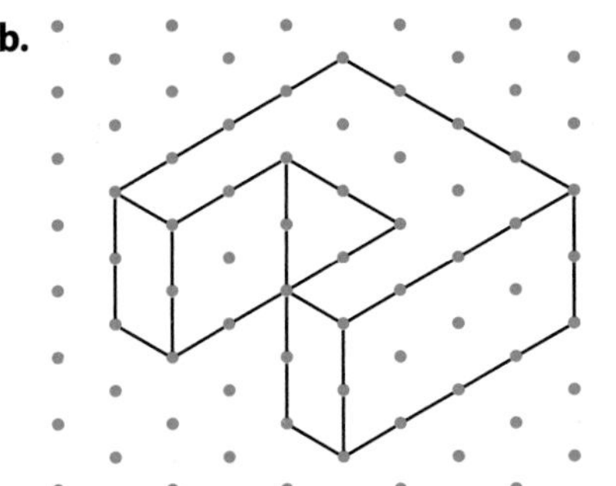

STEP 1 Find the total surface area.

The figure is a $4 \times 4 \times 2$ rectangular prism with a $2 \times 2 \times 2$ rectangular prism removed. The faces of the indentation are congruent to the faces that have been removed from the larger prism, so the formula for its surface area is still:

$SA = 2(\ell w + \ell h + wh)$

$SA = 2[(4 \cdot 4) + (4 \cdot 2) + (4 \cdot 2)] = 2(16 + 8 + 8)$
$= 64$

The total surface area is 64 square units.

STEP 2 Find the volume.

The volume of the figure is the difference between the volume of the $4 \times 4 \times 2$ rectangular prism and the volume of the $2 \times 2 \times 2$ rectangular prism.

$V = (4 \cdot 4 \cdot 2) - (2 \cdot 2 \cdot 2) = 24$

The volume is 24 cubic units.

SEARCH

To see step-by-step videos of these problems, enter the page number into the SWadvantage.com Search Bar.

Need More HELP

For help with finding the volume of a prism, go to *Volumes of Prisms and Cylinders* in *Measurement*, p. 570.

Creating Orthographic Drawings

When you look at an object straight on, your line of sight is perpendicular to the surface of the object. You may see only one side of the object, and not its depth.

An **orthographic drawing** of a three-dimensional object shows up to six views of the object: the front, back, top, bottom, right, and left sides. A heavy segment indicates a break in the surface.

EXAMPLE 1

Given the isometric drawing of a figure, make an orthographic drawing.

Front Right

Front View

Back View

Top View

Bottom View

Right-Side View

Left-Side View

GOT TO KNOW!

Orthographic Drawings

An orthographic drawing shows up to six views: front, back, right side, left side, top, and bottom.

Orthographic drawings are not limited to figures constructed from cubes. You can make an orthographic drawing of any three-dimensional figure, including one with curved surfaces.

EXAMPLE 2

Make an orthographic drawing of the figure below.

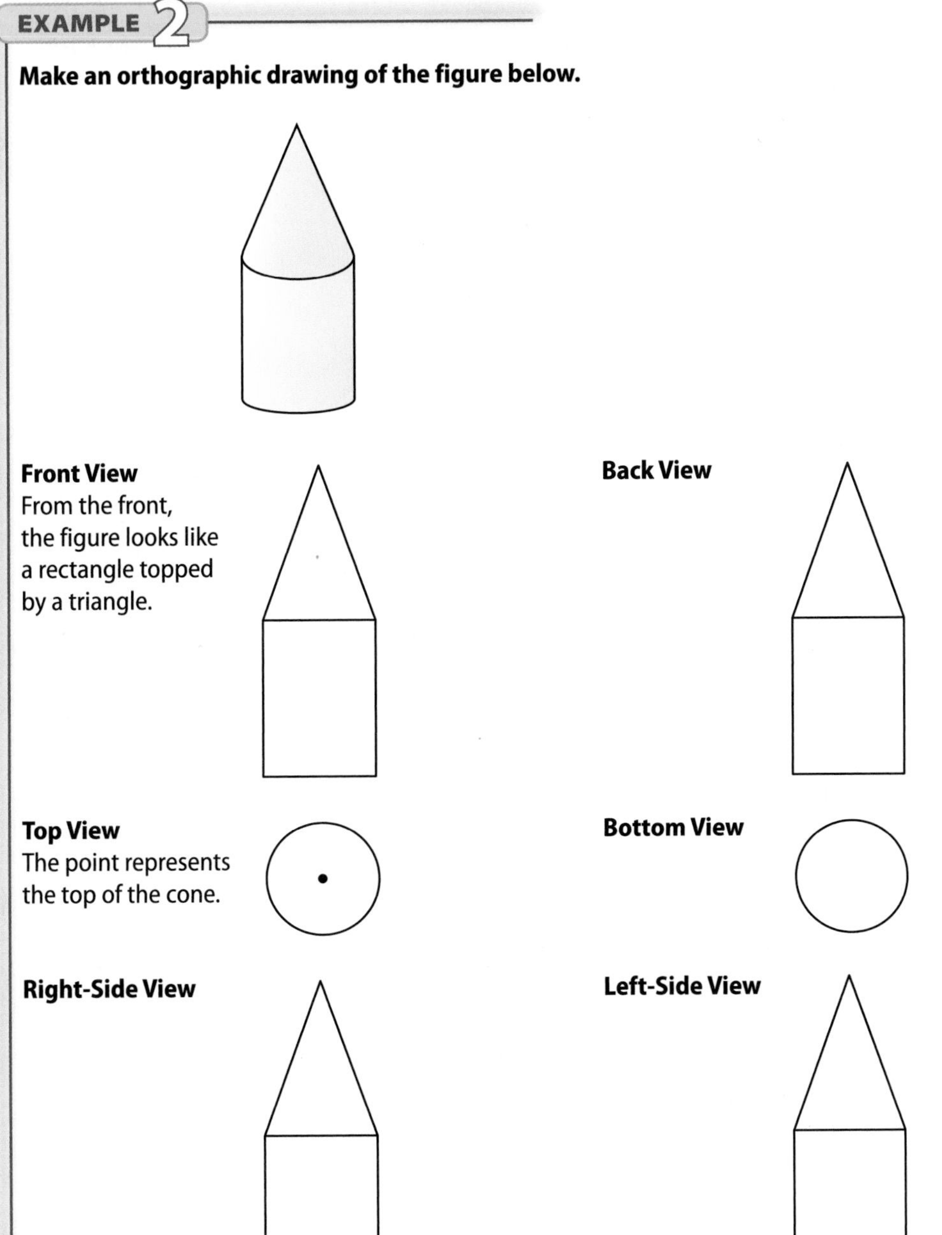

Front View
From the front, the figure looks like a rectangle topped by a triangle.

Back View

Top View
The point represents the top of the cone.

Bottom View

Right-Side View

Left-Side View

SEARCH

To see step-by-step videos of these problems, enter the page number into the SWadvantage.com Search Bar.

Watch Out!

The bottom view is not the same as the top view. Do not include a point at the center of the circle.

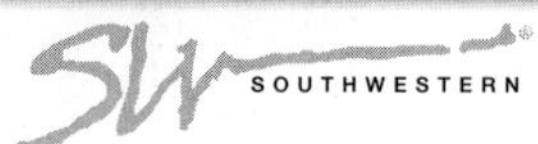

Using Orthographic Drawings

You may not need all six views of an orthographic drawing to create an isometric drawing.

EXAMPLE 3

SEARCH

To see step-by-step videos of these problems, enter the page number into the SWadvantage.com Search Bar.

Given the orthographic drawing of a figure, make an isometric drawing. Then draw the back view and the left-side view.

a.

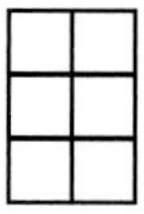

Front 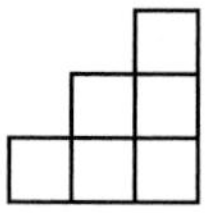 Right Side 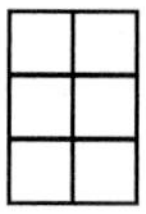 Top

Front Right

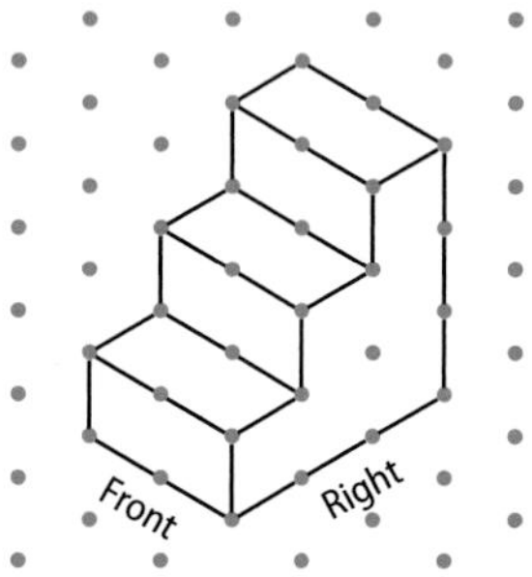

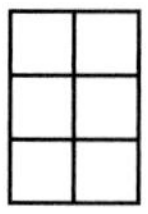

Back 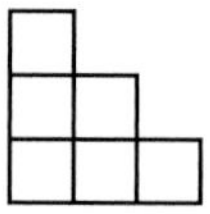 Left Side

b.

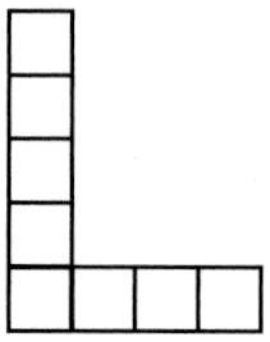

Front 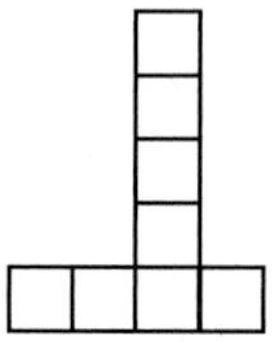 Right Side 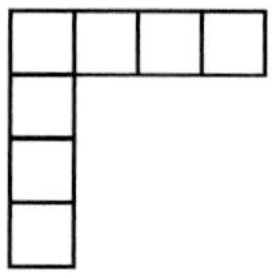 Top

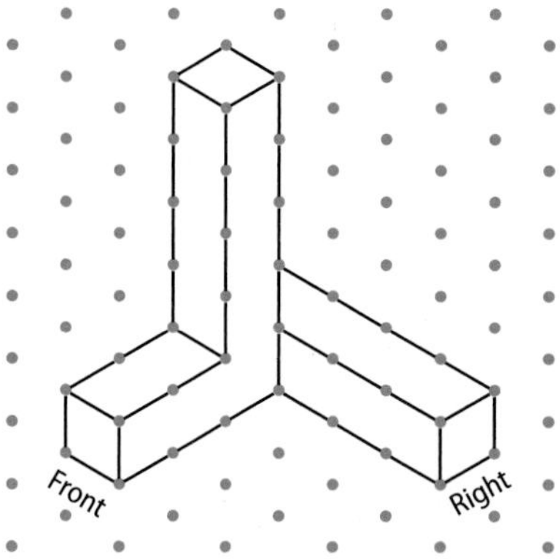

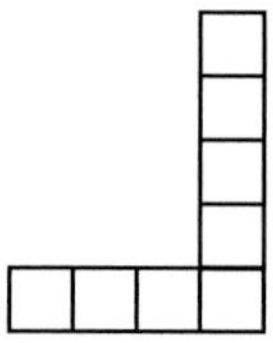

Front Right

Back 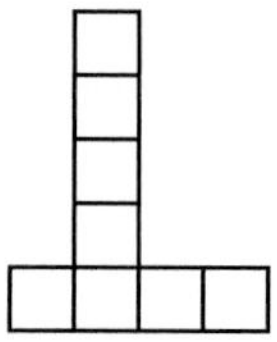 Left Side

You can use an orthographic drawing to calculate the surface area and volume of a solid.

EXAMPLE 4

Name the figure depicted in the orthographic drawing. Use the measurements given to find its surface area and volume.

Front View

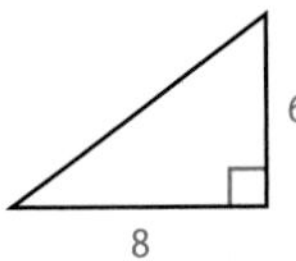

Back View

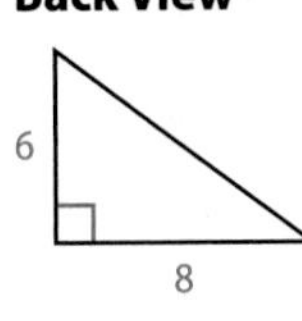

Top View

Bottom View

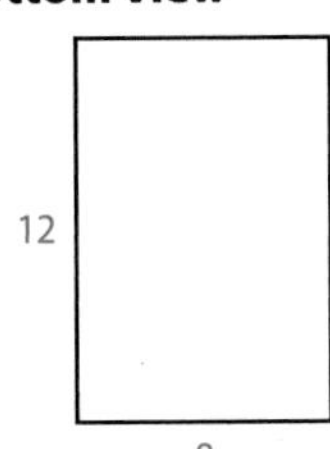

Right-Side View

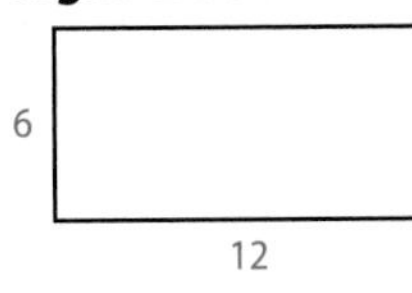

Left-Side View

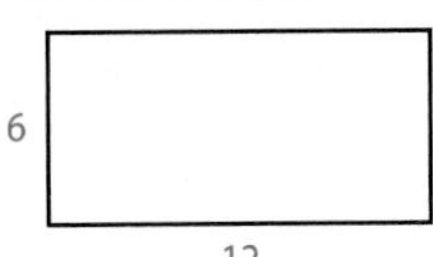

STEP 1 Sketch and identify the figure.

The figure is a right triangular prism.

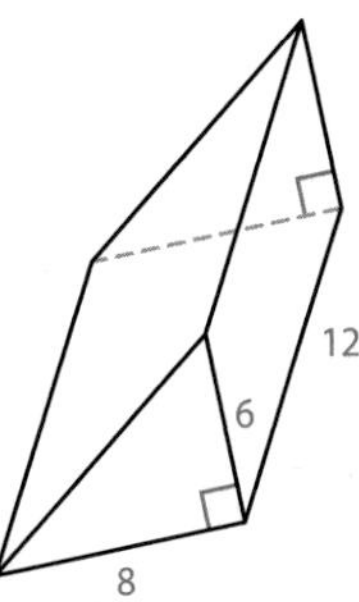

STEP 2 Find the missing dimension.

By the Pythagorean Theorem, the hypotenuse of the triangular base is 10.

STEP 3 Use the formula for surface area, $SA = ph + 2B$, where p = perimeter of a base, h = height of the prism, and B = area of a base.

$B = \frac{1}{2}(8 \cdot 6) = 24$

$SA = ph + 2B$

$SA = (6 + 8 + 10)12 + 2(24)$

$SA = (24)12 + 48$

$SA = 336$ square units

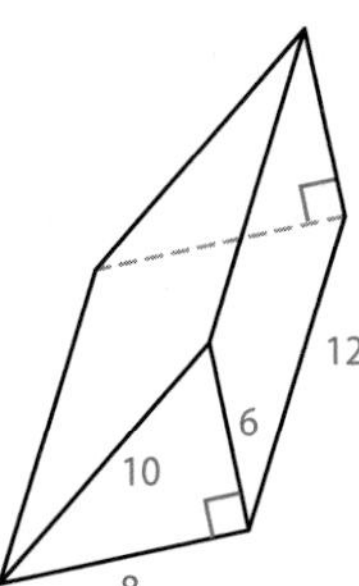

STEP 4 Use the formula for volume, $V = Bh$.

$V = 24(12)$

$V = 288$ cubic units

> **Need More HELP**
> For help with surface area, go to *Surface Area of Prisms*, p. 558.

Creating a Base Design

You can use a *base design* to represent a figure built from cubes. A **base design** shows the shape of the bottom layer of cubes. A number indicates the number of cubes stacked at each position. Another name for a base design is a *foundation drawing*.

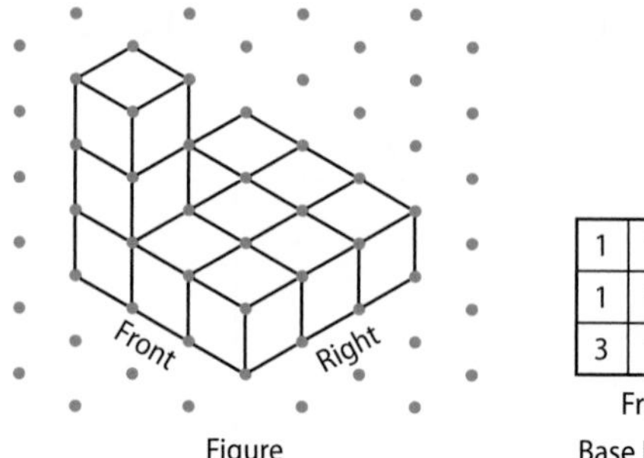

Figure

1	1	1
1	1	1
3	1	1

Front (bottom), Right (right side)

Base Design

EXAMPLE 1

Make a base design of the isometric drawing shown below.

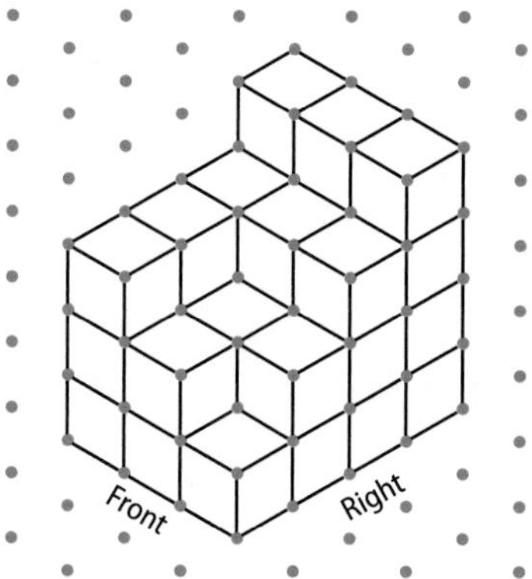

STEP 1 Determine the shape of the base of the figure. The base is a 3×4 rectangle.

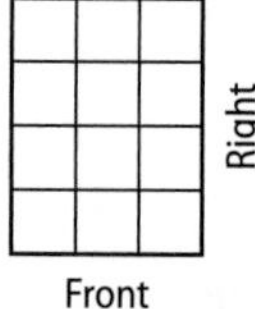

STEP 2 Determine the number of cubes in each position.

4	4	4
3	3	3
3	2	2
3	2	1

Front (bottom), Right (right side)

SEARCH

To see step-by-step videos of these problems, enter the page number into the SWadvantage.com Search Bar.

Since an isometric drawing shows only three sides of a figure, you may have to make educated guesses about the appearances of the hidden sides. Orthographic drawings help take the guesswork away.

EXAMPLE 2

Make a base design of the figure represented by the orthographic drawings below.

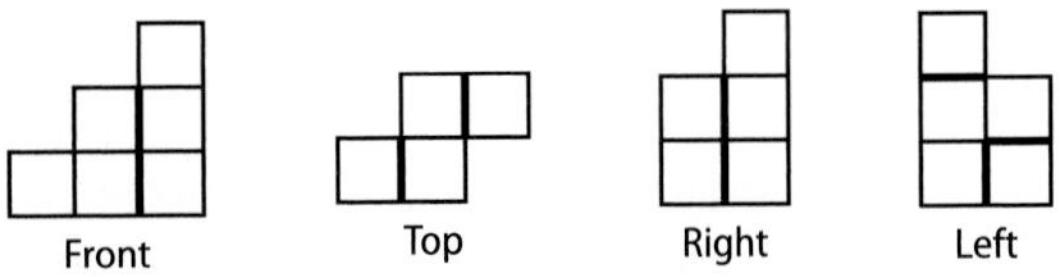

Front Top Right Left

STEP 1 Determine the shape of the base of the figure. A base design is like the floor plan of a building. The top view shows the shape of the base.

Top

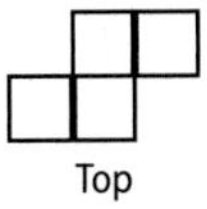

STEP 2 Determine the number of cubes in each position. Remember that bold segments in an orthographic drawing indicate a break in the surface.

Using the front and top views, you can see that there is only one cube in the first column.

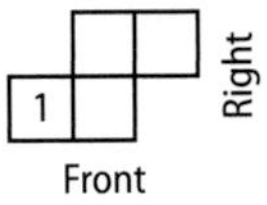

Front Right

STEP 3 The front and right-side views show that there are three cubes in the last column.

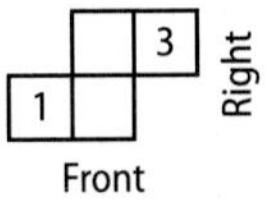

Front Right

STEP 4 The front, right-side, and left-side views show that the remaining columns consist of two cubes each.

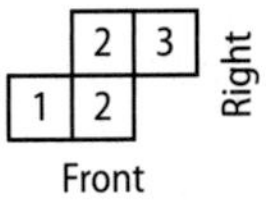

Front Right

Need More HELP

For help with orthographic views of figures built from cubes, go to *Orthographic Drawings*, p. 702.

GOT TO KNOW!

Orthographic Drawings

The top view, not the bottom view, of an orthographic drawing shows the shape of the base.

Using a Base Design

Much like the blueprint for a building, a base design can be used to build or draw a solid constructed from cubes.

Try It This Way

Use shading in your drawing to help you see which cubes are missing.

SEARCH

To see step-by-step videos of these problems, enter the page number into the SWadvantage.com Search Bar.

EXAMPLE 3

Make an isometric drawing of the figure whose base design is given.

4	3	2
3	3	1
2	1	1

Front; Right

STEP 1 Draw the first layer of cubes; these also represent the base shape. The base is a 3 × 3 square.

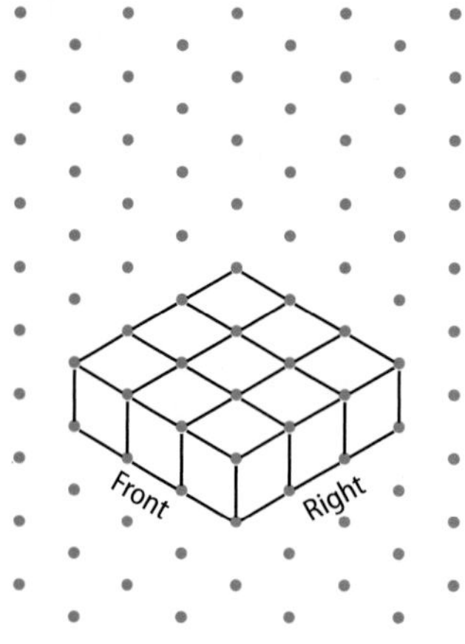
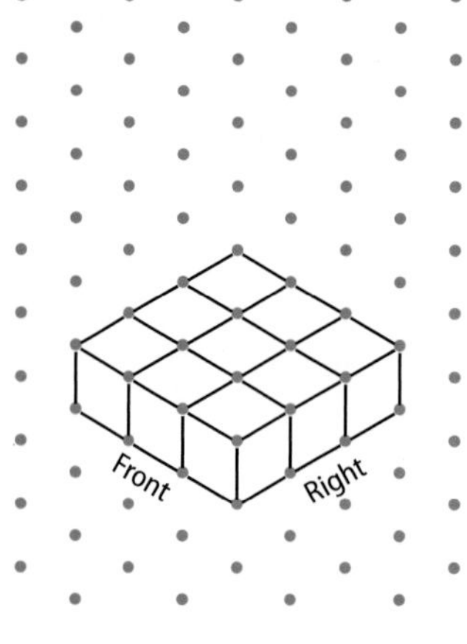

STEP 2 Draw the second layer of cubes. This corresponds to all the squares in the base drawing labeled 2, 3, and 4.

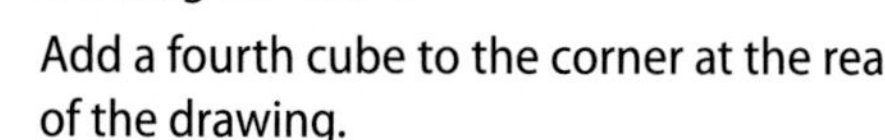

STEP 3 Draw the third layer of cubes. This corresponds to all the squares in the base drawing labeled 3 and 4.

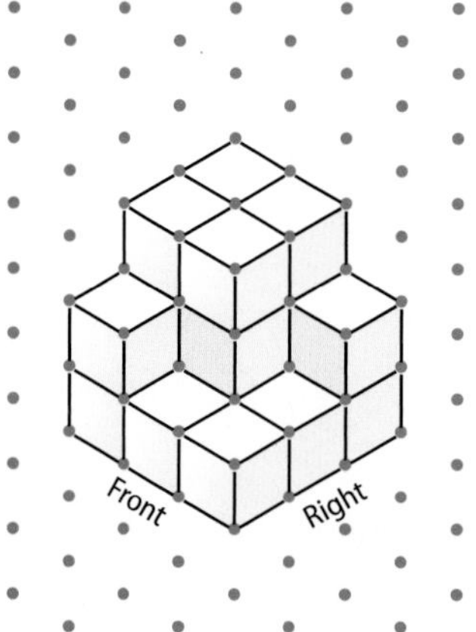

STEP 4 Draw the fourth layer of cubes. This corresponds to all the squares in the base drawing labeled 4.

Add a fourth cube to the corner at the rear of the drawing.

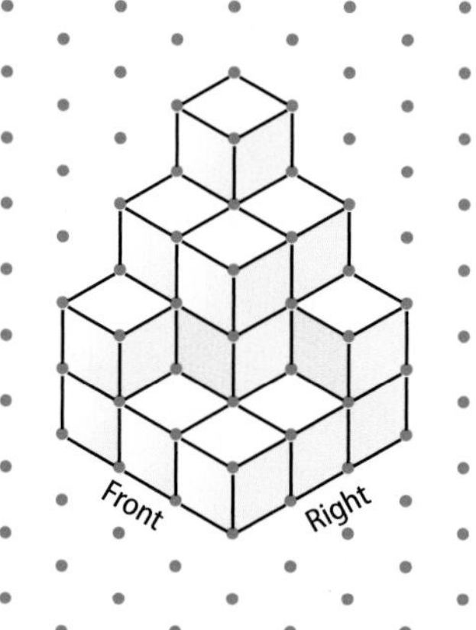

A base design provides the information you need to calculate the surface area and volume of the three-dimensional figure the design represents.

EXAMPLE 4

Calculate the surface area and volume of the solid whose base design is shown below. Each edge of each cube in the solid has a length of 1 cm.

2	3	3	2
2	3	3	2
2	2	2	2

Right

Front

The surface area is the sum of the areas of all the exposed squares. Just count the squares in each view.

STEP 1 Find the number of squares on the bottom.

The bottom is a 4 × 3 rectangle. There are 12 squares on the bottom. The surface area of the bottom is 12 cm^2.

STEP 2 Find the number of squares you can see when you look at the top.

You can see 12 squares when you look down onto the top. The surface area of the top is 12 cm^2.

STEP 3 Find the number of squares you can see when you look at the figure from the front.

From the front, you see a 4 × 2 rectangle topped by a 2 × 1 rectangle. You can see 10 squares. The surface area of the front and back is 10 cm^2 each.

STEP 4 Calculate the surface area of the right side and left side of the figure.

You see a 3 × 2 rectangle topped by a 2 × 1 rectangle. You see 8 squares. The surface area of the right and left side is 8 cm^3 each.

STEP 5 Add all the surface areas.

Total surface area = 2(12 cm^2) + 2(10 cm^2) + 2(8 cm^3)

Total surface area = 60 cm^2

STEP 6 Find the volume of the figure.

The volume of each cube is 1 cm^3. There are 12 cubes in the first layer, 12 cubes in the second layer, and 4 cubes in the third (top) layer, for a total of 28 cubes in the figure. So the volume of the figure is 28 cm^3.

The surface area of the figure is 60 cm^2. The volume of the figure is 28 cm^3.

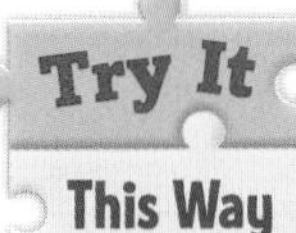

If you are having trouble visualizing the solid represented by a base design, try using blocks or cubes to build the solid.

GOT TO KNOW!

Base Design

A base design shows the base of a figure and the height of each part.

Lateral Areas of Pyramids and Cones

Pyramids

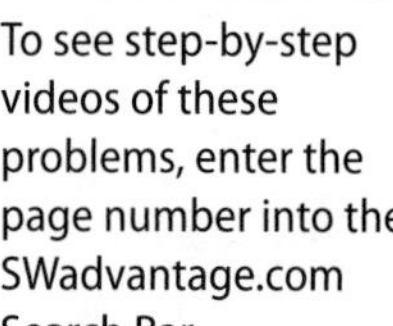

SEARCH

To see step-by-step videos of these problems, enter the page number into the SWadvantage.com Search Bar.

A **pyramid** is a solid figure with a polygonal base and triangular faces determined by edges of the base and that meet in a common point called the **vertex**. A pyramid is named by the shape of its base. For example, a pyramid with a square for its base is a square pyramid and a pyramid with a hexagon for its base is a hexagonal pyramid.

The triangular sides of a pyramid are also known as the **lateral faces** of the pyramid. The number of lateral faces is the same as the number of edges in the base.

GOT TO KNOW!

Naming a Pyramid

One way to name a pyramid identifies the vertex and then the base, separated by a hyphen. So in Example 1, the pyramid in part (a) is *A-BCD* and the pyramid in part (b) is *E-FGHJK*.

EXAMPLE 1

Identify the base and lateral faces in each pyramid.

a. Base: This figure is a triangular pyramid. Since all 4 faces are triangles, any one of them can serve as the base. If we choose the "bottom" triangle as the base, then the base of the triangular pyramid is $\triangle BCD$.

Lateral Faces: The base of this pyramid has 3 sides, so the pyramid has 3 lateral faces. They are $\triangle ABC$, $\triangle ACD$, and $\triangle ADB$.

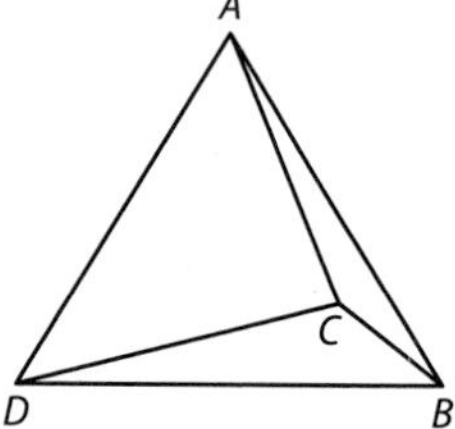

b. Base: This figure is a pentagonal pyramid. The base of the pyramid is pentagon *FGHJK*.

Lateral Faces: The base of this pyramid is a pentagon, so the pyramid has 5 lateral faces. They are $\triangle EFG$, $\triangle EGH$, $\triangle EHJ$, $\triangle EJK$, and $\triangle EKF$.

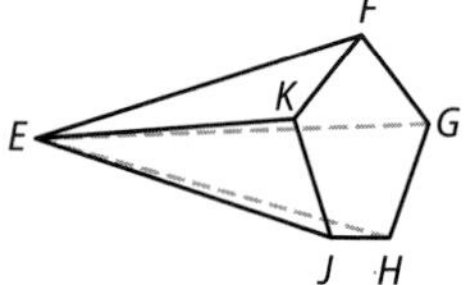

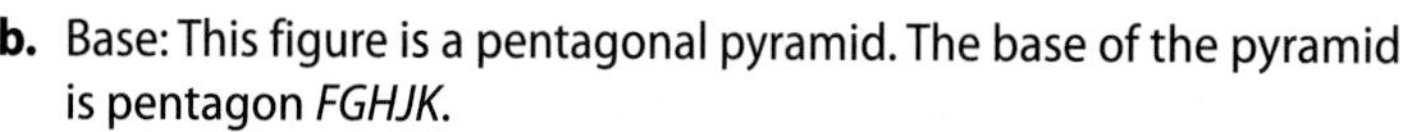

EXAMPLE 2

A pyramid has base *LMNP* and four lateral faces. Sketch the pyramid.

STEP 1 The base of the pyramid is a quadrilateral, so start by drawing quadrilateral *LMNP* to represent the base. Then draw vertex *Q*, not in the same plane as the base.

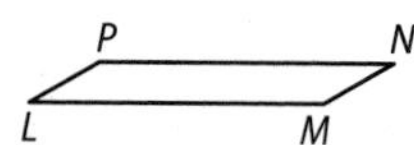

STEP 2 Draw line segments connecting vertex *Q* to vertices *L*, *M*, *N*, and *P*. Use a dashed line to indicate an edge that is hidden from view. The lateral faces of the pyramid are $\triangle QLM$, $\triangle QMN$, $\triangle QNP$, and $\triangle QPL$.

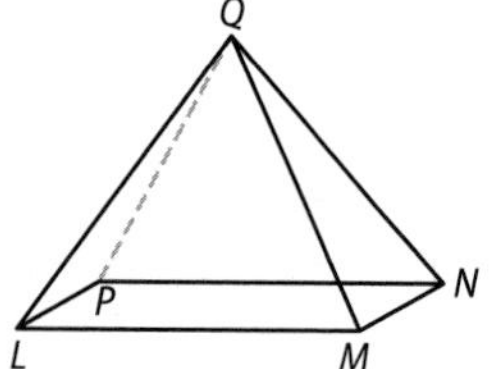

GOT TO KNOW!

Two-dimensional and Three-dimensional Figures

A pyramid is a solid, or three-dimensional, shape. The lateral faces of a pyramid are triangles, which are two-dimensional figures, and the base is a polygon, which is also a two-dimensional figure.

Lateral Area of a Pyramid

A **regular pyramid** has a regular polygon as its base and congruent isosceles triangles as the lateral faces. All the pyramids in the rest of this lesson will be regular pyramids.

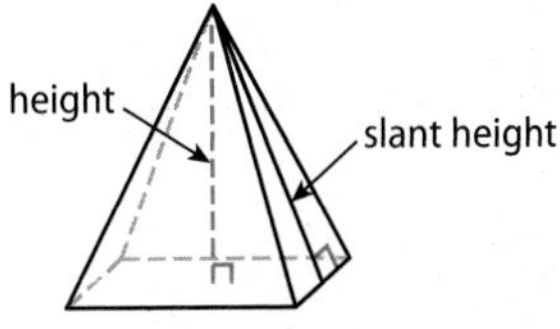

In a pyramid, it is important to distinguish between two distances. One distance, from the vertex and perpendicular to the base, is called the **height of a pyramid**. The other distance, which is the altitude, or height, of each lateral face, is called the **slant height of the pyramid**. For a regular pyramid, all of the lateral faces are congruent triangles so they have the same slant height.

Watch Out !

The slant height of a pyramid is always greater than the height of the pyramid. This is related to the fact that the hypotenuse of a right triangle has to be longer than either leg of the triangle.

EXAMPLE 3

Find the slant height of the pyramid.

Notice that the height and slant height are part of a right triangle, with the slant height of the pyramid being the hypotenuse of that right triangle. Use the Pythagorean Theorem to find the slant height.

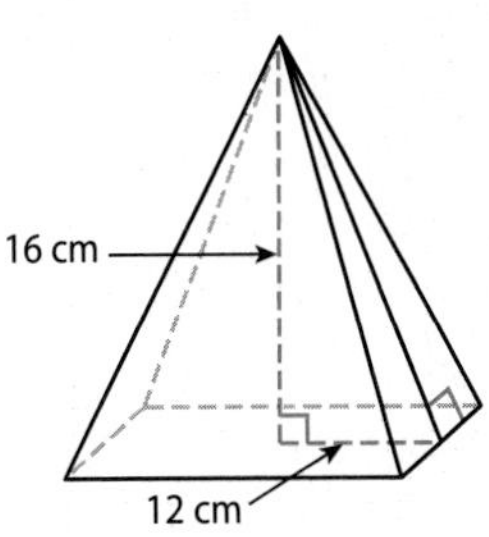

Write the formula.	$c^2 = a^2 + b^2$
Substitute values from the diagram.	$c^2 = 12^2 + 16^2$
Find the squares and add.	$c^2 = 144 + 256 = 400$
Find the square roots of both sides.	$c = 20$

The slant height is 20 cm.

Need More HELP

For help with the Pythagorean Theorem, go to *Pythagorean Theorem*, p. 678.

The **lateral area** of a pyramid is the sum of the areas of its lateral faces. For a regular pyramid, the lateral faces can be rearranged to cover half of a rectangle whose height equals the slant height of the pyramid and whose width equals the perimeter of the pyramid.

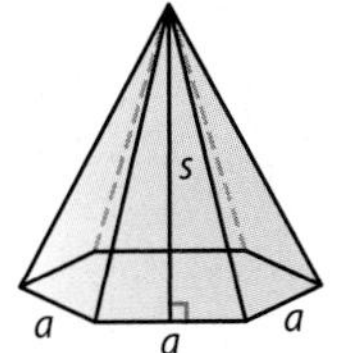

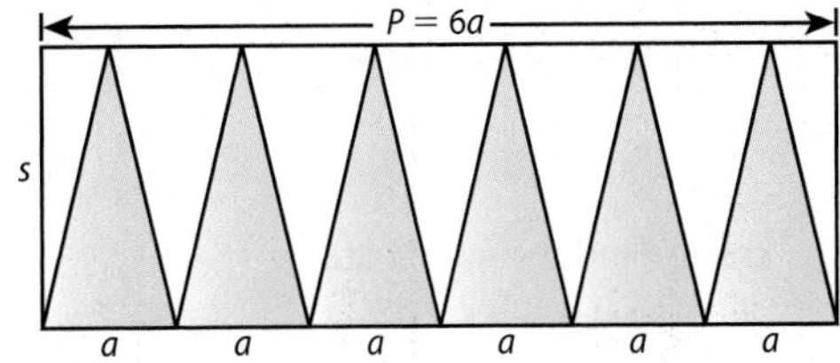

The base of the rectangle is P, the perimeter of the base of the pyramid, and the height of the rectangle is s, the slant height of the faces. So a formula for the lateral area (LA) of a pyramid is $\text{LA} = \frac{1}{2}Ps$.

Watch Out !

The formula for the area A of a triangle with base b and height h is $A = \frac{1}{2}bh$. Don't forget the factor $\frac{1}{2}$!

EXAMPLE 4

Find the lateral area of the regular octagonal pyramid.

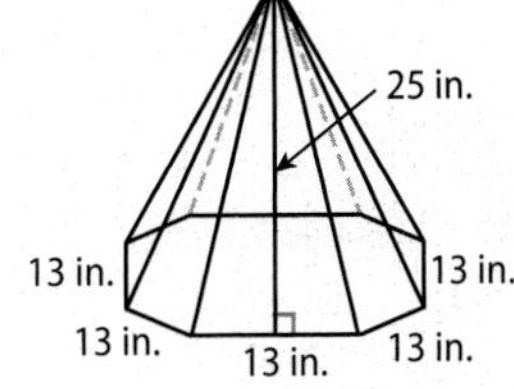

STEP 1 Find the perimeter of the base. Note that the base has 8 sides.

Write the perimeter formula.	$P = 8s$
Substitute values.	$= 8(13)$
Multiply.	$= 104$

STEP 2 Find the lateral area.

Write the formula.	$\text{LA} = \frac{1}{2}Ps$
Substitute values.	$= \frac{1}{2}(104)(25)$
Multiply.	$= 1300$

The lateral area is 1300 in.^{2}.

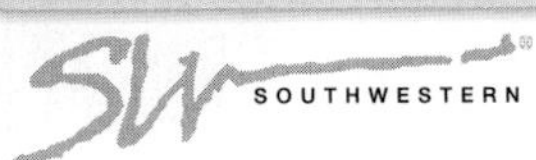

Surface Area of a Pyramid

For a three-dimensional figure, the surface area is the sum of the areas of all of its surfaces. For a pyramid, the surface area is the area of the base plus the lateral area.

EXAMPLE 5

Find the surface area of each pyramid.

a. The figure is a square pyramid.

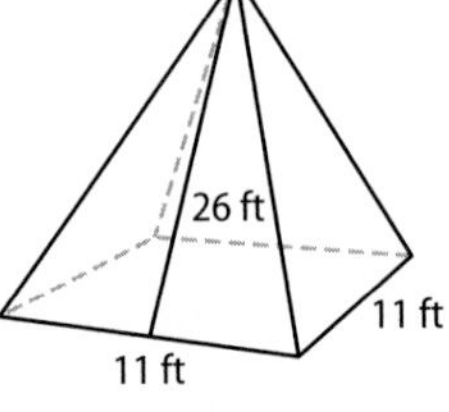

STEP 1 Find the area of the base.

Write the formula. $A = s^2$

Substitute and simplify. $= 11^2 = 121$

STEP 2 Find the lateral area.

Write the formula. $\text{LA} = \frac{1}{2}Ps$

Substitute values. $= \frac{1}{2}(4 \cdot 11)(26)$

Simplify. $= 572$

STEP 3 Add the area of the base and the lateral area.

$121 + 572 = 693$

The surface area of the pyramid is 693 ft^2.

b. The figure is an equilateral triangular pyramid.

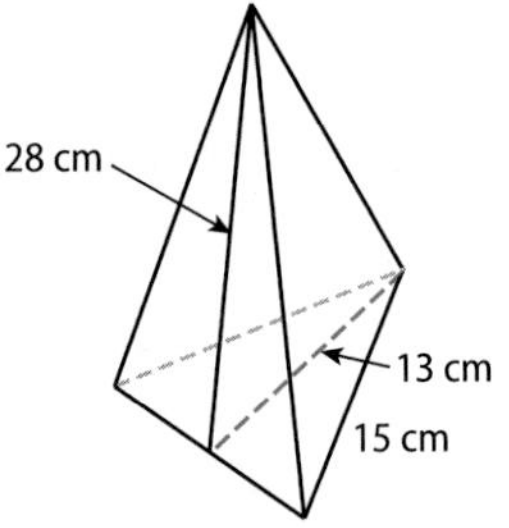

STEP 1 Find the area of the base.

Write the formula. $A = \frac{1}{2}bh$

Substitute values. $= \frac{1}{2}(15)(13) = 97.5$

STEP 2 Find the lateral area.

Write the formula. $\text{LA} = \frac{1}{2}Ps$

Substitute values. $= \frac{1}{2}(3 \cdot 15)(28)$

Simplify. $= 630$

STEP 3 Add the area of the base and the lateral area.

$97.5 + 630 = 727.5$

The surface area of the pyramid is 727.5 cm^2.

GOT TO KNOW!

How Many Bases?

A pyramid has one base. Other solid figures, such as prisms and cylinders, have two bases.

Need More HELP

For help with perimeter, go to *Perimeter* in *Measurement*, p. 524.

SEARCH

To see step-by-step videos of these problems, enter the page number into the SWadvantage.com Search Bar.

GOT TO KNOW!

Surface Area and Lateral Area

The surface area of any solid figure consists of the area of the base(s) plus the lateral area. The lateral area of any solid *does not* include the area of the base(s).

Cones

A **cone** is a three-dimensional figure with a circular base, a **vertex** not in the same plane as the base, and a curved surface determined by the base and the vertex. The curved surface of a cone is called its **lateral surface**.

The **axis of a cone** is the line segment that has one endpoint at the vertex of the cone and the other endpoint at the center of the base. A **right cone** is a cone whose axis is perpendicular to the base. An **oblique cone** is a cone whose axis is not perpendicular to the base. Any segment from the vertex to a point on the boundary of the base is called an **element** of the cone.

An element of a cone is similar to the slant height of a pyramid. Both segments represent the shortest distance from the vertex to the base.

EXAMPLE 6

Determine whether each cone is a right cone or an oblique cone.

To determine whether a cone is right or oblique, form a triangle using a radius of the base, the axis of the cone, and an element of the cone. Then use the Converse of the Pythagorean Theorem to decide if that triangle is a right triangle.

a. Use the cone at the right.

37 ft, 35 ft, 24 ft

STEP 1 Find the radius of the base.

Write the formula. $r = \frac{d}{2}$

Substitute values. $= \frac{24}{2} = 12$

STEP 2 Use the Converse of the Pythagorean Theorem.

Write the formula. $a^2 + b^2 = c^2$

Substitute values. $12^2 + 35^2 \stackrel{?}{=} 37^2$

Find the squares. $144 + 1225 \stackrel{?}{=} 1369$

Add. $1369 = 1369$

The triangle is a right triangle, so the cone is a right cone.

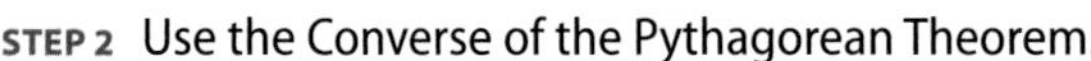

b. Use the cone at the right.

29 m, 21 m, $C = 78.5$ m

STEP 1 Find the radius of the base. Use 3.14 for π.

Write the formula. $r = \frac{C}{2\pi}$

Substitute values. $\approx \frac{78.5}{2(3.14)}$

Simplify. $= 12.5$

STEP 2 Use the Converse of the Pythagorean Theorem.

Write the formula. $a^2 + b^2 = c^2$

Substitute values. $12.5^2 + 21^2 \stackrel{?}{=} 29^2$

Find the squares. $156.25 + 441 \stackrel{?}{=} 841$

Add. $597.25 \neq 841$

The triangle is not a right triangle, so the cone is an oblique cone.

GOT TO KNOW!

Pythagorean Theorem

When you use the Pythagorean Theorem, you start with the fact that $a^2 + b^2 = c^2$ and you find one of the missing values a, b, or c.

Converse of the Pythagorean Theorem

The Converse of the Pythagorean Theorem states that if the lengths of the sides of a triangle satisfy the equation $a^2 + b^2 = c^2$, then the triangle is a right triangle.

Lateral Area of a Cone

As with pyramids, it is important to make a distinction between the *height of a cone* and the *slant height of a cone*. The **height of a cone** is the perpendicular distance from the vertex to the plane containing the base. For a right cone, the height of the cone is equal to the length of the axis. The **slant height of a right cone** is the length of an element of the cone.

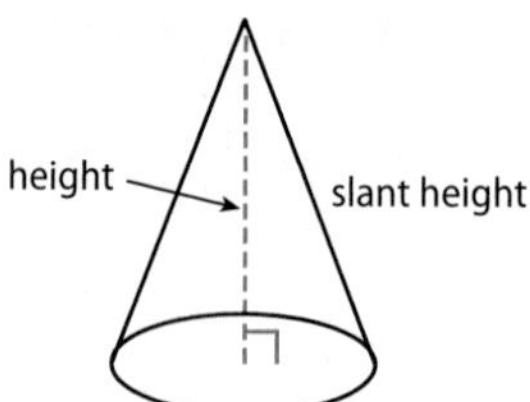

Need More HELP

For help with sectors of a circle, go to *Arcs and Sectors*, p. 728.

The **lateral area of a cone** is the area of its curved surface. To derive a formula for the lateral area of a cone, start by looking at a right cone and its net.

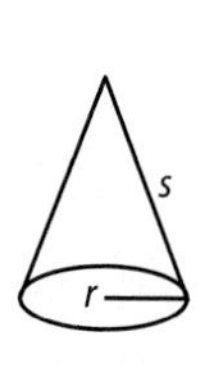

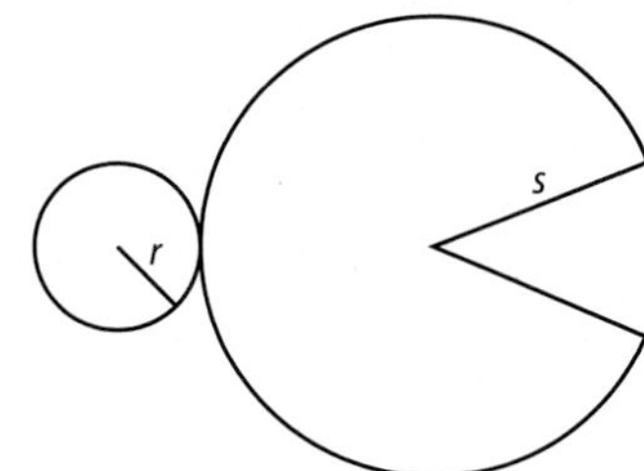

Consider the lateral surface of the cone as it appears in the net above. It is part of a circle, and the radius of that circle is s, the slant height of the cone. The circumference of the partial circle is $2\pi r$ because that is the circumference of the base of the cone.

Watch Out!

A key step in deriving a formula for the lateral area of a cone uses the fact that if you remove a pie-shaped sector of a circle, you take away a proportional part of the area of that circle.

The lateral area of the cone is the same as the area of the partial circle, and that area is a fraction of the area of the circle whose radius is s. That fraction is the ratio $\frac{2\pi r}{2\pi s}$, which simplifies to $\frac{r}{s}$. So:

$$\text{LA} = \frac{r}{s} \times (\text{area of circle with radius } s) = \frac{r}{s} \times (\pi s^2) = \pi rs$$

Therefore, if a cone has a base with radius r and slant height s, a formula for the lateral area of the cone is $\text{LA} = \pi rs$. The total surface area of a cone is the lateral area plus the area of its circular base, so a formula for the total surface area (SA) of a cone is

$$\text{SA} = \pi r^2 + \pi rs$$

SEARCH

To see step-by-step videos of these problems, enter the page number into the SWadvantage.com Search Bar.

EXAMPLE 7

Find the lateral area of the cone. Use 3.14 for π.

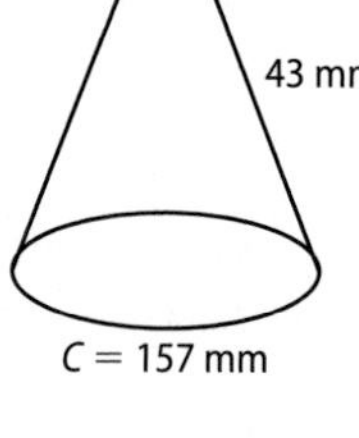

STEP 1 Find the radius of the base.

Write the formula. $r = \frac{C}{2\pi}$

Substitute values and simplify. $\approx \frac{157}{2(3.14)} = \frac{157}{6.28} = 25$

STEP 2 Find the lateral area.

Write the formula. $\text{LA} = \pi rs$

Substitute values from the figure. $\approx (3.14)(25)(43)$

Multiply. $= 3375.5$

The lateral area of the cone is about 3375.5 mm^2.

Surface Area of a Cone

The previous page shows a formula for the surface area (SA) of a cone whose base has radius r and whose slant height is s. That formula is $SA = \pi r^2 + \pi rs$.

EXAMPLE 8

Find the total surface area of each cone. Use 3.14 for π.

a. Use the cone at the right.

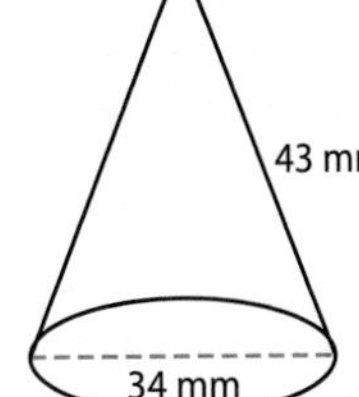

STEP 1 Find the radius.

Write the formula. $r = \frac{d}{2}$

Substitute and simplify. $= \frac{34}{2} = 17$

STEP 2 Find the area of the base.

Write the formula. $A = \pi r^2$
Substitute values. $\approx (3.14)(17^2)$
Simplify. $\approx (3.14)(289)$
$= 907.46$

STEP 3 Find the lateral area.

Write the formula. $LA = \pi rs$
Substitute values. $\approx (3.14)(17)(43)$
Multiply. $= 2295.34$

STEP 4 Add the area of the base and the lateral area.
$907.46 + 2295.34 = 3202.8$

The total surface area of the cone is about 3202.8 mm^2.

b. Use the cone at the right.

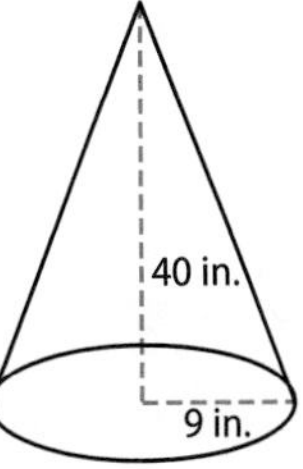

STEP 1 Use the Pythagorean Theorem to find the slant height of the cone.

Write the formula. $a^2 + b^2 = c^2$
Substitute values. $9^2 + 40^2 = c^2$
Find the squares. $81 + 1600 = c^2$
Add. $1681 = c^2$
Find the square roots of both sides. $41 = c$

STEP 2 Find the area of the base.

Write the formula. $A = \pi r^2$
Substitute values. $\approx (3.14)(9^2)$
Simplify. $\approx (3.14)(81) = 254.34$

STEP 3 Find the lateral area.

Write the formula. $LA = \pi rs$
Substitute values. $\approx (3.14)(9)(41)$
Multiply. $= 1158.66$

STEP 4 Add the area of the base and the lateral area.
$254.34 + 1158.66 = 1413$

The total surface area of the cone is about 1413 in.^{2}.

GOT TO KNOW!

Surface Area Formula

In the formula $SA = \pi r^2 + \pi rs$, the term πr^2 is used to calculate the area of the base of the cone. The term πrs is used to calculate the lateral area of the cone.

GOT TO KNOW!

Pyramid and Cone Formulas

For a **regular pyramid** whose base has perimeter P and whose slant height is s,

$LA = \frac{1}{2}Ps$

For a **cone** whose base has radius r and whose slant height is s,

$LA = \pi rs$
$SA = \pi r^2 + \pi rs$

Solids of Revolution

Creating Solids of Revolution

If a figure is revolved about a line, the resulting shape is a **solid of revolution**. The line about which it revolves is the **axis of revolution**. Solids of revolution are figures with curved surfaces, such as cylinders and cones.

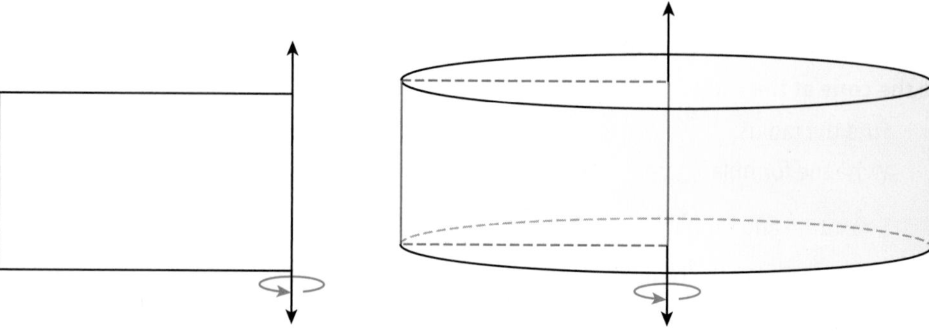

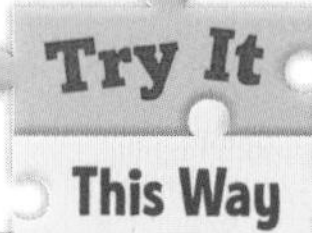

If you are having difficulty visualizing the solid of revolution formed by rotating a two-dimensional figure, try using a physical object with the same general shape. For example, hold a straw at one end, and rotate it around another straw.

EXAMPLE 1

Draw the solid of revolution that results from rotating a line segment as shown.

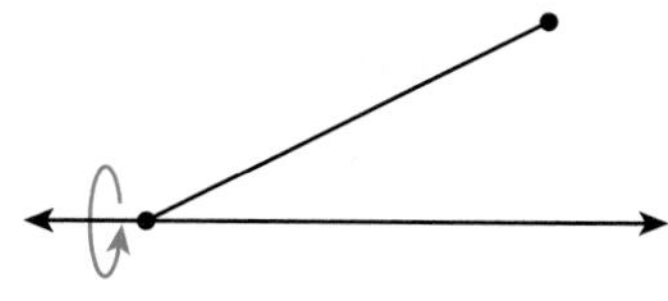

Draw the rotation around the horizontal line.

The vertex at the origin does not move. To picture the rotation of the circle, think of the line spinning, with the point at the origin staying in place. The figure becomes a cone.

Draw a cone with base radius equal to the distance from the end of the segment to the horizontal line.

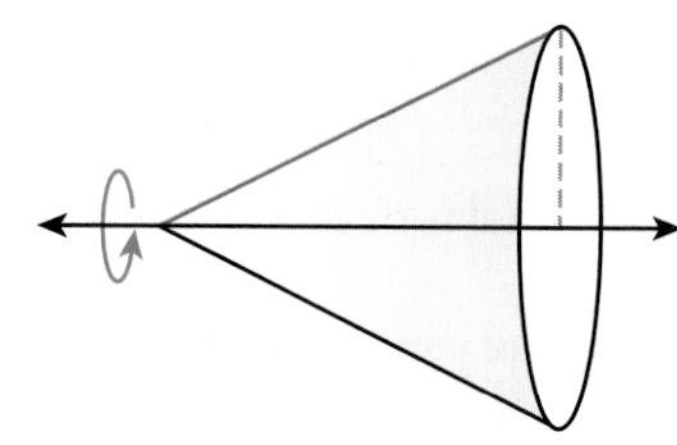

EXAMPLE 2

Draw the solid of revolution that results from rotating a circle around its diameter.

STEP 1 Draw the two-dimensional figure described in the direction. There are no directions of the size of the circle, so draw a circle of any size.

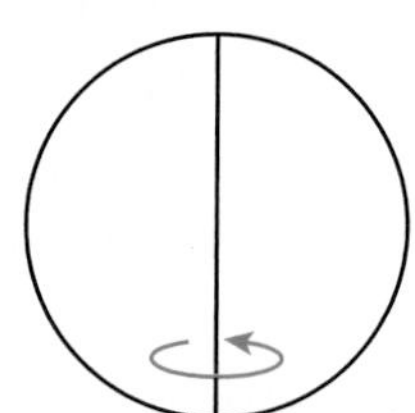

STEP 2 Draw the rotation around the diameter.

To picture the rotation of the circle, think of a coin spinning on its edge. The coin appears to be a solid sphere. So, draw a sphere with the same diameter as the circle from Step 1.

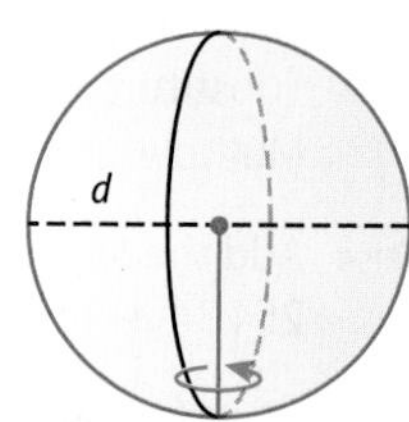

The solid of revolution is a sphere with the same diameter as the circle that formed it.

Solids of revolution have surface area and volume, just like any other three-dimensional figure. Dimensions of the solids can be obtained from information given in the two-dimensional figures forming the solids.

EXAMPLE 3

Rotating a diamond across a line forms two congruent cones. Find the volume of the solid of revolution to the right.

Use the volume formula for a cone.

Multiply by 2 for the two cones. $V = 2 \cdot \frac{1}{3}\pi r^2 h$

Substitute values from the figure. $\approx 2 \cdot \frac{1}{3}(3.14)(4^2)(9)$

Simplify. $\approx 2 \cdot \frac{1}{3}(3.14)(16)(9)$

≈ 301.44

The volume is approximately 301.44 in.^{3}.

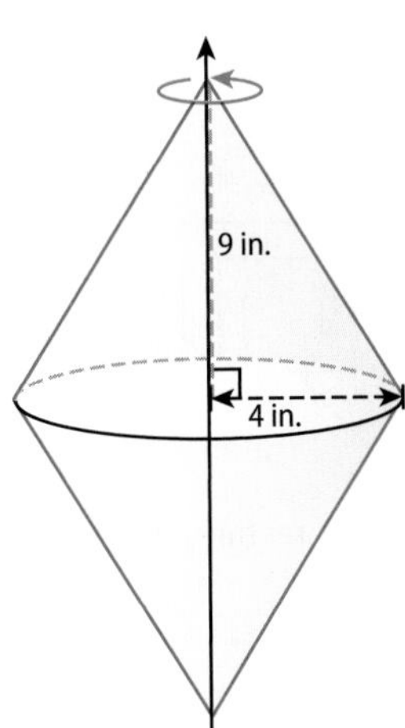

Need More HELP

For help with volumes of cylinders and cones, see *Volumes of Prisms and Cylinders* and *Volumes of Pyramids and Cones* in *Measurement* (pp. 570, 574).

EXAMPLE 4

Find the volume of the solid of revolution formed by rotating the figure as indicated. Use 3.14 for π.

12 cm

8 cm

STEP 1 Draw the solid of revolution.

The solid of revolution looks like a cylinder with height equal to the length of the long leg of the triangle and radius equal to the length of the short leg.

Missing from the cylinder is an inverted cone with the same height and radius as the cylinder.

STEP 2 Find the volume of the cylinder.

Write the formula. $V = \pi r^2 h$

Substitute values from the figure. $\approx (3.14)(8^2)(12)$

Find the square. $\approx (3.14)(64)(12)$

Multiply. ≈ 2411.52

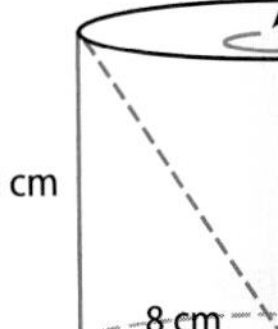
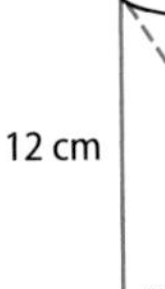

STEP 3 Find the volume of the cone.

Write the formula. $V = \frac{1}{3}\pi r^2 h$

Substitute values from the figure. $\approx \frac{1}{3}(3.14)(8^2)(12)$

Find the square. $\approx \frac{1}{3}(3.14)(64)(12)$

Multiply. ≈ 803.84

STEP 4 Subtract the volumes.

$$2411.52 - 803.84 = 1607.68$$

The volume of the solid of revolution is approximately 1607.68 cm^3.

SEARCH

To see step-by-step videos of these problems, enter the page number into the SWadvantage.com Search Bar.

Cross Sections

Describing Cross Sections

Imagine a pre-packaged loaf of bread that you might buy at the grocery store. As a whole, the loaf is a rectangular prism. Each slice of bread, though, is basically a square.

As with a loaf of bread, we can look at "slices," or *cross sections,* of solid figures. A **cross section** is the intersection of a three-dimensional figure and a plane. Since planes are two-dimensional, cross sections are two-dimensional figures.

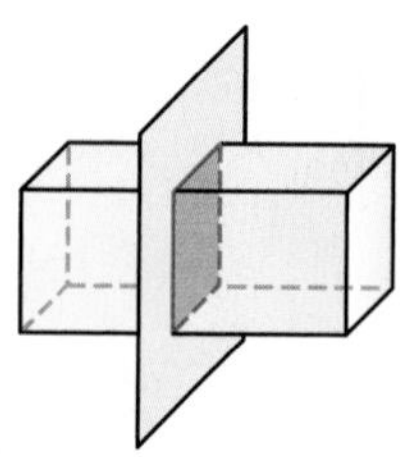

plane intersecting a rectangular prism

square cross section

Watch Out !

The loaf of bread can also be called a "square prism," because the two bases are squares.

One caution, though, is that sometimes a *square prism* refers to a cube, because all six faces are squares.

If you see the term *square prism,* be sure to check the dimensions to determine how many faces are squares.

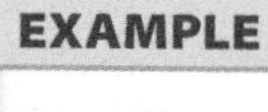

EXAMPLE 1

Describe each cross section.

a.

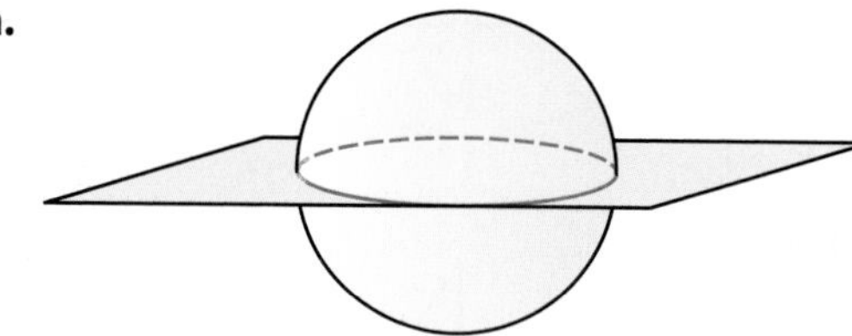

The cross section is a circle.

b.

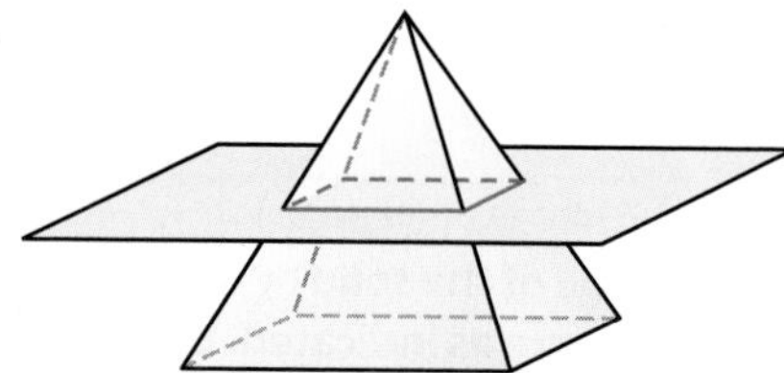

The cross section is a rectangle.

EXAMPLE 2

Describe how to cut a cylinder to make each cross section. Draw the figure.

a. circle

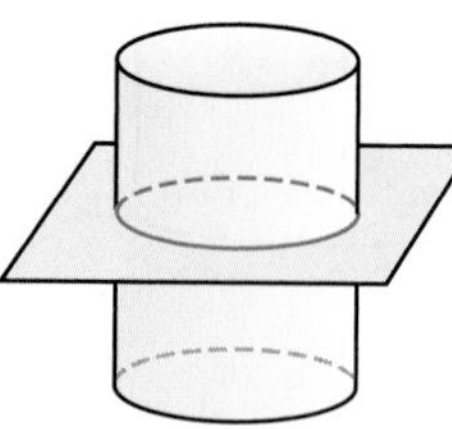

Cut parallel to bases.

b. rectangle

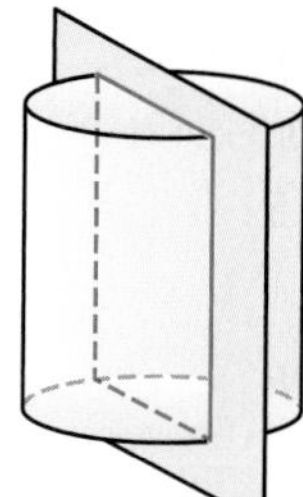

Cut perpendicular to bases.

c. ellipse

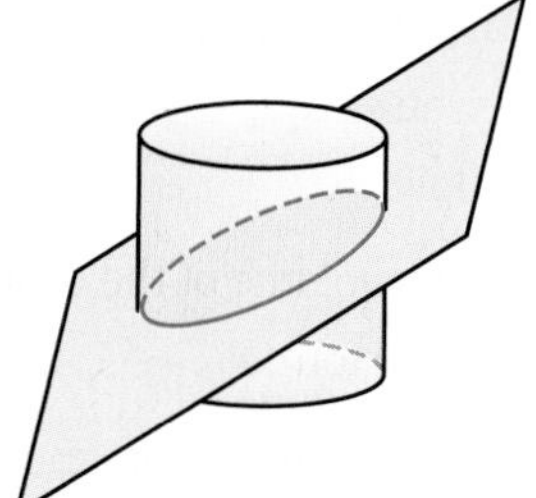

Cut diagonally without cutting the bases.

GOT TO KNOW!

Multiple Cross Sections

Since there are an infinite number of planes that can intersect a three-dimensional figure, each solid figure has an infinite number of possible cross sections.

EXAMPLE 3

Name the two-dimensional figure. Describe and draw two solids that can have this figure as a cross section.

The figure is an acute triangle. It can be a cross section of a triangular pyramid or of a cone.

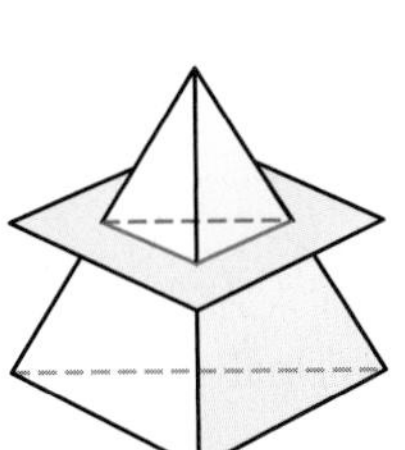

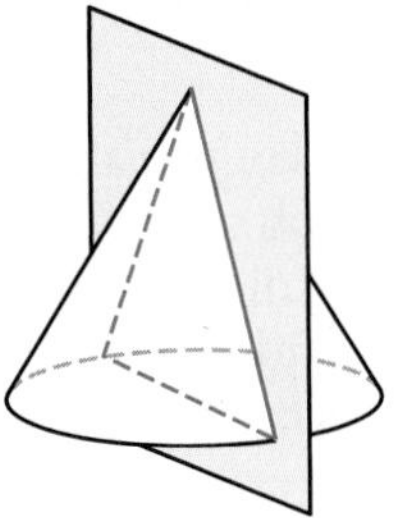

Watch Out !

A triangular prism can also have a triangle as a cross section. For prisms and pyramids, pay close attention to the shape of the base as it will affect the shape of the cross section.

Perimeter and Area of Cross Sections

Cross sections are two-dimensional figures. You can find the perimeter and area of a cross section.

EXAMPLE 4

Find the perimeter and area of the cross section.

The figure is a square prism, and the cross section is a rectangle.

STEP 1 Find the length of the rectangular cross section.

The short edge of the prism, the long edge of the prism, and the long side of the cross section form a right triangle. Use the Pythagorean Theorem to find the length.

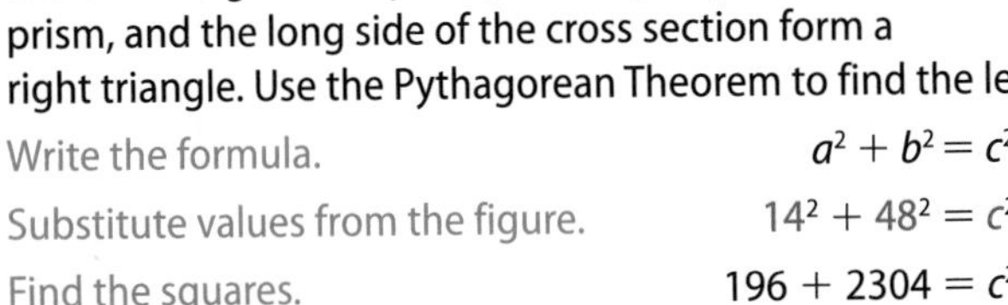

Write the formula.	$a^2 + b^2 = c^2$
Substitute values from the figure.	$14^2 + 48^2 = c^2$
Find the squares.	$196 + 2304 = c^2$
Add.	$2500 = c^2$
Find the square roots of both sides.	$50 = c$

STEP 2 Find the perimeter of the cross section.

Write the formula.	$P = 2\ell + 2w$
Substitute 50 for ℓ and 14 for w.	$= 2(50) + 2(14)$
Multiply.	$= 100 + 28$
Add.	$= 128$

STEP 3 Find the area of the cross section.

Write the formula.	$A = \ell w$
Substitute 50 for ℓ and 14 for w.	$= (50)(14)$
Multiply.	$= 700$

The perimeter of the cross section is 128 in. The area of the cross section is 700 in.^{2}.

To see step-by-step videos of these problems, enter the page number into the SWadvantage.com Search Bar.

Need More HELP

For help with perimeter and area of rectangles, see *Perimeter* and *Areas of Rectangles and Parallelograms* in *Measurement* (pp. 524, 530).

Locus

A Locus in a Plane

The word *locus*, a Latin term, means "location." In mathematics, *locus* has a similar meaning: a **locus** is the set of all points that satisfy a given condition. In other words, a locus is all the points whose locations can be determined using some description, rule, or formula.

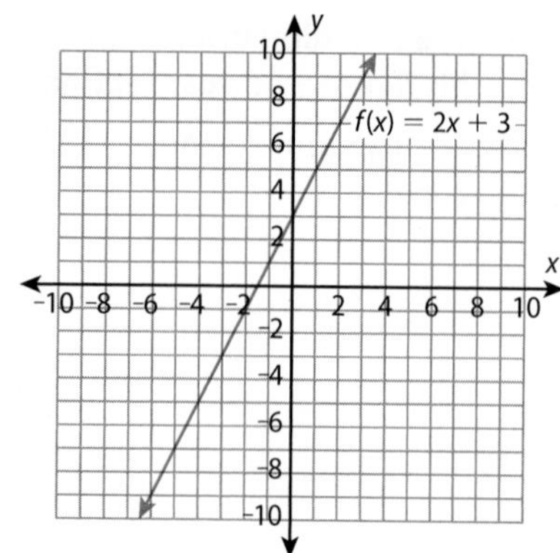

A point, line, or curve on a coordinate graph is a locus. For example, the graph on the right shows the locus of points in a two-dimensional coordinate system that satisfy the condition $y = 2x + 3$. In geometry, a locus of points can form two-dimensional or three-dimensional figures.

EXAMPLE 1

Draw the locus of points that satisfy each condition. Then identify the figure.

a. The locus of points in a plane that are equidistant from the endpoints of $\overline{AB}$

STEP 1 Draw the figure that is given in the condition. Besides the locus, the figure identified in the condition is $\overline{AB}$. Draw and label $\overline{AB}$.

STEP 2 Draw several points that satisfy the given condition, and look for a pattern in the points. The most obvious point that is equidistant from *A* and *B* is the midpoint of the segment. Also, draw a series of isosceles triangles that all have $\overline{AB}$ as their base. The third vertex of each of these triangles is equidistant from *A* and *B*.

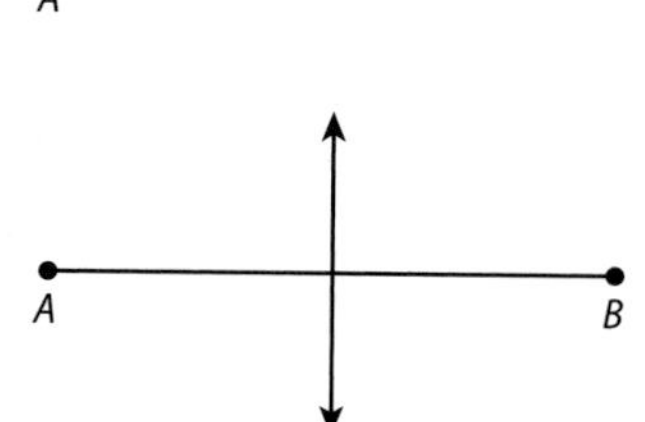

STEP 3 Once the pattern is apparent, connect the points. The points determine a straight line.

The locus of points is the perpendicular bisector of $\overline{AB}$.

Need More HELP

Remember, *equidistant* means "the same distance."

b. The locus of points in a plane that are equidistant from the rays that form ∠*DEF*

STEP 1 Draw any figures that are given in the condition, so draw ∠*DEF*.

STEP 2 Draw several points that satisfy the given condition. To find the distance between each point and the rays, draw segments from the points that are perpendicular to the rays. The pattern is that all the points are on a ray that bisects the angle.

The locus of points is the angle bisector of ∠*DEF*.

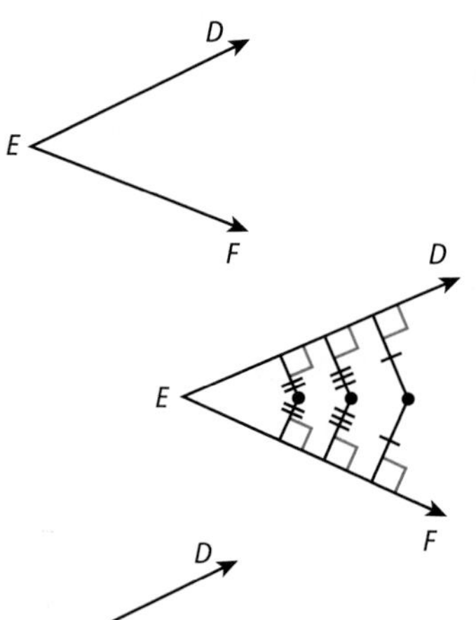

Locus of Points

A *locus of points* consists of all the points, and *only* those points, that satisfy a condition.

EXAMPLE 2

Give the condition that would result in each locus of points.

a.

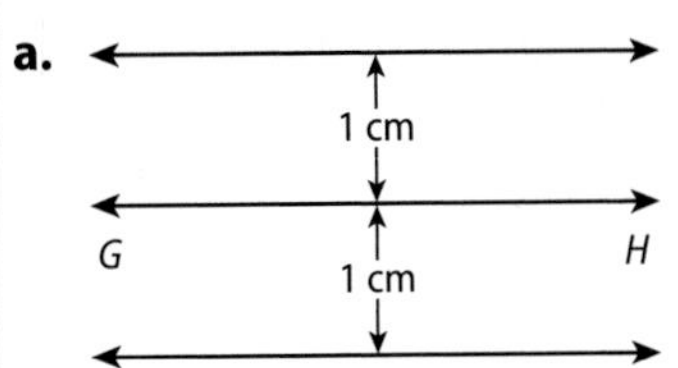

The figure shows $\overleftrightarrow{GH}$ with parallel lines 1 cm above it and 1 cm below it. The locus of points is all points in a plane that are 1 cm away from $\overleftrightarrow{GH}$.

b.

1 in.
J

The figure shows a circle with center *J* and radius 1 in. The locus is all points in a plane that are 1 in. from point *J*.

So far, you have seen loci (the plural of *locus*) that consist of infinite numbers of points. It is possible for a locus to consist of only a few points. One way to achieve this is to describe a *compound locus*. A **compound locus** is the set of all points that satisfy several conditions. Compound loci use the terms "and" or "and also" to separate the conditions.

EXAMPLE 3

Points *K* and *L* are 6 cm apart. Draw the compound locus that shows all points in a plane that are equidistant from *K* and *L* and also 4 cm from *K*.

STEP 1 Draw any figures that are given in the condition.
The only given figures are points *K* and *L*, 6 cm apart.

K L

STEP 2 Draw the locus of points that satisfy the first condition.
From Example 1, you know that the locus of points in a plane that are equidistant from two points is a perpendicular bisector. Use an orange dashed line to show this locus.

K L

STEP 3 Draw the locus of points that satisfy the second condition.
From Example 2, you know that the locus of points in a plane that are the same distance from a given point is a circle. Use a purple dashed line to draw a circle with center *K* and radius 4 cm.

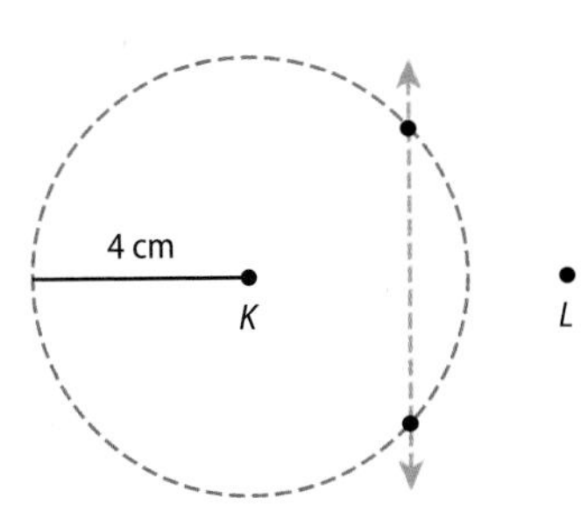

The locus consists of the two points where the circle and the perpendicular bisector intersect.

SEARCH

To see step-by-step videos of these problems, enter the page number into the SWadvantage.com Search Bar.

Watch Out!

Does the circle intersect the perpendicular bisector? The distance from *K* to the perpendicular bisector is half of 6 cm and the radius of circle *K* is 4 cm. So yes, the circle and the perpendicular bisector do intersect.

GOT TO KNOW!

Compound Loci

A compound locus can have more than two conditions. To find a compound locus, consider the conditions one at a time and sketch the points that satisfy that locus. Then find the points common to all the loci.

A Locus in Space

In geometry, *space* is not the "final frontier." Rather, **space** is the set of all points.

Just as in a plane, a locus in space is the set of all points that satisfy a given condition or set of conditions. The only difference in finding a locus in space is that we now have a third dimension to consider. A locus in space can be either a two- or three-dimensional figure.

Need More HELP

For help with points, lines, and planes, see *Points and Lines in a Plane* in *Foundations of Mathematics,* p. 128.

EXAMPLE 4

Draw the locus of points that satisfy each condition. Then identify the figure.

a. Square *MNOP* and its interior are shown at the right. (They are drawn in perspective.) Draw the locus of all points that are 15 mm above *MNOP* or its interior.

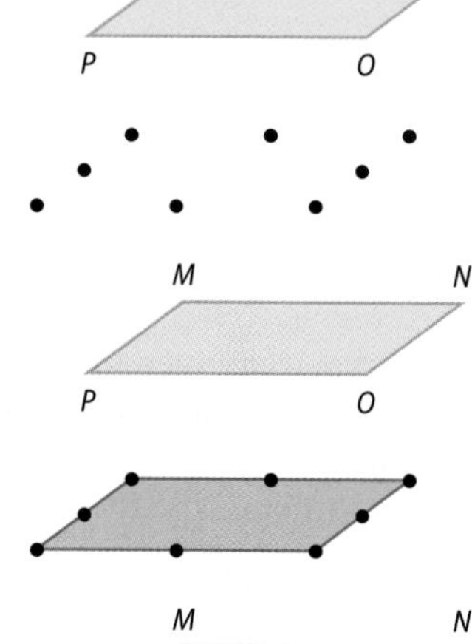

STEP 1 Draw several points that satisfy the given condition, and look for a pattern.

Draw a point 15 mm above each vertex of square *MNOP* and also 15 mm above the midpoint of each segment.

STEP 2 Once the pattern is apparent, connect the points and fill in the interior.

The points form another square and its interior, also shown in perspective.

The locus of points is a square and its interior. The square is congruent to *MNOP* and is 15 mm above it.

b. Draw the locus of points in space satisfying the conditions that each point is on a line segment parallel to a given segment $\overline{QR}$, congruent to $\overline{QR}$, and 1 in. away from $\overline{QR}$.

STEP 1 Start with $\overline{QR}$.

Q R

STEP 2 Draw several points that satisfy the given conditions. Notice that the endpoints of all the satisfying segments lie on a circle around point *Q*, or on a circle around point *R*. Those circles are parallel to each other and both circles are perpendicular to the plane of the page.

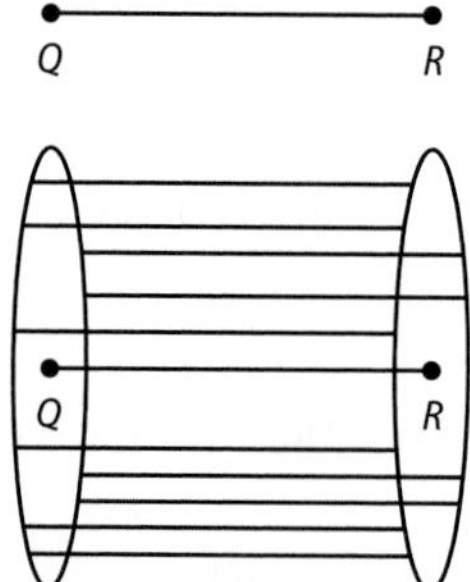

STEP 3 The locus forms a curved surface around $\overline{QR}$.

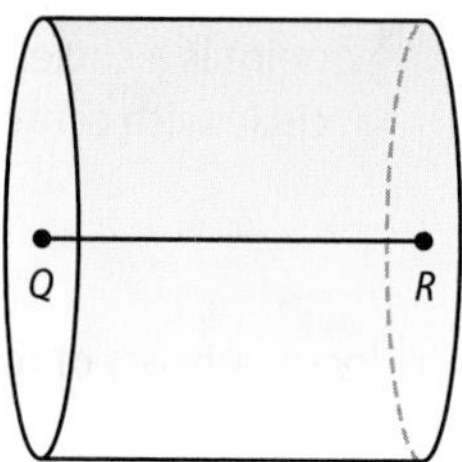

The locus of points is the lateral surface of a cylinder with radius 1 in.

The original figure is usually *not* a part of a locus. Of course, if the locus intersects the original figure, then part(s) of the original figure will be part of the locus.

In every description of a locus, an important distinction is whether the locus consists of points in a plane or points in space.

EXAMPLE 5

Draw each locus of points in a plane and in space. Describe each figure.

a. The locus of points that are $\frac{1}{2}$ in. from a given point

STEP 1 Draw any figures that are given in the condition. The only given figure is a point. Start with two points, one labeled *P* (for *plane*) and one labeled *S* (for *space*), far enough apart so there is room for each locus.

STEP 2 Draw several points that satisfy the given condition, and look for a pattern in the points. For point *P*, we know that the points will form a circle. For point *S*, we need points that are $\frac{1}{2}$ in. away, but not just in one circle. Draw several circles centered at *S*, in different planes.

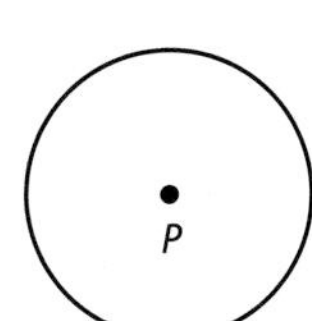

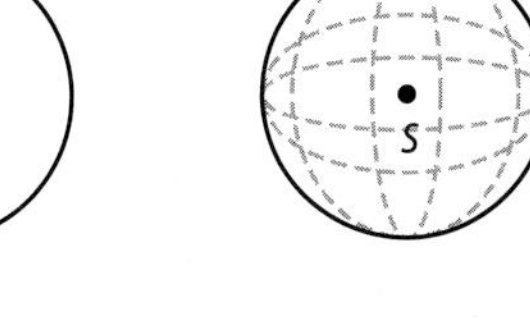

STEP 3 Once the pattern is apparent, draw a figure to represent each locus.

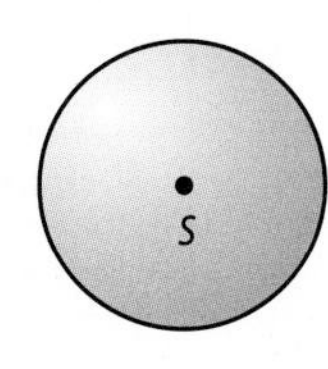

The locus of points around *P* is a circle with center *P* and radius $\frac{1}{2}$ in. The locus of points around *S* is a sphere with center *S* and radius $\frac{1}{2}$ in.

b. The locus of points that are equidistant from two given points

STEP 1 The condition has two given points. Start with two pairs of points, *P* and P_1 (for the plane) and *S* and S_1 (for space). Be sure they are far enough apart.

STEP 2 Draw several points that satisfy the given condition, and look for a pattern in the points. For points *P* and P_1, all the points that satisfy the locus are on the perpendicular bisector of $\overline{PP_1}$. For *S* and S_1, all of the points that satisfy the locus lie on the plane that bisects $\overline{SS_1}$.

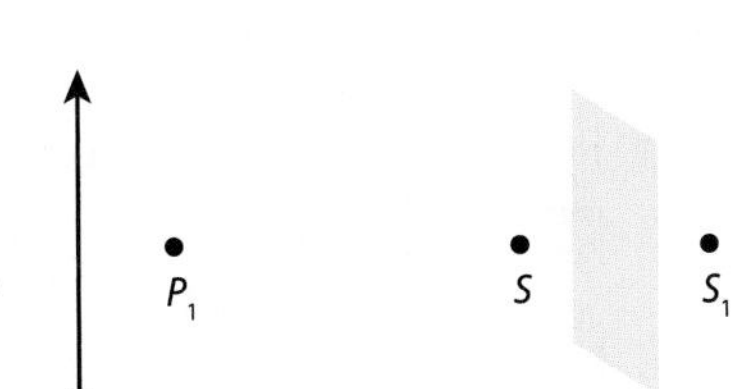

In a plane, the locus of points is a line. In space, the locus of points is a plane.

SEARCH

To see step-by-step videos of these problems, enter the page number into the SWadvantage.com Search Bar.

GOT TO KNOW!

Perspective Drawing

Be sure to work on your skills for showing three-dimensional figures in perspective. That will help you illustrate a locus with a clear drawing.

Euler's Formula

A *polyhedron* is a solid with faces, vertices, and edges. The faces are polygons. An edge is the intersection of two faces. A vertex is the intersection of two or more edges.

SEARCH

To see step-by-step videos of these problems, enter the page number into the SWadvantage.com Search Bar.

EXAMPLE 1

Count the faces, vertices, and edges in each figure. For each figure, find the sum of the number of faces and vertices minus the number of edges.

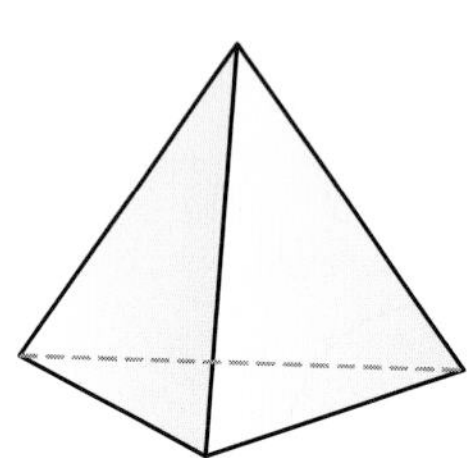

Tetrahedron

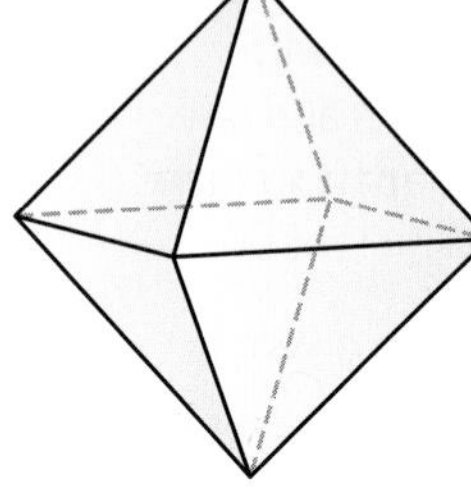

Octahedron

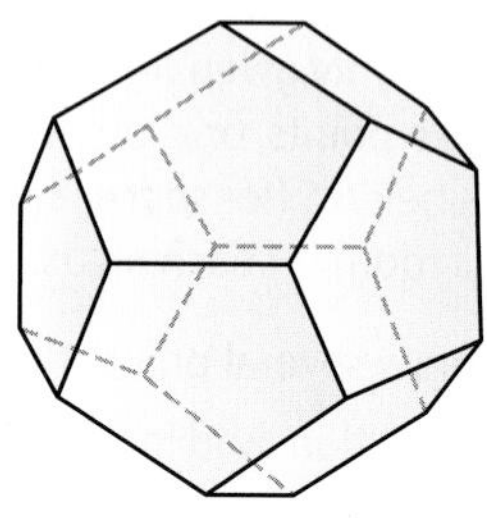

Dodecahedron

STEP 1 Organize your data in a table. Record the number of faces of each figure.

	Faces (*F*)	Vertices (*V*)	Edges (*E*)	$F + V - E$
Tetrahedron	4			
Octahedron	8			
Dodecahedron	12			

STEP 2 Record the number of vertices.

	Faces (*F*)	Vertices (*V*)	Edges (*E*)	$F + V - E$
Tetrahedron	4	4		
Octahedron	8	6		
Dodecahedron	12	20		

STEP 3 Record the number of edges.

	Faces (*F*)	Vertices (*V*)	Edges (*E*)	$F + V - E$
Tetrahedron	4	4	6	
Octahedron	8	6	12	
Dodecahedron	12	20	30	

STEP 4 Find the sum of the numbers of faces and vertices. Then subtract the number of edges.

	Faces (*F*)	Vertices (*V*)	Edges (*E*)	$F + V - E$
Tetrahedron	4	4	6	2
Octahedron	8	6	12	2
Dodecahedron	12	20	30	2

Leonhard Euler (1707–1783) was a Swiss mathematician who first discovered the relationship between the numbers of faces (F), vertices (V), and edges (E) of a polyhedron. **Euler's Formula**, $F + V - E = 2$, is named for him.

EXAMPLE 2

Count the faces and edges in the figure to the right. Then apply Euler's Formula to find the number of vertices.

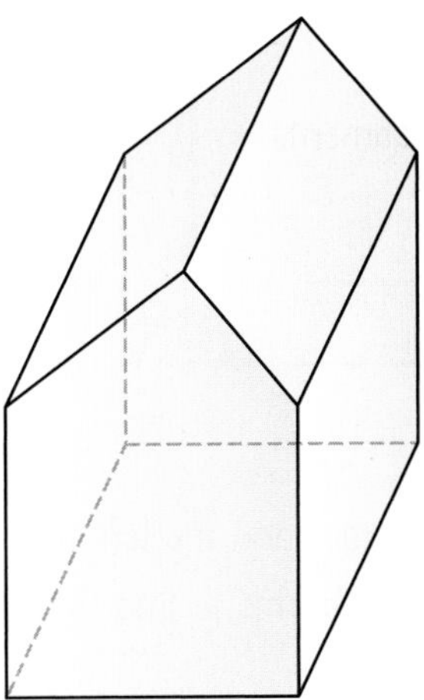

The polyhedron has 2 faces that are pentagons and 5 faces that are rectangles. There are 7 faces in all.

There are 4 edges in the "floor," 4 vertical edges in the "walls," and 7 edges in the "roof." There are 15 edges in all.

$F = 7$ and $E = 15$.

Use Euler's Formula. $F + V - E = 2$

Substitute. $7 + V - 15 = 2$

$V - 8 = 2$

$V = 10$

There are 10 vertices.

You can verify this by counting the 10 vertices in the figure.

EXAMPLE 3

A cube has 6 congruent square faces. Use Euler's Formula to find the number of edges.

$F = 6$ and $V = 8$.

Use Euler's Formula. $F + V - E = 2$

Substitute. $6 + 8 - E = 2$

$14 - E = 2$

$E = 12$

A cube has 12 edges.

To check your answer, draw a cube and count the number of edges.

GOT TO KNOW!

Euler's Formula

The sum of the number of faces (F) and vertices (V) of a polyhedron is two more than the number of edges (E).

$$F + V = E + 2$$

Circles

What Came Before?

- Measures of angles and line segments
- Circumference of a circle

What's This About?

- Finding the area of sectors and the length of arcs in circles
- Using properties and theorems to find the measures of angles and segment lengths
- Relating arc measure to the measures of central, inscribed, and other angles of a circle

Practical Apps

- Civil engineers use properties of arc length to measure the curvature of the Earth when designing roads and bridges.
- Astronomers use tangent lines to take the measurements of planets and moons.

just for FUN!

Q: Which knight started the Round Table?

A: Sir Cumference.

CONTENTS UPLOAD DOWNLOAD Geometry

You can find more practice problems online by visiting:
www.SWadvantage.com

Arcs and Sectors

For a review of the parts of a circle, go to *Circles* in *Foundations of Mathematics*, p. 162.

Types of Arcs

A **circle** is the set of points in a plane a given distance from a given point..That point is the **center** of the circle and the given distance is the length of the **radius**.

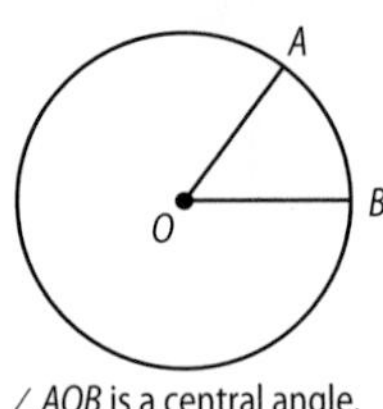

$\angle AOB$ is a central angle.

A **central angle** is an angle whose vertex is the center of a circle.

An **arc** is a part of a circle between two points on the circle. There are three types of arcs:

- The endpoints of a **minor arc** lie on the sides of a central angle. You name a minor arc by naming its endpoints. You read $\widehat{AB}$ as "arc AB."
- The endpoints of a **major arc** lie in the exterior of a central angle. You name a major arc by listing one endpoint, a point on the arc, and then the other endpoint.
- The endpoints of a **semicircle** are the endpoints of a diameter of a circle. You name a semicircle by listing one endpoint, a point on the semicircle, and then the other endpoint.

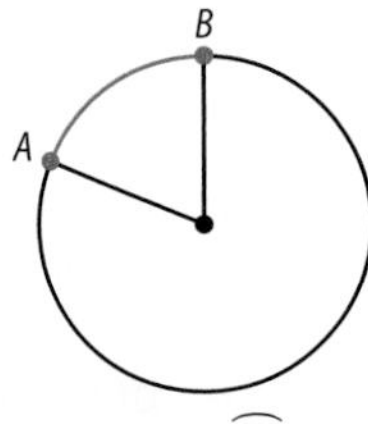

minor $\widehat{AB}$

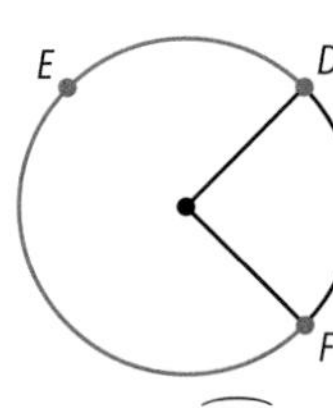

major $\widehat{DEF}$

Q
P R

semicircle $\widehat{PQR}$

EXAMPLE 1

Use the diagram.

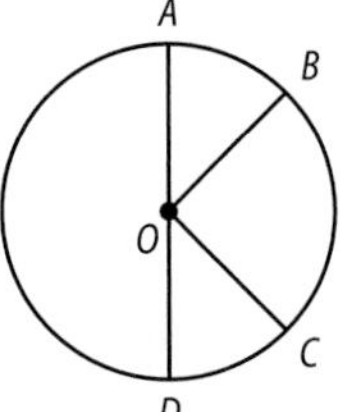

a. Name a semicircle. $\widehat{ABD}$ is a semicircle. Another name for $\widehat{ABD}$ is $\widehat{ACD}$.

b. Name a major arc with endpoints *A* and *C*. $\widehat{ADC}$

c. Name the minor arc with central angle $\angle AOB$. $\widehat{AB}$

SEARCH

To see step-by-step videos of these problems, enter the page number into the SWadvantage.com Search Bar.

The **measure of a minor arc** equals the measure of its central angle. The **measure of a major arc** is 360° minus the measure of the minor arc with the same endpoints. The **measure of a semicircle** is 180°.

Adjacent arcs are arcs of the same circle that share exactly one endpoint. You use the following postulate when adding the measures of adjacent arcs.

Arc Addition Postulate

The measure of an arc formed by two adjacent arcs is the sum of the measures of the two arcs.

$m\widehat{AC} = m\widehat{AB} + m\widehat{BC}$

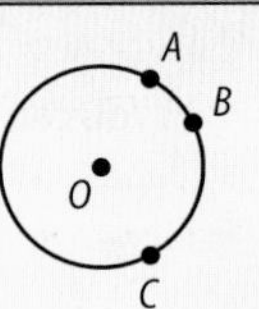

EXAMPLE 2

Find the measure of each arc.

a. $\overset{\frown}{RST}$

$\overset{\frown}{RST}$ is a semicircle; $m\overset{\frown}{RST} = 180°$

b. $\overset{\frown}{QT}$

$m\overset{\frown}{QT} = 180° - m\overset{\frown}{QR}$

$m\overset{\frown}{QT} = 180° - 35°$

$m\overset{\frown}{QT} = 145°$

c. $\overset{\frown}{RS}$

$m\overset{\frown}{RS} = 180° - m\overset{\frown}{ST}$

$m\overset{\frown}{RS} = 180° - 100°$

$m\overset{\frown}{RS} = 80°$

d. $\overset{\frown}{QRS}$

$m\overset{\frown}{QRS} = m\overset{\frown}{QR} + m\overset{\frown}{RS}$

$m\overset{\frown}{QRS} = 35° + 80°$

$m\overset{\frown}{QRS} = 115°$

e. $\overset{\frown}{SRT}$

METHOD 1

$m\overset{\frown}{SRT} = m\overset{\frown}{SR} + m\overset{\frown}{RQT}$

$m\overset{\frown}{SRT} = 80° + 180°$

$m\overset{\frown}{SRT} = 260°$

METHOD 2

$m\overset{\frown}{SRT} = \text{circle} - m\overset{\frown}{ST}$

$m\overset{\frown}{SRT} = 360° - 100°$

$m\overset{\frown}{SRT} = 260°$

Watch Out!

To name a major arc, you must use three points.

Congruent arcs are two arcs that have the same measure and are in the same or congruent circles. The figure shows three circles. ⊙ O and ⊙ P are congruent but ⊙ Q is not the same size. $\overset{\frown}{EF}$ and $\overset{\frown}{GH}$ are parts of congruent circles and $m\overset{\frown}{EF} = m\overset{\frown}{GH}$, so $\overset{\frown}{EF} \cong \overset{\frown}{GH}$. Notice that even though $m\overset{\frown}{GH} = m\overset{\frown}{JK}$, $\overset{\frown}{GH}$ is not congruent to $\overset{\frown}{JK}$.

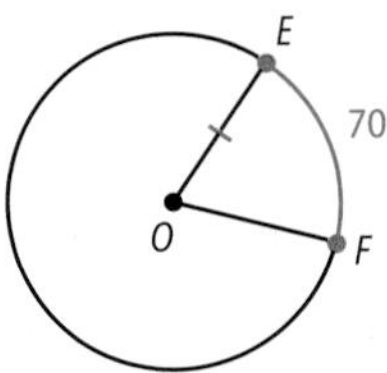

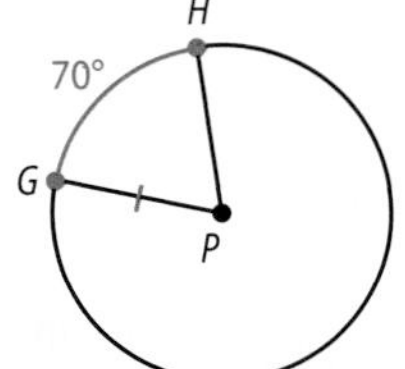

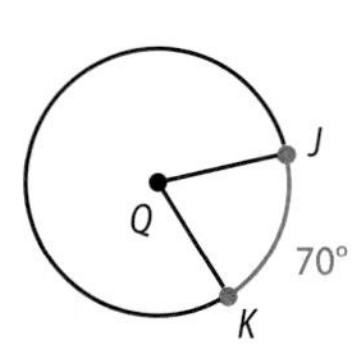

Theorem
In the same circle or in congruent circles, two minor arcs are congruent if and only if their central angles are congruent.

GOT TO KNOW!

Arc Measures

The measure of a **minor arc** equals the measure of its central angle.

The measure of a **major arc** is 360° minus the measure of the minor arc with the same endpoints.

The measure of a **semicircle** is 180°.

Length of an Arc

The length of an arc is a fraction of the circumference of the circle. The fraction is determined by the measure of the arc.

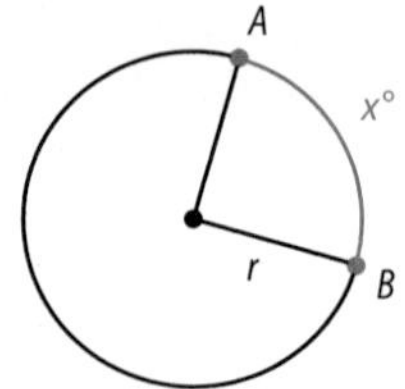

In a circle of radius r, if $m\overset{\frown}{AB} = x°$, then:

length of $\overset{\frown}{AB} = 2\pi r\left(\frac{x°}{360°}\right)$

EXAMPLE 3

SEARCH

To see step-by-step videos of these problems, enter the page number into the SWadvantage.com Search Bar.

Find the length of each arc. Leave your answer in terms of π.

a. $\overset{\frown}{DE}$

Use the formula for the length of an arc with $r = 10$ and $x = 90$.

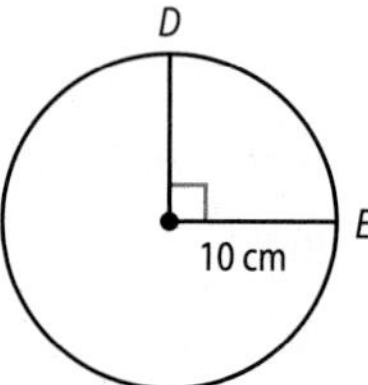

length of $\overset{\frown}{DE} = 2\pi(10)\left(\frac{90°}{360°}\right)$

$= 20\pi\left(\frac{1}{4}\right)$

length of $\overset{\frown}{DE} = 5\pi$ cm

b. $\overset{\frown}{FGH}$

Use the formula for the length of an arc with $r = 9$ and $x = 240$.

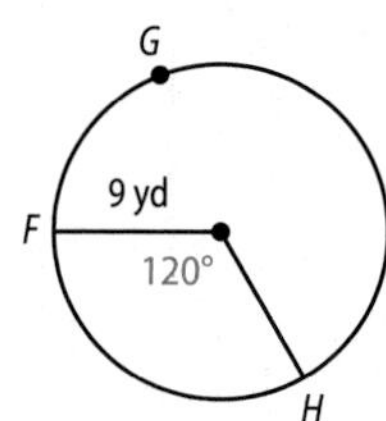

length of $\overset{\frown}{FGH} = 2\pi(9)\left(\frac{240°}{360°}\right)$

$= 18\pi\left(\frac{2}{3}\right)$

length of $\overset{\frown}{FGH} = 12\pi$ yd

c. $\overset{\frown}{AB}$

Use the formula for the length of an arc with $r = 12$ and $x = 45$.

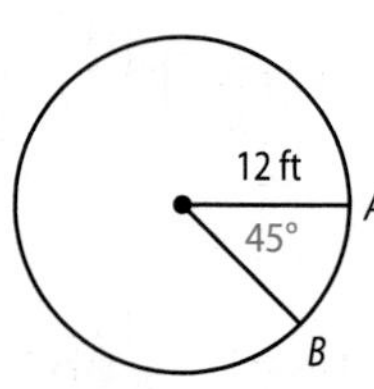

length of $\overset{\frown}{AB} = 2\pi(12)\left(\frac{45°}{360°}\right) = 24\pi\left(\frac{1}{8}\right)$

length of $\overset{\frown}{AB} = 3\pi$ ft

EXAMPLE 4

Find the length of a semicircle with radius 3.6 m.

METHOD 1

Use the formula for the length of an arc with $r = 3.6$ and $x = 180$.

length of semicircle $= 2\pi(3.6)\left(\frac{180°}{360°}\right) = 7.2\pi\left(\frac{1}{2}\right)$

length of semicircle $= 3.6\pi$ m

METHOD 2

A semicircle is half a circle. Its length is half the circumference of the circle.

circumference $= 2\pi r$

$\frac{1}{2}$ circumference $= \pi r = 3.6\pi$

length of semicircle $= 3.6\pi$ m

EXAMPLE 5

The minute hand on a clock is 8.4 cm long. How far does the tip of the minute hand travel in 25 minutes?

STEP 1 Write a proportion to find x, the measure of the central angle.

60 minutes = 1 hour $\frac{x}{360} = \frac{25}{60}$

Cross multiply. $60x = 9{,}000$

Divide by 60. $x = 150$

STEP 2 Use the formula for the length of an arc with $r = 8.4$ and $x = 150$.

$$2\pi r\left(\frac{x}{360}\right) = 2\pi(8.4)\left(\frac{150^\circ}{360^\circ}\right)$$

$$= 16.8\pi\left(\frac{5}{12}\right)$$

$$= 7\pi \text{ cm}$$

The minute hand travels 7π cm, or about 22 cm.

EXAMPLE 6

The length of $\widehat{BC}$ in ⊙ O is 2.15 in. The radius of ⊙ O is 9 in. Find $m\widehat{BC}$.

Let $x^\circ = m\widehat{BC}$. Use the formula for the length of an arc.

$$\text{length of } \widehat{BC} = 2\pi r\left(\frac{x^\circ}{360^\circ}\right)$$

Substitute. $2.15 = 2\pi(9)\left(\frac{x^\circ}{360^\circ}\right)$

Simplify. $2.15 = \frac{\pi}{20}x^\circ$

Solve for x. $x = \frac{20 \cdot 2.15}{\pi} = \frac{43}{\pi}$

Use a calculator. $x \approx 13.7$

$m\widehat{BC} \approx 13.7^\circ$

Watch Out!

Do not confuse arc length with arc measure.

GOT TO KNOW!

Arc Length

The length of an arc is a fraction of the circumference of the circle.

The fraction is determined by the measure of the arc.

In a circle of radius r, if $m\widehat{AB} = x^\circ$, then:

length of $\widehat{AB} = 2\pi r\left(\frac{x^\circ}{360^\circ}\right)$

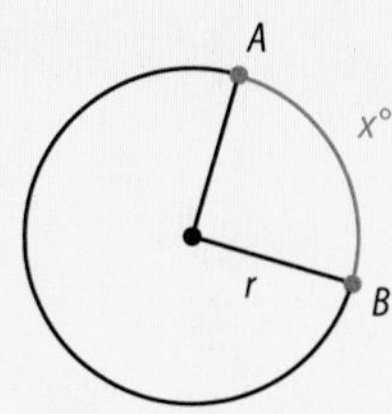

Area of a Sector

A **sector of a circle** is the region bounded by two radii of a circle and an arc. You name a sector with three points—one endpoint, the center of the circle, then the other endpoint.

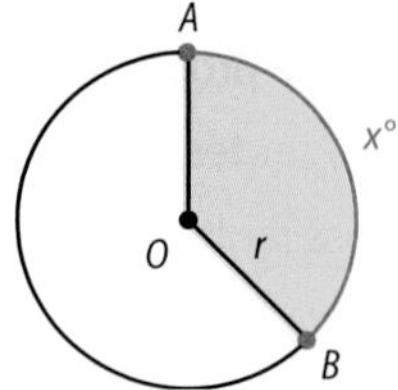

The area of a sector is a fraction of the area of the circle. The fraction is determined by the measure of the arc. In a circle of radius r, if $m\overset{\frown}{AB} = x°$, then:

$$\text{area of sector } AOB = \pi r^2\left(\frac{x°}{360°}\right)$$

EXAMPLE 7

SEARCH

To see step-by-step videos of these problems, enter the page number into the SWadvantage.com Search Bar.

Find the area of the shaded region. Leave your answer in terms of π.

a.

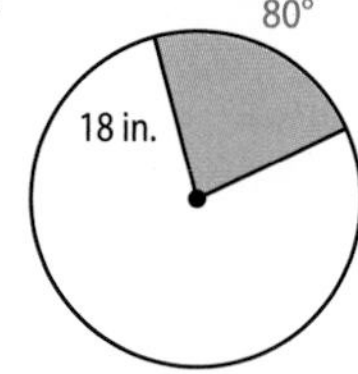

Use the area formula with $r = 18$ and $x = 80$.

$$\text{area} = \pi(18^2)\left(\frac{80°}{360°}\right)$$

$$= 324\pi\left(\frac{2}{9}\right)$$

$$\text{area} = 72\pi \text{ in.}^2$$

b. 120°

6 cm

Use the area formula with $r = 6$ and $x = 240$.

$$\text{area} = \pi(6^2)\left(\frac{240°}{360°}\right)$$

$$= 36\pi\left(\frac{2}{3}\right)$$

$$\text{area} = 24\pi \text{ cm}^2$$

c.

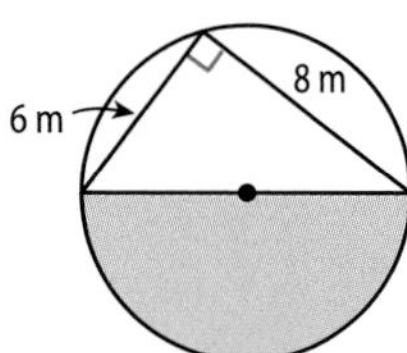

STEP 1 Use the Pythagorean Theorem to find the diameter d of the circle.

$$6^2 + 8^2 = d^2$$

$$36 + 64 = d^2$$

$$d^2 = 100$$

$$d = \sqrt{100} = 10 \text{ m}$$

STEP 2 Find the radius r of the circle.

$$r = 10 \div 2 = 5 \text{ m}$$

STEP 3 Use the area formula with $r = 5$ and $x = 180$.

$$\text{area} = \pi(5^2)\left(\frac{180°}{360°}\right)$$

$$= 25\pi\left(\frac{1}{2}\right)$$

$$\text{area} = 12.5\pi \text{ m}^2$$

EXAMPLE 8

Find the area of the shaded region.

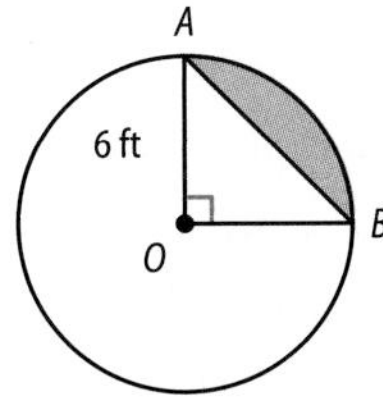

Area of a Sector

In a circle of radius r, if $m\widehat{AB} = x°$, then the area of sector $AOB = \pi r^2\left(\frac{x°}{360°}\right)$.

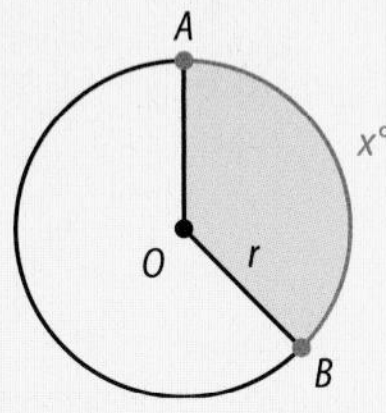

The area of the shaded region equals the area of sector AOB minus the area of $\triangle AOB$.

STEP 1 Find the area of sector AOB.

Use the area formula with $r = 6$ and $x = 90$.

$\text{area} = \pi(6^2)\left(\frac{90°}{360°}\right) = 36\pi\left(\frac{1}{4}\right)$

$\text{area} = 9\pi \text{ ft}^2$

STEP 2 Find the area of $\triangle AOB$.

$\text{area of triangle} = \frac{1}{2} \text{ base} \cdot \text{height}$

$\text{area } \triangle AOB = \frac{1}{2} \cdot 6 \cdot 6$

$\text{area } \triangle AOB = 18 \text{ ft}^2$

STEP 3 Subtract the area of $\triangle AOB$ from the area of sector AOB.

area of the shaded region $= (9\pi - 18) \text{ ft}^2$, or about 10.3 ft^2

EXAMPLE 9

Find the area and perimeter of the figure.

The figure is composed of an equilateral triangle and a semicircle. The radius of the semicircle is 12.

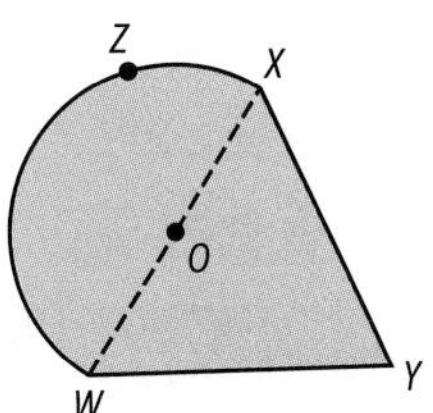

STEP 1 Find the area.

$\text{area of } \triangle WXY = \frac{24^2}{4}\sqrt{3} = 144\sqrt{3}$

$\text{area of semicircle} = \frac{1}{2}\pi(12^2) = 72\pi$

$\text{area of figure} = 144\sqrt{3} + 72\pi$

STEP 2 Find the perimeter.

$\text{perimeter} = WY + YX + \text{length of } \widehat{WZX}$

$= 24 + 24 + 2\pi(12)\left(\frac{180°}{360°}\right)$

$= 24 + 24 + 12\pi$

$\text{perimeter of figure} = 48 + 12\pi$

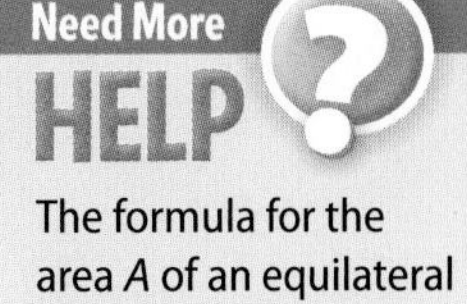

The formula for the area A of an equilateral triangle with side length s is $A = \frac{s^2}{4}\sqrt{3}$.

Chords and Arcs

Chords and Central Angles

A **chord** is a segment whose endpoints lie on a circle.
A **diameter** is a chord that contains the center of a circle.

$\overline{AC}$, $\overline{BF}$, and $\overline{DE}$ are chords. $\overline{BF}$ is a diameter.

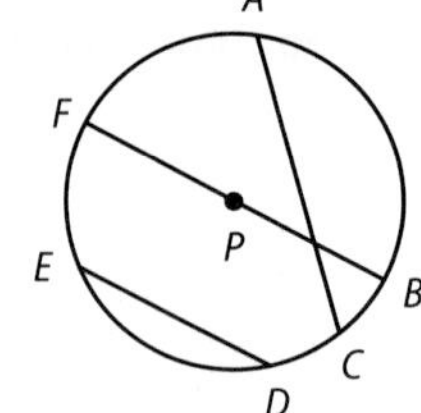

Theorem
In the same circle (or in congruent circles), congruent chords have congruent central angles.

PROOF

Given: $\overline{AD} \cong \overline{BC}$

Prove: $\angle AXD \cong \angle BXC$

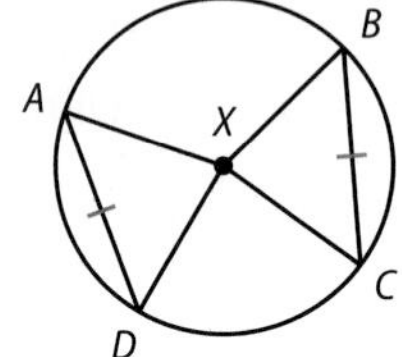

Statements	Reasons
1. $\overline{AD} \cong \overline{BC}$	1. Given
2. $\overline{AX} \cong \overline{BX}, \overline{DX} \cong \overline{CX}$	2. All radii of a circle are $\cong$.
3. $\triangle AXD \cong \triangle BXC$	3. SSS
4. $\angle AXD \cong \angle BXC$	4. CPCTC

The converse of this theorem is also true.

Theorem
In the same circle (or in congruent circles), congruent central angles have congruent chords.

PROOF

Given: $\angle 1 \cong \angle 2$

Prove: $\overline{GK} \cong \overline{HJ}$

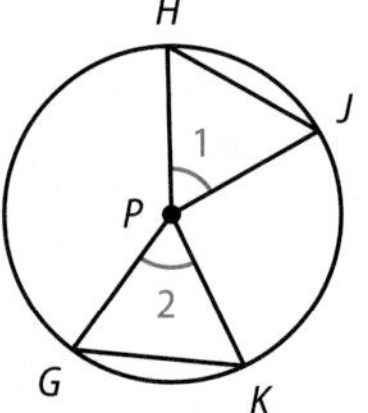

Statements	Reasons
1. $\angle 1 \cong \angle 2$	1. Given
2. $PG = PK = PH = PJ$	2. All radii of a circle are $\cong$.
3. $\triangle GPK \cong \triangle HPJ$	3. SAS
4. $\overline{GK} \cong \overline{HJ}$	4. CPCTC

Watch Out !

$\overline{CF}$ and $\overline{DE}$ have congruent central angles, but they are not congruent chords.

EXAMPLE 1

Name the congruent chords.

In congruent circles, congruent central angles have congruent chords, so $\overline{CF} \cong \overline{BG}$ and $\overline{DE} \cong \overline{AH}$.

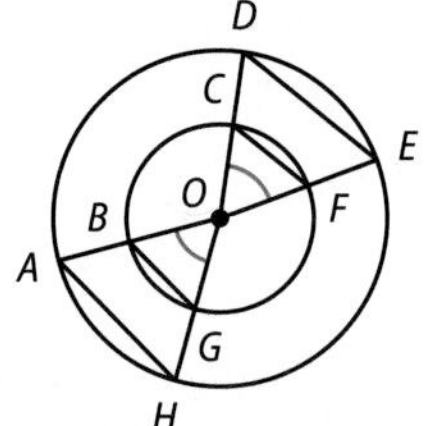

EXAMPLE 2

Find *LM*.

Vertical ∠s are ≅.	$\angle LOM \cong \angle KOJ$
Congruent central ∠s have ≅ chords.	$LM = JK$
Substitute.	$6x + 2 = 13x - 19$
Solve.	$21 = 7x$
	$x = 3$
Substitute 3 for *x*.	$LM = 6(3) + 2$
	$LM = 20$

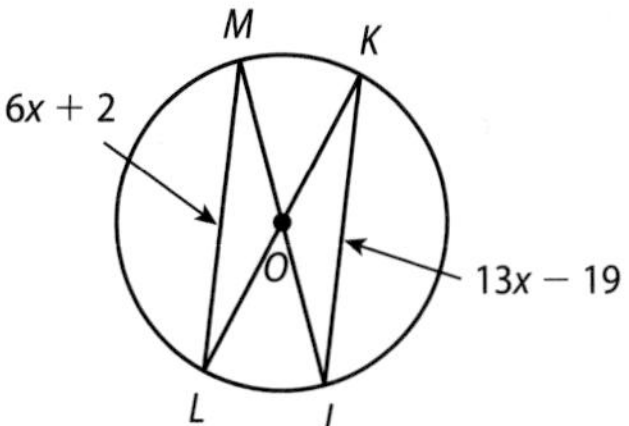

SEARCH

To see step-by-step videos of these problems, enter the page number into the SWadvantage.com Search Bar.

EXAMPLE 3

Find $m\angle EOF$.

Congruent chords have ≅ central ∠s.	$m\angle EOF = m\angle GOH$
Substitute.	$4x - 6 = 6x - 28$
Solve.	$22 = 2x$
	$x = 11$
Substitute 11 for *x*.	$m\angle EOF = 4(11) - 6$
	$m\angle EOF = 38°$

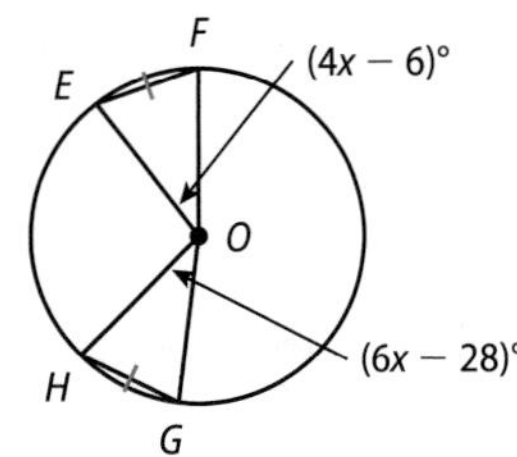

GOT TO KNOW!

Chords and Central Angles

In the same circle (or in congruent circles), congruent chords have congruent central angles.

If $\overline{AD} \cong \overline{BC}$, then $\angle AXD \cong \angle BXC$.

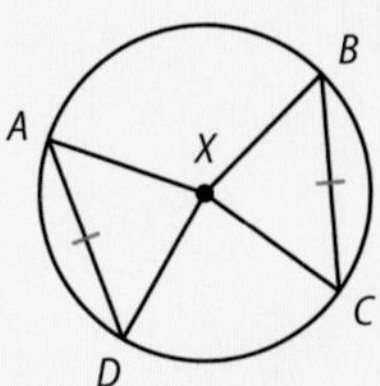

In the same circle (or in congruent circles), congruent central angles have congruent chords.

If $\angle 1 \cong \angle 2$, then $\overline{GK} \cong \overline{HJ}$.

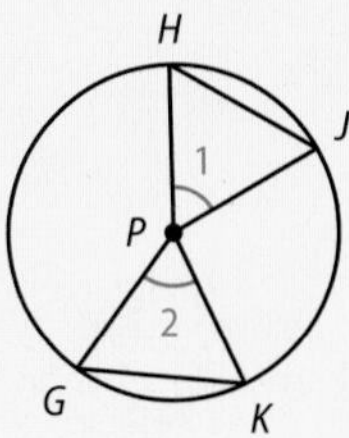

Chords and Arcs

The congruent arcs must be in the same circle or in congruent circles.

Congruent arcs lie in the same circle (or in congruent circles) and have the same measure. A chord that is not a diameter cuts off a minor arc and a major arc. The minor arc is called the **arc of the chord**.

Theorem
In the same circle (or in congruent circles), congruent arcs have congruent chords.

PROOF

Given: $\overset{\frown}{BC} \cong \overset{\frown}{DE}$

Prove: $\overline{BC} \cong \overline{DE}$

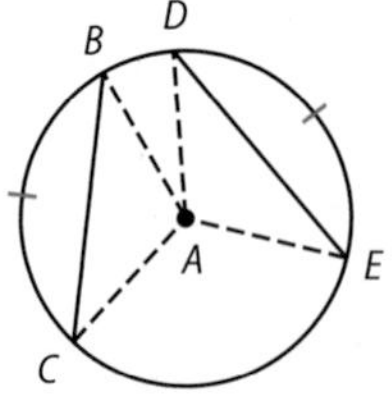

Statements	Reasons
1. $\overset{\frown}{BC} \cong \overset{\frown}{DE}$	1. Given
2. $\angle BAC \cong \angle DAE$	2. Congruent arcs have congruent central $\angle$s.
3. $\overline{BC} \cong \overline{DE}$	3. Congruent central $\angle$s have congruent chords.

The converse of this theorem is also true.

Theorem
In the same circle (or congruent circles), congruent chords have congruent arcs.

PROOF

Given: $\overline{WX} \cong \overline{ZY}$

Prove: $\overset{\frown}{WX} \cong \overset{\frown}{ZY}$

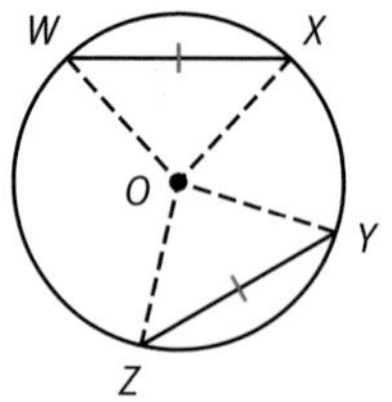

Statements	Reasons
1. $\overline{WX} \cong \overline{ZY}$	1. Given
2. $\angle WOX \cong \angle ZOY$	2. Congruent chords have congruent central $\angle$s.
3. $\overset{\frown}{WX} \cong \overset{\frown}{ZY}$	3. Congruent central $\angle$s have congruent arcs.

Given: $\overset{\frown}{AB} \cong \overset{\frown}{AC}$

Prove: $\angle B \cong \angle C$

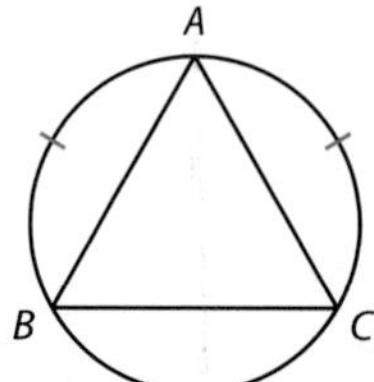

Statements	Reasons
1. $\overset{\frown}{AB} \cong \overset{\frown}{AC}$	1. Given
2. $\overline{AB} \cong \overline{AC}$	2. Congruent arcs have congruent chords.
3. $\angle B \cong \angle C$	3. Base $\angle$s of an isosceles triangle are congruent.

EXAMPLE 5

Find $m\widehat{XY}$.

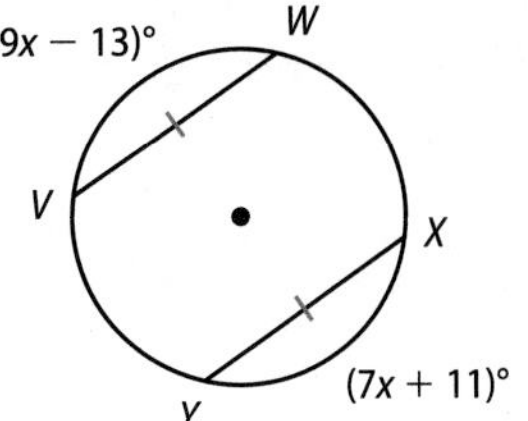

Congruent chords have ≅ arcs. $m\widehat{XY} = m\widehat{VW}$

Substitute. $7x + 11 = 9x - 13$

Solve. $24 = 2x$

$x = 12$

Substitute 12 for x. $m\widehat{XY} = 7(12) + 11$

$m\widehat{XY} = 95°$

SEARCH

To see step-by-step videos of these problems, enter the page number into the SWadvantage.com Search Bar.

EXAMPLE 6

Find GH.

STEP 1 Find $m\widehat{HE}$.

$m\widehat{HE} + m\widehat{GH} + m\widehat{GF} + m\widehat{FE} = 360°$

$m\widehat{HE} + 60 + 110 + 130 = 360$

$m\widehat{HE} = 60°$, so $\widehat{HE} \cong \widehat{GH}$.

STEP 2 Find the value of x.

Congruent arcs have ≅ chords. $GH = EF$

Substitute. $2x + 17 = 10x - 7$

Solve. $24 = 8x$

$x = 3$

STEP 3 Find GH.

$GH = 2x + 17$

Substitute 3 for x. $GH = 2(3) + 17$

$GH = 23$

GOT TO KNOW!

Chords and Arcs

In the same circle (or in congruent circles), congruent arcs have congruent chords.

In the same circle (or in congruent circles), congruent chords have congruent arcs.

$\widehat{AB} \cong \widehat{CD}$ if and only if $\overline{AB} \cong \overline{CD}$.

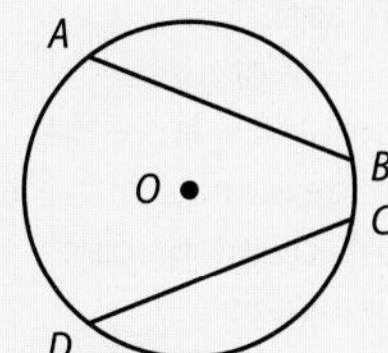

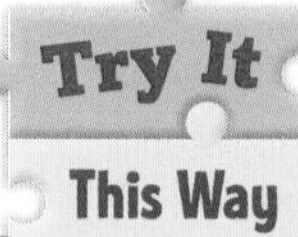

Draw a circle. Label the center and two points on the circle. Fold the circle so that the two points coincide. List your observations.

Bisectors

If M is the midpoint of $\overset{\frown}{AB}$, then $\overset{\frown}{AM} \cong \overset{\frown}{MB}$.
Any line, segment, or ray that contains M **bisects** $\overset{\frown}{AB}$.
$\overline{OM}$ bisects $\overset{\frown}{AB}$.

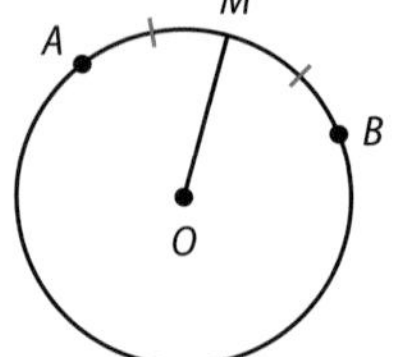

Theorem
If a diameter (or radius) is perpendicular to a chord, then it bisects the chord and its arc.

PROOF
Given: In ⊙O, $\overline{KI} \perp \overline{HJ}$.
Prove: $\overline{HL} \cong \overline{JL}$ and $\overset{\frown}{HI} \cong \overset{\frown}{JI}$

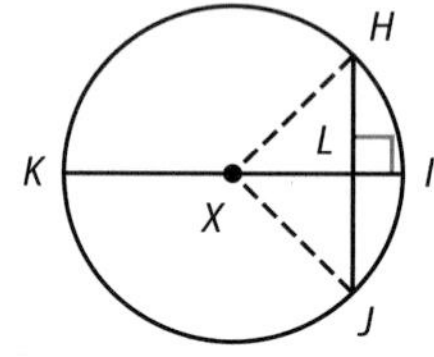

Statements	Reasons
1. $\overline{KI} \perp \overline{HJ}$	1. Given
2. $\angle HLX$ and $\angle JLX$ are right angles.	2. $\perp$ lines form right $\angle$s.
3. $\angle HLX \cong \angle JLX$	3. All right angles are $\cong$.
4. $\overline{XL} \cong \overline{XL}$	4. Reflexive property
5. $\overline{XH} \cong \overline{XJ}$	5. All radii of a circle are $\cong$.
6. $\triangle HLX \cong \triangle JLX$	6. HL
7. $\overline{HL} \cong \overline{JL}$ and $\angle HXL \cong \angle JXL$	7. CPCTC
8. $\overset{\frown}{HI} \cong \overset{\frown}{JI}$	8. Congruent central $\angle$s have $\cong$ arcs.

There are two more important theorems about chords and radii that you should know.

Theorem
If a radius bisects a chord that is not a diameter, then it is perpendicular to the chord.
Theorem
The perpendicular bisector of a chord passes through the center of the circle.

EXAMPLE 7

$CD = 24$. Find OM.

$\overline{OM}$ bisects $\overline{CD}$. $\quad MD = 12$

Use the Pythagorean Theorem. $\quad OM^2 + 12^2 = 13^2$

$$OM^2 + 144 = 169$$
$$OM^2 = 25$$
$$OM = 5$$

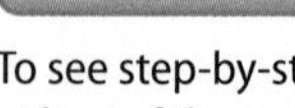

To see step-by-step videos of these problems, enter the page number into the SWadvantage.com Search Bar.

EXAMPLE 8

Find the length of a chord that is 2 cm from the center of a circle with a radius of 6 cm. Round your answer to the nearest tenth.

STEP 1 Draw a diagram.

STEP 2 Use the Pythagorean Theorem to find the value of x.

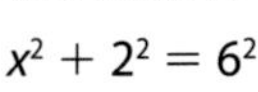

$x^2 + 2^2 = 6^2$

$x^2 + 4 = 36$

$x^2 = 32$

$x = 4\sqrt{2}$

STEP 3 Find AB.

If a radius is perpendicular to a chord, then it bisects the chord, so $AB = 2x$.

$AB = 8\sqrt{2} \approx 11.3$ cm

The length of the chord is about 11.3 cm.

Theorem
If two chords of a circle are congruent, then they are equidistant from the center.
Theorem
If two chords of a circle are equidistant from the center, then they are congruent.

EXAMPLE 9

$\overline{RS} \cong \overline{UT}$. Find VW.

The chords are $\cong$, so they are equidistant from the center.	$VW = XW$
Substitute.	$2x^2 - 10 = x^2 + 3x$
Write in standard form.	$x^2 - 3x - 10 = 0$
Factor.	$(x - 5)(x + 2) = 0$
	$x = 5$ or $x = -2$
Test both roots.	$2x^2 - 10 = 2(25) - 10 = 40$
	$2x^2 - 10 = 2(4) - 10 = -2$

Length must be positive, so $VW = 40$.

Need More HELP

For help with solving quadratic equations, go to *Factoring to Solve Quadratics* in *Algebra* (Book 2, p. 1702).

GOT TO KNOW!

Bisectors

- If a diameter (or radius) is perpendicular to a chord, then it bisects the chord and its arc.
- If a radius bisects a chord that is not a diameter, then it is perpendicular to the chord.
- The perpendicular bisector of a chord passes through the center of the circle.
- Two chords of a circle are congruent if and only if they are equidistant from the center.

Properties of Tangents

Tangent Lines

A **tangent** to a circle is a line in the plane of the circle that intersects the circle in exactly one point, called the **point of tangency**.

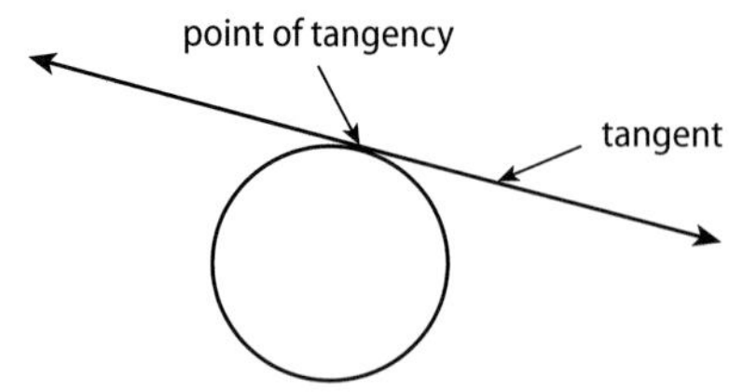

Theorem
If a line is tangent to a circle, then it is perpendicular to the radius drawn to the point of tangency.

Theorem
If a line in the plane of a circle is perpendicular to the radius at a point on the circle, then the line is tangent to the circle.

EXAMPLE 1

$\overleftrightarrow{QS}$ is tangent to $\odot R$ at point Q. Find $m\angle S$.

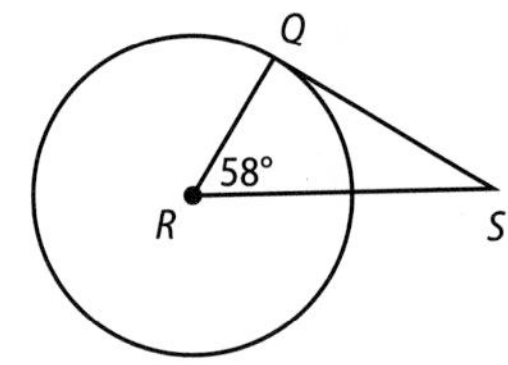

Radii and tangent line are $\perp$.	$m\angle RQS = 90°$
Triangle Angle-Sum Theorem	$m\angle S + m\angle R + m\angle RQS = 180°$
Substitute.	$m\angle S + 58 + 90 = 180$
Solve for $m\angle S$.	$m\angle S = 32°$

EXAMPLE 2

$\overleftrightarrow{HK}$ is tangent to $\odot I$ at point H. If $IJ = 15$ and $HK = 8$, find KJ.

Radii and tangent line are $\perp$.	$m\angle KHI = 90°$
All radii of a $\odot$ are congruent.	$HI = JI = 15$
Use the Pythagorean Theorem.	$HI^2 + HK^2 = KI^2$
Substitute.	$15^2 + 8^2 = KI^2$
	$289 = KI^2$
Take the square root.	$17 = KI$
Segment Addition Postulate	$KJ + JI = KI$
Substitute.	$KJ + 15 = 17$
Solve for KJ.	$KJ = 2$

Need More HELP

For help with the Pythagorean Theorem, go to *Pythagorean Theorem* (p. 678).

Tangent Segments

A **tangent segment** is part of a tangent line. Its endpoints are the point of tangency and another point on the tangent line.

Two-Tangent Theorem
Two tangent segments drawn from a point outside of a circle are congruent.

PROOF

Given: $\overline{QR}$ **and** $\overline{SR}$ **are tangent to** $\odot P$ **at point** Q **and point** S **respectively.**

Prove: $\overline{QR} \cong \overline{SR}$

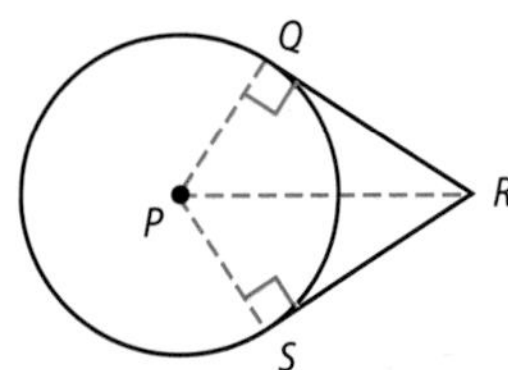

Statements	Reasons
1. $\overline{QR}$ and $\overline{SR}$ are tangent to $\odot P$.	1. Given
2. $\overline{PQ} \perp \overline{QR}$, $\overline{PS} \perp \overline{SR}$	2. Radius and tangent line are $\perp$.
3. $\overline{PR} \cong \overline{PR}$	3. Reflexive property of $\cong$.
4. $\overline{PQ} \cong \overline{PS}$	4. All radii of a circle are $\cong$.
5. $\triangle PQR \cong \triangle PSR$	5. HL
6. $\overline{QR} \cong \overline{SR}$	6. CPCTC

EXAMPLE 3

Find the perimeter of *ABCD*.

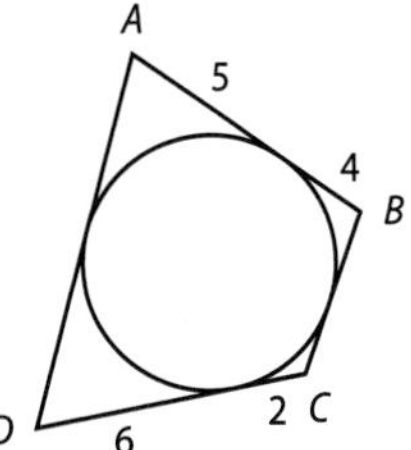

Use the Two-Tangent Theorem to find the missing lengths.

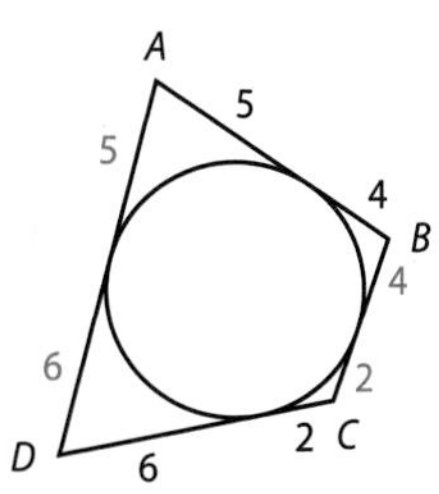

perimeter $= 5 + 5 + 4 + 4 + 2 + 2 + 6 + 6 = 34$

SEARCH

To see step-by-step videos of these problems, enter the page number into the SWadvantage.com Search Bar.

GOT TO KNOW!

Tangent Lines and Tangent Segments

If a line is tangent to a circle, then it is perpendicular to the radius drawn to the point of tangency.

If a line in the plane of a circle is perpendicular to the radius of a circle at a point on the circle, then the line is tangent to the circle.

Two tangent segments drawn from a point outside of a circle are congruent.

Tangent Circles

Two circles are **tangent** if they are coplanar and they intersect in exactly one point.

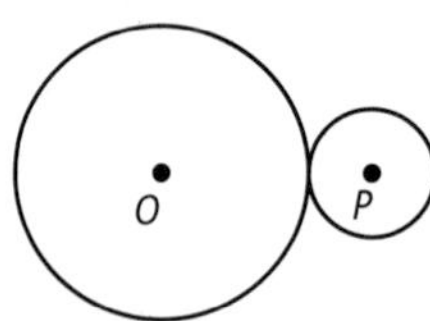

⊙ O and ⊙ P are externally tangent. ⊙ A and ⊙ B are internally tangent.

A line (or segment) that is tangent to two coplanar circles is a **common tangent**.

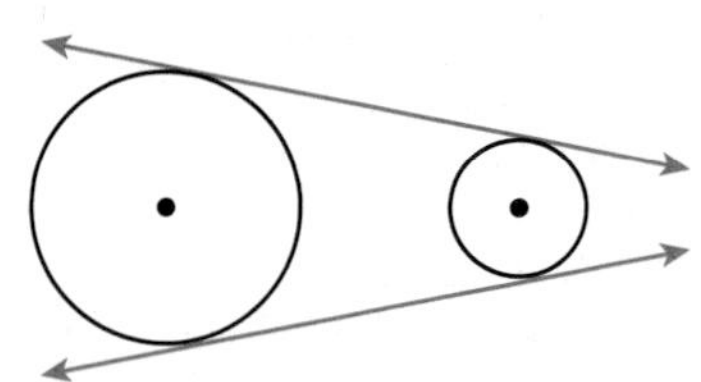

common external tangents

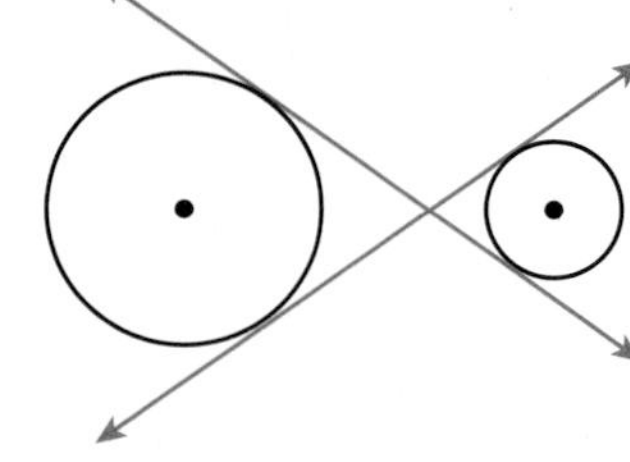

common internal tangents

Watch Out !

Common internal tangents *always* intersect the segment that joins the centers of the circles.

EXAMPLE 4

SEARCH

To see step-by-step videos of these problems, enter the page number into the SWadvantage.com Search Bar.

For each pair of circles, state how many common external and internal tangents can be drawn.

a. 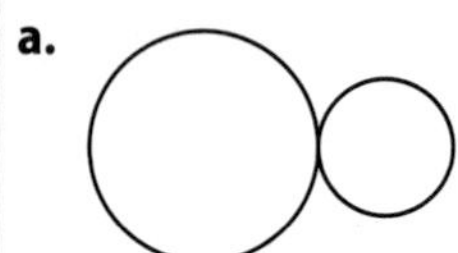

You can draw two common external tangents and one common internal tangent.

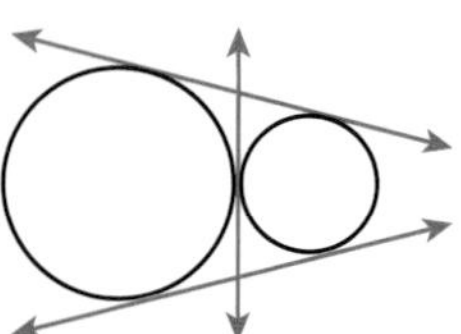

b. 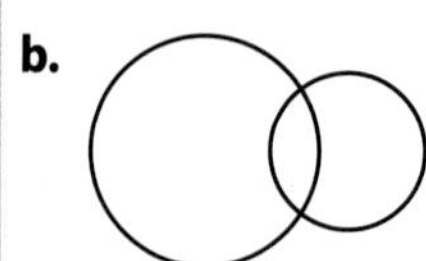

You can draw two common external tangents and no common internal tangent.

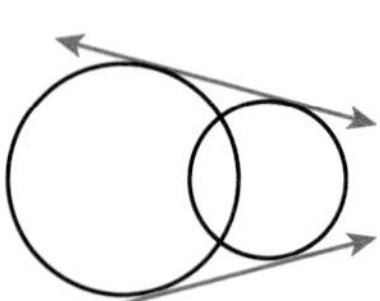

c. 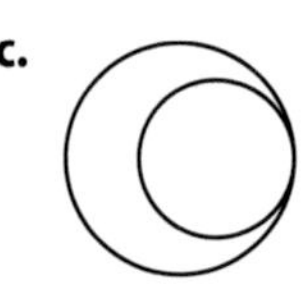

You can draw one common external tangent and no common internal tangents.

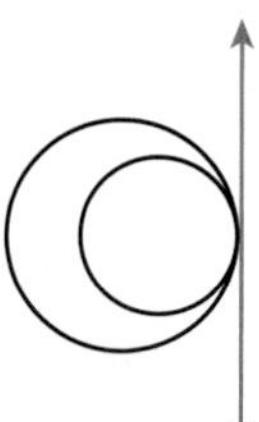

EXAMPLE 5

Circle O and circle P are externally tangent at point A. $OA = 12$ and $PA = 9$.

Find ST, the length of the common external tangent.

STEP 1 Draw $\overline{OP}$.

STEP 2 Draw the radii of the circles to the points of tangency.

STEP 3 Draw $\overline{PR}$ parallel to $\overline{ST}$. Note the following:

Point R divides $\overline{OS}$ into two segments of lengths 9 and 3.
Quadrilateral $OSTP$ contains a rectangle and a right triangle.
$RP = ST$

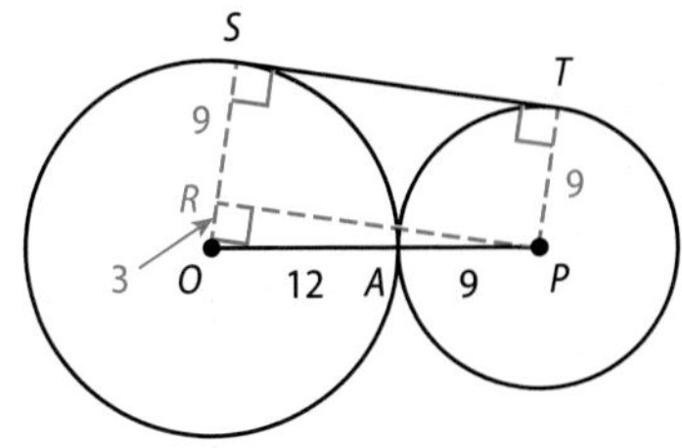

STEP 4 Use the Pythagorean Theorem to find RP.

$OR^2 + RP^2 = OP^2$

$3^2 + RP^2 = 21^2$

$RP = 12\sqrt{3}$

Therefore, $ST = 12\sqrt{3}$.

You follow the same steps to solve a problem involving a common internal tangent.

EXAMPLE 6

$AB = 18$. The radius of circle A is 8, and the radius of circle B is 6.

Find GH, the length of the common internal tangent.

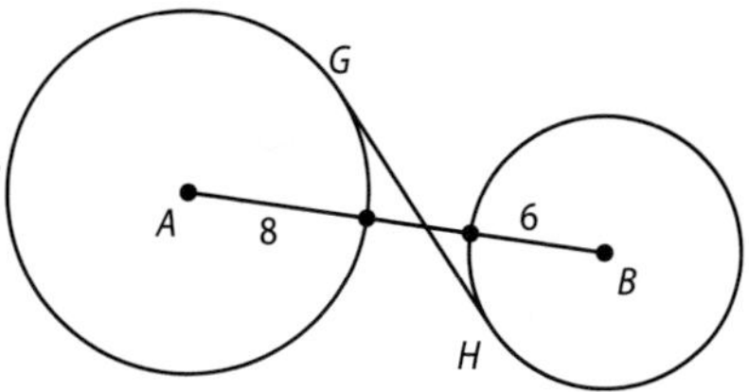

STEP 1 Draw the radii of the circles to the points of tangency.

STEP 2 Draw a line from B parallel to $\overline{GH}$. Extend $\overline{AG}$ to form rectangle $GKBH$.

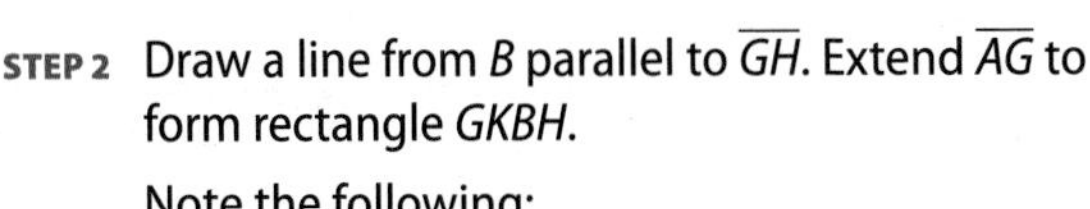

Note the following:
$KB = GH$
$\triangle AKB$ is a right triangle, $AB = 18$, and $AK = 14$.

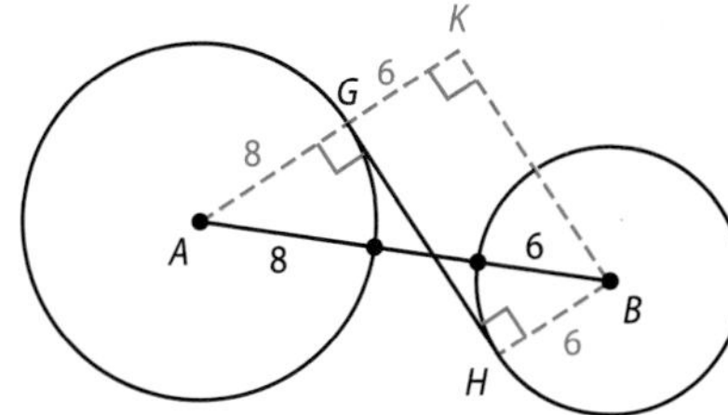

STEP 3 Use the Pythagorean Theorem to find KB.

$AK^2 + KB^2 = AB^2$

$14^2 + KB^2 = 18^2$

$KB = 8\sqrt{2}$

Therefore, $GH = 8\sqrt{2}$.

GOT TO KNOW!

Tangent Circles

Two circles are tangent if they are coplanar and they intersect in exactly one point.

A line (or segment) that is tangent to two coplanar circles is a common tangent.

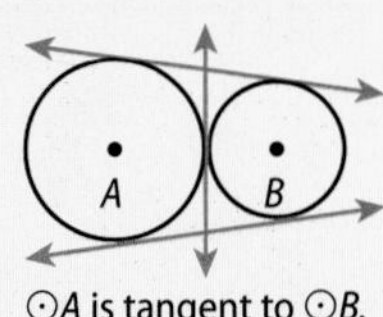

$\odot A$ is tangent to $\odot B$.

Inscribed Angles

Inscribed Angle Theorem

An **inscribed angle** is an angle whose vertex is on a circle and whose sides contain chords of the circle.

$\angle FGH$ is an inscribed angle. It intercepts $\overset{\frown}{FH}$.

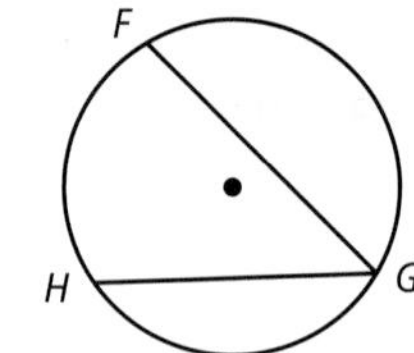

Inscribed Angle Theorem
The measure of an inscribed angle is half the measure of its intercepted arc.

PROOF

There are three cases to consider: (1) the center of the circle lies on one side of the inscribed angle; (2) the center of the circle lies in the interior of the inscribed angle; and (3) the center of the circle lies in the exterior of the inscribed angle. Here is a proof of the first case. The proofs of the other two cases are very similar.

Given: $\angle ACB$ is inscribed in $\odot X$.

Prove: $m\angle ACB = \frac{1}{2} m\overset{\frown}{AB}$

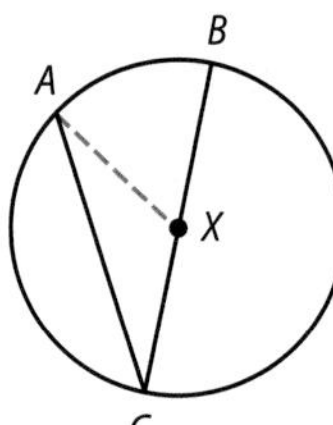

Draw $\overline{XA}$. All radii in a circle are congruent, so $\overline{XA} \cong \overline{XC}$.

Base angles of an isosceles triangle are congruent, so $m\angle XAC = m\angle ACB$.

By the Exterior Angle Theorem, $m\angle AXB = m\angle XAC + m\angle ACB$.

Using substitution, $m\angle AXB = 2(m\angle ACB)$, and $\frac{1}{2} m\angle AXB = m\angle ACB$.

The measure of a central angle equals the measure of its intercepted arc, so $m\angle AXB = m\overset{\frown}{AB}$. By substitution, $m\angle ACB = \frac{1}{2} m\overset{\frown}{AB}$.

EXAMPLE 1

SEARCH

To see step-by-step videos of these problems, enter the page number into the SWadvantage.com Search Bar.

Find each measure.

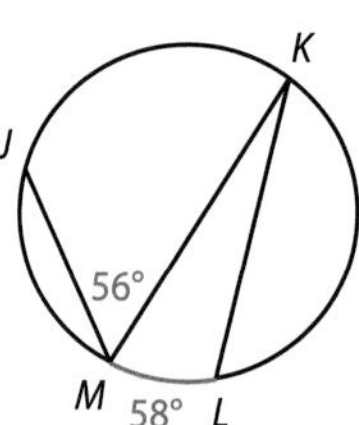

a. $m\angle MKL$

$m\angle MKL = \frac{1}{2} m\overset{\frown}{ML}$

$m\angle MKL = 29°$

b. $m\overset{\frown}{JK}$

$m\angle JMK = \frac{1}{2} m\overset{\frown}{JK}$, so $m\overset{\frown}{JK} = 2(m\angle JMK)$.

$m\overset{\frown}{JK} = 112°$

EXAMPLE 2

Find $m\angle WZY$.

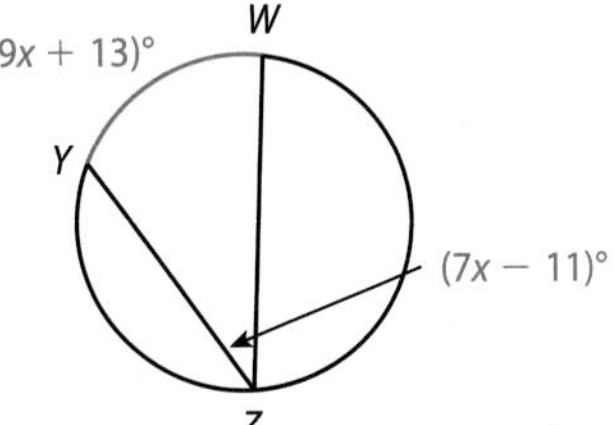

Inscribed ∠ Theorem	$m\angle WZY = \frac{1}{2} m\,\widehat{WY}$
Substitute.	$7x - 11 = \frac{1}{2}(9x + 13)$
Solve for x.	$2(7x - 11) = 9x + 13$
	$14x - 22 = 9x + 13$
	$5x = 35$
	$x = 7$
Substitute for x and simplify.	$m\angle WZY = 7(7) - 11$
	$m\angle WZY = 38°$

EXAMPLE 3

Find $m\angle DEF$ given $m\,\widehat{DEF} = 192°$.

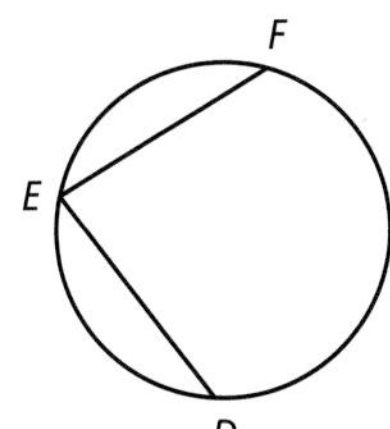

	$m\,\widehat{DF} = 360° - m\,\widehat{DEF}$
Substitute.	$m\,\widehat{DF} = 360° - 192° = 168°$
Inscribed ∠ Theorem	$m\angle DEF = \frac{1}{2} m\,\widehat{DF}$
Substitute for $m\,\widehat{DF}$.	$m\angle DEF = \frac{1}{2}(168°)$
Simplify.	$m\angle DEF = 84°$

Watch Out !

Do not confuse minor arc $\widehat{DF}$ and major arc $\widehat{DEF}$.

There are a few helpful corollaries to the Inscribed Angle Theorem.

Corollary
If two inscribed angles intercept the same arc, then they are congruent.

EXAMPLE 4

Find $m\,\widehat{ST}$.

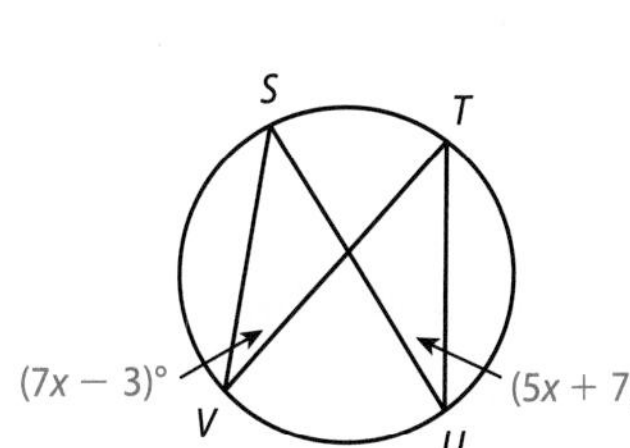

Inscribed ∠s that intercept the same arc are ≅.	$m\angle V = m\angle U$
Substitute.	$7x - 3 = 5x + 7$
Solve for x.	$x = 5$
Substitute for x.	$m\angle V = 7x - 3 = 7(5) - 3 = 32°$
An inscribed ∠ has half the measure of its intercepted arc.	$m\,\widehat{ST} = 64°$

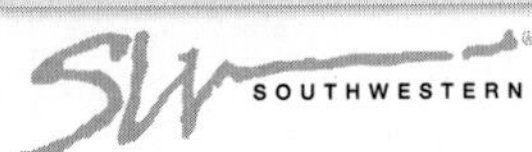

Corollaries

The next corollary follows from the fact that the measure of a semicircle is 180°.

Corollary
An angle inscribed in a semicircle is a right angle.

EXAMPLE 5

$\overline{QS}$ is a diameter. Find $m\angle Q$.

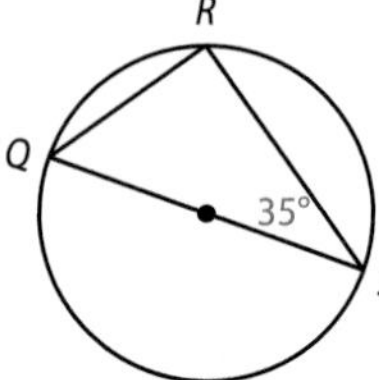

An $\angle$ inscribed in a semicircle is a right $\angle$.	$m\angle QRS = 90°$
Triangle Angle-Sum Theorem	$m\angle Q + 90 + 35 = 180$
	$m\angle Q = 55°$

EXAMPLE 6

Find $m\overset{\frown}{AB}$ given $\overset{\frown}{ABC}$ is a semicircle.

METHOD 1

$m\overset{\frown}{AB} = \frac{1}{2}m\angle C$. Find $m\angle C$.

An $\angle$ inscribed in a semicircle is a right $\angle$.	$m\angle B = 90°$
Triangle Angle-Sum Theorem	$41° + 90° + m\angle C = 180°$
	$m\angle C = 49°$
An inscribed $\angle$ has half the measure of its intercepted arc.	$m\angle C = \frac{1}{2}m\overset{\frown}{AB}$
	$49° = \frac{1}{2}m\overset{\frown}{AB}$
	$98° = m\overset{\frown}{AB}$

METHOD 2

Use the Arc Addition Postulate.

An inscribed $\angle$ has half the measure of its intercepted arc.	$m\angle A = \frac{1}{2}m\overset{\frown}{BC}$
Substitute for $m\angle A$.	$41° = \frac{1}{2}m\overset{\frown}{BC}$
Multiply both sides by 2.	$82° = m\overset{\frown}{BC}$
	$m\overset{\frown}{ABC} = 180°$
Arc Addition Postulate	$m\overset{\frown}{AB} + m\overset{\frown}{BC} = m\overset{\frown}{ABC}$
Substitute.	$m\overset{\frown}{AB} + 82° = 180°$
	$m\overset{\frown}{AB} = 98°$

To review the Arc Addition Postulate, go to *Arcs and Sectors* in *Circles*, p. 728.

A polygon is *inscribed* in a circle if all its vertices lie on the circle.

Corollary
If a quadrilateral is inscribed in a circle, then its opposite angles are supplementary.

EXAMPLE 7

Find $m\angle ADE$.

$m\angle ADC + 107° = 180°$

$m\angle ADC = 73°$

Linear Pair Theorem $m\angle ADE + m\angle ADC = 180°$

$m\angle ADE + 73° = 180°$

$m\angle ADE = 107°$

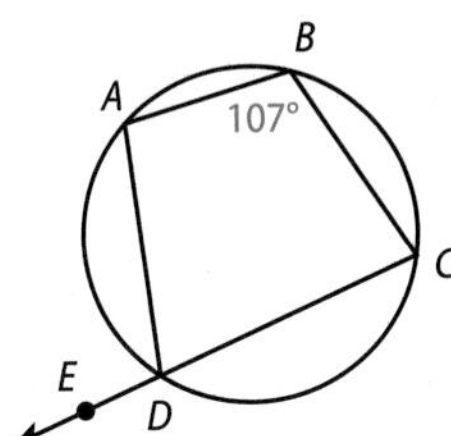

SEARCH

To see step-by-step videos of these problems, enter the page number into the SWadvantage.com Search Bar.

EXAMPLE 8

Find $m\angle I$.

STEP 1 Find the value of x.

Opposite ∠s of an inscribed quadrilateral are supplementary. $m\angle H + m\angle J = 180°$

Substitute. $85 + 11x - 4 = 180$

$x = 9$

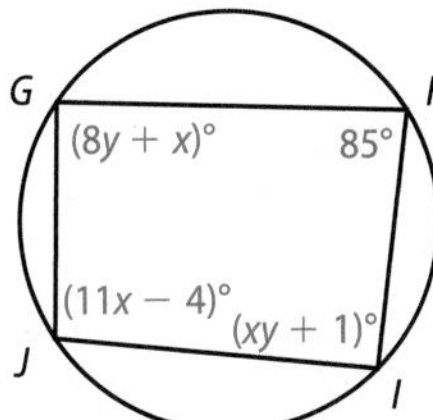

STEP 2 Find the value of y.

Opposite ∠s of an inscribed quadrilateral are supplementary. $m\angle I + m\angle G = 180°$

Substitute. $(xy + 1) + (8y + x) = 180$

Substitute 9 for x. $(9y + 1) + (8y + 9) = 180$

Solve for y. $y = 10$

STEP 3 Use the values of x and y to find $m\angle I$.

$m\angle I = xy + 1$

$m\angle I = (9)(10) + 1$

$m\angle I = 91°$

Properties of Inscribed Angles

The measure of an inscribed angle is half the measure of its intercepted arc.

Inscribed angles that intercept the same arc are congruent.

An angle inscribed in a semicircle is a right angle.

Opposite angles of an inscribed quadrilateral are supplementary.

Tangents, Chords, and Angles

Tangent-Chord Angle Theorem

The measure of an angle formed by a tangent and a chord is determined by the measure of the intercepted arc.

Tangent-Chord Angle Theorem
The measure of an angle whose sides are a tangent and a chord equals half the measure of the intercepted arc.

PROOF

There are three cases to consider: (1) the center of the circle lies on one side of the angle; (2) the center of the circle lies in the interior of the angle; and (3) the center of the circle lies in the exterior of the angle. Case 1 follows directly from this theorem: If a line is tangent to a circle, then it is perpendicular to the radius drawn to the point of tangency. We will prove the second case. The proof of the third case is very similar.

Given: Chord $\overline{AB}$ and tangent $\overline{BC}$ in $\odot O$

Prove: $m\angle ABC = \frac{1}{2} m\widehat{ADB}$

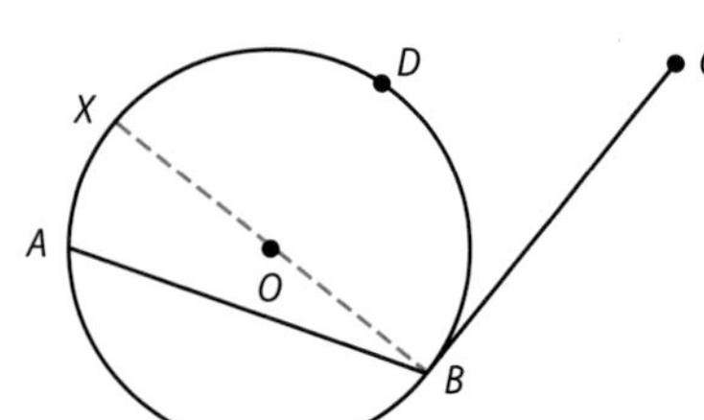

Draw diameter $\overline{XB}$. $\overline{XB}$ is perpendicular to the tangent, so $m\angle XBC = 90°$.

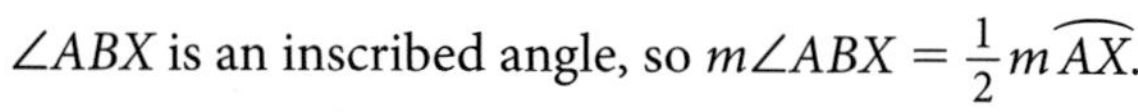

$\angle ABX$ is an inscribed angle, so $m\angle ABX = \frac{1}{2} m\widehat{AX}$.

By the Angle Addition Postulate, $m\angle ABC = m\angle ABX + \angle XBC$. By substitution:

$$m\angle ABC = \frac{1}{2} m\widehat{AX} + 90°$$

$$m\angle ABC = \frac{1}{2} m\widehat{AX} + \frac{1}{2} m\widehat{XDB}$$

$$m\angle ABC = \frac{1}{2}(m\widehat{AX} + m\widehat{XDB})$$

$$m\angle ABC = \frac{1}{2} m\widehat{ADB}$$

EXAMPLE 1

Find $m\angle EFG$.

Tangent-Chord Angle Theorem	$m\angle EFG = \frac{1}{2} m\widehat{EF}$
Substitute.	$m\angle EFG = \frac{1}{2}(104°)$
	$m\angle EFG = 52°$

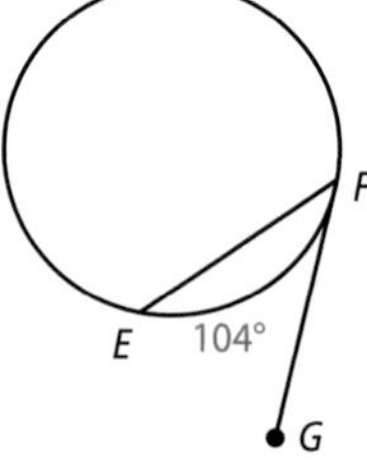

SEARCH

To see step-by-step videos of these problems, enter the page number into the SWadvantage.com Search Bar.

EXAMPLE 2

Find $m\overset{\frown}{JMK}$.

Tangent-Chord Angle Theorem $m\angle JKL = \frac{1}{2}m\overset{\frown}{JMK}$

Substitute. $111° = \frac{1}{2}m\overset{\frown}{JMK}$

$m\overset{\frown}{JMK} = 222°$

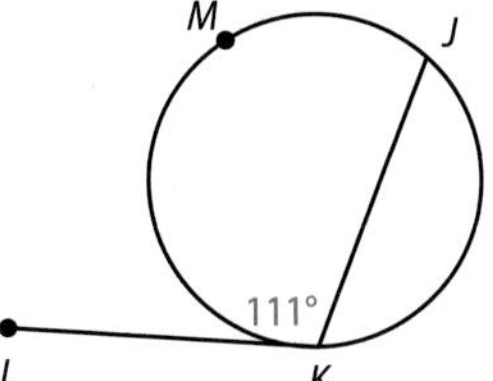

EXAMPLE 3

Find $m\angle TUV$.

$m\overset{\frown}{UWT} = 360° - m\overset{\frown}{UT} = 237°$

Tangent-Chord Angle Theorem $m\angle TUV = \frac{1}{2}m\overset{\frown}{UWT}$

Substitute. $m\angle TUV = \frac{1}{2}(237°)$

Simplify. $m\angle TUV = 118.5°$

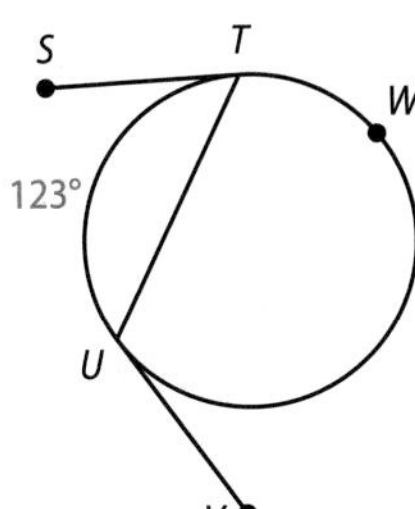

EXAMPLE 4

Find $m\overset{\frown}{PR}$.

STEP 1 Find $m\overset{\frown}{PRS}$.

$m\overset{\frown}{PRS} = 360° - m\overset{\frown}{PS}$

$m\overset{\frown}{PRS} = 360° - 140° = 220°$

STEP 2 Use the Tangent-Chord Angle Theorem to find $m\angle P$.

$m\angle P = \frac{1}{2}m\overset{\frown}{PRS}$

$m\angle P = \frac{1}{2}(220°) = 110°$

STEP 3 Use the Triangle Angle-Sum Theorem to find $m\angle S$.

$m\angle S + m\angle P + m\angle Q = 180°$

$m\angle S + 110° + 30° = 180°$

$m\angle S = 40°$

STEP 4 Use the Inscribed Angle Theorem to find $m\overset{\frown}{PR}$.

$\frac{1}{2}m\overset{\frown}{PR} = m\angle S$

$\frac{1}{2}m\overset{\frown}{PR} = 40°$

$m\overset{\frown}{PR} = 80°$

Try It This Way

Here is another way of stating the Tangent-Chord Angle Theorem: The measure of the arc intercepted by an angle whose sides are a tangent and a chord is twice the measure of the angle.

Watch Out!

You cannot use the Tangent-Chord Angle Theorem with $\angle Q$ because $\overline{SQ}$ is not a chord.

Tangent-Tangent Angle Theorem

When you draw two tangents from a point outside a circle, the angle formed by the tangents intercepts two arcs of the circle—a major arc and a minor arc.

Tangent-Tangent Angle Theorem

The measure of the angle formed by two tangents drawn from a point outside a circle equals half the difference of the measures of the intercepted arcs.

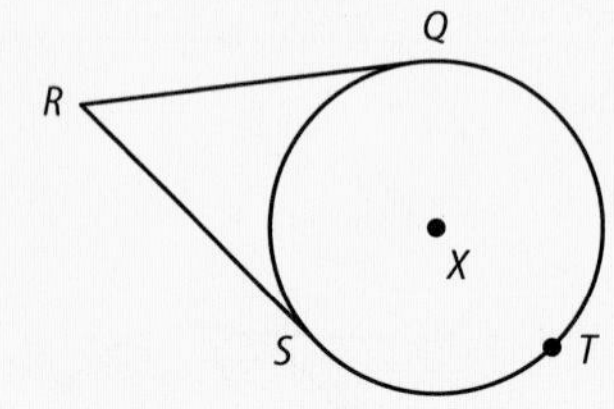

$m\angle QRS = \frac{1}{2}(m\overset{\frown}{QTS} - m\overset{\frown}{QS})$

PROOF

Given: $\overline{RQ}$ and $\overline{RS}$ are tangent to ⊙ X.

Prove: $m\angle R = \frac{1}{2}(m\overset{\frown}{QTS} - m\overset{\frown}{QS})$

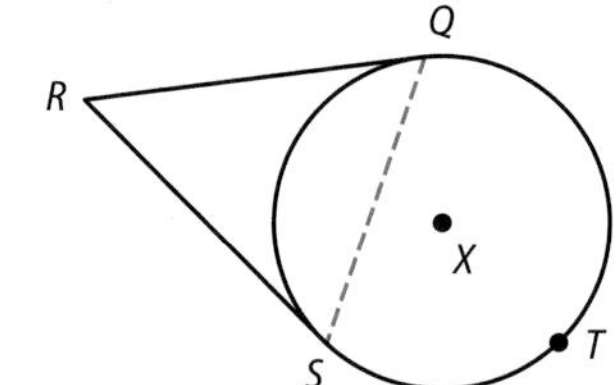

First note that $m\overset{\frown}{QS} + m\overset{\frown}{QTS} = 360°$, so $\frac{1}{2}(m\overset{\frown}{QS} + m\overset{\frown}{QTS}) = 180°$.

Draw chord QS. By the Tangent-Chord Angle Theorem, $m\angle S = \frac{1}{2}m\overset{\frown}{QS}$ and $m\angle Q = \frac{1}{2}m\overset{\frown}{QS}$.

You also know that $m\angle R + m\angle Q + m\angle S = 180°$ by the Triangle Angle-Sum Theorem.

By substitution: $m\angle R + \frac{1}{2}m\overset{\frown}{QS} + \frac{1}{2}m\overset{\frown}{QS} = \frac{1}{2}(m\overset{\frown}{QS} + m\overset{\frown}{QTS})$, which simplifies to $m\angle R = \frac{1}{2}(m\overset{\frown}{QTS} - m\overset{\frown}{QS})$.

Watch Out!

Remember to use three points when you name a major arc.

EXAMPLE 5

Find $m\angle BCD$.

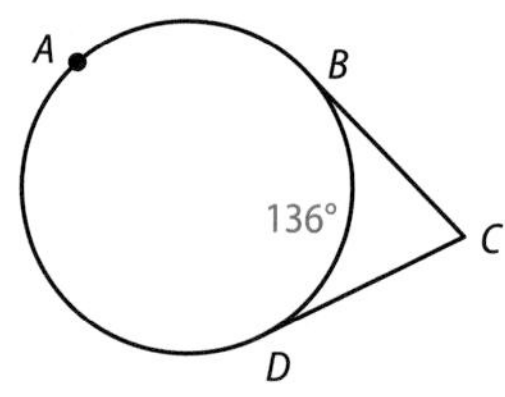

STEP 1 Find $m\overset{\frown}{BAD}$.

$m\overset{\frown}{BAD} + m\overset{\frown}{BD} = 360°$

$m\overset{\frown}{BAD} + 136° = 360°$

$m\overset{\frown}{BAD} = 224°$

STEP 2 Use the Tangent-Tangent Angle Theorem.

$m\angle BCD = \frac{1}{2}(m\overset{\frown}{BAD} - m\overset{\frown}{BD}) = \frac{1}{2}(224° - 136°)$

$m\angle BCD = 44°$

SEARCH

To see step-by-step videos of these problems, enter the page number into the SWadvantage.com Search Bar.

This corollary to the Tangent-Tangent Angle Theorem can make calculations simpler.

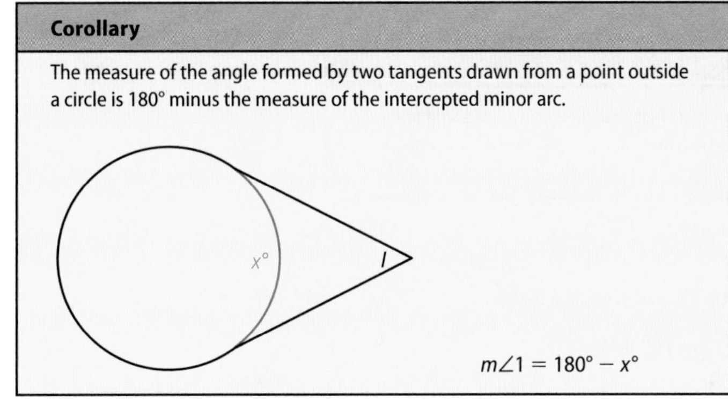

Corollary

The measure of the angle formed by two tangents drawn from a point outside a circle is 180° minus the measure of the intercepted minor arc.

Find $m\angle P$.

METHOD 1

Use the Tangent-Tangent Angle Theorem.

$m\angle P = \frac{1}{2}(m\widehat{QSR} - m\widehat{QR})$

$m\widehat{QR} = 360° - 250° = 110°$

$m\angle P = \frac{1}{2}(250° - 110°)$

$m\angle P = 70°$

METHOD 2

Use the corollary.

$m\angle P = 180° - m\widehat{QR}$

$m\widehat{QR} = 360° - 250° = 110°$

$m\angle P = 180° - 110°$

$m\angle P = 70°$

GOT TO KNOW!

Tangent Angles

The measure of an angle whose sides are a tangent and a chord equals half the measure of the intercepted arc.

The measure of the angle formed by two tangents drawn from a point outside a circle equals half the difference of the measures of the intercepted arcs.

EXAMPLE 7

Find $m\widehat{HJ}$.

Use the corollary.

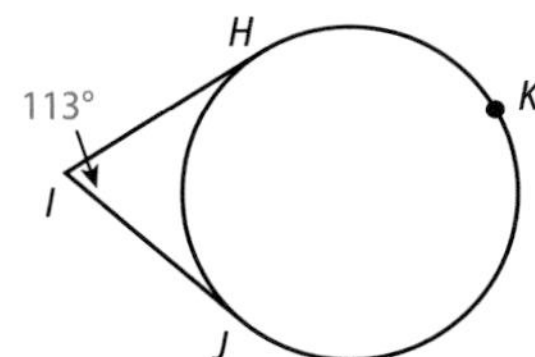

$m\angle HIJ = 180° - m\widehat{HJ}$

$113° = 180° - m\widehat{HJ}$

$m\widehat{HJ} = 67°$

Finding Other Angle Measures

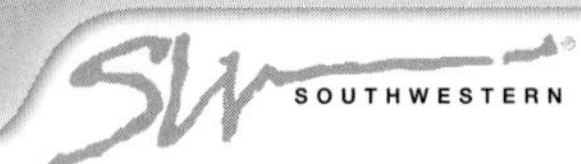

Chord-Chord Angle Theorem

The measure of an angle formed when two chords intersect in a circle is determined by the measures of the intercepted arcs.

Chord-Chord Angle Theorem
If two chords intersect in a circle, the measure of an angle formed is half the sum of the measures of arcs intercepted by the angle and its vertical angle.

PROOF

Given: Intersecting chords $\overline{AC}$ and $\overline{BD}$

Prove: $m\angle BEC = \frac{1}{2}(m\widehat{BC} + m\widehat{AD})$

Begin by drawing $\overline{AB}$.

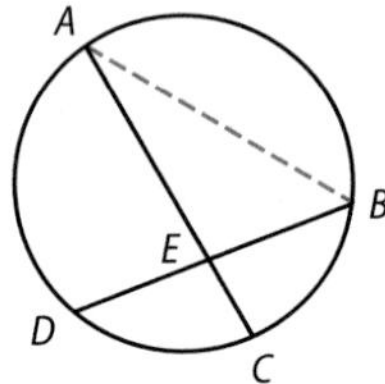

To review the Exterior Angle Theorem, go to *Triangle Angle-Sum Theorem*, p. 668.

Statements	Reasons
1. $m\angle BEC = m\angle A + m\angle B$	1. The measure of an exterior ∠ is the sum of the measures of its remote interior ∠s.
2. $m\angle A = \frac{1}{2}m\widehat{BC}$, $m\angle B = \frac{1}{2}m\widehat{AD}$	2. The measure of an inscribed ∠ is half the measure of its intercepted arc.
3. $m\angle BEC = \frac{1}{2}m\widehat{BC} + \frac{1}{2}m\widehat{AD}$	3. Substitution
4. $m\angle BEC = \frac{1}{2}(m\widehat{BC} + m\widehat{AD})$	4. Distributive Property

EXAMPLE 1

Find each measure.

a. $m\angle GJH$

Chord-Chord Angle Theorem

$m\angle GJH = \frac{1}{2}(145° + 43°)$

$m\angle GJH = 94°$

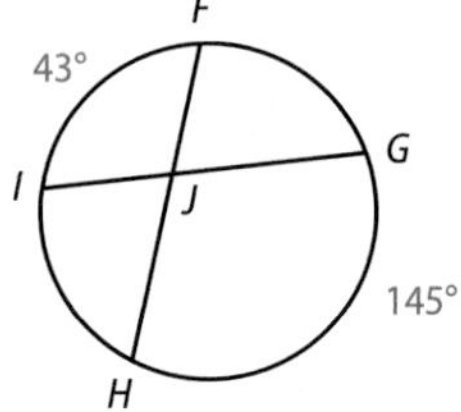

b. $m\widehat{AB}$

Chord-Chord Angle Theorem

$82° = \frac{1}{2}(m\widehat{AB} + 37°)$

$m\widehat{AB} = 127°$

EXAMPLE 2

Find $m\angle SUT$.

METHOD 1

	$m\overset{\frown}{QR} + m\overset{\frown}{RS} + m\overset{\frown}{ST} + m\overset{\frown}{TQ} = 360°$
Substitute given values.	$m\overset{\frown}{QR} + 48° + m\overset{\frown}{ST} + 156° = 360°$
	$m\overset{\frown}{QR} + m\overset{\frown}{ST} = 156°$
Chord-Chord Angle Theorem	$m\angle SUT = \frac{1}{2}(m\overset{\frown}{QR} + m\overset{\frown}{ST})$
Substitute and simplify.	$m\angle SUT = \frac{1}{2}(156°)$
	$m\angle SUT = 78°$

METHOD 2

Chord-Chord Angle Theorem	$m\angle QUT = \frac{1}{2}(m\overset{\frown}{TQ} + m\overset{\frown}{RS})$
Substitute and simplify.	$m\angle QUT = \frac{1}{2}(156° + 48°) = 102°$
Linear Pair Theorem	$m\angle SUT + m\angle QUT = 180°$
Substitute.	$m\angle SUT + 102° = 180°$
	$m\angle SUT = 78°$

SEARCH

To see step-by-step videos of these problems, enter the page number into the SWadvantage.com Search Bar.

EXAMPLE 3

Find $m\overset{\frown}{CD}$.

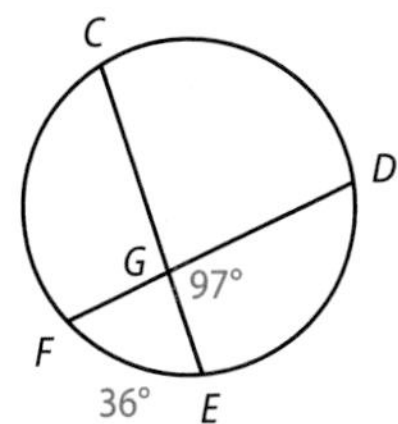

Linear Pair Theorem	$m\angle CGD + m\angle DGE = 180°$
Substitute.	$m\angle CGD + 97° = 180°$
	$m\angle CGD = 83°$
Chord-Chord Angle Theorem	$m\angle CGD = \frac{1}{2}(m\overset{\frown}{CD} + m\overset{\frown}{FE})$
Substitute.	$83° = \frac{1}{2}(m\overset{\frown}{CD} + 36°)$
	$m\overset{\frown}{CD} = 130°$

GOT TO KNOW!

Chord-Chord Angle Theorem

If two chords intersect in a circle, the measure of an angle formed is half the sum of the measures of arcs intercepted by the angle and its vertical angle.

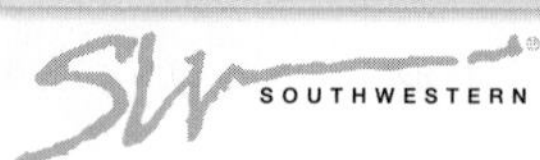

Secant-Secant Angle Theorem

A **secant** is a line that intersects a circle in two points. The angle formed by two secants drawn from a point outside a circle intercepts two arcs.

Secant-Secant Angle Theorem
The measure of the angle formed by two secants drawn from a point outside a circle equals half the difference of the measures of the intercepted arcs.

PROOF

Given: Intersecting secants $\overline{US}$ and $\overline{UW}$

Prove: $m\angle U = \frac{1}{2}(m\overset{\frown}{SW} - m\overset{\frown}{TV})$

Begin by drawing $\overline{VS}$.

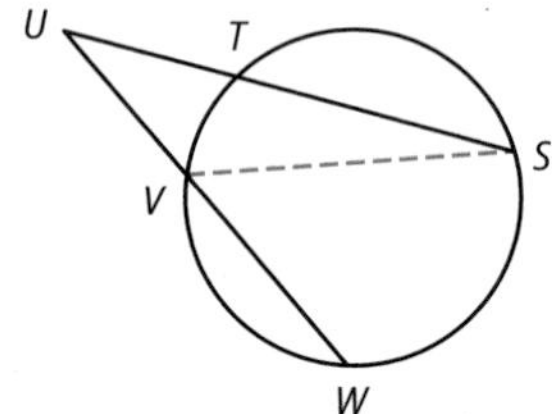

Statements	Reasons
1. $m\angle SVW = \frac{1}{2}m\overset{\frown}{SW}, m\angle S = \frac{1}{2}m\overset{\frown}{TV}$	1. The measure of the inscribed ∠ is half the measure of its intercepted arc.
2. $m\angle SVW = m\angle U + m\angle S$	2. The measure of the exterior ∠ is the sum of the measures of its remote interior∠s.
3. $m\angle U = m\angle SVW - m\angle S$	3. Subtraction Property of Equality
4. $m\angle U = \frac{1}{2}m\overset{\frown}{SW} - \frac{1}{2}m\overset{\frown}{TV}$	4. Substitution
5. $m\angle U = \frac{1}{2}(m\overset{\frown}{SW} - m\overset{\frown}{TV})$	5. Distributive Property

EXAMPLE 4

SEARCH

To see step-by-step videos of these problems, enter the page number into the SWadvantage.com Search Bar.

Find each measure.

a. $m\angle P$

Secant-Secant Angle Theorem $\quad m\angle P = \frac{1}{2}(m\overset{\frown}{AD} - m\overset{\frown}{CB})$

Substitute. $\quad m\angle P = \frac{1}{2}(80° - 40°) = 20°$

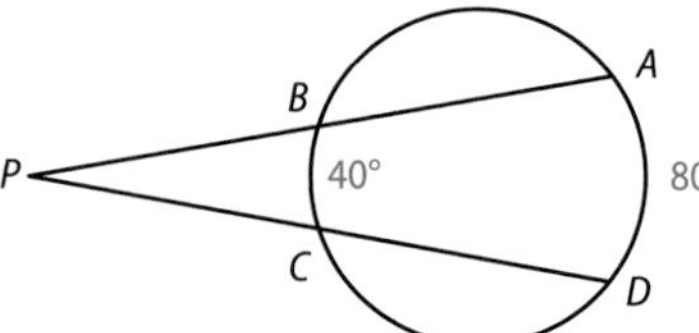

b. $m\overset{\frown}{XY}$

Secant-Secant Angle Theorem $\quad m\angle V = \frac{1}{2}(m\overset{\frown}{WZ} - m\overset{\frown}{XY})$

Substitute. $\quad 45° = \frac{1}{2}(120° - m\overset{\frown}{XY})$

$m\overset{\frown}{XY} = 30°$

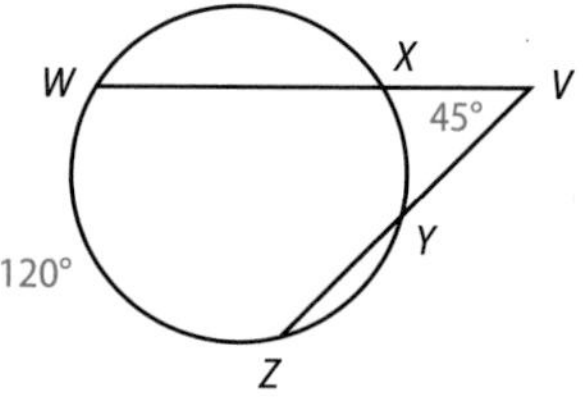

EXAMPLE 5

Find $m\angle J$ in $\odot O$.

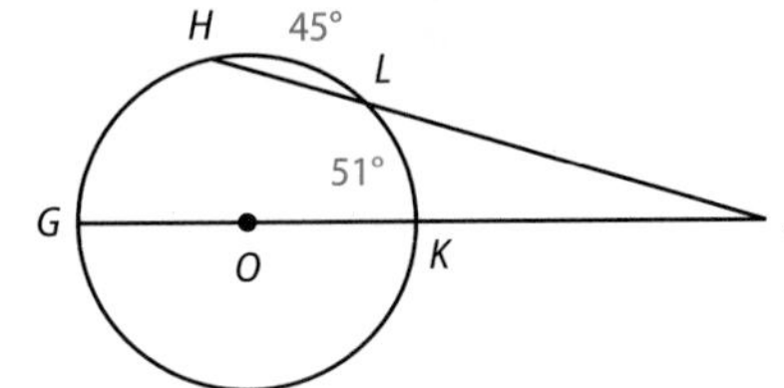

STEP 1 Find $m\overset{\frown}{GH}$.

$\overline{GK}$ is a diameter, so $\overset{\frown}{GHK}$ is a semicircle and $m\overset{\frown}{GHK} = 180°$.

Arc Addition Postulate $\quad m\overset{\frown}{GHK} = m\overset{\frown}{GH} + m\overset{\frown}{HL} + m\overset{\frown}{LK}$

Substitute. $\quad 180° = m\overset{\frown}{GH} + 45° + 51°$

$$m\overset{\frown}{GH} = 84°$$

STEP 2 Use the Secant-Secant Angle Theorem.

$$m\angle J = \frac{1}{2}(m\overset{\frown}{GH} - m\overset{\frown}{LK})$$

Substitute. $\quad m\angle J = \frac{1}{2}(84° - 51°)$

$$m\angle J = 16.5°$$

To review the Arc Addition Postulate, go to *Arcs and Sectors* in *Circles*, p. 728.

EXAMPLE 6

Find $m\overset{\frown}{MO}$.

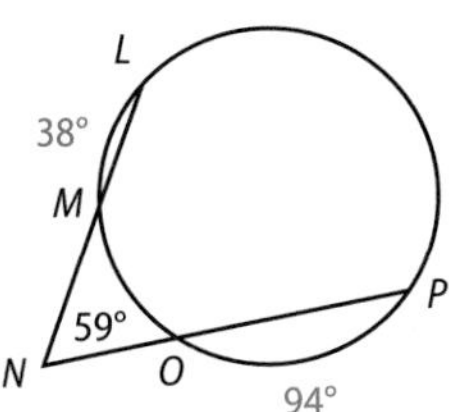

$$m\overset{\frown}{MO} + m\overset{\frown}{OP} + m\overset{\frown}{ML} + m\overset{\frown}{LP} = 360°$$

$$m\overset{\frown}{MO} + 94° + 38° + m\overset{\frown}{LP} = 360°$$

$$m\overset{\frown}{MO} + m\overset{\frown}{LP} = 228°$$

Let $m\overset{\frown}{MO} = x$, then $m\overset{\frown}{LP} = 228 - x$.

Secant-Secant Angle Theorem $\quad m\angle N = \frac{1}{2}(m\overset{\frown}{LP} - m\overset{\frown}{MO})$

Substitute. $\quad m\angle N = \frac{1}{2}(228 - x - x)$

Substitute and simplify. $\quad 59 = \frac{1}{2}(228 - x - x) = \frac{1}{2}(228 - 2x)$

$$59 = 114 - x$$

$$x = 55$$

$m\overset{\frown}{MO} = 55°$

Watch Out

Be sure you use the Distributive Property properly:

$\frac{1}{2}(228 - 2x)$

$= \frac{1}{2}(228) - \frac{1}{2}(2x)$

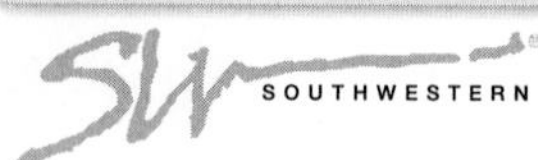

Secant-Tangent Angle Theorem

When you draw a secant and a tangent to a circle from a point outside the circle, the angle formed intercepts two arcs of the circle.

Secant-Tangent Theorem

The measure of the angle formed by a secant and a tangent drawn from a point in the exterior of a circle equals half the difference of the measures of the intercepted arcs.

$m\angle XYZ = \frac{1}{2}(m\overparen{WZ} - m\overparen{XZ})$

PROOF

Given: secant $\overline{WY}$ and tangent $\overline{YZ}$

Prove: $m\angle Y = \frac{1}{2}(m\overparen{WZ} - m\overparen{XZ})$

Begin by drawing $\overline{XZ}$.

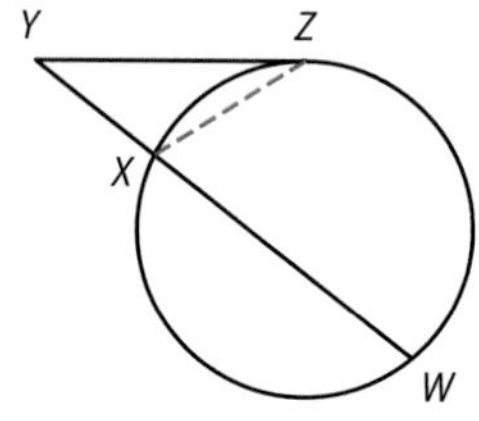

For a review of the Tangent-Chord Angle Theorem, go to *Tangents, Chords, and Angles* in *Circles*, p. 748.

Statements	Reasons
1. $m\angle ZXW = \frac{1}{2}m\overparen{WZ}$	1. The measure of an inscribed ∠ is half the measure of its intercepted arc.
2. $m\angle XZY = \frac{1}{2}m\overparen{XZ}$	2. Tangent-Chord Angle Theorem
3. $m\angle ZXW = m\angle Y + m\angle XZY$	3. The measure of an exterior ∠ is the sum of the measures of its remote interior∠s.
4. $m\angle Y = m\angle ZXW - m\angle XZY$	4. Subtraction Property of Equality
5. $m\angle Y = \frac{1}{2}m\overparen{WZ} - \frac{1}{2}m\overparen{XZ}$	5. Substitution
6. $m\angle Y = \frac{1}{2}(m\overparen{WZ} - m\overparen{XZ})$	6. Distributive Property

EXAMPLE 7

Find $m\angle S$.

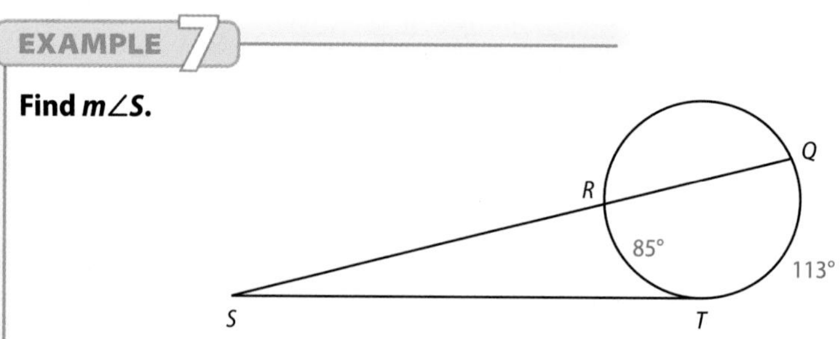

Secant-Tangent Angle Theorem $\quad m\angle S = \frac{1}{2}(m\overparen{QT} - m\overparen{RT})$

Substitute. $\quad m\angle S = \frac{1}{2}(113° - 85°)$

$m\angle S = 14°$

EXAMPLE 8

Find $m\angle X$.

$$m\overset{\frown}{WZ} + m\overset{\frown}{YZ} + m\overset{\frown}{WY} = 360°$$
$$162° + 74° + m\overset{\frown}{WY} = 360°$$
$$m\overset{\frown}{WY} = 124°$$

Secant-Tangent Theorem
$$m\angle X = \frac{1}{2}(m\overset{\frown}{WZ} - m\overset{\frown}{WY})$$
$$m\angle X = \frac{1}{2}(162° - 124°)$$
$$m\angle X = 19°$$

SEARCH

To see step-by-step videos of these problems, enter the page number into the SWadvantage.com Search Bar.

EXAMPLE 9

Find $m\overset{\frown}{BD}$.

Use the Secant-Tangent Theorem.

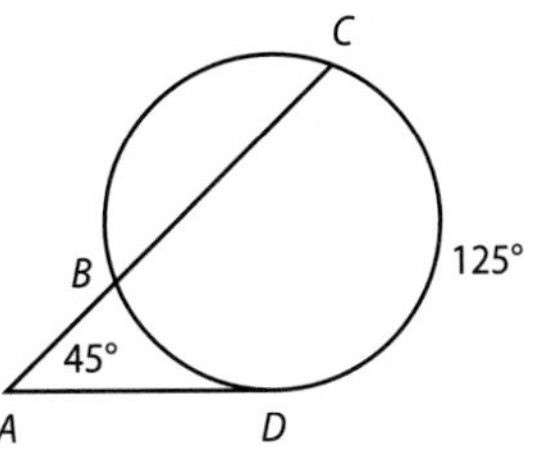

$m\angle A = \frac{1}{2}(m\overset{\frown}{CD} - m\overset{\frown}{BD})$

$45 = \frac{1}{2}(125 - m\overset{\frown}{BD})$

$90 = 125 - m\overset{\frown}{BD}$

$m\overset{\frown}{BD} = 125 - 90 = 35°$

GOT TO KNOW!

Angle Summary

If the vertex of an angle is **ON** a circle, the measure of the angle is **HALF** the measure of the intercepted arc.
- Inscribed Angle Theorem
- Tangent-Chord Angle Theorem

If the vertex of an angle is **INSIDE** a circle, the measure of the angle is **HALF** the **SUM** of the intercepted arcs.
- Chord-Chord Angle Theorem

If the vertex of an angle is **OUTSIDE** a circle, the measure of the angle is **HALF** the **DIFFERENCE** of the intercepted arcs.
- Tangent-Tangent Angle Theorem
- Secant-Secant Angle Theorem
- Secant-Tangent Angle Theorem

Finding Segment Lengths

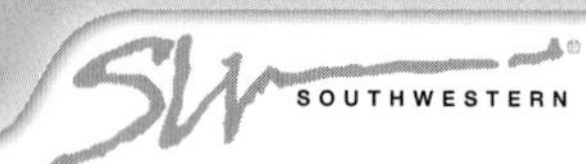

GOT TO KNOW!

Segments and Circles

This theorem deals with chords, which are segments whose endpoints are on a circle. A segment that intersects a circle, and whose endpoints are outside the circle, is part of a secant or a tangent.

Segments Formed by Two Chords

Four segments are formed when two chords intersect in the interior of a circle. The following theorem shows how their lengths are related.

Two-Chords Theorem

If two chords intersect inside a circle, then the product of the segment lengths of one chord is equal to the product of the segment lengths of the other.

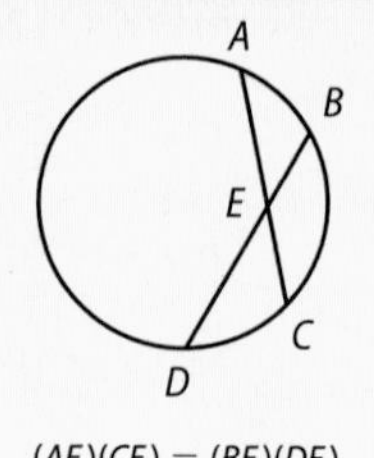

$(AE)(CE) = (BE)(DE)$

PROOF

Given: Chords $\overline{AC}$ and $\overline{BD}$ intersect at point *E*.

Prove: $(AE)(CE) = (BE)(DE)$

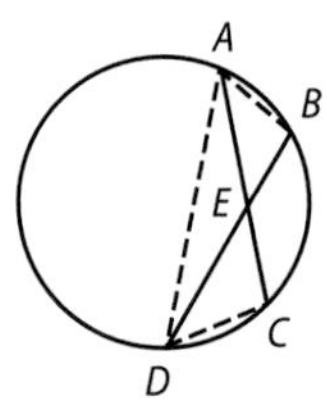

Statements	Reasons
1. $\angle AEB \cong \angle DEC$	1. Vertical angles are congruent.
2. $\angle ABE \cong \angle DCE$	2. Inscribed $\angle$s subtended by same chord are $\cong$.
3. $\triangle AEB \sim \triangle DEC$	3. AA similarity
4. $\frac{AE}{DE} = \frac{BE}{CE}$	4. Properties of similarity
5. $(AE)(CE) = (BE)(DE)$	5. Cross multiply

Need More HELP

For help working with similar triangles, go to *Proving Triangles Similar* on p. 792.

EXAMPLE 1

Find each measure.

a. *QU*

Products of segment lengths are =.	$(QU)(SU) = (TU)(RU)$
Substitute given values.	$(QU)(8) = (16)(9)$
Simplify.	$8(QU) = 144$
Divide both sides by 8.	$QU = 18$

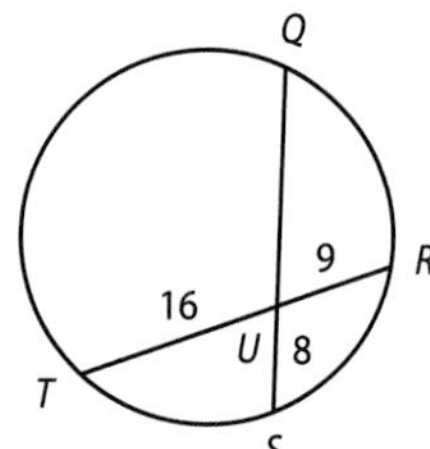

b. *JH*

Products of segment lengths are =.	$(JK)(HK) = (GK)(IK)$
Substitute given values.	$(12)(HK) = (8)(15)$
Simplify.	$12(HK) = 120$
Divide both sides by 12.	$HK = 10$
Segment addition	$JH = JK + HK = 12 + 10 = 22$

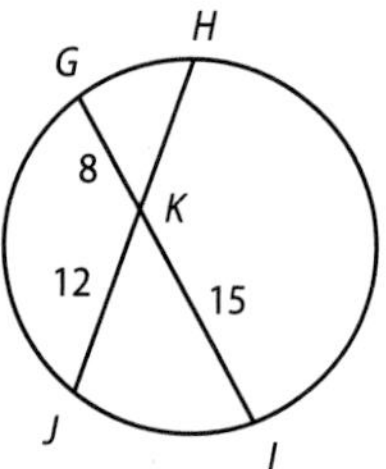

Watch Out!

When you write the products of the segments, be sure the lengths multiplied together represent parts of the *same* segment.

Algebra and Equations

The Two-Chords Theorem may lead to a quadratic equation, or the solution may rely on other relationships between chords, diameters, and arcs. The next example illustrates those kinds of problems.

EXAMPLE 2

a. Find *LP*.

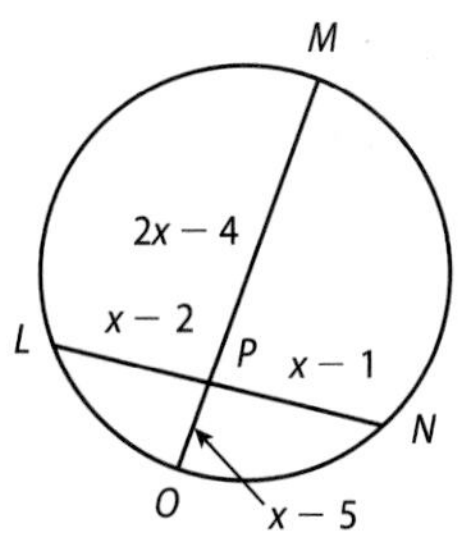

Products of segment lengths are =.	$(LP)(NP) = (MP)(OP)$
Substitute given values.	$(x-2)(x-1) = (2x-4)(x-5)$
Simplify.	$x^2 - 3x + 2 = 2x^2 - 14x + 20$
Combine like terms.	$x^2 - 11x + 18 = 0$
Factor.	$(x-2)(x-9) = 0$
Solve for x.	$x = 2$ or $x = 9$

If $x = 2$, then three of the segment lengths are less than or equal to 0. Length must be positive, so $x = 9$.

Substitute for x.	$LP = (9) - 2 = 7$

b. Find *QU* given *TR* = 53.

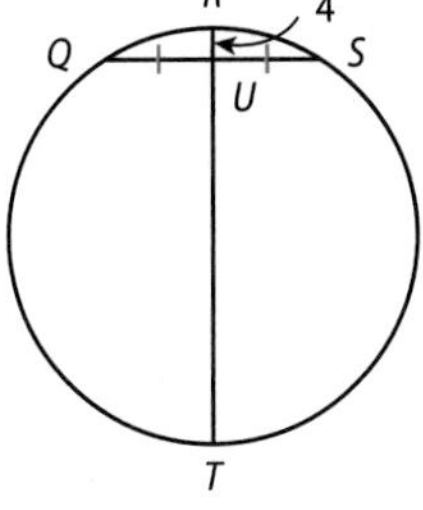

Segment addition	$TU + RU = TR$
Substitute given values.	$TU + 4 = 53$
Solve for TU.	$TU = 49$
Product of segment lengths is =.	$(QU)(SU) = (TU)(RU)$
Substitute. Also, $QU = SU$.	$(QU)(QU) = (49)(4)$
	$(QU)(QU) = 196$
Take the square root of both sides.	$QU = 14$

c. Find *BD*.

(3x + 8)° B 3 (5x − 10)° A C E x D

⊥ diameter bisects arc.	$m\widehat{AB} = m\widehat{BC}$
Substitute given values.	$3x + 8 = 5x - 10$
Solve for x.	$18 = 2x$
	$x = 9$
⊥ diameter bisects chord.	$CE = AE = 9$
Products of segment lengths are =.	$(BE)(DE) = (CE)(AE)$
Substitute.	$(3)(DE) = (9)(9)$
Simplify.	$3(DE) = 81$
Divide both sides by 3.	$DE = 27$
Segment addition	$BD = DE + BE$
Substitute.	$BD = 27 + 3 = 30$

Need More HELP

The algebra skills in Part (a), multiplying binomials and collecting like terms, and then solving a quadratic equation, are reviewed in Book 2, on pp. 1608 and 1702.

SEARCH

To see step-by-step videos of these problems, enter the page number into the SWadvantage.com Search Bar.

GOT TO KNOW!

Math Skills

Even when a question is illustrated using a geometry diagram, algebra skills are often needed to answer that problem. To solve problems, you often have to use your skills from many branches of mathematics.

Segments Formed by Intersecting Secants

Another theorem that relates circles and parts of segments involves secants. A **secant segment**, such as $\overline{AC}$, is a segment of a secant that has one endpoint on a circle and one endpoint outside of the circle. It also crosses the circle at one other point. An **external secant segment**, such as $\overline{AB}$, is the segment between the circle and the endpoint that is outside the circle.

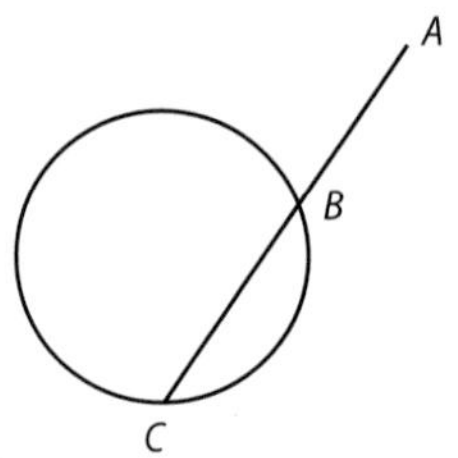

Watch Out!

The "whole secant segment" consists of the chord *plus* the external segment.

Two-Secant Theorem

If two secants intersect outside a circle, then the product of the lengths of one secant segment and its external segment is equal to the product of the other secant segment and its external segment.

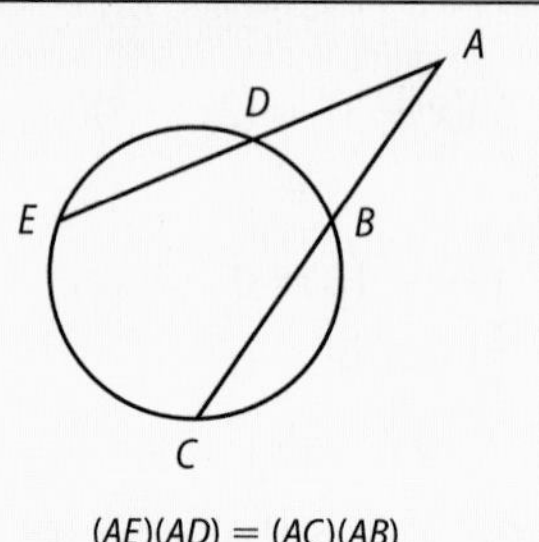

$(AE)(AD) = (AC)(AB)$

PROOF

Given: Secant segments $\overline{AE}$ and $\overline{AC}$ intersect at point *A*.

Prove: $(AE)(AD) = (AC)(AB)$

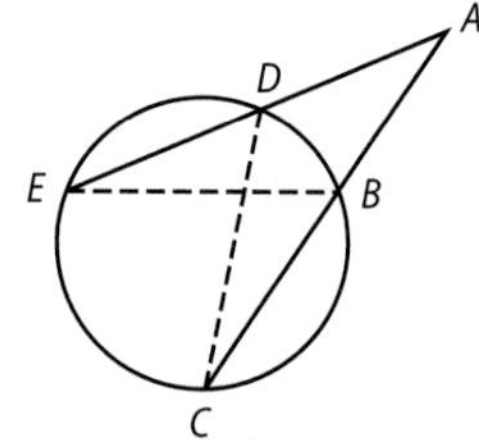

Statements	Reasons
1. $\angle A \cong \angle A$	1. Reflexive property of congruence
2. $\angle AEB \cong \angle ACD$	2. Inscribed $\angle$s subtended by same arc are $\cong$.
3. $\triangle AEB \sim \triangle ACD$	3. AA similarity
4. $\frac{AE}{AC} = \frac{AB}{AD}$	4. Properties of similarity
5. $(AE)(AD) = (AC)(AB)$	5. Cross multiply

EXAMPLE 3

Find *YZ*.

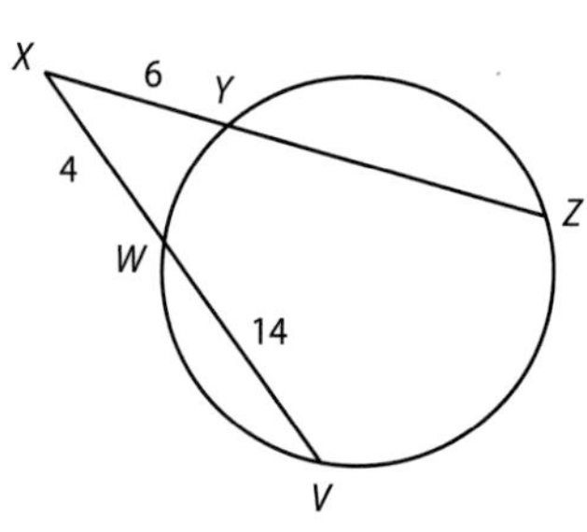

Products of segments lengths are =.	$(XZ)(XY) = (XV)(XW)$
Substitute given values.	$(XZ)(6) = (18)(4)$
Multiply.	$(XZ)(6) = 72$
Divide both sides by 6.	$XZ = 12$
Segment addition	$XY + YZ = XZ$
Substitute.	$6 + YZ = 12$
Subtract 6 from each side.	$YZ = 6$

SEARCH

To see step-by-step videos of these problems, enter the page number into the SWadvantage.com Search Bar.

Multi-Step Problems

The Two-Secant Theorem may be part of a problem that includes solving a quadratic equation, or a single problem may involve both the Two-Secants Theorem and the Two-Chords Theorem. The next example illustrates those kinds of situations.

EXAMPLE 4

a. Find the value of *x*.

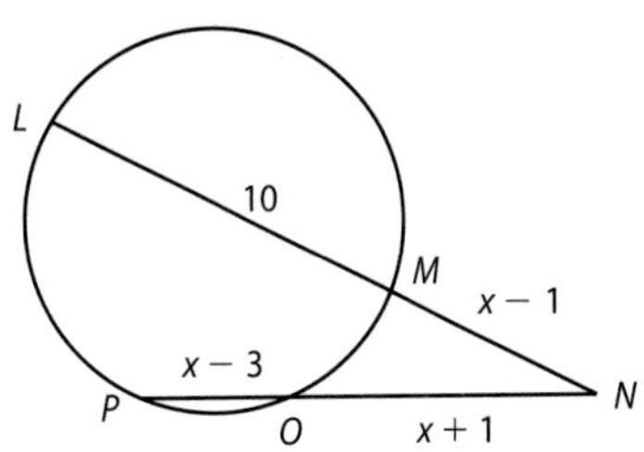

Products of segments are =.	$(PN)(ON) = (LN)(MN)$
Segment addition	$PN = PO + ON$
Substitute and simplify.	$= (x - 3) + (x + 1) = 2x - 2$
Segment addition	$LN = MN + LM$
Substitute and simplify.	$= (x - 1) + (10) = x + 9$
Substitute into the top equation.	$(2x - 2)(x + 1) = (x + 9)(x - 1)$
Multiply.	$2x^2 - 2 = x^2 + 8x - 9$
Combine like terms.	$x^2 - 8x + 7 = 0$
Factor.	$(x - 7)(x - 1) = 0$
Solve for *x*.	$x = 7$ or $x = 1$

If $x = 1$, then two of the segment lengths are less than or equal to 0. The length of a segment cannot be 0, so $x = 7$.

b. Find *RS*. Round to the nearest tenth if answer is not a whole number.

Plan: Use the Two-Chords Theorem to find *UX*. Then use the Two-Secants Theorem.

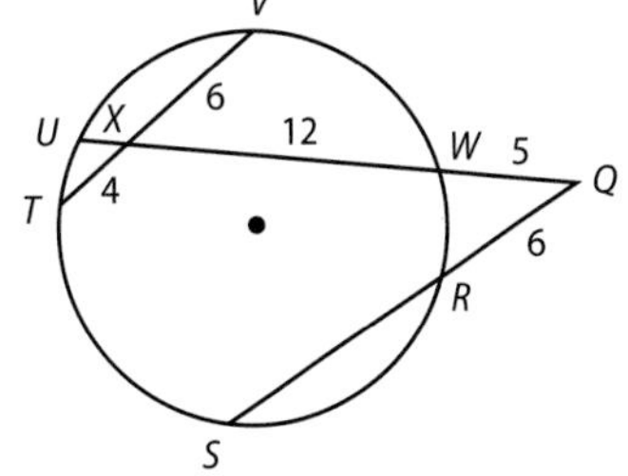

Products of segment lengths are =.	$(WX)(UX) = (VX)(TX)$
Substitute given values.	$(12)(UX) = (6)(4)$
Divide each side by 12.	$UX = 2$
Products of segments are =.	$(QS)(QR) = (QU)(QW)$
Segment addition	$QU = QW + WX + XU$
Substitute.	$= 5 + 12 + 2 = 19$
Substitute.	$(QS)(6) = (19)(5) = 95$
Divide each side by 6.	$QS \approx 15.8$
Segment addition	$QR + RS = QS$
Substitute.	$6 + RS \approx 15.8$
Subtract.	$RS \approx 9.8$

Watch Out!

Be sure you can follow the "flow" of the solution to the Part (a) problem. The first step is to write an equation using two pairs of segments. The second step is to find values for two of the segments, *PN* and *LN*. The third step is to substitute those values for *PN* and *LN* into the top equation and then solve for *x*.

GOT TO KNOW!

Making a Plan

It can be useful to write a plan for a problem. For Part (b), the plan is to use two of the theorems covered in this section.

Segments Formed by Secants and Tangents

Recall that a tangent to a circle touches the circle at exactly one point. A **tangent segment** is a segment of a tangent line that has one endpoint on a circle.

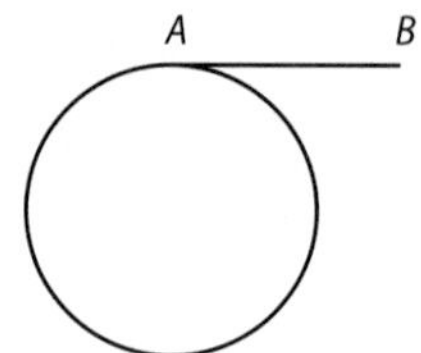

$\overline{AB}$ is a tangent segment.

Secant-Tangent Theorem

If a secant and a tangent intersect outside a circle, then the product of the lengths of the secant segment and its external segment is equal to the length of the tangent segment squared.

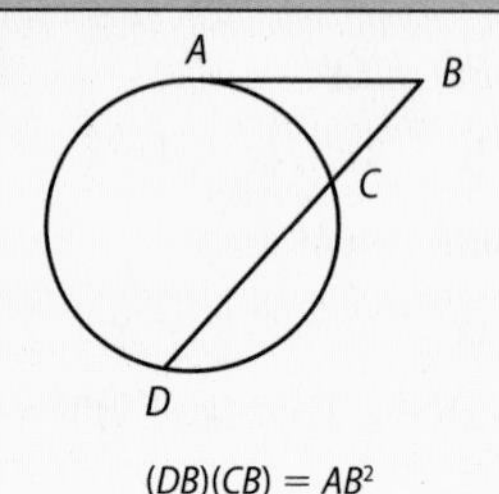

$(DB)(CB) = AB^2$

PROOF

Given: Secant segment $\overline{DB}$ and tangent segment $\overline{AB}$ intersect at point *B*.

Prove: $(DB)(CB) = AB^2$

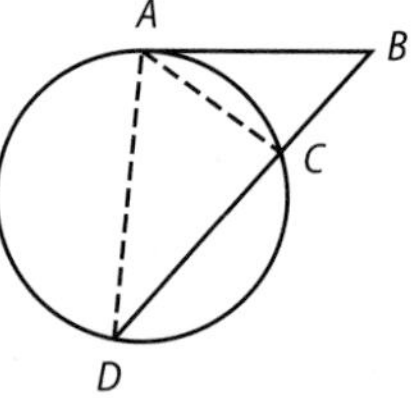

For help with the relationship between a tangent and a chord, go to *Tangents, Chords, and Angles* on p. 748.

Statements	Reasons
1. $\angle B \cong \angle B$	1. Reflexive property of $\cong$
2. $m\angle CAB = \frac{1}{2} m\widehat{AC}$	2. Tangent-Chord Angle Theorem
3. $m\angle ADB = \frac{1}{2} m\widehat{AC}$	3. Inscribed $\angle$ measures half of its intercepted arc.
4. $\angle CAB \cong \angle ADB$	4. Transitive property of $\cong$.
5. $\triangle CAB \sim \triangle ADB$	5. AA similarity
6. $\frac{AB}{DB} = \frac{CB}{AB}$	6. Properties of similarity
7. $(DB)(CB) = AB^2$	7. Cross multiply

EXAMPLE 5

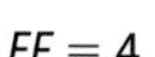

Find *EF*.

Secant-Tangent Theorem	$EF^2 = (FH)(FG)$
Substitute given values.	$EF^2 = (2 + 6)(2)$
Multiply.	$EF^2 = 16$
Solve.	$EF = 4$

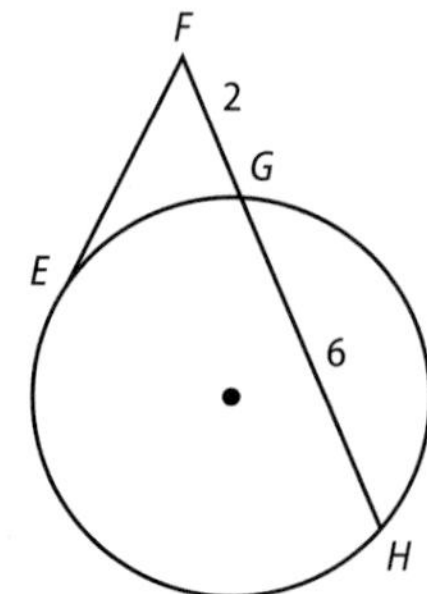

SEARCH

To see step-by-step videos of these problems, enter the page number into the SWadvantage.com Search Bar.

The next example illustrates problems that apply the Secant-Tangent Theorem.

EXAMPLE 6

a. Find *LJ*.

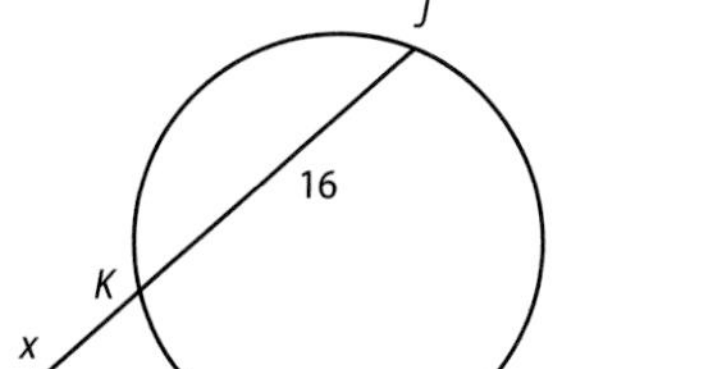

Secant-Tangent Theorem	$LM^2 = (LJ)(LK)$
Segment addition	$LJ = LK + KJ$
	$= x + 16$
Substitute.	$15^2 = (x + 16)x$
Multiply.	$225 = x^2 + 16x$
Write in standard form.	$x^2 + 16x - 225 = 0$
Factor.	$(x + 25)(x - 9) = 0$
Solve for *LK*.	$x = -25$ or $x = 9$

Length cannot be negative, so $x = 9$.

Segment addition	$LJ = 9 + 16 = 25$

b. Find *SU*. Round to the nearest tenth if necessary.

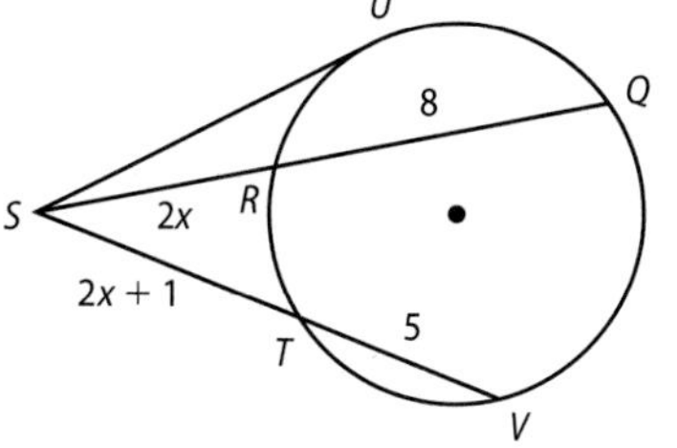

Two-Secants Theorem	$(SV)(ST) = (SQ)(SR)$
Substitute given values.	$(2x + 6)(2x + 1) = (2x + 8)(2x)$
Multiply.	$4x^2 + 14x + 6 = 4x^2 + 16x$
Solve for *x*.	$6 = 2x$
	$3 = x$

The length of $\overline{SR}$ is $2x = 2(3) = 6$.

Secant-Tangent Theorem	$SU^2 = (SQ)(SR)$
Substitute.	$= (6 + 8)(6)$
Multiply.	$= 84$
Take the square root of both sides.	$SU \approx 9.2$

Watch Out!

Be sure to understand the "flow" of the steps for the solution to Part (b). The first step is to write an equation using the segments of two secants and the second step is to solve that equation. The third step is to write an equation using the Secant-Tangent Theorem. The final step is to substitute values into that equation and then solve that equation for the unknown length *SU*.

GOT TO KNOW!

Segment Length Relationships

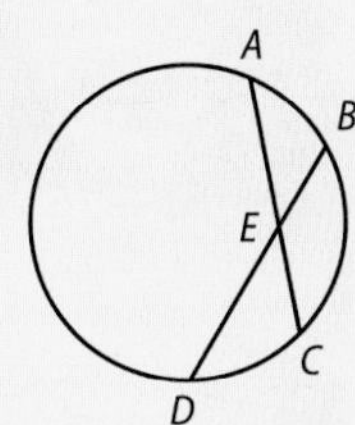

Two-Chords Theorem

$(AE)(CE) = (BE)(DE)$

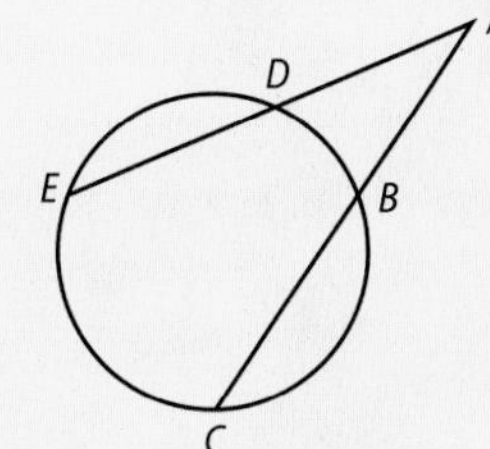

Two-Secants Theorem

$(AE)(AD) = (AC)(AB)$

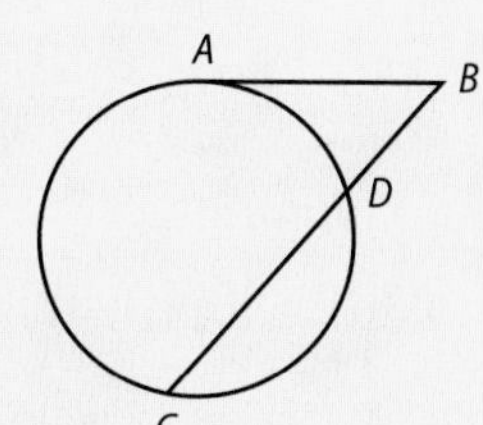

Secant-Tangent Theorem

$(CB)(DB) = AB^2$

Congruence

What Came Before?

- Congruence of angles and line segments
- Properties and classification of triangles

What's This About?

- Proving figures congruent
- Different ways to prove triangles congruent
- Special properties of isosceles and equilateral triangles

Practical Apps

- Landscape artists use congruent figures when designing gardens.
- Truss bridges use congruent triangles to support the weight of the bridge.

just for FUN!

Q: What did the complementary angle say to the isosceles triangle?

A: Nice legs.

CONTENTS UPLOAD DOWNLOAD

Geometry

You can find more practice problems online by visiting:
www.SWadvantage.com

Congruent Figures

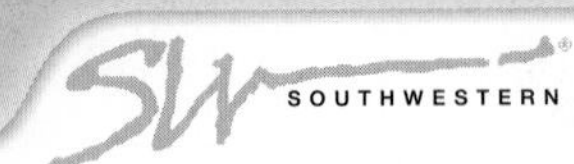

Congruence

Figures that have the exact same size and shape are **congruent**.

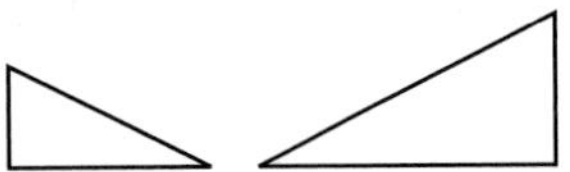

These two figures are the same shape but not the same size. They are not congruent.

These two figures are not the same size and not the same shape. They are not congruent.

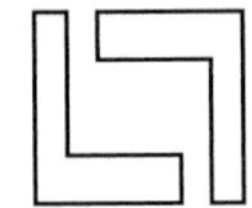

These figures are the same size and shape. They are congruent.

Watch Out !

The way the two figures are positioned does not matter when determining whether they are congruent.

Angles and sides that are in the same position in two different figures are called **corresponding angles** and **corresponding sides**. Two figures are congruent if and only if each pair of corresponding angles and corresponding sides is congruent.

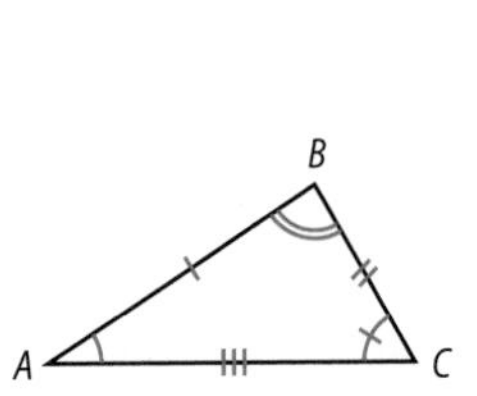

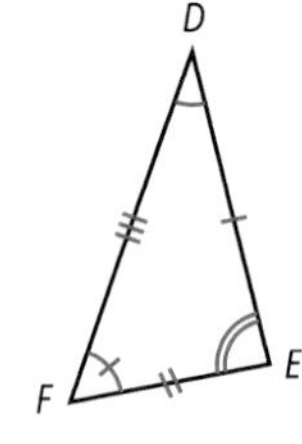

Corresponding Sides	Corresponding Angles	
$\overline{AB} \cong \overline{DE}$	$\angle A \cong \angle D$	
$\overline{BC} \cong \overline{EF}$	$\angle B \cong \angle E$	$\triangle ABC \cong \triangle DEF$
$\overline{CA} \cong \overline{FD}$	$\angle C \cong \angle F$	

Corresponding Sides	Corresponding Angles
$\overline{HI} \cong \overline{QR}$	$\angle H \cong \angle Q$
$\overline{IJ} \cong \overline{RS}$	$\angle I \cong \angle R$
$\overline{JK} \cong \overline{ST}$	$\angle J \cong \angle S$
$\overline{KH} \cong \overline{TQ}$	$\angle K \cong \angle T$

$HIJK \cong QRST$

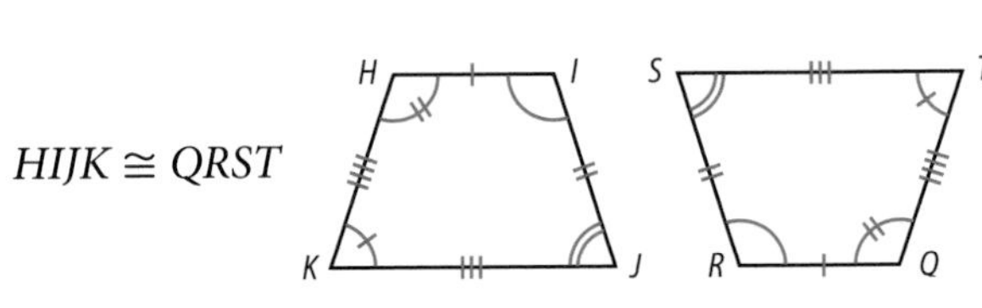

The order in which the vertices are listed in a congruence statement is very important. It indicates which sides and angles correspond to each other.

EXAMPLE 1

Given $\triangle LMN \cong \triangle WXY$, list all pairs of congruent corresponding parts.

Use the order in which the vertices are named.

$\triangle LMN \cong \triangle WXY$

$\angle L \cong \angle W$, $\angle M \cong \angle X$, and $\angle N \cong \angle Y$

$\overline{LM} \cong \overline{WX}$, $\overline{MN} \cong \overline{XY}$, and $\overline{NL} \cong \overline{YW}$

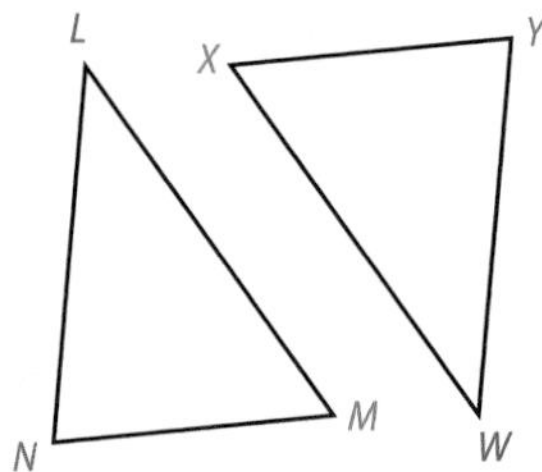

SEARCH

To see step-by-step videos of these problems, enter the page number into the SWadvantage.com Search Bar.

EXAMPLE 2

Given $\triangle DEG \cong \triangle FEG$ and $\angle DGE$ is a right angle, find each value.

a. $m\angle DEG$

Corresponding $\angle$s in $\cong$ $\triangle$s are $\cong$.	$\angle DEG \cong \angle FEG$
Definition of $\cong$ $\angle$s.	$m\angle DEG = m\angle FEG$
Substitute given values.	$9x - 7 = 7x + 5$
Solve for x.	$2x = 12$
	$x = 6$
Substitute for x.	$m\angle DEG = 9(6) - 7$
	$= 47°$

b. y

Sum of $\angle$s in a triangle is 180°.	$m\angle DGE + m\angle DEG + m\angle EDG = 180°$
Subtract.	$m\angle EDG = 180° - m\angle DGE - m\angle DEG$
Substitute.	$m\angle EDG = 180° - (90°) - (47°)$
	$= 43°$
Corresponding $\angle$s in $\cong$ $\triangle$s are $\cong$.	$\angle EFG \cong \angle EDG$
Definition of $\cong$ $\angle$s.	$m\angle EFG = m\angle EDG$
Substitute.	$7y - 20 = 43°$
Solve for y.	$7y = 63$
	$y = 9$

EXAMPLE 3

Given: Parallelograms $QRST$ and $UVWT$, T is the midpoint of $\overline{QU}$ and $\overline{SW}$, $\angle TQR \cong \angle TUV$, and parallel segments as marked

Prove: $QRST \cong UVWT$

Because they are vertical angles, $\angle UTW \cong \angle QTS$. Because opposite angles in a parallelogram are congruent, $\angle UTW \cong \angle UVW$, $\angle QRS \cong \angle QTS$, $\angle TWV \cong \angle TUV$, and $\angle TSR \cong \angle TQR$. $\angle TSR \cong \angle TWV$. $\angle QRS \cong \angle UVW$ by the Transitive Property of Congruence. Therefore, corresponding angles are congruent.

$\overline{TS} \cong \overline{TW}$ and $\overline{QT} \cong \overline{TU}$ by definition of a midpoint. Opposite sides in a parallelogram are congruent, so $\overline{RS} \cong \overline{QT}$, $\overline{TU} \cong \overline{VW}$, $\overline{QR} \cong \overline{TS}$, and $\overline{TW} \cong \overline{UV}$. $\overline{RS} \cong \overline{VW}$ and $\overline{QR} \cong \overline{UV}$ by transitivity. Therefore, corresponding sides are congruent. $QRST \cong UVWT$.

GOT TO KNOW!

Properties of Congruent Figures

Same size

Same shape

Congruent corresponding sides

Congruent corresponding angles

Side-Side-Side Congruence

As you have learned, two triangles are congruent if and only if each pair of corresponding angles is congruent and each pair of corresponding sides is congruent. However, it is not necessary to know all of this to know two triangles are congruent.

The three segments given below can be put together to form a triangle. No matter how you put the segments together, the resulting triangle is the same.

Try It This Way

Put three pencils together to form a triangle. See how many different triangles you can make.

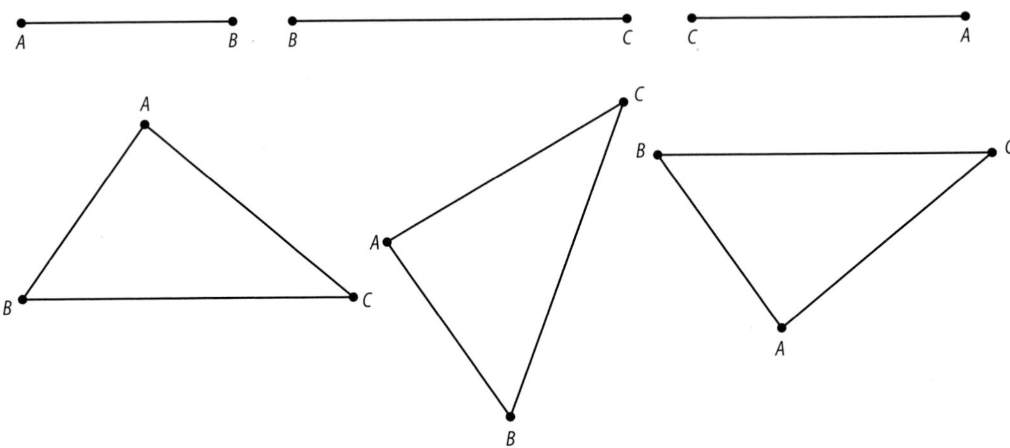

The triangle may be in different positions, but it is still the same triangle. This fact is stated in the following postulate.

Side-Side-Side Congruence Postulate (SSS)

If three sides of one triangle are congruent to the corresponding three sides of another triangle, then the triangles are congruent.

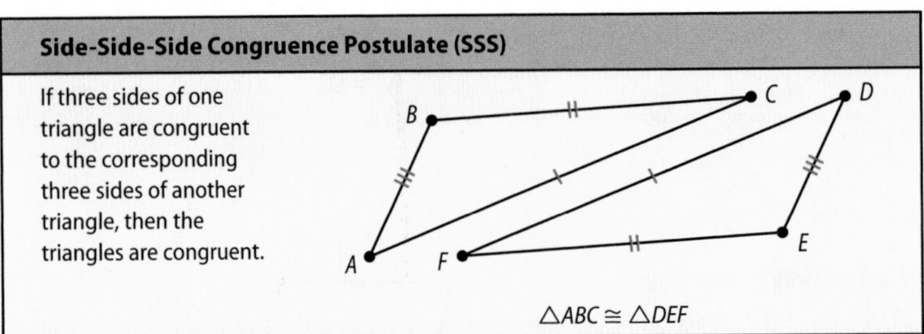

$\triangle ABC \cong \triangle DEF$

EXAMPLE 1

SEARCH

To see step-by-step videos of these problems, enter the page number into the SWadvantage.com Search Bar.

Write and justify a congruence statement that describes each pair of triangles.

a. $\overline{WY} \cong \overline{WY}$ by the Reflexive Property of Congruence. It is given that $\overline{WZ} \cong \overline{WX}$ and $\overline{ZY} \cong \overline{XY}$.

Three pairs of corresponding sides are congruent, so $\triangle WZY \cong \triangle WXY$ by SSS congruence.

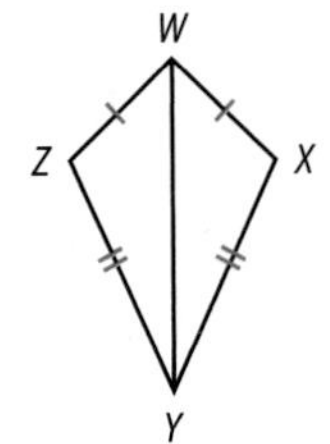

b. Opposite sides are parallel, so the quadrilateral is a parallelogram. This means opposite sides are also congruent, so $\overline{JK} \cong \overline{LM}$ and $\overline{JM} \cong \overline{LK}$. $\overline{KM} \cong \overline{MK}$ by the Reflexive Property of Congruence. Three pairs of corresponding sides are congruent, so $\triangle MJK \cong \triangle KLM$ by SSS congruence.

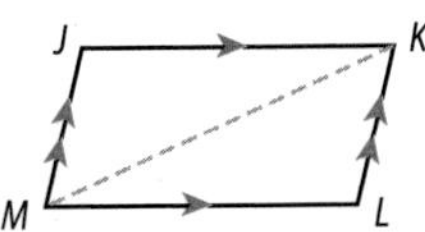

EXAMPLE 2

Given: $\overline{QR} \cong \overline{TU}$, S is the midpoint of $\overline{QT}$ and $\overline{RU}$

Prove: $\triangle QRS \cong \triangle TUS$

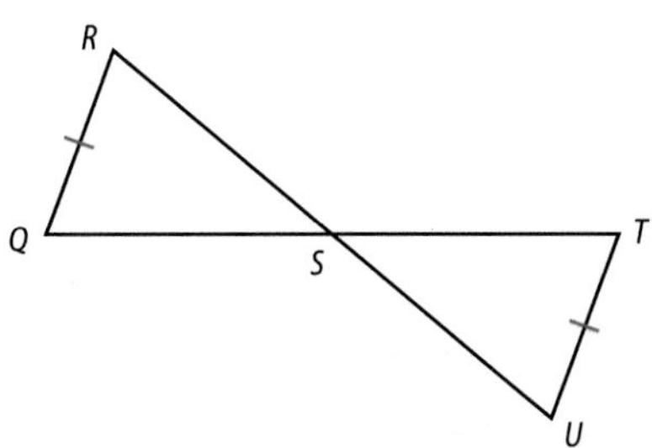

Statements	Reasons
1. $\overline{QR} \cong \overline{TU}$	1. Given
2. S is the midpoint of $\overline{QT}$ and $\overline{RU}$.	2. Given
3. $\overline{SR} \cong \overline{SU}, \overline{SQ} \cong \overline{ST}$	3. Definition of midpoint
4. $\triangle QRS \cong \triangle TUS$	4. SSS congruence

Watch Out!

To say two triangles are congruent, it is not enough to know that there are two corresponding congruent sides (SS). You must know that there are three corresponding congruent sides (SSS).

EXAMPLE 3

Verify that $\triangle GHI \cong \triangle LJK$ given $x = 15$.

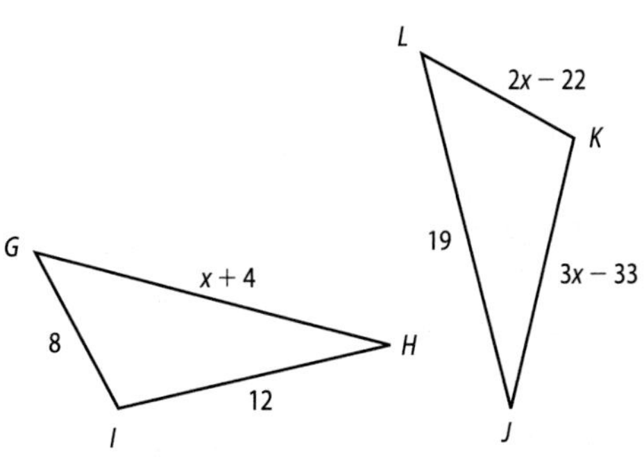

$GH = x + 4$

$= (15) + 4$

$= 19$

$= LJ$

So, $\overline{GH} \cong \overline{LJ}$.

$JK = 3x - 33$

$= 3(15) - 33$

$= 45 - 33$

$= 12$

$= HI$

So, $\overline{HI} \cong \overline{JK}$.

$LK = 2x - 22$

$= 2(15) - 22$

$= 30 - 22$

$= 8$

$= GI$

So, $\overline{GI} \cong \overline{LK}$.

So, $\triangle GHI \cong \triangle LJK$ by SSS congruence.

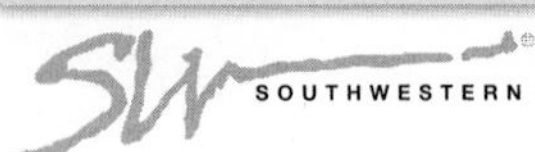

Side-Angle-Side Congruence

Another way to check that two triangles are congruent involves two sides and their *included angle*. An **included angle** is the angle that is formed by two consecutive sides.

The two segments given below can be put together to form the given angle.

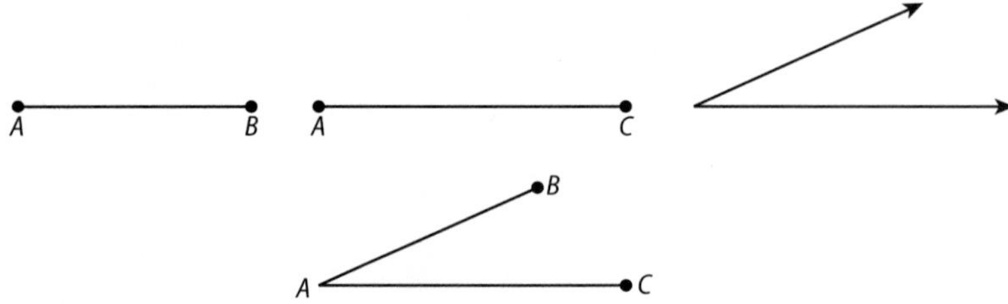

Regardless of the position of $\angle BAC$, to form a triangle, $\overline{BC}$ can have only one length.

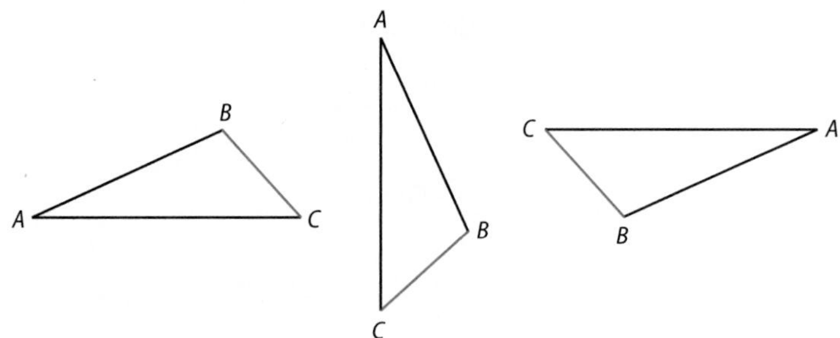

Given any two segments and an included angle, it is possible to make only one triangle. The two sides and an included angle determine the size and shape of a triangle. This fact is stated in the following postulate.

Side-Angle-Side Congruence Postulate (SAS)

If two sides and the included angle of one triangle are congruent to the corresponding sides and included angle of another triangle, then the triangles are congruent.

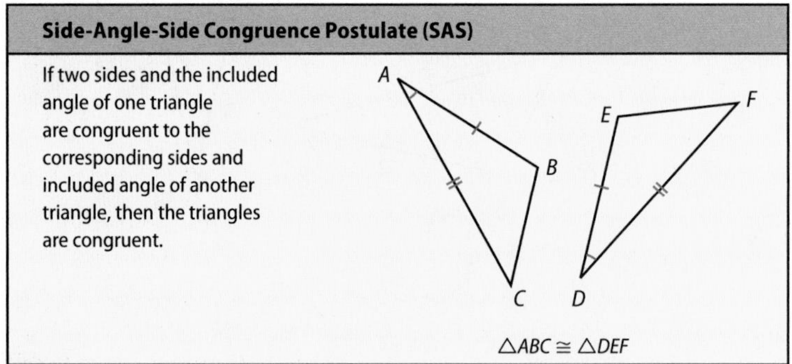

$\triangle ABC \cong \triangle DEF$

GOT TO KNOW!

Two Ways to Show Triangle Congruence

SSS

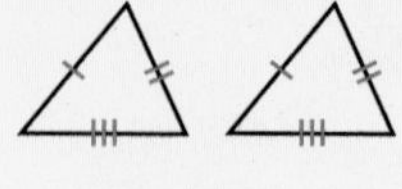

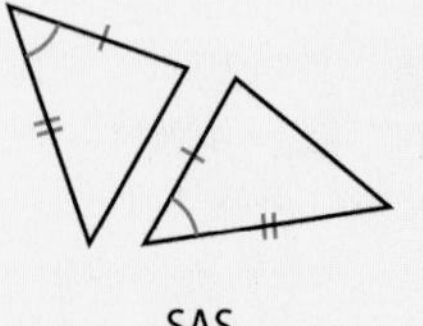

SAS

EXAMPLE 4

Write and justify a congruence statement that describes the two triangles.

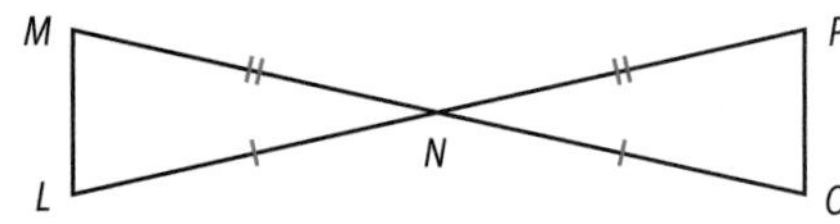

$\angle LNM \cong \angle ONP$ because they are vertical angles.
It is given that $\overline{LN} \cong \overline{ON}$ and $\overline{MN} \cong \overline{PN}$.

Two pairs of corresponding sides and their included angles are congruent, so $\triangle LNM \cong \triangle ONP$ by SAS congruence.

EXAMPLE 5

Given: $\overline{QS} \cong \overline{TR}$, $\angle QST \cong \angle TRQ$, $\angle TSR \cong \angle QRS$

Prove: $\triangle QRS \cong \triangle TSR$

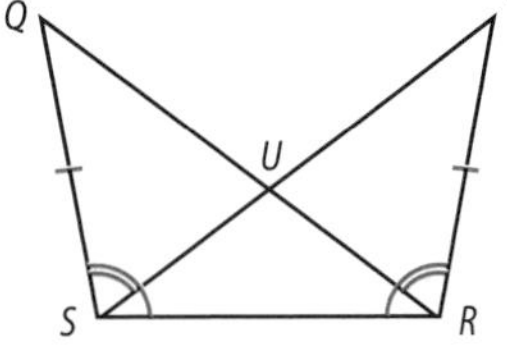

Statements	Reasons
1. $\overline{QS} \cong \overline{TR}$	1. Given
2. $\angle QST \cong \angle TRQ$, $\angle TSR \cong \angle QRS$	2. Given
3. $m\angle QST = m\angle TRQ$, $m\angle TSR = m\angle QRS$	3. Definition of $\cong$ $\angle$s
4. $m\angle QST + m\angle TSR = m\angle TRQ + m\angle QRS$	4. Addition property of equality
5. $m\angle QSR = m\angle QST + m\angle TSR$, $m\angle TRS = m\angle TRQ + m\angle QRS$	5. Angle addition
6. $m\angle QSR = m\angle TRS$	6. Substitution
7. $\angle QSR \cong \angle TRS$	7. Definition of $\cong$ $\angle$s
8. $\overline{SR} \cong \overline{RS}$	8. Reflexive property of congruence
9. $\triangle QRS \cong \triangle TSR$	9. SAS congruence

SEARCH

To see step-by-step videos of these problems, enter the page number into the SWadvantage.com Search Bar.

EXAMPLE 6

Given: $\odot W$, $\overline{VW} \perp \overline{XZ}$

Prove: $\triangle WYZ \cong \triangle WYX$

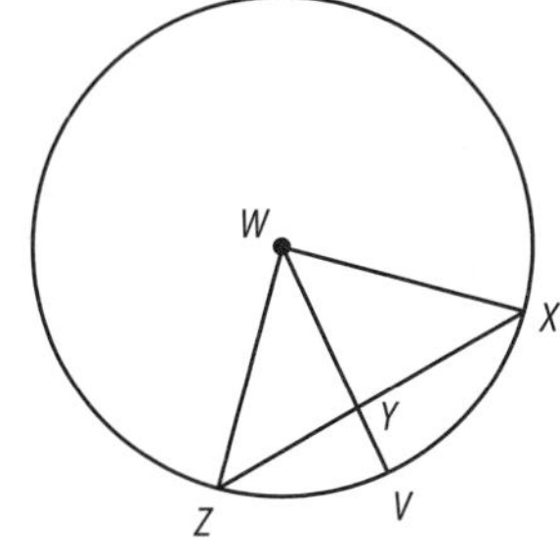

Statements	Reasons
1. $\overline{VW} \perp \overline{XZ}$	1. Given
2. $\overline{VW}$ bisects $\overline{XZ}$	2. If a radius is $\perp$ to a chord, it bisects the chord.
3. $\overline{YZ} \cong \overline{YX}$	3. Definition of bisects
4. $\angle WYZ$ and $\angle WYX$ are right angles	4. Definition of $\perp$
5. $\angle WYZ \cong \angle WYX$	5. All right $\angle$s are $\cong$.
6. $\overline{WY} \cong \overline{WY}$	6. Reflexive property of congruence
7. $\triangle WYZ \cong \triangle WYX$	7. SAS congruence

Using ASA and AAS

Angle-Side-Angle Congruence

An **included side** is a side that is shared by two consecutive angles. Similar to having two segments and an included angle, you can make only one triangle given two angles and the included side.

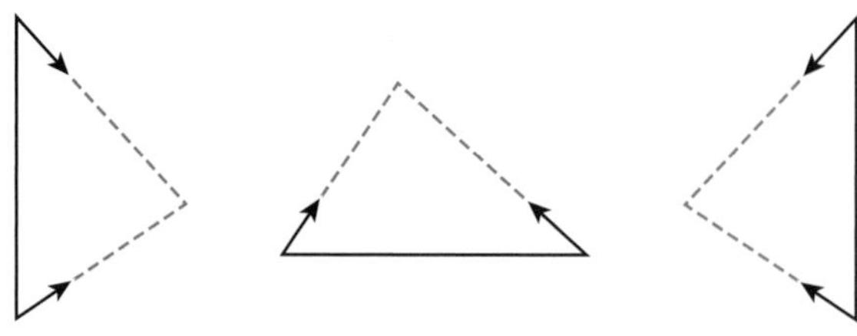

This fact can be used to prove that triangles are congruent and is stated in the following postulate.

Need More HELP

Look at a 30-60-90 triangle. If you are given one side length between a 30° angle and a 60° angle, you can find the other side lengths because there is only one possibility.

Angle-Side-Angle Congruence Postulate (ASA)

If two angles and the included side of one triangle are congruent to the corresponding angles and included side of another triangle, then the triangles are congruent.

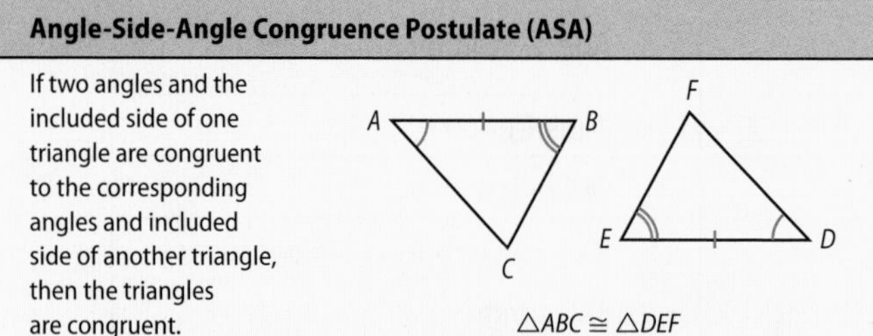

$\triangle ABC \cong \triangle DEF$

EXAMPLE 1

SEARCH

To see step-by-step videos of these problems, enter the page number into the SWadvantage.com Search Bar.

Write and justify a congruence statement that describes each pair of triangles.

a. Given: $\overline{HJ}$ bisects $\angle KHI$ and $\angle KJI$

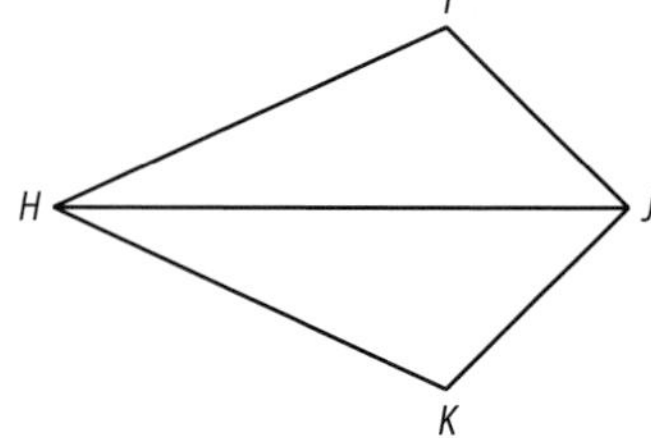

$\overline{HJ} \cong \overline{HJ}$ by the Reflexive Property of Congruence.
It is given that $\angle KHI$ and $\angle KJI$ are bisected by $\overline{HJ}$, so $\angle JHI \cong \angle JHK$ and $\angle HJI \cong \angle HJK$.

Two pairs of corresponding angles and their included sides are congruent. So, $\triangle HIJ \cong \triangle HKJ$ by ASA congruence.

b. Given: $\angle MON$ is a right angle, $\angle NMO \cong \angle LMO$

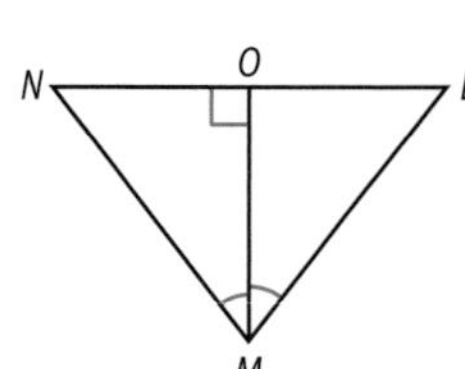

$\overline{OM} \cong \overline{OM}$ by the Reflexive Property of Congruence.

$\angle MON$ and $\angle MOL$ form a linear pair. $\angle MON$ is a right angle, so $\angle MOL$ is also a right angle. All right angles are congruent, so $\angle MON \cong \angle MOL$.

Two pairs of corresponding angles and their included sides are congruent, so $\triangle LOM \cong \triangle NOM$ by ASA congruence.

EXAMPLE 2

Given: $\overline{QR} \parallel \overline{ST}$, $\overline{TQ} \parallel \overline{RS}$, and diagonal $\overline{RT}$

Prove: $\triangle QRT \cong \triangle STR$

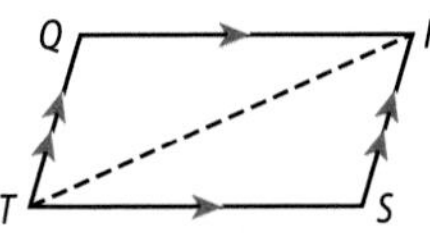

Statements	Reasons
1. $\overline{QR} \parallel \overline{ST}$	1. Given
2. $\angle QRT \cong \angle RTS$	2. Alternate interior $\angle$s are congruent.
3. $\overline{TQ} \parallel \overline{RS}$	3. Given
4. $\angle QTR \cong \angle SRT$	4. Alternate interior $\angle$s are congruent.
5. $\overline{RT} \cong \overline{TR}$	5. Reflexive Property of Congruence
6. $\triangle QRT \cong \triangle STR$	6. ASA congruence

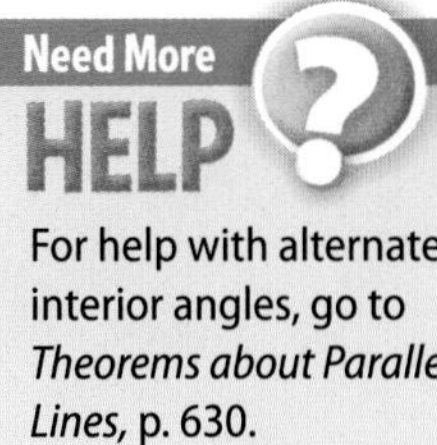

For help with alternate interior angles, go to *Theorems about Parallel Lines*, p. 630.

EXAMPLE 3

Given $x = 7$, determine whether $\triangle UVW \cong \triangle YXW$. If not, find the value of x that does make the triangles congruent.

Definition of $\cong$ segments. $UV \stackrel{?}{=} YX$

Substitute. $3x - 4 \stackrel{?}{=} 4x - 13$

Substitute for x. $3(7) - 4 \stackrel{?}{=} 4(7) - 13$

Simplify. $17 \neq 15$

So, the triangles are not congruent for $x = 7$.

Solve for the true value of x.

$$3x - 4 = 4x - 13$$

$$x = 9$$

Check to see that the angles are congruent when this new value of x is substituted.

$m\angle WVU \stackrel{?}{=} m\angle WXY$

$6x - 2 \stackrel{?}{=} 4x + 16$

$6(9) - 2 \stackrel{?}{=} 4(9) + 16$

$52 = 52$ ✔

$m\angle WUV \stackrel{?}{=} m\angle WYX$

$5x + 2 \stackrel{?}{=} 4x + 11$

$5(9) + 2 \stackrel{?}{=} 4(9) + 11$

$47 = 47$ ✔

So, for $x = 9$, $\triangle UVW \cong \triangle YXW$ by ASA congruence.

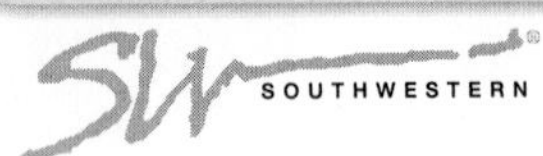

Angle-Angle-Side Congruence

This congruence relationship involves two angles and a side that is not included.

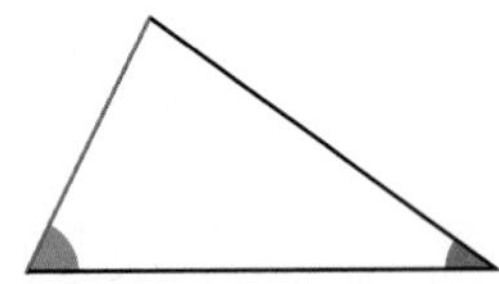

It is not as obvious nor as easy to visualize as the SSS, SAS, and ASA congruencies. AAS cannot just be accepted as true. It must be proven. Therefore, it is stated as a theorem rather than a postulate.

Angle-Angle-Side Congruence Theorem (AAS)
If two angles and a non-included side of one triangle are congruent to the corresponding angles and non-included side of another triangle, then the triangles are congruent.

$\triangle ABC \cong \triangle DEF$

PROOF

Given: $\angle C \cong \angle F$, $\angle B \cong \angle E$, **and** $\overline{AB} \cong \overline{DE}$

Prove: $\triangle ABC \cong \triangle DEF$

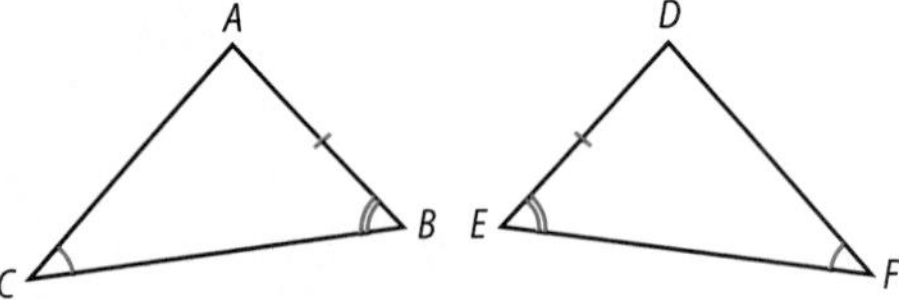

Statements	Reasons
1. $\angle C \cong \angle F$, $\angle B \cong \angle E$	1. Given
2. $\overline{AB} \cong \overline{DE}$	2. Given
3. $\angle A \cong \angle D$	3. If two ∠s of a triangle are ≅ to two ∠s of another triangle, then the third ∠s are ≅.
4. $\triangle ABC \cong \triangle DEF$	4. ASA congruence

EXAMPLE 4

Given $\overline{KL} \cong \overline{HI}$ and $x = 14$, show that $\triangle HIJ \cong \triangle KLM$.

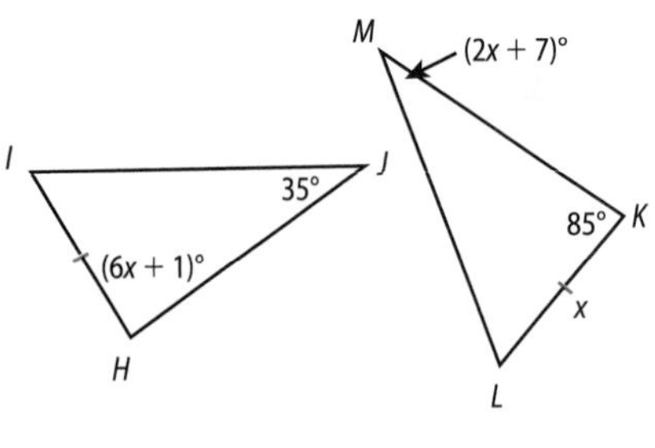

Definition of congruent segments	$KL = HI$
Substitute given values.	$x = 14$
Given	$m\angle JHI = 6x + 1$
Substitute for x.	$= 6(14) + 1$
Simplify.	$= 85°$
Given	$m\angle LMK = 2x + 7$
Substitute for x.	$= 2(14) + 7$
	$= 35°$

Therefore, $\angle JHI \cong \angle MKL$ and $\angle IJH \cong \angle LMK$. So, $\triangle HIJ \cong \triangle KLM$ by AAS congruence.

SEARCH

To see step-by-step videos of these problems, enter the page number into the SWadvantage.com Search Bar.

EXAMPLE 5

Given: $\angle B \cong \angle E, \overline{AD} \cong \overline{CF}$, and $\overline{BC} \parallel \overline{EF}$

Prove: $\triangle ABC \cong \triangle DEF$

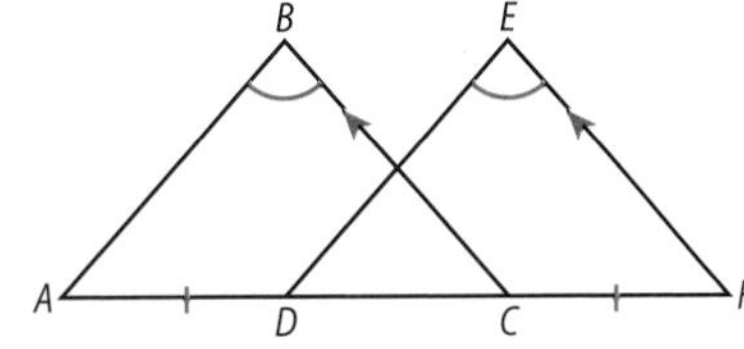

Statements	Reasons
1. $\overline{AD} \cong \overline{CF}$	1. Given
2. $AD = CF$	2. Definition of congruent segments
3. $AD + DC = CF + DC$	3. Addition property of equality
4. $AD + DC = AC, CF + DC = DF$	4. Segment addition
5. $AC = DF$	5. Substitution
6. $\overline{AC} \cong \overline{DF}$	6. Definition of congruent segments
7. $\overline{BC} \parallel \overline{EF}$	7. Given
8. $\angle BCA \cong \angle EFD$	8. Alternate interior $\angle$s are $\cong$.
9. $\angle B \cong \angle E$	9. Given
10. $\triangle ABC \cong \triangle DEF$	10. AAS congruence

Try It This Way

As you find each of the corresponding congruent parts of the two triangles, highlight those parts with color.

EXAMPLE 6

Given: $\overline{VW} \cong \overline{YW}, \overline{UV} \parallel \overline{XY}$

Prove: $\triangle UVW \cong \triangle XYW$

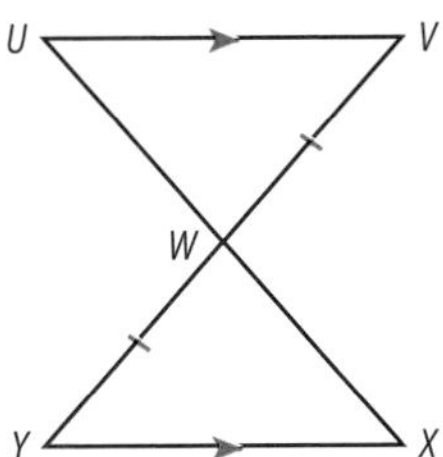

METHOD 1

Statements	Reasons
1. $\overline{UV} \parallel \overline{XY}$	1. Given
2. $\angle UVW \cong \angle XYW$ and $\angle VUW \cong \angle YXW$	2. Alternate interior $\angle$s are $\cong$.
3. $\overline{VW} \cong \overline{YW}$	3. Given
4. $\triangle UVW \cong \triangle XYW$	4. AAS congruence

METHOD 2

You can also use the fact that $\angle UWV$ and $\angle XWY$ are vertical angles and congruent to prove the triangles are congruent using ASA.

GOT TO KNOW!

Two Ways to Show Triangle Congruence Given Two Angles and a Side

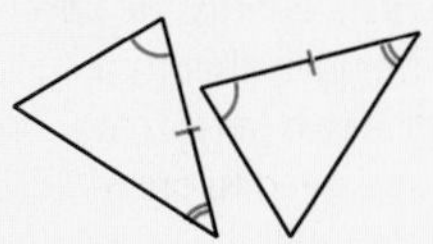

ASA

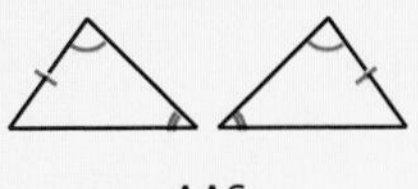

AAS

Using CPCTC

CPCTC

You know that for two triangles to be congruent, they must have six pairs of corresponding congruent parts (three side pairs and three angle pairs).

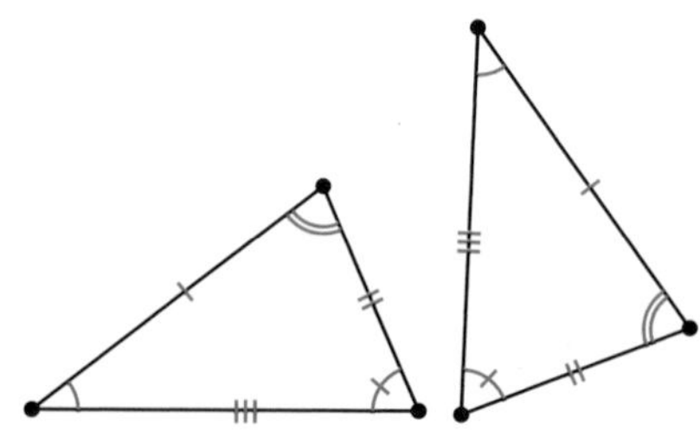

You also know that if you have the right combination of three of these pairs, you can prove that the triangles are congruent (by SSS, SAS, ASA, or AAS).

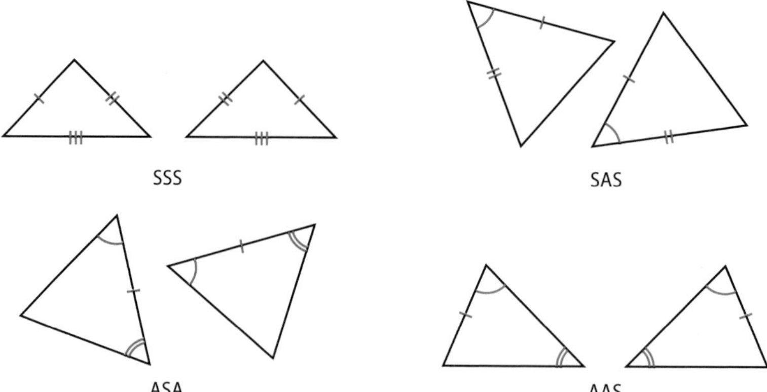

Once you have proven two triangles are congruent, you can answer other questions or prove other congruencies using CPCTC, short for **Corresponding Parts of Congruent Triangles are Congruent.**

EXAMPLE 1

Given: $\overline{AD} \cong \overline{AB}$ **and** $\overline{CD} \cong \overline{CB}$

Prove: $\angle D \cong \angle B$

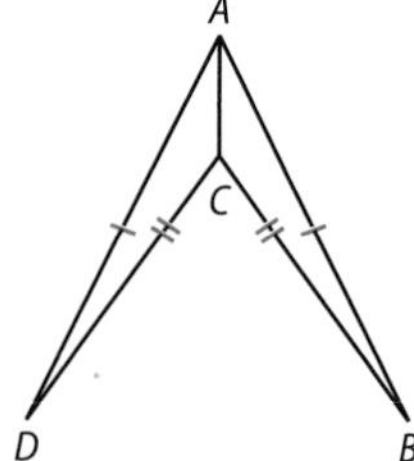

Statements	Reasons
1. $\overline{AD} \cong \overline{AB}$ and $\overline{CD} \cong \overline{CB}$	1. Given
2. $\overline{AC} \cong \overline{AC}$	2. Reflexive Property of Congruence
3. $\triangle ADC \cong \triangle ABC$	3. SSS congruence
4. $\angle D \cong \angle B$	4. CPCTC

Need More HELP

First, identify the two triangles that have the two parts that you need to prove congruent.

EXAMPLE 2

Given: X **is the midpoint of both** $\overline{WY}$ **and** $\overline{VZ}$

Prove: $\angle W \cong \angle Y$

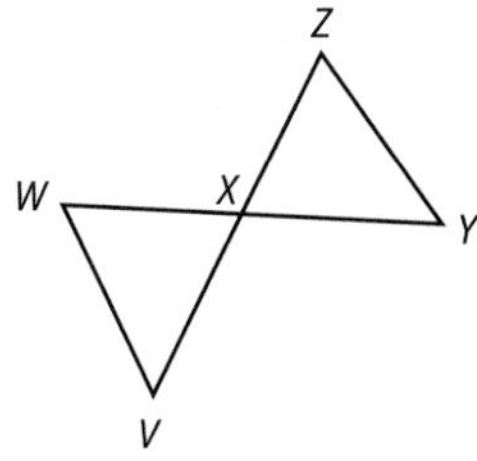

Statements	Reasons
1. X is the midpoint of both $\overline{WY}$ and $\overline{VZ}$.	1. Given
2. $\overline{WX} \cong \overline{YX}$, $\overline{VX} \cong \overline{ZX}$	2. Definition of midpoint
3. $\angle VXW \cong \angle ZXY$	3. Vertical angles are congruent.
4. $\triangle VXW \cong \triangle ZXY$	4. SAS congruence
5. $\angle W \cong \angle Y$	5. CPCTC

EXAMPLE 3

Given: $\overline{MO} \perp \overline{LN}$ **and** $\angle L \cong \angle N$

Prove: $\overline{LM} \cong \overline{NM}$

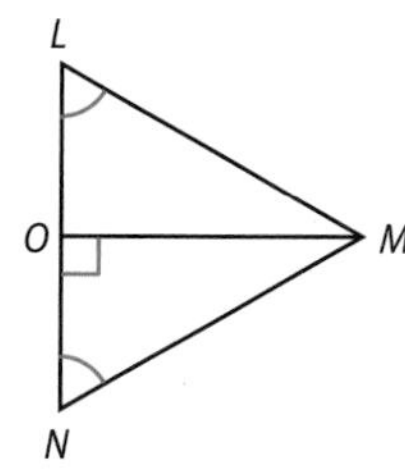

Statements	Reasons
1. $\overline{MO} \perp \overline{LN}$	1. Given
2. $\angle MOL$ and $\angle MON$ are right angles.	2. Definition of $\perp$
3. $\angle MOL \cong \angle MON$	3. All right angles are congruent.
4. $\angle L \cong \angle N$	4. Given
5. $\overline{MO} \cong \overline{MO}$	5. Reflexive Property of Congruence
4. $\triangle MOL \cong \triangle MON$	4. AAS congruence
5. $\overline{LM} \cong \overline{NM}$	5. CPCTC

SEARCH

To see step-by-step videos of these problems, enter the page number into the SWadvantage.com Search Bar.

GOT TO KNOW!

CPCTC

If $\triangle ABC \cong \triangle JKL$, then:

$\angle A \cong \angle J$ $\quad \overline{AB} \cong \overline{JK}$

$\angle B \cong \angle K$ $\quad \overline{BC} \cong \overline{KL}$

$\angle C \cong \angle L$ $\quad \overline{AC} \cong \overline{JL}$

Using CPCTC in Proofs

EXAMPLE 4

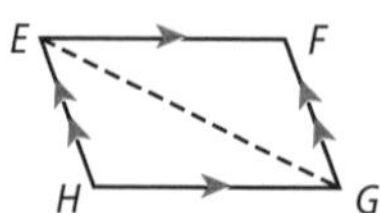

Given: $\overline{EF} \parallel \overline{GH}$ **and** $\overline{EH} \parallel \overline{GF}$**, diagonal** $\overline{EG}$

Prove: $\angle FEH \cong \angle HGF, \overline{EH} \cong \overline{GF}, \overline{GH} \cong \overline{EF}$

Statements	Reasons
1. $\overline{EF} \parallel \overline{GH}$ and $\overline{EH} \parallel \overline{GF}$	1. Given
2. $\angle FEG \cong \angle HGE, \angle FGE \cong \angle HEG$	2. Alternate interior $\angle$s are congruent.
3. $\overline{EG} \cong \overline{GE}$	3. Reflexive Property of Congruence
4. $\triangle GFE \cong \triangle EHG$	4. ASA congruence
5. $m\angle FEG = m\angle HGE, m\angle FGE = m\angle HEG$	5. Definition of $\cong$ $\angle$s
6. $m\angle FEG + m\angle HEG = m\angle HGE + m\angle FGE$	6. Addition Property of Equality
7. $m\angle FEG + m\angle HEG = m\angle FEH$ $m\angle HGE + m\angle FGE = m\angle HGF$	7. Angle addition
8. $m\angle FEH = m\angle HGF$	8. Substitution
9. $\angle FEH \cong \angle HGF$	9. Definition $\cong$ $\angle$s
10. $\overline{EH} \cong \overline{GF}, \overline{GH} \cong \overline{EF}$	10. CPCTC

SEARCH

To see step-by-step videos of these problems, enter the page number into the SWadvantage.com Search Bar.

EXAMPLE 5

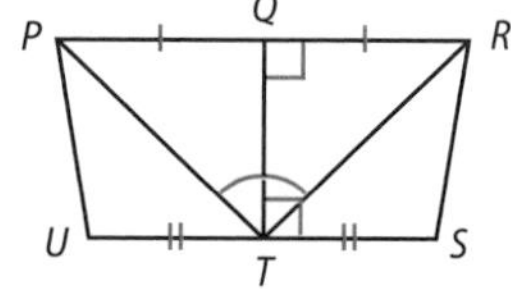

Given: $\overline{QT}$ **is the perpendicular bisector of** $\overline{PR}$ **and** $\overline{SU}$**, and** $\angle QTP \cong \angle QTR$

Prove: $\overline{PU} \cong \overline{RS}$

Statements	Reasons
1. $\overline{QT}$ is the perpendicular bisector of $\overline{PR}$ and $\overline{SU}$.	1. Given
2. $\overline{PQ} \cong \overline{RQ}$, $\angle TQP$ and $\angle TQR$ are right $\angle$s.	2. Definition of $\perp$ bisector
3. $\angle TQP \cong \angle TQR$	3. All right $\angle$s are congruent.
4. $\angle QTP \cong \angle QTR$	4. Given
5. $\triangle TQP \cong \triangle TQR$	5. AAS congruence
6. $\overline{PT} \cong \overline{RT}$	6. CPCTC
7. $\overline{UT} \cong \overline{ST}$, $\angle QTU$ and $\angle QTS$ are right $\angle$s.	7. Definition of $\perp$ bisector
8. $\angle PTU$ and $\angle QTP$ are complementary, and $\angle RTS$ and $\angle QTR$ are complementary.	8. Definition of complementary $\angle$s
9. $\angle PTU \cong \angle RTS$	9. $\angle$s that are complementary to $\cong$ $\angle$s are $\cong$.
10. $\triangle PTU \cong \triangle RTS$	10. SAS congruence
11. $\overline{PU} \cong \overline{RS}$	11. CPCTC

EXAMPLE 6

Given: *HIJK* is a rhombus with diagonal $\overline{HJ}$

Prove: $\overline{HJ}$ bisects $\angle IHK$ and $\angle IJK$

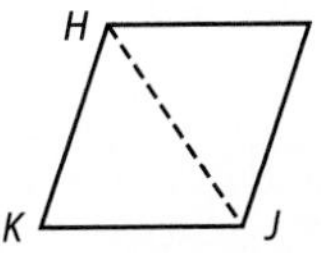

Statements	Reasons
1. *HIJK* is a rhombus.	1. Given
2. $\overline{HI} \cong \overline{HK} \cong \overline{IJ} \cong \overline{KJ}$	2. Definition of a rhombus.
3. $\overline{HJ} \cong \overline{HJ}$	3. Reflexive Property of Congruence
4. $\triangle HIJ \cong \triangle HKJ$	4. SSS congruence
5. $\angle IHJ \cong \angle KHJ$, $\angle IJH \cong \angle KJH$	5. CPCTC
6. $\overline{HJ}$ bisects $\angle IHK$ and $\angle IJK$	6. Definition of bisector

EXAMPLE 7

Given: $\triangle ABC$ and $\triangle DEF$ with coordinates $A(6, -3)$, $B(7, 1)$, $C(1, 0)$, $D(3, 4)$, $E(-1, 5)$, and $F(0, -1)$

Prove: $\angle B \cong \angle E$

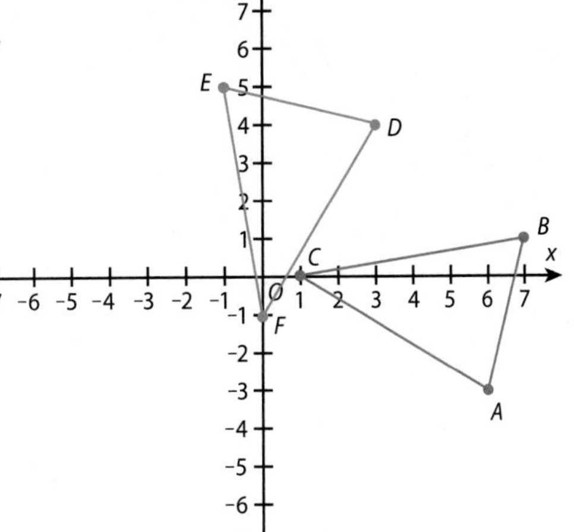

Use the Distance Formula to find the length of each side of the triangles.

$$AB = \sqrt{(7-6)^2 + (1-(-3))^2}$$
$$= \sqrt{1^2 + 4^2}$$
$$= \sqrt{17}$$

$$DE = \sqrt{(3-(-1))^2 + (4-5)^2}$$
$$= \sqrt{4^2 + (-1)^2}$$
$$= \sqrt{17}$$

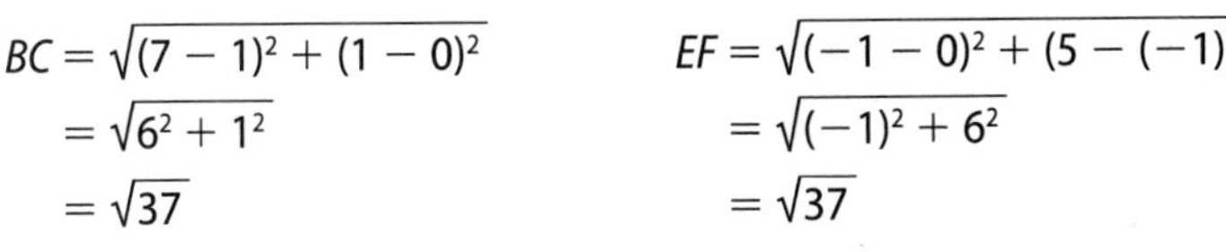

$$BC = \sqrt{(7-1)^2 + (1-0)^2}$$
$$= \sqrt{6^2 + 1^2}$$
$$= \sqrt{37}$$

$$EF = \sqrt{(-1-0)^2 + (5-(-1))^2}$$
$$= \sqrt{(-1)^2 + 6^2}$$
$$= \sqrt{37}$$

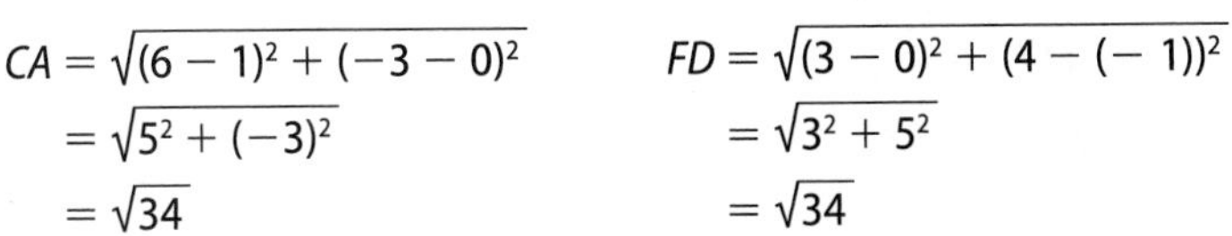

$$CA = \sqrt{(6-1)^2 + (-3-0)^2}$$
$$= \sqrt{5^2 + (-3)^2}$$
$$= \sqrt{34}$$

$$FD = \sqrt{(3-0)^2 + (4-(-1))^2}$$
$$= \sqrt{3^2 + 5^2}$$
$$= \sqrt{34}$$

$\triangle ABC \cong \triangle DEF$ by SSS congruence.

So, $\angle B \cong \angle E$ by CPCTC.

For help with the Distance Formula, go to *Distance Formula*, p. 818.

Congruence in Right Triangles

Congruence Theorems

The following are congruence theorems that can be used with right triangles.

Leg-Leg Congruence (LL) If both legs of a right triangle are congruent to the corresponding legs of another right triangle, then the triangles are congruent.		When you consider that all right angles are congruent, this is really just a specific version of SAS.
Leg-Angle Congruence (LA) If one leg and an acute angle of a right triangle are congruent to the corresponding leg and acute angle of another right triangle, then the triangles are congruent.		This is the same as AAS or ASA, depending on whether the corresponding leg and angle are opposite or adjacent to each other.
Hypotenuse-Angle Congruence (HA) If the hypotenuse and an acute angle of a right triangle are congruent to the hypotenuse and corresponding acute angle of another right triangle, then the triangles are congruent.		This is the same as AAS.
Hypotenuse-Leg Congruence (HL) If the hypotenuse and one leg of a right triangle are congruent to the hypotenuse and corresponding leg of another right triangle, then the triangles are congruent.		This side-side-angle is true only for right triangles. The right triangles must have a pair of legs and the hypotenuses congruent.

Watch Out!

The HL congruence might lead you to think that SSA is a congruence relationship. It is not. This congruence works only with right triangles.

PROOF

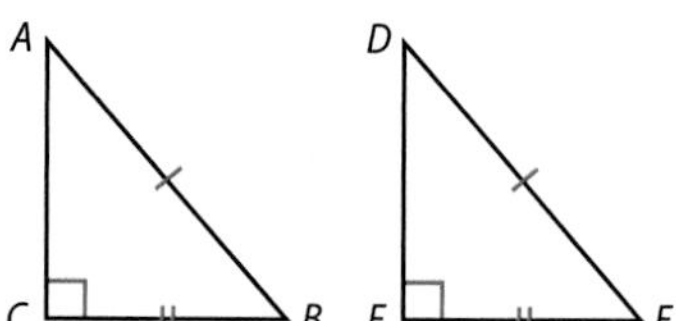

Given: $\triangle ABC$ and $\triangle DEF$ are right triangles, $\overline{AB} \cong \overline{DE}$, and $\overline{BC} \cong \overline{EF}$

Prove: $\triangle ABC \cong \triangle DEF$

Because you know $\triangle ABC$ and $\triangle DEF$ are right triangles, you can apply the Pythagorean Theorem.

$AC^2 + BC^2 = AB^2$ $\quad$ $DF^2 + EF^2 = DE^2$

$AC^2 = AB^2 - BC^2$ $\quad$ $DF^2 = DE^2 - EF^2$

By definition of congruence, $AB = DE$ and $BC = EF$.

Using substitution, $DF^2 = AB^2 - BC^2$.

So, by transitivity $AC^2 = DF^2$.

Taking the square root of both sides results in $AC = DF$, so $\overline{AC} \cong \overline{DF}$.

Now you know all three pairs of corresponding sides are congruent.

So, $\triangle ABC \cong \triangle DEF$ by SSS congruence.

EXAMPLE 1

Given: $\triangle DEF$ and $\triangle FGD$ are right triangles, $\overline{EF} \cong \overline{GD}$

Prove: $\triangle DEF \cong \triangle FGD$

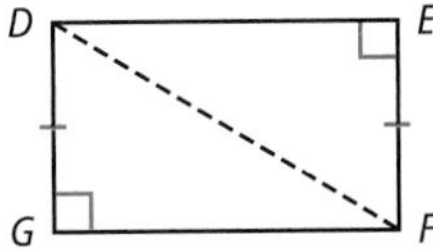

Statements	Reasons
1. $\triangle DEF$ and $\triangle FGD$ are right triangles, $\overline{EF} \cong \overline{GD}$	1. Given
2. $\overline{DF} \cong \overline{FD}$	2. Reflexive Property of Congruence
3. $\triangle DEF \cong \triangle FGD$	3. HL congruence

SEARCH

To see step-by-step videos of these problems, enter the page number into the SWadvantage.com Search Bar.

EXAMPLE 2

Given: $\angle HKJ$ and $\angle HIJ$ are right angles, $\overline{HJ}$ bisects $\angle KJI$

Prove: $\triangle HKJ \cong \triangle HIJ$

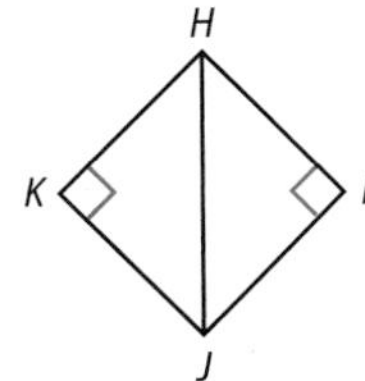

Statements	Reasons
1. $\angle HKJ$ and $\angle HIJ$ are right angles.	1. Given
2. $\triangle HKJ$ and $\triangle HIJ$ are right triangles.	2. Definition of right triangle
3. $\overline{HJ} \cong \overline{HJ}$	3. Reflexive Property of Congruence
4. $\overline{HJ}$ bisects $\angle KJI$.	4. Given
5. $\angle HJK \cong \angle HJI$	5. Definition of bisector
6. $\triangle HKJ \cong \triangle HIJ$	6. HA congruence

EXAMPLE 3

Given: $\overline{RT}$ is the perpendicular bisector of $\overline{QS}$

Prove: $\triangle RTQ \cong \triangle RTS$

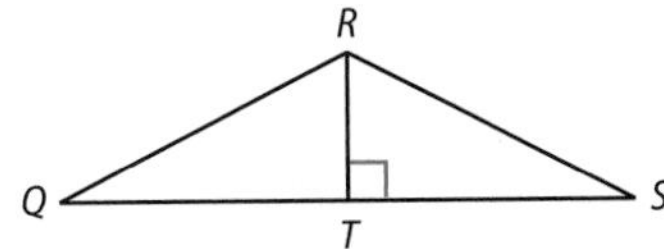

Statements	Reasons
1. $\overline{RT}$ is the perpendicular bisector of $\overline{QS}$.	1. Given
2. $\angle RTQ$ and $\angle RTS$ are right angles.	2. Definition of perpendicular
3. $\triangle RTQ$ and $\triangle RTS$ are right triangles.	3. Definition of right triangle
4. $\overline{TQ} \cong \overline{TS}$	4. Definition of bisector
5. $\overline{RT} \cong \overline{RT}$	5. Reflexive Property of Congruence
6. $\triangle RTQ \cong \triangle RTS$	6. LL congruence

Watch Out!

Before using a right triangle congruence, you must first establish that the triangles are right triangles.

Right Triangle Proofs

SEARCH

To see step-by-step videos of these problems, enter the page number into the SWadvantage.com Search Bar.

EXAMPLE 4

Given: $\triangle KLM$ and $\triangle MNK$ are right triangles, $\angle KLM \cong \angle MNK$

Prove: $\triangle KLM \cong \triangle MNK$

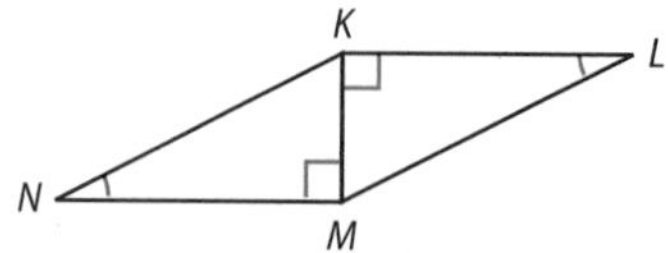

Statements	Reasons
1. $\triangle KLM$ and $\triangle MNK$ are right triangles, $\angle KLM \cong \angle MNK$.	1. Given
2. $\overline{KM} \cong \overline{MK}$	2. Reflexive Property of Congruence
3. $\triangle KLM \cong \triangle MNK$	3. LA congruence

EXAMPLE 5

Given: $\angle LNM$ and $\angle LPM$ are right angles, $\overline{LP} \cong \overline{MN}$

a. Prove: $\triangle LMN \cong \triangle MLP$

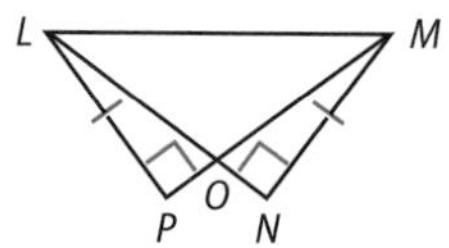

Statements	Reasons
1. $\angle LNM$ and $\angle LPM$ are right angles.	1. Given
2. $\triangle LMN$ and $\triangle MLP$ are right triangles.	2. Definition of right triangle
3. $\overline{LM} \cong \overline{ML}$	3. Reflexive Property of Congruence
4. $\overline{LP} \cong \overline{MN}$	4. Given
5. $\triangle LMN \cong \triangle MLP$	5. HL congruence

b. Prove: $\triangle MON \cong \triangle LOP$

Statements	Reasons
1. $\angle LNM$ and $\angle LPM$ are right angles.	1. Given
2. $\triangle MON$ and $\triangle LOP$ are right triangles.	2. Definition of right triangle
3. $\angle MON \cong \angle LOP$	3. Vertical angles are congruent.
4. $\overline{LP} \cong \overline{MN}$	4. Given
5. $\triangle MON \cong \triangle LOP$	5. LA congruence

EXAMPLE 6

Given: $\angle ACB$ and $\angle DBC$ are right angles, $\overline{DC} \perp \overline{AB}$, $\overline{AC} \cong \overline{BC} \cong \overline{DB}$

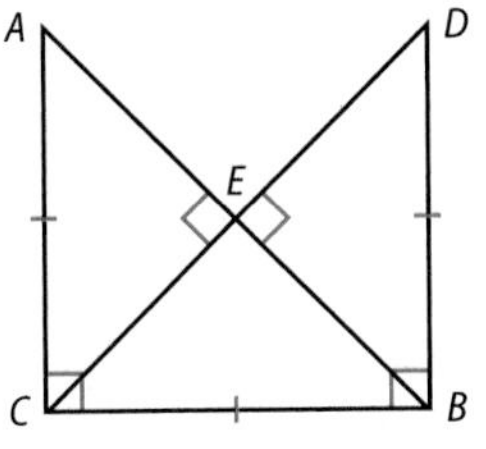

a. Prove: $\triangle ABC \cong \triangle DCB$

Statements	Reasons
1. $\angle ACB$ and $\angle DBC$ are right angles.	1. Given
2. $\triangle ABC$ and $\triangle DCB$ are right triangles.	2. Definition of right triangle
3. $\overline{BC} \cong \overline{CB}$	3. Reflexive Property of Congruence
4. $\overline{AC} \cong \overline{DB}$	4. Given
5. $\triangle ABC \cong \triangle DCB$	5. LL congruence

b. Prove: $\triangle AEC \cong \triangle BEC$

Statements	Reasons
1. $\overline{DC} \perp \overline{AB}$	1. Given
2. $\angle AEC$ and $\angle BEC$ are right angles.	2. Definition of perpendicular
3. $\triangle AEC$ and $\triangle BEC$ are right triangles.	3. Definition of right triangle
4. $\overline{EC} \cong \overline{EC}$	4. Reflexive Property of Congruence
5. $\overline{AC} \cong \overline{BC}$	5. Given
6. $\triangle AEC \cong \triangle BEC$	6. HL congruence

c. Prove: $\triangle AEC \cong \triangle DEB$

$\angle AEC$ and $\angle DEB$ are right angles because they are angles formed by perpendicular segments. That makes $\triangle AEC$ and $\triangle DEC$ right triangles. It is given that $\overline{AC} \cong \overline{BD}$, so you know the two right triangles have congruent hypotenuses.

In part (b) you showed that $\triangle AEC \cong \triangle BEC$. Using CPCTC, $\angle ACE \cong \angle BCE$. $\angle ACE$ and $\angle BCE$ form a right angle, so they are complementary. If two congruent angles are complementary, they each measure 45°, so $m\angle ACE = m\angle BCE = 45°$. $\angle CEB$ is a right angle, so $\angle BCE$ and $\angle CBE$ must be complementary, making $m\angle CBE = 45°$. $\angle CBE$ and $\angle DBE$ are complementary. $\angle ACE$ and $\angle DBE$ are both complementary to 45° angles so they must be congruent. So $\triangle AEC \cong \triangle DEB$ by HA.

For help with the Congruent Complements theorem, go to *Proving Angles Congruent* (p. 624).

Right Triangle Congruencies

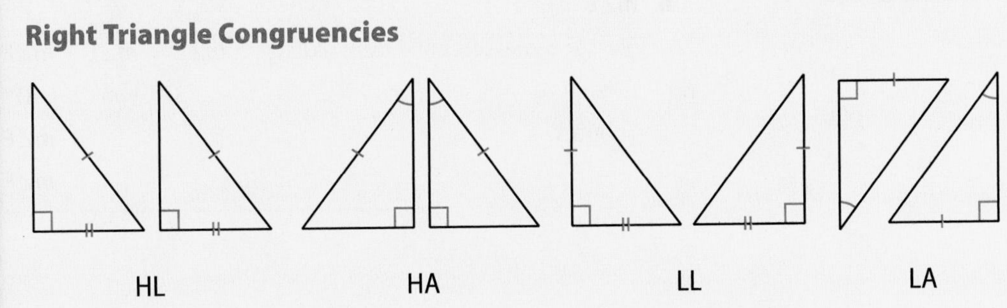

Isosceles and Equilateral Triangles

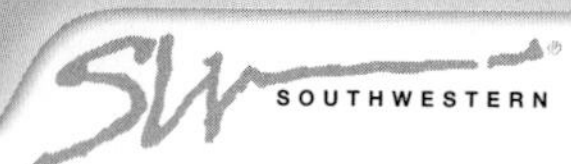

Isosceles Triangles

An **isosceles triangle** has at least two congruent sides. These sides are called **legs**. The third side is the **base**. The angles adjacent to the base are **base angles**. The angle opposite the base is the **vertex angle**.

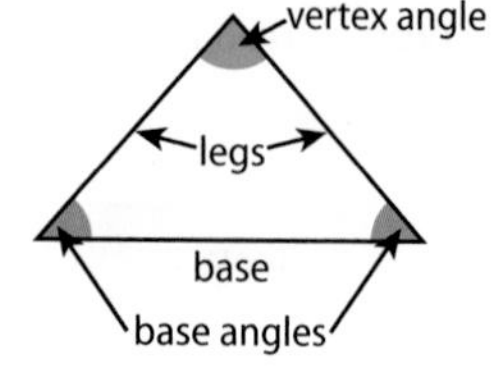

Base Angles Theorem

If two sides of a triangle are congruent, then the angles opposite those sides are congruent.

B
A C

$\angle A \cong \angle C$

Theorem

If two angles of a triangle are congruent, then the sides opposite those angles are congruent.

B
A C

$\overline{AB} \cong \overline{BC}$

PROOF

Given: $\overline{AB} \cong \overline{CB}$

Prove: $\angle A \cong \angle C$

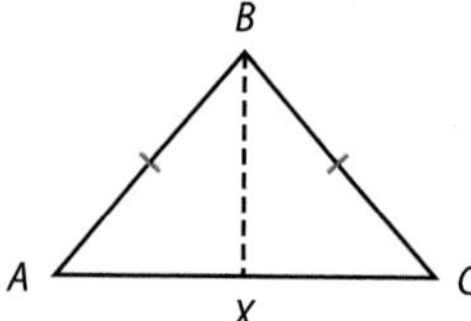

Draw $\overline{BX}$ so that X is the midpoint of $\overline{AC}$. By definition of midpoint, $\overline{XA} \cong \overline{XC}$. It is given that $\overline{AB} \cong \overline{CB}$. $\overline{BX} \cong \overline{BX}$ by the Reflexive Property of Congruence. So $\triangle BXA \cong \triangle BXC$ by SSS congruence. Using CPCTC, $\angle A \cong \angle C$.

EXAMPLE 1

SEARCH

To see step-by-step videos of these problems, enter the page number into the SWadvantage.com Search Bar.

Given $\triangle DEF$ with $\overline{DE} \cong \overline{EF}$, find each measure.

D 37° E F

a. $m\angle F$

$\angle$s opposite $\cong$ sides of a $\triangle$ are $\cong$.	$\angle F \cong \angle D$
Definition of congruent $\angle$s	$m\angle F = m\angle D$
Substitute given value.	$m\angle F = 37°$

b. $m\angle E$

Sum of $\angle$ measures of a $\triangle$ is 180°.	$m\angle D + m\angle E + m\angle F = 180°$
Substitute.	$37° + m\angle E + 37° = 180°$
Subtract.	$m\angle E = 180 - 37 - 37$
	$m\angle E = 106°$

EXAMPLE 2

Given $\triangle HIJ$ with $\overline{IJ} \cong \overline{IH}$, find x.

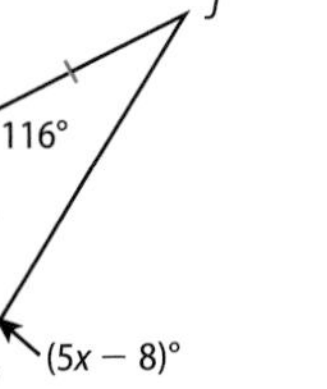

METHOD 1

Sum of $\angle$ measures of a $\triangle$ is 180°.	$m\angle H + m\angle I + m\angle J = 180°$
$\angle$s opposite $\cong$ sides of a $\triangle$ are $\cong$.	$\angle H \cong \angle J$
Definition of congruent $\angle$s	$m\angle H = m\angle J$
Substitute.	$(5x - 8) + 116 + (5x - 8) = 180$
Combine like terms.	$10x + 100 = 180$
Subtract.	$10x = 80$
Divide.	$x = 8$

METHOD 2

Sum of $\angle$ measures of a $\triangle$ is 180°.	$m\angle H + m\angle I + m\angle J = 180°$
$\angle$s opposite $\cong$ sides of a $\triangle$ are $\cong$.	$\angle H \cong \angle J$
Definition of congruent $\angle$s	$m\angle H = m\angle J$
Substitute.	$m\angle H + 116 + m\angle H = 180$
Simplify.	$2m\angle H + 116 = 180$
Subtract.	$2m\angle H = 64$
Divide.	$m\angle H = 32$
Substitute for $m\angle H$.	$5x - 8 = 32$
Add.	$5x = 40$
Divide.	$x = 8$

Watch Out!

A base angle will share only one side with a congruent leg and will measure less than 90°.

EXAMPLE 3

Given $\triangle KLM$ with $\overline{KM} \cong \overline{KL}$, find $m\angle K$.

$\angle$s opposite $\cong$ sides of a $\triangle$ are $\cong$.	$\angle M \cong \angle L$
Definition of congruent $\angle$s	$m\angle M = m\angle L$
Substitute.	$9x + 2 = 6x + 14$
Combine like terms.	$3x = 12$
Divide.	$x = 4$
Substitute for x.	$m\angle M = 9(4) + 2$
	$= 38°$
	$m\angle L = 6(4) + 14$
	$= 38°$
Sum of $\angle$ measures of a $\triangle$ is 180°.	$m\angle K + m\angle L + m\angle M = 180°$
Substitute.	$m\angle K + 38 + 38 = 180$
Simplify.	$m\angle K + 76 = 180$
Subtract.	$m\angle K = 104°$

Equilateral Triangles

An **equilateral triangle** has three congruent sides. An **equiangular triangle** has three congruent angles. These two theorems state that there is no difference between the two.

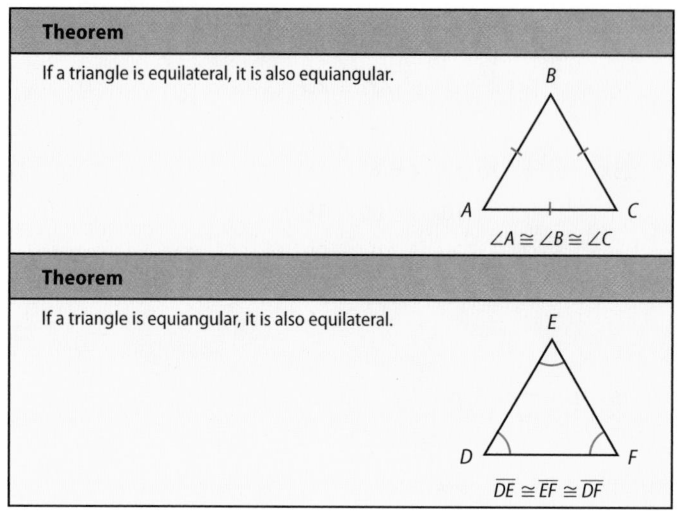

Theorem	
If a triangle is equilateral, it is also equiangular.	$\angle A \cong \angle B \cong \angle C$

Theorem	
If a triangle is equiangular, it is also equilateral.	$\overline{DE} \cong \overline{EF} \cong \overline{DF}$

Note that since an equilateral triangle has at least two congruent sides, it is also an isosceles triangle.

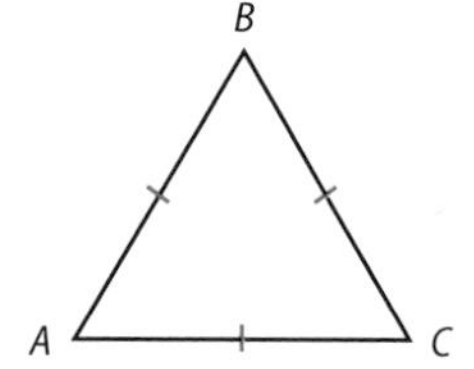

PROOF

Given: $\triangle ABC$ is equilateral.

Prove: $\triangle ABC$ is equiangular.

You are given that $\overline{AB} \cong \overline{BC}$. So $\angle A \cong \angle C$ because angles opposite congruent sides of a triangle are congruent. Also, $\overline{AB} \cong \overline{AC}$. So $\angle C \cong \angle B$ for the same reason. Using either the same method one more time or the Transitive Property of Congruence, you get $\angle A \cong \angle B$. Therefore, $\triangle ABC$ is equiangular.

GOT TO KNOW!

Triangles with Congruent Sides

Base angles of an isosceles triangle are congruent.

If two angles of a triangle are congruent, then the sides opposite those angles are congruent.

A triangle has three congruent angles if and only if it has three congruent sides.

A triangle has three congruent sides if and only if it has three congruent angles.

EXAMPLE 4

Given that $\triangle NOP$ is equilateral, find x.

Equilateral $\triangle$ is equiangular.	$\triangle NOP$ is equiangular.
Each $\angle$ of an equiangular $\triangle$ measures 60°.	$m\angle O = 60°$
Substitute.	$13x - 5 = 60$
Add.	$13x = 65$
Divide.	$x = 5$

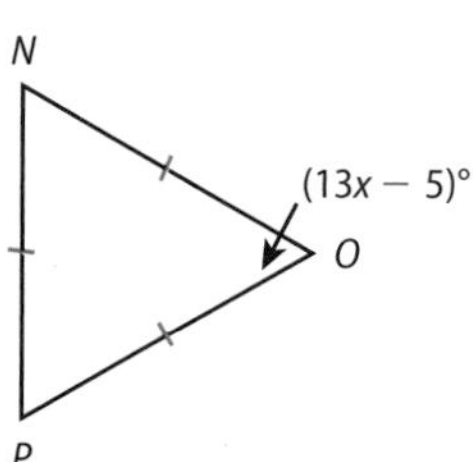

For help with angle relationships in triangles, go to *Triangle Angle Sum Theorem*, p. 668.

EXAMPLE 5

Given $\triangle TUV$ is equiangular, find TV.

Equiangular △ is equilateral.	$\triangle TUV$ is equilateral.
Definition of equilateral	$TV = TU = UV$
Substitute for TU and TV.	$7x - 12 = 3x + 20$
Solve for x.	$4x = 32$
	$x = 8$
Substitute for x.	$TV = 7(8) - 12 = 44$

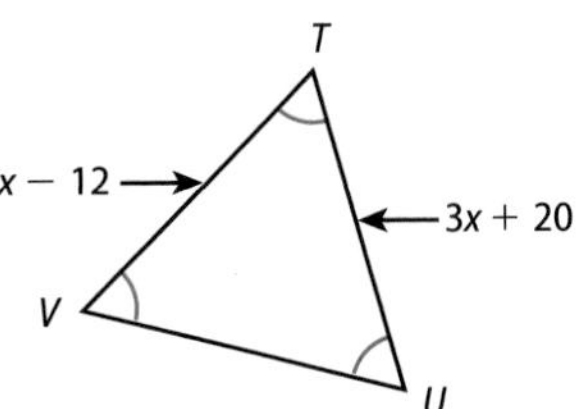

SEARCH

To see step-by-step videos of these problems, enter the page number into the SWadvantage.com Search Bar.

EXAMPLE 6

Given $\triangle QRS$ is equilateral, find y.

Equilateral △ is equiangular.	$\triangle QRS$ is equiangular.
Each ∠ of an equiangular △ measures 60°.	$m\angle Q = 60°$
Substitute for $m\angle Q$.	$22x - 6 = 60$
Add.	$22x = 66$
Divide.	$x = 3$
Each ∠ of an equiangular △ measures 60°.	$m\angle R = 60°$
Substitute for $m\angle R$.	$2xy + 18 = 60$
Substitute for x.	$2(3)y + 18 = 60$
Simplify and subtract.	$6y = 42$
Divide.	$y = 7$

R
(2xy + 18)°
(22x − 6)°
Q
S

EXAMPLE 7

Given $\triangle WYZ$ is equilateral, $\angle XYZ$ is a right angle, and $\overline{WY} \cong \overline{XY}$, find x.

Definition of a right ∠.	$m\angle XYZ = 90°$
Equilateral △ is equiangular.	$\triangle WYZ$ is equiangular.
Each ∠ of an equiangular △ measures 60°.	$m\angle WYZ = 60°$
Angle addition	$m\angle WYZ + m\angle XYW = m\angle XYZ$
Substitute for $m\angle WYZ$ and $m\angle XYZ$.	$60° + m\angle XYW = 90°$
Subtract.	$m\angle XYW = 30°$
∠s opposite ≅ sides of a △ are ≅.	$\angle YWX \cong \angle YXW$
Definition of congruent ∠s	$m\angle YWX = m\angle YXW$
Sum of ∠ measures of a △ is 180°.	$m\angle XYW + m\angle YWX + m\angle YXW = 180°$
Substitute.	$30 + (6x + 9) + (6x + 9) = 180$
Combine like terms.	$12x + 48 = 180$
Subtract.	$12x = 132$
Divide.	$x = 11$

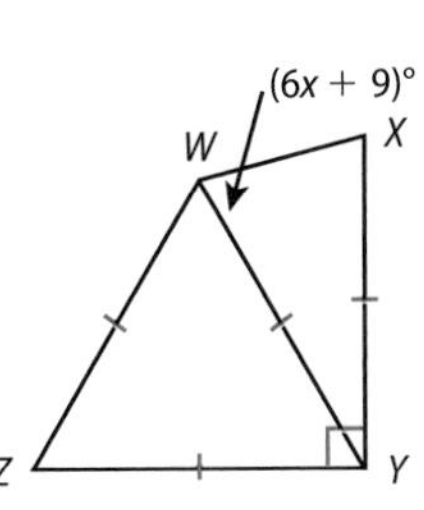

Similarity

What Came Before?

- Properties of right triangles
- Proving triangles and other figures congruent

What's This About?

- Defining and proving similarity of figures
- Using proportions to solve for missing measures in similar figures
- Designing and creating fractals

Practical Apps

- Scale drawings use similar figures to represent large structures.
- Cell phone antennas have fractal designs so that they can receive multiple signals.

just for FUN!

TEACHER: Class, take out your rulers.

STUDENT: I don't have mine. Can I just measure indirectly?

CONTENTS UPLOAD DOWNLOAD

Geometry

You can find more practice problems online by visiting:
www.SWadvantage.com

Similar Polygons

Similarity

Figures that have the exact same shape but not necessarily the same size are **similar**.

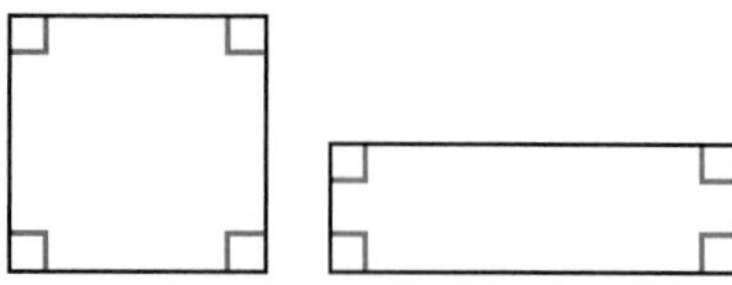

These figures are not the exact same shape, so they are not similar.

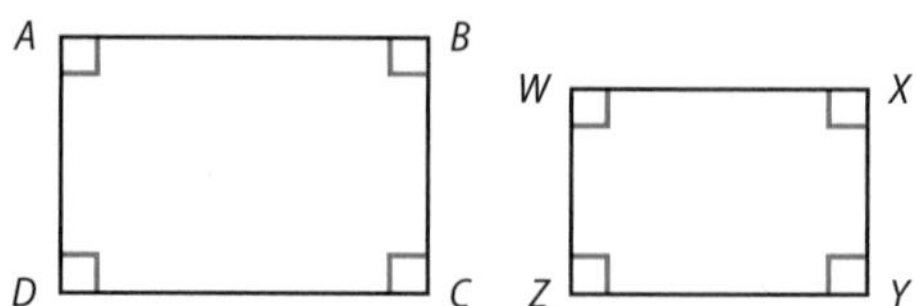

These figures are the exact same shape, so $ABCD \sim WXYZ$ (read *ABCD* is similar to *WXYZ*).

For help with proportions, go to *Equivalent Ratios and Proportions* in *Numbers and Operations,* p. 368.

Two figures are similar if and only if each pair of corresponding angles is congruent and each pair of corresponding sides is proportional.

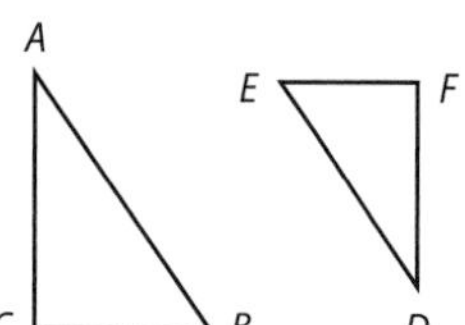

Corresponding Sides

$$\frac{AB}{DE} = \frac{BC}{EF} = \frac{CA}{FD}$$

Corresponding Angles

$\angle A \cong \angle D$
$\angle B \cong \angle E$
$\angle C \cong \angle F$

$$\triangle ABC \sim \triangle DEF$$

As with congruence, the order in which the vertices are listed in a similarity statement indicates which sides and angles correspond to each other.

The ratio of the lengths of corresponding sides of similar figures is called the **similarity ratio**. The similarity ratio of *GHIJ* to *KLMN* is $\frac{3}{5}$. The similarity ratio of *KLMN* to *GHIJ* is $\frac{5}{3}$.

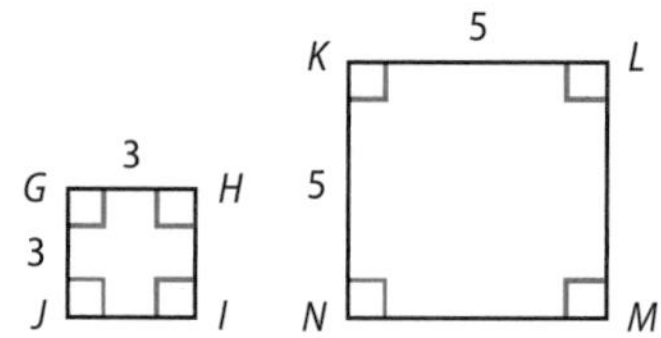

EXAMPLE 1

Determine whether the rectangles are similar.

All angles in rectangles are right angles, so the angles are congruent.

Now check that the sides are proportional.

$\frac{PS}{TW} = \frac{8}{6} = \frac{4}{3}$ $\quad$ $\frac{PQ}{TU} = \frac{12}{10} = \frac{6}{5}$ $\quad$ $\frac{4}{3} \neq \frac{6}{5}$

Corresponding sides are not proportional, so *PQRS* is not similar to *TUVW*.

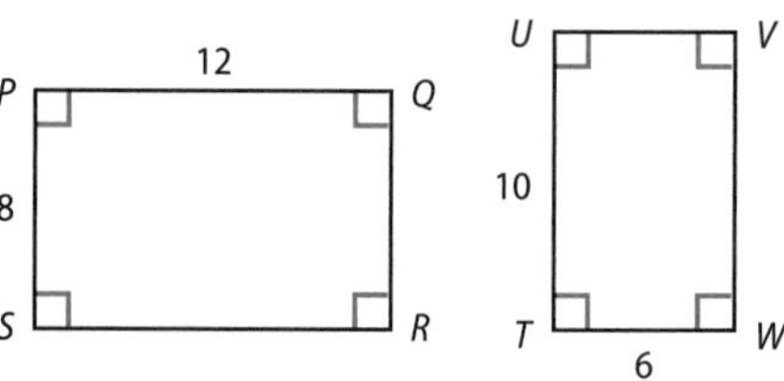

GOT TO KNOW!

Characteristics of Similar Figures

The have the exact same shape.

They may or may not be the same size.

Their corresponding angles are congruent.

Their corresponding sides are proportional.

EXAMPLE 2

Determine whether the triangles are similar.

It is given that $\angle A \cong \angle X$ and $\angle B \cong \angle Y$. This means that the third angles in the triangles must be congruent, so $\angle C \cong \angle Z$. So, all the corresponding angles are congruent.

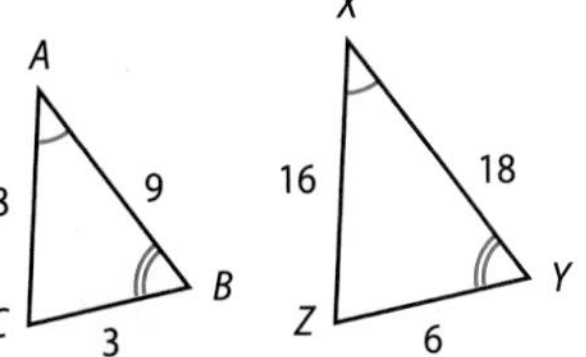

Now check that the sides are proportional.

$\frac{BC}{YZ} = \frac{3}{6} = \frac{1}{2}$ $\quad \frac{CA}{ZX} = \frac{8}{16} = \frac{1}{2}$ $\quad \frac{AB}{XY} = \frac{9}{18} = \frac{1}{2}$

Corresponding sides are proportional with a similarity ratio of $\frac{1}{2}$. So, $\triangle ABC \sim \triangle XYZ$.

> **SEARCH**
> To see step-by-step videos of these problems, enter the page number into the SWadvantage.com Search Bar.

EXAMPLE 3

Given *DEFG* ~ *HIJK*. Solve for *x*.

Since the rectangles are similar, their side lengths must be proportional.

$$\frac{DG}{HK} = \frac{DE}{HI}$$

Substitute the given values in the proportion.

$$\frac{4}{x-1} = \frac{6}{2x-5}$$

Cross multiply to find the value for x.

$$4(2x - 5) = 6(x - 1)$$
$$8x - 20 = 6x - 6$$
$$2x = 14$$
$$x = 7$$

A **golden rectangle** is a rectangle that can be divided into a square and a rectangle so that the rectangles are similar. The new, smaller rectangle is also a golden rectangle. All golden rectangles are similar to each other. In the diagram, $ACDF \sim EBCD$.

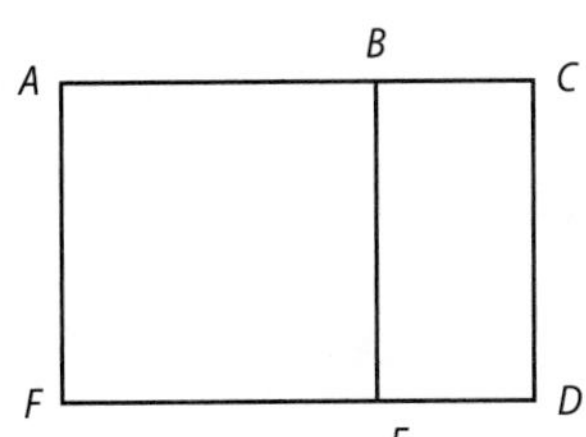

EXAMPLE 4

***MPUL* is a golden rectangle.**

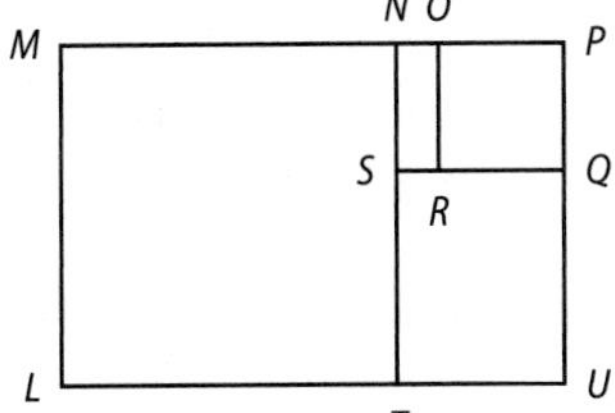

a. Identify all similar rectangles.

MPUL, *TNPU*, *NPQS*, and *SNOR* are all golden rectangles, so they are all similar to each other.

$MPUL \sim TNPU \sim NPQS \sim SNOR$

b. Identify all sides that correspond to $\overline{ML}$.

You can tell by looking at the similarity statements that $\overline{TU}$, $\overline{NS}$, and $\overline{SR}$ all correspond to $\overline{ML}$.

Proving Triangles Similar

Triangle Similarity

As you have learned, two triangles are similar if and only if all pairs of corresponding angles are congruent and all pairs of corresponding sides are proportional. But as with congruence, it is not necessary to know all of this to know two triangles are similar. This lesson gives you three ways to show triangles are similar using the minimum amount of information.

Angle-Angle Similarity Postulate (AA)

If two angles of one triangle are congruent to the corresponding angles of another triangle, then the triangles are similar.

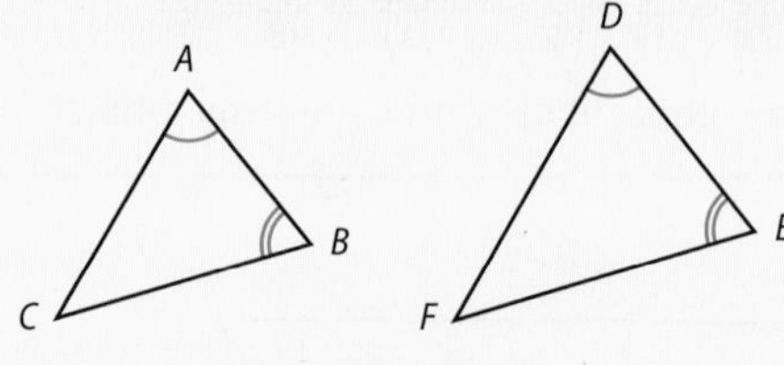

$\angle A \cong \angle D$
$\angle B \cong \angle E$

$\triangle ABC \sim \triangle DEF$

Watch Out!

The SSS and SAS theorems for similarity are not the same as for congruence.

Side-Side-Side Similarity Theorem (SSS)

If three sides of one triangle are proportional to the corresponding sides of another triangle, then the triangles are similar.

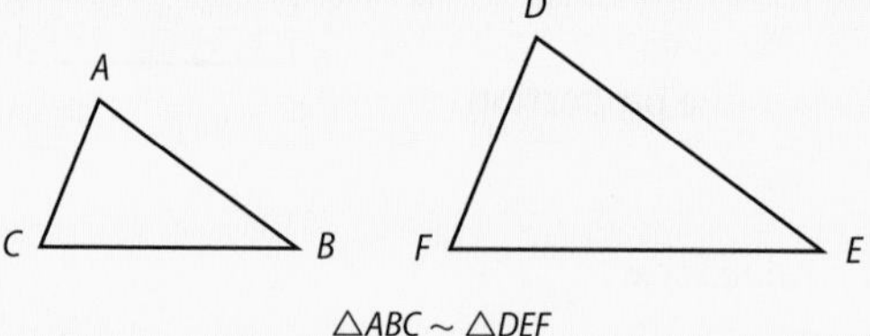

$\frac{AB}{DE} = \frac{BC}{EF} = \frac{AC}{DF}$

$\triangle ABC \sim \triangle DEF$

Side-Angle-Side Similarity Theorem (SAS)

If two sides of one triangle are proportional to the corresponding sides of another triangle and the included angles are congruent, then the triangles are similar.

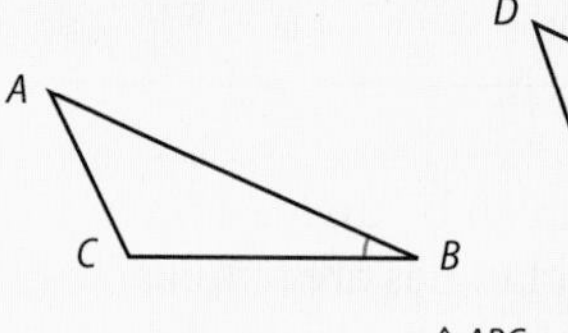

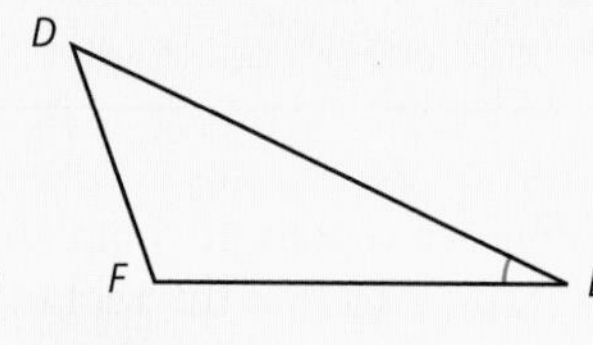

$\frac{AB}{DE} = \frac{BC}{EF}$
$\angle B \cong \angle E$

$\triangle ABC \sim \triangle DEF$

SEARCH

To see step-by-step videos of these problems, enter the page number into the SWadvantage.com Search Bar.

EXAMPLE 1

Write and justify a similarity statement for the triangles.

Vertical ∠s are ≅.	$\angle ACB \cong \angle DCE$
Given	$\overline{AB} \parallel \overline{DE}$
Alternate interior ∠s are ≅.	$\angle A \cong \angle D$

Two pairs of corresponding angles are congruent, so $\triangle ACB \sim \triangle DCE$ by AA similarity.

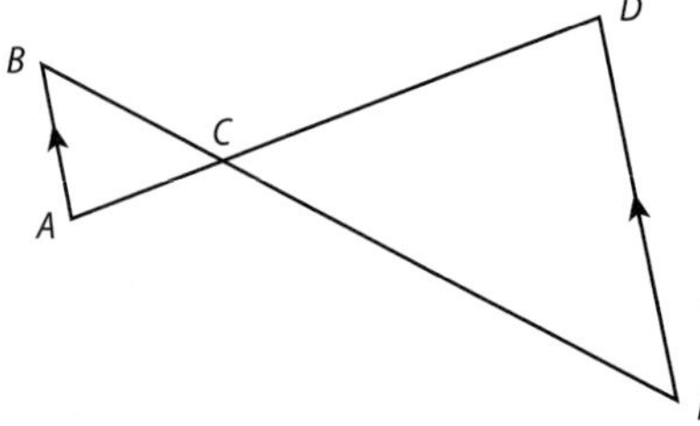

EXAMPLE 2

Write and justify a similarity statement for each pair of triangles.

a. **$\triangle GHI$ and $\triangle JKL$**

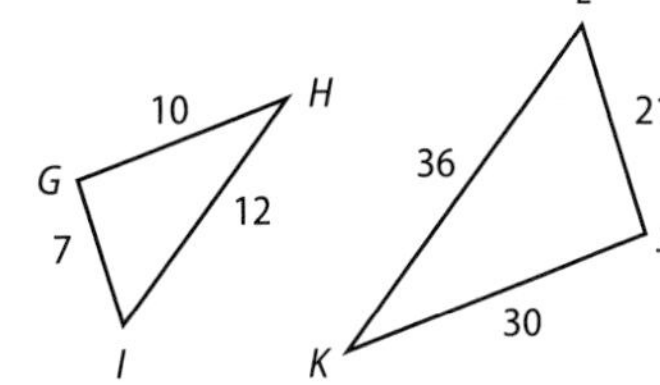

Find the ratio of each pair of corresponding sides.

$\frac{GH}{JK} = \frac{10}{30} = \frac{1}{3}$ $\quad \frac{HI}{KL} = \frac{12}{36} = \frac{1}{3}$ $\quad \frac{GI}{JL} = \frac{7}{21} = \frac{1}{3}$

All three pairs of corresponding sides are proportional.
So, $\triangle GHI \sim \triangle JKL$ by SSS similarity.

b. **$\triangle PON$ and $\triangle QOM$**

Reflexive property of $\cong$ $\quad \angle O \cong \angle O$

Find the ratio of corresponding sides.

$\frac{NO}{MO} = \frac{10}{10+5} = \frac{10}{15} = \frac{2}{3}$ $\quad \frac{PO}{QO} = \frac{8}{8+4} = \frac{8}{12} = \frac{2}{3}$

Two pairs of corresponding sides are proportional and their included angles are congruent.
So, $\triangle PON \sim \triangle QOM$ by SAS similarity.

EXAMPLE 3

Write and justify a similarity statement.
Then find *UV*.

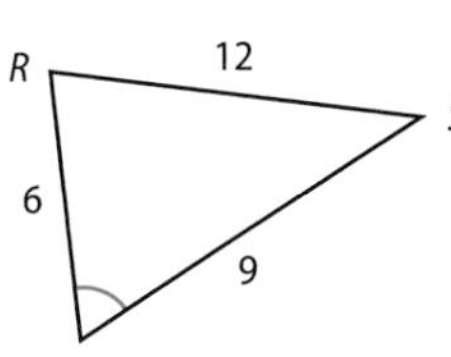

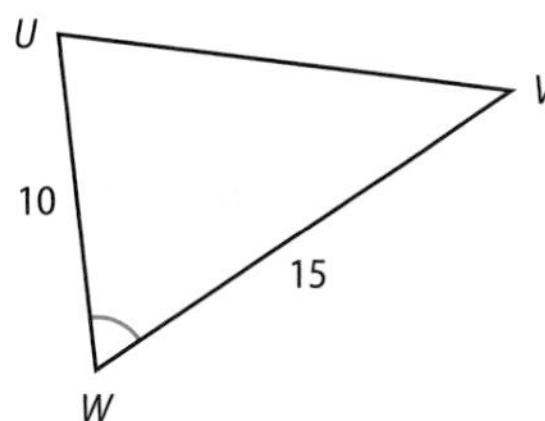

Given $\quad \angle T \cong \angle W$

Find the ratio of corresponding sides.

$\frac{RT}{UW} = \frac{6}{10} = \frac{3}{5}$ $\quad \frac{ST}{VW} = \frac{9}{15} = \frac{3}{5}$

Two pairs of corresponding sides are proportional and their included angles are congruent.
So, $\triangle RST \sim \triangle UVW$ by SAS similarity.

Since the triangles are similar, you know $\frac{RS}{UV} = \frac{ST}{VW} = \frac{RT}{UW}$. So, $\frac{12}{UV} = \frac{3}{5}$.

Cross multiply.	$(5)(12) = 3(UV)$
Simplify.	$60 = 3(UV)$
Divide both sides by 3.	$20 = UV$

Conditions for Triangle Similarity

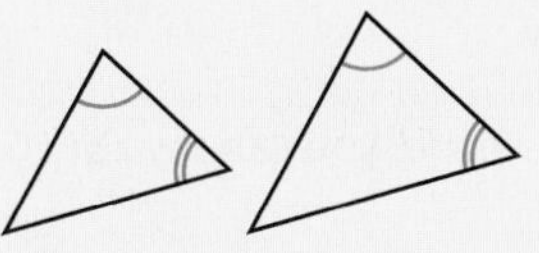

AA

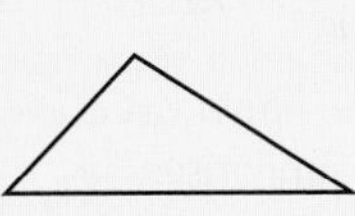

SSS

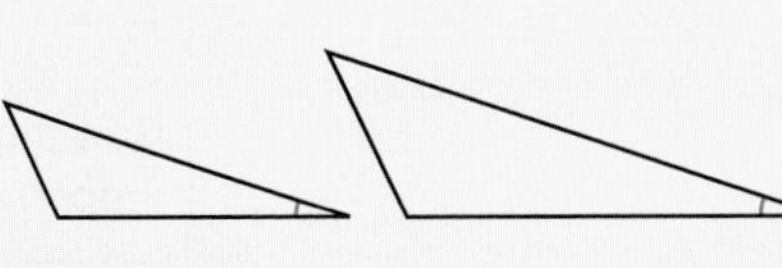

SAS

Using Similar Triangles in Proofs

EXAMPLE 4

SEARCH

To see step-by-step videos of these problems, enter the page number into the SWadvantage.com Search Bar.

Given: Isosceles triangles *ABC* and *XYZ*, with $\angle B \cong \angle Y$

Prove: $\triangle ABC \sim \triangle XYZ$

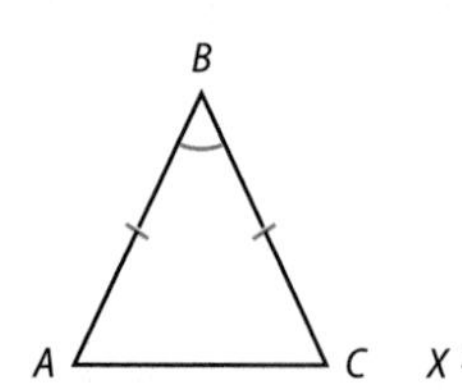

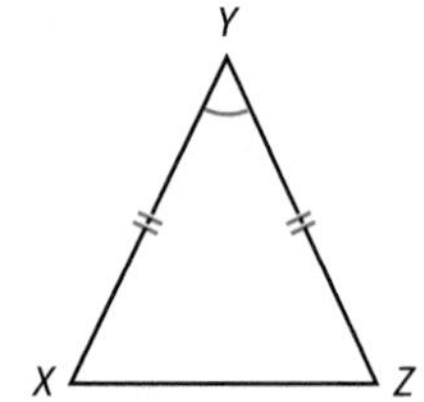

Statements	Reasons
1. $\overline{AB} \cong \overline{BC}, \overline{XY} \cong \overline{YZ}$	1. Given
2. $AB = BC, XY = YZ$	2. Definition of ≅ segments
3. $\frac{AB}{XY} = \frac{BC}{YZ}$	3. Division property of equality
4. $\angle B \cong \angle Y$	4. Given
5. $\triangle ABC \sim \triangle XYZ$	5. SAS similarity

As there are for equality and congruence, there are helpful properties that hold for similarity.

Properties of Similarity	
Reflexive Property of Similarity	$\triangle ABC \sim \triangle ABC$
Symmetric Property of Similarity	If $\triangle ABC \sim \triangle XYZ$, then $\triangle XYZ \sim \triangle ABC$.
Transitive Property of Similarity	If $\triangle ABC \sim \triangle XYZ$ and $\triangle XYZ \sim \triangle LMN$, then $\triangle ABC \sim \triangle LMN$.

EXAMPLE 5

Given: $\overline{DF} \parallel \overline{CG}$

Prove: $\triangle CEG \sim \triangle HIJ$

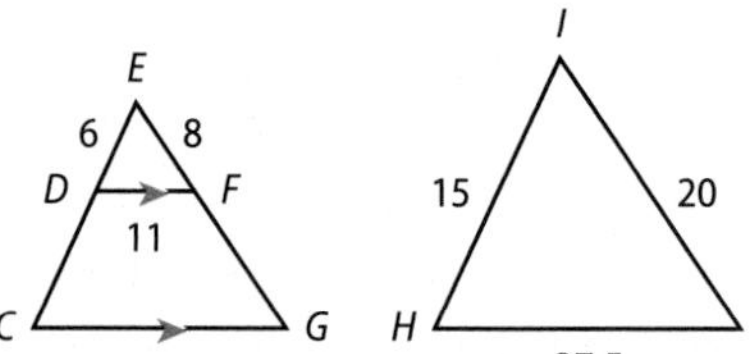

It is given that $\overline{DF} \parallel \overline{CG}$, so $\angle EDF \cong \angle ECG$ and $\angle EFD \cong \angle EGC$ because they are corresponding angles. That makes $\triangle CEG \sim \triangle DEF$ by AA similarity.

Now check the relationship between the corresponding side lengths of $\triangle DEF$ and $\triangle HIJ$.

$\frac{DE}{HI} = \frac{6}{15} = \frac{2}{5}$ $\quad$ $\frac{EF}{IJ} = \frac{8}{20} = \frac{2}{5}$ $\quad$ $\frac{FD}{JH} = \frac{11}{27.5} = \frac{2}{5}$

$\frac{DE}{HI} = \frac{EF}{IJ} = \frac{FD}{JH}$, so $\triangle DEF \sim \triangle HIJ$ by SSS similarity.

Now that you know $\triangle CEG \sim \triangle DEF$ and $\triangle DEF \sim \triangle HIJ$, you can say $\triangle CEG \sim \triangle HIJ$ by the Transitive Property of Similarity.

EXAMPLE 6

Given: $\overline{LN}$ **bisects** $\overline{KM}$ **and** $\overline{OM}$

Prove: $\triangle LMN \sim \triangle KMO$

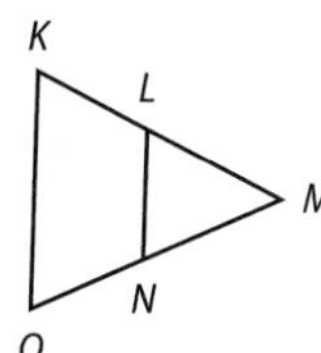

Statements	Reasons
1. $\overline{LN}$ bisects $\overline{KM}$ and $\overline{OM}$	1. Given
2. $\overline{KL} \cong \overline{LM}, \overline{ON} \cong \overline{NM}$	2. Definition of bisect
3. $KL = LM, ON = NM$	3. Definition of $\cong$ segments
4. $KL + LM = KM, ON + NM = OM$	4. Segment addition
5. $LM + LM = KM, NM + NM = OM$	5. Substitution
6. $2(LM) = KM, 2(NM) = OM$	6. Addition
7. $2 = \frac{KM}{LM}, 2 = \frac{OM}{NM}$	7. Division
8. $\frac{OM}{NM} = \frac{KM}{LM}$	8. Transitive property of equality
9. $\angle M \cong \angle M$	9. Reflexive property of congruence
10. $\triangle LMN \sim \triangle KMO$	10. SAS similarity

Once you prove triangles congruent, you can use CPCTC to prove other things about the triangles. You can also use corresponding parts to prove things true about similar triangles.

EXAMPLE 7

Given: $\overline{ST} \cong \overline{SR}$ **and** $\angle Q \cong \angle U$

Prove: $\angle P \cong \angle V$

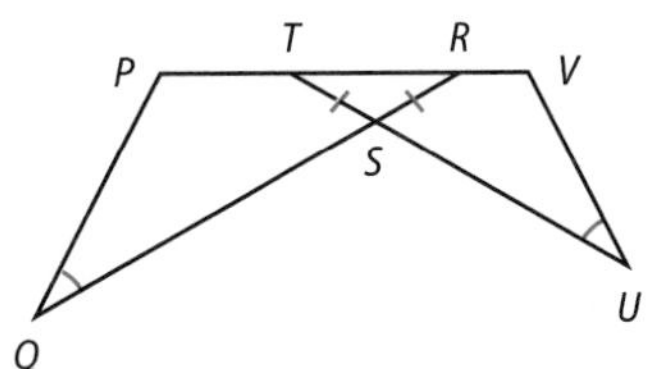

Statements	Reasons
1. $\overline{ST} \cong \overline{SR}$	1. Given
2. $\angle SRT \cong \angle STR$	2. $\angle$s opposite $\cong$ sides of a triangle are $\cong$.
3. $\angle Q \cong \angle U$	3. Given
4. $\triangle PQR \sim \triangle VUT$	4. AA similarity
5. $\angle P \cong \angle V$	5. Corresponding $\angle$s in similar triangles are $\cong$.

Watch Out !

You can use similarity to show only that corresponding sides are proportional, not congruent.

Similarity in Right Triangles

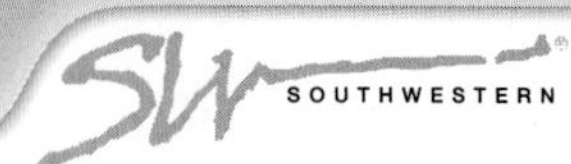

Right Triangle Similarity

Useful relationships occur when the altitude is drawn in a right triangle.

Theorem

If the altitude is drawn to the hypotenuse of a right triangle, then the two triangles formed are similar to the original triangle and to each other.

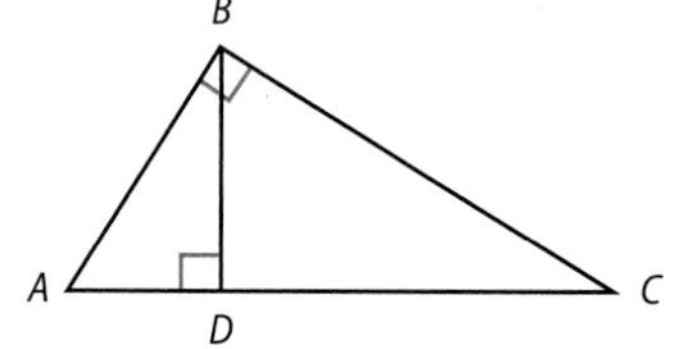

$\triangle ABC \sim \triangle BDC \sim \triangle ADB$

PROOF

Given: right $\triangle ABC$ with altitude $\overline{BD}$

Prove: $\triangle ABC \sim \triangle BDC \sim \triangle ADB$

Statements	Reasons
1. $\angle ABC$, $\angle BDC$, and $\angle BDA$ are right angles.	1. Given
2. $\angle ABC \cong \angle BDC \cong \angle BDA$	2. All right angles are congruent.
3. $\angle C \cong \angle C$, $\angle A \cong \angle A$	3. Reflexive property of $\cong$
4. $\triangle ABC \sim \triangle BDC$, $\triangle ABC \sim \triangle ADB$	4. AA similarity
5. $\triangle ABC \sim \triangle BDC \sim \triangle ADB$	5. Transitive property of congruence

EXAMPLE 1

Write a similarity statement that describes the set of triangles.

Given: $\triangle HIJ$ with altitude $\overline{IK}$

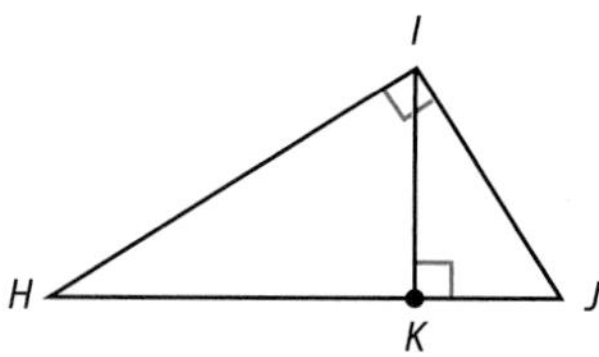

It may help to redraw the triangles separately.

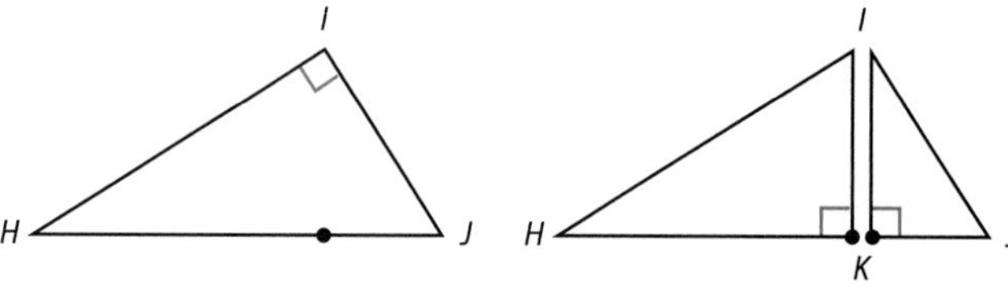

Reflexive property of $\cong$. $\angle H \cong \angle H$ and $\angle J \cong \angle J$

$\triangle HIJ \sim \triangle HKI \sim \triangle IKJ$

To see step-by-step videos of these problems, enter the page number into the SWadvantage.com Search Bar.

The **geometric mean** of two positive numbers is the positive square root of their product. So, the geometric mean of x and y is $\sqrt{xy}$. If we let the geometric mean of x and y be a, then $a^2 = xy$.

EXAMPLE 2

Find the geometric mean *a* for each pair of numbers.

a. 9 and 16

STEP 1 Find the product of the numbers.

$$a^2 = (9)(16)$$
$$= 144$$

STEP 2 Take the positive square root of the product.

$$a = \sqrt{144}$$
$$= 12$$

b. 8 and 12

STEP 1 Find the product of the numbers.

$$a^2 = (8)(12)$$
$$= 96$$

STEP 2 Take the positive square root of the product.

$$a = \sqrt{96}$$
$$a = \sqrt{16} \cdot \sqrt{6}$$
$$= 4\sqrt{6}$$

The geometric mean comes from solving a proportion in which the means are the same—$\frac{x}{a} = \frac{a}{y}$. You encounter this kind of proportion when comparing similar triangles formed by drawing the altitude to the hypotenuse.

Need More HELP

If you have forgotten the difference between means and extremes in a proportion, go to *Equivalent Ratios and Proportions* in *Numbers and Operations*, p. 368.

EXAMPLE 3

Use the sides of the triangles to write proportions that have the means that are the same length.

STEP 1 Look for sides that are shared by two of the three triangles.

$\overline{MO}$ is the shorter leg on one triangle and the longer leg of another.

$\overline{OP}$ is the shorter leg on one triangle and the hypotenuse of another.

$\overline{NO}$ is the longer leg on one triangle and the hypotenuse of another.

STEP 2 Write proportions using each of the above listed side lengths as the means.

$$\frac{NM}{MO} = \frac{MO}{MP} \qquad \frac{MP}{OP} = \frac{OP}{PN} \qquad \frac{PN}{NO} = \frac{NO}{MN}$$

Geometric Mean

The solution to the last example is an introduction to and an explanation of the following corollaries that involve the geometric mean.

Corollary

The length of the altitude drawn to the hypotenuse of a right triangle is the geometric mean of the lengths of the segments into which it divides the hypotenuse.

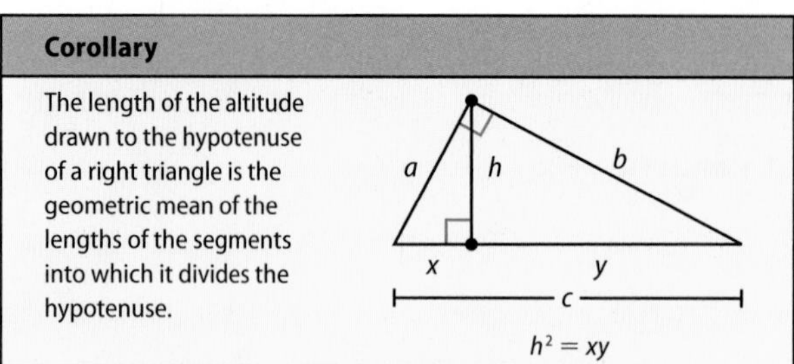

$h^2 = xy$

EXAMPLE 4

Find the value of *x*.

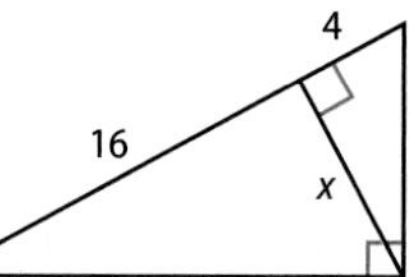

Geometric mean $\quad x^2 = (4)(16)$

$= 64$

Take the square root. $\quad x = \sqrt{64}$

$= 8$

Corollary

The length of a leg of a right triangle is the geometric mean of the lengths of the hypotenuse and the adjacent segment of the hypotenuse.

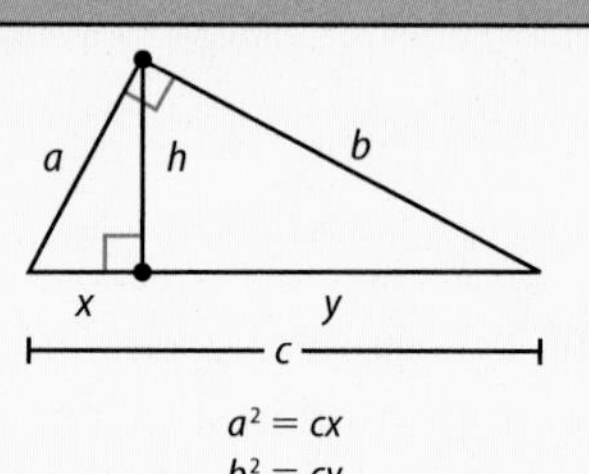

$a^2 = cx$

$b^2 = cy$

EXAMPLE 5

Find the value of *x* in each triangle.

a.

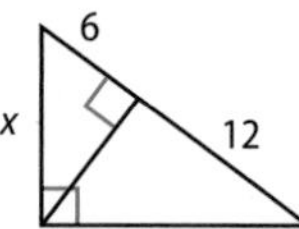

Geometric mean $\quad x^2 = 6(6 + 12)$

$= 6(18)$

$= 108$

Take the square root. $\quad x = \sqrt{108}$

$= 6\sqrt{3}$

b.

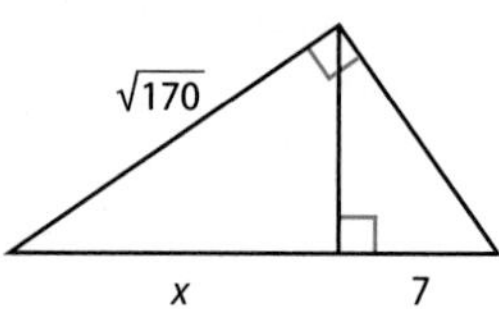

Geometric mean $\quad (\sqrt{170})^2 = x(x + 7)$

Simplify. $\quad 170 = x^2 + 7x$

Subtract. $\quad 0 = x^2 + 7x - 170$

Factor. $\quad 0 = (x + 17)(x - 10)$

Solve for *x*. $\quad x = -17$ or $x = 10$

Length must be positive, so $x = 10$.

SEARCH

To see step-by-step videos of these problems, enter the page number into the SWadvantage.com Search Bar.

EXAMPLE 6

Find the value of *x*, *y*, and *z* in each right triangle.

a.

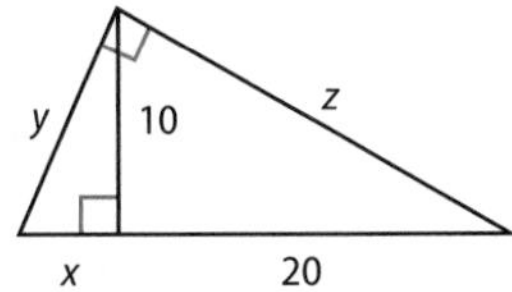

Geometric mean	$10^2 = 20x$
	$100 = 20x$
Divide.	$5 = x$
Geometric mean	$y^2 = 5(5 + 20)$
Simplify.	$= 5(25)$
Multiply.	$= 125$
Take the square root.	$y = \sqrt{125} = 5\sqrt{5}$
Geometric mean	$z^2 = 20(20 + 5)$
Simplify.	$= 20(25)$
Multiply.	$= 500$
Take the square root.	$z = \sqrt{500} = 10\sqrt{5}$

b.

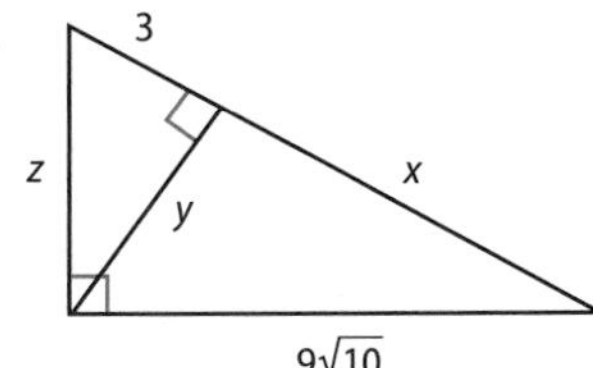

Geometric mean	$(9\sqrt{10})^2 = x(x + 3)$
Simplify.	$810 = x^2 + 3x$
Subtract.	$0 = x^2 + 3x - 810$
Factor.	$0 = (x + 30)(x - 27)$
Solve for *x*.	$x = -30$ or $x = 27$

Length must be positive, so $x = 27$.

Geometric mean	$y^2 = 3(27)$
Multiply.	$= 81$
Take the square root.	$y = \sqrt{81}$
	$y = 9$
Geometric mean	$z^2 = 3(3 + 27)$
Simplify.	$= 3(30)$
Multiply.	$= 90$
Take the square root.	$z = \sqrt{90} = 3\sqrt{10}$

Need More HELP

Remember, you can always check your answer using the Pythagorean Theorem.

GOT TO KNOW!

Relationships When an Altitude Is Drawn in a Right Triangle

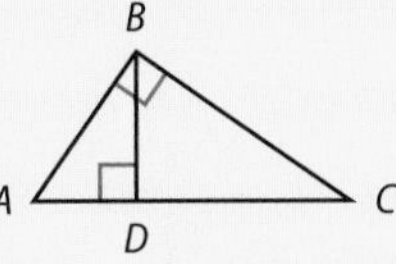

$\triangle ABC \sim \triangle BDC \sim \triangle ADB$

$BD^2 = (AD)(DC)$

$BA^2 = (AD)(AC)$

$BC^2 = (CD)(AC)$

Indirect Measurement

Shadows

There may be a time when you want to measure a length that you cannot measure directly by hand. Using similar triangles to find this length is called **indirect measurement**.

One method of indirect measurement involves similar triangles and shadows. Look at the diagram below. It would be difficult to directly measure the telephone pole's height by hand. However, you can assume that the person and the pole are perpendicular to the ground. Therefore, each makes a right angle with the ground.

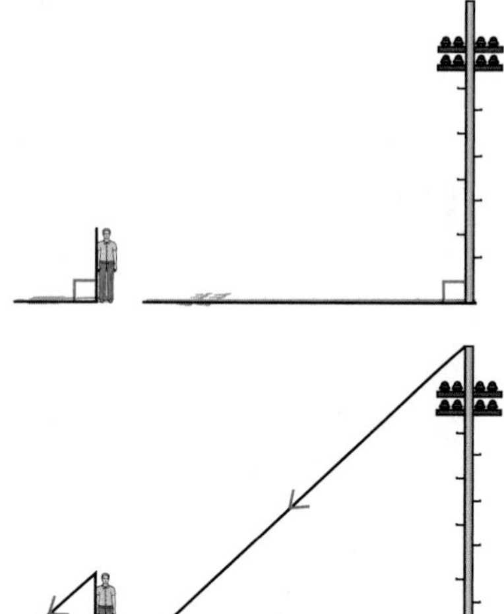

The sun's rays are parallel to each other. So, congruent corresponding angles are formed.

The triangles formed are similar using AA similarity. You can use the person's height, the lengths of the shadows, and proportions to find the height of the telephone pole.

SEARCH

To see step-by-step videos of these problems, enter the page number into the SWadvantage.com Search Bar.

EXAMPLE 1

Find each height.

a. height of the taller building

$\angle ABC \cong \angle DEF$ and $\angle ACB \cong \angle DFE$. So, $\triangle ABC \sim \triangle DEF$.

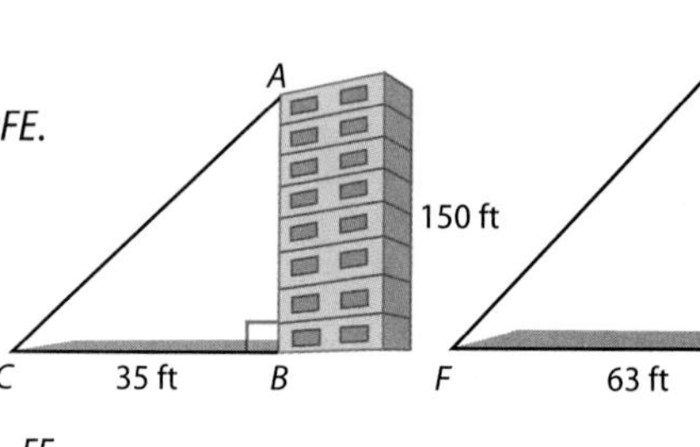

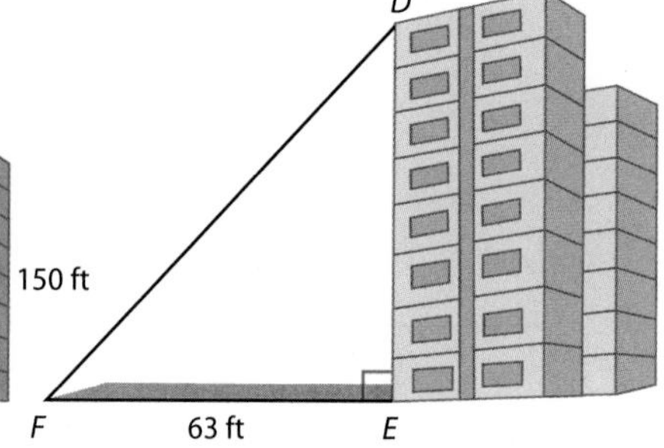

Write a proportion. $\frac{DE}{AB} = \frac{EF}{BC}$

Substitute. $\frac{DE}{150} = \frac{63}{35} = \frac{9}{5}$

Cross multiply. $5(DE) = (150)(9)$

Solve. $DE = (30)(9)$

$= 270 \text{ ft}$

The building is 270 feet tall.

b. height of the streetlight

$\angle GHI \cong \angle JKL$ and $\angle GIH \cong \angle JLK$. So, $\triangle GHI \sim \triangle JKL$.

Write a proportion. $\frac{JL}{GI} = \frac{KL}{HI}$

Substitute. $\frac{JL}{1.2} = \frac{1.8}{0.4} = \frac{4.5}{1}$

Cross multiply. $JL = (1.2)(4.5)$

$= 5.4 \text{ m}$

The streetlight is 5.4 meters tall.

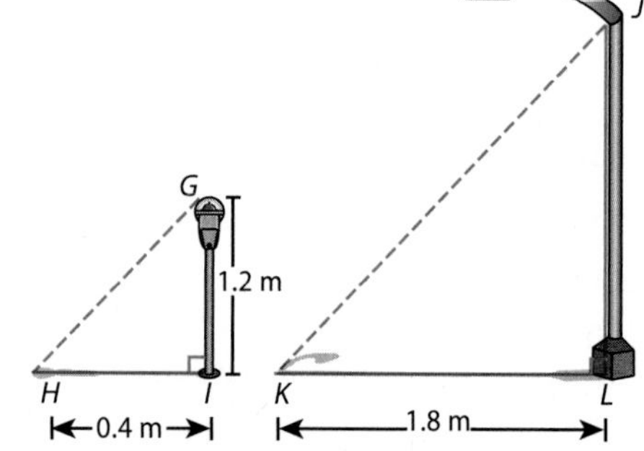

Mirrors

Another method of indirect measurement involves using mirrors.

If you place a mirror between you and a tall object, similar triangles are formed by your line of sight and the line of declination from the top of the object.

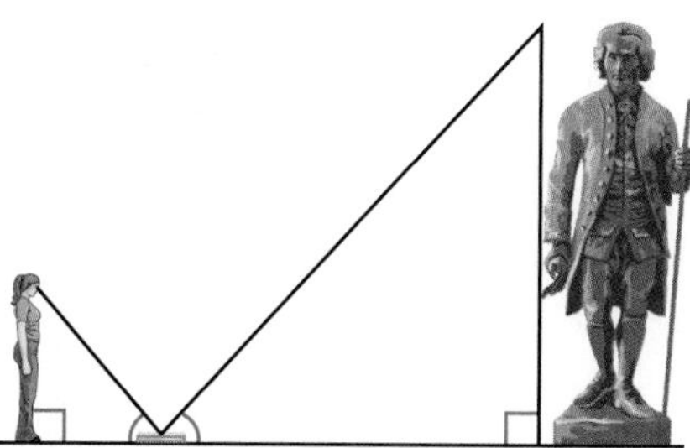

Because light reflects off a mirror at the same angle it hits the mirror, a second corresponding congruent angle is formed. So, now you know these two triangles are similar.

To find the object's height, write and solve a proportion using your height and the distances between the mirror and you and between the mirror and the object.

EXAMPLE 2

Find the height of the tree.

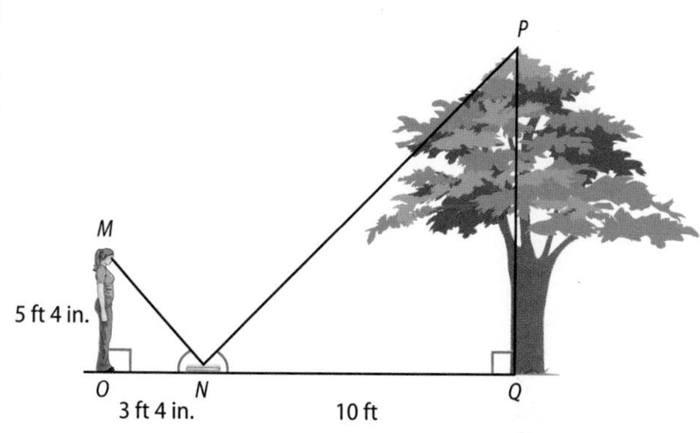

STEP 1 Change all measurements to the same unit.

$MO = 5$ ft 4 in. $= 64$ in.

$NO = 3$ ft 4 in. $= 40$ in.

$NQ = 10$ ft $= 120$ in.

STEP 2 Use similar triangles to write a proportion.

$\angle MNO \cong \angle PNQ$ and $\angle MON \cong \angle PQN$. So, $\triangle MNO \sim \triangle PNQ$ and $\frac{PQ}{MO} = \frac{NQ}{NO}$.

STEP 3 Solve for the height.

Substitute. $\frac{PQ}{64} = \frac{120}{40} = \frac{3}{1}$

Cross multiply. $PQ = (64)(3)$

$= 192$ in. $= 16$ ft

The tree is 192 inches, or 16 feet, tall.

Watch Out!

It does not matter what unit you use, just be sure to change all measurements to the same unit.

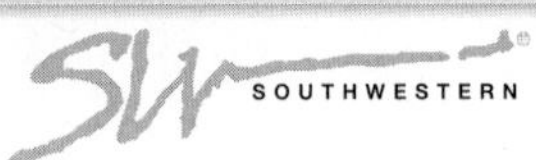

More Examples of Indirect Measurement

EXAMPLE 3

Find the width of the lake.

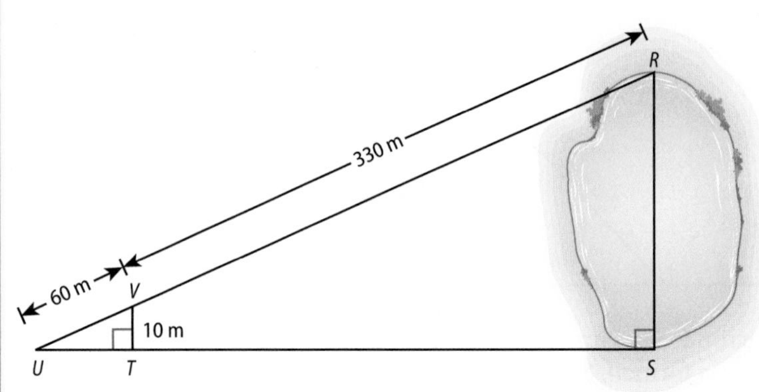

$\angle RSU \cong \angle VTU$ and $\angle U \cong \angle U$. So, $\triangle RSU \sim \triangle VTU$ and $\frac{RS}{VT} = \frac{UR}{UV}$.

Substitute. $\frac{RS}{10} = \frac{330 + 60}{60} = \frac{390}{60}$

Cross multiply. $60(RS) = (10)(390)$

Solve. $RS = \frac{(10)(390)}{60}$

$= 65$ m

The lake is 65 meters wide.

Need More HELP

For help working with similar triangles, go to *Proving Triangles Similar*, p. 792.

EXAMPLE 4

Find the height of the tower.

$\angle ACB \cong \angle DEB$ and $\angle B \cong \angle B$.

So, $\triangle ACB \sim \triangle DEB$ and $\frac{AC}{DE} = \frac{CB}{EB}$.

Substitute. $\frac{AC}{6} = \frac{100 + 2}{2} = \frac{102}{2}$

Cross multiply. $2(AC) = (6)(102)$

Solve. $AC = \frac{(6)(102)}{2}$

$= 306$ ft

The tower is 306 feet tall.

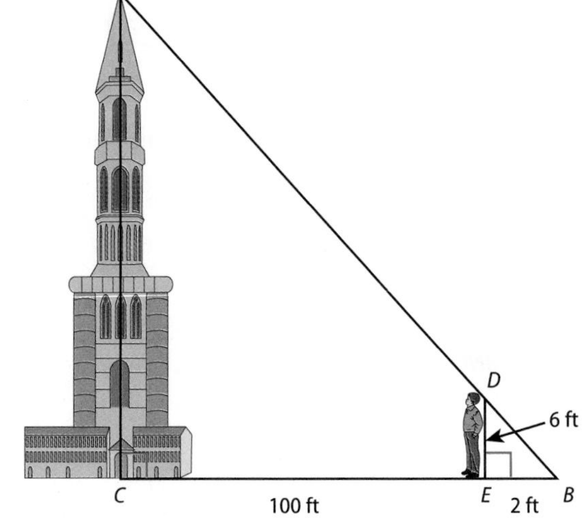

EXAMPLE 5

Find XU.

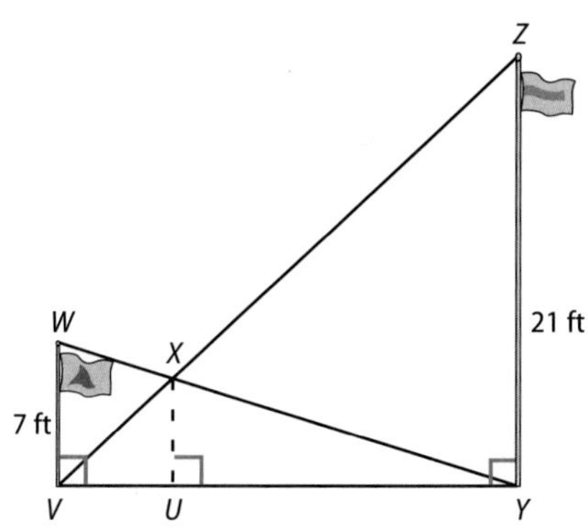

The flagpoles are perpendicular to the ground, so $\overline{WV} \parallel \overline{ZY}$. $\angle VWX \cong \angle ZYX$ and $\angle WVX \cong \angle YZX$ because each pair are alternate interior angles. So $\triangle VWX \sim \triangle ZYX$ and $\frac{WV}{ZY} = \frac{7}{21} = \frac{1}{3}$.

The altitudes in similar triangles are in the same proportion as the sides.

VU and UY are the lengths of the altitudes of $\triangle VWX$ and $\triangle ZYX$ respectively. So, $\frac{VU}{UY} = \frac{1}{3}$.

Find UY in terms of VU.

Cross multiply. $UY = 3VU$

Find VY in terms of VU.

Segment addition $VY = VU + UY$

Substitute for UY. $VY = VU + 3VU$

$VY = 4VU$

Both $\overline{WV}$ and the altitude $\overline{XU}$ make right angles with the ground and $\angle WYV \cong \angle WYV$.

So, $\triangle VWY \sim \triangle UXY$ and $\frac{XU}{WV} = \frac{UY}{VY}$.

Substitute values for WV, UY, and VY. $\frac{XU}{7} = \frac{3(VU)}{4(VU)} = \frac{3}{4}$

Cross multiply. $4(XU) = (7)(3)$

Solve. $XU = \frac{21}{4}$

$XU = 5.25$ ft

SEARCH

To see step-by-step videos of these problems, enter the page number into the SWadvantage.com Search Bar.

GOT TO KNOW!

Tips for Using Indirect Measurement

Using shadows—

Sunlight rays are parallel, causing proportional shadows.

Using mirrors—

Light reflects off a mirror at the same angle at which it hits.

Proportions in Triangles

Proportional Sides

You have learned that an altitude drawn in a right triangle creates a proportional relationship between side lengths. In this lesson you look at segments drawn in other triangles that create proportional relationships.

Theorem

If a segment that is parallel to a side of a triangle intersects the other two sides, then it divides those two sides into proportional segments.

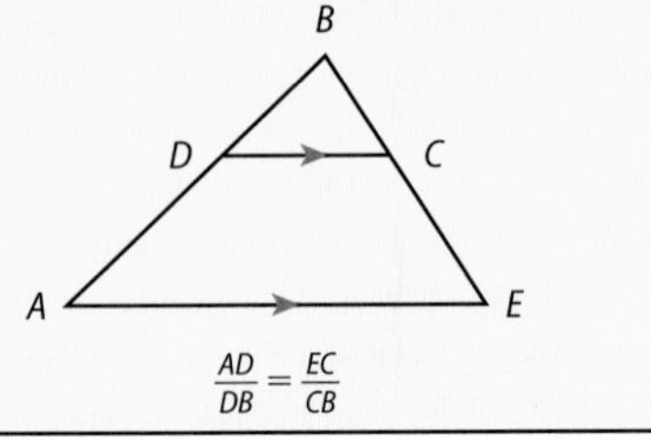

$\frac{AD}{DB} = \frac{EC}{CB}$

The converse of this theorem is also true.

Theorem

If a segment divides two sides of a triangle into proportional segments, then it is parallel to the third side.

EXAMPLE 1

SEARCH

To see step-by-step videos of these problems, enter the page number into the SWadvantage.com Search Bar.

Find each value.

a. ***x***

$\overline{RV} \parallel \overline{SU}$, so $\frac{TS}{SR} = \frac{TU}{UV}$.

Substitute given values. $\frac{7}{5} = \frac{6}{x}$

Cross multiply. $7x = 30$

Divide. $x = 4\frac{2}{7}$

b. ***FH***

$\overline{GJ} \parallel \overline{HI}$, so $\frac{JI}{FJ} = \frac{GH}{FG}$.

Substitute given values. $\frac{2}{12} = \frac{4}{FG}$

Cross multiply. $2(FG) = 48$

Divide. $FG = 24$

Segment addition $FH = FG + GH$

Substitute. $FH = 24 + 4$

$FH = 28$

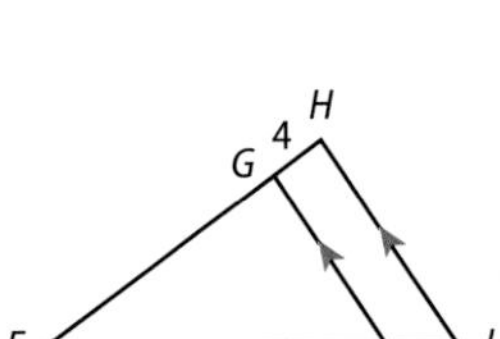

Theorem

An angle bisector of a triangle divides the opposite sides into two segments that are proportional to the other two sides of the triangle.

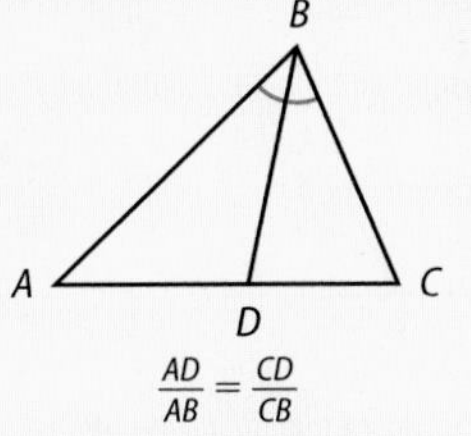

PROOF

Given: $\overline{BD}$ is the angle bisector of $\angle ABC$.

Prove: $\frac{AD}{AB} = \frac{CD}{CB}$

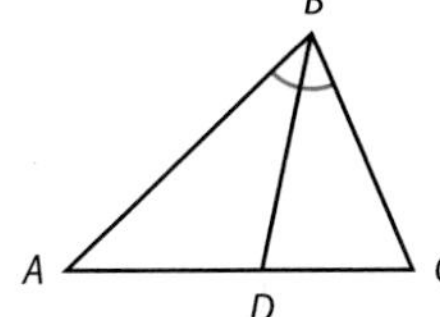

Draw $\overline{CE}$ so that $\overline{CE} \parallel \overline{DB}$, and extend $\overline{AB}$ to form $\triangle AEC$. Since $\overline{DB}$ is a segment parallel to one side of $\triangle AEC$, it divides $\overline{AC}$ and $\overline{AE}$ proportionally. So $\frac{AD}{AB} = \frac{CD}{EB}$.

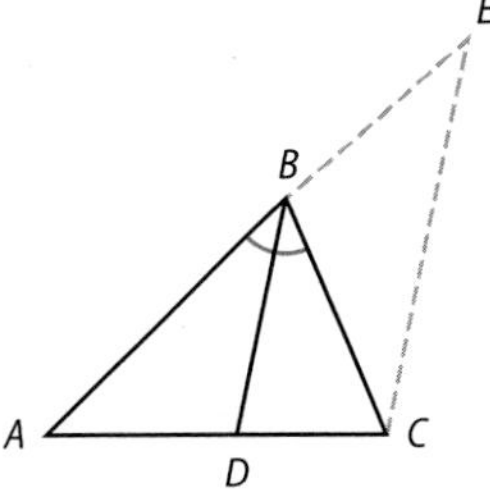

$\angle BEC$ and $\angle ABD$ are corresponding angles, so $\angle BEC \cong \angle ABD$. By definition of a bisected angle, $\angle ABD \cong \angle DBC$. $\angle DBC$ and $\angle BCE$ are alternate interior angles, so $\angle DBC \cong \angle BCE$. Using these three congruence statements and the Transitive Property of Congruence, $\angle BEC \cong \angle BCE$. The sides opposite congruent angles in a triangle are congruent, so $\overline{CB} \cong \overline{EB}$ and $CB = EB$. Substituting CB for EB in the proportion results in $\frac{AD}{AB} = \frac{CD}{CB}$.

EXAMPLE 2

Find each value.

a. *JI*

$\angle$ bisector divides opposite sides proportionally.	$\frac{HG}{GJ} = \frac{HI}{IJ}$
Substitute given values.	$\frac{9}{15} = \frac{12}{IJ}$
Cross multiply.	$9(IJ) = 180$
Divide.	$IJ = 20$

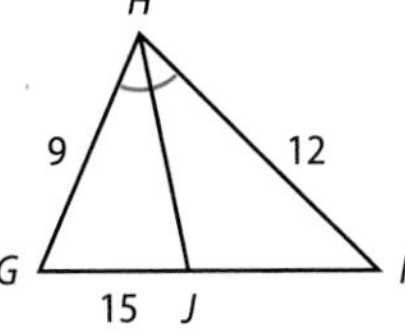

b. *x*

$\angle$ bisector divides opposite sides proportionally.	$\frac{XW}{WZ} = \frac{XY}{YZ}$
Substitute given values.	$\frac{6}{2x - 8} = \frac{15}{3x - 8}$
Cross multiply.	$18x - 48 = 30x - 120$
Solve for x.	$72 = 12x$
	$x = 6$

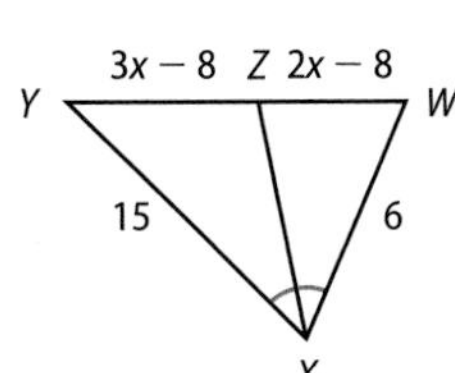

Need More HELP

For help with angle relationships when parallel lines are cut by a transversal, go to *Theorems About Parallel Lines*, p. 630.

Midsegment Theorem

The **midsegment** of a triangle is the segment that has its endpoints on the midpoints of two sides of a triangle.

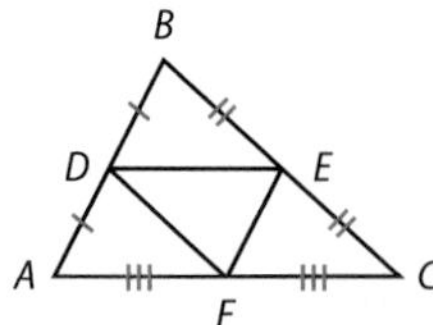

$\overline{DE}$, $\overline{EF}$, and $\overline{DF}$ are midsegments of $\triangle ABC$. $\triangle DEF$ is called the **midsegment triangle**. The midsegment theorem, stated below, is a special case of the first theorem given in this lesson.

Theorem	
A midsegment of a triangle is parallel to one side of the triangle and is half as long as that side.	$\overline{DE} \parallel \overline{AC}$ and $DE = \frac{1}{2}AC$

PROOF

Given: $\overline{DE}$ **is a midsegment of** $\triangle ABC$

Prove: $\overline{DE} \parallel \overline{AC}$ **and** $DE = \frac{1}{2}AC$

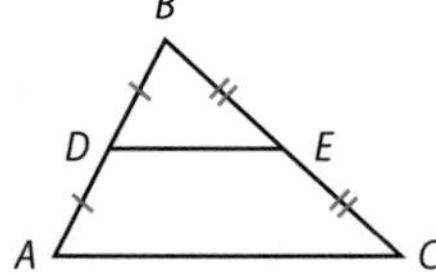

Statements	Reasons
1. $\overline{DE}$ is a midsegment of $\triangle ABC$	1. Given
2. $BD = DA$, $BE = EC$	2. Definition of midsegment
3. $\frac{BD}{DA} = 1$, $\frac{BE}{EC} = 1$	3. Division property of equality
4. $\frac{BD}{DA} = \frac{BE}{EC}$	4. Transitive property of equality
5. $\overline{DE} \parallel \overline{AC}$	5. If a segment divides two sides of a triangle proportionally, it is $\parallel$ to the third side.
6. $\angle BDE \cong \angle A$, $\angle BED \cong \angle C$	6. Corresponding $\angle$s are $\cong$.
7. $\triangle DBE \sim \triangle ABC$	7. AA similarity
8. $DB = \frac{1}{2}AB$	8. Definition of midsegment
9. $DE = \frac{1}{2}AC$	9. Corresponding sides of similar triangles are proportional.

EXAMPLE 3

Find each value.

a. ***SU***

Midsegment is $\frac{1}{2}$ as long as third side.	$SU = \frac{1}{2}QR$
Substitute given value.	$SU = \frac{1}{2}(26.8)$
	$SU = 13.4$

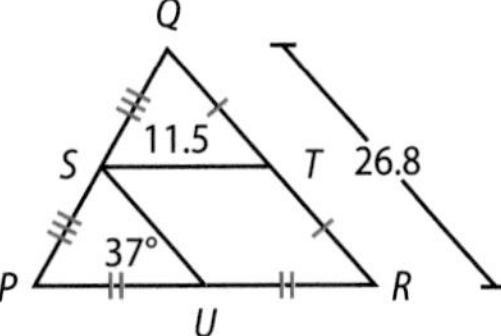

b. ***PR***

Midsegment is $\frac{1}{2}$ as long as third side.	$ST = \frac{1}{2}PR$
Substitute given value.	$11.5 = \frac{1}{2}PR$
Multiply by 2.	$PR = 23$

c. ***m∠QTS***

Midsegment is ∥ to third side.	$\overline{ST} \parallel \overline{PR}$
Alternate interior ∠s are ≅.	$\angle UST \cong \angle SUP$
Midsegment is ∥ to third side.	$\overline{SU} \parallel \overline{QR}$
Alternate interior ∠s are ≅.	$\angle QTS \cong \angle UST$
Transitive property of ≅	$\angle QTS \cong \angle SUP$
Definition of ≅ ∠s	$m\angle QTS = m\angle SUP$
Substitute given value.	$m\angle QTS = 37°$

Need More HELP

If a diagram shows that a segment splits two sides of a triangle into congruent parts, that segment is a midsegment.

SEARCH

To see step-by-step videos of these problems, enter the page number into the SWadvantage.com Search Bar.

EXAMPLE 4

Find the value of *x*.

Midsegment is $\frac{1}{2}$ as long as third side.	$3x + 1 = \frac{1}{2}(x^2 + 2x + 2)$
Multiply both sides by 2.	$6x + 2 = x^2 + 2x + 2$
Subtract.	$0 = x^2 - 4x$
Factor.	$0 = x(x - 4)$
Use the Zero Product Property.	$x = 0$ or $x = 4$

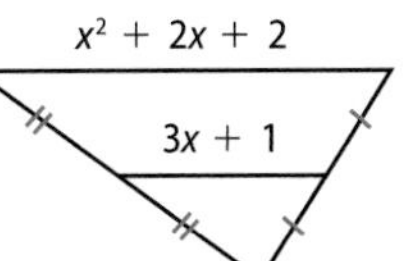

GOT TO KNOW!

Parallel Segment in Triangle

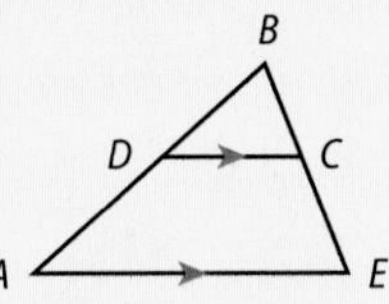

$\frac{AD}{DB} = \frac{EC}{CB}$

If $AD = DB$, then $DC = \frac{1}{2}AE$.

Self-Similarity

A figure is considered **self-similar** if it can be divided into parts that are similar to the entire figure. Some self-similar figures you have already learned about are shown below.

A right triangle with the altitude drawn to the hypotenuse is self-similar.

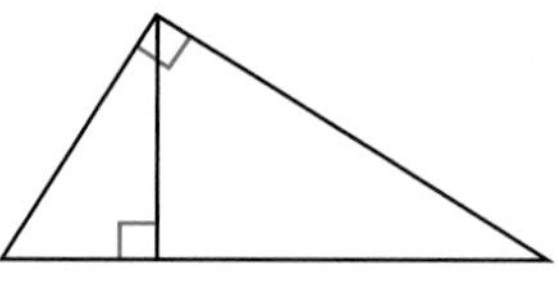

A golden rectangle divided into other golden rectangles is self-similar.

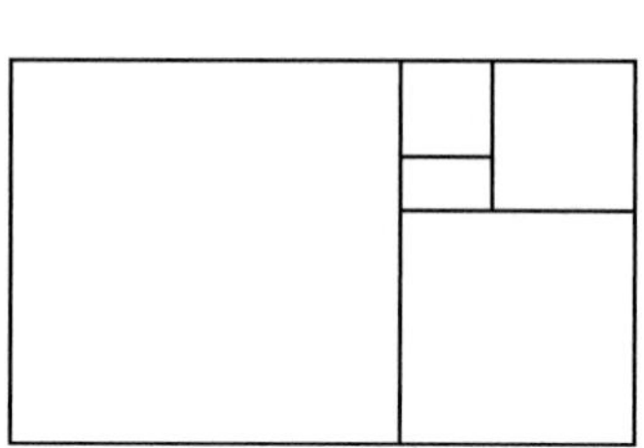

Need More
HELP
For more information about golden rectangles, go to *Similar Polygons*, p. 790.

Self-similar figures are formed by a process called **iteration**, that is, repeatedly performing a rule. Below is an example of an iteration, the Cantor set, formed by removing the middle third of a segment.

You can see the same rule is applied to each new part of the figure during each iteration.

Another example you may be more familiar with is that of a tree diagram.

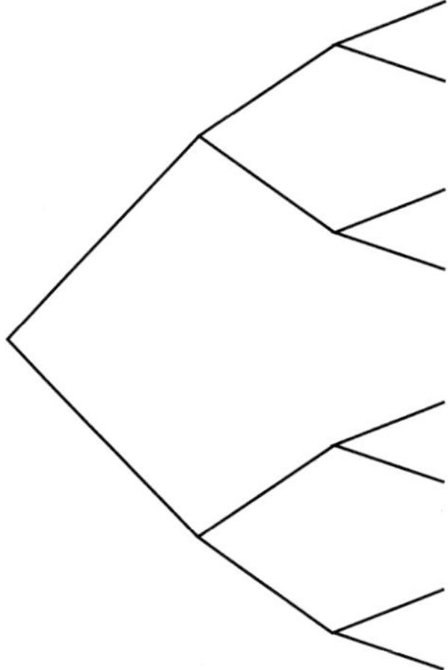

You start with a "V" shape. During each iteration, you add a "V" to the end of each branch.

A **fractal** is a self-similar figure made by iteration. A well-known example is the Sierpinski triangle. To make a Sierpinski triangle, follow the steps below.

Start with an equilateral triangle.

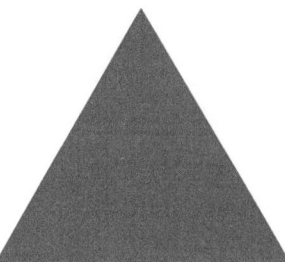

Remove the midsegment triangle. This is the first iteration.

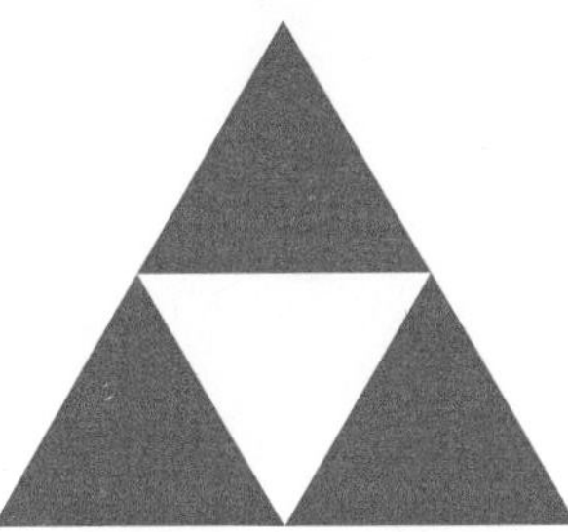

Now remove the midsegment triangle from each of the three newly formed triangles. This is the second iteration.

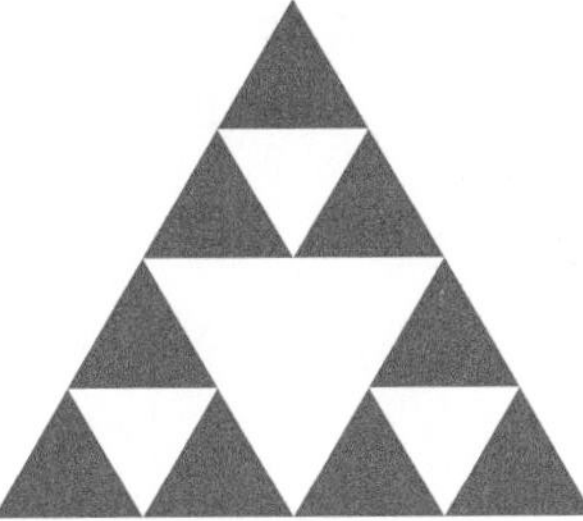

This is the third iteration.

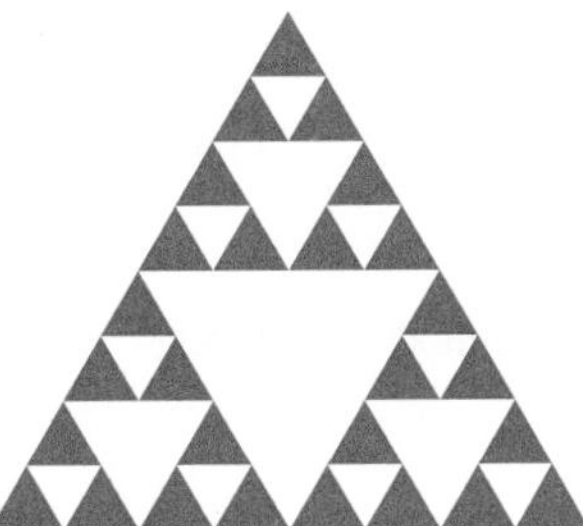

Repeating the process two more times results in the following figure.

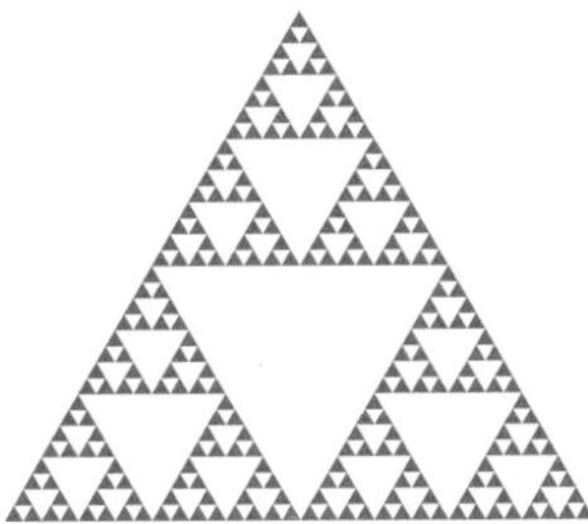

SEARCH

To see step-by-step videos of these problems, enter the page number into the SWadvantage.com Search Bar.

Forming Fractals

The Koch snowflake is another example of a fractal that begins with a triangle. To make a Koch snowflake, follow the steps below.

Start with an equilateral triangle.

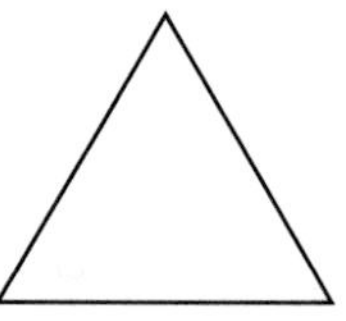

Add an equilateral triangle, one-third the size of the original, to the center of each side.

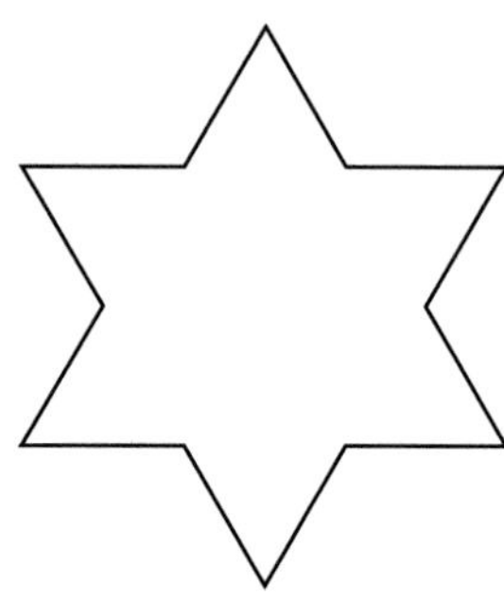

EXAMPLE 1

Draw the next two iterations of the Koch snowflake.

Starting with the first iteration, add a triangle to the center of each side to get the following figure.

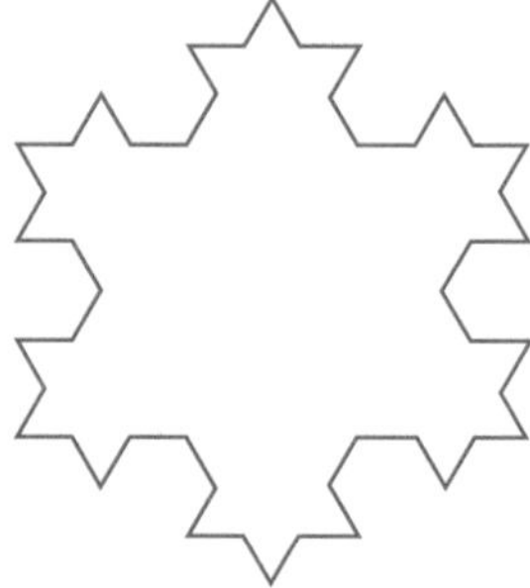

Repeat the process to get the next iteration.

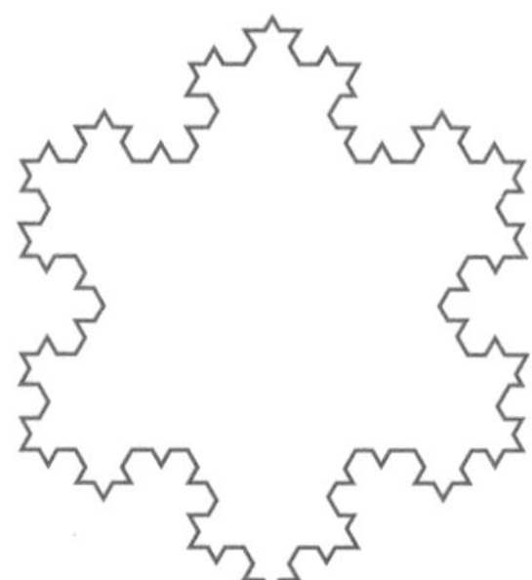

GOT TO KNOW!

Characteristics of Fractals

A small part is similar to the whole figure.

They are formed by a repeated process.

EXAMPLE 2

Describe the rule for the fractal given by the following figure and first iteration. Then draw the next two iterations.

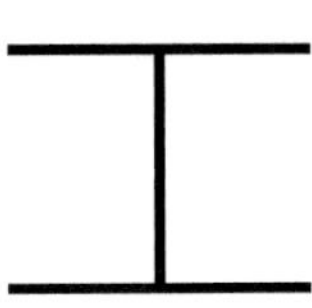

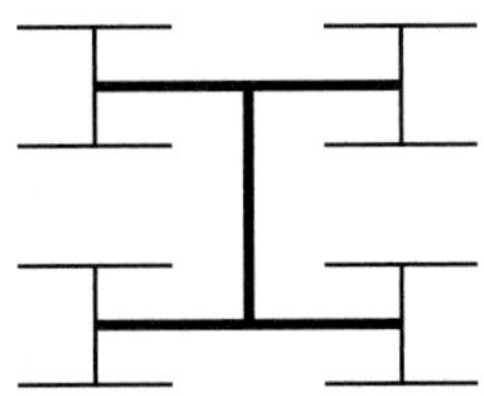

A sideways "H" is placed on each of the four corners at the midpoint of each new H.

This shows the second and third iterations.

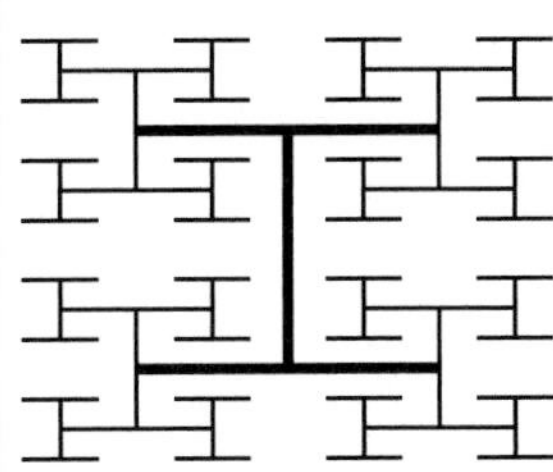

EXAMPLE 3

The Sierpinski carpet is a fractal formed by dividing a square into 9 congruent squares, removing the center square, and then repeating this process. Draw the first three iterations.

Start with a square.

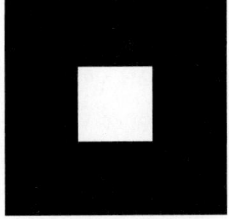

The first iteration removes 1 center square.

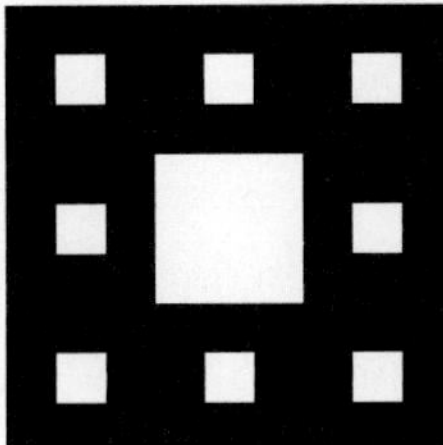

The second iteration removes 8 center squares.

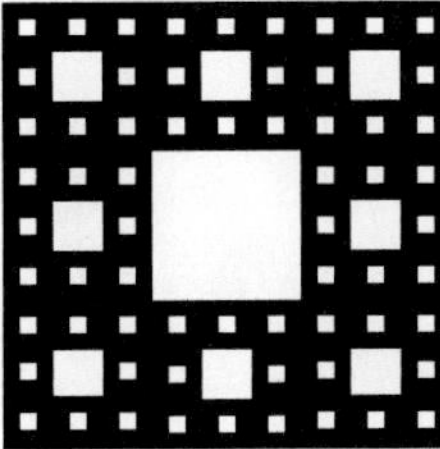

The third iteration removes 64 center squares.

SEARCH

To see step-by-step videos of these problems, enter the page number into the SWadvantage.com Search Bar.

For the second iteration, do to each of the eight remaining squares what you did to the original square.

Coordinate Geometry

What Came Before?

- Graphing linear equations on the coordinate plane
- The Pythagorean Theorem

What's This About?

- Determining if graphs of linear equations are parallel or perpendicular
- Finding distances and midpoints on the coordinate plane
- Using theorems and spatial reasoning to prove statements

Practical Apps

- Coordinate geometry can be used in city map navigation.
- The distance formula can be used with photos taken from satellites to calculate the distance between two locations.

just for FUN!

I'm trying to find the distance around this circle, but I can't find the endpoints!

CONTENTS UPLOAD DOWNLOAD

Geometry

You can find more practice problems online by visiting:
www.SWadvantage.com

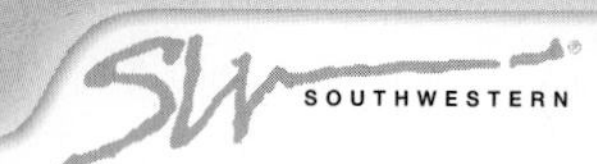

Slopes of Parallel Lines

The **slope** m of the line containing points (x_1, y_1) and (x_2, y_2) is given by the formula:

$$m = \frac{y_2 - y_1}{x_2 - x_1}$$

By looking at the slope of a line, you can determine many properties about the line—how steep it is, whether it rises or falls from left to right, and whether it is vertical or horizontal. When you compare the slopes of two lines, you can determine whether they intersect or are parallel.

Theorem
If two non-vertical lines are parallel, then their slopes are equal.

The converse of this theorem is also true.

Theorem
If the slopes of two non-vertical lines are equal, then the lines are parallel.

If two lines are vertical, they are parallel and their slopes are undefined.

SEARCH

To see step-by-step videos of these problems, enter the page number into the SWadvantage.com Search Bar.

EXAMPLE 1

Find the slope of a line parallel to the line through the points $A(-3, 2)$ and $B(5, 1)$.

The slope of $\overleftrightarrow{AB} = \frac{1 - 2}{5 - (-3)} = -\frac{1}{8}$.

Therefore, the slope of every line parallel to $\overleftrightarrow{AB}$ is $-\frac{1}{8}$.

Try It This Way

To visually model the slope, first sketch the line with equation $2x + 3y = 9$ on a coordinate grid. Then find its slope.

Draw another line parallel to the first line. Then find its slope and compare that to the slope of the first line.

EXAMPLE 2

Find the slope of a line parallel to the line with equation $2x + 3y = 9$.

STEP 1 Rewrite the given equation in slope-intercept form.

$$2x + 3y = 9$$

Subtract $2x$ from both sides. $\quad 3y = -2x + 9$

Divide both sides by 3. $\quad y = -\frac{2}{3}x + 3$

STEP 2 Identify the slope of the given line.

$y = -\frac{2}{3}x + 3$ is in the form $y = mx + b$, where m is the slope of the line.

$m = -\frac{2}{3}$

The slope of a line parallel to the line with equation $2x + 3y = 9$ is $-\frac{2}{3}$.

EXAMPLE 3

Write an equation of the line through (−1, 4) that is parallel to the line with equation $x - 2y = 6$.

STEP 1 Find the slope of the given line.

$$x - 2y = 6$$

Rewrite the equation in slope-intercept form. $y = \frac{1}{2}x - 3$

The slope of the line is $\frac{1}{2}$.

STEP 2 Use the point-slope form to write an equation of the line parallel to $x - 2y = 6$.

$y - y_1 = m(x - x_1)$, where m = slope and (x_1, y_1) is a point on the line.

Substitute $\frac{1}{2}$ for m, −1 for x_1, and 4 for y_1. $y - 4 = \frac{1}{2}(x - (-1))$

Multiply both sides by 2. $2y - 8 = x + 1$

Add 8 to both sides. $2y = x + 9$

Divide both sides by 2. $y = \frac{1}{2}x + 4.5$

Watch Out!

Subtracting a negative number is the same as adding its opposite.

EXAMPLE 4

a. Find the slopes of the sides of quadrilateral *ABCD*.

Slope of $\overline{AB} = \frac{2 - (-1)}{-1 - (-2)} = \frac{2 + 1}{-1 + 2} = \frac{3}{1} = 3$

Slope of $\overline{BC} = \frac{5 - 2}{4 - (-1)} = \frac{3}{5}$

Slope of $\overline{CD} = \frac{-1 - 5}{2 - 4} = \frac{6}{2} = 3$

Slope of $\overline{AD} = \frac{-1 - (-1)}{2 - (-2)} = \frac{-1 + 1}{2 + 2} = 0$

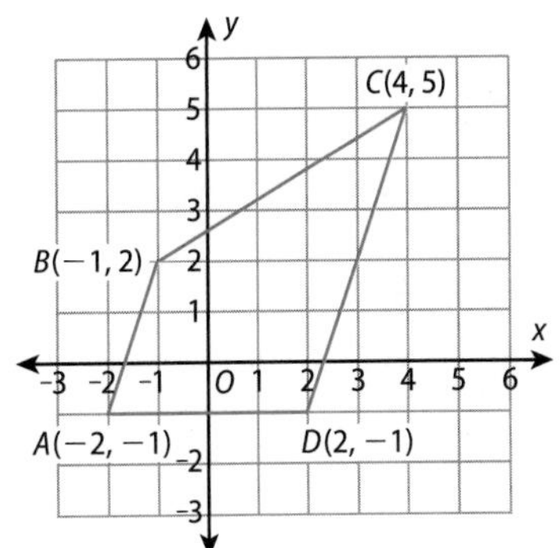

b. What kind of quadrilateral is *ABCD*?

The slope of $\overline{AB}$ = the slope of $\overline{CD}$ = 3, so $\overline{AB} \parallel \overline{CD}$.

The slope of $\overline{BC} \neq$ the slope of $\overline{AD}$, so $\overline{BC}$ is not parallel to $\overline{AD}$.

Quadrilateral *ABCD* has exactly one pair of parallel sides, so it is a trapezoid.

EXAMPLE 5

$\overline{PQ}$ with endpoints $P(-3, 0)$ and $Q(1, -1)$ is parallel to $\overline{RS}$ with endpoints $R(4, 2)$ and $S(-1, c)$. Find the value of c.

Slope of $\overline{PQ} = \frac{-1 - 0}{1 - (-3)} = -\frac{1}{4}$ Slope of $\overline{RS} = \frac{c - 2}{-1 - 4} = \frac{c - 2}{-5}$

Parallel lines have equal slopes. $-\frac{1}{4} = \frac{c - 2}{-5}$

Cross-multiply. $5 = 4c - 8$

Solve for c. $c = \frac{13}{4} = 3.25$

Slopes of Perpendicular Lines

Two numbers are **negative reciprocals** if their product is -1. For example, $\frac{2}{3}$ and $-\frac{3}{2}$ are negative reciprocals because $\frac{2}{3}\left(-\frac{3}{2}\right) = -1$. You can use slope to determine whether lines are perpendicular.

Theorem
If two non-vertical lines are perpendicular, then their slopes are negative reciprocals.

The converse of this theorem is also true.

Watch Out!

The slope of a vertical line is not defined.

Theorem
If the slopes of two non-vertical lines are negative reciprocals, then the lines are perpendicular.

A vertical line is always perpendicular to a horizontal line.

SEARCH

To see step-by-step videos of these problems, enter the page number into the SWadvantage.com Search Bar.

EXAMPLE 6

Are the lines with the given slopes parallel or perpendicular?

a. $m_1 = 0.25, m_2 = \frac{2}{8}$

$m_1 = 0.25 = \frac{1}{4} = \frac{2}{8} = m_2$

The slopes are equal, so the lines are parallel.

b. $m_1 = -0.5, m_2 = 2$

$(m_1)(m_2) = (-0.5)(2) = -1$

The slopes are negative reciprocals, so the lines are perpendicular.

EXAMPLE 7

Find the slope of a line perpendicular to the line with equation $3x - 4y = 12$.

STEP 1 Rewrite the given equation in slope-intercept form.

$3x - 4y = 12$

Add $4y$ to both sides. $3x = 4y + 12$

Subtract 12 from both sides. $4y = 3x - 12$

Divide both sides by 4. $y = \frac{3}{4}x - 3$

STEP 2 Identify the slope of the given line.

The slope of the line with equation $y = \frac{3}{4}x - 3$ is $\frac{3}{4}$.

STEP 3 Find m, the slope of the perpendicular line.

The slopes of $\perp$ lines are negative reciprocals. $m\left(\frac{3}{4}\right) = -1$

$m = -\frac{4}{3}$

EXAMPLE 8

Write an equation of the line through (1, −3) perpendicular to the line with equation $x + 4y = -8$.

STEP 1 Find the slope of the given line.

Rewrite $x + 4y = -8$ in slope-intercept form. $y = -\frac{1}{4}x - 2$

The given line has slope $-\frac{1}{4}$.

STEP 2 Find m, the slope of the perpendicular line.

The slopes of ⊥ lines are negative reciprocals. $m\left(-\frac{1}{4}\right) = -1$

$m = 4$

STEP 3 Write an equation of the perpendicular line.

METHOD 1

Use the point-slope form. $y - y_1 = m(x - x_1)$

Substitute 1 for x_1, −3, for y_1, and 4 for m. $y - (-3) = 4(x - 1)$

Simplify. $y + 3 = 4(x - 1)$

METHOD 2

Use the slope-intercept form. $y = mx + b$

Substitute 4 for m. $y = 4x + b$

Substitute 1 for x, −3 for y, and solve for b. $-3 = 4(1) + b$

Simplify. $b = -7$

Write the equation using the value of b. $y = 4x - 7$

EXAMPLE 9

Find the slope of the altitude of △*ABC* from *C*.

The altitude from C is perpendicular to $\overline{AB}$.

The slope of $\overline{AB} = \frac{-2 - (-1)}{5 - (-2)} = -\frac{1}{7}$.

The negative reciprocal of $-\frac{1}{7}$ is 7.

The slope of the altitude from C is 7.

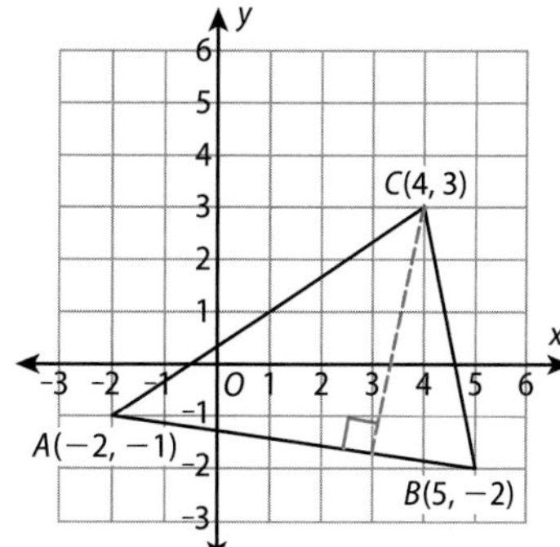

Need More HELP

For a review of the point-slope form, go to *The Point-Slope Form of a Linear Equation* in *Algebra* (Book 2, p. 1544).

GOT TO KNOW!

Slopes of Parallel and Perpendicular Lines

Slopes	Lines
Equal	Parallel
Negative Reciprocals	Perpendicular

Distance Formula

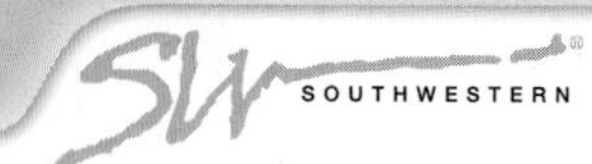

Finding the Distance Between Two Points

Finding the distance between two points in the coordinate plane is easy when the points lie on a vertical line or a horizontal line. All you have to do is count squares.

$AB = 3$ and $BC = 4$

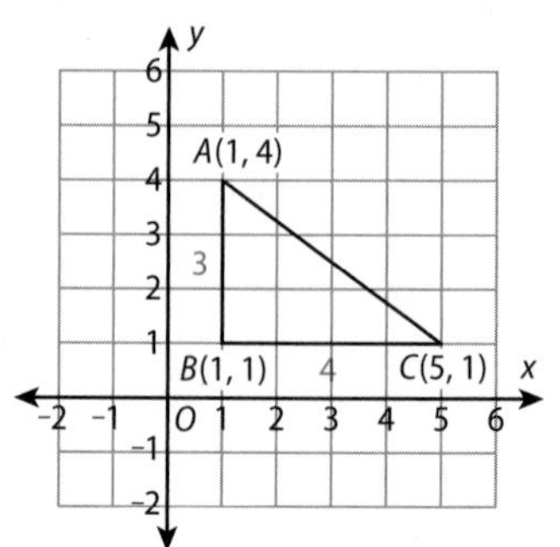

Points A and C do not lie on a vertical line or a horizontal line. But $\triangle ABC$ is a right triangle, so you can use the Pythagorean Theorem to find AC.

$$AB^2 + BC^2 = AC^2$$
$$3^2 + 4^2 = AC^2$$
$$25 = AC^2$$
$$AC = 5$$

Using the same method, you can derive a formula for the distance between any two points $P(x_1, y_1)$ and $Q(x_2, y_2)$. First draw a right triangle. The coordinates of point T are (x_2, y_1). Now apply the Pythagorean Theorem.

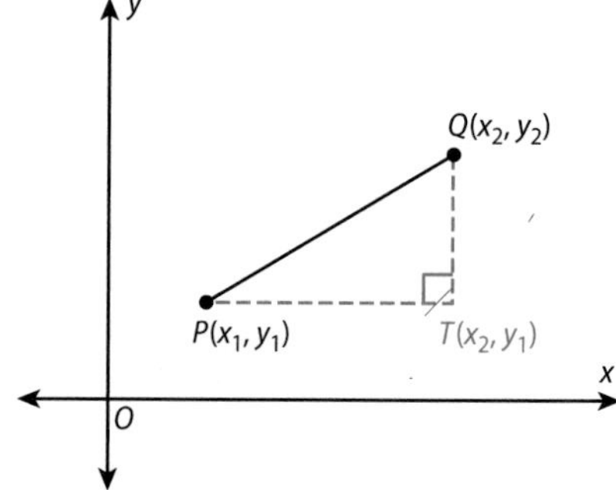

$$PQ^2 = PT^2 + QT^2$$
$$PQ^2 = (x_2 - x_1)^2 + (y_2 - y_1)^2$$
$$PQ = \sqrt{(x_2 - x_1)^2 + (y_2 - y_1)^2}$$

The Distance Formula

The distance d between the points with coordinates (x_1, y_1) and (x_2, y_2) is given by:

$$d = \sqrt{(x_2 - x_1)^2 + (y_2 - y_1)^2}$$

EXAMPLE 1

To review simplifying radicals, go to *Square Roots* in *Algebra* (Book 2, p. 1400).

Find the length of the segment with endpoints $D(-2, 3)$ and $E(4, 1)$.

METHOD 1

Draw a right triangle and use the Pythagorean Theorem.

The coordinates of F are $(-2, 1)$, $DF = 2$, and $FE = 6$.

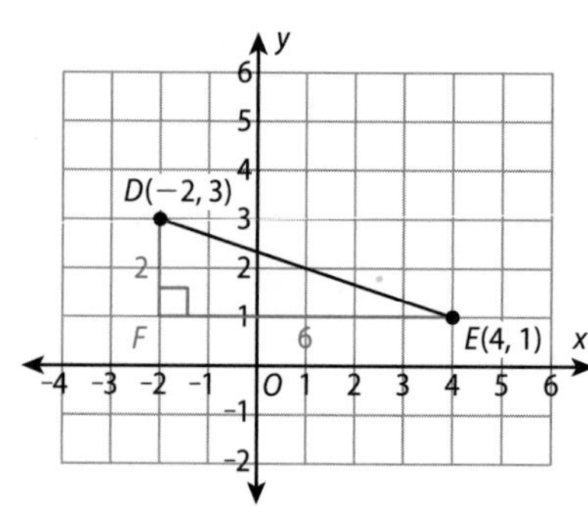

$$DF^2 + FE^2 = DE^2$$
$$2^2 + 6^2 = DE^2$$
$$4 + 36 = DE^2$$
$$DE = \sqrt{40} = \sqrt{4} \cdot \sqrt{10} = 2\sqrt{10}$$

METHOD 2

Use the distance formula.

Let $(x_1, y_1) = (-2, 3)$ and $(x_2, y_2) = (4, 1)$.

$$DE = \sqrt{[4 - (-2)]^2 + (1 - 3)^2} = \sqrt{(4 + 2)^2 + (-2)^2} = \sqrt{36 + 4} = \sqrt{40} = \sqrt{4} \cdot \sqrt{10} = 2\sqrt{10}$$

EXAMPLE 2

Show that the triangle with vertices $A(-2, -2)$, $B(4, 2)$ and $C(2, 4)$ is isosceles.

STEP 1 Find the lengths of the three sides.

$$AB = \sqrt{[4-(-2)]^2 + [2-(-2)]^2}$$
$$= \sqrt{(4+2)^2 + (2+2)^2}$$
$$= \sqrt{6^2 + 4^2} = \sqrt{36 + 16}$$
$$AB = \sqrt{52} = 2\sqrt{13}$$
$$BC = \sqrt{(2-4)^2 + (4-2)^2}$$
$$= \sqrt{(-2)^2 + 2^2} = \sqrt{4+4}$$
$$BC = \sqrt{8} = 2\sqrt{2}$$
$$AC = \sqrt{[2-(-2)]^2 + [4-(-2)]^2}$$
$$= \sqrt{(2+2)^2 + (4+2)^2}$$
$$= \sqrt{4^2 + 6^2} = \sqrt{16 + 36}$$
$$AC = \sqrt{52} = 2\sqrt{13}$$

STEP 2 Determine which sides are congruent.

$AB = 2\sqrt{13} = AC$, so $\triangle ABC$ must be isosceles.

Watch Out!

Remember to put negative numbers in parentheses when you substitute into the distance formula.

EXAMPLE 3

Find the area of the circle that passes through $Q(7, -13)$ and whose center is $P(2, 1)$.

STEP 1 Find the length of a radius, PQ.

$$PQ = \sqrt{(2-7)^2 + [1-(-13)]^2}$$
$$PQ = \sqrt{(-5)^2 + 14^2}$$
$$PQ = \sqrt{25 + 196} = \sqrt{221}$$

STEP 2 Use the formula for the area A of a circle.

In the formula, r is the radius. $A = \pi r^2$

Substitute $\sqrt{221}$ for r. $A = \pi(\sqrt{221})^2$

$A = 221\pi$ square units

SEARCH

To see step-by-step videos of these problems, enter the page number into the SWadvantage.com Search Bar.

GOT TO KNOW!

The Distance Formula

The distance d between the points with coordinates (x_1, y_1) and (x_2, y_2) is given by:

$$d = \sqrt{(x_2 - x_1)^2 + (y_2 - y_1)^2}$$

Midpoint Formula

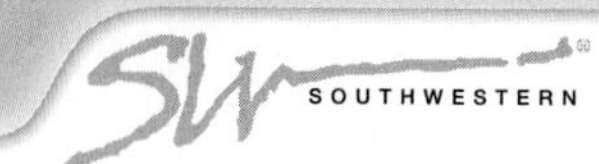

Finding the Midpoint

The point that divides a segment into two congruent segments is the **midpoint** of the segment. The coordinate of the midpoint of a segment whose endpoints are on a number line is the average of their coordinates.

If A and B have coordinates a and b, then the coordinate of M, the midpoint of $\overline{AB}$, is $\frac{a+b}{2}$.

A M B

a $\frac{a+b}{2}$ b

You can apply this idea to find the coordinates of the midpoint of a vertical segment or a horizontal segment.

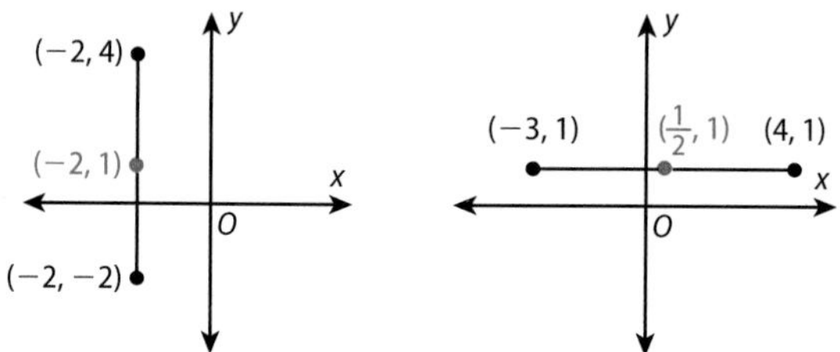

To find the coordinates of the midpoint of any other segment, you apply this idea twice. In the diagram below, M is the midpoint of $\overline{AB}$ with endpoints $A(x_1, y_1)$ and $B(x_2, y_2)$. Draw right $\triangle ABC$. The coordinates of C are (x_2, y_1). The coordinates of M_1, the midpoint of $\overline{AC}$, are $\left(\frac{x_1 + x_2}{2}, y_1\right)$. The coordinates of M_2, the midpoint of $\overline{BC}$, are $\left(x_2, \frac{y_1 + y_2}{2}\right)$. So, the coordinates of M are $\left(\frac{x_1 + x_2}{2}, \frac{y_1 + y_2}{2}\right)$.

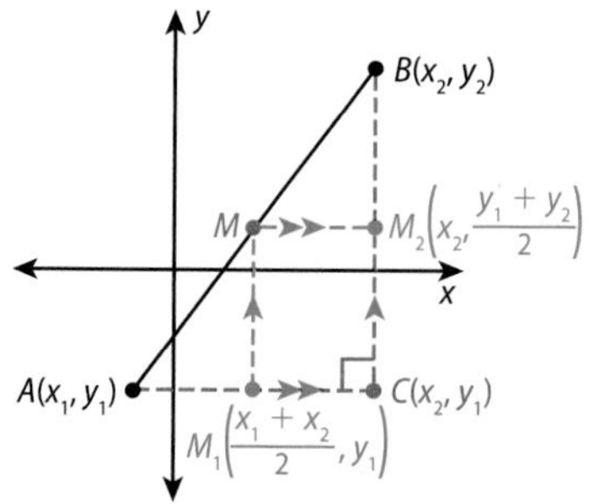

The Midpoint Formula
The coordinates of the midpoint of the segment with endpoints (x_1, y_1) and (x_2, y_2) are $\left(\frac{x_1 + x_2}{2}, \frac{y_1 + y_2}{2}\right)$.

EXAMPLE 1

Find the coordinates of the midpoint of the segment with the given endpoints.

a. (11, 5) and (7, 2)

The *x*-coordinate of the midpoint is $\frac{11 + 7}{2} = 9$.

The *y*-coordinate of the midpoint is $\frac{5 + 2}{2} = 3.5$.

The coordinates of the midpoint are (9, 3.5).

b. (−8, 1) and (−2, −3)

The *x*-coordinate of the midpoint is $\frac{-8 + (-2)}{2} = -5$.

The *y*-coordinate of the midpoint is $\frac{1 + (-3)}{2} = -1$.

The coordinates of the midpoint are (−5, −1).

Try It This Way

Use graph paper to find the coordinates of the midpoints in Example 1 and Example 3.

EXAMPLE 2

***M*(−2, 5) is the midpoint of $\overline{AB}$ and the coordinates of *A* are (6, 1). Find the coordinates of *B*.**

Let (x_1, y_1) represent the coordinates of *B*. Use the Midpoint Formula.

$$-2 = \frac{6 + x_1}{2} \qquad 5 = \frac{1 + y_1}{2}$$

$$-4 = 6 + x_1 \qquad 10 = 1 + y_1$$

$$x_1 = -10 \qquad y_1 = 9$$

The coordinates of *B* are (−10, 9).

SEARCH

To see step-by-step videos of these problems, enter the page number into the SWadvantage.com Search Bar.

EXAMPLE 3

The coordinates of the endpoints of the diameter of a circle are (8, −2) and (13, −6). Find the coordinates of the center of the circle.

The center of the circle is the midpoint of the diameter. Let (x_1, y_1) represent the coordinates of the center. Use the Midpoint Formula.

STEP 1 Find the *x*-coordinate of the center.

$$x_1 = \frac{8 + 13}{2} = \frac{21}{2}$$

$$x_1 = 10.5$$

STEP 2 Find the *y*-coordinate of the center.

$$y_1 = \frac{-2 + (-6)}{2} = \frac{-8}{2}$$

$$y_1 = -4$$

The coordinates of the center of the circle are (10.5, −4).

Using the Midpoint Formula

A **median** of a triangle is a segment whose endpoints are a vertex of the triangle and the midpoint of the opposite side.

In the figure, $\overline{PM}$ is a median of $\triangle PQR$.

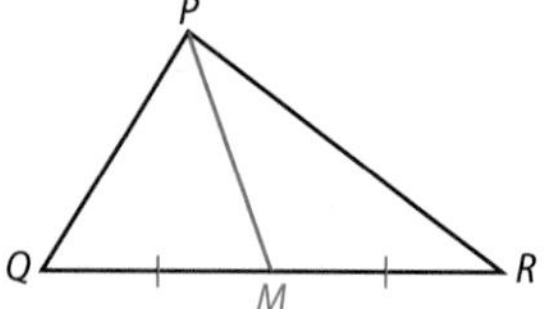

EXAMPLE 4

$\triangle ABC$ has vertices $A(-2, -1)$, $B(6, 3)$, and $C(0, 5)$. Find the length of the median from C.

STEP 1 Find the coordinates of the midpoint of $\overline{AB}$.

$x\text{-coordinate} = \frac{-2+6}{2} = \frac{4}{2} = 2 \qquad y\text{-coordinate} = \frac{-1+3}{2} = \frac{2}{2} = 1$

The coordinates of the midpoint of $\overline{AB}$ are (2, 1).

STEP 2 Use the Distance Formula to find the distance d from $C(0, 5)$ to (2, 1).

$$d = \sqrt{(x_2 - x_1)^2 + (y_2 - y_1)^2} = \sqrt{(2-0)^2 + (1-5)^2}$$
$$= \sqrt{2^2 + (-4)^2} = \sqrt{4 + 16} = \sqrt{20} = 2\sqrt{5}$$

The length of the median from C is $2\sqrt{5}$.

SEARCH

To see step-by-step videos of these problems, enter the page number into the SWadvantage.com Search Bar.

EXAMPLE 5

Write an equation of the perpendicular bisector of the segment joining $D(-4, -2)$ and $E(2, 6)$.

STEP 1 Find the slope of $\overline{DE}$.

$$\text{slope of } \overline{DE} = \frac{6-(-2)}{2-(-4)}$$
$$= \frac{8}{6} = \frac{4}{3}$$

STEP 2 Find the slope of a line perpendicular to $\overline{DE}$.

Let m = the slope of a line perpendicular to $\overline{DE}$. If two lines are perpendicular, their slopes are negative reciprocals.

$m\left(\frac{4}{3}\right) = -1, m = -\frac{3}{4}$

STEP 3 Find the coordinates of the midpoint of $\overline{DE}$.

$x\text{-coordinate} = \frac{-4+2}{2} = -1 \qquad y\text{-coordinate} = \frac{(-2)+6}{2} = 2$

The coordinates of the midpoint of $\overline{DE}$ are $(-1, 2)$.

STEP 4 Write an equation of the line with slope $-\frac{3}{4}$ that contains the point $(-1, 2)$.

Start with the point-slope form of a linear equation.

	$y - 2 = -\frac{3}{4}(x - (-1))$
Multiply both sides by 4.	$4y - 8 = -3(x + 1)$
Distributive Property	$4y - 8 = -3x - 3$
	$3x + 4y = 5$

Need More HELP

The perpendicular bisector of a segment is the line that is perpendicular to the segment at its midpoint.

EXAMPLE 6

***A*, *B*, *C*, and *D* are the midpoints of the sides of quadrilateral *PQRS*.**

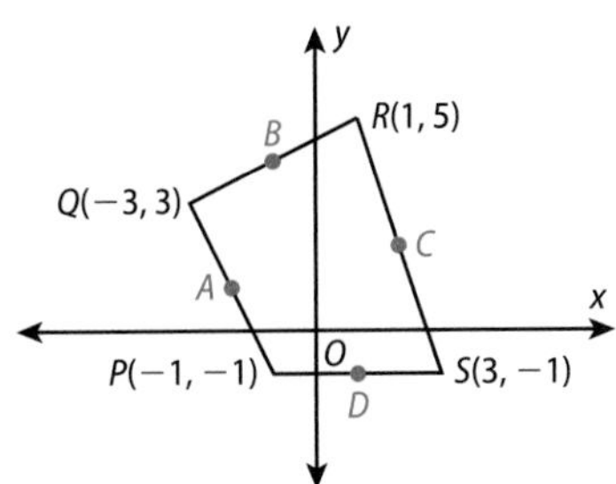

a. Find the coordinates of *A*, *B*, *C*, and *D*.

The coordinates of *A* are $\left(\frac{-1+(-3)}{2}, \frac{-1+3}{2}\right) = (-2, 1)$.

The coordinates of *B* are $\left(\frac{-3+1}{2}, \frac{3+5}{2}\right) = (-1, 4)$.

The coordinates of *C* are $\left(\frac{1+3}{2}, \frac{5+(-1)}{2}\right) = (2, 2)$.

The coordinate of *D* are $\left(\frac{-1+3}{2}, \frac{-1+(-1)}{2}\right) = (1, -1)$.

b. Show that quadrilateral *ABCD* is a parallelogram.

Use slope to show that $\overline{AB} \parallel \overline{CD}$ and $\overline{BC} \parallel \overline{AD}$.

Slope of $\overline{AB} = \frac{4-1}{-1-(-2)} = 3$ Slope of $\overline{CD} = \frac{2-(-1)}{2-1} = 3$

Slope of $\overline{BC} = \frac{4-2}{-1-2} = -\frac{2}{3}$ Slope of $\overline{AD} = \frac{1-(-1)}{-2-1} = -\frac{2}{3}$

Lines with equal slopes are parallel, so $\overline{AB} \parallel \overline{CD}$ and $\overline{BC} \parallel \overline{AD}$.

A quadrilateral with two pairs of parallel lines is, by definition, a parallelogram.

GOT TO KNOW!

Formulas in Coordinate Geometry

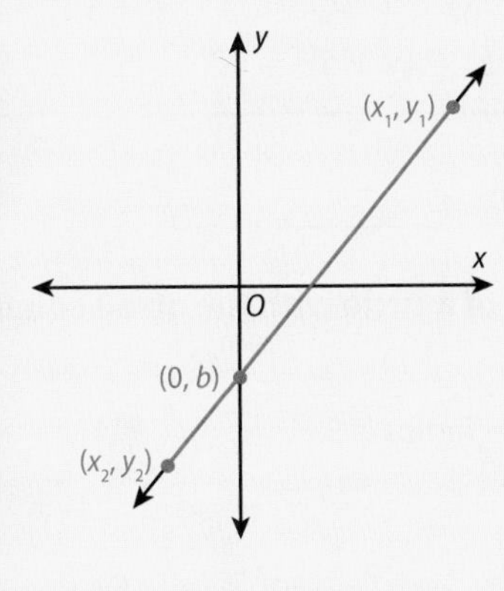

Slope *m*

$m = \frac{y_2 - y_1}{x_2 - x_1}$

Slope-Intercept Form of an Equation for a Line

$y = mx + b$

Point-Slope Form of an Equation for a Line

$y - y_1 = m(x - x_1)$

Distance Formula

The distance *d* from (x_1, y_1) to (x_2, y_2):

$d = \sqrt{(x_2 - x_1)^2 + (y_2 - y_1)^2}$

Midpoint Formula

The midpoint *M* between (x_1, y_1) and (x_2, y_2):

$M\left(\frac{x_1 + x_2}{2}, \frac{y_1 + y_2}{2}\right)$

Equations of Circles

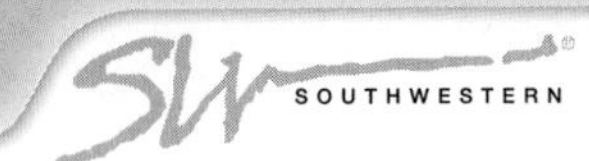

Circles in the Coordinate Plane

You can use the Distance Formula to derive an equation of a circle.

Let $P(x, y)$ be any point on the circle with center $C(h, k)$ and radius r. Then:

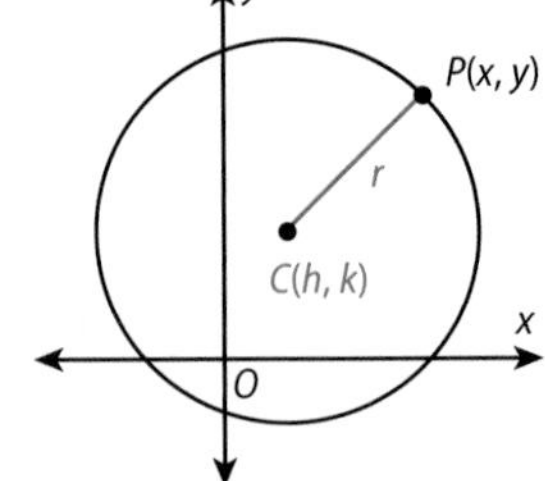

$$PC = r$$

Distance Formula $\sqrt{(x-h)^2 + (y-k)^2} = r$

Square both sides. $(x-h)^2 + (y-k)^2 = r^2$

The Equation of a Circle
The equation of a circle with center (h, k) and radius r is $(x-h)^2 + (y-k)^2 = r^2$

SEARCH

To see step-by-step videos of these problems, enter the page number into the SWadvantage.com Search Bar.

EXAMPLE 1

Write an equation of a circle with the given center and radius.

a. center $(-1, 4)$, radius 3

Let $h = -1$, $k = 4$, and $r = 3$.

$$(x-h)^2 + (y-k)^2 = r^2$$

Substitute. $(x-(-1))^2 + (y-4)^2 = 3^2$

Simplify. $(x+1)^2 + (y-4)^2 = 9$

b. center $(0, -5)$, radius $2\sqrt{3}$

Let $h = 0$, $k = -5$, and $r = 2\sqrt{3}$.

$$(x-h)^2 + (y-k)^2 = r^2$$

Substitute. $(x-0)^2 + (y-(-5))^2 = (2\sqrt{3})^2$

Simplify. $x^2 + (y+5)^2 = 12$

EXAMPLE 2

Find the center and radius of a circle with the given equation.

a. $(x-2)^2 + (y-1)^2 = 25$

The center is $(2, 1)$ and the radius is 5.

b. $(x+6)^2 + y^2 = \frac{4}{9}$

Rewrite the equation in the form $(x-h)^2 + (y-k)^2 = r^2$.

$$(x-(-6))^2 + (y-0)^2 = \left(\frac{2}{3}\right)^2$$

The center is $(-6, 0)$ and the radius is $\frac{2}{3}$.

EXAMPLE 3

Graph the equation $(x + 1)^2 + (y - 3)^2 = 4$.

The equation represents a circle with center $(-1, 3)$ and radius 2.

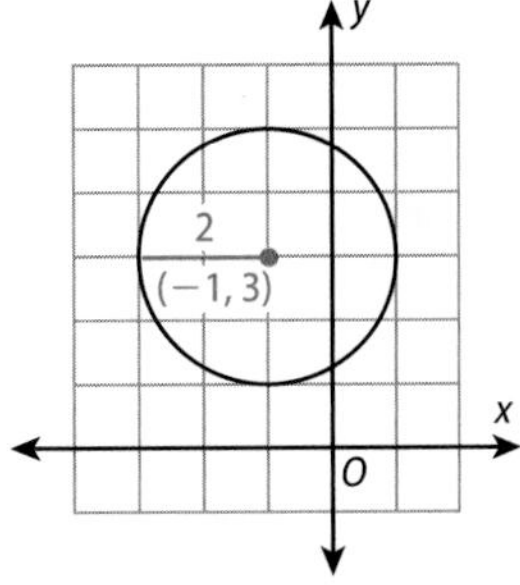

EXAMPLE 4

Write an equation of a circle whose graph is given.

The center of the circle is $(0, -2)$. Let $h = 0$, $k = -2$, and $r = 3$.

$$(x - h)^2 + (y - k)^2 = r^2$$

Substitute. $$(x - 0)^2 + (y - (-2))^2 = 3^2$$

Simplify. $$x^2 + (y + 2)^2 = 9$$

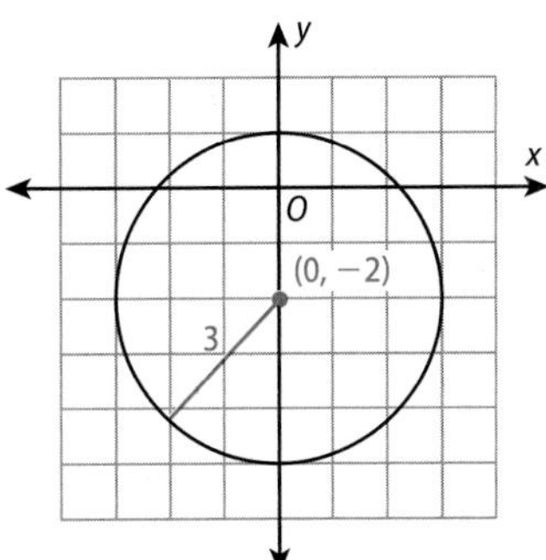

EXAMPLE 5

Graph the inequality $(x - 5)^2 + (y + 4)^2 < 16$.

The inequality represents the interior of the circle with center $(5, -4)$ and radius 4.

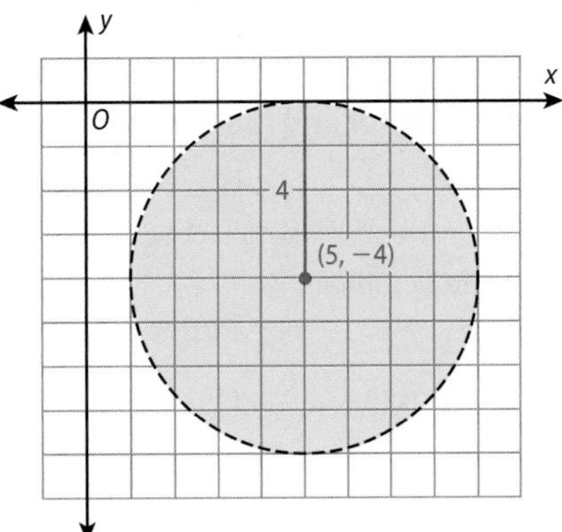

Watch Out!

The points on the circle are not part of the graph of the inequality. Use a dashed line to graph the circle.

GOT TO KNOW!

Equation of a Circle

The equation of a circle with center (h, k) and radius r is $(x - h)^2 + (y - k)^2 = r^2$.

Using the Equation of a Circle

Try It This Way

In Example 6, you can check your answer by graphing the equation and the point.

EXAMPLE 6

Circle *P* has equation $(x + 3)^2 + (y + 1)^2 = 12$. Does the point $(0, -4)$ lie on the circle, in the interior of the circle, or in the exterior of the circle?

Substitute 0 for x and -4 for y. $\quad (0 + 3)^2 + ((-4) + 1)^2 = 3^2 + (-3)^2$

Simplify. $\quad = 9 + 9$

$= 18$

$18 > 12$, so the point lies in the exterior of the circle.

SEARCH

To see step-by-step videos of these problems, enter the page number into the SWadvantage.com Search Bar.

EXAMPLE 7

Find the area and circumference of a circle with equation $\frac{(x-5)^2}{3} + \frac{(y+8)^2}{3} = 27$.

STEP 1 Find the radius r of the circle. $\quad \frac{(x-5)^2}{3} + \frac{(y+8)^2}{3} = 27$

Multiply both sides by 3. $\quad (x - 5)^2 + (y + 8)^2 = 81$

Find the square root of the right side. $\quad (x - 5)^2 + (y + 8)^2 = 9^2$

$r = 9$

STEP 2 Find the area and the circumference.

Area $= \pi r^2$

$= \pi(9^2)$

$= 81\pi$ square units

Circumference $= 2\pi r$

$= 2\pi(9)$

$= 18\pi$ units

To review how to complete the square in order to factor an equation, go to *Completing the Square* in *Algebra* (Book 2, p. 1706).

EXAMPLE 8

Find the center and radius of a circle with equation $x^2 - 6x + y^2 + 4y = 12$. Then graph the equation.

Complete the square. $\quad x^2 - 6x + 9 + y^2 + 4y + 4 = 12 + 9 + 4$

Write the binomials. $\quad (x - 3)^2 + (y + 2)^2 = 25$

Find the square root of the right side. $\quad (x - 3)^2 + (y + 2)^2 = 5^2$

The center is $(3, -2)$ and the radius is 5.

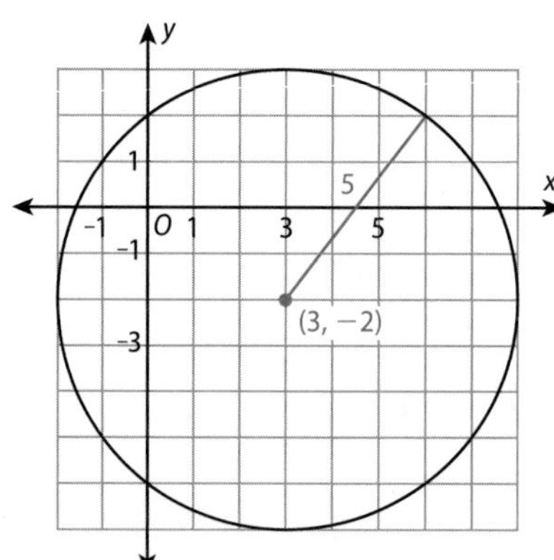

EXAMPLE 9

Find the x- and y-intercepts of a line that is tangent to the circle $x^2 + y^2 = 25$ at the point (3, 4).

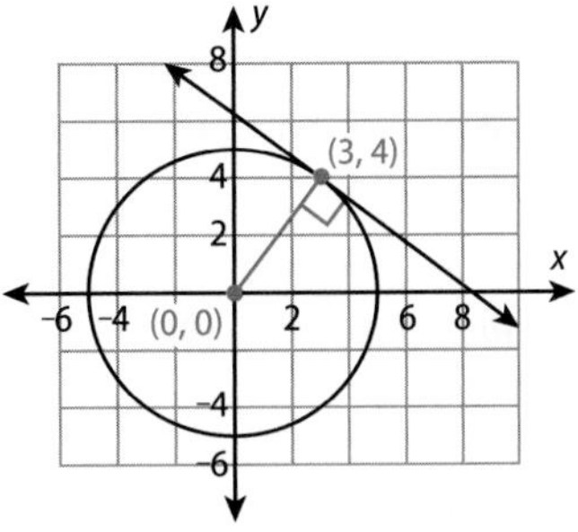

STEP 1 Find the slope of the tangent line.

The slope of the radius is $\frac{4}{3}$. The radius drawn to the point of tangency is perpendicular to the tangent. So, the slope of the tangent line is $-\frac{3}{4}$.

STEP 2 Use the point-slope form of a linear equation to write an equation of a line.

Point-slope equation	$y - y_1 = m(x - x_1)$
$x_1 = 3, y_1 = 4$, and $m = -\frac{3}{4}$	$y - 4 = -\frac{3}{4}(x - 3)$
Multiply both sides by 4.	$4y - 16 = -3(x - 3)$
Distributive Property	$4y - 16 = -3x + 9$
	$3x + 4y = 25$

STEP 3 Find the x-intercept.

Let $y = 0$. Solve for x.	$3x + 4(0) = 25$
	$x = \frac{25}{3} = 8\frac{1}{3}$

STEP 4 Find the y-intercept.

Let $x = 0$. Solve for y.	$3(0) + 4y = 25$
	$y = \frac{25}{4} = 6\frac{1}{4}$

Need More HELP

For a review of the point-slope equation of a line, go to *Point-Slope Form of a Linear Equation* in *Algebra* (Book 2, p. 1544).

EXAMPLE 10

Find the coordinates of the points where the line $x + y = 2$ intersects the circle $x^2 + y^2 = 10$.

Use substitution to solve the equation: $x^2 + y^2 = 10$ (1)

$x + y = 2$ (2)

STEP 1 Solve Equation (2) for y. $y = 2 - x$

STEP 2 Substitute into Equation (1).

Substitute into Equation (1).	$x^2 + (2 - x)^2 = 10$
Square the binomial.	$x^2 + 4 - 4x + x^2 = 10$
Combine like terms.	$2x^2 - 4x - 6 = 0$
Divide both sides by 2.	$x^2 - 2x - 3 = 0$
Factor.	$(x - 3)(x + 1) = 0$
	$x = 3$ or $x = -1$

STEP 3 Find the corresponding values of y.

If $x = 3$, then $y = 2 - 3 = -1$. If $x = -1$, then $y = 2 - (-1) = 3$.

The points of intersection are $(3, -1)$ and $(-1, 3)$.

Proofs Using Coordinate Geometry

Placing a Figure

You have written paragraph proofs and two-column proofs. Now you will learn a third kind of proof: *coordinate proof.* A proof that involves figures in the coordinate plane is a **coordinate proof**. You can use coordinate geometry to prove properties of lines, triangles, quadrilaterals, and other figures.

The first step in writing a coordinate proof is choosing where to place the figure in the coordinate plane. Where you place a figure relative to the axes and the origin can make a big difference.

SEARCH

To see step-by-step videos of these problems, enter the page number into the SWadvantage.com Search Bar.

EXAMPLE 1

Position and label a square with side length *s* on the coordinate plane.

To maximize the number of times 0 is a coordinate of a vertex, follow these steps.

- Use the origin as a vertex.
- Place one side on the *x*-axis and one side on the *y*-axis.
- Label the vertices *O*, *P*, *Q*, *R*.
- Supply the coordinates of *P*, *Q*, and *R*.

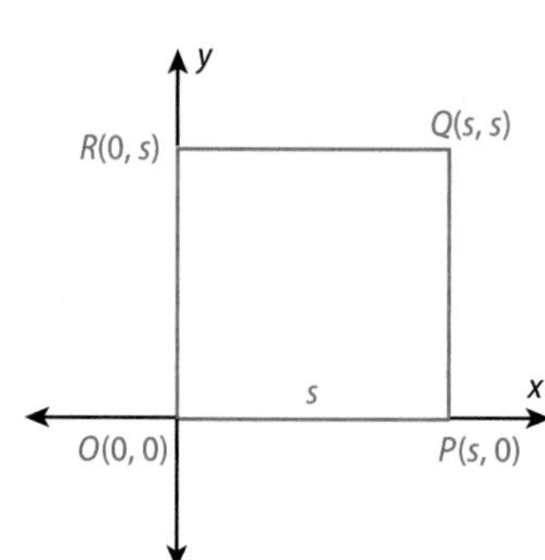

When a proof involves the Midpoint Formula, it may help to use coordinates that are multiples of 2.

EXAMPLE 2

$\triangle AOB$ is a right triangle. What are the coordinates of the midpoint *M* of the hypotenuse?

Use the Midpoint Formula.

The coordinates of *M* are

$\left(\frac{2a + 0}{2}, \frac{0 + 2b}{2}\right) = (a, b)$.

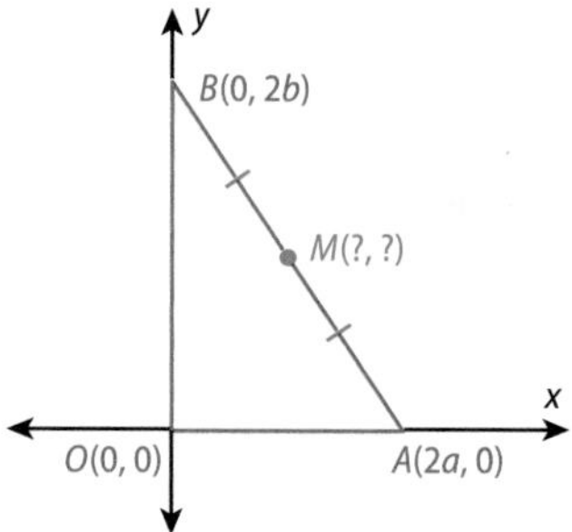

EXAMPLE 3

***OJKL* is a parallelogram. Supply the coordinates of *K* without using any new letters.**

Points *J* and *K* are the same distance from the *x*-axis, so they have the same *y*-coordinate, *c*.

Opposite sides of a parallelogram are congruent, so $JK = OL = a$. Therefore, the *x*-coordinate of *K* must be $a + b$ because $JK = (a + b) - b = b$.

The coordinates of *K* are $(a + b, c)$.

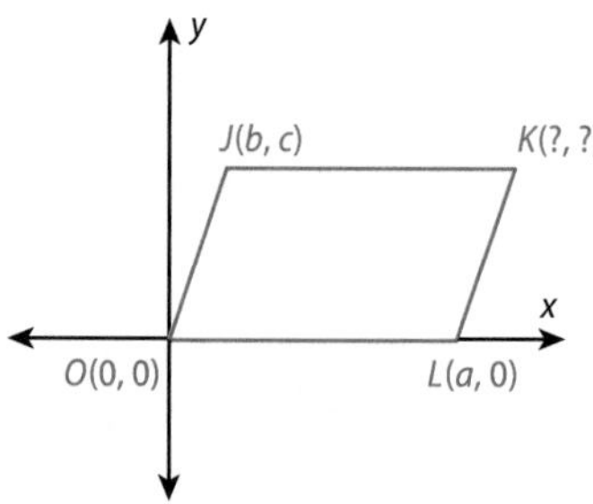

Now it's time to write a coordinate proof. This one uses the Midpoint Formula.

EXAMPLE 4

Prove that the diagonals of a rectangle bisect each other.

Given: *ABCD* is a rectangle.

Prove: $\overline{AC}$ bisects $\overline{BD}$.

Plan: Find the coordinates of the midpoint of each diagonal. Show that they are the same.

STEP 1 Draw the figure in the coordinate plane.

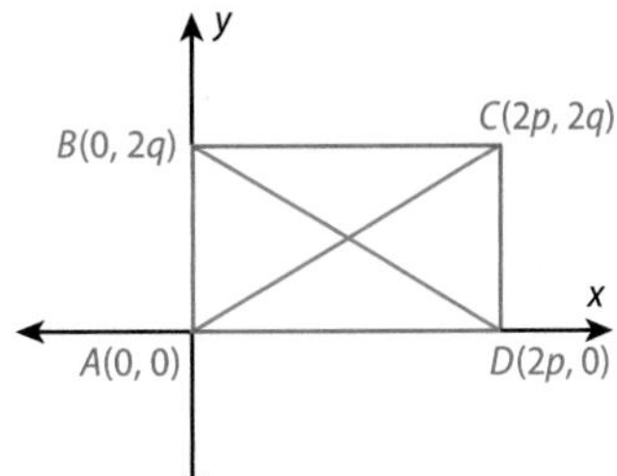

STEP 2 Use the Midpoint Formula to find the coordinates of the midpoint of each diagonal.

Midpoint of $\overline{AC}$ $\left(\frac{0 + 2p}{2}, \frac{0 + 2q}{2}\right) = (p, q)$

Midpoint of $\overline{BD}$ $\left(\frac{0 + 2p}{2}, \frac{2q + 0}{2}\right) = (p, q)$

The midpoints of the diagonals are the same point, so $\overline{AC}$ bisects $\overline{BD}$.

The next proof uses slope.

EXAMPLE 5

Use coordinate geometry to prove that the diagonals of a square are perpendicular.

Place a square on the coordinate plane, and label the vertices as shown.

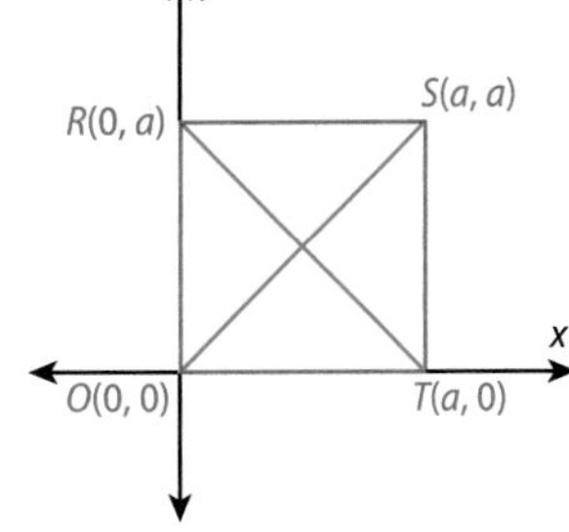

Slope of $\overline{OS} = \frac{a - 0}{a - 0} = 1$ Slope of $\overline{RT} = \frac{a - 0}{0 - a} = -1$

Slope of $\overline{OS}$ • Slope of $\overline{RT} = -1$

Since their slopes are negative reciprocals, $\overline{OS} \perp \overline{RT}$.

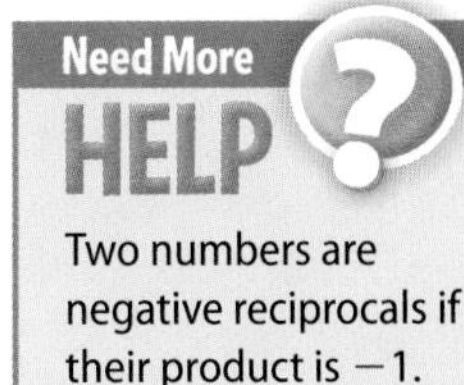

Two numbers are negative reciprocals if their product is -1.

GOT TO KNOW!

Placing a Figure in the Coordinate Plane

These suggestions may simplify calculations.

- Use the origin as one vertex.
- Place one or more sides along an axis to maximize the number of times 0 is a coordinate of a vertex.
- Assign coordinates to points using as few variables as possible.

More Proofs

The proof in Example 6 uses the Distance Formula.

SEARCH

To see step-by-step videos of these problems, enter the page number into the SWadvantage.com Search Bar.

EXAMPLE 6

Use coordinate geometry to prove that the diagonals of an isosceles trapezoid are congruent.

Given: $PQRS$ is an isosceles trapezoid with $\overline{PQ} \parallel \overline{SR}$ and $\overline{PS} \cong \overline{QR}$.

Prove: $\overline{PR} \cong \overline{QS}$.

Plan: Find the length of each diagonal. Show that the lengths are equal.

The trapezoid is isosceles. Place the trapezoid so that the y-axis is a line of symmetry and one base is on the x-axis. Label the vertices as shown.

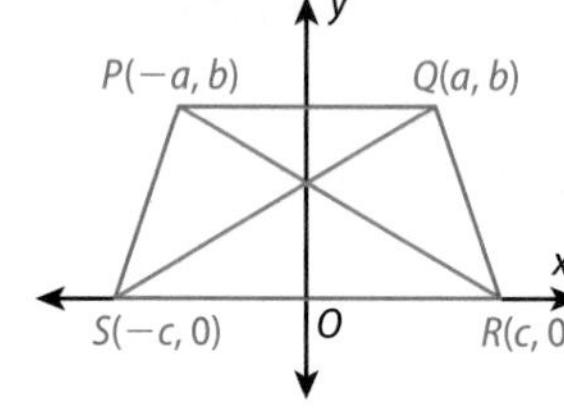

Use the Distance Formula to find the length of each diagonal.

$PR = \sqrt{(c - (-a))^2 + (0 - b)^2} = \sqrt{(c + a)^2 + b^2}$

$QS = \sqrt{(a - (-c))^2 + (b - 0)^2} = \sqrt{(a + c)^2 + b^2}$

The lengths of the diagonals are equal, so the diagonals are congruent.

EXAMPLE 7

Use coordinate geometry to prove that the median to the hypotenuse of a right triangle is half the length of the hypotenuse.

Given: $\triangle AOB$ is a right triangle with right angle $\angle AOB$; M is the midpoint of $\overline{AB}$.

Prove: $OM = \frac{1}{2}AB$

Plan: Find the lengths of the median and $\overline{AB}$. Show that the length of the median is half of AB.

Place the triangle so that the legs coincide with the x-axis and the y-axis. Since the proof involves the midpoint of $\overline{AB}$, label the vertices as shown.

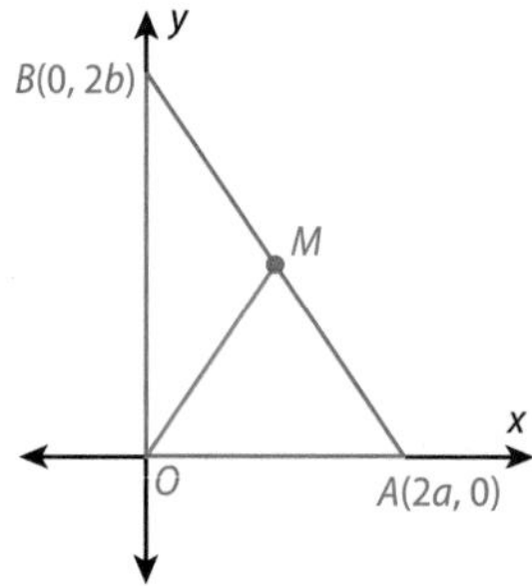

Use the Midpoint Formula to find the coordinates of M. $\left(\frac{0 + 2a}{2}, \frac{2b + 0}{2}\right) = (a, b)$

Use the Distance Formula to find OM. $OM = \sqrt{(a - 0)^2 + (b - 0)^2} = \sqrt{a^2 + b^2}$

Use the Distance Formula to find AB. $AB = \sqrt{(2a - 0)^2 + (0 - 2b)^2} = \sqrt{(2a)^2 + (2b)^2}$

$= \sqrt{4a^2 + 4b^2} = \sqrt{4(a^2 + b^2)} = 2\sqrt{a^2 + b^2}$

$AB = 2(OM)$, so $OM = \frac{1}{2}AB$.

$\sqrt{a^2 + b^2} \neq a + b$

Three lines are **concurrent** if they intersect at the same point. This theorem about the concurrency of the altitudes of a triangle is difficult to prove without the use of coordinate geometry.

Theorem
The lines that contain the altitudes of a triangle are concurrent.

EXAMPLE 8

Given: $\triangle PQR$ with lines a, b, and c containing the altitudes of the triangle.

Prove: Lines a, b, and c are concurrent.

Plan: Show that the intersection of lines a and b is the same as the intersection of lines b and c.

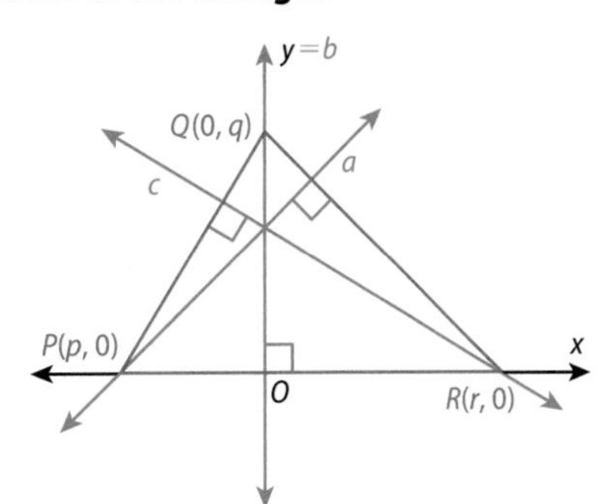

Place the triangle so one side coincides with the x-axis and one altitude coincides with the y-axis.

STEP 1 Find the slope of line a.

Slope of $\overline{QR} = \frac{0-q}{r-0} = -\frac{q}{r}$

Line $a \perp \overline{QR}$, so the slope of line $a = \frac{r}{q}$.

STEP 2 Write an equation of line a.

Use the point-slope form. $\quad y - 0 = \frac{r}{q}(x - p)$, or $y = \frac{r}{q}(x - p)$

STEP 3 Write an equation of line b.

Line b is the y-axis. Its equation is: $\quad x = 0$

STEP 4 Find the intersection of lines a and b.

Substitute 0 for x in the equation for line a. $\quad y = \frac{r}{q}(0 - p) = -\frac{pr}{q}$

The lines intersect at the point $\left(0, -\frac{pr}{q}\right)$.

STEP 5 Find the slope of line c.

Slope of $\overline{PQ} = \frac{q-0}{0-p} = -\frac{q}{p}$

Line $c \perp \overline{PQ}$, so the slope of line $c = \frac{p}{q}$.

STEP 6 Write an equation of line c.

Use the point-slope form. $\quad y - 0 = \frac{p}{q}(x - r)$, or $y = \frac{p}{q}(x - r)$

STEP 7 Find the intersection of lines b and c.

Substitute 0 for x in the equation for line c. $\quad y = \frac{p}{q}(0 - r) = -\frac{pr}{q}$

The lines intersect at $\left(0, -\frac{pr}{q}\right)$.

The intersection of lines a and b is the same as the intersection of lines b and c, so lines a, b, and c are concurrent.

For a review of the point-slope equation of a line, go to *The Point-Slope Form of a Linear Equation* in *Algebra*, (Book 2, p. 1544).

Transformations

What Came Before?

- Congruence and similarity of figures
- Properties of polygons

What's This About?

- Translations, reflections, rotations, and dilations of figures
- Types of symmetry
- Properties of figures in tessellations

Practical Apps

- Graphic artists use dilations to make large copies of their compositions.
- Tessellations are used in making quilts and designing floor tiles.

just for FUN!

Q: What was the clone's favorite geometry lesson?

A: Tessellations.

CONTENTS UPLOAD DOWNLOAD Geometry

You can find more practice problems online by visiting: **www.SWadvantage.com**

Translations

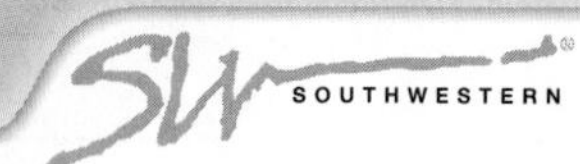

What Is a Transformation?

A **transformation** is a function that maps each point P in the plane onto a unique point in the plane P', called the **image** of P. The point P is called the **pre-image** of P'.

One way to describe a transformation is with arrow notation (→). Points of the image are often labeled with prime notation ($'$), using the same letter for both.

$$A \to A'$$

A' is the image of A and A is the pre-image of A'. In the diagrams in this lesson, the blue figure is the pre-image and the red figure is the image.

$$ABCD \to A'B'C'D'$$

An **isometry** is a transformation that preserves lengths and angle measures.

Remember—a function is a relationship that matches each element of a first set to an element of a second set in such a way that no element of the first set is assigned to two different elements of the second set.

Translations and Coordinate Notation

A **translation** is an isometry in which all the points in the plane are moved the same distance in the same direction. Translations preserve congruency: the image of a polygon after a translation is congruent to the original polygon. Translations also preserve orientation: after a translation, the orientation of the image of a figure is the same as the orientation of the original figure.

You can use *coordinate notation* to describe a translation. The function rule below shows the result of translating a point (x, y) horizontally by a units and vertically by b units.

$$(x, y) \to (x + a, y + b)$$

In the translation shown at the top of this page, $a = 5$ and $b = 0$: $(x, y) \to (x + 5, y)$.

Watch Out!

When a translation moves points to the right, a is positive; when it moves points to the left, a is negative. When a translation moves points up, b is positive; when a translation moves points down, b is negative.

EXAMPLE 1

Graph the image of $P(4, 3)$ after a translation of 6 units to the left and 2 units down. Write the coordinates of the image.

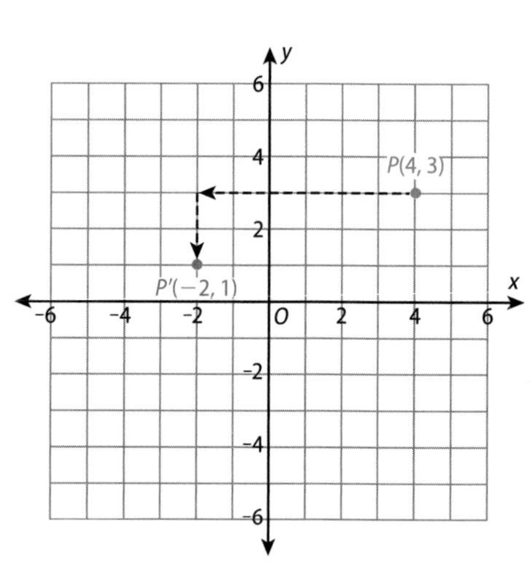

METHOD 1

Count the units on the graph.

6 units to the left and 2 units down from (4, 3) is (−2, 1).

METHOD 2

Use coordinate notation.

Left 6 units means $a = -6$. Down 2 units means $b = -1$.

$$(x, y) \to (x + a, y + b)$$

$$P(4, 3) \to P'(4 + (-6), 3 + (-2)) = P'(4 - 6, 3 - 2) = P'(-2, 1)$$

Translations

Translations preserve congruency and orientation.

EXAMPLE 2

Find the endpoints of the image of $\overline{MN}$ after the translation $(x, y) \rightarrow (x + 5, y - 4)$. Graph the image.

Find the endpoints of $\overline{MN}$.

M is at $(-4, -1)$. N is at $(-2, 3)$.

For each endpoint, add 5 to the x-value and -4 to the y-value.

Pre-image $\rightarrow$ Image

$M(-4, -1) \rightarrow M'(-4 + 5, -1 - 4) = M'(1, -5)$

$N(-2, 3) \rightarrow N'(-2 + 5, 3 - 4) = N'(3, -1)$

The endpoints of the image are $M'(1, -5)$ and $N'(3, -1)$.

Draw $\overline{M'N'}$.

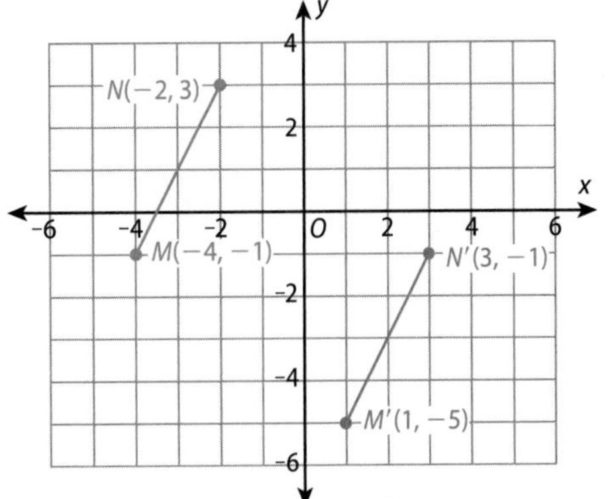

Need More HELP

List corresponding points of the pre-image and image in the same order. This is similar to how you label corresponding points of congruent figures.

EXAMPLE 3

Write a rule to describe the translation $\triangle HJK \rightarrow \triangle H'J'K'$.

Choose corresponding points on the pre-image and image. Use $H(5, -2)$ and its image $H'(0, 0)$.

To find the horizontal change, subtract the x-coordinate of the pre-image from the x-coordinate of the image.

horizontal change: $a = 0 - 5 = -5$

To find the vertical change, subtract the y-coordinate of the pre-image from the y-coordinate of the image.

vertical change: $b = 0 - (-2) = 2$

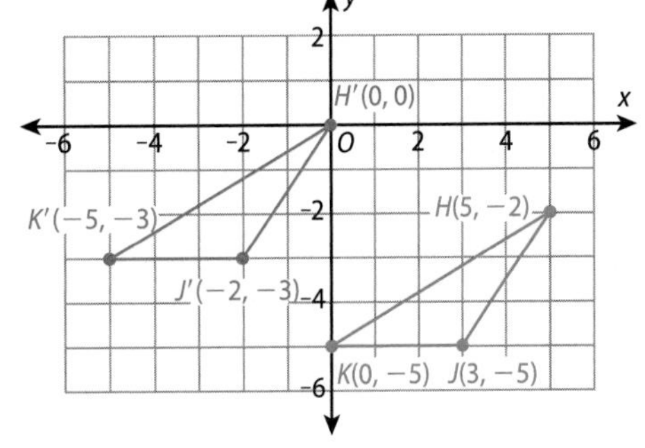

Need More HELP

Since the transformation is a translation, $\triangle HJK$ is congruent to $\triangle H'J'K'$.

GOT TO KNOW!

Translations in the Coordinate Plane

A **translation** maps the point $A(x, y)$ to the point $A'(x + a, y + b)$.

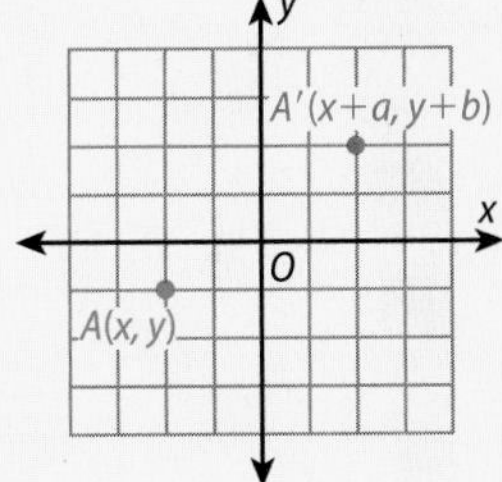

A **horizontal translation** maps the point $B(x, y)$ to the point $B'(x + a, y)$.

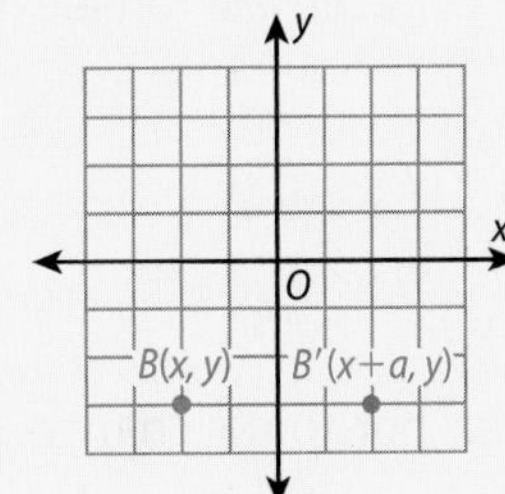

A **vertical translation** maps the point $C(x, y)$ to the point $C'(x, y + b)$.

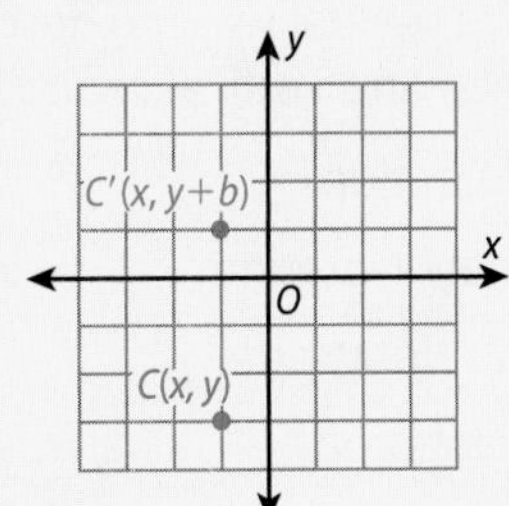

Function Notation

Another way to describe a translation is to use the function notation $T_{a,\,b}$, where a represents the horizontal change and b represents the vertical change.

$$T_{a,\,b}(x, y) \longrightarrow (x + a, y + b)$$

EXAMPLE 4

SEARCH To see step-by-step videos of these problems, enter the page number into the SWadvantage.com Search Bar.

The point $F(-1, 5)$ is translated using the translation $T_{4,\,-7}$. Describe the translation, and then find the coordinates of the image.

For $T_{4,\,-7}$, $a = 4$ and $b = -7$. The translation is 4 units to the right and 7 units down.

Write $T_{4,\,-7}$ in the form $T_{a,\,b}(x, y) \longrightarrow (x + a, y + b)$.	$T_{4,\,-7}(x, y) \longrightarrow (x + 4, y - 7)$
Substitute -1 for x and 5 for y.	$T_{4,\,-7}(-1, 5) \longrightarrow (-1 + 4, 5 - 7)$
Simplify.	$T_{4,\,-7}(-1, 5) \longrightarrow (3, -2)$

The image of $(-1, 5)$ is $(3, -2)$.

EXAMPLE 5

Need More HELP Since the transformation is a translation, parallelogram *RSUV* is congruent to parallelogram *R′S′U′V′*.

Use function notation to represent the translation that maps parallelogram *RSUV* to parallelogram *R′S′U′V′*.

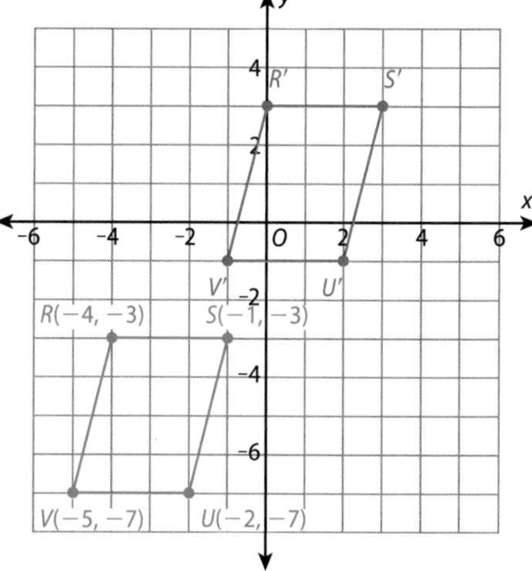

Choose two corresponding points.

$R(-4, -3) \longrightarrow R'(0, 3)$

horizontal change: $a = 0 - (-4) = 4$

vertical change: $b = 3 - (-3) = 6$

Substitute the numbers for a and b into $T_{a,\,b}$.

$T_{a,b} = T_{4,6}$

CHECK Choose another pair of points.

$S(-1, -3) \longrightarrow S'(3, 3)$

horizontal change: $a = 3 - (-1) = 4$ ✔

vertical change: $b = 3 - (-3) = 6$ ✔

The rule for the translation is $T_{4,6}(x, y) \longrightarrow (x + 4, y + 6)$.

GOT TO KNOW!

Notation for Translations

There are several ways to describe a translation. Only the last three explicitly show the horizontal and vertical change.

Arrow Notation	$\triangle ABC \longrightarrow \triangle A'B'C'$
Coordinate Notation	$(x, y) \longrightarrow (x + a, y + b)$
Function Notation	$T_{a,b}(x, y) \longrightarrow (x + a, y + b)$
Vector Notation	$\langle a, b \rangle$ where a indicates horizontal change, b indicates vertical change

Representing Translations Using Vectors

Because a translation maps all points of a figure the same distance and in the same direction, you can use a *vector* to represent a translation. A **vector** can be written as $\langle a, b \rangle$, where a is the horizontal change and b is the vertical change. So, the translation vector $v = \langle 5, -9 \rangle$ represents a translation of 5 units to the right and 9 units down.

Watch Out !

Use brackets, ⟨ ⟩, rather than parentheses, ( ), to write a vector.

EXAMPLE 6

Find the vertices of the image of $\triangle XYZ$ for the translation vector $\mathbf{v} = \langle -3, 1 \rangle$. Graph the image.

The vector $\langle -3, 1 \rangle$ indicates moving to the left 3 units and up 1 unit.

Find the coordinates of the vertices of the image.

Pre-Image $\rightarrow$ image

$X(1, 2) \rightarrow X'(1 - 3, 2 + 1) = X'(-2, 3)$

$Y(3, -4) \rightarrow Y'(3 - 3, -4 + 1) = Y'(0, -3)$

$Z(1, -4) \rightarrow Z'(1 - 3, -4 + 1) = Z'(-2, -3)$

Draw $\triangle X'Y'Z'$.

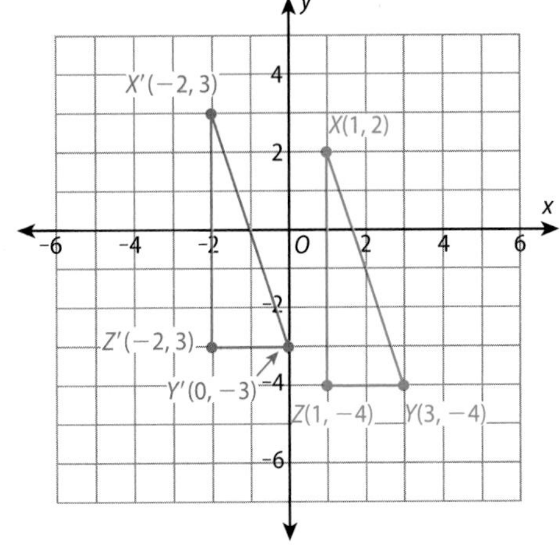

To review vectors, go to *Vectors* in *Trigonometry*, p. 1066.

EXAMPLE 7

In chess, the pieces can be moved only in certain ways. The game board shows moves for three chess pieces. Write the translation vector for each piece and describe the translation.

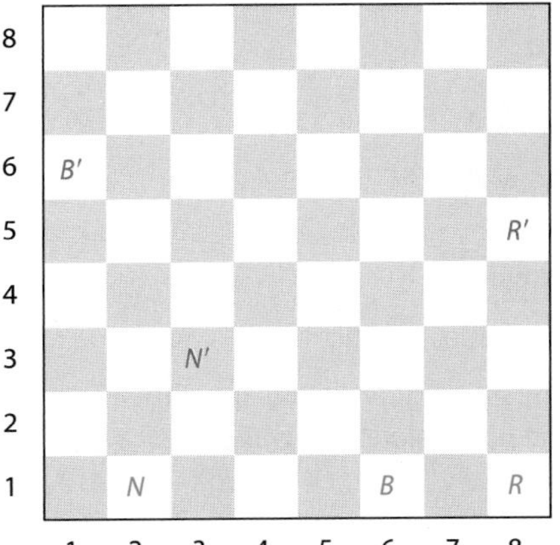

a. rook *R*

$R(8, 1) \rightarrow R'(8, 5)$

horizontal change: $a = 8 - 8 = 0$
vertical change: $b = 5 - 1 = 4$

$\mathbf{v} = \langle 0, 4 \rangle$

The rook moved up in a straight line.

b. bishop *B*

$B(6, 1) \rightarrow B'(1, 6)$

horizontal change: $a = 1 - 6 = -5$ vertical change: $b = 6 - 1 = 5$

$\mathbf{v} = \langle -5, 5 \rangle$

The bishop moved on a diagonal.

c. knight *N*

$N(2, 1) \rightarrow N'(3, 3)$

horizontal change: $a = 3 - 2 = 1$ vertical change: $b = 3 - 1 = 2$

$\mathbf{v} = \langle 1, 2 \rangle$

The knight moved up 2 units and to the right 1 unit.

Reflections

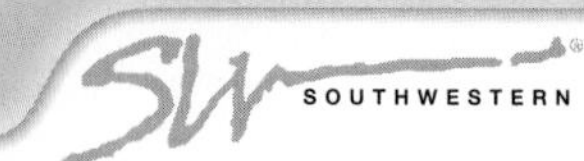

Watch Out !

A reflection changes the orientation of a figure. Notice that the vertices *A*, *B*, *C* are in counterclockwise order, but the vertices *A′*, *B′*, *C′* of its image are in clockwise order!

SEARCH

To see step-by-step videos of these problems, enter the page number into the SWadvantage.com Search Bar.

What Is a Reflection?

A *reflection* is an isometry that *flips* a figure over a line, called the *line of reflection.* In a **reflection**, each point of the original figure is the same distance from the line of reflection as the corresponding point in the image. The **line of reflection** is the perpendicular bisector of each segment connecting a point and its image.

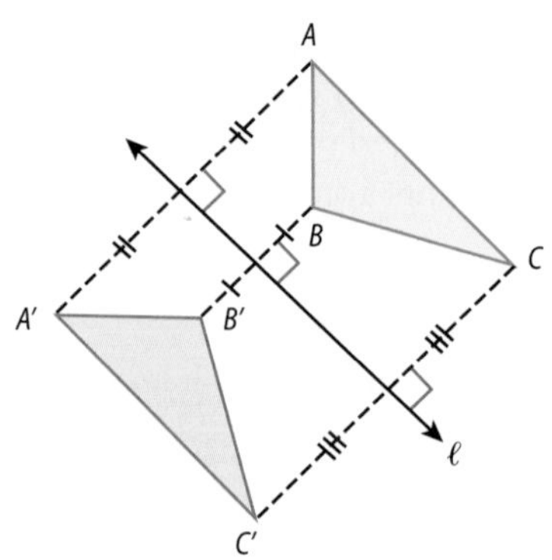

The diagram shows $\triangle ABC$ and its image $\triangle A'B'C'$ after a reflection over line ℓ. You can represent the reflection symbolically as:

$\triangle ABC \rightarrow \triangle A'B'C'$

Line ℓ is the perpendicular bisector of $\overline{AA'}$, $\overline{BB'}$, and $\overline{CC'}$.

EXAMPLE 1

Graph the reflection of $\triangle ABC$ over the *y*-axis. Write the coordinates of the vertices of the image.

METHOD 1

For each vertex, find the point that is the same distance from the *y*-axis, but in the opposite direction.

Pre-image		Image
$A(-3, 4)$	$\rightarrow$	$A'(3, 4)$
$B(3, 0)$	$\rightarrow$	$B'(-3, 0)$
$C(-2, 6)$	$\rightarrow$	$C'(2, 6)$

Draw $\triangle A'B'C'$.

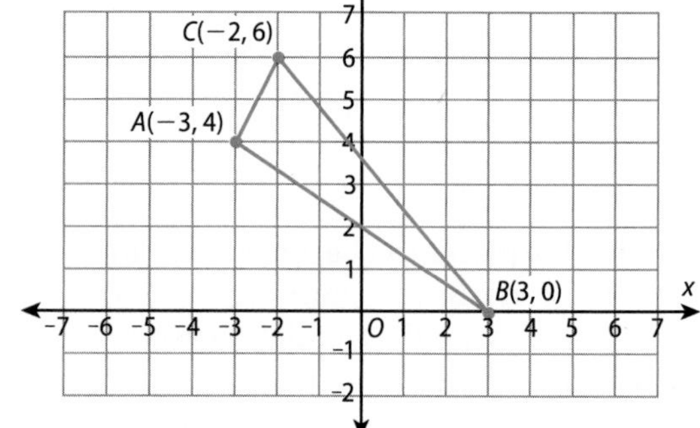

METHOD 2

Use paper-folding.

Copy the figure onto graph paper. Then fold the paper along the *y*-axis. Push a pin or the point of your pencil through vertices *A*, *B*, and *C*. Open the paper.

Label the pinpoints $A'(3, 4)$, $B'(-3, 0)$, and $C'(2, 6)$.

Draw $\triangle A'B'C'$.

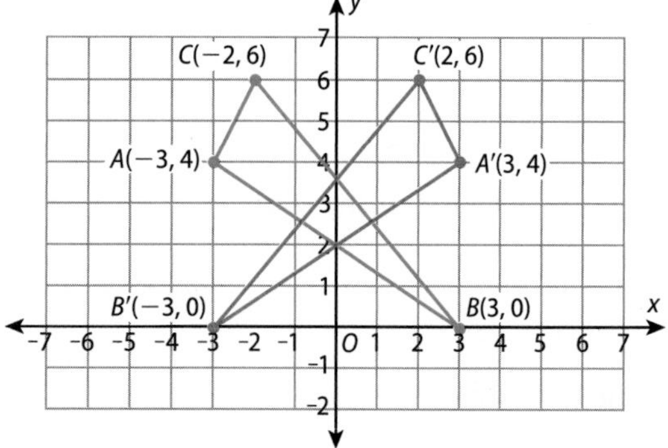

Compare the coordinates of the vertices of the original figure to the coordinates of their reflections.

- A reflection over the *y*-axis maps the point (x, y) to the point $(-x, y)$.

When you reflect a point over the *x*-axis, you will see a different pattern in the coordinates.

- A reflection over the *x*-axis maps the point (x, y) to the point $(x, -y)$.

If a point is on an axis, then its reflection over that axis is the point itself.

EXAMPLE 2

Graph $\overline{PQ}$ with endpoints $P(-2, -3)$ and $Q(1, 2)$. Find the coordinates of the vertices of the image after a reflection over the x-axis. Then graph the image.

METHOD 1

Use the fact that a reflection over the x-axis maps the point (x, y) to $(x, -y)$.

Pre-image		Image
$P(-2, -3)$	$\rightarrow$	$P'(-2, 3)$
$Q(1, 2)$	$\rightarrow$	$Q'(1, -2)$

Draw $\overline{P'Q'}$.

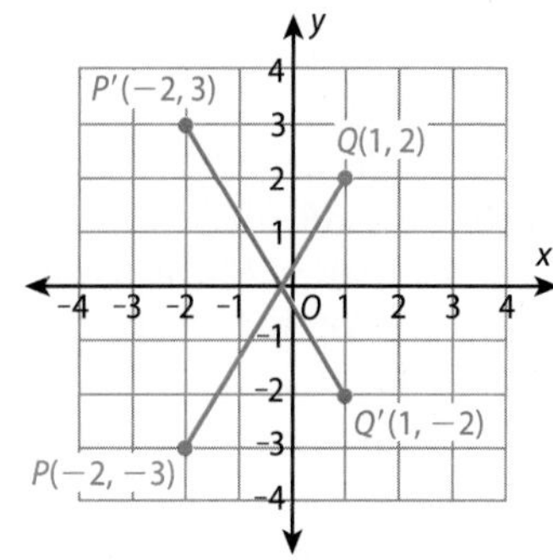

METHOD 2

Locate points P' and Q' so that the x-axis is the perpendicular bisector of $\overline{PP'}$ and $\overline{QQ'}$.

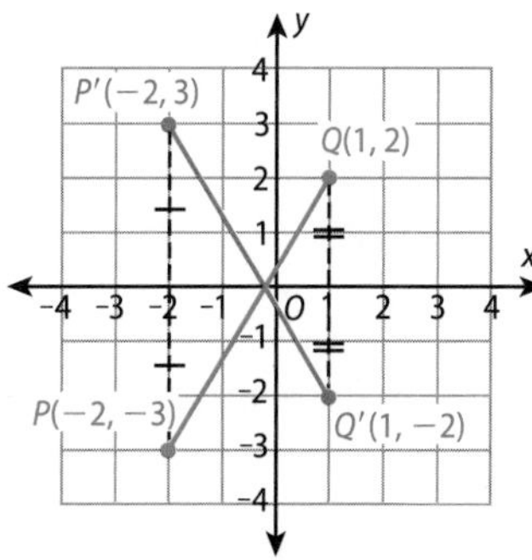

Need More HELP

You read $P \longrightarrow P'$ as "P maps onto P prime."

GOT TO KNOW!

Reflections

A **reflection** is a transformation that flips a figure over a line.

A reflection preserves congruency but not orientation.

Reflections Over an Axis

A **reflection over the *x*-axis** maps the point $A(x, y)$ to the point $A'(x, -y)$.

A(x, y)

A′(x, −y)

A **reflection over the *y*-axis** maps the point $B(x, y)$ to the point $B'(-x, y)$.

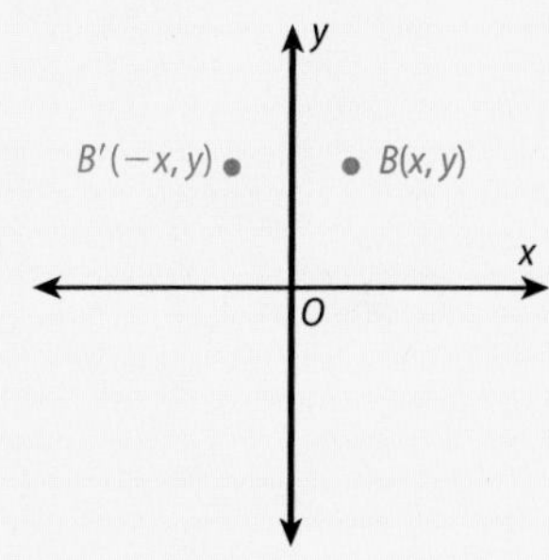

Other Lines of Reflection

The line of reflection will not always be the x-axis or the y-axis.

- A reflection over the line $y = x$ maps the point (x, y) to the point (y, x).
- A reflection over the line $y = -x$ maps the point (x, y) to the point $(-y, -x)$.

Watch Out!

The image of a point lying on the line of reflection will coincide with the original point.

EXAMPLE 3

Graph $\triangle STU$ with vertices $S(-2, -2)$, $T(3, 5)$, and $U(4, 0)$. Find the coordinates of the vertices of the image after a reflection over the line $y = x$. Then graph the image.

STEP 1 Use the fact that a reflection over the line $y = x$ maps the point (x, y) to the point (y, x). Switch the x- and y-coordinates to find the coordinates of the vertices of the image.

Pre-image		Image
$S(-2, -2)$	$\rightarrow$	$S'(-2, -2)$
$T(3, 5)$	$\rightarrow$	$T'(5, 3)$
$U(4, 0)$	$\rightarrow$	$U'(0, 4)$

STEP 2 Plot the points and draw the triangle.

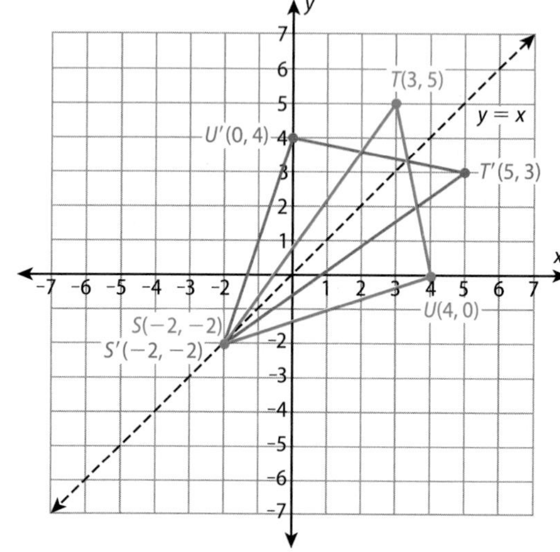

SEARCH

To see step-by-step videos of these problems, enter the page number into the SWadvantage.com Search Bar.

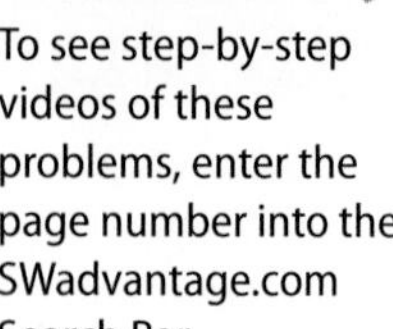

EXAMPLE 4

Graph the reflection of quadrilateral *ABCD* over the line $x = 2$.

When you flip the figure over the line $x = 2$, the figure does not move vertically, only horizontally. This means that the y-coordinates of the image points do not change. Follow these steps to find the x-coordinates of the image points.

STEP 1 Find the distance from each given vertex to the line $x = 2$.

Vertex	Distance to $x = 2$
A	4 units
B	1 unit
C	2 units
D	5 units

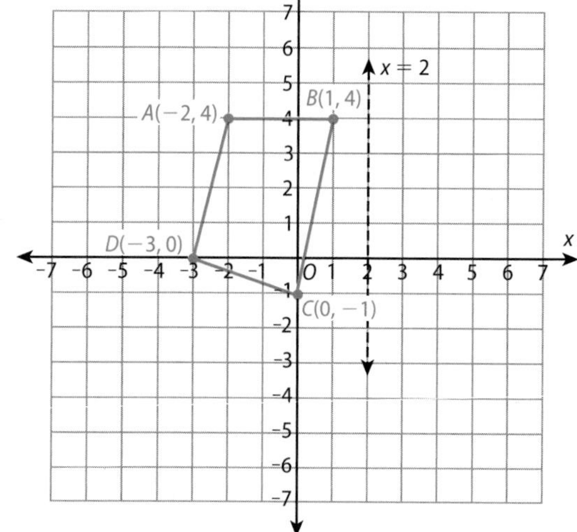

STEP 2 Each image point is the same distance from the line $x = 2$ but on the other side of the line. To find the x-coordinate of the image, add 2 to the distance each vertex is from $x = 2$.

$A(-2, 4) \rightarrow A'(2 + 4, 4) = A'(6, 4)$
$B(1, 4) \rightarrow B'(2 + 1, 4) = B'(3, 4)$
$C(0, -1) \rightarrow C'(2 + 2, -1) = C'(4, -1)$
$D(-3, 0) \rightarrow D'(2 + 5, 0) = D'(7, 0)$

STEP 3 Graph quadrilateral $A'B'C'D'$.

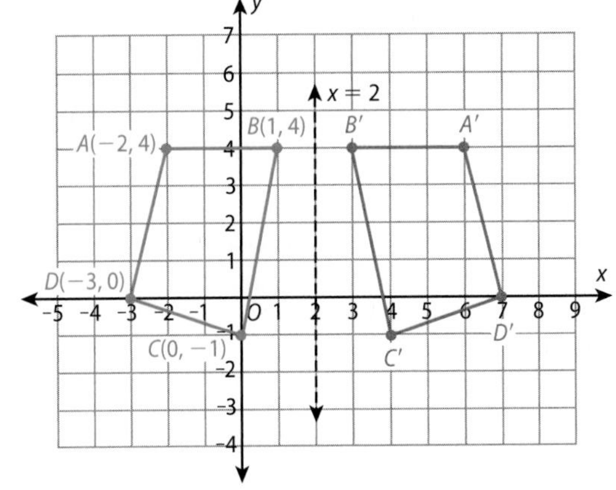

Using Reflections

EXAMPLE 5

Frank is playing mini-golf and hopes to make a hole-in-one. There is a pool of water directly in front of the hole *H*. How should Frank putt the ball *F* so that it will go into the hole and miss the water?

He should imagine reflecting the point H over the line determined by one of the walls.

Then imagine $\overline{FH'}$, the line segment connecting the golf ball to the reflection of the hole.

If he aims his putt at P, the point where $\overline{FH'}$ intersects the wall, the ball will bounce off the wall and go into the hole!

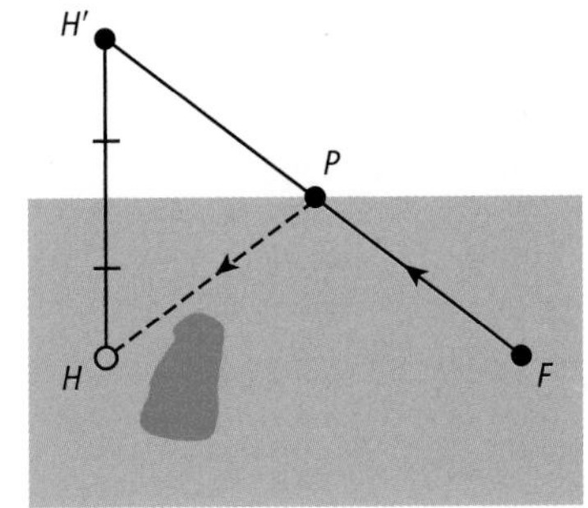

GOT TO KNOW!

Reflections Over a Line

A reflection over the line $y = x$ maps the point $A(x, y)$ to the point $A'(y, x)$.

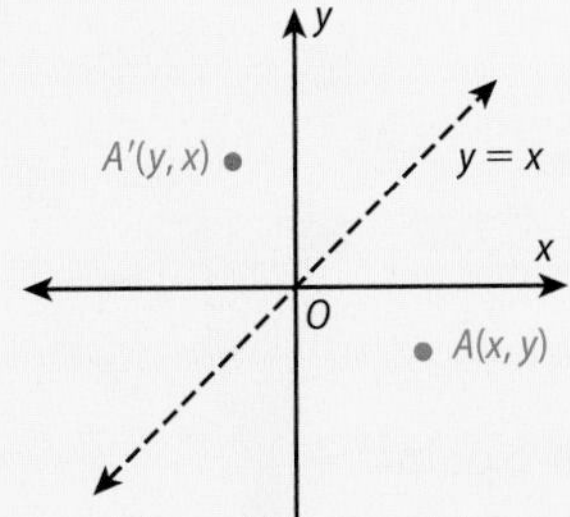

A reflection over the line $y = -x$ maps the point $B(x, y)$ to the point $B'(-y, -x)$.

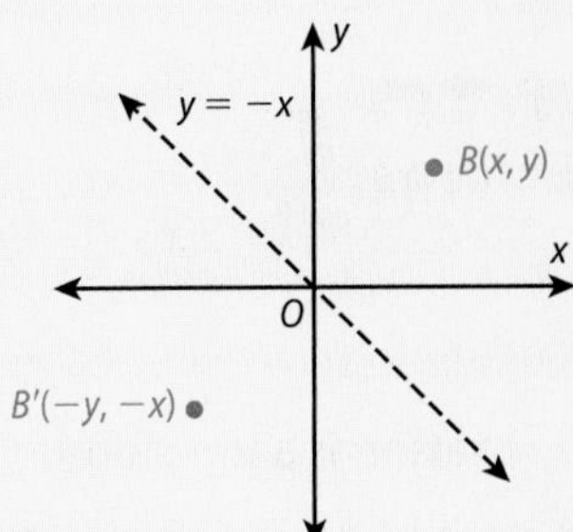

Rotations

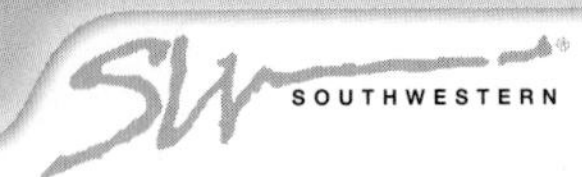

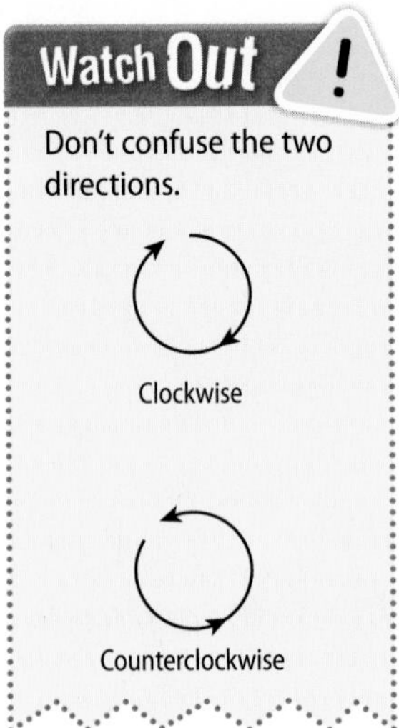

Don't confuse the two directions.

About Rotations

A **rotation** is an isometry that turns a figure about a point called the **center of rotation**. Rays from the center of rotation to corresponding points on the pre-image and image determine the **angle of rotation**.

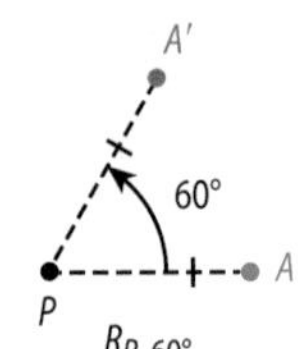

A rotation can be clockwise or counterclockwise. A clockwise rotation has a negative angle of rotation. A counterclockwise rotation has a positive angle of rotation.

To describe a rotation, you must identify the center of rotation and the angle of rotation. The notation $R_{P,60°}$ denotes a counterclockwise rotation of 60° about point P, as shown in the figure.

A 360° rotation maps a point to itself. The figure at the right shows a 405° rotation of point B about point P. The image is the same as if you had rotated point B 45° about point P.

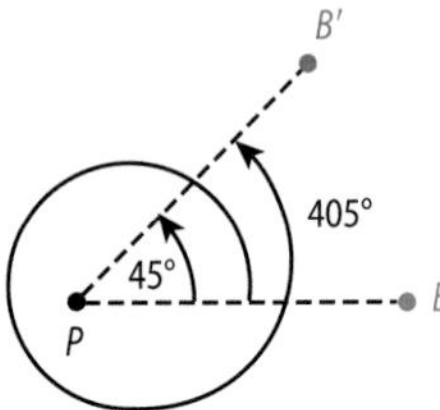

EXAMPLE 1

Find another name for each rotation.

a. $R_{P,-90°}$

Draw a sketch.

$90 + 270 = 360$

$R_{P,-90°} = R_{P,270°}$

b. $R_{P,315°}$

Draw a sketch.

$315 + 45 = 360$

$R_{P,315°} = R_{P,-45°}$

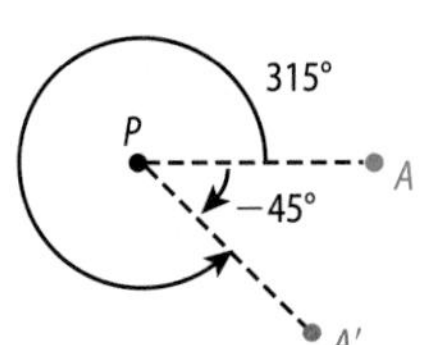

SEARCH

To see step-by-step videos of these problems, enter the page number into the SWadvantage.com Search Bar.

Rotations

A **rotation** is a transformation that turns a figure about a point.

A rotation preserves congruency and orientation.

Drawing a Rotation Image

You can use a ruler and a protractor to draw the image of a figure after a rotation.

EXAMPLE 2

Draw the image of $\triangle DEF$ after a rotation of 90° about point P.

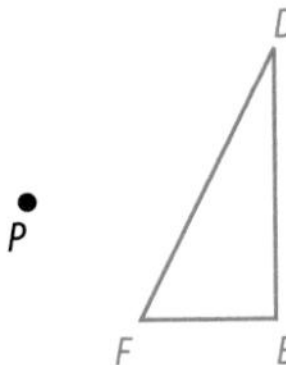

STEP 1 Use a protractor to draw a 90° angle with center P and side $\overline{DP}$.

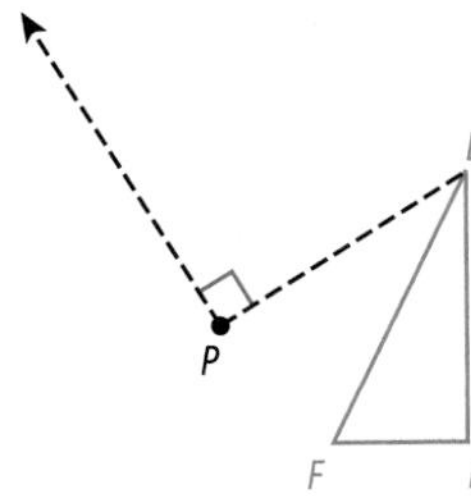

STEP 2 Use a ruler to locate D' so that $\overline{PD'} \cong \overline{PD}$.

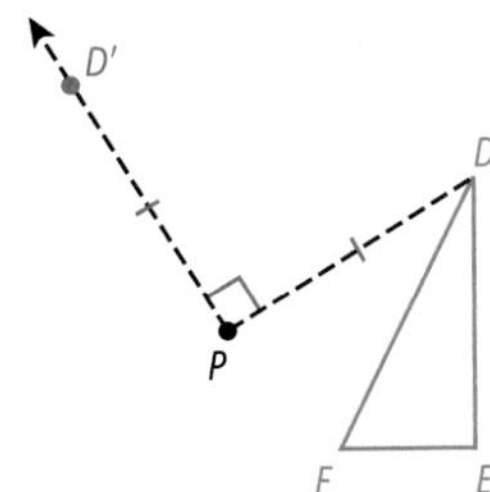

STEP 3 Repeat Steps 1 and 2 to locate E' and F'. Draw $\triangle D'E'F'$.

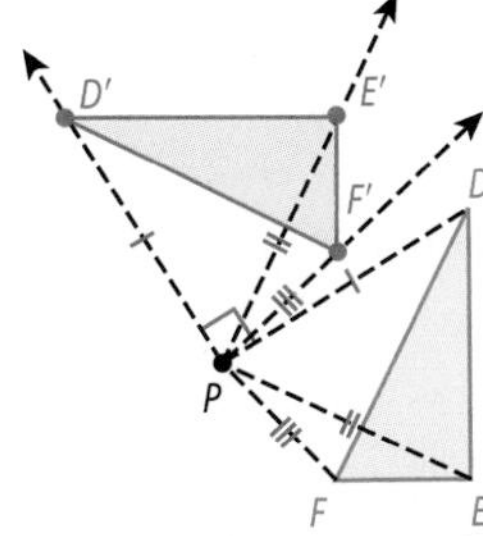

Try It This Way

Some graphing calculators can do rotations. Check your calculator for a Rotation Tool.

Rotations in the Coordinate Plane

When rotating a figure in the coordinate plane, this book assumes that the origin $O(0, 0)$ is the center of rotation. A rotation of 90° or −90° is a **quarter-turn**. A rotation of 180° or −180° is a **half-turn**. In a half-turn, the origin is the midpoint of each segment joining a point and its image. For quarter-turns and half-turns, you can use the rules in the *Got to Know!* box shown below to find the coordinates of the image points.

SEARCH

To see step-by-step videos of these problems, enter the page number into the SWadvantage.com Search Bar.

EXAMPLE 3

Graph the image of $\triangle ABC$ after a half-turn about the origin.

METHOD 1

Use the fact that the origin O is the midpoint of $\overline{AA'}$, $\overline{BB'}$, $\overline{CC'}$ to locate A', B', and C'. In the figure, $AO = OA'$, $BO = OB'$, and $CO = OC'$.

Draw $\triangle A'B'C'$.

METHOD 2

A half-turn is a rotation of 180° about the origin O. Use the rule $R_{O, 180°}(x, y) \rightarrow (-x, -y)$ to find the coordinates of A', B', and C'.

Pre-image		Image
$A(1, 1)$	→	$A'(-1, -1)$
$B(1, 4)$	→	$B'(-1, -4)$
$C(3, 1)$	→	$C'(-3, -1)$

Draw $\triangle A'B'C'$.

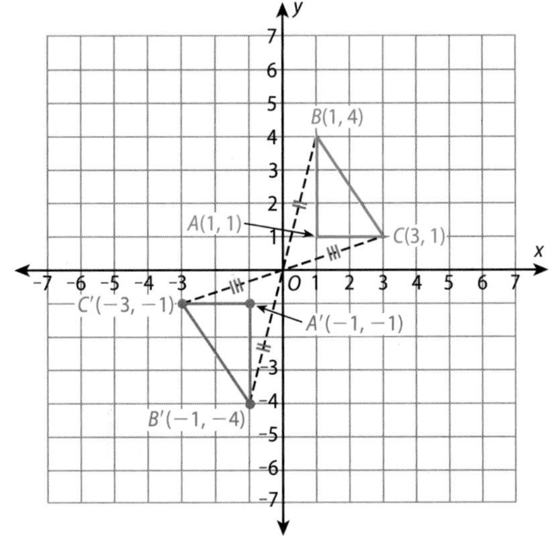

EXAMPLE 4

Graph quadrilateral $PQTS$ with vertices $P(-1, -1)$, $Q(-4, -1)$, $T(-5, -4)$, and $S(-1, -4)$. Find the coordinates of the vertices of the image after a rotation of −90°. Then graph the image.

A rotation of −90° is a clockwise quarter-turn. Use the rule $R_{O, -90°}(x, y) \rightarrow (y, -x)$ to find the coordinates of P', Q', T', and S'.

Pre-image		Image
$P(-1, -1)$	→	$P'(-1, 1)$
$Q(-4, -1)$	→	$Q'(-1, 4)$
$T(-5, -4)$	→	$T'(-4, 5)$
$S(-1, -4)$	→	$S'(-4, 1)$

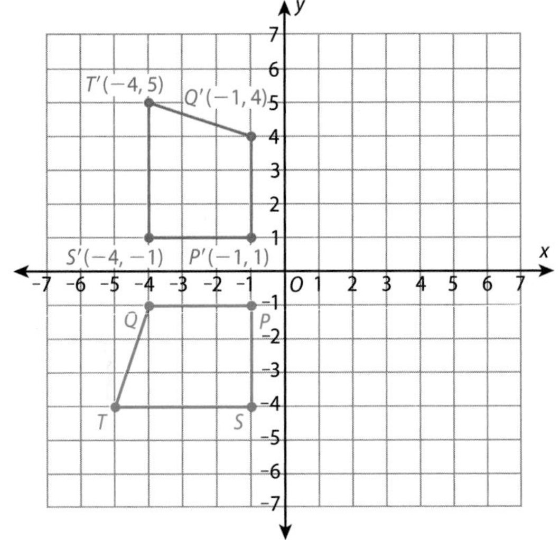

GOT TO KNOW!

Half-turns

$R_{O, 180°}(x, y) \rightarrow (-x, -y)$

$R_{O, -180°}(x, y) \rightarrow (-x, -y)$

Quarter-turns

$R_{O, 90°}(x, y) \rightarrow (-y, x)$

$R_{O, -90°}(x, y) \rightarrow (y, -x)$

Finding the Center of Rotation

You can use the perpendicular-bisector construction to find the center of a rotation if you are given at least two points and their images.

Find the center of rotation for this transformation.

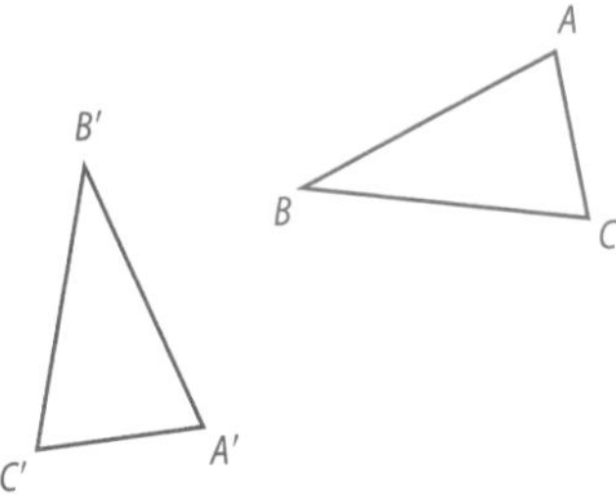

STEP 1 Draw $\overline{AA'}$.

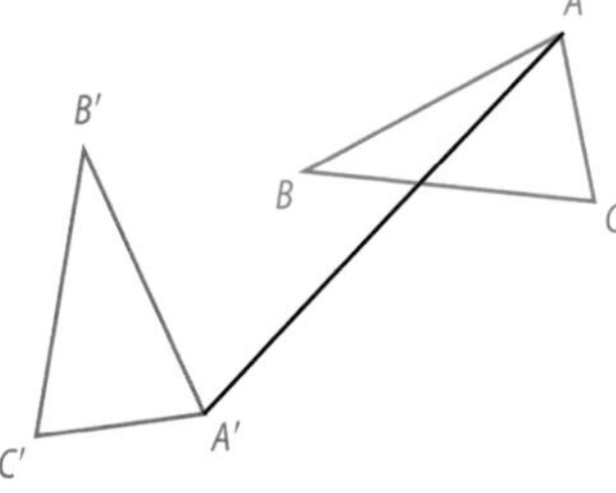

STEP 2 Construct the perpendicular bisector of $\overline{AA'}$.

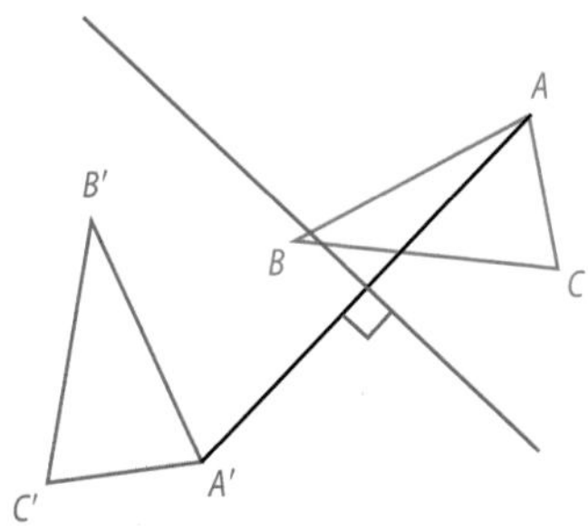

STEP 3 Draw $\overline{BB'}$.

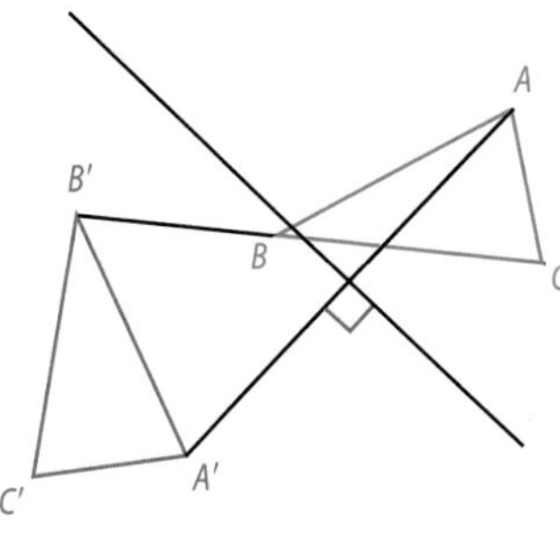

STEP 4 Construct the perpendicular bisector of $\overline{BB'}$. Label the intersection of the two perpendicular bisectors as point P. P is the center of rotation.

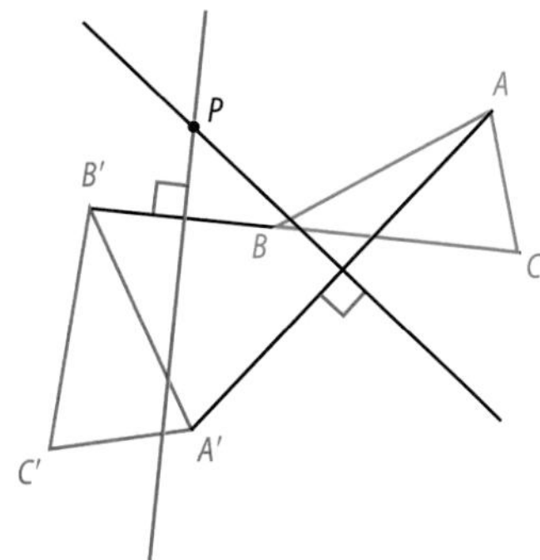

Need More HELP

For help with constructing the perpendicular bisector of a segment, go to *Perpendicular Bisector of a Segment* in *Constructions* (p. 864).

Symmetry

Line Symmetry

When a transformation maps a figure onto itself, the figure has **symmetry**.

If you can reflect a figure over a line and the figure maps onto itself, the figure has **line symmetry**. The reflection line is the **line of symmetry**. Line symmetry is also called **reflection symmetry**.

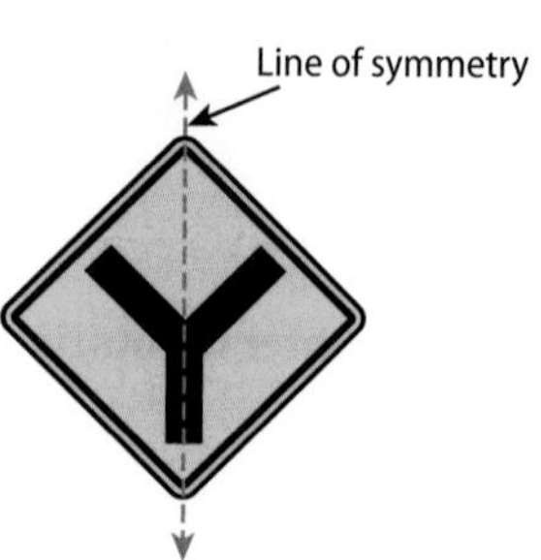

EXAMPLE 1

Do the rectangle and the square have the same number of lines of symmetry?

Draw all possible lines that divide each figure into mirror-image congruent halves.

The rectangle has 2 lines of symmetry.

The square has 4 lines of symmetry.

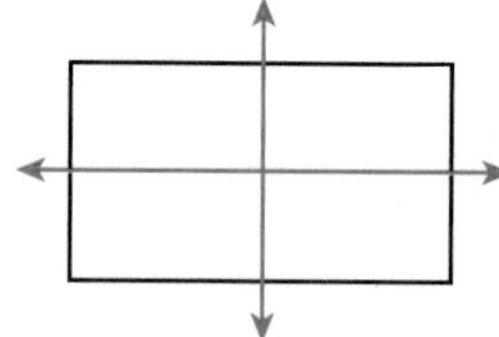

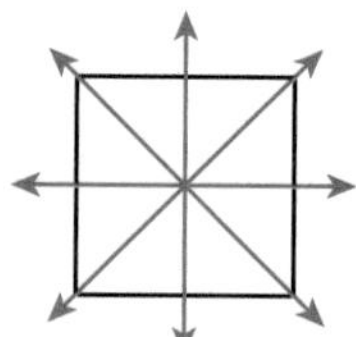

The figures do *not* have the same number of lines of symmetry.

Try It This Way

Trace the shape onto a piece of paper. Then fold the paper so that the two halves exactly match. Each fold line is a line of symmetry.

EXAMPLE 2

Complete the figure so that it has symmetry in line *t*.

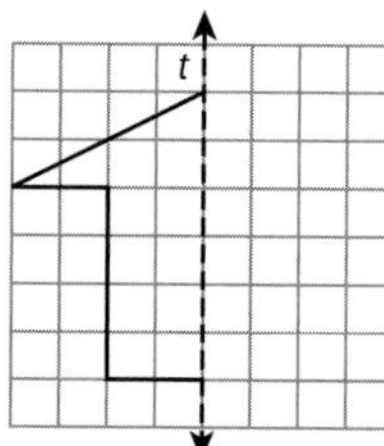

STEP 1 Graph the reflection of each vertex over line t.

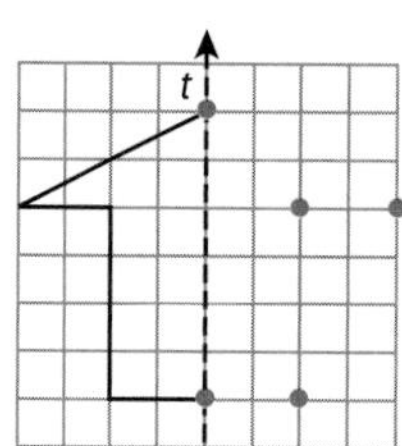

STEP 2 Draw the figure.

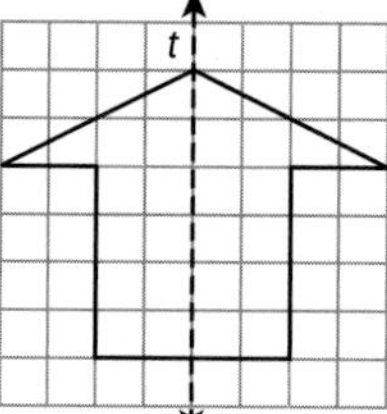

Need More HELP

For help with reflecting a figure over a line, go to *Reflections* on page 838.

Rotational Symmetry

If you can rotate a figure less than 360° so that the figure coincides with itself, the figure has **rotational symmetry**. The point around which the figure is rotated is the **center of rotation**. The smallest angle the figure needs to be rotated to show symmetry is the **angle of rotation**.

The **order of symmetry** is the number of rotations of the smallest angle greater than 0° and less than or equal to 360° that produce an image that coincides with the original. In a regular polygon, the order of symmetry is the same as the number of sides.

For help with rotations, go to *Rotations* on page 842.

EXAMPLE 3

What is the order of symmetry for this regular hexagon?

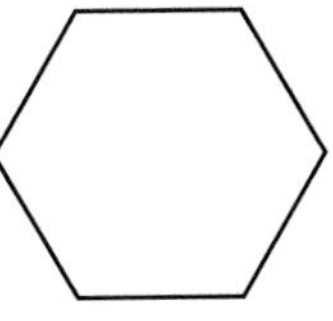

There are six rotations less than or equal to 360° that produce an image that coincides with the original:

60°, 120°, 180°, 240°, 300°, and 360°

A regular hexagon has rotational symmetry of order 6.

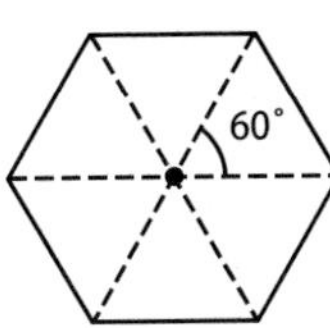

EXAMPLE 4

Does the figure have rotational symmetry? If so, find the angle of rotation and the order of symmetry.

Yes, the figure has rotational symmetry.

To find the angle of rotation and the order of symmetry, follow these steps:

STEP 1 Find the angle of rotation.

$360° \div 5 = 72°$

The angle of rotation is 72°.

STEP 2 Find the order of symmetry.

There are five rotations less than or equal to 360° that produce an image coincident with the original:

72°, 144°, 216°, 288°, 360°.

The order of symmetry is 5.

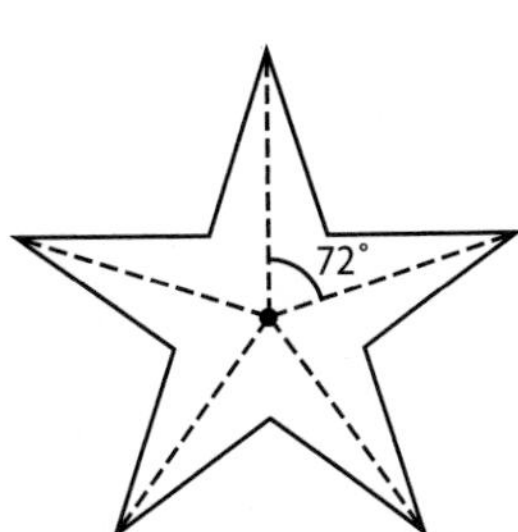

SEARCH

To see step-by-step videos of these problems, enter the page number into the SWadvantage.com Search Bar.

Point Symmetry

> **Watch Out !**
> A figure with point symmetry always has rotational symmetry. However, a figure with rotational symmetry may not always have point symmetry.

A figure that has 180° rotational symmetry has **point symmetry**. You can test for point symmetry by turning the figure upside down to see if it looks the same.

EXAMPLE 5

Which of these letters have point symmetry?

M N T S X

STEP 1 Turn this book upside down.

STEP 2 Identify the letters that appear the same upside down or right side up.
N, S, and X appear the same.
M and T do not appear the same.

STEP 3 Classify the letters that appear the same as having point symmetry.
The letters N, S, and X have point symmetry.

A point P is a **point of symmetry** if you can rotate a figure 180° about P and the result coincides with the original figure.

EXAMPLE 6

Does the command symbol on a computer keyboard have point symmetry? If so, find the point of symmetry.

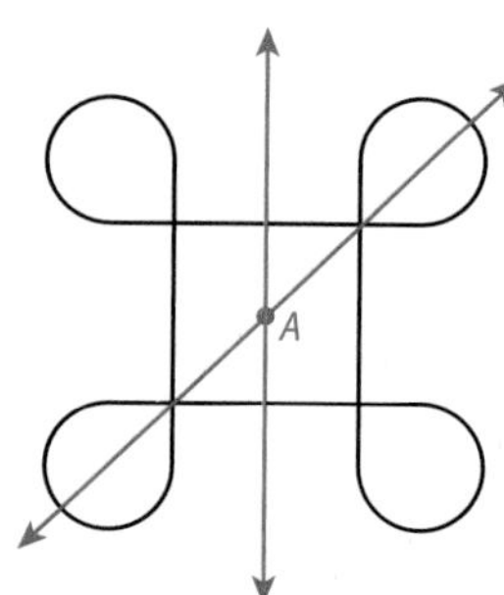

Yes, the figure has point symmetry.

To find the point of symmetry, follow these steps:

STEP 1 Draw at least two lines of symmetry.

STEP 2 Find the point where the lines intersect.
Point A is the point of symmetry.

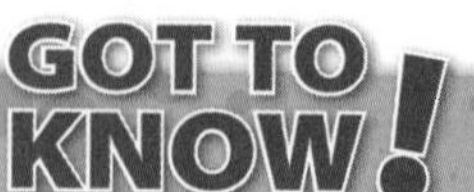

Types of Symmetry

If a figure maps onto itself after a reflection over a line, then the figure has **line symmetry**.

If a figure maps onto itself after a rotation less than 360°, then the figure has **rotational symmetry**.

If a figure maps onto itself after a rotation of 180°, then the figure has **point symmetry**.

Identifying Types of Symmetry

Some figures have more than one type of symmetry.

EXAMPLE 7

What types of symmetry does this figure have?

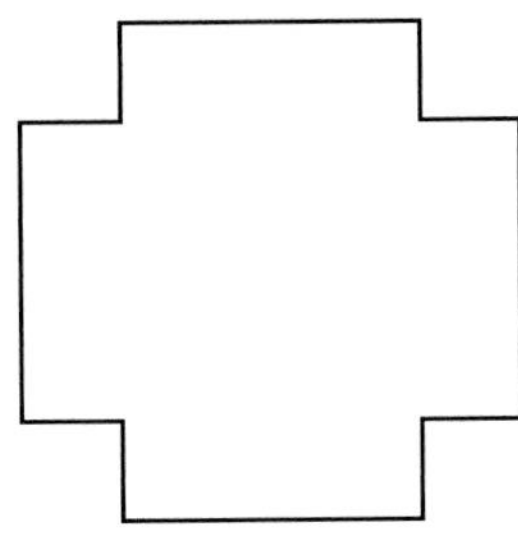

The figure has line symmetry with 4 lines of symmetry.

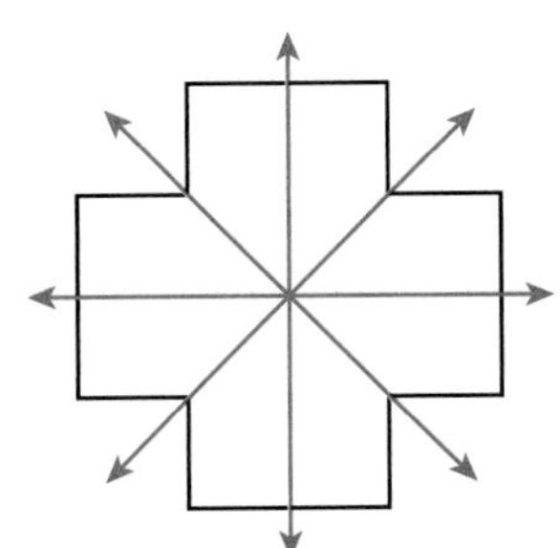

The figure has rotational symmetry of order 4. The angle of rotation is 90°.

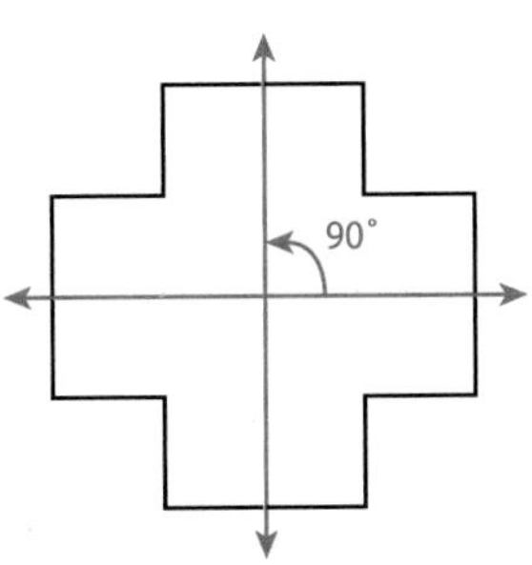

The figure has rotational symmetry of 180°, so the figure also has point symmetry.

SEARCH

To see step-by-step videos of these problems, enter the page number into the SWadvantage.com Search Bar.

EXAMPLE 8

Describe the symmetry of an equilateral triangle.

Draw an equilateral triangle.

The triangle has line symmetry with 3 lines of symmetry.

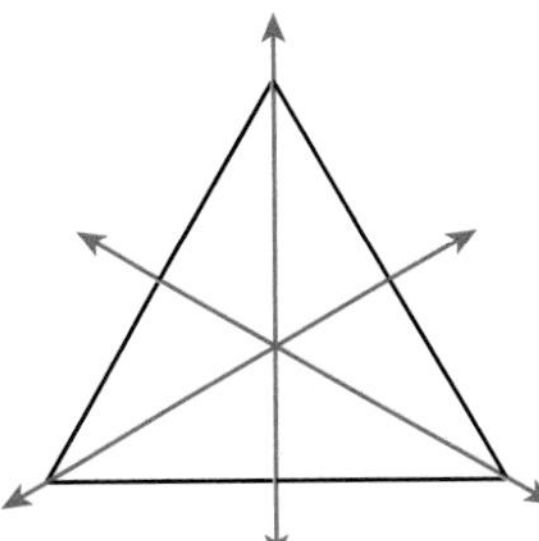

The triangle has rotational symmetry of order 3. The angle of rotation is 120°.

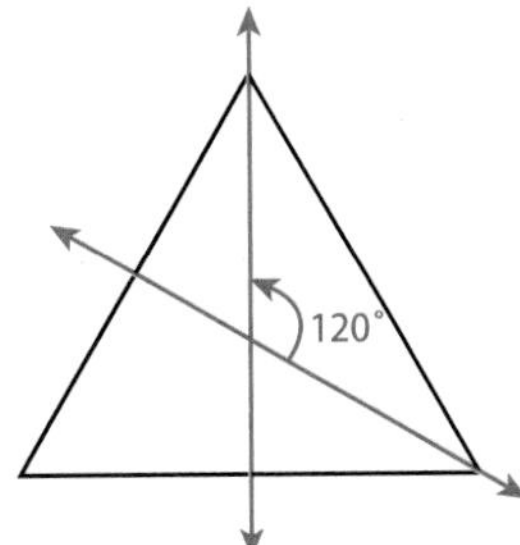

The triangle does not have point symmetry.

Dilations

What Is a Dilation?

All the transformations you have seen so far are isometries—they preserve congruence. A **dilation**, on the other hand, is a transformation that produces an image similar to the original figure. Another name for a dilation is a **similarity transformation**.

A dilation with **scale factor** r and **center** P maps a point A to point A' according to these rules:

1. **If $r > 0$, A' lies on $\overrightarrow{PA}$ and $PA' = r \cdot PA$.**
2. **If $r < 0$, A' lies on the ray opposite to $\overrightarrow{PA}$ and $PA' = |r| \cdot PA$.**

If $|r| > 1$, the image is larger than the original. The dilation is an **enlargement**.

If $|r| < 1$, the image is smaller than the original. The dilation is a **reduction**.

EXAMPLE 1

$A'B'C'D'$ is the dilation image of $ABCD$. The center of the dilation is P.

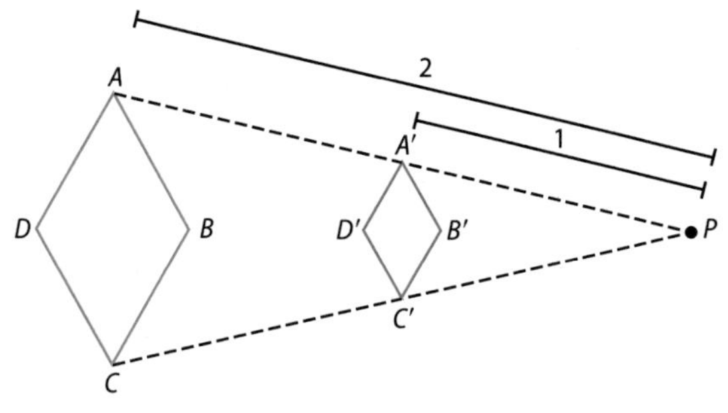

a. Is the dilation an enlargement or reduction?

The image is smaller than the pre-image. The dilation is a reduction.

b. Find the scale factor.

A' lies on $\overrightarrow{PA}$, so the scale factor $r > 0$.

$r = \frac{PA'}{PA} = \frac{1}{2}$

Need More HELP

In similar figures, corresponding angles are congruent and corresponding sides are proportional.

EXAMPLE 2

$\triangle R'S'T'$ is the image of $\triangle RST$ under a dilation. Describe the dilation.

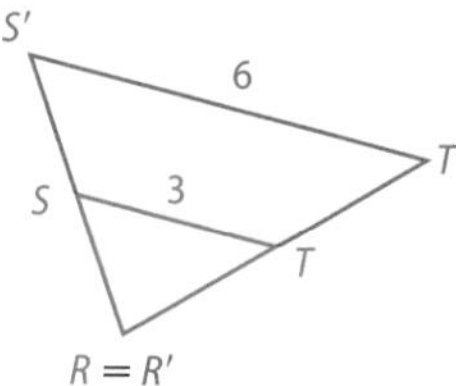

The image is larger than the pre-image, so the dilation is an enlargement. The center of the dilation is R. The scale factor is $\frac{S'T'}{ST} = \frac{6}{3} = 2$.

The dilation is an enlargement with center R and scale factor 2.

Scale Factor

A dilation has a scale factor of r.

If $|r| > 1$, the dilation is an enlargement.

If $|r| < 1$, the dilation is a reduction.

If $|r| = 1$, the dilation is an isometry.

Dilations in the Coordinate Plane

You can use coordinates to describe a dilation with center at the origin of the coordinate plane.

A dilation with center $O(0, 0)$ and scale factor r maps (x, y) to (rx, ry).

EXAMPLE 3

Rectangle $ABCD$ has vertices $A(1, 1)$, $B(1, 3)$, $C(2, 2)$, and $D(2, 1)$. Draw its image after a dilation with center $O(0, 0)$ and scale factor 3.

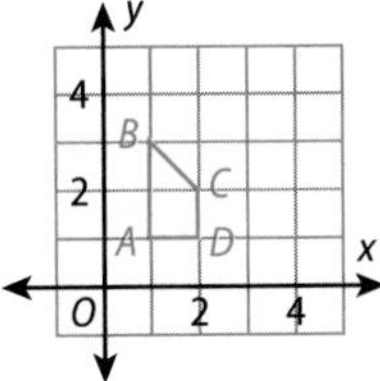

STEP 1 Find the image of each vertex.

$(x, y) \rightarrow (rx, ry)$

$A(1, 1) \rightarrow A'(3, 3)$

$B(1, 3) \rightarrow B'(3, 9)$

$C(2, 2) \rightarrow C'(6, 6)$

$D(2, 1) \rightarrow D'(6, 3)$

STEP 2 Graph $A'B'C'D'$.

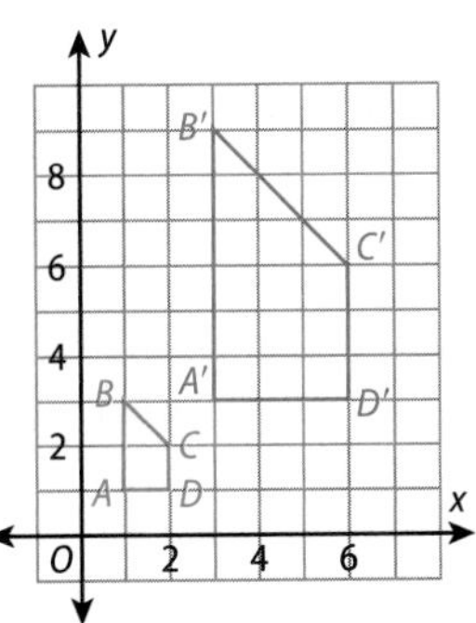

Watch Out!

Remember that the pre-image is the figure before dilation. It is shown in blue and labeled *ABCD*. The image is the figure after dilation. It is shown in red and labeled *A'B'C'D'*.

EXAMPLE 4

Triangle DEF has vertices $D(4, 0)$, $E(-2, 4)$, and $F(-2, -2)$. Graph the triangle and its image after a dilation with center $O(0, 0)$ and scale factor $-\frac{1}{2}$.

STEP 1 Find the image of each vertex.

$(x, y) \rightarrow (rx, ry)$

$D(4, 0) \rightarrow D'(-2, 0)$

$E(-2, 4) \rightarrow E'(1, -2)$

$F(-2, -2) \rightarrow F'(1, 1)$

STEP 2 Graph $\triangle DEF$ and $\triangle D'E'F'$.

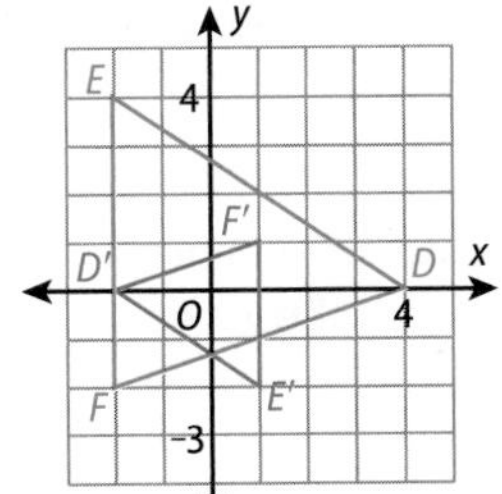

SEARCH

To see step-by-step videos of these problems, enter the page number into the SWadvantage.com Search Bar.

GOT TO KNOW!

Dilations in the Coordinate Plane

A dilation with center $O(0, 0)$ and scale factor r maps (x, y) to (rx, ry).

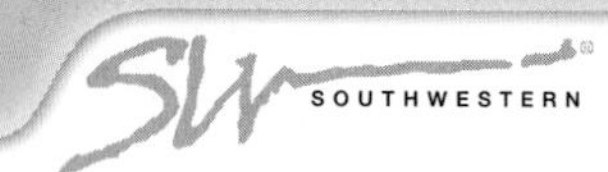

Glide Reflections

When two or more transformations are combined to produce a single transformation, the result is called a **composition** of the original transformations.

A **glide reflection** is a composition of a translation (glide) and a reflection over a line that is parallel to the direction of the translation. You get the same result whether you do the translation first and then the reflection or the reflection first and then the translation.

Need More HELP

For help with translations, go to *Translations* on pp. 834–837.

EXAMPLE 1

Find the image of this triangle after the translation $(x, y) \rightarrow (x + 5, y)$ and then reflection over the x-axis.

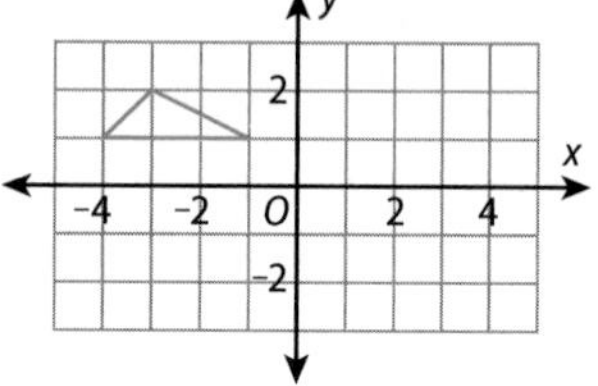

STEP 1 Translate each vertex of the triangle by adding 5 to the x-coordinate.

$(-4, 1) \rightarrow (1, 1)$

$(-3, 2) \rightarrow (2, 2)$

$(-1, 1) \rightarrow (4, 1)$

The result is the red triangle.

STEP 2 Reflect the red triangle over the x-axis. Remember that when you reflect a point (x, y) over the x-axis, $(x, y) \rightarrow (x, -y)$.

$(1, 1) \rightarrow (1, -1)$

$(2, 2) \rightarrow (2, -2)$

$(4, 1) \rightarrow (4, -1)$

The composition of the two transformations is a glide reflection because the line of reflection is parallel to the direction of the translation.

Need More HELP

For help with reflecting over a line, go to *Reflections* on pp. 838–841.

EXAMPLE 2

Describe the glide reflection used to translate the blue pre-image to the green image.

STEP 1 Find the reflection first.

To change the pre-image so it faces the same way as the image, it must be reflected over the y-axis.

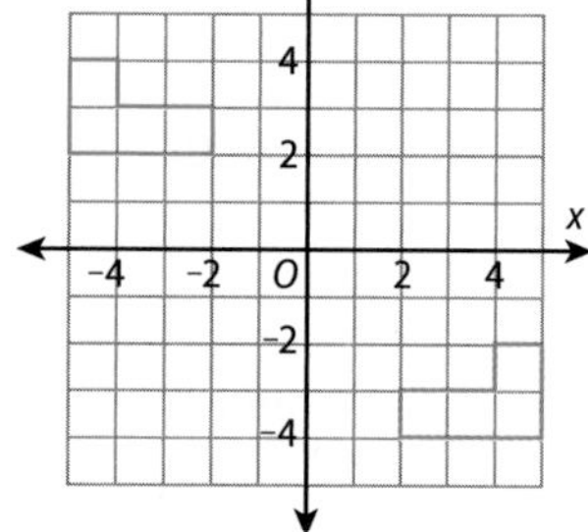

STEP 2 Choose corresponding points and figure out how many units right or left and how many units up or down the translation needs to be.

The red figure is then translated 6 units down to get to the green figure. The translation is $(x, y) \rightarrow (x, y - 6)$.

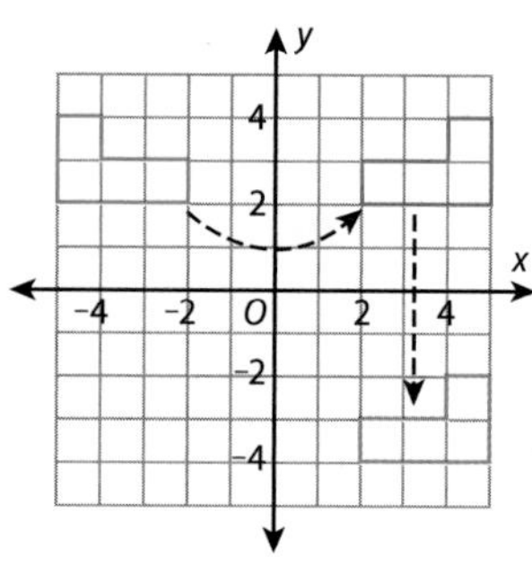

The translation is $(x, y) \rightarrow (x, y - 6)$. The reflection is over the y-axis. The line of reflection is parallel to the direction of the translation.

Order of Composition

The order in which transformations in a composition are performed can affect the final image.

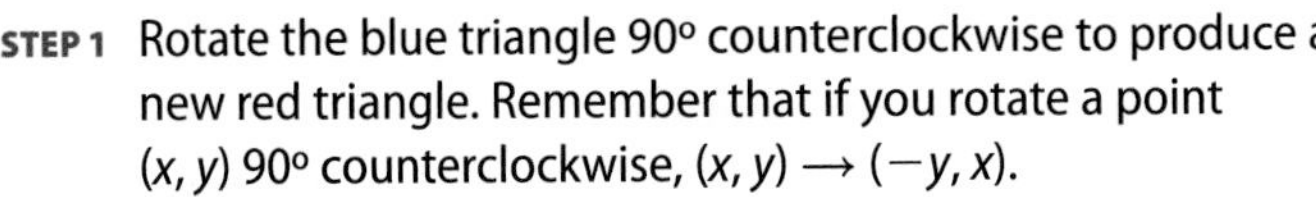

EXAMPLE 3

In this composition, the blue pre-image was reflected over the *y*-axis to produce the red image and then rotated about the origin 90° counterclockwise to produce the green image. If you do the transformations in the opposite order, what are the vertices of the image? Does the order that the transformations are performed make a difference?

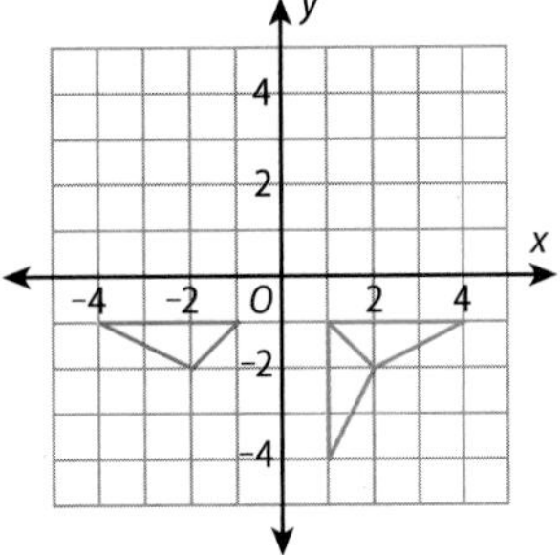

STEP 1 Rotate the blue triangle 90° counterclockwise to produce a new red triangle. Remember that if you rotate a point (x, y) 90° counterclockwise, $(x, y) \rightarrow (-y, x)$.

$(1, -1) \rightarrow (1, 1)$

$(4, -1) \rightarrow (1, 4)$

$(2, -2) \rightarrow (2, 2)$

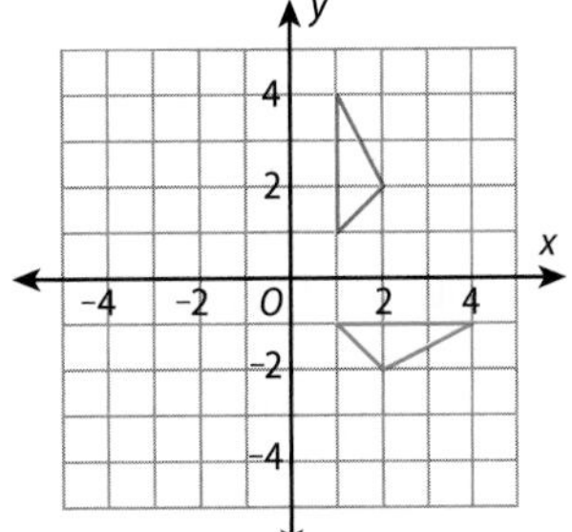

STEP 2 Reflect the red triangle over the *y*-axis. Remember that if you reflect a point (x, y) over the *y*-axis, $(x, y) \rightarrow (-x, y)$.

$(1, 1) \rightarrow (-1, 1)$

$(1, 4) \rightarrow (-1, 4)$

$(2, 2) \rightarrow (-2, 2)$

The vertices of the image for this composition are:

$(-1, 1), (-1, 4), (-2, 2)$

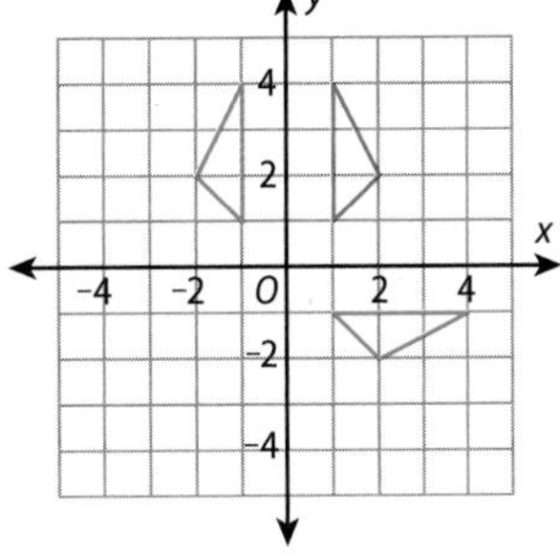

Compare the diagram at the top of the page with the diagram at the right. The order that the transformations are performed does make a difference. The green triangle is in a different location from when the transformations were performed in the reverse order.

Need More HELP

For help with rotations, go to *Rotations* on pp. 842–845.

SEARCH

To see step-by-step videos of these problems, enter the page number into the SWadvantage.com Search Bar.

Composition of Transformations

When two or more transformations are performed one after another, the result is called a composition.

The order in which transformations in a composition are performed can affect the final image. For a glide reflection, the result is the same whether you do the translation first and then the reflection or the reflection first and then the translation.

Regular Tessellations

A **tessellation** is an arrangement of shapes that cover the plane with no overlaps and no gaps. A tessellation is said to **tessellate** the plane. A tessellation consisting of congruent copies of a regular polygon is called a **regular tessellation**.

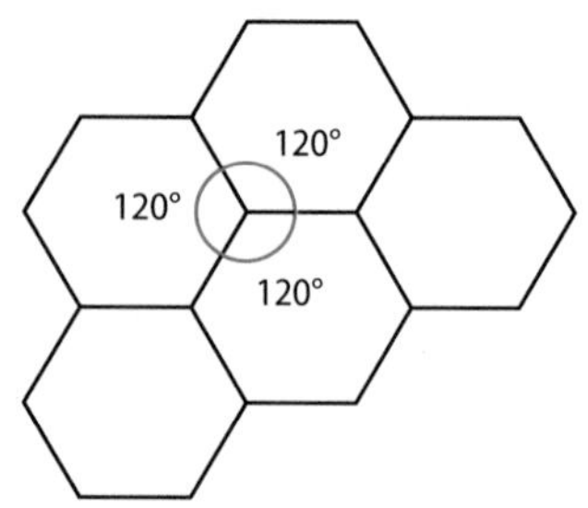

These hexagons form a regular tessellation. The measure of each interior angle of a regular hexagon is 120°. Notice that the sum of the measures of the interior angles at each vertex of the tessellation is 360°.

EXAMPLE 1

Which regular polygons can be used to form a regular tessellation?

STEP 1 Find the measures of the interior angles of regular polygons with 8 or fewer sides.

STEP 2 For each of the regular polygons in the table, divide 360° by the measure of the interior angles.

Number of Sides	Interior Angle	$\frac{360°}{\text{Interior Angle}}$
3	60°	6
4	90°	4
5	108°	$3\frac{1}{3}$
6	120°	3
7	$128\frac{4}{7}°$	2.8
8	135°	$2\frac{2}{3}$

A whole number of copies of the regular polygon must meet at each vertex of a tessellation to form a 360° angle; otherwise there will be a gap or overlap. So 360° divided by the measure of the interior angles of the polygon must be a whole number. The whole number tells how many of that polygon will meet at each vertex.

At least 3 regular polygons must meet at each vertex. If a regular polygon has more than 6 sides, then the measure of its interior angles is greater than 120°. So the sum of the measures at each vertex would be more than 360°. Therefore, the only regular polygons that can be used to form a regular tessellation are those with 3, 4, or 6 sides; in other words, equilateral triangles, squares, or regular hexagons.

Need More HELP

Remember—the formula for finding the measure of the interior angle of a regular polygon with n sides is: $\frac{180(n-2)}{n}$.

GOT TO KNOW!

Tessellations

A tessellation is an arrangement of shapes that cover the plane with no overlaps and no gaps.

A tessellation of congruent copies of a regular polygon is called a regular tessellation. There are only three polygons that can form regular tessellations: equilateral triangles, squares, and hexagons. These diagrams show the way each type of shape can fit together to cover the whole plane.

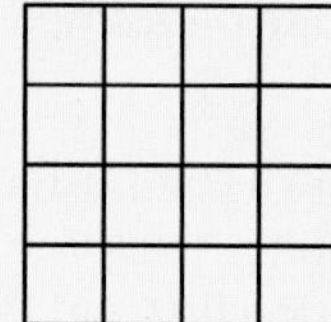

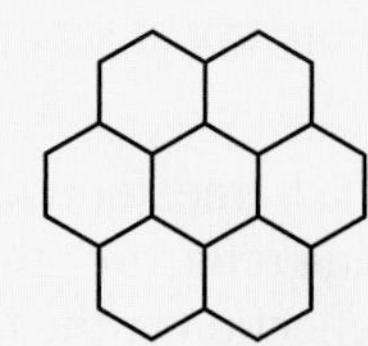

Semi-Regular Tessellations

A tessellation is a **semi-regular tessellation** if it consists of more than one type of regular polygon and the arrangement of polygons is the same at each vertex. The tessellation shown here is a semi-regular tessellation.

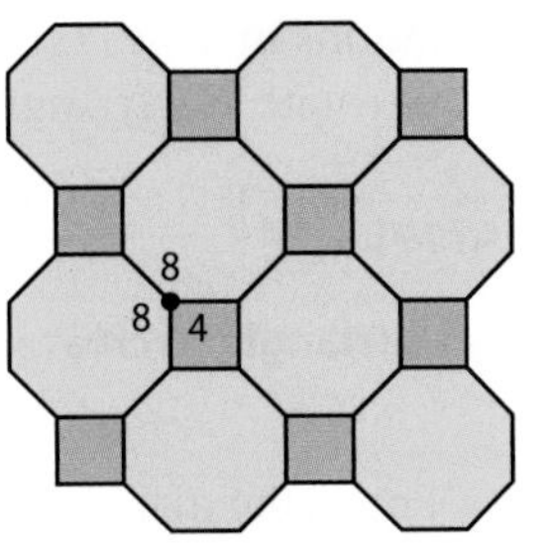

A vertex of a tessellation can be described by the number of sides of the polygons that meet at the vertex. For example, the vertex arrangement of a tessellation of equilateral triangles, shown on the previous page, is 3-3-3-3-3-3 because there are six equilateral triangles that meet at each vertex. The vertex arrangement of the tessellation shown here is 4-8-8 because a square, a regular octagon, and another regular octagon meet at each vertex. To describe a vertex arrangement, start with the number of sides of the polygon with the fewest sides.

Need More HELP

For help with rotations, go to *Rotations* on pp. 842–845.

EXAMPLE 2

Describe the vertex arrangement of this semi-regular tessellation.

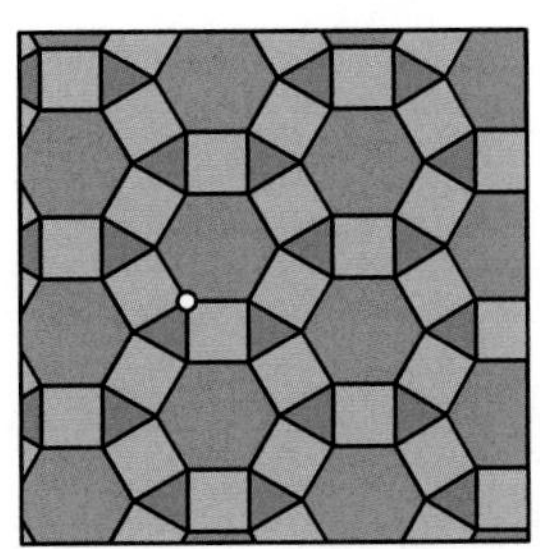

Since you know this is a semi-regular tessellation, you know that the arrangement of polygons is the same at each vertex. The triangle has the fewest sides, so the first number is 3. The next shape is a square, the next is a hexagon, and the last is another square.

So the vertex arrangement is 3-4-6-4.

SEARCH

To see step-by-step videos of these problems, enter the page number into the SWadvantage.com Search Bar.

EXAMPLE 3

Is this tessellation regular, semi-regular, or neither?

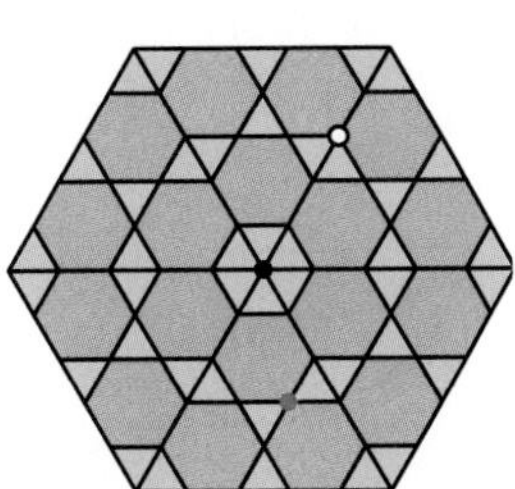

STEP 1 Decide whether the tessellation is regular.

All the shapes are regular congruent polygons, but there is more than one type of polygon, so the tessellation is not regular.

STEP 2 Decide whether the tessellation is semi-regular.

The arrangement of polygons is not the same at each vertex. The vertex arrangement at the vertex marked with the white dot is 3-3-6-6. The vertex arrangement at the vertex marked with the black dot is 3-3-3-3-3-3. The vertex arrangement at the vertex marked with the red dot is 3-6-3-6. So this is not a semi-regular tessellation.

This tessellation is neither regular nor semi-regular.

Tessellations with Triangles and Quadrilaterals

Tessellations may be composed of triangles and quadrilaterals that are not regular polygons. You can rotate any triangle and any quadrilateral to create a figure that tessellates.

SEARCH

To see step-by-step videos of these problems, enter the page number into the SWadvantage.com Search Bar.

EXAMPLE 4

Use this triangle to create a tessellation.

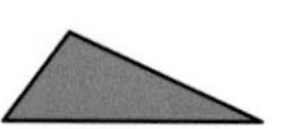

STEP 1 Rotate the triangle about the midpoint of its longest side to make a parallelogram.

STEP 2 Make copies of the parallelogram and translate them to create a tessellation.

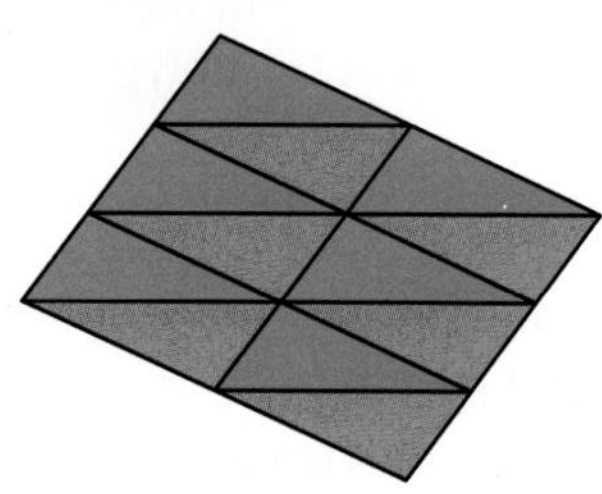

EXAMPLE 5

Use this quadrilateral to create a tessellation.

Rotating a quadrilateral about the midpoints of its sides creates a figure that will tessellate.

STEP 1 Rotate copies of the quadrilateral about the midpoints of each of its sides like this:

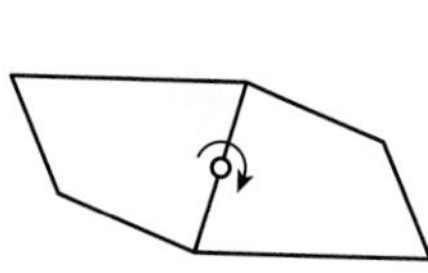

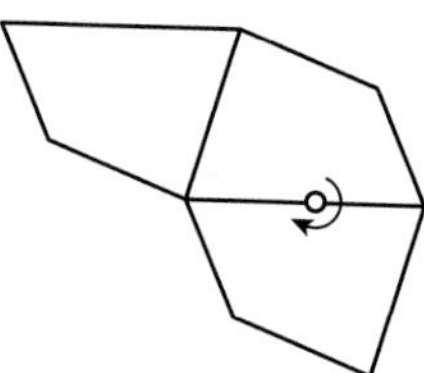

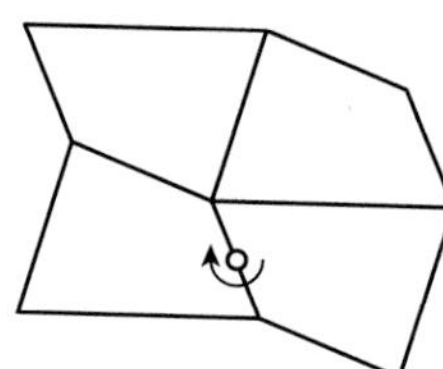

STEP 2 Make copies of the new figure and translate them to create a tessellation.

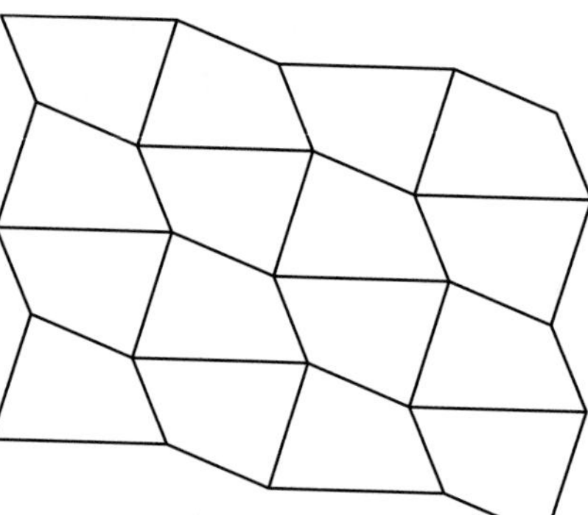

Tessellations with Figures That Are Not Polygons

There are many ways to create tessellations. One way is to start with a polygon that tessellates.

Use this parallelogram to create a tessellation.

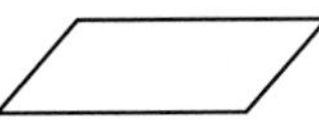

METHOD 1

Make a Drawing

STEP 1 Copy the parallelogram. Draw a curve to replace one side of the parallelogram.

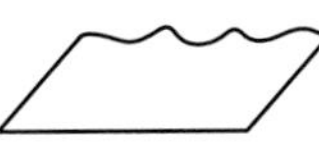

STEP 2 Copy the curve and use it to replace the opposite side.

STEP 3 Draw a curve to replace one of the remaining parallel sides.

STEP 4 Copy the curve and use it to replace the opposite side.

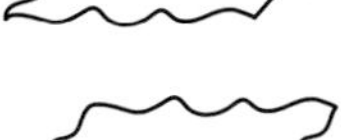

STEP 5 Copy the figure over and over to create a tessellation.

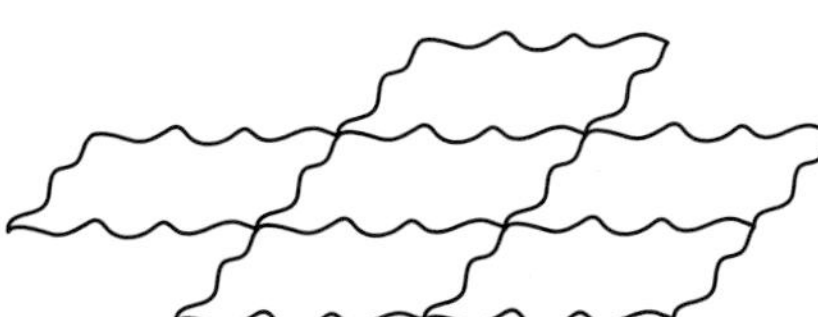

METHOD 2

Cut and Tape

You can use the diagrams for each step above to guide you for the corresponding step in Method 2.

STEP 1 Copy the parallelogram on paper. Cut out the parallelogram by cutting along its sides. Cut a curve out of one side of the parallelogram.

STEP 2 Tape the piece you cut off to the opposite side.

STEP 3 Cut a curve from one of the remaining parallel sides.

STEP 4 Tape the piece you cut off to the opposite side.

STEP 5 Copy the figure over and over and create a tessellation.

For help with rotations, go to *Rotations* on pp. 842–845.

Constructions

What Came Before?

- Measurement and congruence of segments and angles
- Characteristics of parallel and perpendicular lines

What's This About?

- Using a compass and a straightedge to draw segments, angles, and lines
- Bisecting angles and line segments
- Constructing triangles within and outside of circles

Practical Apps

- Product designers, drafters and architects use constructions for blueprints.
- Origami figures are made by folding paper and using the properties of geometric construction.

just for FUN!

Q: What do you call your geometry class during this unit?

A: A construction site.

CONTENTS UPLOAD DOWNLOAD

Geometry

You can find more practice problems online by visiting:
www.SWadvantage.com

Congruent Segments

Constructing a Congruent Segment

A **construction** is a geometric drawing that is made using only a straightedge and a compass. It is understood that you are also allowed to use a pencil or a pen. Anything that can be used to draw a straight line is a straightedge. When you are making a construction, you are not allowed to measure angles with a protractor or to measure lengths with a ruler.

EXAMPLE 1

Construct a segment congruent to segment $\overline{AB}$.

A B

STEP 1 Use a straightedge to draw a segment longer than $\overline{AB}$. Label one of the endpoints of the new segment as C.

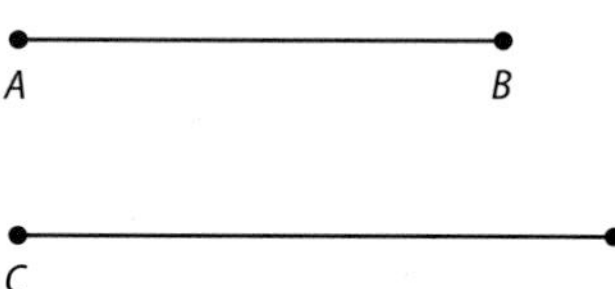

STEP 2 Set your compass at the length of $\overline{AB}$.

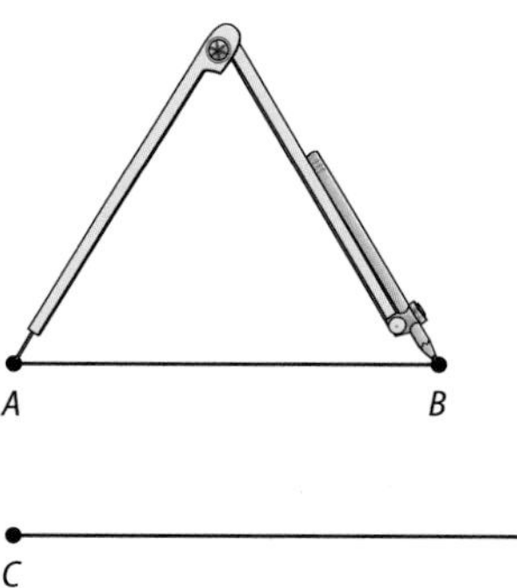

C

STEP 3 Keep the compass adjusted to the same radius, and place the compass point on C. Draw an arc intersecting the new segment. Label the point of intersection of the arc and the segment as D. Then $\overline{CD}$ is congruent to $\overline{AB}$.

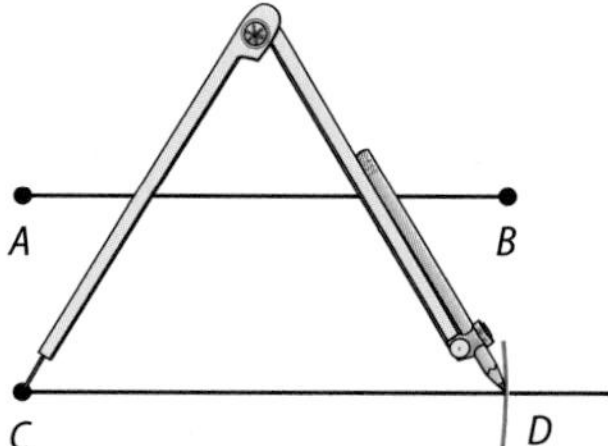

The distance between the compass point and the pencil point in Steps 2 and 3 is the length of the original segment, so the measure of the original segment and the measure of the constructed segment are the same.

Draw a segment *EF*. Measure its length.

Use a ruler to draw another segment the same length as segment *EF*.

Construct a third segment congruent to segment *EF* using a straightedge and compass.

Compare the segment you drew by measuring with a ruler with the segment you drew using a straightedge and compass.

Adding Segments

If you know how to construct congruent segments, you can do other constructions.

EXAMPLE 2

Construct a segment the length of which is equal to the sum of the lengths of $\overline{AB}$ and $\overline{CD}$.

A B

C D

STEP 1 Use a straightedge to draw a segment that is longer than the sum of the lengths of $\overline{AB}$ and $\overline{CD}$. Label one of the endpoints of the segment as *G*.

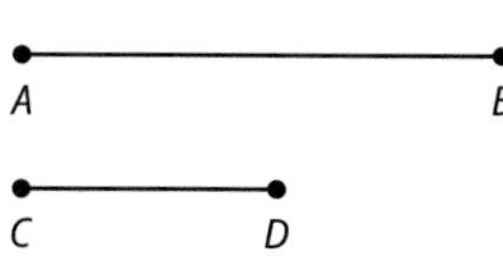

G

STEP 2 Set the compass at the length of $\overline{AB}$. Put the compass point on *G*. Draw an arc with radius *AB* intersecting the new segment.

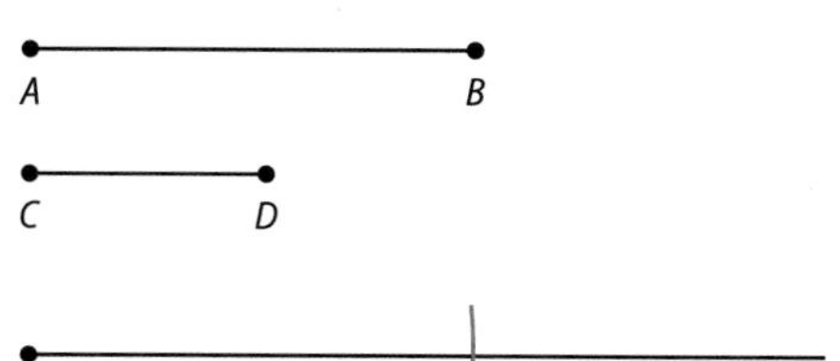

STEP 3 Set the compass radius at the length of $\overline{CD}$.

Place the compass point on the point of intersection of the arc and the segment.

Draw a new arc intersecting the segment as shown.

Label the point where the new arc intersects the segment as *H*.

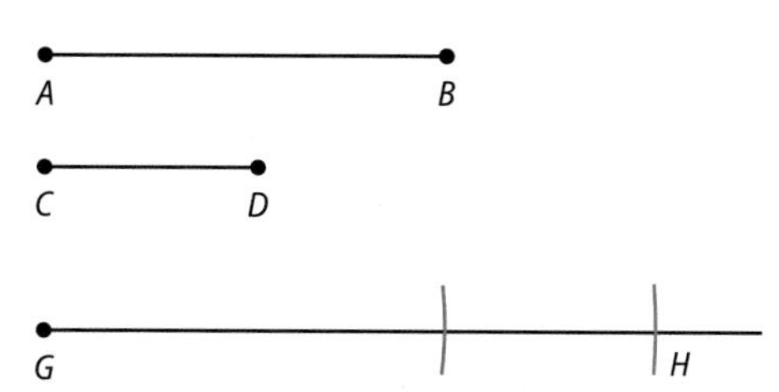

The length of $\overline{GH}$ is equal to the sum of the lengths of $\overline{AB}$ and $\overline{CD}$. In symbols, $GH = AB + CD$.

SEARCH

To see step-by-step videos of these problems, enter the page number into the SWadvantage.com Search Bar.

Congruent Angles

Copying an Angle

You can copy any angle using a compass and straightedge.

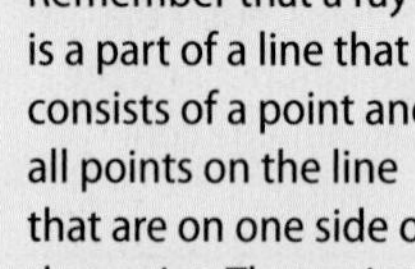

Remember that a ray is a part of a line that consists of a point and all points on the line that are on one side of that point. That point is called the endpoint of the ray.

To see step-by-step videos of these problems, enter the page number into the SWadvantage.com Search Bar.

EXAMPLE 1

Construct an angle congruent to angle *A*.

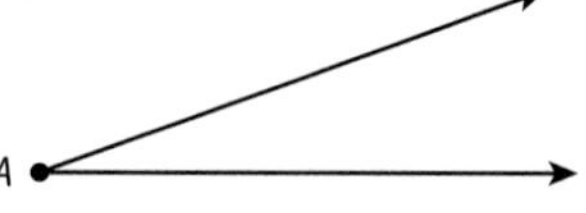

STEP 1 Use a straightedge to draw a ray. Label the endpoint *P*.

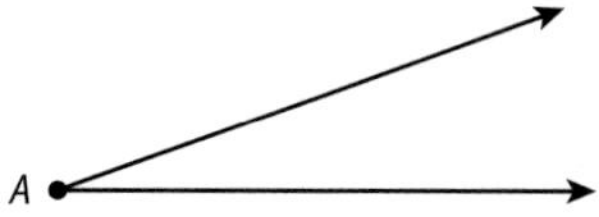

STEP 2 Set the radius of the compass at any convenient length. Place the compass point on *A*. Draw an arc that intersects both rays of the angle. Label the points where the arc crosses the rays as *B* and *C*.

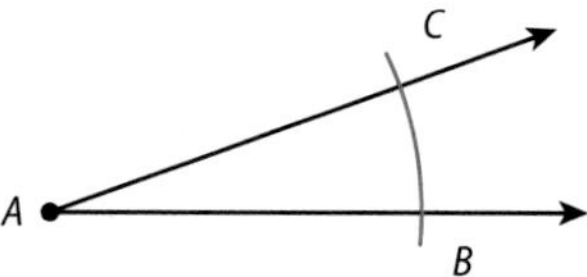

STEP 3 Without changing the compass setting, place the point of the compass on *P* and draw an arc. Label the point where the arc crosses the ray as *Q*.

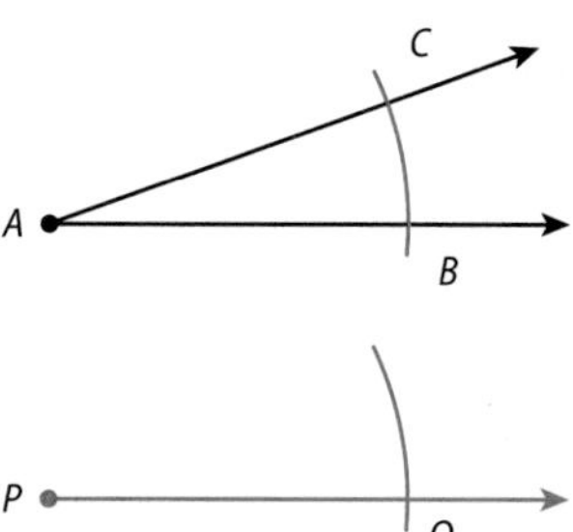

STEP 4 Place the point of the compass on B, and set it so the pencil point is on C.

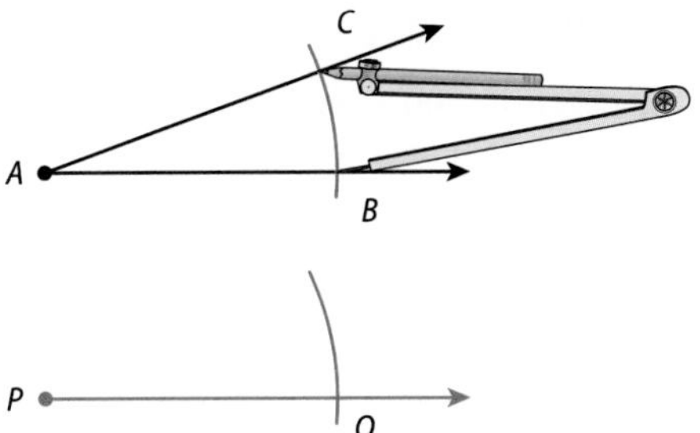

STEP 5 Without changing the compass setting, place the point of the compass on Q and draw an arc intersecting the first arc. Label the point where the arcs intersect R.

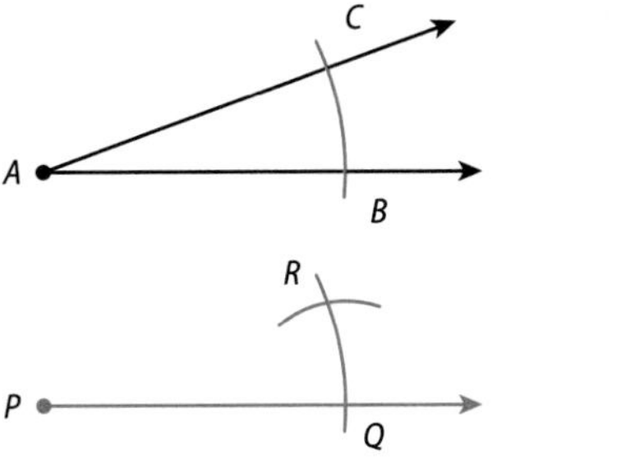

STEP 6 Use a straightedge to draw a ray with endpoint P that passes through R.

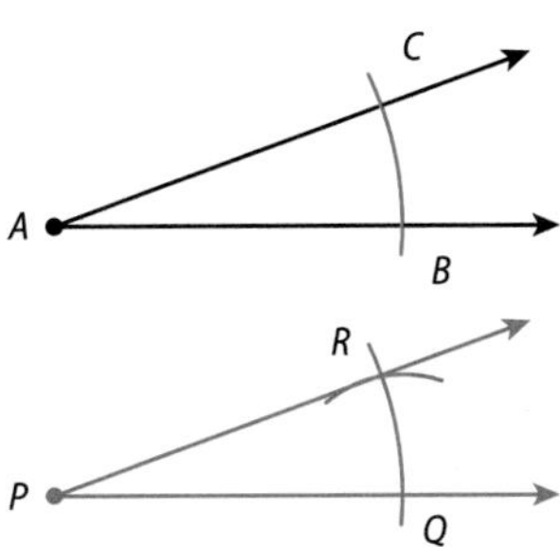

Angle P is congruent to angle A.

Form triangles by drawing a segment connecting B and C, and a segment connecting Q and R. You can prove that angle P is congruent to angle A by using SSS, the Side-Side-Side Congruence Postulate.

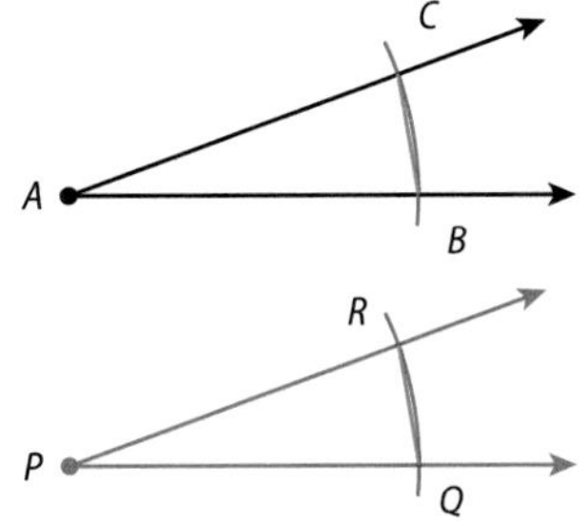

$\overline{AB} \cong \overline{PQ}$ because the radius of the arc with its center at A is the same as the radius of the arc with its center at P. For a similar reason, $\overline{AC} \cong \overline{PR}$. Because of the way point R was obtained, $\overline{BC} \cong \overline{QR}$. Therefore, $\triangle CAB \cong \triangle RPQ$. $\angle A$ and $\angle P$ are corresponding angles. Hence $\angle A \cong \angle P$.

Need More HELP

For help with using the Side-Side-Side Congruence Postulate, see *Using SSS and SAS* on page 768.

Constructing a Perpendicular Bisector

A **perpendicular bisector of a segment** is a line, ray, or segment that is perpendicular to the given segment at its midpoint.

EXAMPLE 1

Construct a perpendicular bisector of the segment on the right.

STEP 1 Place the compass on one endpoint of the segment. Open the compass to about two-thirds the length of the segment.

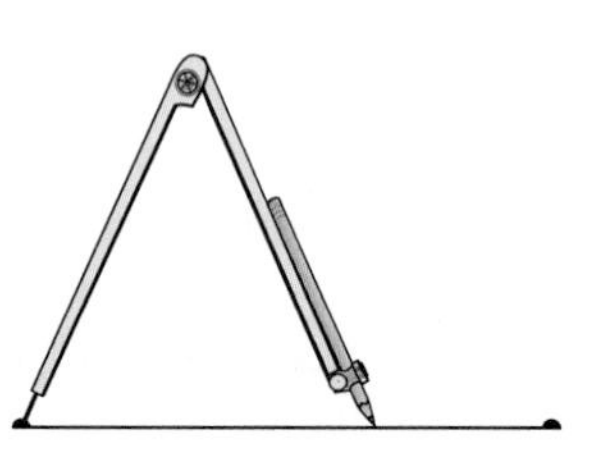

STEP 2 Draw an arc on each side of the segment.

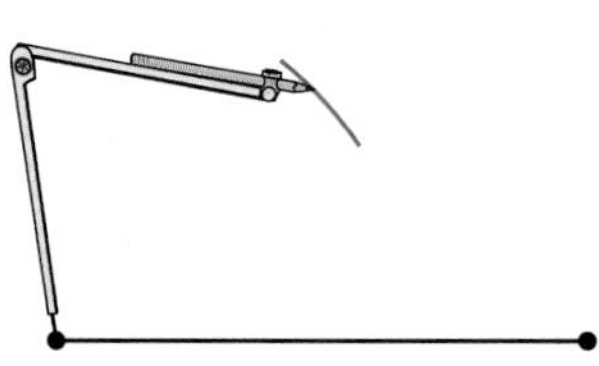

STEP 3 Without changing the compass setting, place the point on the other endpoint of the segment and draw two arcs that intersect the first arcs.

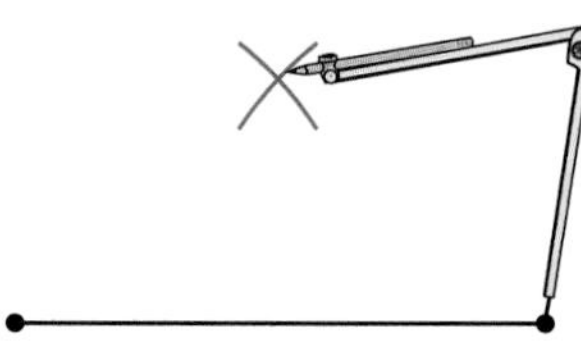

STEP 4 Use a straightedge to draw a line through the two points where the arcs intersect.

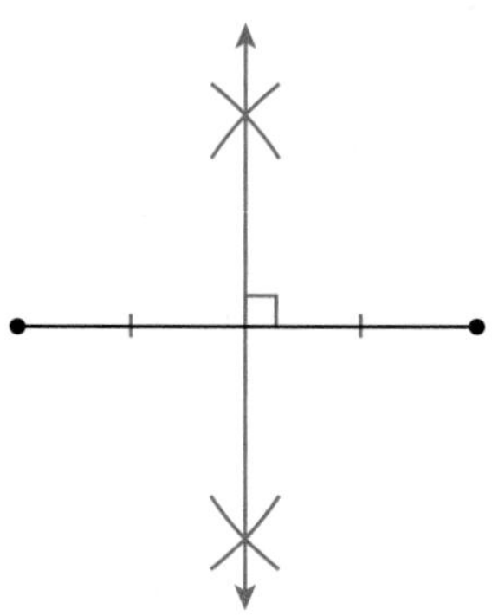

The line is perpendicular to the segment and intersects the segment at its midpoint.

Remember that the midpoint of a segment divides a segment into two congruent parts.

Constructing the Median of a Triangle

A **median of a triangle** is a line segment connecting a vertex of the triangle with the midpoint of the side opposite that vertex. Each triangle has three medians.

EXAMPLE 2

Construct a median of this triangle.

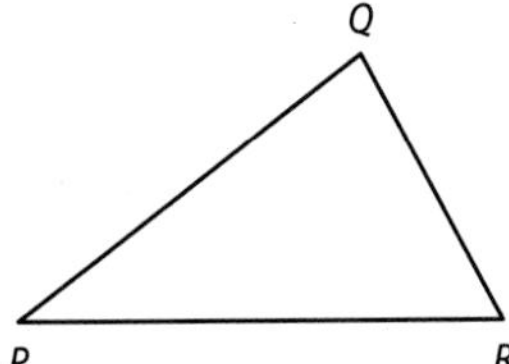

STEP 1 Choose a side of the triangle and construct a perpendicular bisector of that side, following the steps of Example 1.

In this example, a perpendicular bisector of $\overline{PQ}$ is constructed.

The point where the segment crosses $\overline{PQ}$ is its midpoint.

Label the midpoint *S*.

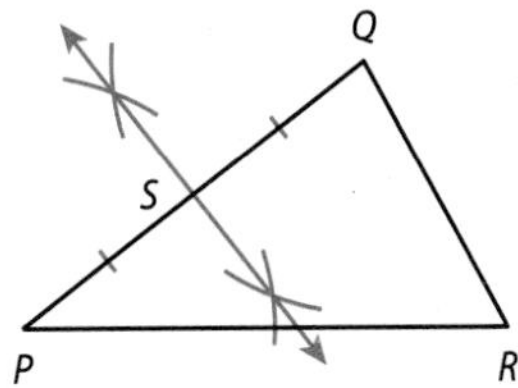

STEP 2 Use a straightedge to draw a segment from *S* to the angle opposite side $\overline{PQ}$, angle *R*.

Segment *RS* is a median of triangle *PQR*.

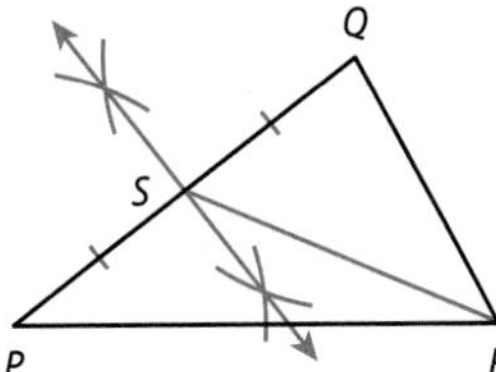

SEARCH To see step-by-step videos of these problems, enter the page number into the SWadvantage.com Search Bar.

Segment *RS* is one of the three medians of triangle *PQR*. You can construct the other two medians by following Steps 1–2 for each of the other two sides of the triangle.

The medians of a triangle have a special property, which you will explore in Example 3.

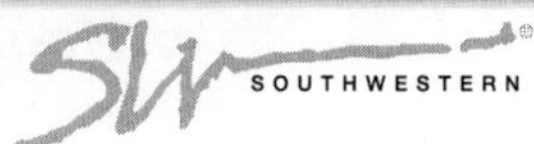

Constructing the Centroid of a Triangle

The three medians of a triangle meet at a single point. The point is called the **centroid** of the triangle. The centroid is the balancing point of the triangle.

EXAMPLE 3

Find the centroid of this triangle.

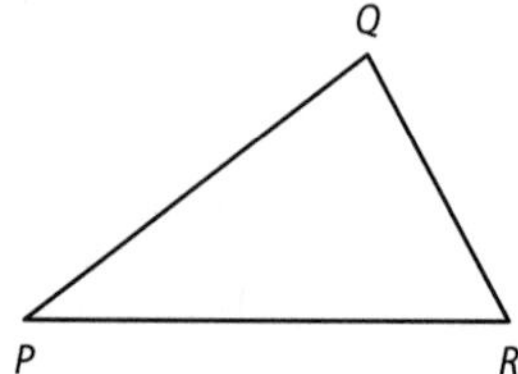

STEP 1 Construct the median to one side of the triangle. Example 2 shows how to construct the median to side $\overline{PQ}$.

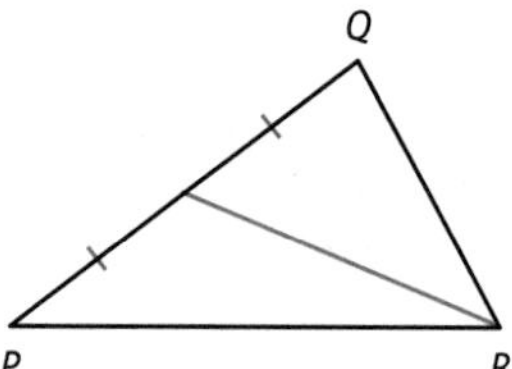

STEP 2 Construct the median to another side of the triangle.

The point where the two medians intersect is the centroid of the triangle. It is not necessary to draw all three medians to find the centroid. Continue with Step 3 to illustrate that all three medians meet at the centroid.

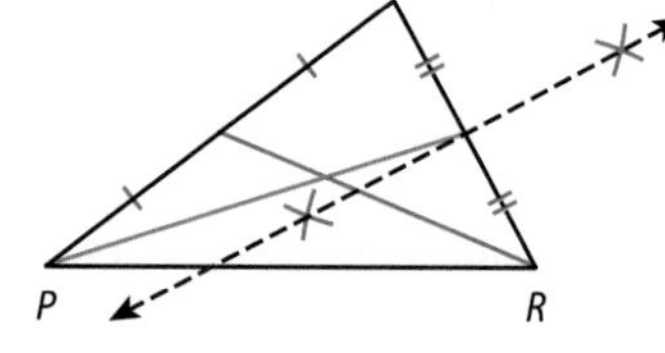

STEP 3 Construct the median to the remaining side of the triangle.

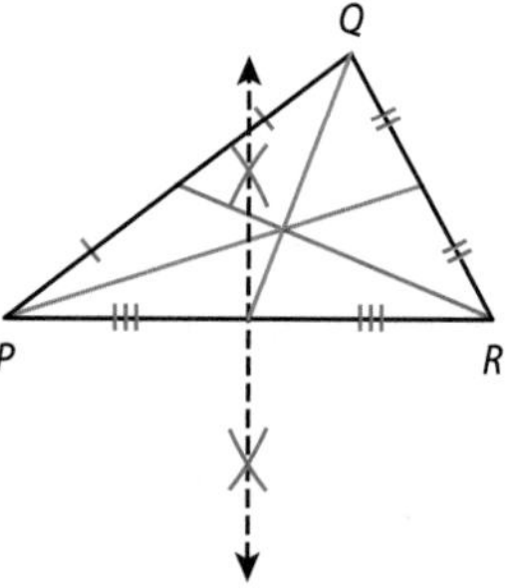

The centroid of the triangle is the point where the medians of the three sides of the triangle meet.

Draw a triangle on paper using a straightedge. Construct the centroid of the triangle using a compass and straightedge. Cut out the triangle and trace its outline on cardboard or stiff paper. Cut along the outline to make a model of the triangle. Find and mark the point on which the triangular model will balance on the tip of a pencil. Compare the centroid of the triangle with the point on which the triangular model balances.

Three or more lines in the same plane that intersect at the same point are called **concurrent lines**. The point of intersection of the lines is called the **point of concurrency**. The centroid of a triangle is one example of a point of concurrency. Here is another example of concurrent lines. The colored lines meet at the point of concurrency.

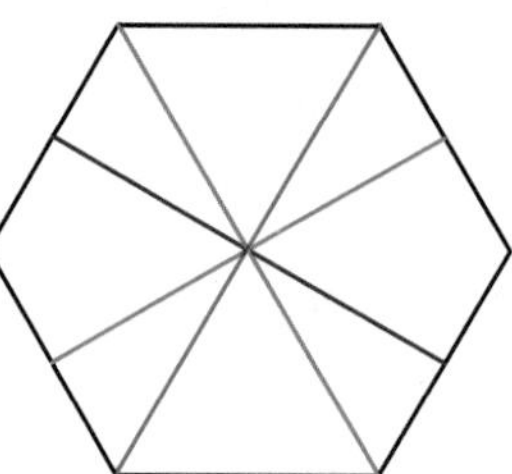

Distance of the Centroid from the Vertices

EXAMPLE 4

The figure shows the medians of the triangle. For each median, find this ratio:

$$\frac{\textbf{Distance from the vertex to the centroid}}{\textbf{Length of the median}}$$

What conclusion can you draw?

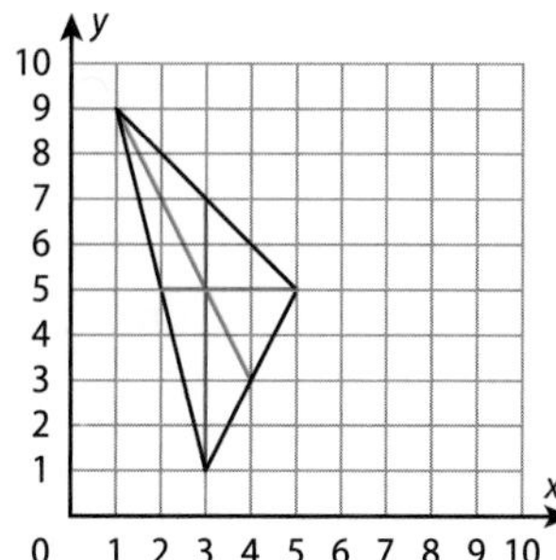

STEP 1 Find the ratio for the blue median.

$$\frac{4 \text{ units}}{6 \text{ units}} = \frac{2}{3}$$

STEP 2 Find the ratio for the red median.

$$\frac{2 \text{ units}}{3 \text{ units}} = \frac{2}{3}$$

STEP 3 Find the ratio for the green median.

Use the distance formula. The vertex is at (1, 9), the centroid is at (3, 5), and the midpoint of the opposite side is at (4, 3). The distance from the vertex to the centroid is given by

$$\sqrt{(x_2 - x_1)^2 + (y_2 - y_1)^2} = \sqrt{(1 - 3)^2 + (9 - 5)^2} = \sqrt{4 + 16} = \sqrt{20} = 2\sqrt{5}$$

The length of the median is given by

$$\sqrt{(x_2 - x_1)^2 + (y_2 - y_1)^2} = \sqrt{(1 - 4)^2 + (9 - 3)^2} = \sqrt{9 + 36} = \sqrt{45} = 3\sqrt{5}$$

The ratio for the green median is given by

$$\frac{2\sqrt{5}}{3\sqrt{5}} = \frac{2}{3}$$

Therefore, the centroid of the triangle is two-thirds of the distance from each vertex to the midpoint of the opposite side.

SEARCH

To see step-by-step videos of these problems, enter the page number into the SWadvantage.com Search Bar.

The property that is true for the triangle in Example 4 is true for every triangle: In any triangle the medians intersect at a point that is two-thirds of the distance from each vertex to the midpoint of the opposite side.

GOT TO KNOW!

Location of Centroids

The centroid of any triangle is two-thirds of the distance from each vertex to the midpoint of the opposite side.

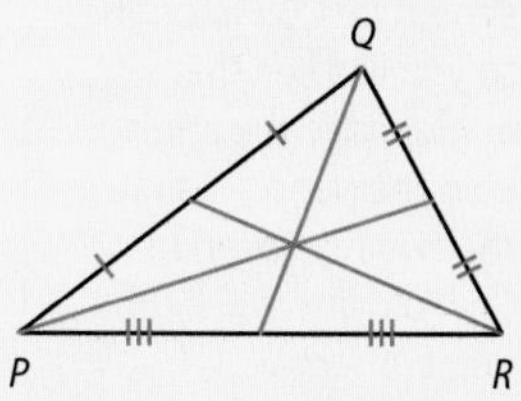

Angle Bisector

Bisecting an Angle

An **angle bisector** is a ray that divides an angle into two adjacent angles that are congruent.

EXAMPLE 1

Use a compass and a straightedge to bisect angle *A*.

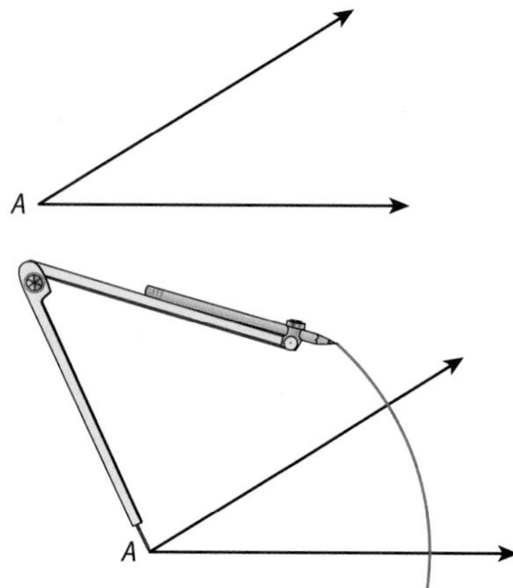

STEP 1 Place the compass point on vertex *A*. Draw an arc that intersects both rays.

STEP 2 Move the compass point to the intersection of one of the rays and the arc. Draw an arc on the interior of the angle.

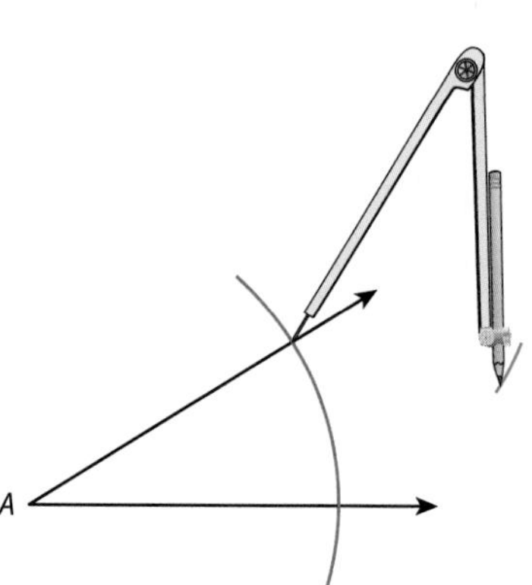

STEP 3 Without changing the compass setting, move the point of the compass to the other point of intersection of the other ray and the arc. Draw another arc that intersects the arc that you drew in Step 2.

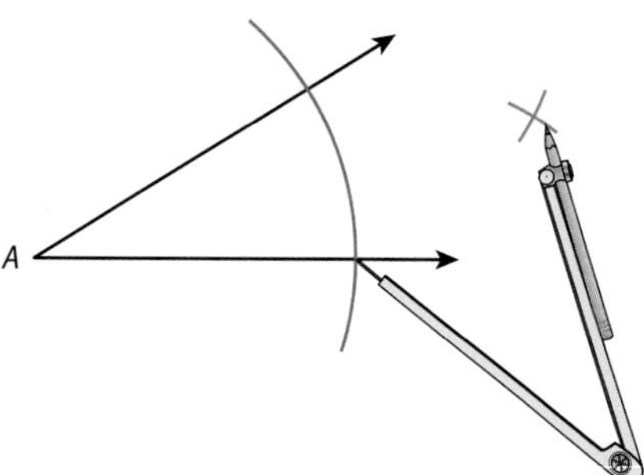

STEP 4 Use a straightedge to draw a ray from vertex *A* through the point where the two arcs intersect. The ray is the angle bisector of angle *A*.

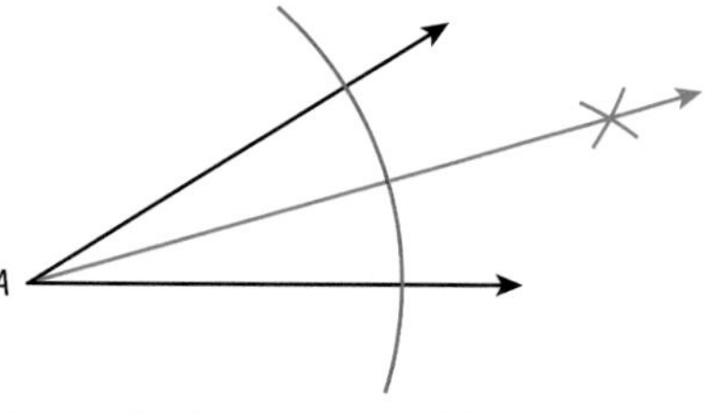

Try It This Way

Place a piece of paper over an angle to be bisected. The paper should be thin enough so you can see the angle. Trace the angle. Fold the paper so that the two rays overlap. The fold line will be the angle bisector.

Dividing an Angle into Four Congruent Parts

You can divide an angle into four congruent angles by bisecting the angle and then bisecting each of the resulting angles, using the method in Example 1.

EXAMPLE 2

Use a compass and straightedge to divide this angle into four congruent angles.

STEP 1 Put the point of the compass on the vertex and draw an arc that crosses both rays.

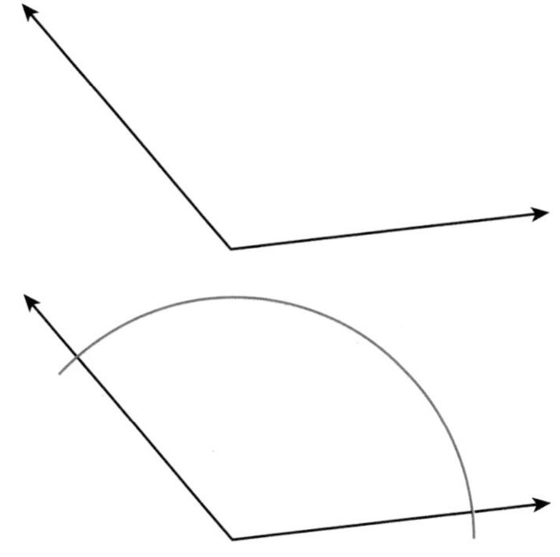

STEP 2 Draw arcs from the intersection of the first arc and each ray to construct an angle bisector as shown in Example 1.

The angle is now divided into two congruent angles.

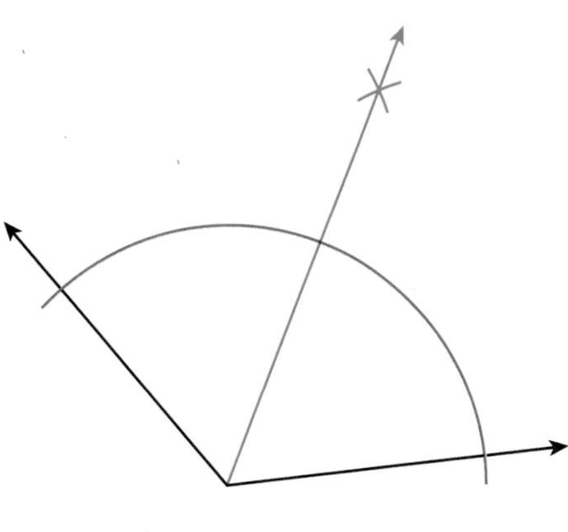

STEP 3 Bisect each of the two congruent angles using the same process.

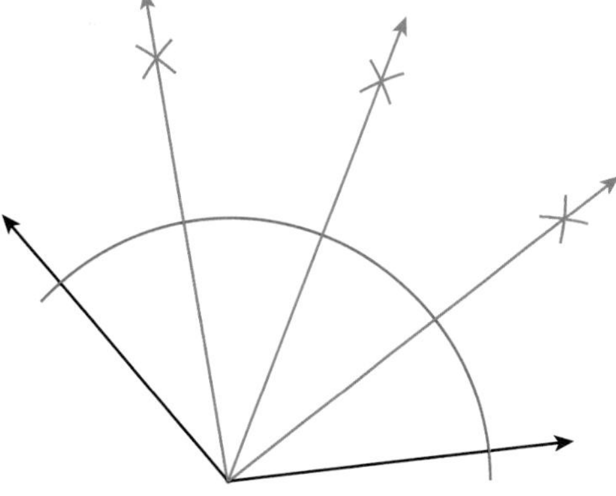

The angle is now divided into four congruent angles.

SEARCH

To see step-by-step videos of these problems, enter the page number into the SWadvantage.com Search Bar.

Perpendicular Line Through a Point on a Line

A compass and straightedge can be used to construct a line that is perpendicular to a given line and passes through a point on the line.

Try It This Way

Start with a line drawn on a piece of paper and a point *P* on the line. Fold the piece of paper so that the fold passes through point *P* and the parts of the line on either side of *P* overlap. The fold line will be perpendicular to the given line, and it will pass through the point *P*.

EXAMPLE 1

Construct a line perpendicular to the given line at point *P*.

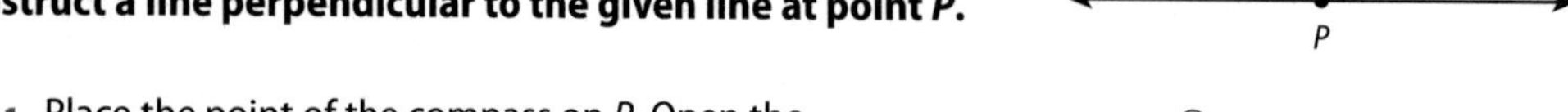

STEP 1 Place the point of the compass on *P*. Open the compass and draw an arc intersecting the line on either side of *P*.

Label the points of intersection *Q* and *R*.

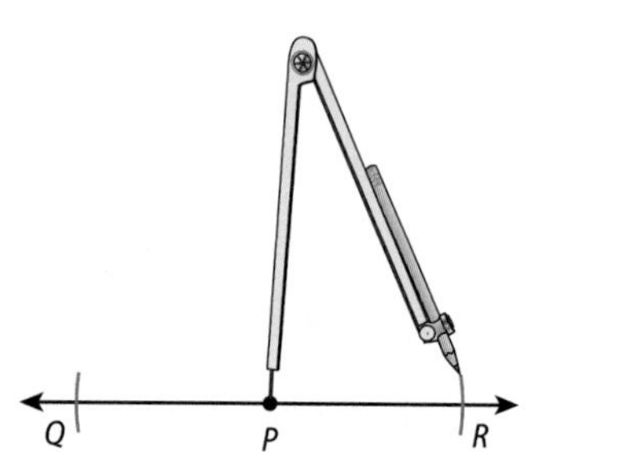

STEP 2 Widen the compass setting. Place the point of the compass on *Q*, and draw an arc above the line.

With the compass at the same setting, place the point of the compass on *R* and draw an arc above the line.

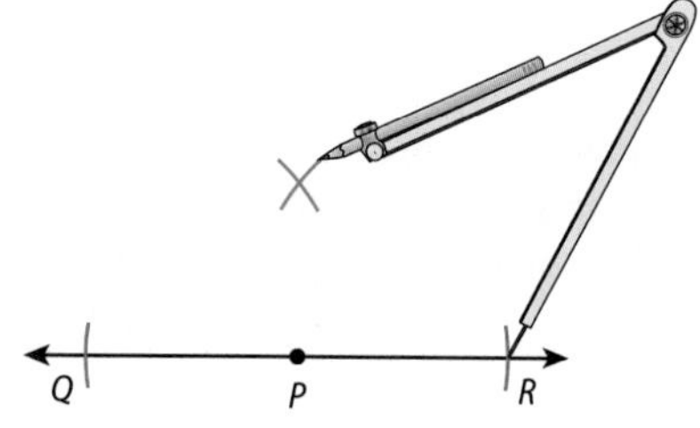

STEP 3 Use a straightedge to draw a line that passes through *P* and the point of intersection of the two arcs.

The line is perpendicular to the given line at point *P*.

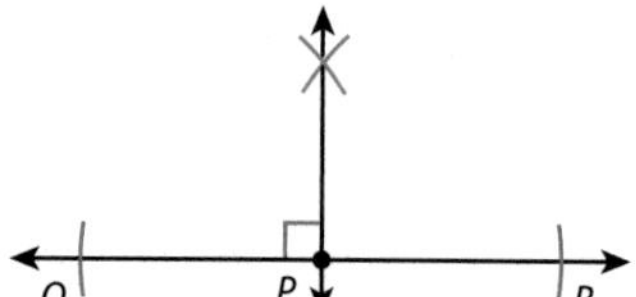

Perpendicular Line Through a Point Not on a Line

You can also use a compass and straightedge to construct a line that is perpendicular to a given line and passes through a point that is not on the line.

EXAMPLE 2

Construct a line perpendicular to the given line through point *K*.

K

STEP 1 Place the point of the compass on *K*.

Open the compass so that it is greater than the distance from *K* to the line.

Draw arcs across the line on each side of *K*.

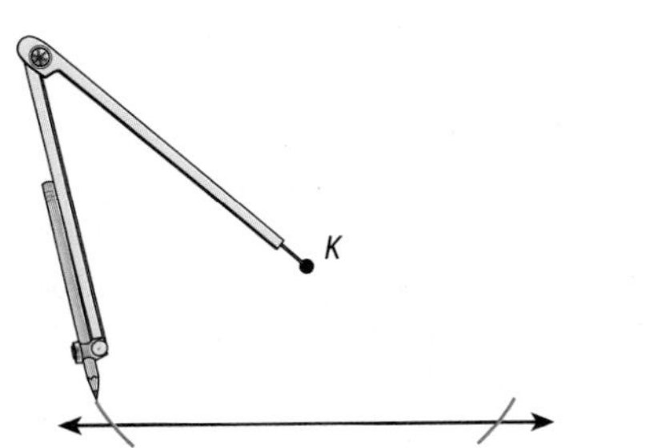

STEP 2 Do not change the compass setting. From the point where each arc intersects the line, draw an arc below the line so that the arcs intersect.

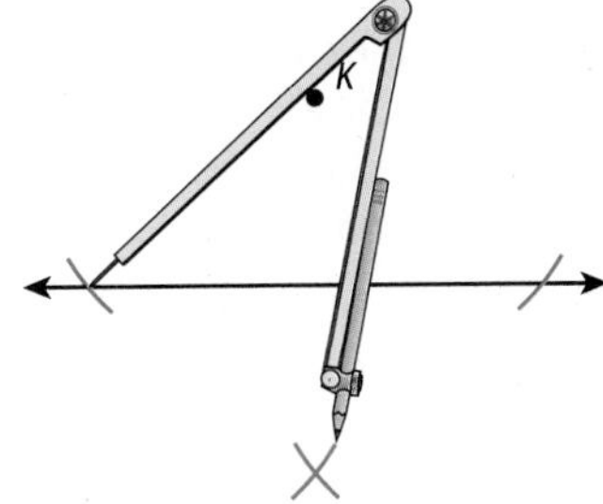

STEP 3 Use a straightedge to draw a line passing through *K* and the point where the arcs intersect.

This line is perpendicular to the original line and passes through point *K*, *which is not on the line.*

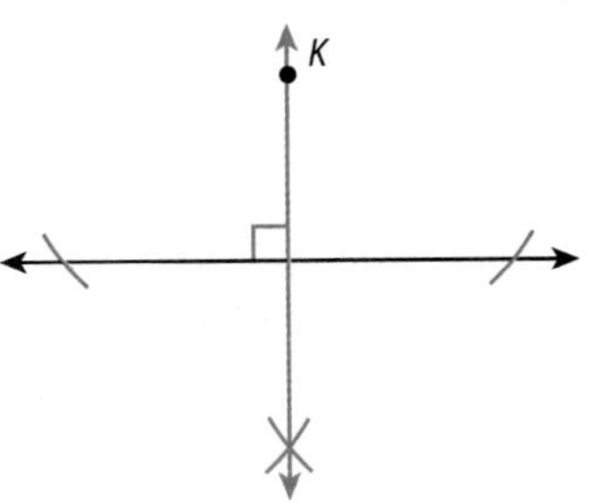

SEARCH

To see step-by-step videos of these problems, enter the page number into the SWadvantage.com Search Bar.

Constructing the Altitude of a Triangle

An **altitude** of a triangle is a perpendicular segment from a vertex to a line containing the side opposite the vertex. An altitude can be inside or outside of the triangle.

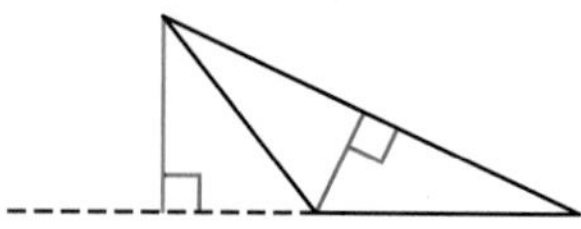

EXAMPLE 3

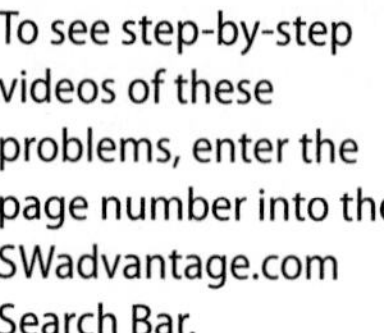

To see step-by-step videos of these problems, enter the page number into the SWadvantage.com Search Bar.

Construct an altitude to side *PR* from *Q*.

Construct a line perpendicular to side *PR* from point *Q*.

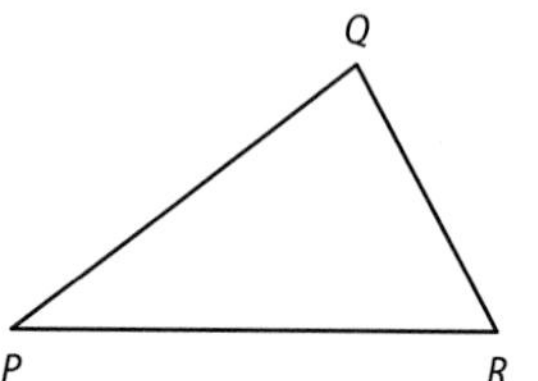

STEP 1 For this example, you can use a straightedge to extend $\overline{PR}$. Place the point of the compass on point *Q*. Open the compass so that it is longer than the distance from *Q* to *R*. Draw arcs intersecting $\overline{PR}$ on either side of *Q*.

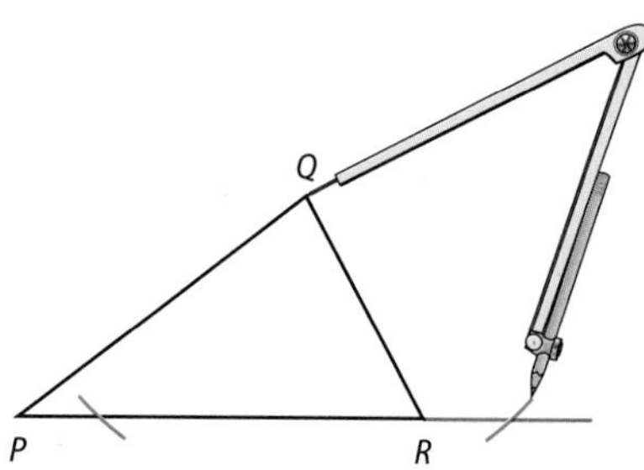

STEP 2 Move the compass point to each of the points where the arcs intersect line *PR*, and draw intersecting arcs with the same compass setting on the outside of the triangle.

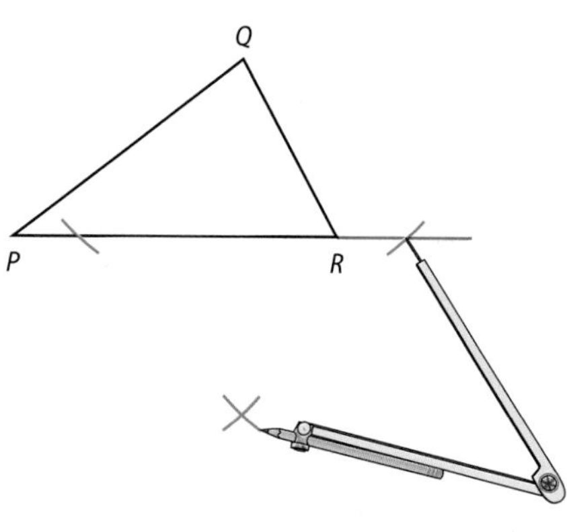

STEP 3 Position a straightedge on *Q* and the intersection of the two arcs. Draw a segment from *Q* to side *PR*. This is the altitude.

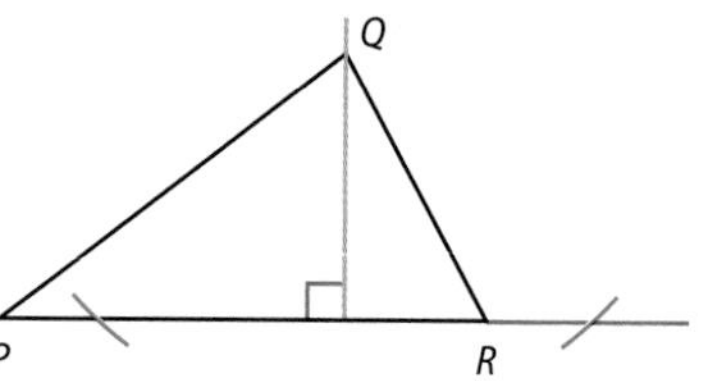

Orthocenter of a Triangle

Every triangle has three altitudes. The altitudes of a triangle are concurrent. That is, all three intersect at one point. The point is called the **orthocenter** of the triangle. In the obtuse triangle, shown here in black, the orthocenter is outside of the triangle.

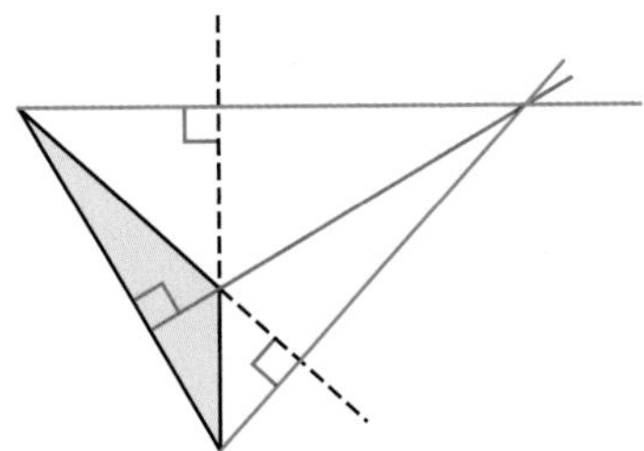

GOT TO KNOW!

Location of Orthocenters

The location of the orthocenter of a triangle depends upon the type of triangle.

The orthocenter of an acute triangle is inside the triangle.

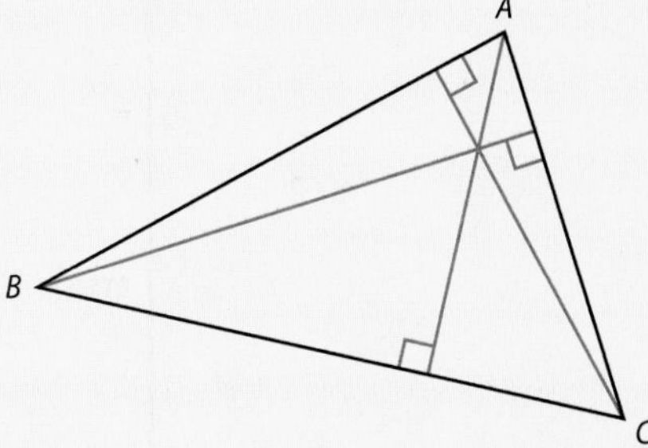

The orthocenter of a right triangle is the vertex of the right angle.

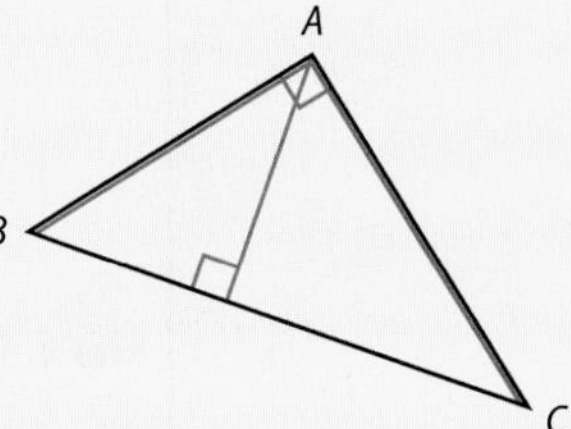

The orthocenter of an obtuse angle is outside the triangle.

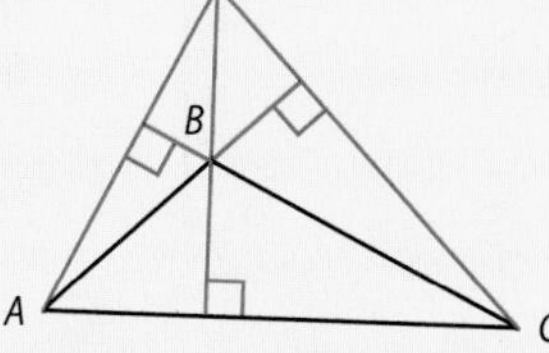

Constructing a Parallel Line Through a Given Point

You can use a straightedge and compass to construct a line that passes through a given point and that is parallel to a given line. To do it, you can draw a line that will become a transversal and construct congruent corresponding angles.

EXAMPLE 1

Construct a line that passes through point *P* and is parallel to line *m*.

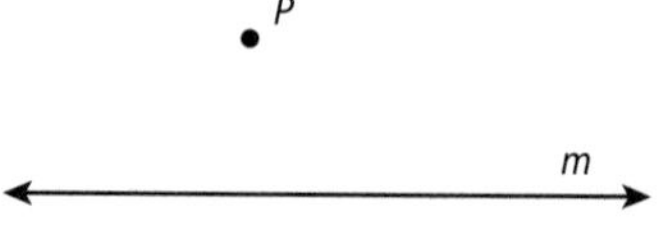

STEP 1 Draw points *Q* and *R* on *m*. Use a straightedge to draw line *PQ*.

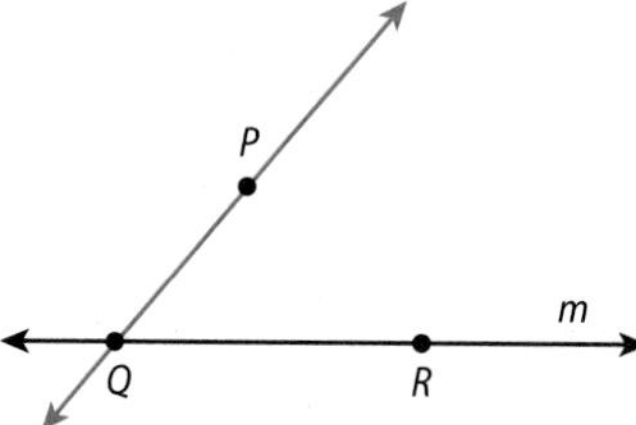

STEP 2 Place the point of the compass on point *Q*. Draw an arc that crosses $\overline{QP}$ and $\overline{QR}$.

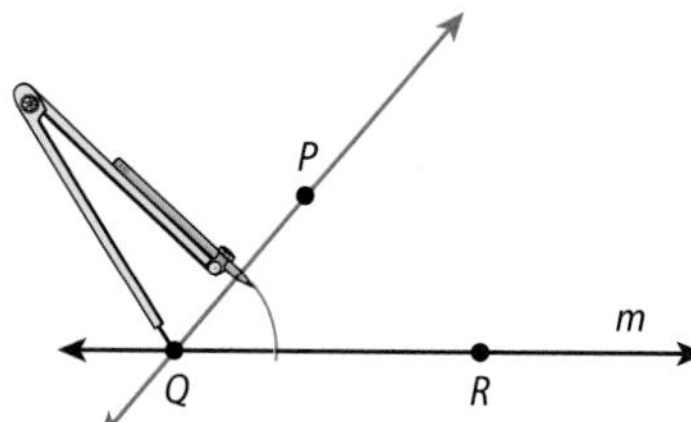

STEP 3 Use the same compass setting. Place the point of the compass on *P*, and draw another arc.

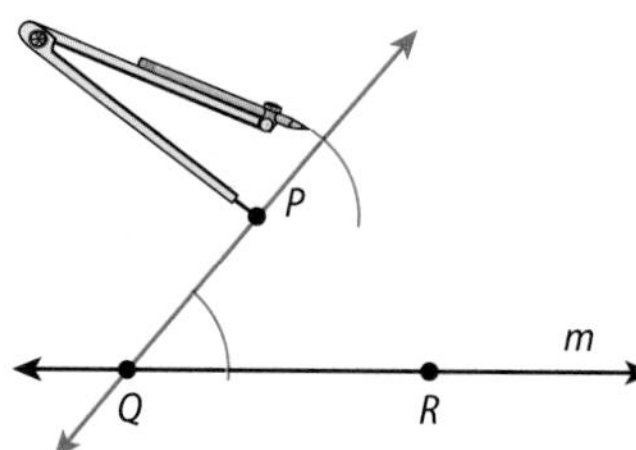

STEP 4 Set the compass so that the point of the compass is on the point of intersection of the first arc and $\overline{QP}$ and the point of the pencil is on the intersection of the first arc and $\overline{QR}$.

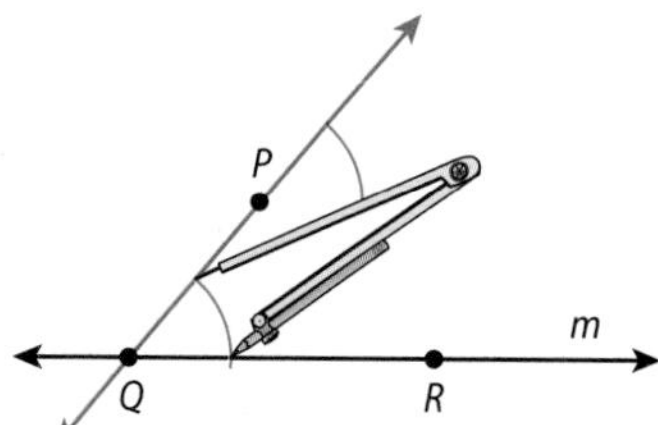

Need More HELP

Remember that a transversal is a line that intersects two or more lines in the same plane at different points.

For help with corresponding angles formed by parallel lines and a transversal, see *Theorems about Parallel Lines* (p. 630).

STEP 5 Without changing the compass setting, place the point of the compass at the intersection of $\overline{QP}$ and the upper arc. Draw an arc across the upper arc.

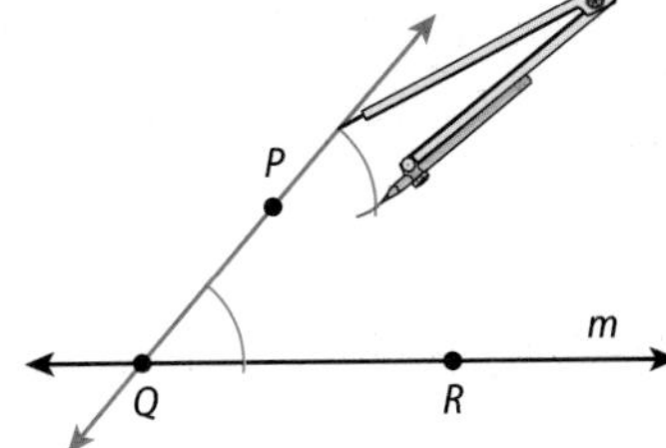

STEP 6 Draw a line through *P* and the intersection of the two arcs. The line is parallel to *m*.

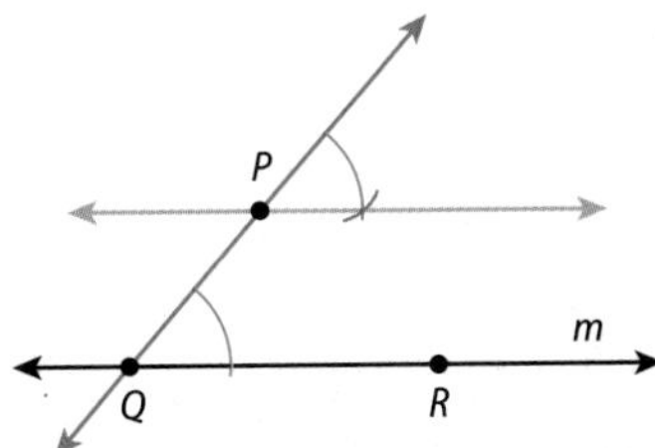

SEARCH

To see step-by-step videos of these problems, enter the page number into the SWadvantage.com Search Bar.

This construction is justified by the Converse of the Corresponding Angles Postulate: If two lines are cut by a transversal and corresponding angles are congruent, then the lines are parallel.

GOT TO KNOW!

Constructing Parallel Lines

You can use a straightedge and a compass to construct a line parallel to a given line through a point. To do it, you construct congruent angles. Because the two angles are congruent and are on the same side of the transversal, the constructed line is parallel to the given line.

By constructing two pairs of parallel lines you can construct a parallelogram.

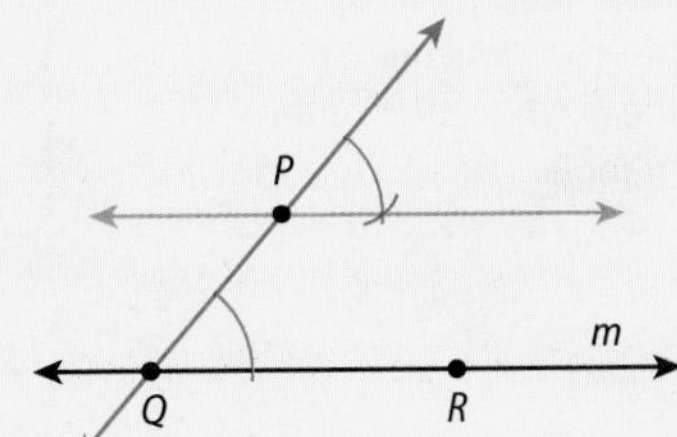

Constructing Perpendicular Bisectors of a Triangle

A **perpendicular bisector of a triangle** is a line (or ray or segment) that is perpendicular to a side of the triangle and passes through the midpoint of the side. Each triangle has three perpendicular bisectors, and they are concurrent; that is, they meet at a point.

EXAMPLE 1

Construct the perpendicular bisectors of the sides of triangle *PQR*, and locate the point of concurrency.

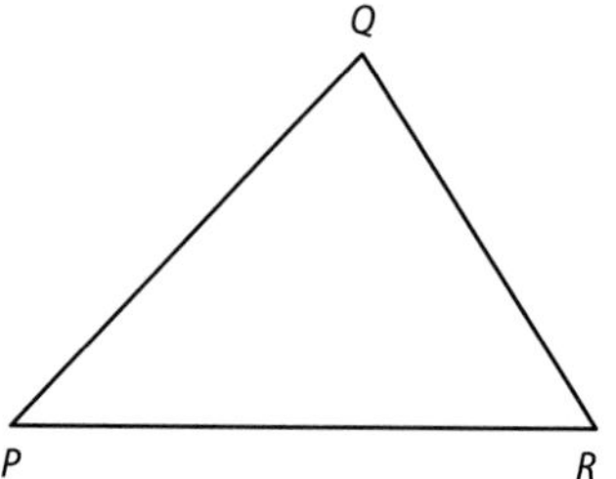

STEP 1 Construct a perpendicular bisector for side *PQ*.

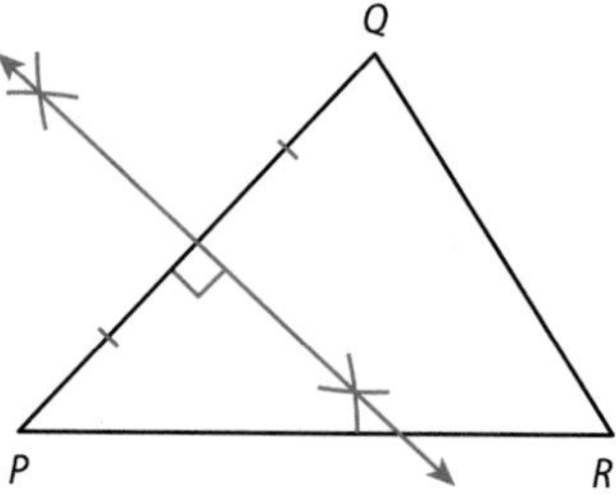

STEP 2 Construct a perpendicular bisector for side *QR*.

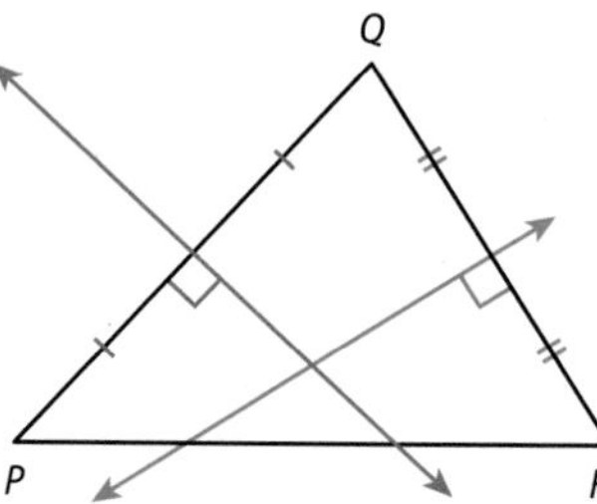

STEP 3 Construct a perpendicular bisector for side *PR*. Point *C* is the point of concurrency.

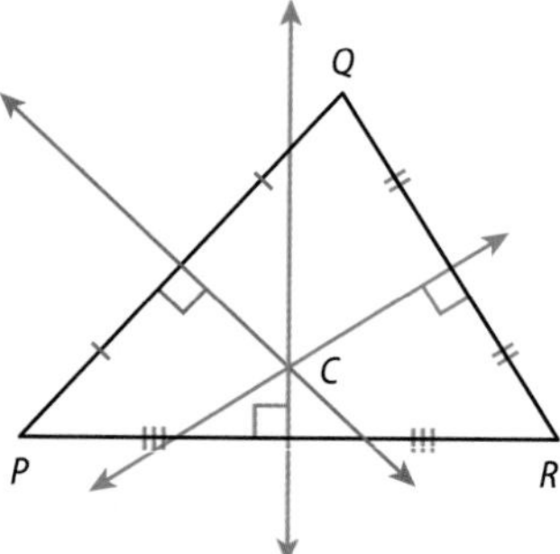

The point of concurrency of the perpendicular bisectors is called the **circumcenter** of the triangle.

Need More HELP

For help with constructing a perpendicular bisector of a segment, go to *Perpendicular Bisector of a Segment* in *Geometry*, p. 864.

Try It This Way

Trace and cut out triangle *PQR*. Fold each vertex to meet the adjacent vertex. Each fold line will be the perpendicular bisector of one of the sides. The fold lines of the three perpendicular bisectors will meet at the circumcenter of the triangle.

Circumscribing a Triangle

A circle that passes through all of the vertices of a polygon is called a **circumcircle of the polygon**. We say that the circle **circumscribes** the polygon. To circumscribe a triangle, find the point of concurrency of its perpendicular bisectors and draw a circle with that center.

EXAMPLE 2

Circumscribe a circle about triangle *ABC*.

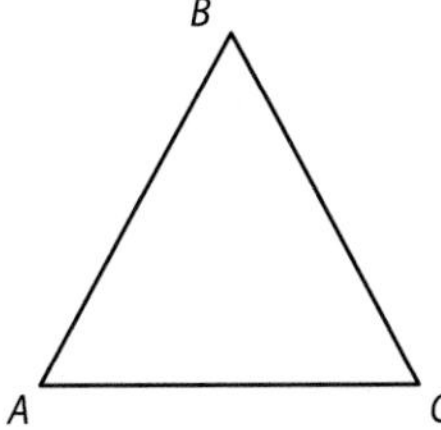

STEP 1 Construct a perpendicular bisector for side *AC*.

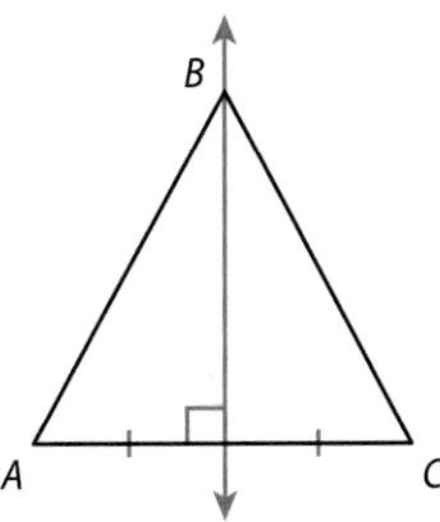

STEP 2 Construct a perpendicular bisector for side *BC*.

The point of intersection of the two perpendicular bisectors is the circumcircle of the triangle because the third perpendicular bisector would intersect them at the same point.

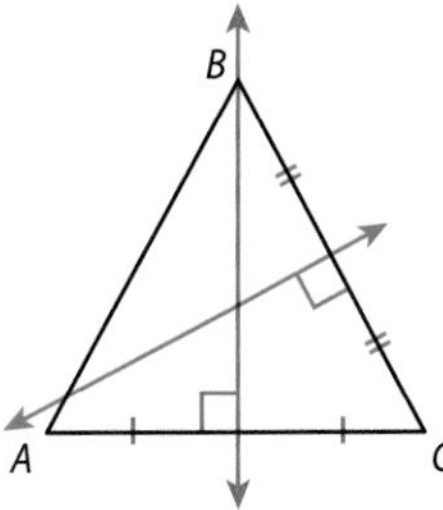

STEP 3 Place the point of a compass on the intersection of the two perpendicular bisectors and the pencil on one of the vertices.

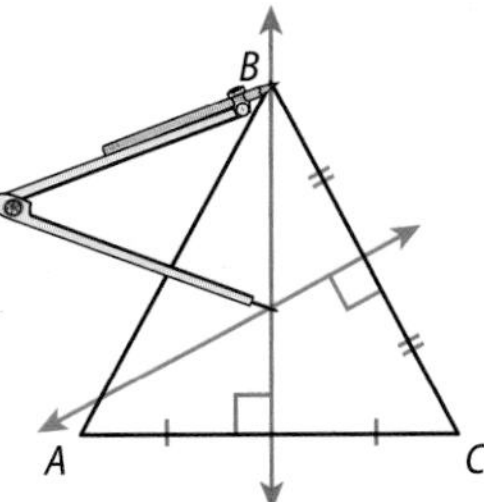

STEP 4 Draw the circle.

The circle circumscribes the triangle. In other words, the vertices of the triangle lie on the circle.

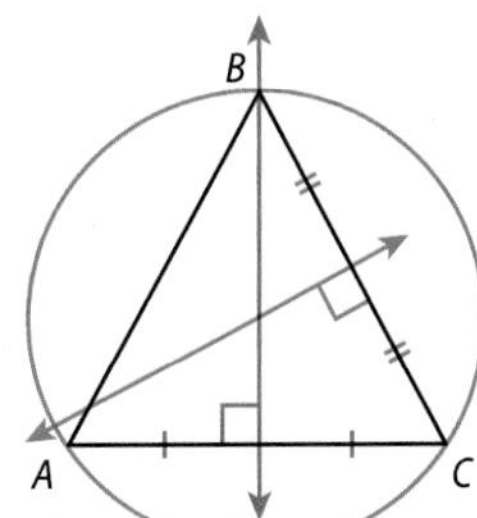

SEARCH

To see step-by-step videos of these problems, enter the page number into the SWadvantage.com Search Bar.

Distance of the Circumcenter from the Vertices

EXAMPLE 3

Compare the lengths from the vertices to the circumcenter of triangle *PQR*.

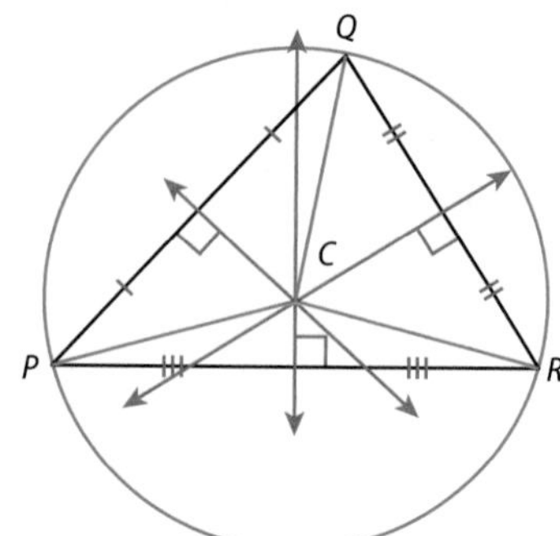

Use a compass to compare the lengths.

STEP 1 Place the point of a compass on vertex *P*, and open the compass so the pencil is on the circumcenter.

STEP 2 Without changing the compass setting, move it so the point is on vertex *Q*. Do you have to increase the compass opening, decrease it, or leave it the same for the pencil to be on the circumcenter?

STEP 3 Without changing the compass setting, move it so the point is on vertex *R*. Do you have to increase the compass opening, decrease it, or leave it the same for the pencil to be on the circumcenter?

The compass setting stays the same for all three measurements. The length from each vertex to the circumcenter is the same.

GOT TO KNOW!

Perpendicular Bisectors and Triangle Circumcenters

For all triangles, the perpendicular bisectors of the sides are concurrent (all intersect) at the *circumcenter* of the triangle. The distance from each vertex to the circumcenter is the same. It is the radius of the circumcircle.

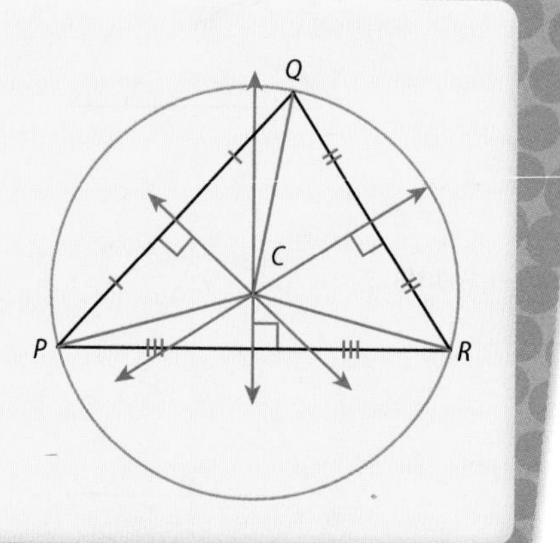

Circumcenter Locations

The location of the circumcenter depends upon the type of triangle being circumscribed.

EXAMPLE 4

Find the location of the circumcenter in an acute triangle, a right triangle, and an obtuse triangle.

Decide if each circumcenter is located within the triangle, outside the triangle, or on the triangle.

STEP 1 Draw an acute triangle, and draw perpendicular bisectors to find the circumcenter.

The circumcenter of any acute triangle is located within the triangle.

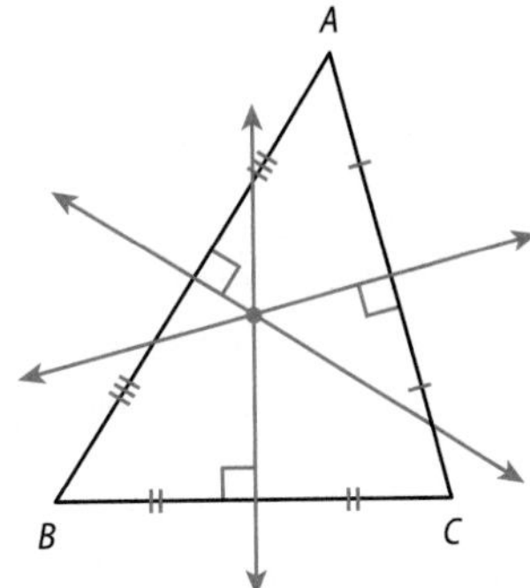

STEP 2 Draw a right triangle, and draw perpendicular bisectors to find the circumcenter.

The circumcenter of any right triangle is located at the midpoint of the hypotenuse of the right triangle.

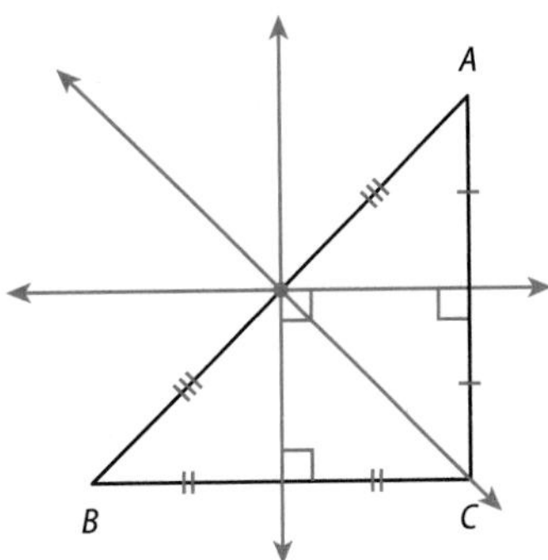

STEP 3 Draw an obtuse triangle, and draw perpendicular bisectors to find the circumcenter.

The circumcenter of any obtuse triangle is located outside of the triangle.

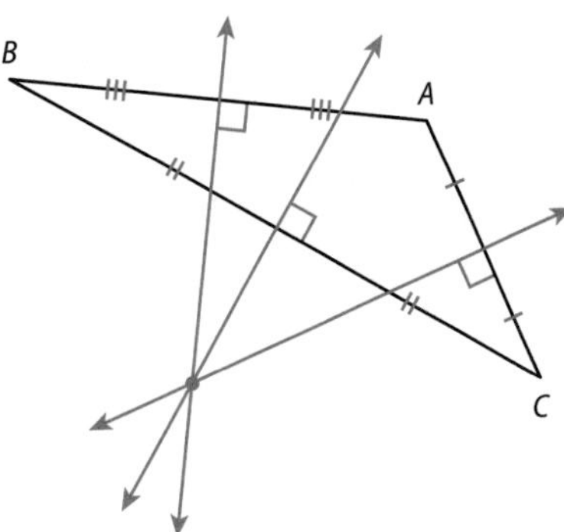

SEARCH

To see step-by-step videos of these problems, enter the page number into the SWadvantage.com Search Bar.

Inscribe a Circle in a Triangle

For help with bisecting an angle, go to *Angle Bisector* on p. 868.

Angle Bisectors of a Triangle

An **angle bisector** of a triangle is a bisector of an angle of the triangle. The three angle bisectors of a triangle are concurrent. That is, they meet at a point. The point of concurrency is called the **incenter of the triangle**.

SEARCH

To see step-by-step videos of these problems, enter the page number into the SWadvantage.com Search Bar.

EXAMPLE 1

Construct the angle bisectors for triangle *ABC*, and find the point of concurrency.

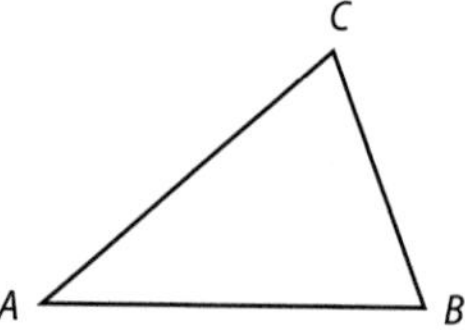

STEP 1 Bisect angle *A* as follows.

Use a compass with its point on vertex *A* to draw an arc. Draw intersecting arcs by placing the point of the compass at the intersection of the first arc and each of the two sides. Draw a ray from *A* through the intersecting arcs.

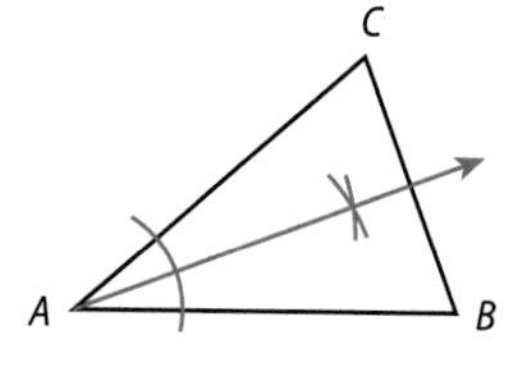

STEP2 Bisect angle *B* by following the same procedure.

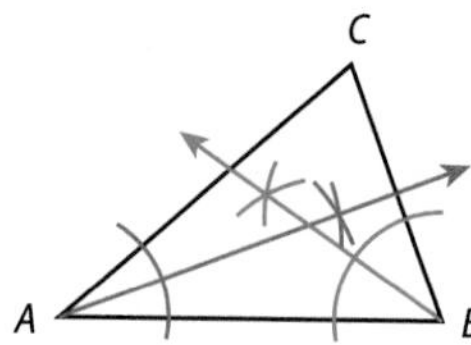

STEP 3 Bisect angle *C* by following the same procedure. Label the point where the three angle bisectors meet as point *D*.

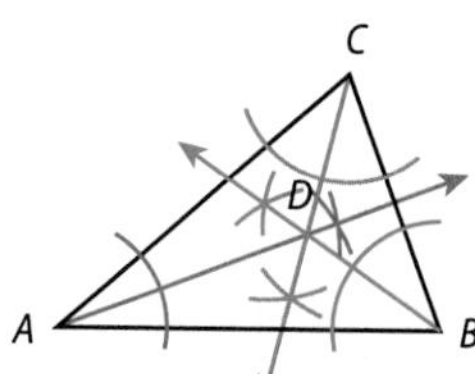

Point *D* is the incenter of triangle *ABC*.

Incenters

The angle bisectors of any triangle are concurrent. The point of concurrency is called the incenter of the triangle.

Perpendiculars from the Incenter

EXAMPLE 2

Construct perpendiculars from the incenter *D* of triangle *ABC* through each side of the triangle.

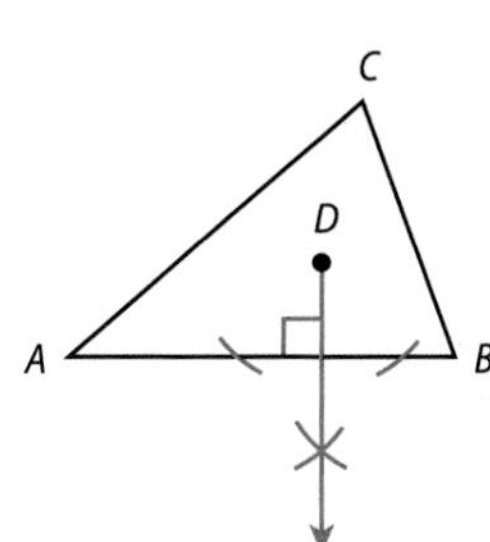

STEP 1 Construct a ray from *D* perpendicular to side *AB* as follows.

With the point of the compass on *D*, draw arcs that intersect side *AB* at two different points. Draw intersecting arcs by placing the point of the compass at the intersections of the first arcs and the side. Draw a line from *D* through the intersecting arcs.

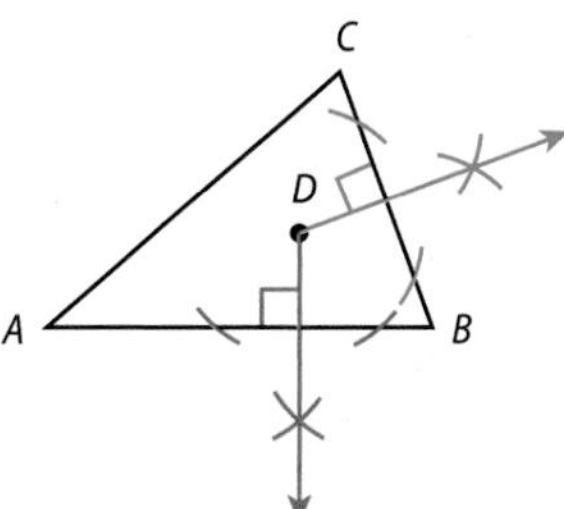

STEP 2 Construct a ray from *D* perpendicular to side *CB* by following the same procedure.

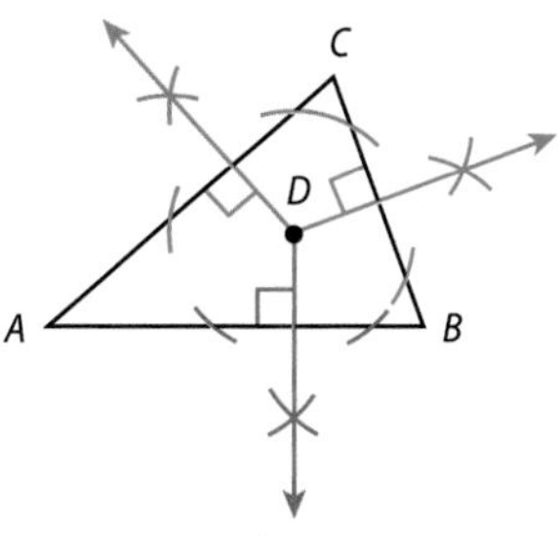

STEP 3 Construct a ray from *D* perpendicular to side *AC* by following the same procedure.

Need More HELP

For help with constructing a line that is perpendicular to a given line through a point not on the line, go to *Perpendicular Lines* on p. 871.

Incenter Distance from the Sides of a Triangle

You can use the perpendiculars from the incenter of a triangle to measure the length from the sides of the triangle to the incenter.

EXAMPLE 3

Compare the lengths of the perpendiculars from the incenter to the sides of triangle *ABC*.

Use a compass to compare the lengths.

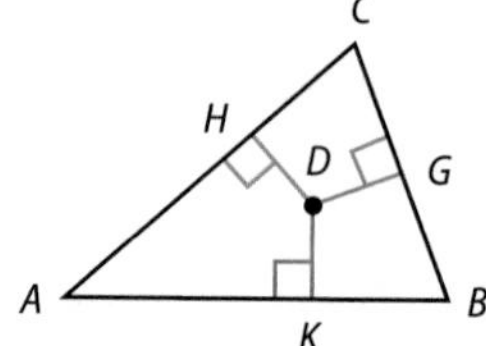

STEP 1 Use a compass to measure the length of the segment *DG* by placing the point of the compass at *D* and the pencil point at *G*.

STEP 2 Keep the point of the compass on *D*. Without changing the setting of the compass, move the pencil point to the segment *DH*. Do you have to increase, decrease, or leave the compass setting the same for the pencil point to touch point *H*?

The compass setting remains the same.

STEP 3 Keep the point of the compass on *D*. Without changing the setting of the compass, move the pencil point to the segment *DK*. Do you have to increase, decrease, or leave the compass setting the same for the pencil point to touch point *K*?

The compass setting remains the same.

STEP 4 Compare the lengths of the perpendiculars.

The perpendiculars from the incenter to the sides of triangle *ABC* are all the same length.

SEARCH

To see step-by-step videos of these problems, enter the page number into the SWadvantage.com Search Bar.

GOT TO KNOW!

Location of Incenters of a Triangle

The incenter of any triangle is equidistant from the three sides of the triangle. In this diagram, $PD = PE = PF$.

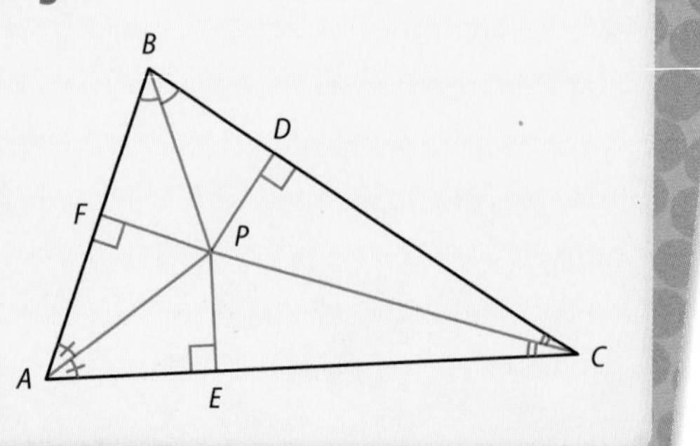

Inscribing a Circle in a Triangle

A circle that is tangent to each side of a polygon is said to be **inscribed** in the polygon. By constructing two angle bisectors and a perpendicular from their point of intersection to one of the sides of the triangle, you can inscribe a circle within a triangle.

EXAMPLE 4

Inscribe a circle within triangle *DEF*.

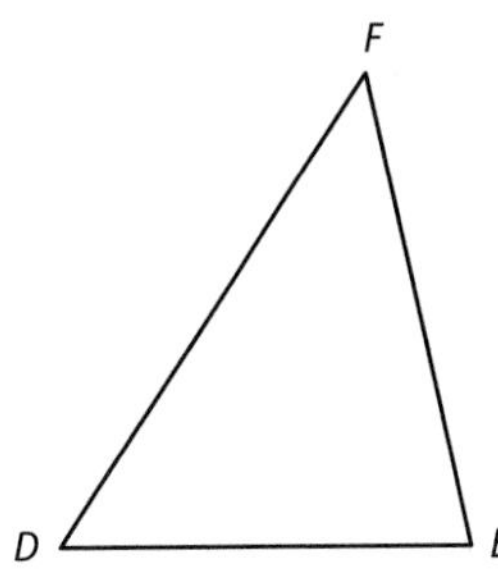

STEP 1 Bisect angle *D* and angle *E*. Label the point where the bisectors intersect as point *C*.

Point *C* is the incenter of the triangle because the third angle bisector would pass through the same point.

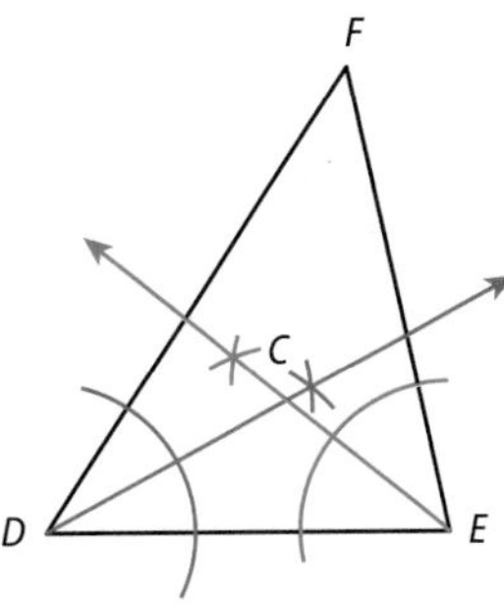

STEP 2 Construct a perpendicular ray from point *C* through one of the sides of the triangle. Label the point where the ray intersects side *DE* as point *G*.

The radius of an inscribed circle will be the length of the segment *CG*.

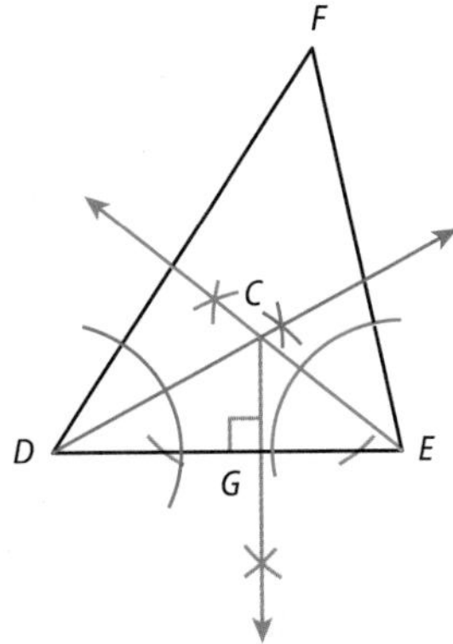

STEP 3 Place the point of the compass on the incenter, point *C*. Open the compass to the length of segment *CG*. Draw the circle.

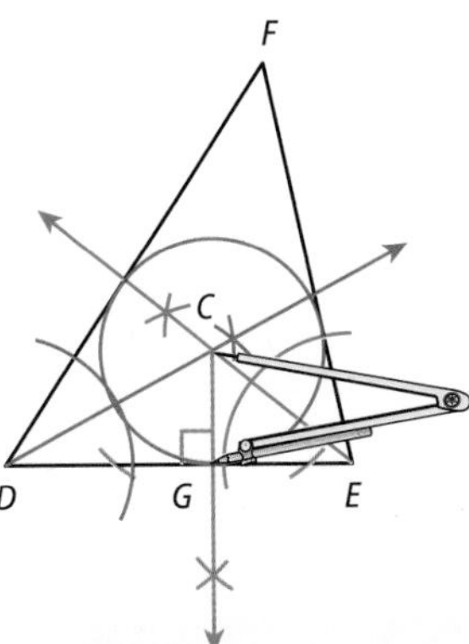

The circle is inscribed in triangle *DEF*.

Geometry

Formulas

Distance Formula	$d = \sqrt{(x_2 - x_1)^2 + (y_2 - y_1)^2}$	Lateral Area of a Regular Pyramid	$LA = \frac{1}{2}Ps$
Midpoint Formula	$\left(\frac{x_1 + x_2}{2}, \frac{y_1 + y_2}{2}\right)$	Lateral Area of a Regular Cone	$LA = \pi rs$
Slope m	$m = \frac{y_2 - y_1}{x_2 - x_1}$	Euler's Formula	$F + V = E + 2$
Slope-Intercept Form of an Equation for a Line	$y = mx + b$	Length of an Arc	$\ell = 2\pi r\left(\frac{x°}{360°}\right)$
Point-Slope Form of an Equation for a Line	$y - y_1 = m(x - x_1)$	Area of a Sector	$A = \pi r^2\left(\frac{x°}{360°}\right)$
Equation of a Circle	$(x - h)^2 + (y - k)^2 = r^2$ with center (h, k) and radius r		

Perimeter, Area, and Volume

Figure	Perimeter Formula	Area Formula
Regular Polygon	$P = ns$	$A = \frac{1}{2}ap$
Triangle	$P = s_1 + s_2 + s_3.$	$A = \frac{1}{2}bh$
Square	$P = 4s$	$A = s^2$
Rectangle	$P = 2\ell + 2w$ or $2(\ell + w)$	$A = \ell \cdot w$
Parallelogram	$P = 2(s_1 + s_2)$	$A = b \cdot h$
Trapezoid	$P = s_1 + s_2 + s_3 + s_4$	$A = \frac{1}{2}h(b_1 + b_2)$
Circle	circumference: $C = \pi d$ or $C = 2\pi r$	$A = \pi r^2$
Figure	**Surface Area Formula**	**Volume Formula**
Cube	$SA = 6s^2$	$V = s^3$
Rectangular Prism	$SA = Ph + 2B$	$V = Bh$
Pyramid	$SA = \frac{1}{2}P\ell + B$	$V = \frac{1}{3}Bh$
Cylinder	$SA = 2\pi rh + 2\pi r^2$	$V = \pi r^2 h$
Cone	$SA = \pi r\ell + \pi r^2$	$V = \frac{1}{3}\pi r^2 h$
Sphere	$SA = 4\pi r^2$	$V = \frac{4}{3}\pi r^3$

Congruence Properties

Property	Segments	Angles
Reflexive	$\overline{AB} \cong \overline{AB}$	$\angle X \cong \angle X$
Symmetric	If $\overline{AB} \cong \overline{CD}$, then $\overline{CD} \cong \overline{AB}$.	If $\angle X \cong \angle Y$, then $\angle Y \cong \angle X$.
Transitive	If $\overline{AB} \cong \overline{CD}$ and $\overline{CD} \cong \overline{EF}$, then $\overline{AB} \cong \overline{EF}$.	If $\angle X \cong \angle Y$ and $\angle Y \cong \angle Z$, then $\angle X \cong \angle Z$.

Logic Statements

Statement	In Words	In Symbols
Conditional	If p, then q.	$p \rightarrow q$
Inverse	If not p, then not q.	$\sim p \rightarrow \sim q$
Converse	If q, then p.	$q \rightarrow p$
Contrapositive	If not q, then not p.	$\sim q \rightarrow \sim p$
Biconditional	p if and only if q.	$p \leftrightarrow q$

Math SMART!

Truth Table for $p \rightarrow q$

Hypothesis p	Conclusion q	Conditional $p \rightarrow q$	Converse $q \rightarrow p$	Biconditional $p \leftrightarrow q$
T	T	T	T	T
T	F	F	T	F
F	T	T	F	F
F	F	T	T	T

Laws of Logic

The Law of Detachment

If $p \rightarrow q$ is true and p is true, then q is true.

Law of Syllogism

If $p \rightarrow q$ is true and $q \rightarrow r$ is true, then $p \rightarrow r$ must be true.

Types of Reasoning

Deductive Reasoning	• Uses properties, rules, definitions, theorems, given facts, and the laws of logic to arrive at a conclusion. • The conclusion must be true if the hypotheses are true.
Inductive Reasoning	• Uses observations and patterns. • The conclusion is not necessarily true.

p if and only if q

Geometry: Postulates, Theorems, and Corollaries

Angles

Angle Addition Postulate: If point M is in the interior of $\angle JKL$, then $m\angle JKM + m\angle MKL = m\angle JKL$.

Linear Pair Theorem: If two angles form a linear pair, then they are supplementary.

Congruent Supplements Theorem: If two angles are supplementary to the same angle (or to congruent angles), then the angles are congruent.

Congruent Complements Theorem: If two angles are complementary to the same angle (or to congruent angles), then the angles are congruent.

Vertical Angles Theorem: Vertical angles are congruent.

Right Angle Congruence Theorem: All right angles are congruent.

Theorem (p. 628): If two angles are congruent and supplementary, then each angle is a right angle.

Corresponding Angles Postulate: If two parallel lines are cut by a transversal, then corresponding angles are congruent.

Converse of the Corresponding Angles Postulate: If two lines are cut by a transversal and corresponding angles are congruent, then the lines are parallel.

Alternate Interior Angles Theorem: If two parallel lines are cut by a transversal, then alternate interior angles are congruent.

Converse of the Alternate Interior Angles Theorem: If two lines are cut by a transversal and alternate interior angles are congruent, then the lines are parallel.

Alternate Exterior Angles Theorem: If two parallel lines are cut by a transversal, then alternate exterior angles are congruent.

Converse of the Alternate Exterior Angles Theorem: If two lines are cut by a transversal and alternate exterior angles are congruent, then the lines are parallel.

Same-Side Interior Angles Theorem: If two parallel lines are cut by a transversal, then same-side interior angles are supplementary.

Converse of the Same-Side Interior Angles Theorem: If two lines are cut by a transversal and same-side interior angles are supplementary, then the lines are parallel.

Polygons

Polygon Interior Angle-Sum Theorem: The sum of the measures of the interior angles of a polygon with n sides is $(n - 2)180°$.

Polygon Exterior Angle-Sum Theorem: The sum of the measures of the exterior angles of a polygon is 360°.

Parallel and Perpendicular Lines

Theorem (p. 633): In a plane, if two lines are perpendicular to the same line, then they are parallel.

Theorem (p. 814): If two non-vertical lines are parallel, then their slopes are equal.

Theorem (p. 814): If the slopes of two non-vertical lines are equal, then the lines are parallel.

Theorem (p. 816): If two non-vertical lines are perpendicular, then their slopes are negative reciprocals.

Theorem (p. 816): If the slopes of two non-vertical lines are negative reciprocals, then the lines are perpendicular.

Parallel Postulate: Given a line and a point not on the line, there is exactly one line through the point parallel to the line.

Circles

Arc Addition Postulate: The measure of an arc formed by two adjacent arcs is the sum of the measures of the two arcs. $m\widehat{AC} = m\widehat{AB} + m\widehat{BC}$	**Inscribed Angle Theorem:** The measure of an inscribed angle is half the measure of its intercepted arc.
Theorem (p. 728): In the same circle or in congruent circles, two minor arcs are congruent if and only if their central angles are congruent.	**Corollary:** If two inscribed angles intercept the same arc, then they are congruent.
Theorem (p. 734): In the same circle (or in congruent circles), congruent chords have congruent central angles.	**Corollary:** An angle inscribed in a semicircle is a right angle.
Converse of Theorem (p. 734): In the same circle (or in congruent circles), congruent central angles have congruent chords.	**Corollary:** If a quadrilateral is inscribed in a circle, then its opposite angles are supplementary.
Theorem (p. 736): In the same circle (or in congruent circles), congruent arcs have congruent chords.	**Tangent-Chord Angle Theorem:** The measure of an angle whose sides are a tangent and a chord equals half the measure of the intercepted arc.
Converse of Theorem (p. 736): In the same circle (or congruent circles), congruent chords have congruent arcs.	**Tangent-Tangent Angle Theorem:** The measure of the angle formed by two tangents drawn from a point outside a circle equals half the difference of the measures of the intercepted arcs.
Theorem (p. 738): If a diameter (or radius) is perpendicular to a chord, then it bisects the chord and its arc.	**Corollary:** The measure of the angle formed by two tangents drawn from a point outside a circle is 180° minus the measure of the intercepted minor arc.
Theorem (p. 738): If a radius bisects a chord that is not a diameter, then it is perpendicular to the chord.	**Chord-Chord Angle Theorem:** If two chords intersect in a circle, the measure of an angle formed is half the sum of the measures of arcs intercepted by the angle and its vertical angle.
Theorem (p. 738): The perpendicular bisector of a chord passes through the center of the circle.	**Secant-Secant Angle Theorem:** The measure of the angle formed by two secants drawn from a point outside a circle equals half the difference of the measures of the intercepted arcs.
Theorem (p. 739): If two chords of a circle are congruent, then they are equidistant from the center.	**Secant-Tangent Theorem:** The measure of the angle formed by a secant and a tangent drawn from a point in the exterior of a circle equals half the difference of the measures of the intercepted arcs.
Theorem (p. 739): If two chords of a circle are equidistant from the center, then they are congruent.	**Theorem (p. 758):** If two chords intersect inside a circle, then the product of the segment lengths of one chord is equal to the product of the segment lengths of the other.
Theorem (p. 740): If a line is tangent to a circle, then it is perpendicular to the radius drawn to the point of tangency.	**Theorem (p. 760):** If two secants intersect outside a circle, then the product of the lengths of one secant segment and its external segment is equal to the product of the other secant segment and its external segment.
Theorem (p. 740): If a line in the plane of a circle is perpendicular to the radius at a point on the circle, then the line is tangent to the circle.	**Theorem (p. 762):** If a secant and a tangent intersect outside a circle, then the product of the lengths of the secant segment and its external segment is equal to the length of the tangent segment squared.
Two-Tangent Theorem: Two tangent segments drawn from a point not on a circle are congruent.	

Geometry: Postulates, Theorems, and Corollaries

Quadrilaterals

Theorem (p. 644): If both pairs of opposite sides of a quadrilateral are congruent, then the quadrilateral is a parallelogram.

Theorem (p. 645): If two sides of a quadrilateral are both congruent and parallel, then the quadrilateral is a parallelogram.

Theorem (p. 650): The diagonals of a rectangle are congruent.

Theorem (p. 651): If a parallelogram has one right angle, then it is a rectangle.

Theorem (p. 652): The diagonals of a rhombus are perpendicular.

Theorem (p. 652): The diagonals of a rhombus bisect the angles of the rhombus.

Trapezoid Midsegment Theorem: The midsegment of a trapezoid is parallel to each of the bases, and its length is half the sum of the lengths of the bases.

Theorem (p. 658): The base angles of an isosceles trapezoid are congruent.

Theorem (p. 659): The diagonals of an isosceles trapezoid are congruent.

Theorem (p. 660): If a quadrilateral is a kite, then exactly one pair of opposite angles is congruent.

Theorem (p. 661): The diagonals of a kite are perpendicular.

Triangles

Triangle Inequality Theorem: The sum of the lengths of any two sides of a triangle is always greater than the length of the third side.

Hinge Theorem: If two sides of one triangle are congruent to two sides of another triangle, but their included angles are not congruent, then the side opposite the larger included angle is longer than the side opposite the smaller included angle.

Converse of Hinge Theorem: If two sides of one triangle are congruent to two sides of another triangle, but the third sides are not congruent, then the angle opposite the longer side is larger than the angle opposite the shorter side.

Triangle Angle-Sum Theorem: The sum of the angle measures of a triangle is 180°.

Corollary: The acute angles of a right triangle are complementary.

Corollary: The measure of each angle of an equiangular triangle is 60°.

Exterior Angle Theorem: The measure of an exterior angle of a triangle equals the sum of the measures of its remote interior angles.

Pythagorean Inequality Theorem: Given: a, b, and c are the side lengths of a triangle with c the length of the longest side:

If $c^2 < a^2 + b^2$, then $\triangle ABC$ is acute.
If $c^2 > a^2 + b^2$, then $\triangle ABC$ is obtuse.

Side-Side-Side Congruence Postulate (SSS): If three sides of one triangle are congruent to the corresponding three sides of another triangle, then the triangles are congruent.

Side-Angle-Side Congruence Postulate (SAS): If two sides and the included angle of one triangle are congruent to the corresponding sides and included angle of another triangle, then the triangles are congruent.

Angle-Side-Angle Congruence Postulate (ASA): If two angles and the included side of one triangle are congruent to the corresponding angles and included side of another triangle, then the triangles are congruent.

Angle-Angle-Side Congruence Theorem (AAS): If two angles and a non-included side of one triangle are congruent to the corresponding angles and non-included side of another triangle, then the triangles are congruent.

Angle-Angle Similarity Postulate (AA): If two angles of one triangle are congruent to the corresponding angles of another triangle, then the triangles are similar.

Triangles (continued)

CPCTC: Corresponding Parts of Congruent Triangles are Congruent.

Theorem (p. 784): If two sides of a triangle are congruent, then the angles opposite those sides are congruent.

Theorem (p. 784): If two angles of a triangle are congruent, then the sides opposite those angles are congruent.

Theorem (p. 786): If a triangle is equilateral, it is also equiangular.

Theorem (p. 786): If a triangle is equiangular, it is also equilateral.

Side-Side-Side Similarity Theorem (SSS): If three sides of one triangle are proportional to the corresponding sides of another triangle, then the triangles are similar.

Side-Angle-Side Similarity Theorem (SAS): If two sides of one triangle are proportional to the corresponding sides of another triangle and the included angles are congruent, then the triangles are similar.

Theorem (p. 804): If a segment that is parallel to a side of a triangle intersects the other two sides, then it divides those two sides into proportional segments.

Theorem (p. 804): If a segment divides two sides of a triangle into proportional segments, then it is parallel to the third side.

Theorem (p. 805): An angle bisector of a triangle divides the opposite sides into two segments that are proportional to the other two sides of the triangle.

Theorem (p. 806): A midsegment of a triangle is parallel to one side of the triangle and is half as long as that side.

Theorem (p. 831): The lines that contain the altitudes of a triangle are concurrent.

Right Triangles

Pythagorean Theorem: The sum of the squares of the lengths of the legs of a right triangle equals the square of the length of the hypotenuse.

$a^2 + b^2 = c^2$

Converse of the Pythagorean Theorem: If the sum of the squares of the lengths of two sides of a triangle is equal to the square of the length of the third side, then the triangle is a right triangle.

45°–45°–90° Triangle Theorem: In a 45°–45°–90° triangle, the length of the hypotenuse is $\sqrt{2}$ times the length of a leg.

30°–60°–90° Triangle Theorem: In a 30°–60°–90° triangle, the hypotenuse is twice the length of the shorter leg, and the longer leg is $\sqrt{3}$ times the length of the shorter leg.

Leg-Leg Congruence (LL): If both legs of a right triangle are congruent to the corresponding legs of another right triangle, then the triangles are congruent.

Leg-Angle Congruence (LA): If one leg and an acute angle of a right triangle are congruent to the corresponding leg and acute angle of another right triangle, then the triangles are congruent.

Hypotenuse-Angle Congruence (HA): If the hypotenuse and an acute angle of a right triangle are congruent to the hypotenuse and corresponding acute angle of another right triangle, then the triangles are congruent.

Hypotenuse-Leg Congruence (HL): If the hypotenuse and one leg of a right triangle are congruent to the hypotenuse and corresponding leg of another right triangle, then the triangles are congruent.

Theorem (p. 796): If the altitude is drawn to the hypotenuse of a right triangle, then the two triangles formed are similar to the original triangle and to each other.

Corollary: The length of the altitude drawn to the hypotenuse of a right triangle is the geometric mean of the lengths of the segments into which it divides the hypotenuse.

Corollary: The length of a leg of a right triangle is the geometric mean of the lengths of the hypotenuse and the adjacent segment of the hypotenuse.

Trigonometry

Makers of amusement park rides have to meet safety codes in angular velocity that depend on the radius of the ride.

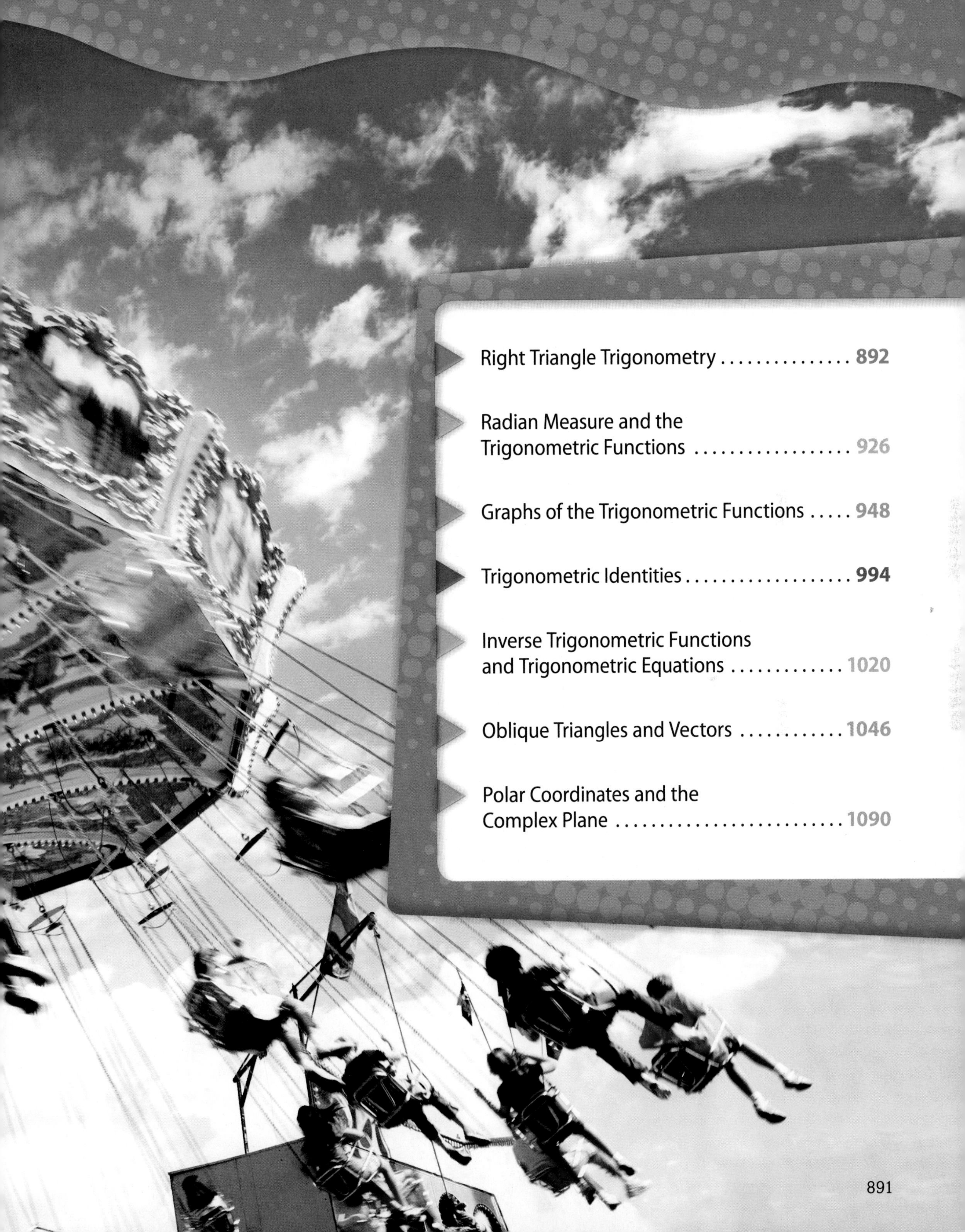

Right Triangle Trigonometry

What Came Before?

- Special right triangles
- The Pythagorean Theorem and side lengths of a right triangle

What's This About?

- Finding the trigonometric ratios of acute angles
- Finding angle measures and side lengths by using trigonometric ratios
- Using trigonometric ratios to solve right triangles

Practical Apps

- Surveyors use right triangle trigonometry to find distances by using angles of elevation and depression.
- Astronomers use trigonometric ratios to find diameters of planets and their distances from Earth.

just for FUN!

Q: What is the tangent of 90 degrees?

A: That's a trig question!

CONTENTS UPLOAD DOWNLOAD *Trigonometry*

You can find more practice problems online by visiting:
www.SWadvantage.com

Angles and Degree Measure

For a review of classifying angles, go to *Classifying Angles* and *Special Pairs of Angles* in Foundations of Mathematics (pp. 140, 146).

Angles

A basic figure in trigonometry is the angle. In geometry, you learned that an angle is the union of two rays with a common endpoint. In trigonometry, it is helpful to define an angle differently: An **angle** is formed by rotating a ray around its endpoint. The endpoint is at the origin and is the **vertex** of the angle. The **initial side** of the angle is the side that lies on the x-axis. The other side of the angle is the **terminal side**.

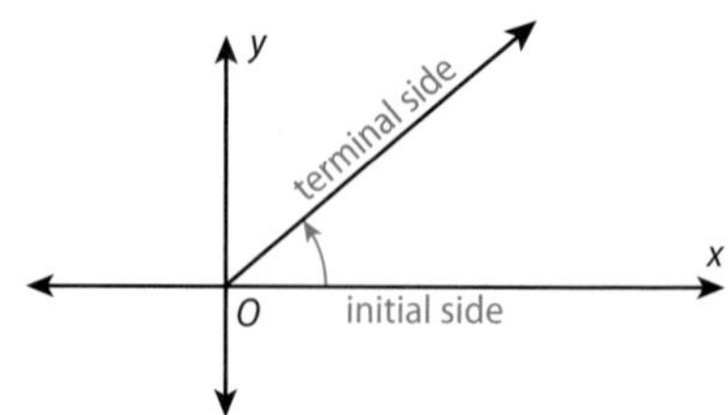

You can classify an angle by its measure. For example, a 90° angle is a **right angle**. An **acute angle** has measure greater than 0° and less than 90°. An **obtuse angle** has measure greater than 90° and less than 180°. If the measure of an angle is 180°, the angle is a **straight angle**.

Pairs of angles also have special names. **Complementary angles** are two angles the sum of whose measures is 90°. **Supplementary angles** are two angles the sum of whose measures is 180°.

SEARCH

To see step-by-step videos of these problems, enter the page number into the SWadvantage.com Search Bar.

EXAMPLE 1

Find $m\angle ABD$ and $m\angle CBD$. Then classify each angle.

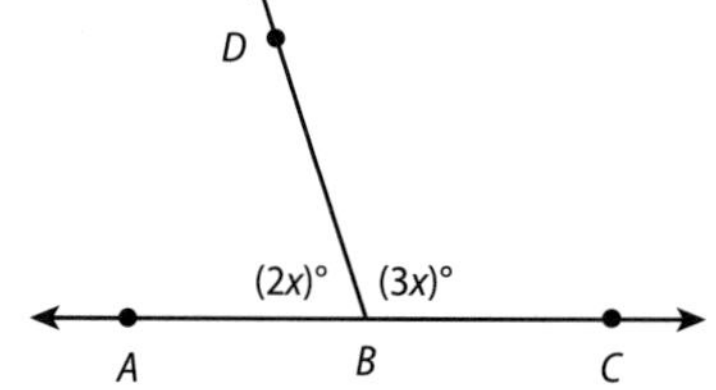

STEP 1 Since $\angle ABC$ is a straight angle, its measure is 180°. Write and solve an equation to find x.

Write the equation.	$2x + 3x = 180$
Combine like terms.	$5x = 180$
Divide both sides by 5.	$x = 36$

STEP 2 Find the measures of the two angles.

$m\angle ABD = 2x = 2(36) = 72°$ $\qquad$ $m\angle CBD = 3x = 3(36) = 108°$

STEP 3 Classify the angles by their measures.

$\angle ABD$ is acute. $\qquad$ $\angle CBD$ is obtuse.

GOT TO KNOW!

Classifying Angles and Angle Pairs

Right angle
$m\angle A = 90°$

Acute angle
$0° < m\angle B < 90°$

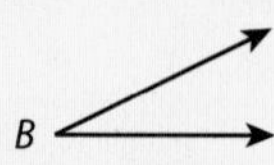

Complementary angles
$m\angle 1 + m\angle 2 = 90°$

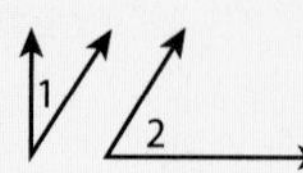

Straight angle
$m\angle DEF = 180°$

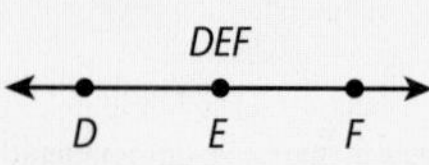

Obtuse angle
$90° < m\angle Q < 180°$

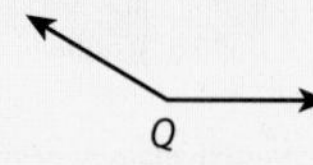

Supplementary angles
$m\angle 3 + m\angle 4 = 180°$

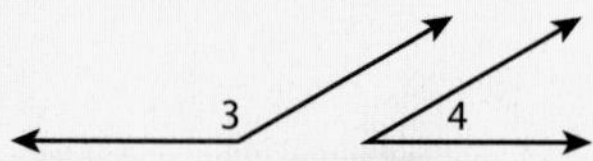

Angles in Standard Position

An angle is in **standard position** if the vertex is at the origin and the initial side lies on the positive x-axis. An angle in standard position is said to lie in the quadrant that contains its terminal side. Remember that the x- and y-axes divide the coordinate plane into four quadrants; I, II, III, and IV, labeled counterclockwise starting at the top right.

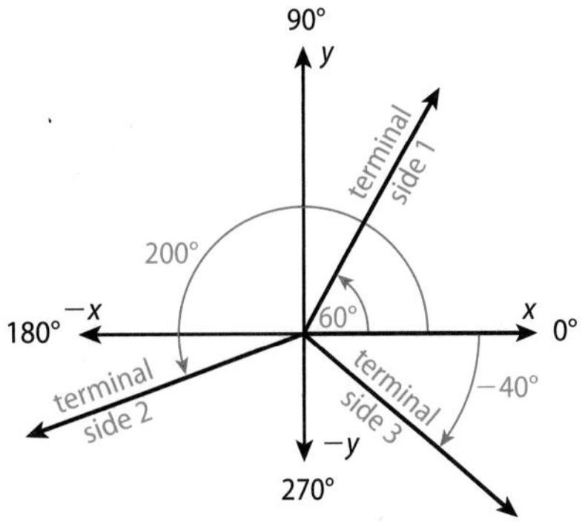

A counterclockwise rotation determines a **positive** angle. If the rotation is clockwise, the angle is **negative**. The figure shows angles of 60°, 200°, and −40°.

If the terminal side of an angle lies on the x-axis or the y-axis, the angle is a **quadrantal** angle. The measure of a quadrantal angle is always a multiple of 90°. Two angles in standard position that have the same terminal side are **coterminal**. Every angle has infinitely many coterminal angles.

EXAMPLE 2

Find two angles, one positive and one negative, that are coterminal with a 55° angle.

To find a positive angle, add a multiple of 360°.

A positive angle that is coterminal with a 55° angle is 55° + 360° = 415°.

To find a negative angle, subtract a multiple of 360°.

A negative angle that is coterminal with a 55° angle is 55° − 360° = −305°.

EXAMPLE 3

Sketch each angle in standard position.

a. 290°

Rotate the ray 290° counterclockwise.

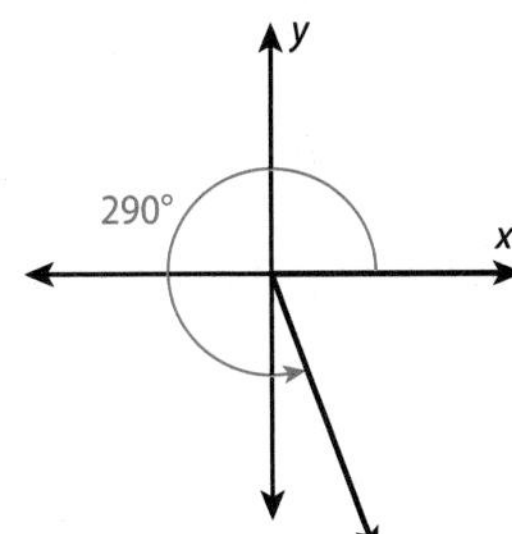

b. −100°

Rotate the ray 100° clockwise.

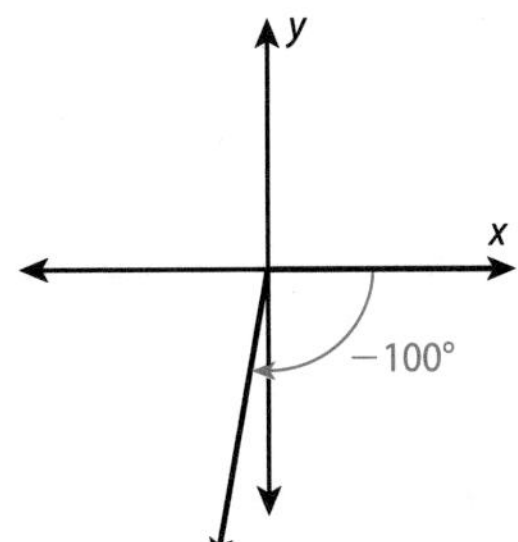

Ways to REMEMBER

To help remember the degree measures for the quadrants, you may want to sketch a small diagram of a coordinate system.

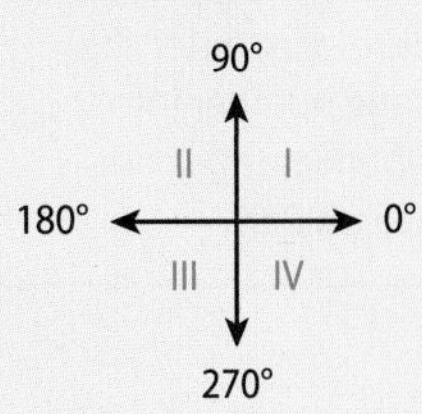

Computing with Angle Measures

Graphing calculators and many scientific calculators can convert back and forth between DMS (degrees/minutes/seconds) and decimal degrees. Make sure your calculator is set on degree mode and not radian mode.

Parts of a Degree

When stating an angle measurement, it is important to be precise. Angle measures may be given in **decimal degrees** or in **DMS** (degrees/minutes/seconds) notation. DMS is based on the fact that there are 360 degrees in a circle. Each degree of an angle is divided into 60 **minutes** and each minute is divided into 60 **seconds**. The symbols for minutes and seconds are ' and ", respectively.

minutes: $1° = 60'$ $\quad 1' = \frac{1}{60}°$ $\qquad$ seconds: $1' = 60''$ $\quad 1'' = \frac{1}{60}' = \frac{1}{3600}°$

For example, $20°30' = 20.5°$. Both ways of recording angle measures are now used, so you need to be able to convert from one type of measure to the other.

EXAMPLE 1

Convert 35.4° to degrees/minutes/seconds.

STEP 1 Multiply the decimal part of the angle measure by 60 to get minutes.

$0.4(60') = 24'$

STEP 2 Add.

$35° + 24' = 35°24'$

$35.4° = 35°24'$

SEARCH

To see step-by-step videos of these problems, enter the page number into the SWadvantage.com Search Bar.

EXAMPLE 2

Convert 48°50'22" to decimal degrees. Round to three decimal places.

STEP 1 Write the minutes and seconds as fractions.

$48°50'22'' = 48° + \left(\frac{50}{60}\right)° + \left(\frac{22}{3{,}600}\right)°$

STEP 2 Change the fractions to decimals.

$48°50'22'' \approx 48° + 0.833° + 0.006°$

$48°50'22'' \approx 48.839°$

EXAMPLE 3

Convert 24.683° to degrees/minutes/seconds.

STEP 1 Multiply the decimal part of the angle measure by 60 to get minutes.

$0.683(60') = 40.98'$

STEP 2 Multiply the decimal part of the minutes by 60 to get seconds.

$0.98(60'') = 58.8''$

STEP 3 Add.

$24° + 40' + 58.8''$

$24.683° = 24°40'58.8''$

Computing with Angle Measures

Adding and subtracting angle measures given in degrees, minutes, and seconds may involve renaming.

EXAMPLE 4

Find the sum 47°35' + 70°48'.

STEP 1 Vertically align the angle measures. Then add the degrees and minutes separately.

$$\begin{array}{r} 47°35' \\ +\ 70°48' \\ \hline 117°83' \end{array}$$

STEP 2 Rename 83'. Change 83' to degrees and minutes.

83' = 60' + 23'
= 1°23'

STEP 3 Add.

117° + 1°23' = 118°23'

47°35' + 70°48' = 118°23'

Watch Out !

Be careful not to confuse DMS notation with decimal degrees.

The sum 47°35' + 70°48' is *not* equal to 117.83°.

EXAMPLE 5

Find the difference 180° − 113°28'.

STEP 1 Rename 180°.

180° = 179° + 1°
= 179°60'

STEP 2 Vertically align the angle measures. Subtract the degrees and minutes separately.

$$\begin{array}{r} 179°60' \\ -\ 113°28' \\ \hline 66°32' \end{array}$$

180° − 113°28' = 66°32'

EXAMPLE 6

Find $m\angle 2$ if $m\angle 1$ = 64°37'17".

STEP 1 The angles are complementary, so the sum of their measures is 90°. Write an equation.

$m\angle 1 + m\angle 2 = 90°$, or $m\angle 2 = 90° - m\angle 1$

STEP 2 Rename 90°: 90° = 89°59'60"

STEP 3 To find $m\angle 2$, subtract $m\angle 1$ from 90°.

$$\begin{array}{r} 89°59'60" \\ -\ 64°37'17" \\ \hline 25°22'43" \end{array}$$

$m\angle 2$ = 25°22'43"

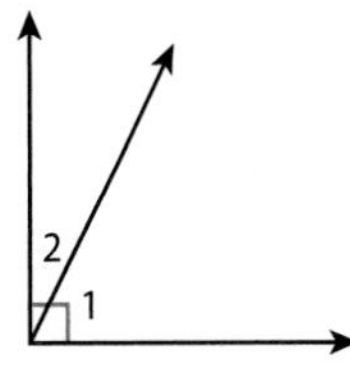

Special Triangles and Angles

45°–45°–90° Triangles

Every angle corresponds to a fractional part of a circle. Recall, there are 360 degrees in a circle.

Degrees	30°	45°	60°	90°	120°	135°	180°
Fractional Part of a Circle	$\frac{1}{12}$	$\frac{1}{8}$	$\frac{1}{6}$	$\frac{1}{4}$	$\frac{1}{3}$	$\frac{3}{8}$	$\frac{1}{2}$

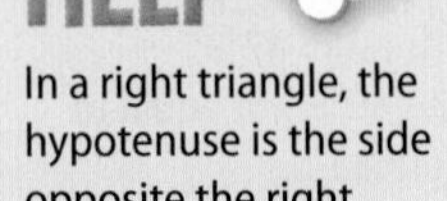

In a right triangle, the hypotenuse is the side opposite the right angle. For more review of the Pythagorean Theorem, go to *Pythagorean Theorem* in *Geometry* (p. 678).

Because angles whose measures are multiples of 30 and 45 appear so frequently in trigonometry, you should know some facts about them. In particular, it is very helpful to know the properties of two special right triangles, the 45°–45°–90° triangle and the 30°–60°–90° triangle.

When you draw a diagonal of a square, you create two congruent 45°–45°–90° triangles, also known as isosceles right triangles. If each leg has length x and the hypotenuse has length c, you can use the Pythagorean Theorem to solve for c in terms of x.

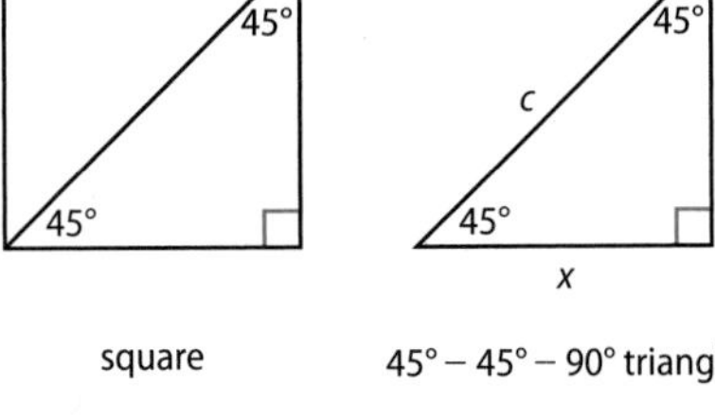

$$x^2 + x^2 = c^2$$

$$2x^2 = c^2$$

$$x\sqrt{2} = c$$

All isosceles right triangles are similar. In every 45°–45°–90° triangle, the legs are congruent and the length of the hypotenuse is $\sqrt{2}$ times the length of a leg.

EXAMPLE 1

Find the value of *h*. Round your answer to the nearest tenth.

Use the properties of a 45°–45°–90° triangle.

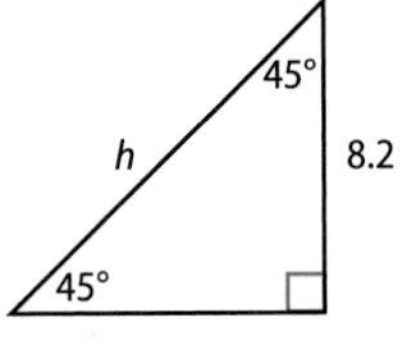

Hypotenuse $= \sqrt{2} \cdot$ leg $\qquad h = \sqrt{2}(8.2)$

Use a calculator and round to the nearest tenth. $\qquad h \approx (1.41421)(8.2)$

≈ 11.6

$h \approx 11.6$

SEARCH

To see step-by-step videos of these problems, enter the page number into the SWadvantage.com Search Bar.

GOT TO KNOW!

The Pythagorean Theorem

In a right triangle with legs of length a and b and hypotenuse of length c, $a^2 + b^2 = c^2$.

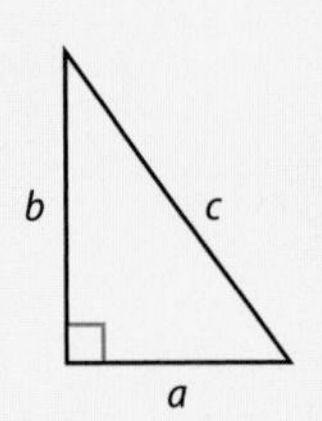

EXAMPLE 2

Find the exact value of *x*.

Use the properties of a 45°–45°–90° triangle.

Hypotenuse $= \sqrt{2} \cdot$ leg	$60 = x\sqrt{2}$
Divide both sides by $\sqrt{2}$.	$x = \frac{60}{\sqrt{2}}$
Rationalize the denominator.	$x = \frac{60}{\sqrt{2}} \cdot \frac{\sqrt{2}}{\sqrt{2}}$
Simplify.	$x = 30\sqrt{2}$

Watch Out!

If a problem asks for an "exact answer," leave the square root in your answer and write the square root in simplified form.

EXAMPLE 3

A walking path through a square park is 85 yd long. Find the dimensions of the park.

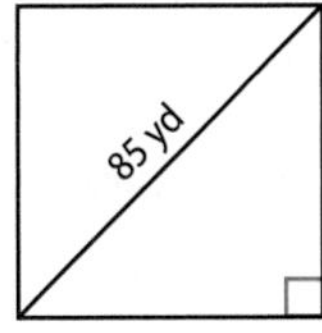

METHOD 1

Use the Pythagorean Theorem.

Let a = length of each side of the square.	$a^2 + a^2 = 85^2$
Simplify.	$2a^2 = 7{,}225$
Divide both sides by 2.	$a^2 = 3{,}612.5$
Use a calculator. Round to the nearest tenth.	$a \approx 60.1$

METHOD 2

Use the properties of a 45°–45°–90° triangle.

Hypotenuse $= \sqrt{2} \cdot$ leg	$85 = a\sqrt{2}$
Divide both sides by $\sqrt{2}$.	$a = \frac{85}{\sqrt{2}}$
Use a calculator. Round to the nearest tenth.	$a \approx 60.1$

The park is about 60.1 yd wide and 60.1 yd long.

Need More HELP

For a review of rationalizing the denominator, go to *Dividing Radical Expressions* in *Advanced Algebra* (Book 2, p. 1962).

GOT TO KNOW!

45°–45°–90° Triangle Theorem

In a 45°–45°–90° triangle, the legs are congruent and the length of the hypotenuse is $\sqrt{2}$ times the length of a leg.

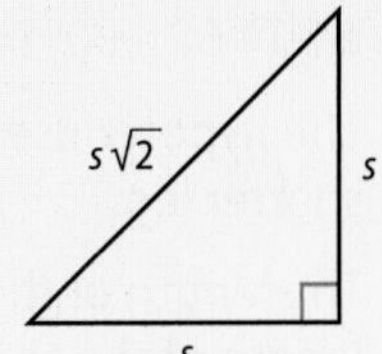

30°–60°–90° Triangles

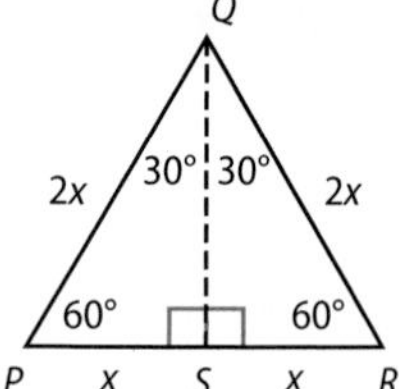

The measure of each angle of an equilateral triangle is 60° and the side lengths are congruent. The bisector of $\angle PQR$ is also the perpendicular bisector of $\overline{PR}$. $\triangle QPS$ is a 30°–60°–90° triangle.

You can use the Pythagorean Theorem to find an expression for QS in terms of x.

Use the Pythagorean Theorem.	$PS^2 + QS^2 = PQ^2$
Substitute.	$x^2 + QS^2 = (2x)^2$
Simplify.	$QS^2 = 3x^2$
Solve for QS.	$QS = x\sqrt{3}$

All 30°–60°–90° triangles are similar. In every 30°–60°–90° triangle, the hypotenuse is twice as long as the shorter leg, and the longer leg is $\sqrt{3}$ times the shorter leg.

EXAMPLE 4

Find the exact values of *x* and *y*.

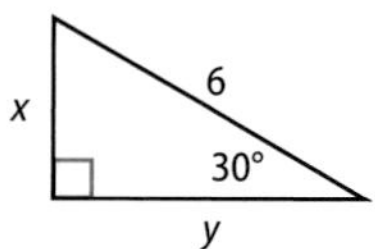

STEP 1 Find the value of x.

2 • shorter leg = hypotenuse	$2x = 6$
Solve for x.	$x = 3$

STEP 2 Find the value of y.

longer leg = $\sqrt{3}$ • shorter leg	$y = x\sqrt{3}$
Substitute 3 for x.	$y = 3\sqrt{3}$

Watch Out!

The shorter leg in a 30°–60°–90° triangle is half the length of the hypotenuse. It is not half the length of the longer leg.

GOT TO KNOW!

30°–60°–90° Triangle Theorem

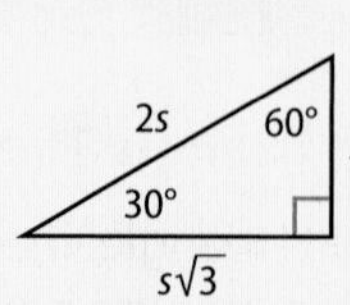

In a 30°–60°–90° triangle,

- The hypotenuse is twice the length of the shorter leg.
- The length of the longer leg is $\sqrt{3}$ times the length of the shorter leg.

EXAMPLE 5

Find the exact values of p and t.

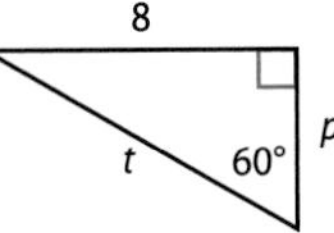

STEP 1 Find the length of the shorter leg.

$\sqrt{3}$ • shorter leg = longer leg $\quad \sqrt{3} \cdot p = 8$

Divide both sides by $\sqrt{3}$. $\quad p = \frac{8}{\sqrt{3}}$

Rationalize the denominator. $\quad p = \frac{8\sqrt{3}}{3}$

STEP 2 Find the hypotenuse.

hypotenuse = 2 • shorter leg $\quad t = 2 \cdot \frac{8\sqrt{3}}{3}$

Simplify. $\quad t = \frac{16\sqrt{3}}{3}$

EXAMPLE 6

A 24-ft ladder leans against the side of a house. The ladder makes a 60° angle with the ground. How far up the side of the house does the ladder reach?

STEP 1 Make a sketch.

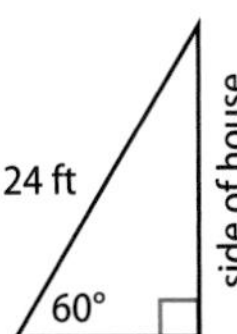

STEP 2 Find the length of the shorter leg.

Divide the hypotenuse by 2. $\quad \frac{24}{2} = 12$

STEP 3 Find the length of the longer leg.

Multiply the shorter leg by $\sqrt{3}$. $\quad 12\sqrt{3}$

Use a calculator. $\quad 12\sqrt{3} \approx 20.8$

The ladder reaches about 20.8 ft up the side of the house.

SEARCH

To see step-by-step videos of these problems, enter the page number into the SWadvantage.com Search Bar.

EXAMPLE 7

An equilateral triangle with sides 1 in. long is inscribed in circle *E*. Find the radius of the circle.

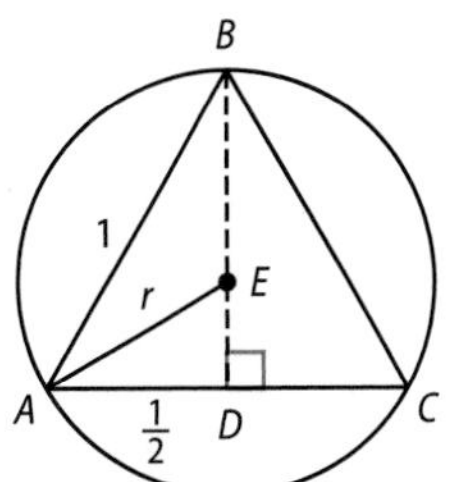

Since $\overline{BD}$ bisects $\angle ABC$, $\triangle BAD$ is a 30°–60°–90° triangle.

Since $\overline{BD}$ bisects $\overline{AC}$, $AD = \frac{1}{2}$. Radius EA bisects $\angle BAD$, so $m\angle EAD = 30°$ and $\triangle AED$ is also a 30°–60–90° triangle. Let $EA = r$. Then $ED = \frac{r}{2}$.

Use the Pythagorean Theorem. $\quad \left(\frac{1}{2}\right)^2 + \left(\frac{r}{2}\right)^2 = r^2$

Simplify. $\quad \frac{1}{4} + \frac{r^2}{4} = r^2$

Multiply both sides by 4. $\quad 1 + r^2 = 4r^2$

Solve for r. $\quad r = \frac{\sqrt{3}}{3}$

The radius of the circle is $\frac{\sqrt{3}}{3}$.

Need More HELP

For more review of special triangles, go to *Special Right Triangles* in *Geometry* (p. 684).

Trigonometric Ratios

Sine, Cosine, and Tangent Ratios

The Pythagorean Theorem relates the lengths of the sides of a right triangle. So does *trigonometry*. The word **trigonometry** comes from the Greek language and means "triangle measurement."

The ratios of side lengths in a right triangle have special names: *sine*, *cosine*, and *tangent ratios*. The definitions are given below.

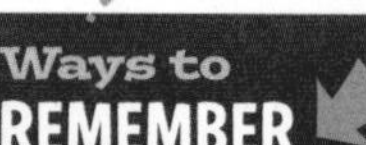

Use SOH CAH TOA to remember the definitions of sine, cosine, and tangent.

SOH stands for "Sine: Opposite over Hypotenuse."

CAH stands for "Cosine: Adjacent over Hypotenuse."

TOA stands for "Tangent: Opposite over Adjacent.

Definition

sine of $\angle A = \frac{\text{leg opposite } \angle A}{\text{hypotenuse}}$

cosine of $\angle A = \frac{\text{leg adjacent to } \angle A}{\text{hypotenuse}}$

tangent of $\angle A = \frac{\text{leg opposite } \angle A}{\text{leg adjacent to } \angle A}$

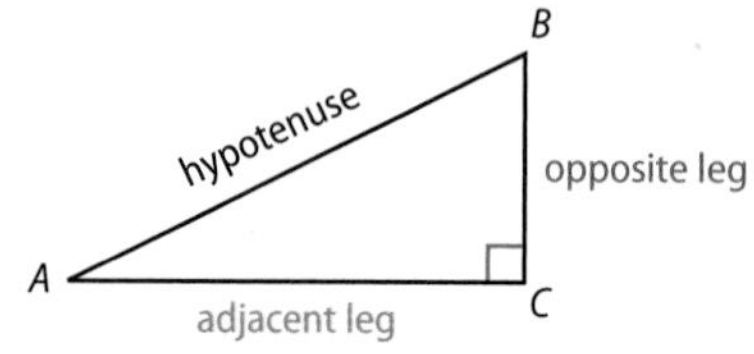

Short Form

$\sin A = \frac{\text{opposite}}{\text{hypotenuse}}$

$\cos A = \frac{\text{adjacent}}{\text{hypotenuse}}$

$\tan A = \frac{\text{opposite}}{\text{adjacent}}$

EXAMPLE 1

Write sin *P*, cos *P*, and tan *P* as ratios.

$\sin P = \frac{\text{opposite}}{\text{hypotenuse}} = \frac{7}{25}$

$\cos P = \frac{\text{adjacent}}{\text{hypotenuse}} = \frac{24}{25}$

$\tan P = \frac{\text{opposite}}{\text{adjacent}} = \frac{7}{24}$

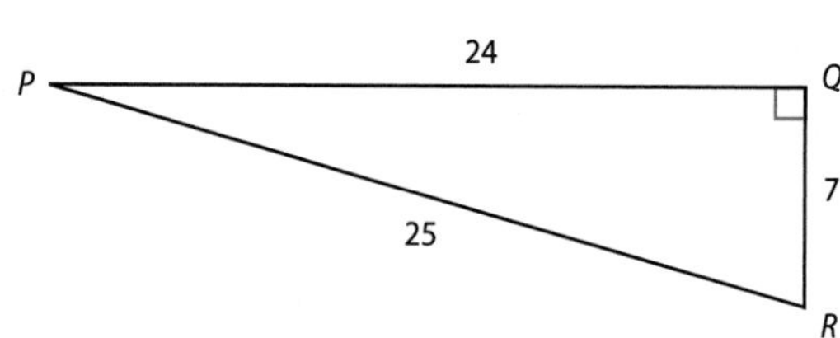

GOT TO KNOW!

Trigonometric Ratios

$\sin A = \frac{\text{opposite}}{\text{hypotenuse}}$

$\cos A = \frac{\text{adjacent}}{\text{hypotenuse}}$

$\tan A = \frac{\text{opposite}}{\text{adjacent}}$

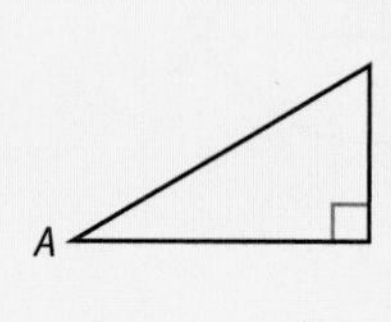

EXAMPLE 2

Find the sine, cosine, and tangent of $\angle A$. Round your answers to the nearest hundredth.

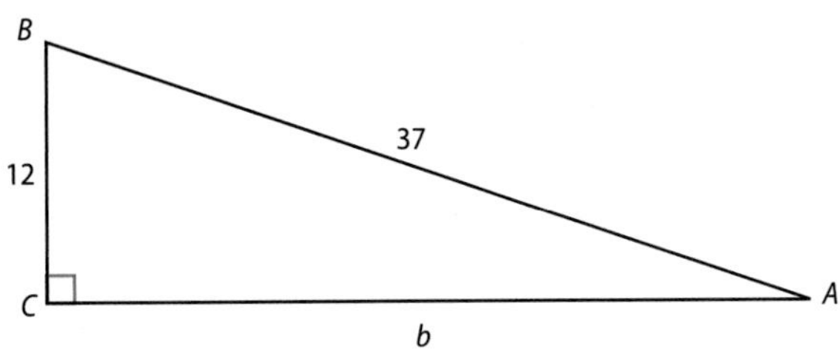

STEP 1 Use the Pythagorean Theorem to find the value of b.

Pythagorean Theorem $12^2 + b^2 = 37^2$

Simplify. $144 + b^2 = 1{,}369$

$b^2 = 1{,}225$

$b = 35$

STEP 2 Write the ratios.

$$\sin A = \frac{\text{opposite}}{\text{hypotenuse}} = \frac{12}{37} \approx 0.32$$

$$\cos A = \frac{\text{adjacent}}{\text{hypotenuse}} = \frac{35}{37} \approx 0.95$$

$$\tan A = \frac{\text{opposite}}{\text{adjacent}} = \frac{12}{35} \approx 0.34$$

Watch Out !

Be careful not to confuse sine and cosine. Make sure you use the opposite side for sine and the adjacent side for cosine.

EXAMPLE 3

If $\cos \theta = \frac{7}{9}$, find the values of $\sin \theta$ and $\tan \theta$.

STEP 1 By definition of cosine, you know that

$$\frac{\text{side adjacent to } \theta}{\text{hypotenuse}} = \frac{7}{9}.$$

Draw a right triangle in which the hypotenuse is 9 and the leg adjacent to θ is 7.

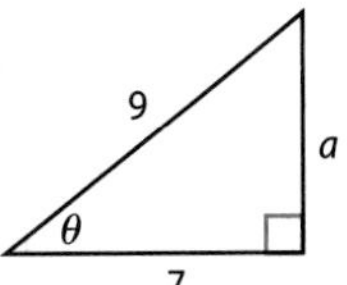

STEP 2 Use the Pythagorean Theorem to find the missing side.

Pythagorean Theorem $a^2 + 7^2 = 9^2$

$a^2 = 81 - 49$

$a^2 = 32$

Take the positive square root. $a = \sqrt{32}$

Simplify the radical. $a = \sqrt{16 \cdot 2}$

$a = 4\sqrt{2}$

STEP 3 Write the sine and tangent of θ.

$$\sin \theta = \frac{\text{opposite}}{\text{hypotenuse}} = \frac{4\sqrt{2}}{9} \qquad \tan \theta = \frac{\text{opposite}}{\text{adjacent}} = \frac{4\sqrt{2}}{7}$$

SEARCH

To see step-by-step videos of these problems, enter the page number into the SWadvantage.com Search Bar.

Cosecant, Secant, and Cotangent Ratios

The reciprocals of the sine, cosine, and tangent ratios are the **cosecant**, **secant**, and **cotangent** ratios, abbreviated csc, sec, and cot, respectively.

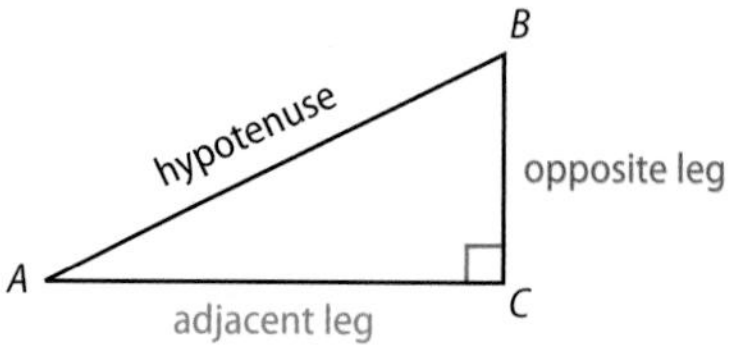

$\sin A = \dfrac{\text{leg opposite } \angle A}{\text{hypotenuse}}$ $\qquad \cos A = \dfrac{\text{leg adjacent to } \angle A}{\text{hypotenuse}}$ $\qquad \tan A = \dfrac{\text{leg opposite } \angle A}{\text{leg adjacent to } \angle A}$

$\csc A = \dfrac{\text{hypotenuse}}{\text{leg opposite } \angle A}$ $\qquad \sec A = \dfrac{\text{hypotenuse}}{\text{leg adjacent to } \angle A}$ $\qquad \cot A = \dfrac{\text{leg adjacent to } \angle A}{\text{leg opposite } \angle A}$

Need More HELP

To write the reciprocal of a fraction, mentally FLIP the fraction.

A **trigonometric identity** is an equation that is true for all acceptable values of the variables in the equation. Here are the six **reciprocal identities**. You will use identities in later topics to simplify trigonometric expressions and to solve trigonometric equations.

$\sin \theta = \dfrac{1}{\csc \theta}$ $\qquad \cos \theta = \dfrac{1}{\sec \theta}$ $\qquad \tan \theta = \dfrac{1}{\cot \theta}$

$\csc \theta = \dfrac{1}{\sin \theta}$ $\qquad \sec \theta = \dfrac{1}{\cos \theta}$ $\qquad \cot \theta = \dfrac{1}{\tan \theta}$

EXAMPLE 4

Find the values of sin *P*, cos *P*, tan *P*, csc *P*, sec *P*, and cot *P*.

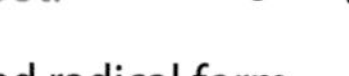

STEP 1 Use the Pythagorean Theorem to find the hypotenuse.

Pythagorean Theorem	$3^2 + 8^2 = c^2$
	$9 + 64 = c^2$
	$c^2 = 73$
Take the positive square root.	$c = \sqrt{73}$

STEP 2 Write the ratios in simplified radical form.

$\sin P = \dfrac{3}{\sqrt{73}} = \dfrac{3\sqrt{73}}{73}$ $\qquad \cos P = \dfrac{8}{\sqrt{73}} = \dfrac{8\sqrt{73}}{73}$ $\qquad \tan P = \dfrac{3}{8}$

$\csc P = \dfrac{\sqrt{73}}{3}$ $\qquad \sec P = \dfrac{\sqrt{73}}{8}$ $\qquad \cot P = \dfrac{8}{3}$

GOT TO KNOW!

Reciprocal Identities

$\csc \theta = \dfrac{1}{\sin \theta}$ $\qquad \sec \theta = \dfrac{1}{\cos \theta}$ $\qquad \cot \theta = \dfrac{1}{\tan \theta}$

$\sin \theta = \dfrac{1}{\csc \theta}$ $\qquad \cos \theta = \dfrac{1}{\sec \theta}$ $\qquad \tan \theta = \dfrac{1}{\cot \theta}$

Cofunctions

In every right triangle, the acute angles are complementary. In the figure, $\angle A$ and $\angle B$ are complementary. Notice that $\sin A = \cos B$ and $\sin B = \cos A$. In other words, the sine of an angle equals the cosine of its complement. Sine and cosine are called **cofunctions**. Tangent and cotangent are also cofunctions, as are secant and cosecant.

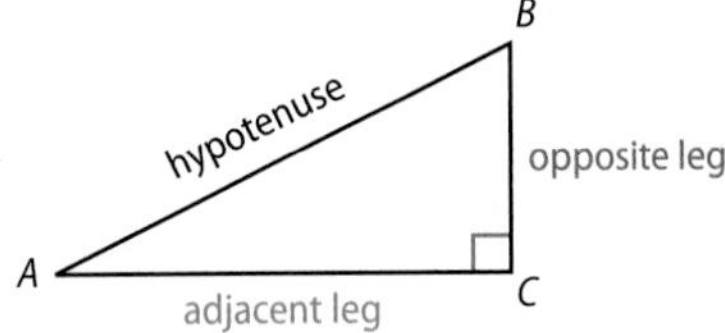

The following list shows six more identities, the **cofunction identities**.

$\sin\theta = \cos(90° - \theta)$ $\quad$ $\tan\theta = \cot(90° - \theta)$ $\quad$ $\sec\theta = \csc(90° - \theta)$

$\cos\theta = \sin(90° - \theta)$ $\quad$ $\cot\theta = \tan(90° - \theta)$ $\quad$ $\csc\theta = \sec(90° - \theta)$

EXAMPLE 5

Use a cofunction identity to find the value of *x*.

a. $\cos 63° = \sin x°$

Use a cofunction identity. $\cos 63° = \sin(90° - 63°)$
$= \sin 27°$

$x = 27$

b. $\tan 24° = \cot x°$

Use a cofunction identity. $\tan 24° = \cot(90° - 24°)$
$= \cot 66°$

$x = 66$

SEARCH

To see step-by-step videos of these problems, enter the page number into the SWadvantage.com Search Bar.

EXAMPLE 6

Find the value of *x* that satisfies the equation $\cos(x + 8)° = \sin(2x - 14)°$.

Since cosine and sine are cofunctions, you can write an equation showing that the sum of the two expressions is 90.

Write the equation.	$(x + 8) + (2x - 14) = 90$
Combine like terms.	$3x - 6 = 90$
Add 6 to both sides.	$3x = 96$
Divide both sides by 3.	$x = 32$

Cofunction Identities

$\sin\theta = \cos(90° - \theta)$ $\quad$ $\tan\theta = \cot(90° - \theta)$ $\quad$ $\sec\theta = \csc(90° - \theta)$

$\cos\theta = \sin(90° - \theta)$ $\quad$ $\cot\theta = \tan(90° - \theta)$ $\quad$ $\csc\theta = \sec(90° - \theta)$

Using a Calculator

You can use the SIN, COS, and TAN keys of your calculator to find the values of the sine, cosine, and tangent ratios, respectively. When you are given the measure of an angle in degrees, make sure your calculator is in degree mode (DEG), and not in radian mode (RAD) or gradian mode (GRA). The degree mode is the default mode on most calculators. If you see RAD or GRA on your calculator screen, you are not in degree mode.

Most trigonometric values (like most square roots) are irrational numbers. The tangent of 45° equals 1 and the cosine of 60° equals 0.5, but these are exceptions. When you use trigonometric ratios, round your answer to a reasonable number of decimal places. If the answer is a rounded value, be sure to use the approximate symbol when you state your answer.

Your calculator may be able to convert from DMS (degree, minutes, seconds) to decimal degrees. Make sure the calculator is in degree mode first.

EXAMPLE 1

Use a calculator to evaluate each expression. Round your answer to three decimal places.

a. tan 75°

TAN 7 5 ENTER **3.732050808**

tan 75° ≈ 3.732

b. cos 28.6°

COS 2 8 . 6 ENTER **0.877982975**

cos 28.6° ≈ 0.878

c. sin 110°

SIN 1 1 0 ENTER **0.93969262208**

sin 110° ≈ 0.937

Always check the angle mode on your calculator.

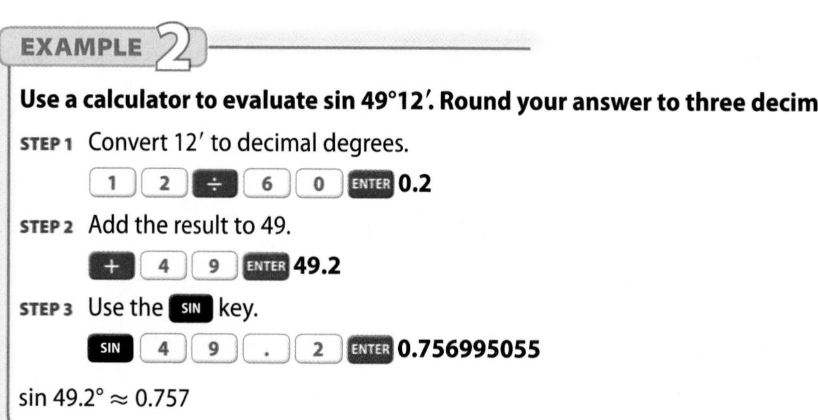

EXAMPLE 2

Use a calculator to evaluate sin 49°12′. Round your answer to three decimal places.

STEP 1 Convert 12′ to decimal degrees.

1 2 ÷ 6 0 ENTER **0.2**

STEP 2 Add the result to 49.

\+ 4 9 ENTER **49.2**

STEP 3 Use the SIN key.

SIN 4 9 . 2 ENTER **0.756995055**

sin 49.2° ≈ 0.757

The Reciprocal Ratios

Your calculator has keys for the sine, cosine, and tangent ratios. But, there may be no keys for the other three functions—cosecant, secant, and cotangent. So how do you use a calculator to evaluate these ratios? First of all, remember that these are reciprocal functions.

$$\csc\theta = \frac{1}{\sin\theta} \qquad \sec\theta = \frac{1}{\cos\theta} \qquad \cot\theta = \frac{1}{\tan\theta}$$

To use a calculator to determine the values for cosecant, secant, and tangent, use the SIN, COS, and TAN keys, respectively, followed by the reciprocal x^{-1} key.

EXAMPLE 3

Use a calculator to evaluate each expression. Round your answer to three decimal places.

a. cot 53°

Use your calculator to evaluate $\frac{1}{\tan 53°}$. TAN 5 3) x^{-1} ENTER **0.75355405**

cot 53° ≈ 0.754

b. sec 14.3°

Use your calculator to evaluate $\frac{1}{\cos 14.3°}$. COS 1 4 . 3) x^{-1} ENTER **1.03197499**

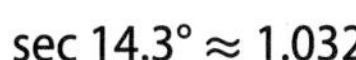

sec 14.3° ≈ 1.032

Watch Out!

The order in which you use the keys varies from calculator to calculator. On some calculators you press TAN and then the angle measure. On others, you enter the angle measure first.

EXAMPLE 4

Use a calculator to evaluate csc 52°10′. Round your answer to three decimal places.

STEP 1 Convert 10′ to decimal degrees.

1 0 ÷ 6 0 = **0.166666666**

STEP 2 Add the result to 52.

+ 5 2 = **52.16666667**

STEP 3 Because $\csc\theta = \frac{1}{\sin\theta}$, use the SIN key, followed by the x^{-1} key.

SIN 52.16666667) x^{-1} ENTER **1.266146047**

csc 52°10′ ≈ 1.266

SEARCH

To see step-by-step videos of these problems, enter the page number into the SWadvantage.com Search Bar.

Finding Trigonometric Values with a Calculator

Function	sine	cosine	tangent	cosecant	secant	cotangent
Keys	SIN	COS	TAN	SIN x^{-1}	COS x^{-1}	TAN x^{-1}

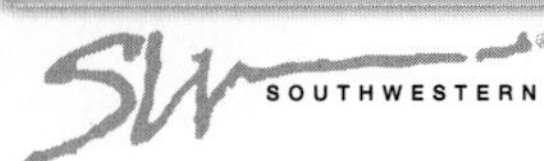

Solving Problems with Right Triangles

You can use trigonometric ratios to solve many types of problems. To find an unknown length in a right triangle you need only two pieces of information—the lengths of two sides or the measure of one acute angle and the length of one side.

Watch Out

Copy the drawing carefully and use it to help you solve the problem. If a drawing is not provided, then make one.

EXAMPLE 5

The shadow of a flagpole extends 30 ft from the flagpole. A line from the top of the flagpole to the end of the shadow makes a 50° angle with the ground. Find x, the height of the flagpole.

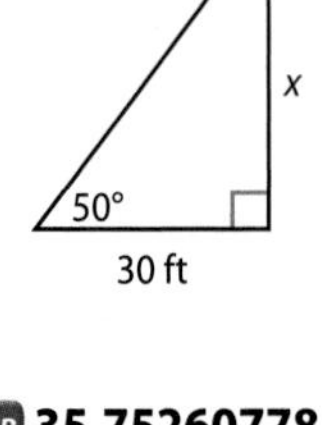

STEP 1 Write an equation.

$\tan 50° = \frac{\text{opposite}}{\text{adjacent}} = \frac{x}{30}$

STEP 2 Solve the equation.

Multiply both sides by 30. $30 \cdot \tan 50° = x$

Use a calculator. 3 0 × TAN 5 0 ENTER **35.75260778**

Round your answer to the nearest foot. $x \approx 36$

The flagpole is about 36 ft tall.

EXAMPLE 6

Triangle PQR is isosceles. The base angles measure 70° and the legs are 12 cm long. Find the area of $\triangle PQR$.

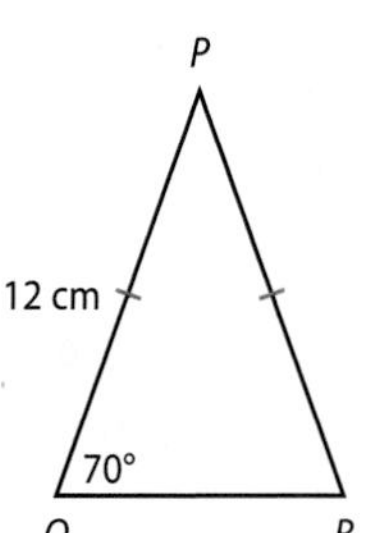

To find the area of a triangle, use the formula $A = \frac{1}{2}bh$, where A is the area, b is the length of the base, and h is the height of the triangle.

STEP 1 Draw the altitude from the vertex P to the base of the triangle. Because the triangle is isosceles, the altitude bisects the base.

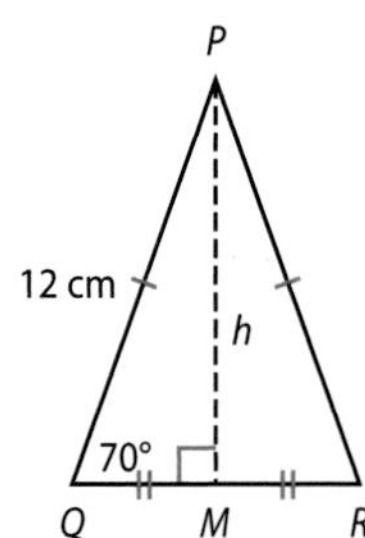

STEP 2 Find the height h.

Use a trigonometric ratio. $\sin \theta = \frac{\text{opposite}}{\text{hypotenuse}}$

Write an equation. $\sin 70° = \frac{h}{12}$

Solve the equation for h. $h = 12(\sin 70°) \approx 11.276$

STEP 3 Find the length of the base.
The length of the base QR is $2(QM)$.
Use the Pythagorean Theorem to find QM.

Pythagorean Theorem $QM^2 + PM^2 = PQ^2$

Substitute. $QM^2 + 11.276^2 = 12^2$

Solve for QM. $QM \approx 4.105$

$QR = 2(QM) \approx 8.21$

STEP 4 Substitute into the area formula.

$A = \frac{1}{2}bh = \frac{1}{2}(8.21)(11.276) \approx 46.3$

The area of $\triangle PQR$ is about 46.3 cm^2.

Using a Table

Before there were calculators, mathematicians and scientists used tables like this one to compute trigonometric ratios. The earliest known table of trigonometric ratios is part of a Babylonian cuneiform tablet.

θ Degrees	θ Radians	sin θ	cos θ	tan θ	cot θ	sec θ	csc θ		
6	.1047	.1045	.9945	.1051	9.514	1.006	9.567	1.4661	**84**
7	.1222	.1219	.9925	.1228	8.144	1.008	8.206	1.4486	**83**
8	.1396	.1392	.9903	.1405	7.115	1.010	7.185	1.4312	**82**
9	.1571	.1564	.9877	.1584	6.314	1.012	6.392	1.4137	**81**
10	.1745	.1736	.9848	.1763	5.671	1.015	5.759	1.3963	**80**
11	.1920	.1908	.9816	.1944	5.145	1.019	5.241	1.3788	**79**
12	.2094	.2079	.9781	.2126	4.705	1.022	4.810	1.3614	**78**
		cos θ	**sin θ**	**cot θ**	**tan θ**	**csc θ**	**sec θ**	**θ Radians**	**θ Degrees**

Watch Out!

If you use the angle measures in the right column, be sure to use the column names at the bottom—not the top.

For now, ignore the column labeled *Radians*. You will learn more about radians in *Radian Measure and Trigonometric Functions* starting on page 926.

In the table above, only angles from 6° to 12° and from 78° to 84° are shown. In the complete table, for angles from 0° to 45°, use the angles in the left-hand column and the trigonometric ratios listed at the top. For angles from 45° to 90°, use the angles in the right-hand column and the trigonometric ratios listed at the bottom.

EXAMPLE 7

Use the table to find the value of each trigonometric ratio.

a. sin 6°

Start at the top of the table.
Find the column headed "sin θ."
Go to the row that contains 6 in the "Degrees" column on the left.

$\sin 6° \approx 0.1045$

b. tan 81°

Start at the bottom of the table.
Find the column labeled "tan θ."
Go up to the row that contains 81 in the "Degrees" column on the right.

$\tan 81° \approx 6.314$

SEARCH

To see step-by-step videos of these problems, enter the page number into the SWadvantage.com Search Bar.

Trigonometric Ratios of Special Angles

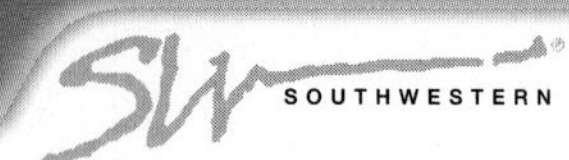

0° and 90° Angles

There are some angles that have exact trigonometric values. These appear so often in problem situations that it is a good idea to memorize their values.

To gain understanding of the trigonometric ratios for angles of 0° and 90°, consider a right triangle in the coordinate plane.

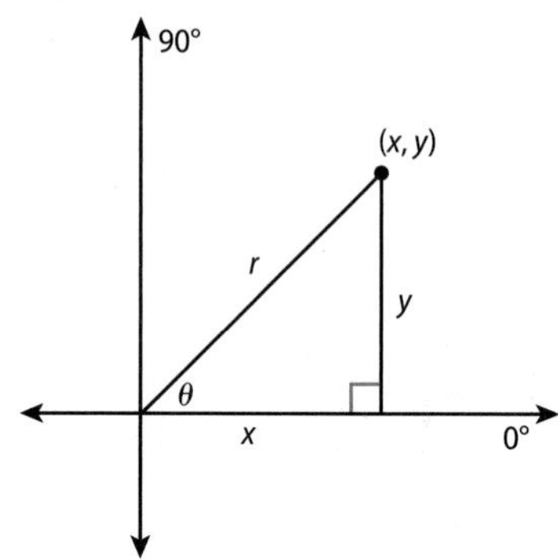

Based on this figure, the trigonometric functions can be redefined as follows:

$$\sin\theta = \frac{y}{r},\ \cos\theta = \frac{x}{r},\ \tan\theta = \frac{y}{x}$$

When θ equals 0°, what happens to x, y, and r? You can see that the value of y reduces to 0 and that the values of r and x will become equal. Next, imagine θ increasing to 90°. Now the value of x reduces to 0 and the values of r and y become equal. These ideas are used in the next example.

You cannot divide by 0. Division by 0 is undefined.

EXAMPLE 1

Find the six trigonometric ratios for angles of 0° and 90°.

STEP 1 For 0°, use $x = 1$, $y = 0$, and $r = 1$. Write the six ratios.

$\sin 0° = \frac{y}{r} = \frac{0}{1} = 0$ $\qquad$ $\csc 0° = \frac{1}{\sin 0°} = \frac{1}{0}$ undefined

$\cos 0° = \frac{x}{r} = \frac{1}{1} = 1$ $\qquad$ $\sec 0° = \frac{1}{\cos 0°} = \frac{1}{1} = 1$

$\tan 0° = \frac{y}{x} = \frac{0}{1} = 0$ $\qquad$ $\cot 0° = \frac{1}{\tan 0°} = \frac{1}{0}$ undefined

STEP 2 For 90°, use $x = 0$, $y = 1$, and $r = 1$. Write the six ratios.

$\sin 90° = \frac{y}{r} = \frac{1}{1} = 1$ $\qquad$ $\csc 90° = \frac{1}{\sin 90°} = \frac{1}{1} = 1$

$\cos 90° = \frac{x}{r} = \frac{0}{1} = 0$ $\qquad$ $\sec 90° = \frac{1}{\cos 90°} = \frac{1}{0}$ undefined

$\tan 90° = \frac{y}{x} = \frac{1}{0}$ undefined $\qquad$ $\cot 90° = \frac{1}{\tan 90°} = \frac{0}{1} = 0$

GOT TO KNOW!

Trigonometric Ratios of 0° and 90° Angles

$\sin 0° = 0$	$\cos 0° = 1$	$\tan 0° = 0$	$\csc 0°$ undefined	$\sec 0° = 1$	$\cot 0°$ undefined
$\sin 90° = 1$	$\cos 90° = 0$	$\tan 90°$ undefined	$\csc 90° = 1$	$\sec 90°$ undefined	$\cot 90° = 0$

30° and 60° Angles

In a 30°- 60°- 90° right triangle, the shorter leg is opposite the 30° angle and the longer leg is opposite the 60° angle. The hypotenuse is twice as long as the shorter leg. The length of the longer leg is $\sqrt{3}$ times the shorter leg.

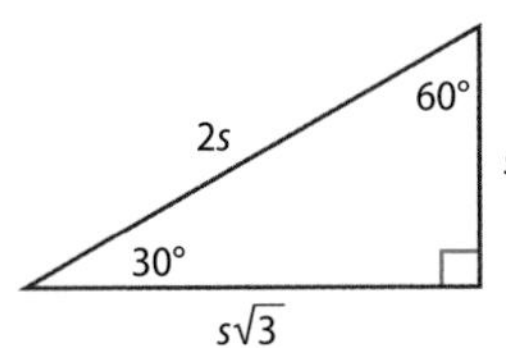

Need More HELP

For a review of 30°- 60°- 90° triangles, go to *Angles and Degree Measure* on page 894.

EXAMPLE 2

Without using a calculator, find the six trigonometric ratios of a 30° angle.

STEP 1 Draw a 30°- 60°- 90° right triangle with hypotenuse 2.

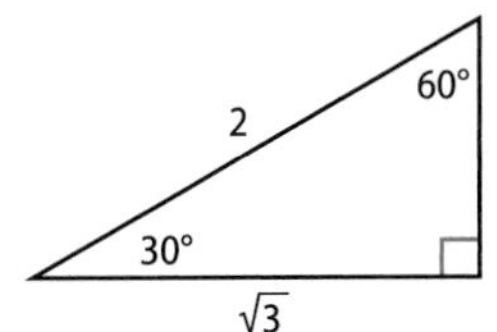

STEP 2 Find the sine, cosine, and tangent of 30°.

$$\sin 30° = \frac{\text{opposite}}{\text{hypotenuse}} = \frac{1}{2}$$

$$\cos 30° = \frac{\text{adjacent}}{\text{hypotenuse}} = \frac{\sqrt{3}}{2}$$

$$\tan 30° = \frac{\text{opposite}}{\text{adjacent}} = \frac{1}{\sqrt{3}} \cdot \frac{\sqrt{3}}{\sqrt{3}} = \frac{\sqrt{3}}{3}$$

STEP 3 Use the reciprocal relationships to find the cosecant, secant, and cotangent of 30°.

$$\csc 30° = \frac{1}{\sin 30°} = \frac{2}{1} = 2$$

$$\sec 30° = \frac{1}{\cos 30°} = \frac{2}{\sqrt{3}} \cdot \frac{\sqrt{3}}{\sqrt{3}} = \frac{2\sqrt{3}}{3}$$

$$\cot 30° = \frac{1}{\tan 30°} = \frac{\sqrt{3}}{1} = \sqrt{3}$$

SEARCH

To see step-by-step videos of these problems, enter the page number into the SWadvantage.com Search Bar.

EXAMPLE 3

A board that is 2.35 m long braces a gate in a fence. The brace makes a 30° angle with the bottom of the gate. How tall is the gate? Round your answer to the nearest hundredth.

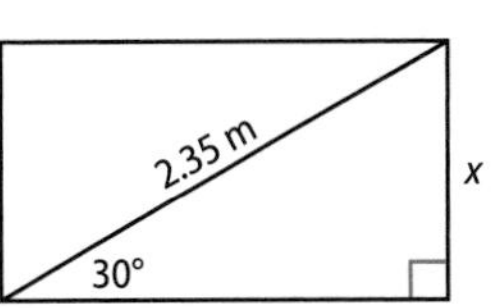

You are given the hypotenuse in a 30°- 60°- 90° right triangle. You need to find the measure of the side opposite the 30° angle. Use the sine ratio to find the unknown measure.

Write an equation.	$\sin 30° = \frac{x}{2.35}$
Multiply both sides by 2.35.	$x = 2.35 \cdot \sin 30°$
Simplify.	$x = 2.35 \cdot \frac{1}{2} = 1.175$

The gate is about 1.18 m tall.

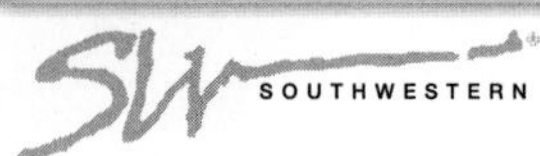

60° Angles

EXAMPLE 4

Without using a calculator, find the six trigonometric ratios of a 60° angle.

STEP 1 Draw a 30°- 60°- 90° right triangle with hypotenuse 2.

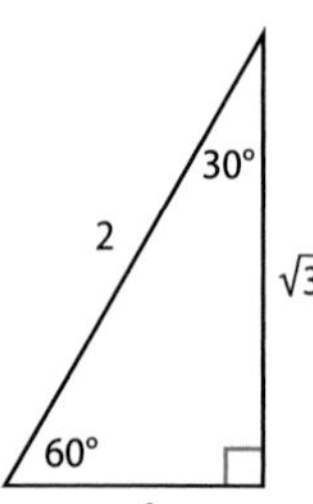

STEP 2 Find the sine, cosine, and tangent of 60°.

$$\sin 60° = \frac{\text{opposite}}{\text{hypotenuse}} = \frac{\sqrt{3}}{2}$$

$$\cos 60° = \frac{\text{adjacent}}{\text{hypotenuse}} = \frac{1}{2}$$

$$\tan 60° = \frac{\text{opposite}}{\text{adjacent}} = \frac{\sqrt{3}}{1} = \sqrt{3}$$

STEP 3 Use the reciprocal relationships to find the cosecant, secant, and cotangent of 60°.

$$\csc 60° = \frac{1}{\sin 60°} = \frac{2}{\sqrt{3}} \cdot \frac{\sqrt{3}}{\sqrt{3}} = \frac{2\sqrt{3}}{3}$$

$$\sec 60° = \frac{1}{\cos 60°} = \frac{2}{1} = 2$$

$$\cot 60° = \frac{1}{\tan 60°} = \frac{1}{\sqrt{3}} \cdot \frac{\sqrt{3}}{\sqrt{3}} = \frac{\sqrt{3}}{3}$$

EXAMPLE 5

A right triangle has one 60° angle. The leg opposite this angle is 8 units long. Find the exact value of *x*.

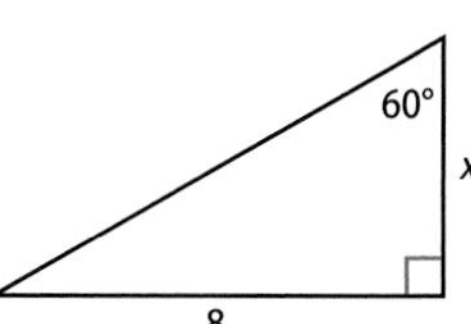

SEARCH

To see step-by-step videos of these problems, enter the page number into the SWadvantage.com Search Bar.

METHOD 1

Use the cotangent ratio.

Write an equation. $\cot 60° = \frac{x}{8}$

Substitute $\frac{\sqrt{3}}{3}$ for cot 60°. $\frac{\sqrt{3}}{3} = \frac{x}{8}$

Multiply both sides by 8. $x = \frac{8\sqrt{3}}{3}$

METHOD 2

Use the tangent ratio.

Write an equation. $\tan 60° = \frac{8}{x}$

Substitute $\sqrt{3}$ for tan 60°. $\sqrt{3} = \frac{8}{x}$

Multiply both sides by x. $x\sqrt{3} = 8$

Divide both sides by $\sqrt{3}$. $x = \frac{8}{\sqrt{3}}$

Rationalize the denominator. $x = \frac{8}{\sqrt{3}} \cdot \frac{\sqrt{3}}{\sqrt{3}} = \frac{8\sqrt{3}}{3}$

45° Angles

In every 45°-45°-90° triangle, the legs are congruent and the length of the hypotenuse is $\sqrt{2}$ times the length of a leg.

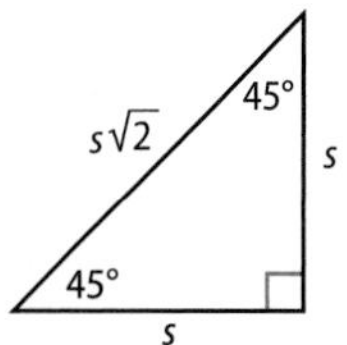

EXAMPLE 6

Without using a calculator, find the six trigonometric ratios of a 45° angle.

STEP 1 Draw a 45°-45°-90° right triangle with legs of length 1 and hypotenuse $\sqrt{2}$.

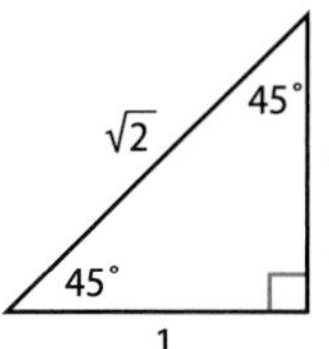

STEP 2 Find the sine, cosine, and tangent of 45°.

$$\sin 45° = \frac{\text{opposite}}{\text{hypotenuse}} = \frac{1}{\sqrt{2}} \cdot \frac{\sqrt{2}}{\sqrt{2}} = \frac{\sqrt{2}}{2}$$

$$\cos 45° = \frac{\text{adjacent}}{\text{hypotenuse}} = \frac{1}{\sqrt{2}} \cdot \frac{\sqrt{2}}{\sqrt{2}} = \frac{\sqrt{2}}{2}$$

$$\tan 45° = \frac{\text{opposite}}{\text{adjacent}} = \frac{1}{1} = 1$$

STEP 3 Use the reciprocal relationships to find the cosecant, secant, and cotangent of 45°.

$$\csc 45° = \frac{1}{\sin 45°} = \frac{\sqrt{2}}{1} = \sqrt{2}$$

$$\sec 45° = \frac{1}{\cos 45°} = \frac{\sqrt{2}}{1} = \sqrt{2}$$

$$\cot 45° = \frac{1}{\tan 45°} = \frac{1}{1} = 1$$

GOT TO KNOW!

Trigonometric Ratios of a 30° Angle

$\sin 30° = \frac{1}{2}$ $\quad\cos 30° = \frac{\sqrt{3}}{2}$ $\quad\tan 30° = \frac{1}{\sqrt{3}} = \frac{\sqrt{3}}{3}$

$\csc 30° = 2$ $\quad\sec 30° = \frac{2}{\sqrt{3}} = \frac{2\sqrt{3}}{3}$ $\quad\cot 30° = \sqrt{3}$

Trigonometric Ratios of a 60° Angle

$\sin 60° = \frac{\sqrt{3}}{2}$ $\quad\cos 60° = \frac{1}{2}$ $\quad\tan 60° = \sqrt{3}$

$\csc 60° = \frac{2}{\sqrt{3}} = \frac{2\sqrt{3}}{3}$ $\quad\sec 60° = 2$ $\quad\cot 60° = \frac{1}{\sqrt{3}} = \frac{\sqrt{3}}{3}$

Trigonometric Ratios of a 45° Angle

$\sin 45° = \frac{1}{\sqrt{2}} = \frac{\sqrt{2}}{2}$ $\quad\cos 45° = \frac{1}{\sqrt{2}} = \frac{\sqrt{2}}{2}$ $\quad\tan 45° = 1$

$\csc 45° = \sqrt{2}$ $\quad\sec 45° = \sqrt{2}$ $\quad\cot 45° = 1$

Finding Angle Measures

Special Angles

To see step-by-step videos of these problems, enter the page number into the SWadvantage.com Search Bar.

You know how to use trigonometric ratios to find the lengths of the sides of a right triangle given one side and an angle. Now you will learn how to use trigonometric ratios to find an angle measure when you are given two sides of a right triangle.

When you are looking for an unknown angle measure, first check to see if it is one of the special angles: 0°, 30°, 45°, 60°, or 90°. If you have not memorized the trigonometric ratios for special angles, use the table below.

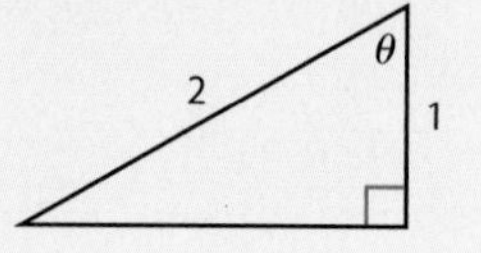

To find an angle whose cosine is $\frac{1}{2}$, start by drawing a right triangle with a leg of length 1 and a hypotenuse of length 2. Label the included angle θ.

EXAMPLE 1

Find the value of θ, $0° \leq \theta \leq 90°$, that satisfies each equation.

a. $\sin \theta = 1$

$\theta = 90°$

b. $\cos \theta = 0.5$

$0.5 = \frac{1}{2}$, so $\theta = 60°$.

c. $\tan \theta = \frac{\sqrt{3}}{3}$

$\theta = 30°$

d. $\sec \theta = \frac{1}{2}$

$\sec \theta = \frac{1}{2}$ is equivalent to the equation $\cos \theta = 2$. The value of cosine θ is never greater than 1.

The equation has no solution.

GOT TO KNOW!

Trigonometric Ratios of Special Angles

θ	$\sin \theta$	$\cos \theta$	$\tan \theta$	$\csc \theta$	$\sec \theta$	$\cot \theta$
0°	0	1	0	undefined	1	undefined
30°	$\frac{1}{2}$	$\frac{\sqrt{3}}{2}$	$\frac{\sqrt{3}}{3}$	2	$\frac{2\sqrt{3}}{3}$	$\sqrt{3}$
45°	$\frac{\sqrt{2}}{2}$	$\frac{\sqrt{2}}{2}$	1	$\sqrt{2}$	$\sqrt{2}$	1
60°	$\frac{\sqrt{3}}{2}$	$\frac{1}{2}$	$\sqrt{3}$	$\frac{2\sqrt{3}}{3}$	2	$\frac{\sqrt{3}}{3}$
90°	1	0	undefined	1	undefined	0

Using a Calculator

In most trigonometric equations, the angle you are looking for is probably not one of the special angles. To find the measure of such an angle, you will use the idea of an *inverse operation*. You have seen inverse operations before. They undo each other. Addition and subtraction are inverse operations; so are squaring a number and taking the square root. You can use inverse operations to write equivalent trigonometric equations.

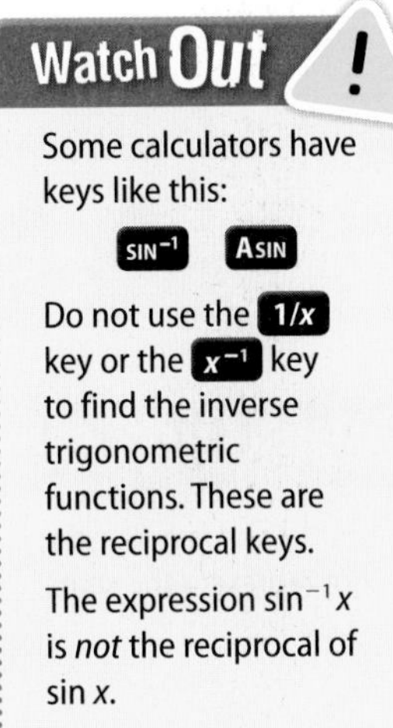

Watch Out !
Some calculators have keys like this:
SIN⁻¹ ASIN
Do not use the 1/x key or the x⁻¹ key to find the inverse trigonometric functions. These are the reciprocal keys.
The expression sin⁻¹x is *not* the reciprocal of sin x.

The most often used inverse trig functions are:

Notation	Read
$\sin^{-1}$	inverse sine, or arcsine
$\cos^{-1}$	inverse cosine, or arccosine
$\tan^{-1}$	inverse tangent, or arctangent

In a right triangle, the inverse trig relations are defined as:

If $\sin y = x$ and $0° \leq y \leq 90°$, then $y = \sin^{-1} x$.

If $\cos y = x$ and $0° \leq y \leq 90°$, then $y = \cos^{-1} x$.

If $\tan y = x$ and $0° \leq y \leq 90°$, then $y = \tan^{-1} x$.

Locate the inverse sine, cosine, and tangent keys on your calculator. On many calculators, they are often the second functions above the corresponding keys.

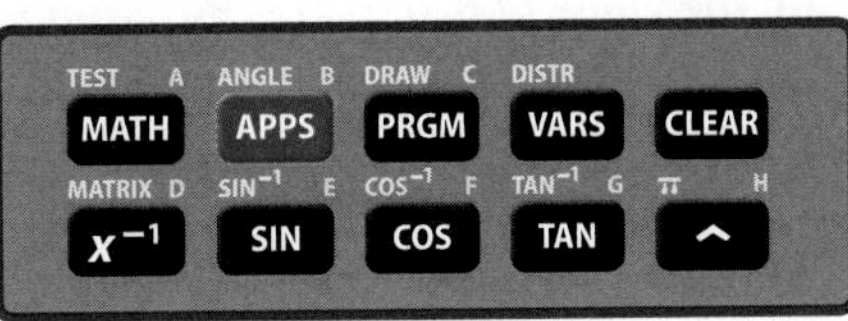

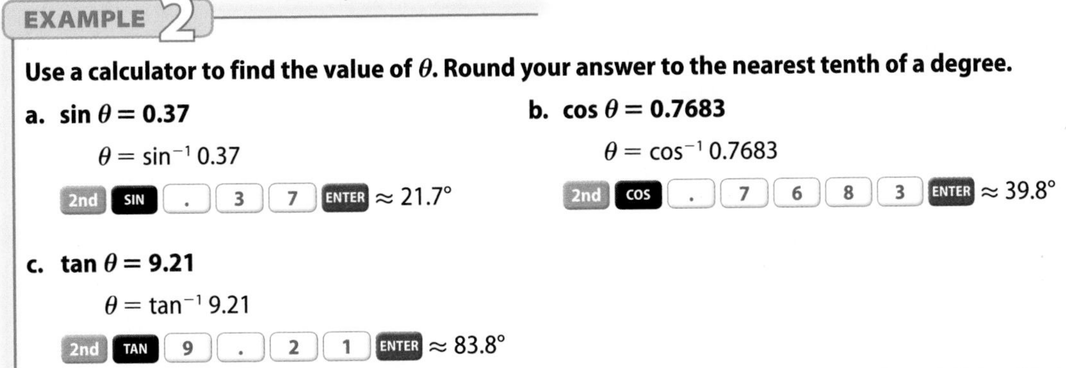

EXAMPLE 2

Use a calculator to find the value of θ. Round your answer to the nearest tenth of a degree.

a. $\sin \theta = 0.37$

$\theta = \sin^{-1} 0.37$

2nd SIN . 3 7 ENTER $\approx 21.7°$

b. $\cos \theta = 0.7683$

$\theta = \cos^{-1} 0.7683$

2nd COS . 7 6 8 3 ENTER $\approx 39.8°$

c. $\tan \theta = 9.21$

$\theta = \tan^{-1} 9.21$

2nd TAN 9 . 2 1 ENTER $\approx 83.8°$

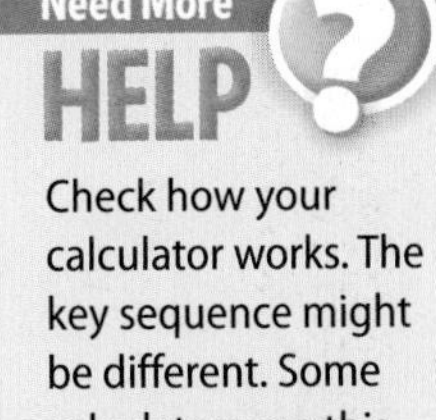

Check how your calculator works. The key sequence might be different. Some calculators use this sequence:

.37 2nd SIN

Inverse Sine, Cosine, and Tangent in a Right Triangle

Inverse sine: If $\sin y = x$ and $0° \leq y \leq 90°$, then $y = \sin^{-1} x$.

Inverse cosine: If $\cos y = x$ and $0° \leq y \leq 90°$, then $y = \cos^{-1} x$.

Inverse tangent: If $\tan y = x$ and $0° \leq y \leq 90°$, then $y = \tan^{-1} x$.

Inverse Cosecant, Secant, and Cotangent

Your calculator has keys for the inverse sine, the inverse cosine, and the inverse tangent. As you have seen, the inverse keys are marked $\sin^{-1}$, $\cos^{-1}$, and $\tan^{-1}$. But, there are no keys for inverses of the cosecant, secant, and tangent. To solve an equation like $\cot \theta = 0.64$, you need to use one of the reciprocal identities.

Cosecant, secant, and cotangent are reciprocals of sine, cosine, and tangent, respectively.

$$\csc \theta = \frac{1}{\sin \theta} \qquad \sec \theta = \frac{1}{\cos \theta} \qquad \cot \theta = \frac{1}{\tan \theta}$$

To find values for these measures, you will need to use the reciprocal key **1/x**.

Watch Out!

$\sin^{-1} x$ and $(\sin \theta)^{-1}$ do not represent the same quantity.

It is important to understand how $\sin^{-1} x$ differs from $(\sin \theta)^{-1}$.

- Arcsine, or $\sin^{-1} x$, represents an angle measure.
- The reciprocal of sine, or $(\sin \theta)^{-1}$, represents the cosecant ratio, not an angle measure.

$$\cos 60° = \frac{1}{2} \qquad \cos^{-1}\left(\frac{1}{2}\right) = 60° \qquad (\cos 60°)^{-1} = \frac{1}{\cos 60°} = 2$$

EXAMPLE 3

Find the value of θ, $0° \le \theta \le 90°$, that satisfies $\cot \theta = 0.64$.

STEP 1 Rewrite the equation to use tangent.

$\cot \theta = 0.64 \longrightarrow \frac{1}{\tan \theta} = 0.64$

STEP 2 Take the reciprocal of both sides.

$\tan \theta = \frac{1}{0.64}$

STEP 3 Use the inverse tangent key on a calculator.

$\tan^{-1}\left(\frac{1}{0.64}\right) = \tan^{-1}(1.5625) \approx 57.38°$

$\theta \approx 57.38°$

EXAMPLE 4

Solve $2 \sec \theta = 8$, $0° \le \theta \le 90°$.

Rewrite the equation to use cosine. $2 \sec \theta = 8 \longrightarrow \frac{2}{\cos \theta} = 8$

Multiply both sides by $\cos \theta$. $2 = 8 \cos \theta$

Divide both sides by 8. $0.25 = \cos \theta$

Use the inverse cosine key on a calculator. **2nd** **COS** 0.25 **ENTER** ≈ 75.52

$\theta \approx 75.52°$

To see step-by-step videos of these problems, enter the page number into the SWadvantage.com Search Bar.

Solving Problems with Right Triangles

Using a given trigonometric ratio to approximate an angle will help you solve applied problems. A common type of problem is finding an unknown angle in a right triangle. You need only two pieces of information, the lengths of two sides.

EXAMPLE 5

A 30-ft ladder reaches 28 ft up the side of a building. Find the angle the ladder makes with the ground. Round your answer to the nearest hundredth.

You are given the hypotenuse (the ladder) and the side opposite the angle. So, use the sine function to determine the measure of the angle.

Write an equation. $\sin\theta = \frac{28}{30}$

Use a calculator. $\theta = \sin^{-1}\left(\frac{28}{30}\right) \approx 68.96°$

The ladder makes about a 68.96° angle with the ground.

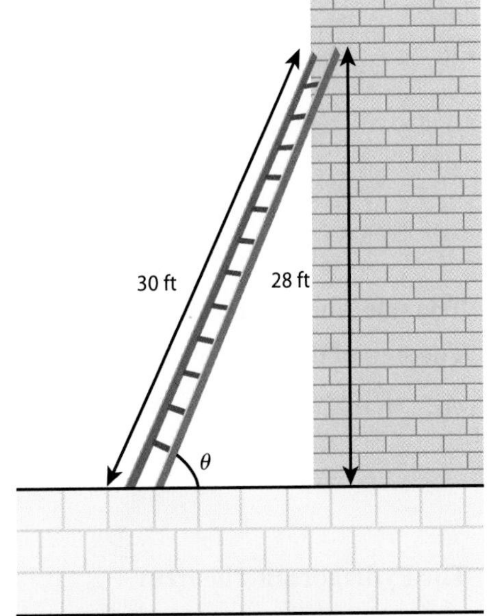

EXAMPLE 6

A cable television pole is 25 yd high. The bracing wire at the ground is 15 yd from the base of the pole. Find the measure of the angle where the wire meets the ground.

You know the length of the side adjacent to the angle and the length of the side opposite the angle. Use the tangent ratio.

Write an equation. $\tan\theta = \frac{25}{15}$

Use a calculator. $\theta = \tan^{-1}\left(\frac{25}{15}\right) \approx 59.04°$

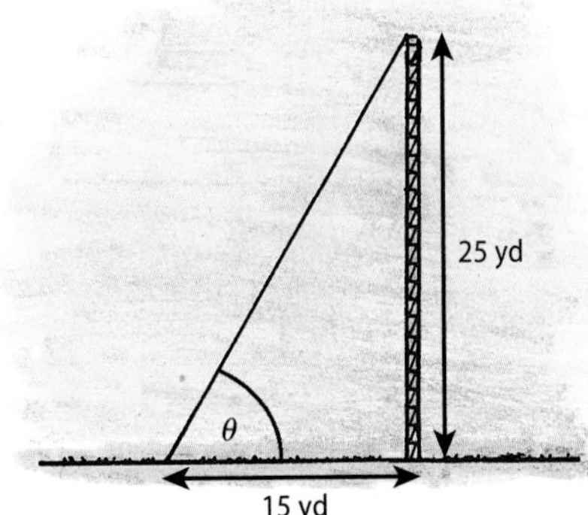

CHECK $\tan 59.04 \stackrel{?}{=} \frac{25}{15}$

$1.666914379 \approx 1.666666667$ ✔

The wire makes about a 59.04° angle with the ground.

Solving Right Triangles

Useful Things to Know

To solve a triangle means to determine the measures of the three sides and the three angles of a given triangle. The following definitions and theorems are often useful when solving a triangle.

Complementary Angles in a Right Triangle

The two acute angles in a right triangle are complementary.

$m\angle A + m\angle B = 90°$

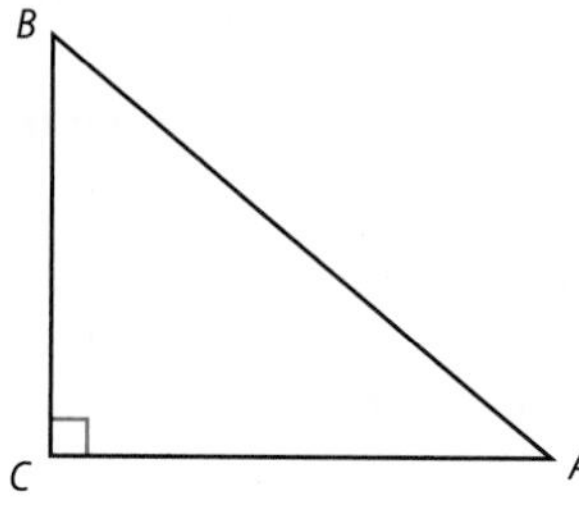

Triangle Angle Sum Theorem

The sum of the angle measures in any triangle is 180°.

$m\angle 1 + m\angle 2 + m\angle 3 = 180°$

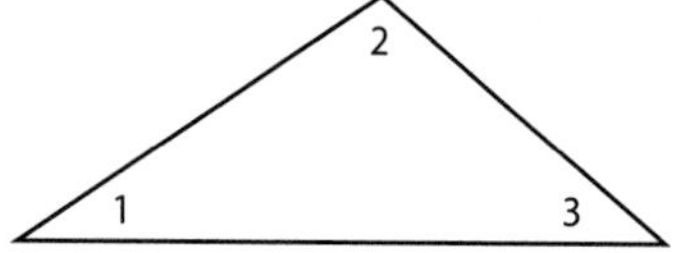

The Pythagorean Theorem

In a right triangle with legs of length a and b and hypotenuse of length c, $a^2 + b^2 = c^2$.

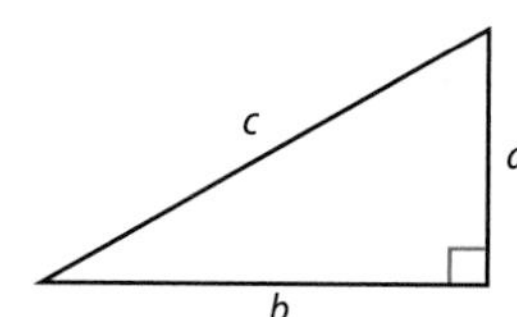

The Trigonometric Ratios

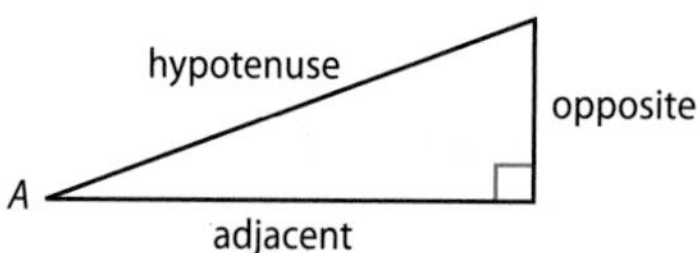

$\sin A = \frac{\text{opposite}}{\text{hypotenuse}}$ $\quad \cos A = \frac{\text{adjacent}}{\text{hypotenuse}}$ $\quad \tan A = \frac{\text{opposite}}{\text{adjacent}}$

$\csc A = \frac{\text{hypotenuse}}{\text{opposite}}$ $\quad \sec A = \frac{\text{hypotenuse}}{\text{adjacent}}$ $\quad \cot A = \frac{\text{adjacent}}{\text{opposite}}$

Converting DMS Notation to Decimal Degrees

$x°y'z'' = \left(x + \frac{y}{60} + \frac{z}{3600}\right)°$

EXAMPLE 1

Tell how you would solve each problem. There may be more than one way.

a. You know two sides in a right triangle. You want to find the length of the third side.

Use the Pythagorean Theorem. Substitute the two given side lengths and solve for the third side.

b. You know one acute angle in a right triangle and want to find the other acute angle.

METHOD 1

Two angles are given. Add their measures and subtract the sum from 180°.

METHOD 2

Subtract the acute angle measure from 90°.

c. You know one side length and one acute angle in a right triangle. You want to find the length of the side opposite the given angle.

Use the sine or tangent ratio, depending on which side length you are given.

Using One Side and One Angle

When you know the length of a side and the measure of an acute angle in a right triangle, you can use trigonometry to find the lengths of the other sides.

EXAMPLE 2

Find the values of a and c.

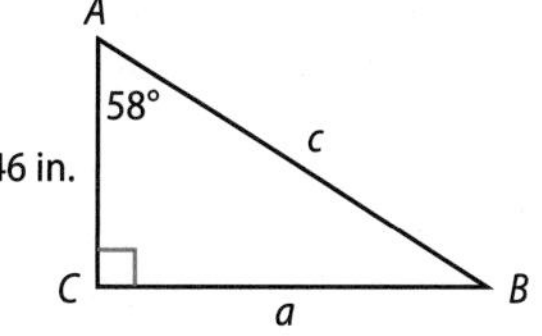

STEP 1 Find the value of a.

Use the tangent ratio: $\tan A = \frac{\text{opposite}}{\text{adjacent}}$

Substitute. $\tan 58° = \frac{a}{46}$

Use a calculator. $a = 46 \cdot \tan 58° \approx 73.6$

STEP 2 Find the value of c.

METHOD 1

Use the cosine ratio.

$$\cos A = \frac{\text{adjacent}}{\text{hypotenuse}}$$

$$\cos 58° = \frac{46}{c}$$

$$c = \frac{46}{\cos 58°} \approx 86.8$$

METHOD 2

Use the Pythagorean Theorem.

$$73.6^2 + 46^2 = c^2$$

$$c^2 = 7{,}532.96$$

$$c \approx 86.8$$

$a \approx 73.6$ and $c \approx 86.8$

SEARCH

To see step-by-step videos of these problems, enter the page number into the SWadvantage.com Search Bar.

Using One Side and One Angle

EXAMPLE 3

Find m∠Q, QR, and PR.

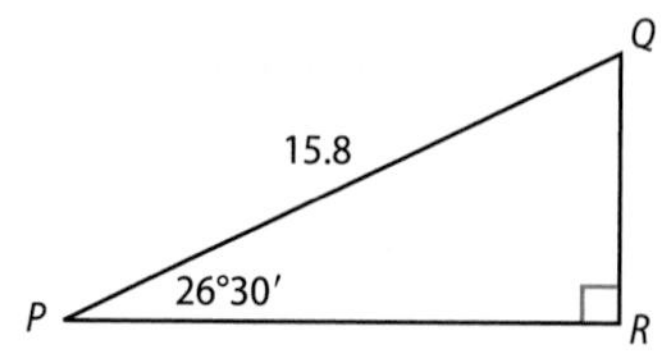

STEP 1 Find $m\angle Q$.

$\angle P$ and $\angle Q$ are complementary. $m\angle P + m\angle Q = 90°$

Substitute. $26°30' + m\angle Q = 90°$

$m\angle Q = 63°30'$

STEP 2 Find QR.

$\overline{QR}$ is opposite $\angle P$. $\sin P = \dfrac{\text{opposite}}{\text{hypotenuse}}$

Substitute values from the triangle. $\sin 26°30' = \dfrac{QR}{15.8}$

Write the degrees as a decimal. $\sin 26.5° = \dfrac{QR}{15.8}$

Simplify. $QR = 15.8 \cdot \sin 26.5° \approx 7.05$

STEP 3 Find PR.

$\overline{PR}$ is adjacent to $\angle P$. $\cos P = \dfrac{\text{adjacent}}{\text{hypotenuse}}$

Substitute values from the triangle. $\cos 26°30' = \dfrac{PR}{15.8}$

Write the degrees as a decimal. $\cos 26.5° = \dfrac{PR}{15.8}$

Simplify. $PR = 15.8 \cdot \cos 26.5° \approx 14.14$

Try It This Way

Use the Pythagorean Theorem to find PR.

$PR^2 + QR^2 = PQ^2$

$PR^2 + 7.05^2 = 15.8^2$

$PR \approx 14.14$

EXAMPLE 4

The legs of an isosceles triangle are 25 cm long. The measure of the vertex angle is 62°. Find the length of the base.

The altitude to the base determines two congruent right triangles.

$\sin 31° = \dfrac{DM}{25}$

$DM = 25 \sin 31° \approx 12.9$

$DF = 2(DM) \approx 25.8$

The base is about 25.8 cm long.

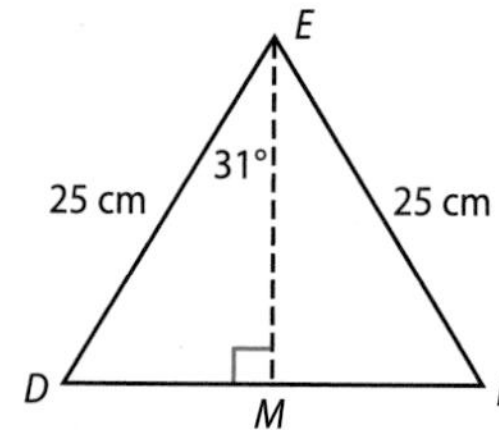

Using Two Sides

In another type of problem, you are given the lengths of two sides of a right triangle and asked to find the measures of the angles.

EXAMPLE 5

Find $m\angle A$ and $m\angle B$ to the nearest tenth of a degree.

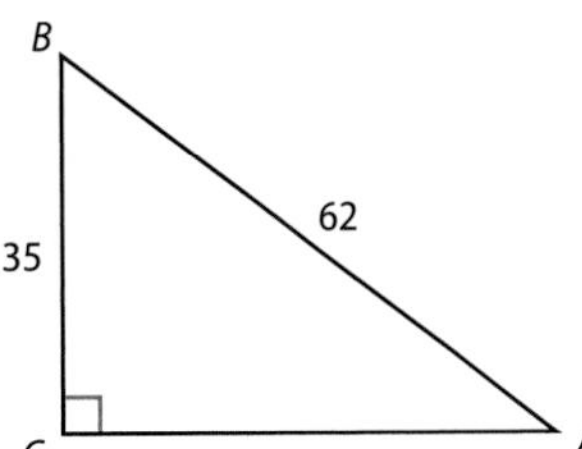

STEP 1 Find $m\angle A$.

$$\sin A = \frac{\text{opposite}}{\text{hypotenuse}} \qquad \sin A = \frac{35}{62}$$

$$m\angle A = \sin^{-1}\frac{35}{62}$$

Use a calculator. $m\angle A \approx 34.4°$

STEP 2 Find $m\angle B$.

$\angle A$ and $\angle B$ are complementary. $m\angle A + m\angle B = 90°$

Substitute. $34.4° + m\angle B = 90°$

$$m\angle B = 55.6°$$

SEARCH

To see step-by-step videos of these problems, enter the page number into the SWadvantage.com Search Bar.

EXAMPLE 6

A wheelchair ramp is 15 ft long and has a rise of 14 in. Find the measure of the angle θ between the ramp and the ground. Round your answer to the nearest tenth of a degree.

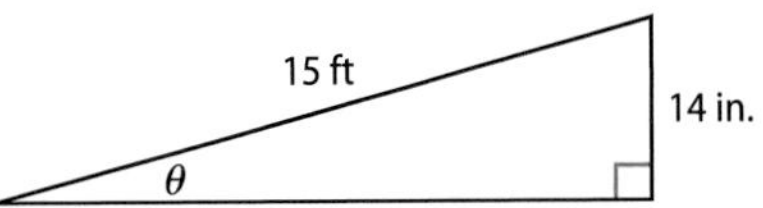

STEP 1 Convert feet to inches.

$15 \text{ ft} \longrightarrow 15(12) = 180 \text{ in.}$

STEP 2 Use the sine ratio.

$$\sin\theta = \frac{\text{opposite}}{\text{hypotenuse}} = \frac{14}{180}$$

$$\theta = \sin^{-1}\frac{14}{180} \approx 4.5°$$

Solving a Right Triangle

To solve a right triangle, use the given lengths and angle measures to find the unknown parts of the triangle. You can use:

- the Pythagorean Theorem
- trigonometric ratios
- the fact that the acute angles of a right triangle are complementary

Applications of Right Triangles

Indirect Measurement

In practical situations, it is often difficult or impossible to measure a length or an angle directly. In such cases, you may use trigonometry to make an indirect measurement.

Try It This Way

Practice your reading skills. Cover the figure with an index card. Read the problem and try making your own sketch first.

EXAMPLE 1

Plans call for building a bridge across the river from point *C* to point *A*. The surveyor walks 100 m along the riverbank from point *C*, and then measures the angle to point *A*. The measure of the angle is 63°. Find the length of the bridge.

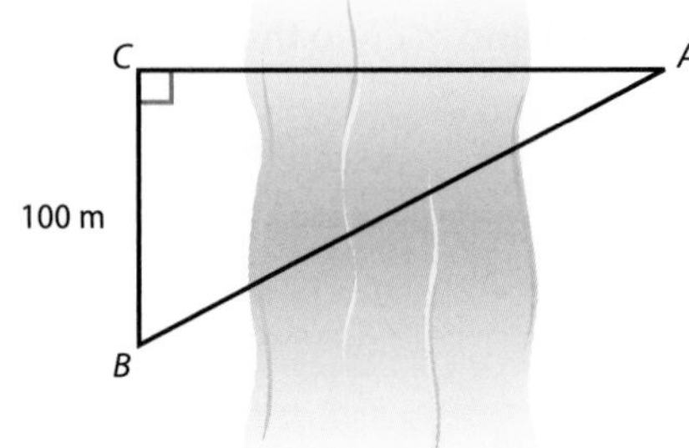

You need to find *AC*, the length of the longer leg of a right triangle. You know $m\angle B$ and the length of the leg adjacent to $\angle B$. So, use the tangent ratio.

Write an equation. $\tan 63° = \frac{AC}{100}$

Solve for *AB*. $AC = 100 \cdot \tan 63° \approx 196.26$

The bridge will be about 196 m long.

Need More HELP

When possible, use the sine, cosine, and tangent rather than cosecant, secant, and cotangent. The sine, cosine, and tangent are easier to find with a calculator or a table.

EXAMPLE 2

A guy wire attached to the top of a pole meets the ground at a 73° angle, 20 ft from the base of the pole. How tall is the pole?

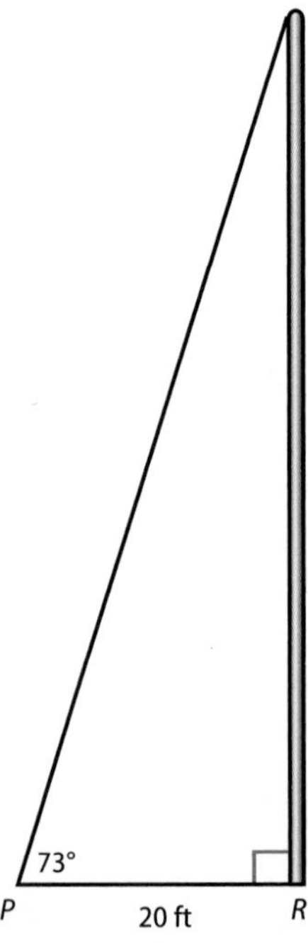

You are given an angle and the length of a leg adjacent to that angle. You want to find *QR*, the length of the leg opposite the given angle. Use the tangent ratio.

Write an equation. $\tan 73° = \frac{QR}{20}$

Solve for *QR*. $QR = 20 \cdot \tan 73° \approx 65.4$

The pole is about 65 ft tall.

EXAMPLE 3

In a stiff wind, a kite pulls its string tight at an angle of 28° from the ground. If 137 m of string are let out, how high is the kite above the ground?

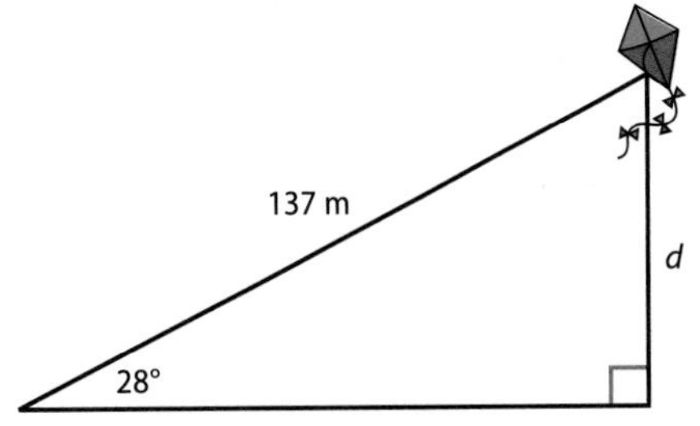

You are given the hypotenuse and an angle. You want to find the length of the leg opposite that angle. Use the sine ratio.

Write an equation. $\sin 28° = \frac{d}{37}$

Solve for d. $d = 137 \cdot \sin 28° \approx 64.32$

The kite is about 64.3 m above the ground.

SEARCH

To see step-by-step videos of these problems, enter the page number into the SWadvantage.com Search Bar.

EXAMPLE 4

A ladder on a fire truck is mounted 4 m above the ground and is 32 m long. It extends from the truck at an angle of 80°. Find the distance the ladder will reach up the side of a building.

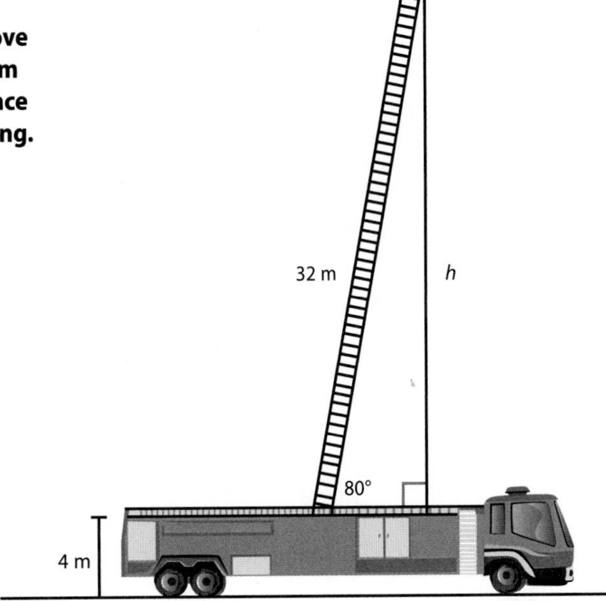

Find the height h. Then add 4 m.

You are given the hypotenuse and an angle. You want to find the length of the leg opposite the angle. Use the sine ratio.

Write an equation. $\sin 80° = \frac{h}{32}$

Solve for h. $h = 32 \cdot \sin 80° \approx 31.5$

Since the ladder is mounted 4 m above the ground, add 4 m. $31.5 + 4 = 35.5$

The ladder can reach about 35.5 m up the side of a building.

Angles of Elevation and Depression

The angle formed by a line of sight and a horizontal line is the **angle of elevation** if the observer is looking up, and the **angle of depression** if the observer is looking down.

The figure shows the angle of elevation for a person looking up at an airplane and the corresponding angle of depression for the pilot looking down at the ground. As you can see, the angle of elevation is congruent to the angle of depression. That's because the horizontal lines are parallel, and the two angles are alternate interior angles.

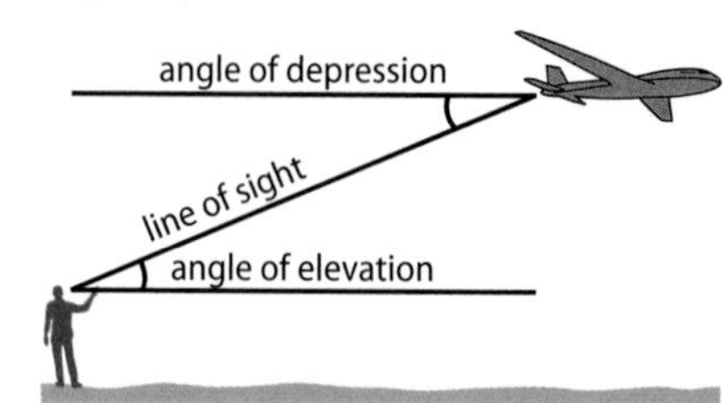

Need More HELP

For a review of alternate interior angles, go to *Theorems about Parallel Lines* in *Geometry* (p. 630).

Watch Out!

Both the angle of elevation and the angle of depression are measured between the line of sight and the *horizontal*. Make sure you aren't using a vertical line instead of a horizontal one.

EXAMPLE 5

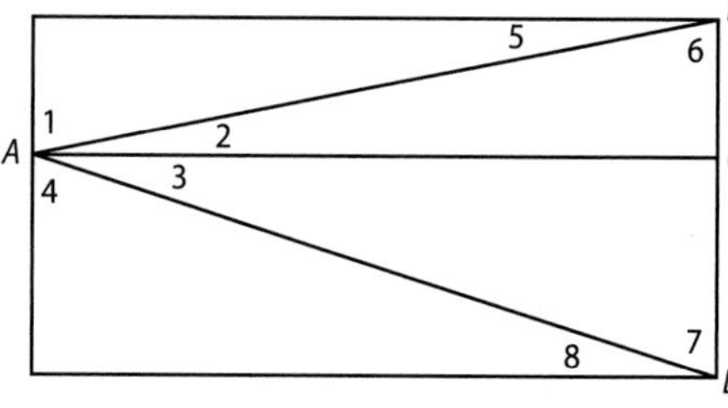

a. What is the angle of elevation from *A* to *B*?

$\angle 2$

b. What is the angle of depression from *A* to *D*?

$\angle 3$

c. What is the angle of depression from *B* to *A*?

$\angle 5$

EXAMPLE 6

An observer lies on level ground 50 ft from the bottom of a cell phone tower. The angle of elevation to the top of the tower is 75°. Find the height of the tower.

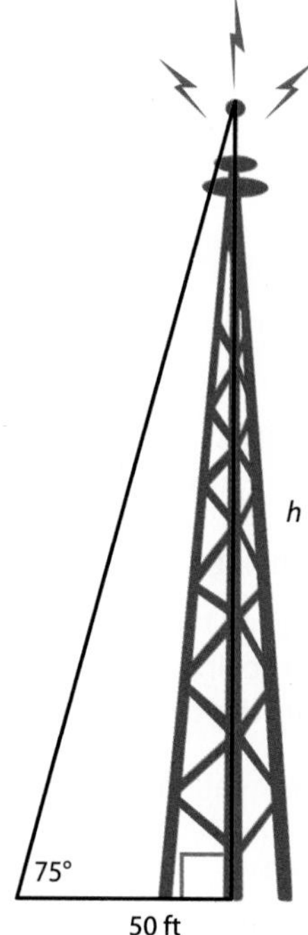

METHOD 1

Use tan 75°.

$$\tan 75° = \frac{h}{50}$$

$$h = 50(\tan 75°)$$

$$\approx 186.6$$

METHOD 2

Use tan 15°.

$$\tan 15° = \frac{50}{h}$$

$$h = \frac{50}{\tan 15°}$$

$$\approx 186.6$$

The cell phone tower is about 187 ft high.

EXAMPLE 7

The angle of depression from an airplane flying at 12,500 m to the airport control tower is 51°15′.

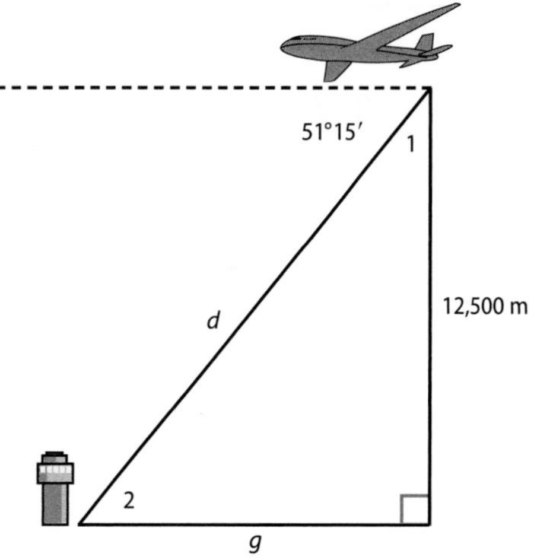

a. Find the travel distance d from the airplane to the tower.

STEP 1 Convert 51°15′ to decimal degrees.
$51°15' = 51.25°$

STEP 2 Find $m\angle 1$.
$m\angle 1 = 90° - 51.25° = 38.75°$

STEP 3 Write and solve an equation.

$$\cos 38.75° = \frac{12{,}500}{d}$$

Use a calculator.
$$d = \frac{12{,}500}{\cos 38.75°}$$

$$d \approx 16{,}028$$

The travel distance is about 16,028 m.

b. Find the ground distance g from the tower to the airplane.

STEP 1 Find $m\angle 2$.
The angle of elevation is congruent to the angle of depression, so $m\angle 2 = 51.25°$.

STEP 2 Write and solve an equation.

$$\tan 51.25° = \frac{12{,}500}{g}$$

Use a calculator.
$$g = \frac{12{,}500}{\tan 51.25°}$$

$$g \approx 10{,}032$$

The ground distance is about 10,032 m.

SEARCH

To see step-by-step videos of these problems, enter the page number into the SWadvantage.com Search Bar.

Watch Out!

You need to find the measures of the angles in the triangle. The angle of depression is complementary to $\angle 1$.

GOT TO KNOW!

Angles of Elevation and Depression

The **angle of elevation** is the angle between a horizontal line and the line of sight from an observer to an object at a higher level.

The **angle of depression** is the angle between a horizontal line and the line of sight from an observer to an object at a lower level.

Radian Measure and the Trigonometric Functions

What Came Before?

- Trigonometric ratios of acute angles
- Calculating angle measures using trigonometric ratios

What's This About?

- Converting between degree measure and radian measure
- Finding linear and angular velocities
- Using the Unit Circle to find the trigonometric ratios of common angles

Practical Apps

- Manufacturers of CD and DVD players use angular and linear velocity to make sure the laser moves correctly to play the disc.
- Carousel makers have to meet safety codes in angular velocity that depend on the radius of the ride.

Just for FUN!

Q: When were trigonometry tables used?

A: B.C. (Before Calculators)

CONTENTS UPLOAD DOWNLOAD

Trigonometry

Measures of Rotations of Angles

Directed Angles

In geometry, most angles you work with have measures between 0° and 180°. In trigonometry, you will also use angles with measures greater than 180° and less than 0°. You can generate any angle by using a rotation that moves one of the rays forming the angle, called the *initial side*, onto the other ray, called the *terminal side*.

Counterclockwise rotations produce *positive angles* and *clockwise* rotations produce *negative angles*. An angle generated in this manner is called a *directed angle*.

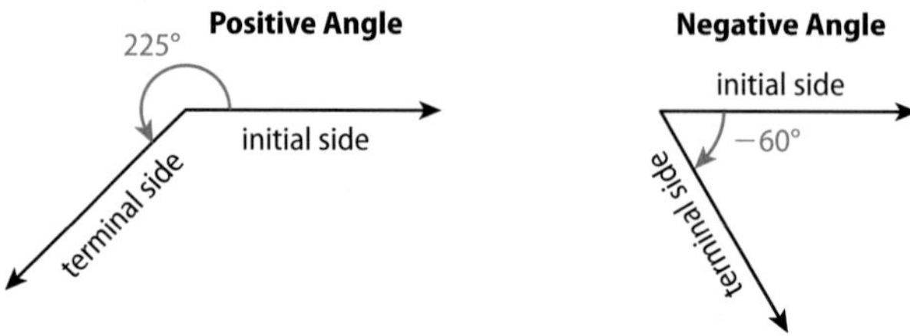

Remember the four quadrants of the coordinate plane.

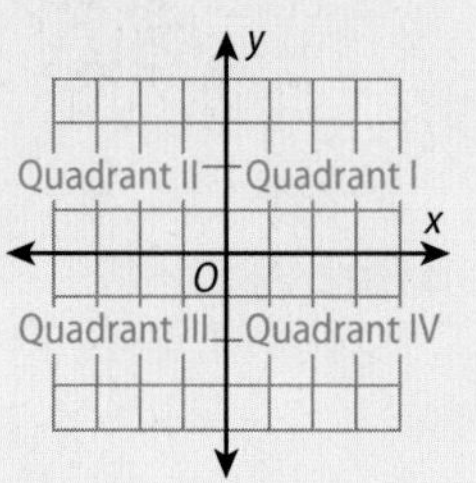

The four divisions made by the x- and y-axes are called quadrants. You can form an angle by placing the initial side of the angle on the x-axis and rotating the terminal side around the four quadrants. An angle is in standard position when its initial side coincides with the positive x-axis. The terminal side of the angle will fall in one of the four quadrants or on one of the axes.

EXAMPLE 1

Sketch the angle with the given revolution in standard position, and give the degree measure.

Begin by placing the initial side of the angle on the x-axis.

a. $\frac{1}{4}$ clockwise

$\frac{1}{4}$ of 360° is 90°. A clockwise angle is negative.

The angle is on the negative y-axis.

The degree measure is −90°.

The sketch is on the right in blue.

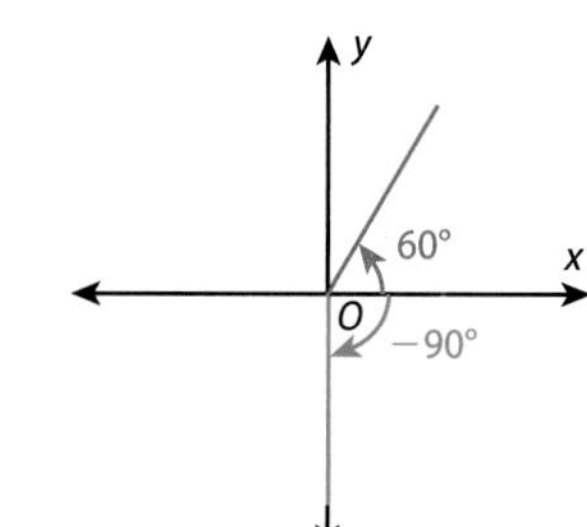

b. $\frac{1}{6}$ counterclockwise revolution

$\frac{1}{6}$ of 360° is 60°. A counterclockwise revolution is positive.

The angle is between 0° and 90°, so its terminal side is in Quadrant I.

The degree measure is 60°.

The sketch is on the right in red.

General Angles

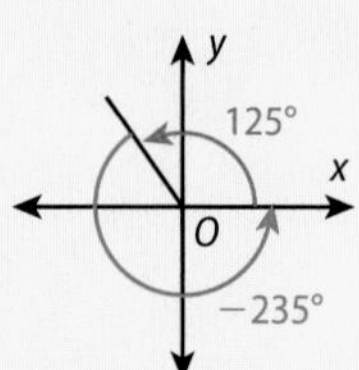

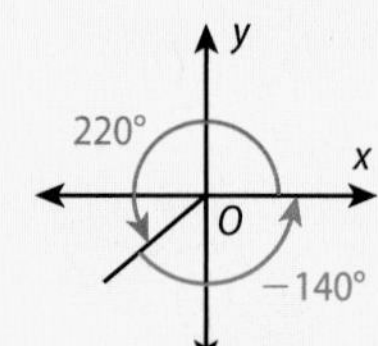

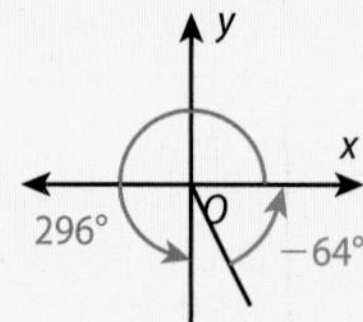

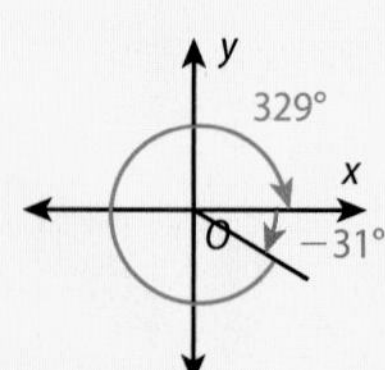

Being able to visualize angles on a coordinate plane will help you to understand trigonometric relationships.

EXAMPLE 2

Sketch each of the following angles in standard position.

a. 130° **b. 250°** **c. −40°** **d. 310°**

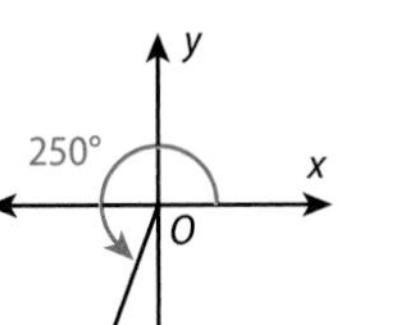

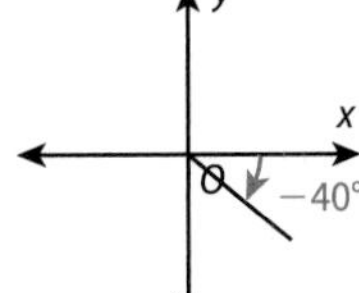

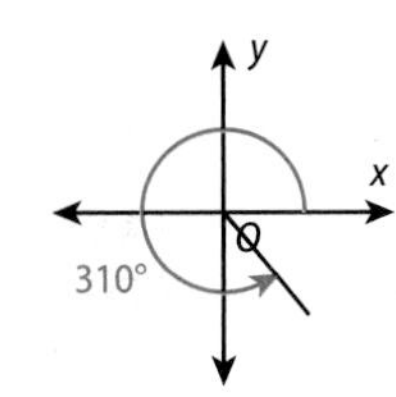

SEARCH

To see step-by-step videos of these problems, enter the page number into the SWadvantage.com Search Bar.

Sometimes all you need to know is the quadrant in which the angle lies. This will be sufficient to draw a sketch of the angle. It helps to know the four *quadrantal angles.* An angle whose terminal side falls on an axis is called a **quadrantal angle**.

EXAMPLE 3

In which quadrant, or on which axis, does the terminal side of each angle lie?

a. 85°

An 85° angle is greater than 0° and less than 90°.

The terminal side of an 85° angle is in Quadrant I.

b. 240°

A 240° angle is greater than 180° and less than 270°.

The terminal side of a 240° angle is in Quadrant III.

c. −240°

A −240° angle is less than −180° and greater than −270°.

The terminal side of a −240° angle is in Quadrant II.

d. 290°

A 290° angle is greater than 270° and less than 360°.

The terminal side of a 290° angle is in Quadrant IV.

GOT TO KNOW!

Quadrantal Angles

The **quadrantal angles** are 0° (or 360°), 90° (or −270°), 180° (or −180°), 270° (or −90°), 360° (or 0°), 360° + 90°, and so on.

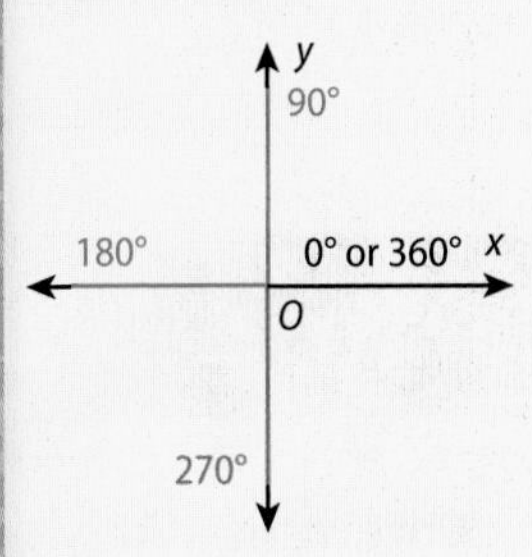

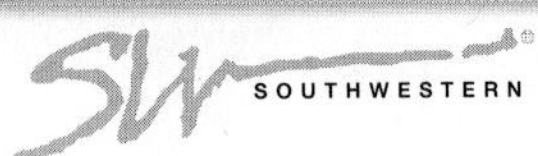

Coterminal Angles

If the terminal sides of two angles in standard position coincide, the angles are said to be **coterminal**. For example, angles of 30°, −330°, and 390° are coterminal. The measure of all angles coterminal to 30° is $30° + n(360°)$.

$$30° + (-1)(360°) = -330°$$

$$30° + (1)(360°) = 390°$$

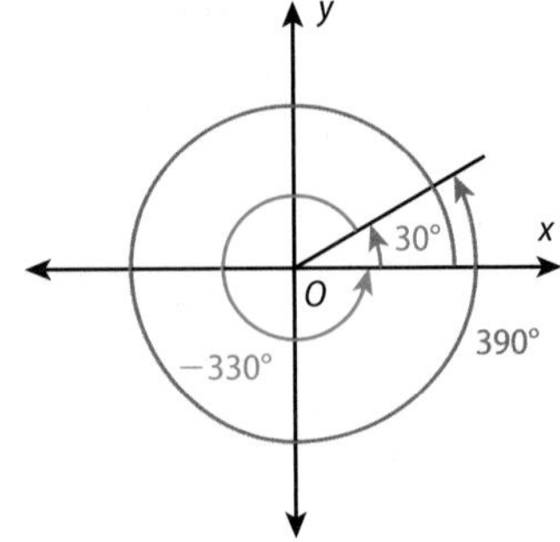

EXAMPLE 4

What is a coterminal angle for each of the following angles?

a. −110°

$-110° + (1)(360°) = 250°$

A 250° angle is coterminal with a −110° angle.

b. 420°

$420° - (1)(360°) = 60°$

A 60° angle is coterminal with a 420° angle.

c. 750°

$750° - (2)(360°) = 750° - 720° = 30°$

A 30° angle is coterminal with a 750° angle.

GOT TO KNOW!

Coterminal Angles

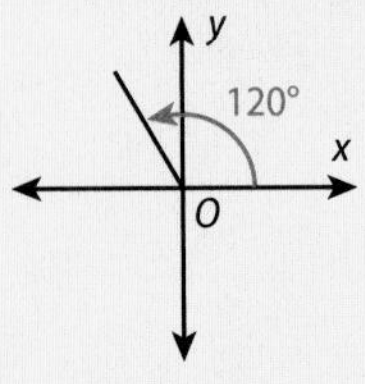

120° + (0)360°

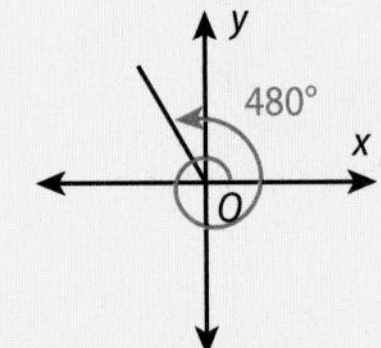

120° + (1)360°

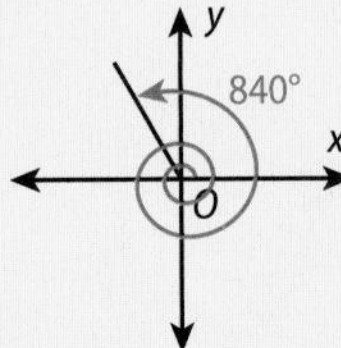

120° + (2)360°

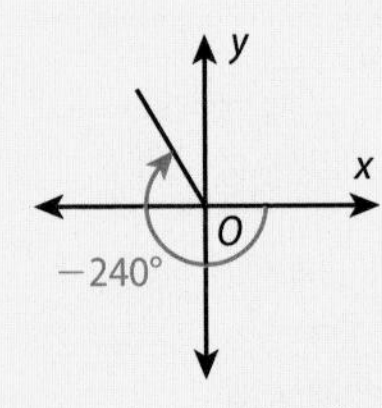

120° + (−1)360°

EXAMPLE 5

Determine the coterminal angles (one positive and one negative) for the given angles.

a.

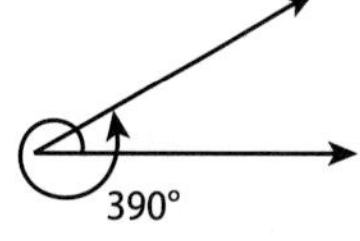

b.

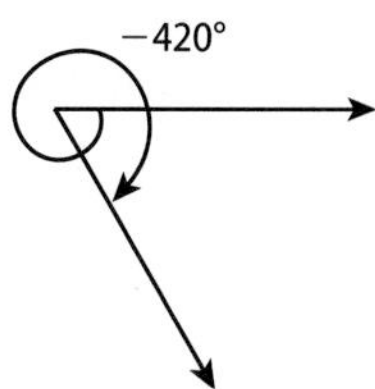

METHOD 1

a. The angle is positive. Subtract 360°.

$390° - 360° = 30°$ positive

Subtract 360° from 30°.

$30° - 360° = -330°$ negative

b. The angle is negative. Add 360°.

$-420° + 360° = -60°$ negative

Add 360° to −60°.

$-60° + 360° = 300°$ positive

METHOD 2

Sketch each angle. Begin with the initial side.

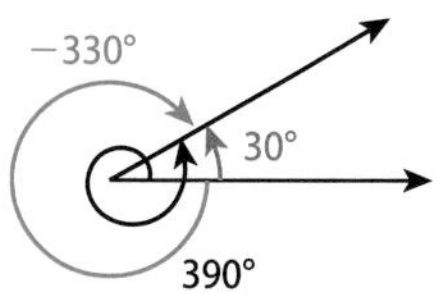

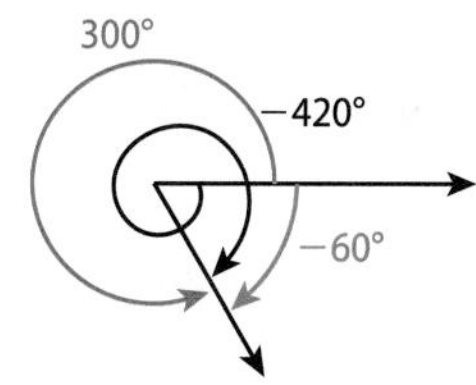

Remember:
A *counterclockwise* revolution is *positive*.
A *clockwise* revolution is *negative*.

SEARCH

To see step-by-step videos of these problems, enter the page number into the SWadvantage.com Search Bar.

Reference Angles

A **reference angle** θ' of a given angle θ in standard notation is the smallest positive acute angle determined by the x-axis and the terminal side of θ.

EXAMPLE 6

θ is a 250° angle. Find its reference angle θ'.

A 250° angle is in Quadrant III. $\theta' = 250° - 180° = 70°$

GOT TO KNOW!

Reference Angles

The diagrams show the relationship between θ and θ' in all four quadrants.

$\theta' = \theta$

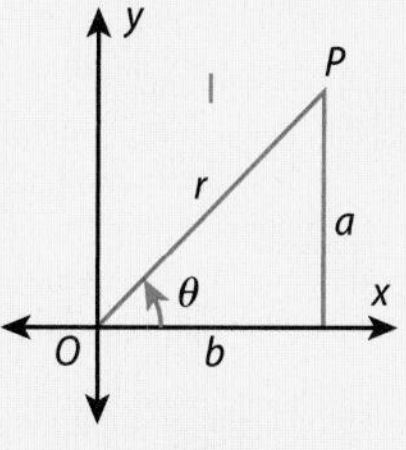

$\theta' = 180° - \theta$

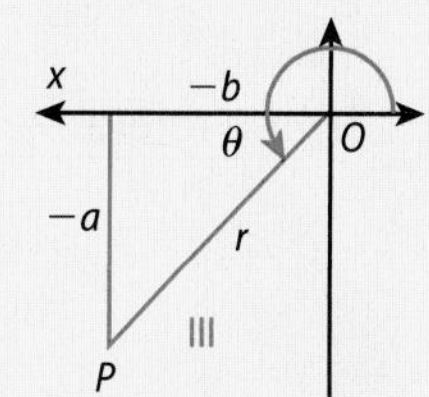

$\theta' = \theta - 180°$

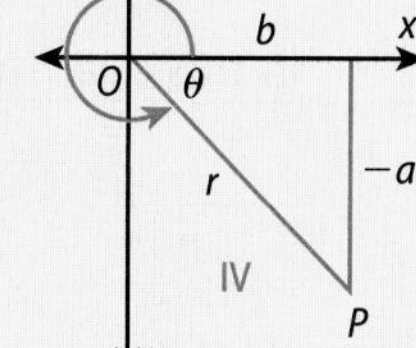

$\theta' = 360° - \theta$

Functions of Non-Acute Angles

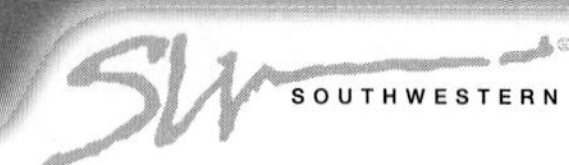

Reference Angles

The quadrants in a coordinate system are numbered counterclockwise using Roman numerals.

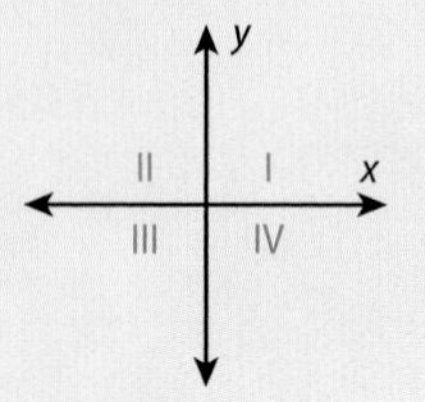

To find the trigonometric values for angles greater than 90° or less than 0°, you need to use a reference angle. If θ is a non-quadrantal angle in standard position, then the **reference angle** θ' is the smallest acute angle that the terminal side of θ makes with the x-axis.

An angle with its terminal side in Quadrant I equals its reference angle. To find the reference angle for an angle in Quadrant II, subtract from 180°. For Quadrant III, subtract 180°. And, for Quadrant IV, subtract from 360°.

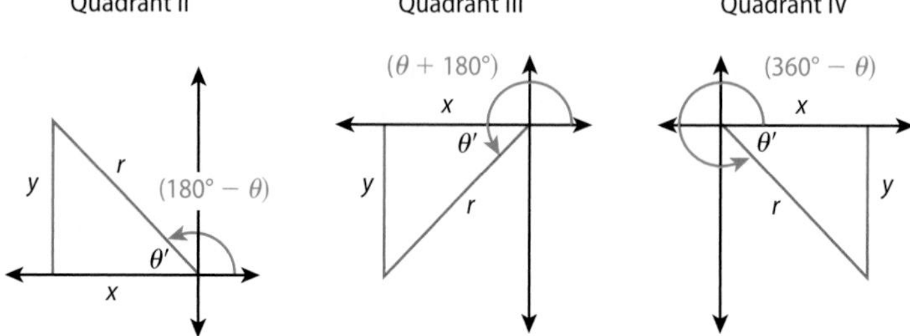

EXAMPLE 1

Try It This Way

Be sure to start by identifying the quadrant. It may help to sketch the angle first.

Find the reference angle for each angle.

a. 280°

Identify the quadrant.	$270° < 280° < 360°$	Quadrant IV
Subtract from 360°.	$360° - 280° = 80°$	

The reference angle is 80°.

b. 140°

Identify the quadrant.	$90° < 140° < 180°$	Quadrant II
Subtract from 180°.	$180° - 140° = 40°$	

The reference angle is 40°.

c. 210°

Identify the quadrant.	$180° < 210° < 270°$	Quadrant III
Subtract 180°.	$210° - 180° = 30°$	

The reference angle is 30°.

GOT TO KNOW!

Reference Angles

If θ is in this quadrant	the reference angle θ' equals
I	θ
II	$180° - \theta$
III	$\theta - 180°$
IV	$360° - \theta$

Angles Smaller than 0° or Larger than 360°

The trigonometric functions are defined by a point on the terminal side of the angle, and not by the amount of rotation. So, the trigonometric function values for coterminal angles are equal. This results in six **identities for coterminal angles**.

$\sin\theta = \sin(360° + \theta)$ $\cos\theta = \cos(360° + \theta)$ $\tan\theta = \tan(360° + \theta)$

$\csc\theta = \csc(360° + \theta)$ $\sec\theta = \sec(360° + \theta)$ $\cot\theta = \cot(360° + \theta)$

You can use these identities to find a coterminal angle in the range $0 \leq \theta \leq 360°$. Just add or subtract multiples of 360° as many times as needed.

EXAMPLE 2

Find the coterminal angle, then find the reference angle.

a. −140°

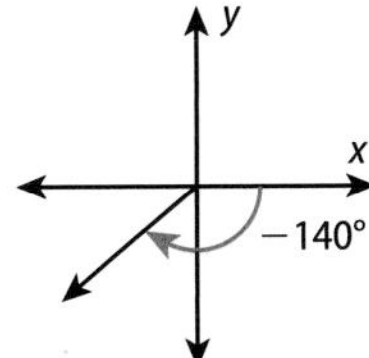

Add 360° to find the coterminal angle. $360° + (-140°) = 220°$

Subtract 180° to find the reference angle. $220° - 180° = 40°$

coterminal angle: 220°; reference angle: 40°

b. 765°

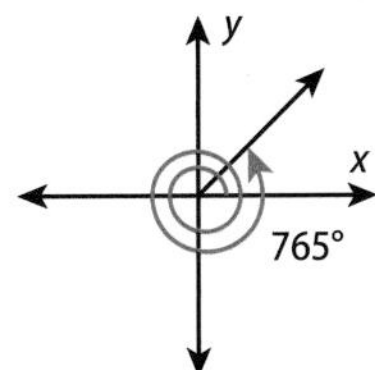

Divide by 360° to find the number of full rotations to subtract. $765° \div 360° = 2.1$

Subtract 2 multiples of 360° to find the coterminal angle. $765° - (2 \cdot 360°) = 45°$

This angle is in Quadrant I, so the reference angle is the same. 45°

coterminal angle: 45°; reference angle: 45°

c. −570°

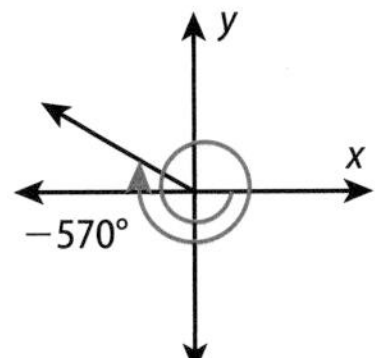

Add 2 multiples of 360° to find the coterminal angle. $-570° + (2 \cdot 360°) = 150°$

Subtract from 180° to find the reference angle. $180° - 150° = 30°$

coterminal angle: 150°; reference angle: 30°

Watch Out!

If an angle is not between 0° and 360°, first find the coterminal angle in this range. Then find the reference angle.

SEARCH

To see step-by-step videos of these problems, enter the page number into the SWadvantage.com Search Bar.

GOT TO KNOW!

Coterminal Identities

$\sin\theta = \sin(360° + \theta)$

$\cos\theta = \cos(360° + \theta)$

$\tan\theta = \tan(360° + \theta)$

$\csc\theta = \csc(360° + \theta)$

$\sec\theta = \sec(360° + \theta)$

$\cot\theta = \cot(360° + \theta)$

Ways to REMEMBER

The mnemonic device, **A**ll **S**tudents **T**ake **C**alculus, can help you remember the signs of the functions for each quadrant.

A is in the first quadrant and stands for ALL. All six trigonometric functions are positive in the first quadrant.

S is in the second quadrant and stands for SINE. This means that SINE and its reciprocal, COSECANT, are positive in the second quadrant.

T is in Quadrant III and stands for TANGENT.

C is in Quadrant IV and stands for COSINE.

Signs in Quadrants I, II, III, and IV

To use reference angles, you need to know the signs of the trigonometric functions in the four quadrants. To find these signs, think of the triangle used to define the trigonometric functions.

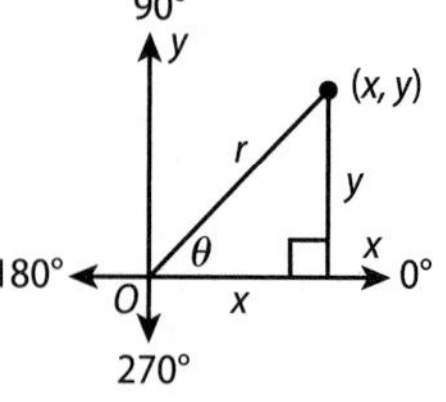

The value of r is always a positive number, but x and y can be positive or negative. It depends on which quadrant contains the terminal side of the angle θ.

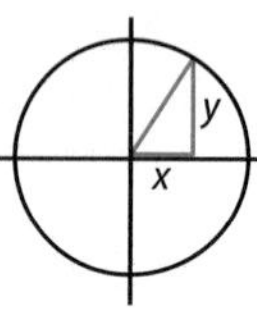

Quadrant I

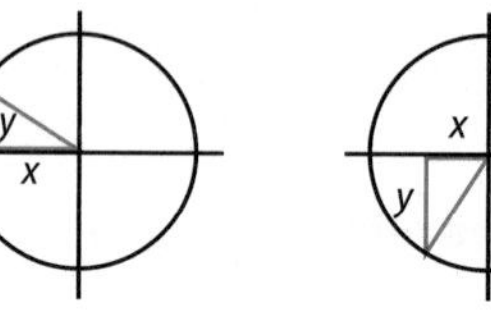

Quadrant II

Quadrant III

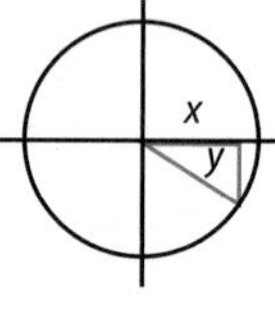

Quadrant IV

EXAMPLE 3

Identify each value as positive, negative, 0, or undefined.

a. tan 200°

Identify the quadrant.	$180° < 200° < 270°$	Quadrant III
Identify the sign.	positive	

b. sec 140°

Identify the quadrant.	$90° < 140° < 180°$	Quadrant II
Identify the sign.	negative	

c. cos 550°

Find the coterminal angle.	$550° - 360° = 190°$	
Identify the quadrant.	$180° < 190° < 270°$	Quadrant III
Identify the sign.	negative	

d. cot 1,620°

Find the coterminal angle.	$1{,}620° - (4 \cdot 360°) = 180°$
Identify the quadrant.	quadrantal angle
Find cot 180°.	undefined

Signs of the Trigonometric Functions

Quadrant	I	II	III	IV
sin or csc	+	+	−	−
cos or sec	+	−	−	+
tan or cot	+	−	+	−

Trigonometric Function Values for Any Angle

To find the value of a trigonometric function for any angle, follow these steps.

STEP 1 If the angle is not in the range $0° < \theta < 360°$, find the smallest positive coterminal angle in that range.

STEP 2 If the result is not in Quadrant I, find the reference angle.

STEP 3 Find the value of the trigonometric function.

STEP 4 Use the correct sign.

EXAMPLE 4

Find the exact value of tan 315°.

STEP 1 The angle, 315°, is between 0° and 360°.

STEP 2 Find the reference angle.
Subtract from 360°. $360° - 315° = 45°$

STEP 3 Find the exact value of the function.
Use the special angle value. $\tan 45° = 1$

STEP 4 Find the sign.
315° is in Quadrant IV. tangent is negative

$\tan 315° = -1$

SEARCH

To see step-by-step videos of these problems, enter the page number into the SWadvantage.com Search Bar.

EXAMPLE 5

Find the exact value of sin 600°.

STEP 1 Find the coterminal angle in the range $0° < \theta < 360°$.
Subtract 1 multiple of 360°. $600° - 360° = 240°$

STEP 2 Find the reference angle.
Subtract 180°. $240° - 180° = 60°$

STEP 3 Find the exact value of the function.
Use the special angle value. $\sin 60° = \frac{\sqrt{3}}{2}$

STEP 4 Find the sign.
240° is in Quadrant III. sine is negative

$\sin 600° = -\frac{\sqrt{3}}{2}$

EXAMPLE 6

Find a value for csc 203° 15′ to the nearest hundredth.

STEP 1 Convert to decimal degrees.

$203°15' = \left(203 + \frac{15}{60}\right)° = 203.25°$

STEP 2 Use a calculator.

$(\sin 203.25°)^{-1} \approx -2.53$

Radian Measure

Remember that there are 360° in a circle.

The distance around a circle, or its circumference, is $2\pi r$.

Converting Between Radian Measure and Degrees

Up to this point you have been working with angles measured in degrees. In trigonometry, angles are often measured in *radians*. A **radian** is the measure of a central angle that cuts off an arc whose length is equal to the radius of the circle. Therefore, $360° = 2\pi$.

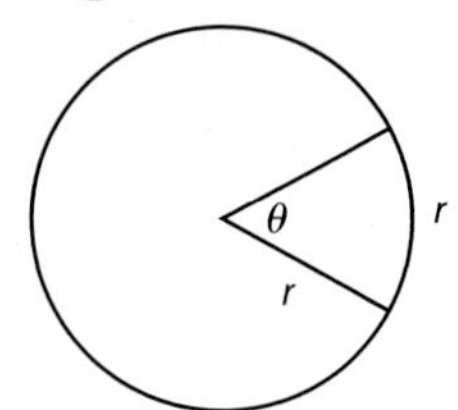

Note that a central angle of 1 radian (1 rad) intercepts an arc of length r regardless of the length of the radius of the circle.

Since $360° = 2\pi$ radians

$180° = \pi$ radians

Thus, $1° = \frac{\pi}{180}$ rad and 1 rad $= \frac{180}{\pi}$.

To convert the degree measure of an angle to radians, multiply the number of degrees by $\frac{\pi \text{ radians}}{180°}$.

To convert the radian measure of an angle to degrees, multiply the number of radians by $\frac{180°}{\pi \text{ radians}}$.

EXAMPLE 1

Need More **HELP**

Scientific and graphing calculators have special keys or modes that will allow you to change from degrees to radians and vice versa.

Convert each degree measure to radians.

a. 36°

Multiply the number of degrees by $\frac{\pi \text{ radians}}{180°}$.

$$36° = 36° \cdot \frac{\pi \text{ radians}}{180°}$$
$$= \frac{\pi}{5} \text{ rad}$$

b. −120°

$$-120° = -120° \cdot \frac{\pi \text{ radians}}{180°}$$
$$= -\frac{2\pi}{3} \text{ rad}$$

EXAMPLE 2

Convert each radian measure to degrees.

a. $\frac{\pi}{12}$

Multiply the number of radians by $\frac{180°}{\pi \text{ radians}}$.

$$\frac{\pi}{12} = \frac{\pi}{12} \cdot \frac{180°}{\pi \text{ radians}}$$
$$= 15°$$

b. -5π

$$-5\pi = -5\pi \cdot \frac{180°}{\pi \text{ radians}}$$

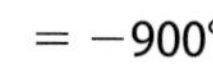

$$= -900°$$

GOT TO KNOW!

Degrees to Radians	Multiply the number of degrees by $\frac{\pi \text{ radians}}{180°}$ and simplify.
Radians to Degrees	Multiply the number of radians by $\frac{180°}{\pi \text{ radians}}$ and simplify.

Radian Measure of Special Angles

Think of fractional parts of a circle to determine the radian measure of special angles.

EXAMPLE 3

Find the radian measure of the following special angles.

a. 90° **b. 60°** **c. 45°**

Determine what fractional part of a circle equals each angle.

$\frac{90°}{360°} = \frac{1}{4}$ $\frac{60°}{360°} = \frac{1}{6}$ $\frac{45°}{360°} = \frac{1}{8}$

Multiply 2π by the fraction you found.

$\frac{1}{4}(2\pi) = \frac{\pi}{2}$ $\frac{1}{6}(2\pi) = \frac{\pi}{3}$ $\frac{1}{8}(2\pi) = \frac{\pi}{4}$

90° is $\frac{\pi}{2}$ radians. 60° is $\frac{\pi}{3}$ radians. 45° is $\frac{\pi}{4}$ radians.

SEARCH

To see step-by-step videos of these problems, enter the page number into the SWadvantage.com Search Bar.

You can apply what you learned about coterminal angles in degree measure to angles in radian measure.

EXAMPLE 4

Find an angle between 0 and 2π that is coterminal with $\theta = \frac{7\pi}{3}$. Sketch this angle.

STEP 1 For this angle, subtract one revolution (2π).

$$\frac{7\pi}{3} - 2\pi = \frac{7\pi}{3} - \frac{6\pi}{3}$$
$$= \frac{\pi}{3}$$

So, $\frac{7\pi}{3}$ is coterminal with $\frac{\pi}{3}$.

STEP 2 Sketch this angle.

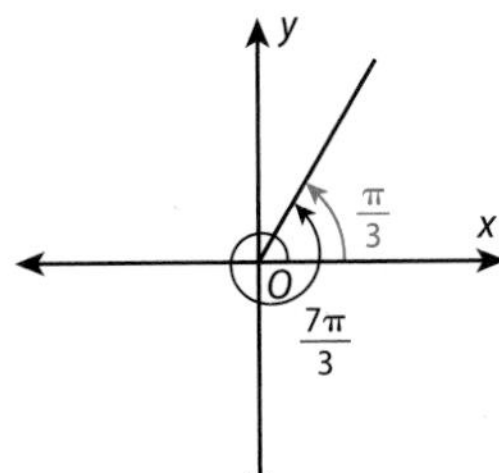

GOT TO KNOW!

Special Angle Measures in Degrees and Radians

Degrees	30°	45°	60°	90°	180°	360°
Radians	$\frac{\pi}{6}$	$\frac{\pi}{4}$	$\frac{\pi}{3}$	$\frac{\pi}{2}$	π	2π

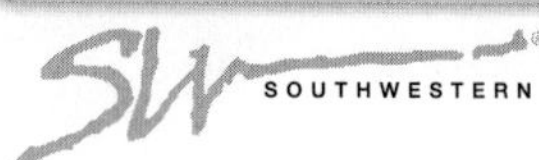

Trigonometric Values of Special Angles

You can use a reference triangle to determine the trigonometric values of special angles in radian measure.

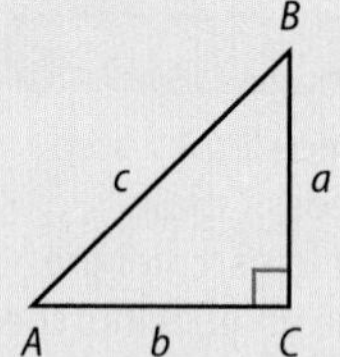

The six trig values for angle A are:

$\sin A = \frac{a}{c}$ $\csc A = \frac{c}{a}$

$\cos A = \frac{b}{c}$ $\sec A = \frac{c}{b}$

$\tan A = \frac{a}{b}$ $\cot A = \frac{b}{a}$

If a radical is in the denominator of a fraction, multiply both the numerator and the denominator by the radical to simplify.

EXAMPLE 5

Find the sin, cos, and tan of $\frac{\pi}{4}$.

STEP 1 Sketch the reference triangle.

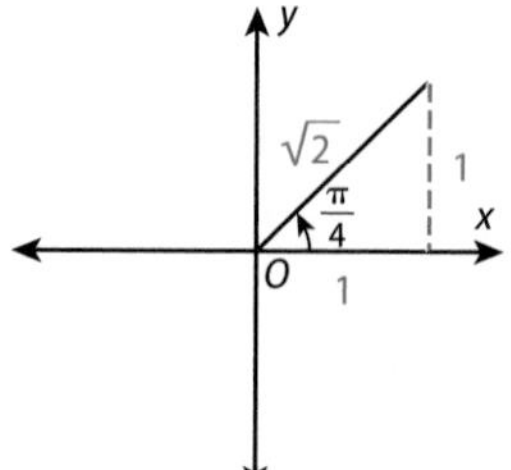

STEP 2 Use the reference triangle to determine the value of each trigonometric function.

$$\sin\frac{\pi}{4} = \frac{1}{\sqrt{2}} = \frac{1}{\sqrt{2}} \cdot \frac{\sqrt{2}}{\sqrt{2}} = \frac{\sqrt{2}}{2}$$

$$\cos\frac{\pi}{4} = \frac{1}{\sqrt{2}} = \frac{1}{\sqrt{2}} \cdot \frac{\sqrt{2}}{\sqrt{2}} = \frac{\sqrt{2}}{2}$$

$$\tan\frac{\pi}{4} = \frac{1}{1} = 1$$

So, $\sin\frac{\pi}{4}$ is $\frac{\sqrt{2}}{2}$, $\cos\frac{\pi}{4}$ is $\frac{\sqrt{2}}{2}$, and $\tan\frac{\pi}{4}$ is 1.

EXAMPLE 6

Find the six trigonometric functions of $\frac{10\pi}{3}$.

STEP 1 Sketch the reference triangle.

Begin with the angle $\frac{10\pi}{3}$. Next, sketch the coterminal angle $\left(\frac{10\pi}{3} - 2\pi = \frac{4\pi}{3}\right)$. Then, find the reference angle $\left(\frac{4\pi}{3} - \pi = \frac{\pi}{3}\right)$. Last, sketch the reference triangle.

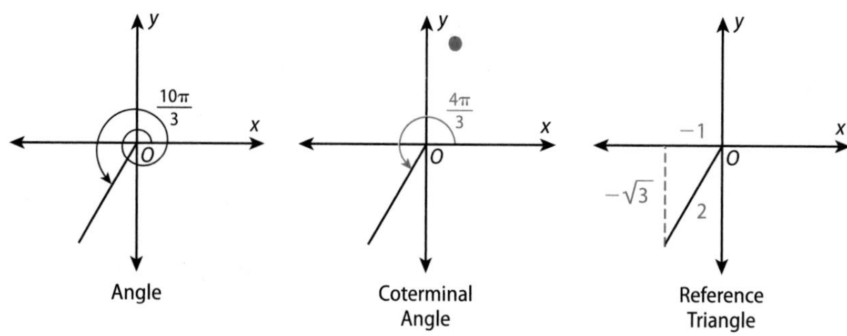

STEP 2 The reference angle is $\frac{\pi}{3}$. Use the reference triangle to determine the value of each trigonometric function.

$$\sin\frac{10\pi}{3} = \frac{-\sqrt{3}}{2} = -\frac{\sqrt{3}}{2} \qquad \cos\frac{10\pi}{3} = \frac{-1}{2} = -\frac{1}{2} \qquad \tan\frac{10\pi}{3} = \frac{-\sqrt{3}}{-1} = \sqrt{3}$$

$$\csc\frac{10\pi}{3} = -\frac{2}{\sqrt{3}} \cdot \frac{\sqrt{3}}{\sqrt{3}} = -\frac{2\sqrt{3}}{3} \qquad \sec\frac{10\pi}{3} = -\frac{2}{1} = -2 \qquad \cot\frac{10\pi}{3} = \frac{-1}{-\sqrt{3}} \cdot \frac{\sqrt{3}}{\sqrt{3}} = \frac{\sqrt{3}}{3}$$

You do not need to draw a reference triangle to find the trigonometric value of θ if θ is a special angle in any quadrant. All you need to know are the trigonometric values of the special angles from 0 to $\frac{\pi}{2}$ radians and the sign of the trigonometric functions in the quadrant in which the terminal side of θ falls.

EXAMPLE 7

Find the six trigonometric functions of $-\frac{5\pi}{6}$.

STEP 1 Add 2π to find the coterminal angle.

$$2\pi + \left(-\frac{5\pi}{6}\right) = \frac{12\pi}{6} - \frac{5\pi}{6} = \frac{7\pi}{6} \qquad \text{Quadrant III}$$

STEP 2 Subtract π to find the reference angle. $\frac{7\pi}{6} - \pi = \frac{7\pi}{6} - \frac{6\pi}{6} = \frac{\pi}{6}$

STEP 3 Identify the trigonometric values for $\frac{\pi}{6}$. Determine the sign of each value for Quadrant III.

$$\sin\left(-\frac{5\pi}{6}\right) = -\frac{1}{2} \qquad \cos\left(-\frac{5\pi}{6}\right) = -\frac{\sqrt{3}}{2} \qquad \tan\left(-\frac{5\pi}{6}\right) = \frac{\sqrt{3}}{3}$$

$$\csc\left(-\frac{5\pi}{6}\right) = -2 \qquad \sec\left(-\frac{5\pi}{6}\right) = -\frac{2\sqrt{3}}{3} \qquad \cot\left(-\frac{5\pi}{6}\right) = \sqrt{3}$$

SEARCH

To see step-by-step videos of these problems, enter the page number into the SWadvantage.com Search Bar.

The terminal side of quadrantal angles 0°, $\frac{\pi}{2}$ (90°), π (180°), $\frac{3\pi}{2}$ (270°), 2π (360°), and so on, lie along one of the axes. To find the trigonometric functions of these angles, think of their position on the coordinate plane.

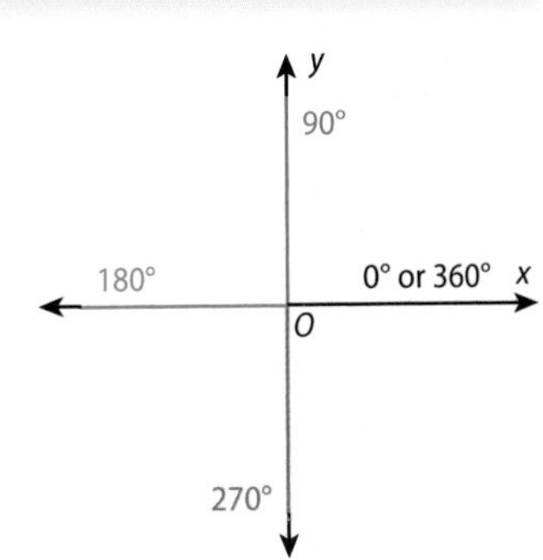

For an angle of 0 radians, the terminal side lies along the x-axis, with $x = r$ and $y = 0$, so

$$\sin 0 = \frac{0}{r} = 0 \qquad \cos 0 = \frac{r}{r} = 1 \qquad \tan 0 = \frac{0}{r} = 0$$

GOT TO KNOW!

Trigonometric Values of the Special Angles

Degrees	Radians	$\sin\theta$	$\cos\theta$	$\tan\theta$	$\csc\theta$	$\sec\theta$	$\cot\theta$
0	0	0	1	0	undefined	1	undefined
30	$\frac{\pi}{6}$	$\frac{1}{2}$	$\frac{\sqrt{3}}{2}$	$\frac{\sqrt{3}}{3}$	2	$\frac{2\sqrt{3}}{3}$	$\sqrt{3}$
45	$\frac{\pi}{4}$	$\frac{\sqrt{2}}{2}$	$\frac{\sqrt{2}}{2}$	1	$\sqrt{2}$	$\sqrt{2}$	1
60	$\frac{\pi}{3}$	$\frac{\sqrt{3}}{2}$	$\frac{1}{2}$	$\sqrt{3}$	$\frac{2\sqrt{3}}{3}$	2	$\frac{\sqrt{3}}{3}$
90	$\frac{\pi}{2}$	1	0	undefined	1	undefined	0

Applications of Radian Measure

Length of an Arc and Area of a Sector

You can use radian measure to write simple formulas for finding the length of an arc (s) and area of a sector (A). In the formulas in the *Got To Know!* box, r is the radius of the circle and θ is the radian measure of the central angle.

SEARCH

To see step-by-step videos of these problems, enter the page number into the SWadvantage.com Search Bar.

EXAMPLE 1

A central angle of a circle of radius 6 centimeters measures 1.5 radians. Find each measure.

a. the length of the intercepted arc

Use the arc length formula.	$s = r\theta$
Substitute 6 for r and 1.5 for θ.	$= (6)(1.5)$
Multiply.	$= 9$

The length of the intercepted arc is 9 cm.

b. the area of the sector

Use the area of a sector formula.	$A = \frac{1}{2}r^2\theta$
Substitute 6 for r and 1.5 for θ.	$= \frac{1}{2}6^2(1.5)$
Multiply.	$= 18(1.5) = 27$

The area of the sector is 27 cm^2.

EXAMPLE 2

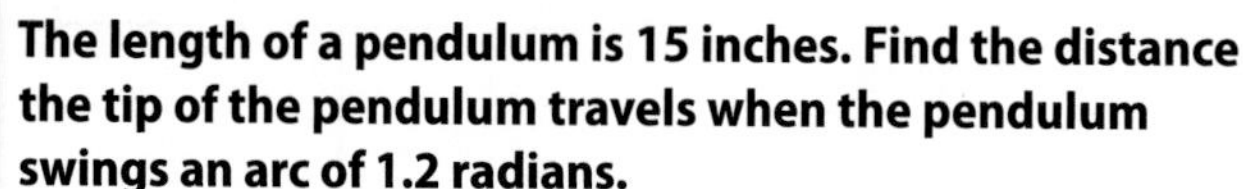

The length of a pendulum is 15 inches. Find the distance the tip of the pendulum travels when the pendulum swings an arc of 1.2 radians.

Use the arc length formula.	$s = r\theta$
Substitute 15 for r and 1.2 for θ.	$= (15)(1.2)$
Multiply.	$= 18$ in.

The tip of the pendulum travels 18 inches.

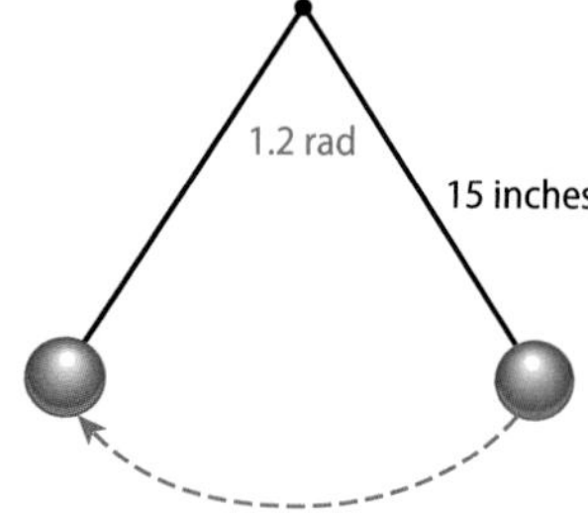

GOT TO KNOW!

Arc Length

$s = r\theta$

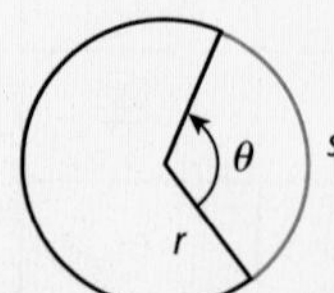

Area of a Sector

$A = \frac{1}{2}r^2\theta$

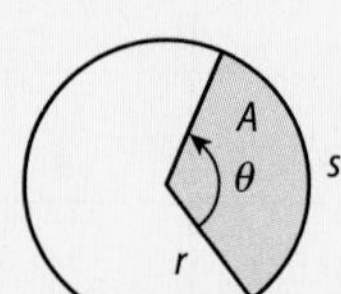

Latitude

Measuring latitude is a way of locating places on earth with respect to the equator. Lines of latitude are parallel to the equator. The position of these lines is given by an angle θ whose vertex is at the center of the earth.

$$\theta = \frac{s}{r}$$

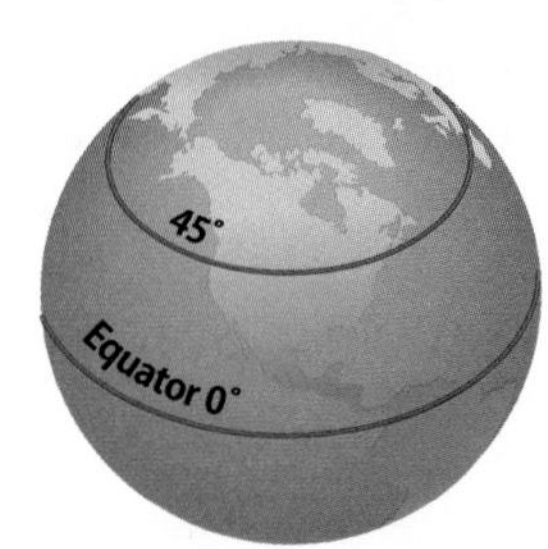

EXAMPLE 3

Find the latitude of Chicago, which is 2,890 miles north of the equator. Assume the earth is a sphere with radius of 3,960 miles.

STEP 1 Write the latitude formula. $\theta = \frac{s}{r}$

STEP 2 Substitute 2,890 for *s* and 3,960 for *r*. Then simplify. $\theta = \frac{2{,}890}{3{,}960} = \frac{289}{396}$

STEP 3 Convert the result to degrees. $\theta = \frac{289}{396} \cdot \frac{180°}{\pi} \approx 41.81°$

The latitude of Chicago is about 41.81° North.

EXAMPLE 4

The latitude of Pittsburgh is 40° 27′ N. How far is Pittsburgh from the equator?

STEP 1 Convert 40° 27′ to decimal degrees. $40°\ 27' = 40° + \left(\frac{27}{60}\right)°$

$= 40° + 0.45° = 40.45°$

STEP 2 Convert 40.45° to radians. $\theta = 40.45° \times \frac{\pi}{180°} \approx 0.7$ radians

STEP 3 Write the formula. $\theta = \frac{s}{r}$

STEP 4 Substitute 0.7 for θ and 3,960 for *r*. $0.7 = \frac{s}{3{,}960}$

STEP 5 Solve for *s*. $2{,}772 = s$

Pittsburgh is about 2,772 miles from the equator.

Need More HELP

To convert an angle in minutes into degrees, first write $27' = \left(\frac{27}{60}\right)°$. Then change the fraction to a decimal and add the decimal to 40°.

For the formula, θ is in radians. Change degrees to radians.

GOT TO KNOW!

Latitude

$\theta = \frac{s}{r}$

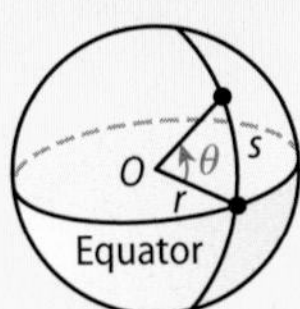

Linear and Angular Velocity

Linear Velocity

Suppose that a particle moves with a constant speed, V, around a circle of radius r centimeters. If the particle travels s centimeters in t seconds, its speed is:

$$V = \frac{s}{t} \text{ cm/s}$$

The **linear velocity** of a point on a rotating object is the *distance* per unit time that the point travels along the circular path.

EXAMPLE 1

The second hand of a clock is 9 centimeters long. What is the linear velocity of the tip of the second hand as it travels around the clock?

The tip of the second hand travels 2π radians in 1 minute or 60 seconds.

Write the formula. Substitute $r\theta$ for s, the distance traveled. $V = \frac{s}{t} = \frac{r\theta}{t}$

Substitute 60 for t and $9(2\pi)$ for $r\theta$. $= \frac{9(2\pi)}{60}$

Simplify. ≈ 0.94 cm/s

The tip of the second hand of the clock travels 0.94 centimeters per second.

Need More HELP

Arc length is equal to the radius times the angle measure in radians.

$s = r\theta$

(See page 940.)

Angular Velocity

Another kind of speed associated with a point on a rotating object is *angular velocity*. The **angular velocity** of a point on a rotating object is the number of degrees (radians, or revolutions) per unit time through which the point turns. The Greek letter ω is usually used to represent angular velocity.

$$\omega = \frac{\theta}{t}$$

EXAMPLE 2

The wheel of a truck turns at 6 revolutions per second (rps). What is the angular velocity of the wheel in radians per second?

Multiply the revolutions per second times the radians per revolution. The wheel travels 2π in 1 revolution. $\omega = \frac{6}{1} \times \frac{2\pi}{1} = 12\pi$ rad/s

The angular velocity of the truck wheel is 12 radians per second.

Note that the angular velocity of all points on a rotating object is the *same*. However, the linear velocity depends on how far the point is from the axis of rotation.

There is a simple relationship between the angular velocity and the linear velocity of the same point. If a point travels in a circular path with radius r at a constant speed, the linear velocity V is equal to the angular velocity times the radius of the path. See the *Got To Know!* box.

EXAMPLE 3

Ana rides an electronic tricycle at 15 miles per hour. The tires have a radius of 24 inches.

a. Find the angular velocity of a tricycle tire in radians per minute.

First change the units of linear velocity from miles per hour to inches per minute.

$$V = \frac{15\text{ mi}}{\text{h}} \cdot \frac{5{,}280\text{ ft}}{1\text{ mi}} \cdot \frac{12\text{ in.}}{1\text{ ft}} \cdot \frac{1\text{ h}}{60\text{ min}} = 15{,}840\text{ in./min}$$

Then use the formula $\omega = \frac{V}{r}$ to find the angular velocity.

$$\omega = \frac{V}{r} = \frac{15{,}840}{24} = 660\text{ rad/min}$$

The angular velocity of a tire on Ana's tricycle is 660 radians per minute.

b. How many revolutions per minute does the tricycle tire make?

To find the number of revolutions per minute, divide ω by 2π.

$$\frac{660}{2\pi} \approx 105\text{ rpm}$$

The tricycle tire travels at a speed of 105 revolutions per minute.

Need More HELP

It is important to use consistent units of measure when working problems involving linear and angular velocity.

EXAMPLE 4

A Ferris wheel with a radius of 25 feet makes one revolution in 2 minutes.

a. Find the speed of a seat on the outer rim of the Ferris wheel.

In one revolution, the seat travels a distance of the circumference or $2\pi r$.

$$V = \frac{s}{t} = \frac{50\pi}{2} = 25\pi \approx 78.5\text{ ft/min}$$

b. Find the angular speed.

In one revolution, the Ferris wheel turns 360° or 2π radians.

$$\omega = \frac{\theta}{t} = \frac{2\pi}{2} = \pi \approx 3.1\text{ rad/min}$$

SEARCH

To see step-by-step videos of these problems, enter the page number into the SWadvantage.com Search Bar.

GOT TO KNOW!

Linear and Angular Velocity

Linear Velocity	**Angular Velocity**
$V = \frac{s}{t}$	$\omega = \frac{\theta}{t}$

$$V = \frac{s}{t} = r\frac{\theta}{t} = r\omega$$

The Unit Circle

SOUTHWESTERN

Values of Trigonometric Functions on the Unit Circle

The key trigonometric functions, sine and cosine, may be defined using the *unit circle*. A **unit circle** is simply a circle centered at the origin with radius equal to one unit. Since $r = 1$, the sine and cosine simplify to $\sin\theta = y$ and $\cos\theta = x$.

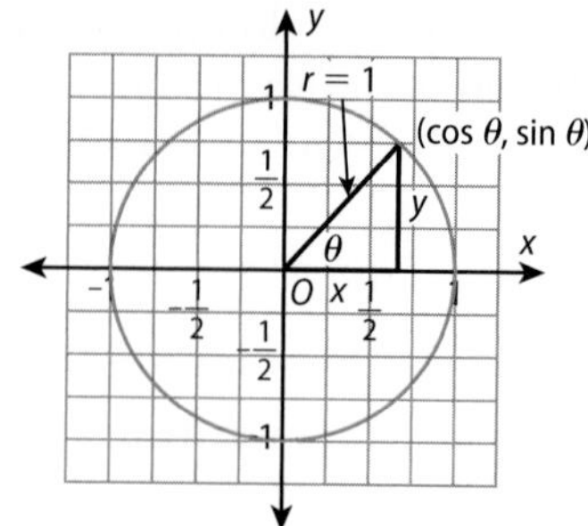

So, for a given angle θ, every x-coordinate of a point on a unit circle is the cosine of the angle and every y-coordinate is the sine of the angle. Thus, the coordinates x and y are two functions of θ. We can use these coordinates to define the six trigonometric functions of θ for any point on the unit circle.

EXAMPLE 1

Find the value of each of the six trigonometric functions when $\theta = \frac{\pi}{3}$.

$\frac{\pi}{3}$ is $\frac{1}{6}$ of 2π or $\frac{1}{6}$ of the unit circle.

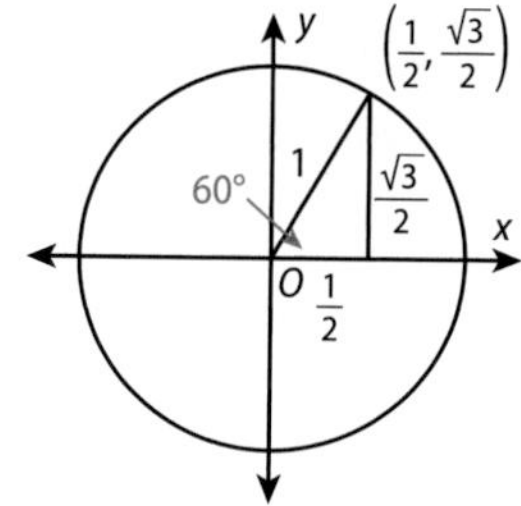

The radius drawn to the terminal side of the angle forms a 60° angle with the x-axis. This is a 30°–60°–90° right triangle with a radius of 1.

So, the coordinates of the point on the circle are $\left(\frac{1}{2}, \frac{\sqrt{3}}{2}\right)$.

$\sin\frac{\pi}{3} = y = \frac{\sqrt{3}}{2}$ $\qquad \csc\frac{\pi}{3} = \frac{1}{y} = \frac{2}{\sqrt{3}} = \frac{2\sqrt{3}}{3}$

$\cos\frac{\pi}{3} = x = \frac{1}{2}$ $\qquad \tan\frac{\pi}{3} = \frac{y}{x} = \frac{\frac{\sqrt{3}}{2}}{\frac{1}{2}} = \sqrt{3}$

$\sec\frac{\pi}{3} = \frac{1}{x} = 2$ $\qquad \cot\frac{\pi}{3} = \frac{x}{y} = \frac{1}{\sqrt{3}} = \frac{\sqrt{3}}{3}$

Need More HELP

In a 30°–60°–90° right triangle, the length of the sides and the length of the hypotenuse are related in a very special way (See page 686.)

SEARCH

To see step-by-step videos of these problems, enter the page number into the SWadvantage.com Search Bar.

GOT TO KNOW!

Trigonometric Functions of a Point on the Unit Circle

$\sin\theta = y$	$\cos\theta = x$	$\tan\theta = \frac{y}{x}, x \neq 0$
$\csc\theta = \frac{1}{y}, y \neq 0$	$\sec\theta = \frac{1}{x}, x \neq 0$	$\cot\theta = \frac{x}{y}, y \neq 0$

Special Angles

Because the angles 30° ($\frac{\pi}{6}$), 45° ($\frac{\pi}{4}$), and 60° ($\frac{\pi}{3}$) occur frequently in trigonometry, it is a good idea to memorize their function values or to be able to construct the triangles from which you can determine the function values of the points on the unit circle associated with these angles.

EXAMPLE 2

Find the coordinates of the point on the unit circle when $\theta = \frac{\pi}{4}$. Then find the value of each of the six trigonometric functions at this point.

STEP 1 Draw the reference triangle.

$\frac{\pi}{4}$ is $\frac{1}{4}$ of 180° or 45°. The reference triangle is a 45°–45°–90° right triangle. The hypotenuse is the radius of the circle which is 1.

$\left(\frac{\sqrt{2}}{2}, \frac{\sqrt{2}}{2}\right)$, 1, $\frac{\sqrt{2}}{2}$, x, y, O, $\frac{\sqrt{2}}{2}$

STEP 2 Use the Pythagorean theorem to calculate the length of the legs of this triangle.

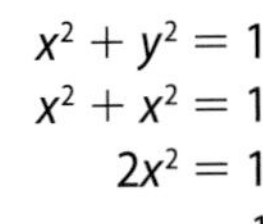

$$x^2 + y^2 = 1$$
$$x^2 + x^2 = 1$$
$$2x^2 = 1$$
$$x^2 = \frac{1}{2}$$
$$x = \sqrt{\frac{1}{2}} = \frac{\sqrt{2}}{2}$$

STEP 3 Use $\left(\frac{\sqrt{2}}{2}, \frac{\sqrt{2}}{2}\right)$ to find the value of the six trigonometric functions when $\theta = \frac{\pi}{4}$.

$\sin\frac{\pi}{4} = y = \frac{\sqrt{2}}{2}$ $\quad$ $\cos\frac{\pi}{4} = x = \frac{\sqrt{2}}{2}$ $\quad$ $\tan\frac{\pi}{4} = \frac{y}{x} = \frac{\frac{\sqrt{2}}{2}}{\frac{\sqrt{2}}{2}} = 1$

$\csc\frac{\pi}{4} = \frac{1}{y} = \frac{1}{\frac{\sqrt{2}}{2}} = \sqrt{2}$ $\quad$ $\sec\frac{\pi}{4} = \frac{1}{y} = \frac{1}{\frac{\sqrt{2}}{2}} = \sqrt{2}$ $\quad$ $\cot\frac{\pi}{4} = \frac{x}{y} = \frac{\frac{\sqrt{2}}{2}}{\frac{\sqrt{2}}{2}} = 1$

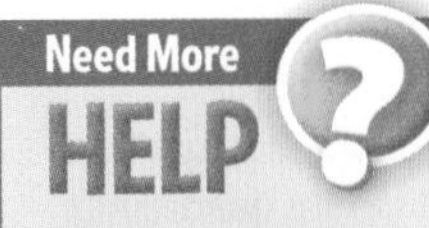

The Pythagorean theorem states that

$$a^2 + b^2 = c^2$$

where a and b are the lengths of the sides and c is the length of the hypotenuse. (See page 678.)

GOT TO KNOW!

Sine and Cosine Values of the Special Angles on the Unit Circle

The unit circle shows the sine and cosine values for the special angles 0, $\frac{\pi}{6}, \frac{\pi}{4}, \frac{\pi}{3}, \frac{\pi}{2}$, and their multiples up to 2π.

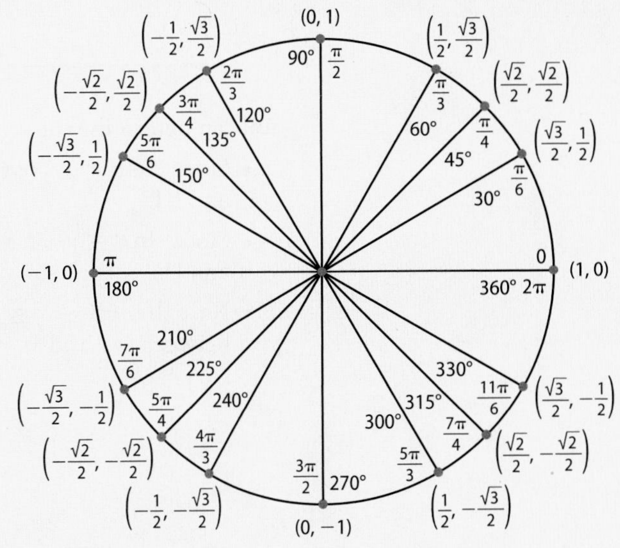

Finding the Angle Measures

If you are given the trigonometric value of a special angle, you can determine the angle.

EXAMPLE 3

Find two values of θ that satisfy each function.

a. $\cos\theta = -\frac{\sqrt{2}}{2}$

Determine the coordinate and the quadrant.

$\cos\theta = x$

x is negative in Quadrant II and III.

$x = -\frac{\sqrt{2}}{2}$

Find the angle with that coordinate on the unit circle.

θ could be $\frac{3\pi}{4}$ or 135°, and $\frac{5\pi}{4}$ or 225°.

b. $\csc\theta = \frac{2\sqrt{3}}{2}$

$\csc\theta = \frac{1}{y}$

y is positive in Quadrant I and II.

$\frac{1}{y} = \frac{2\sqrt{3}}{3}$

$y = \frac{3}{2\sqrt{3}} = \frac{\sqrt{3}}{2}$

θ could be $\frac{\pi}{3}$ or 60°, and $\frac{2\pi}{3}$ or 120°.

Need More HELP

For more about the signs of the trigonometric functions in different quadrants, see page 934.

You can also find the value of a trigonometric function at a given point.

EXAMPLE 4

Find the value of each trigonometric function at the given point.

a. $\sin\frac{\pi}{2}$

Find the coordinates of the angle on the unit circle.

(0, 1) are the coordinates associated with $\frac{\pi}{2}$.

Identify the coordinate(s) associated with the trigonometric function. Simplify if needed.

$\sin\theta = y$

$\sin\frac{\pi}{2} = 1$

b. $\tan\pi$

$(-1, 0)$ are the coordinates associated with π.

$\tan\theta = \frac{y}{x}$

$\tan\pi = \frac{0}{-1} = 0$

c. $\cos\frac{4\pi}{3}$

$\left(-\frac{1}{2}, -\frac{\sqrt{3}}{2}\right)$ are the coordinates associated with $\frac{4\pi}{3}$.

$\cos\theta = x$

$\cos\frac{4\pi}{3} = -\frac{1}{2}$

SEARCH

To see step-by-step videos of these problems, enter the page number into the SWadvantage.com Search Bar.

You can determine the signs of the functions in each of the four quadrants.

- Since $\cos\theta = x$, $\cos\theta$ is positive in Quadrants I and IV and negative in Quadrants II and III.
- Since $\sin\theta = y$, $\sin\theta$ is positive in Quadrants I and II and negative in Quadrants II and IV.
- Note that $-1 \le x \le 1$ and $-1 \le y \le 1$, so the values of $\sin\theta$ and $\cos\theta$ also have a range between -1 and 1.

Circular Functions

The trigonometric functions are often called *circular functions* because of their association with the unit circle.

Suppose you are on a Ferris wheel. You step onto the Ferris wheel at its lowest point. As the wheel turns, you rise until your seat reaches the highest point. It then descends. As you pass the starting position, the cycle repeats itself. A graph of this function is shown below.

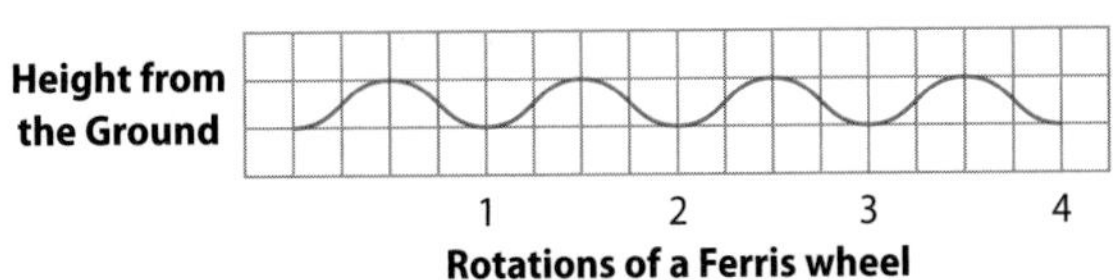

Functions that continually repeat themselves are called ***periodic functions***.

A point on the unit circle can travel around the circle over and over again. Thus the domain consists of all positive real numbers. Since the point can travel in a clockwise direction, the domain includes all negative real numbers. The range is from -1 to 1.

EXAMPLE 5

Find the value (ordered pair) in the range of the circular function that corresponds to the real number $\frac{3\pi}{2}$.

STEP 1 Find what part of a revolution $\frac{3\pi}{2}$ represents. $\qquad \frac{\frac{3\pi}{2}}{2\pi} = \frac{3}{4}$

One revolution is 2π. Divide by 2π.

STEP 2 Draw and label a unit circle.

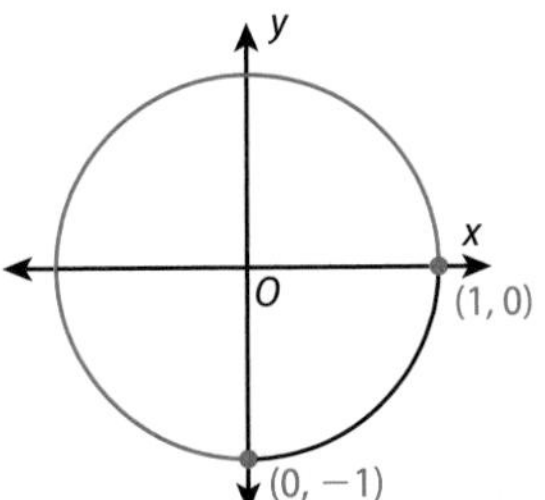

$\frac{3\pi}{2}$ corresponds to the point $(0, -1)$.

EXAMPLE 6

Find the value (ordered pair) in the range of the circular function that corresponds to the real number $-\pi$.

Draw a diagram to represent $-\pi$.

$-\pi$ is in a clockwise direction that represents $\frac{1}{2}$ a revolution.

$-\pi$ corresponds to the point $(-1, 0)$.

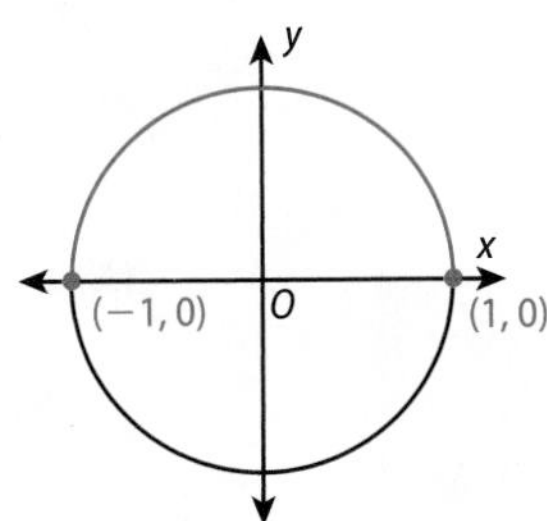

Graphs of the Trigonometric Functions

What Came Before?

- Graphing functions on the coordinate plane
- The Unit Circle

What's This About?

- Using the values in the Unit Circle to graph the trigonometric functions
- Transforming trigonometric functions
- Modeling real world applications with trigonometric functions

Practical Apps

- Radio and cell phone signals are sine waves that produce sounds.
- The path of the pendulum of a grandfather clock can be modeled by harmonic motion.

Just for FUN!

I can prove that six = 6 using trigonometry!

$\frac{1}{n}\sin x = 6$

$\frac{1}{\not n}\text{si}\not n\, x = 6$

$\text{six} = 6$

CONTENTS UPLOAD DOWNLOAD

Trigonometry

Topics	Vocabulary	Pages
Periodic Functions	*function* *periodic function* *period of the function*	950–951
Graphs of the Sine and Cosine Functions	*amplitude*	952–957
Using a Graphing Calculator		958–961
Transformations	*phase shift* *argument*	962–967
Graphs of the Tangent and Cotangent Functions	*asymptotes*	968–971
Graphs of the Secant and Cosecant Functions		972–975
Other Transformations		976–981
Combining Trigonometric Functions		982–985
Harmonic Motion		986–989
Modeling with Trigonometric Functions		990–993

You can find more practice problems online by visiting:
www.SWadvantage.com

Definition of a Periodic Function

Need More HELP

The domain of a function is the set of all first coordinates in an ordered pair. The range is the set of all second coordinates.

A **periodic function** is a function f such that $f(x) = f(x + np)$, where x is any real number in the domain of f, n is an integer, and p is a positive real number. The smallest possible value of p is called the **period of the function**.

The graph of a periodic function repeats in a regular pattern over equal intervals. The length of the smallest horizontal interval between corresponding points is the *period* of the function.

Watch Out!

The length of p is always positive and equals $|x_1 - x_2|$, where x_1 and x_2 are the endpoints of a horizontal segment.

EXAMPLE 1

What is the period in the graph of the periodic function shown?

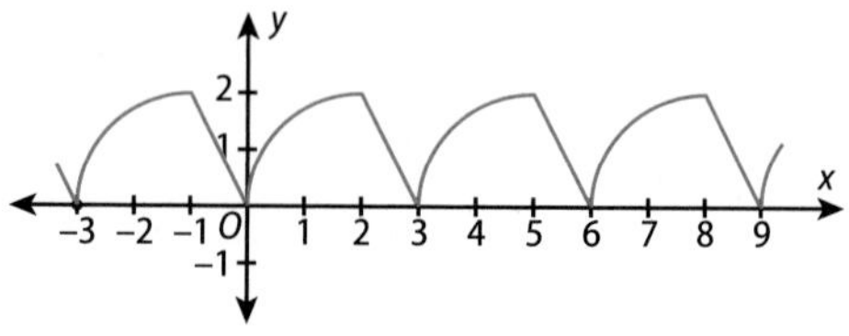

To determine the period p, draw one or more horizontal segments between corresponding points on the graph. Then find p by calculating the difference of the absolute value of the x-coordinates of the endpoints of one of the segments.

The period of this function is 3.

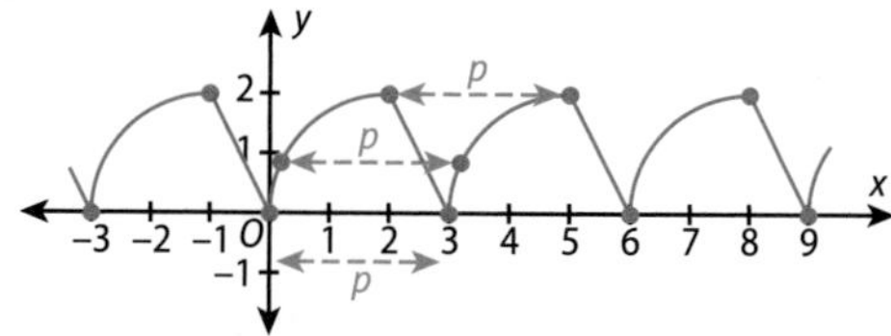

EXAMPLE 2

SEARCH

To see step-by-step videos of these problems, enter the page number into the SWadvantage.com Search Bar.

What is the period of this square function?

The square function repeats over the set of all real numbers. Its pattern looks like this: ⎽⎍

The shortest length of a horizontal segment between corresponding points is: $|3 - (-1)| = 4$.

The period p of this function is 4.

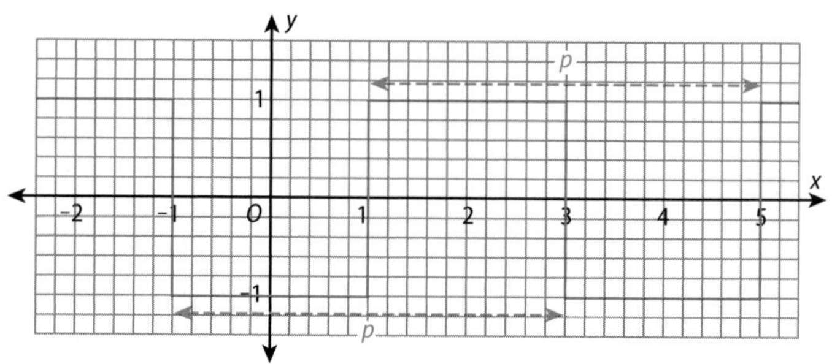

EXAMPLE 3

What is the period in the graph of the saw tooth function shown?

The equation of the saw tooth function is $f(x) = x - [x]$, where x is a real number. The expression $[x]$ is the greatest integer less than or equal to x. Horizontal segments between corresponding "teeth" of the graph are always 1. So, the period of this function is 1.

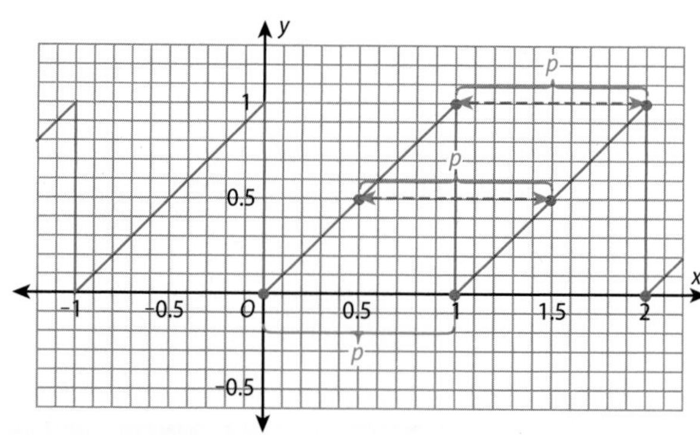

EXAMPLE 4

What is the period of this function?

This function is an example of a periodic function that is not defined for all real numbers x. Each branch of the curve is asymptotic to a vertical line through those values of x.

Using the coordinates along the x-axis, the period p is equal to $|-1.9 - (-7.1)| = 5.2$.

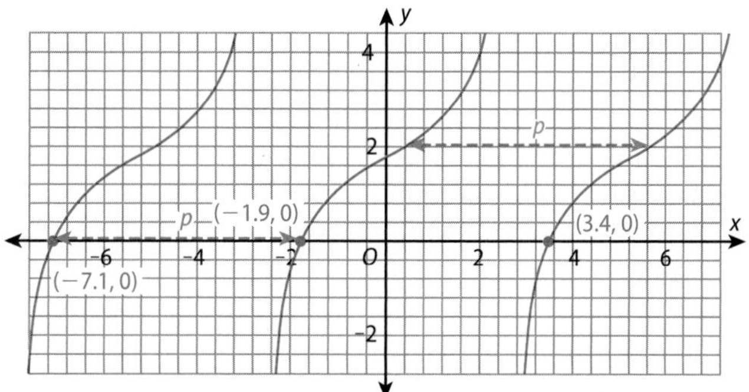

Need More HELP

An asymptote is a line that a curve approaches but never intersects.

EXAMPLE 5

What is the period of this function?

This function is defined for all real numbers x. Using the values of x at the start and end of the pattern, the period of this function is $|2 - 0)| = 2$.

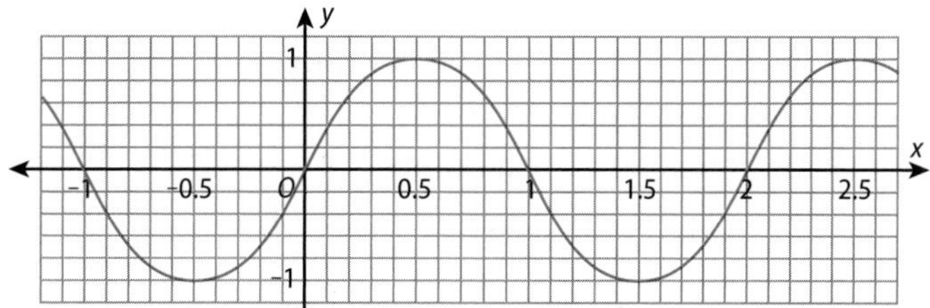

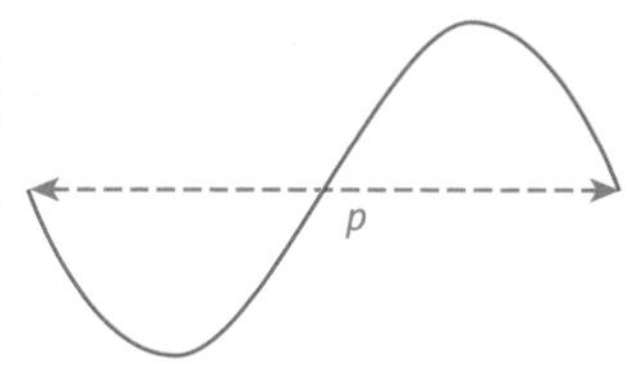

Watch Out!

You can start anywhere on the graph of a periodic function to determine its period.

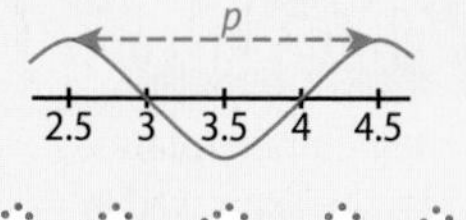

GOT TO KNOW!

Periodic Functions

- For all real numbers x in the domain of the function, a periodic function $f(x)$ is defined as $f(x) = f(x + np)$, where n is an integer, and p is a positive real number. The smallest possible value of p is the period of the function.
- The period of a function equals $|x_1 - x_2|$, where x_1 and x_2 are the endpoints of the shortest horizontal segment between corresponding points on the graph of the function.

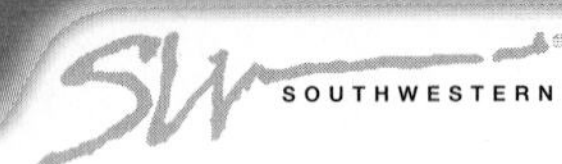

A unit circle has a radius of 1 and its center is at the origin.

Graphs of $y = a \sin(x)$

The definition of the sine function is expressed in terms of the y-coordinate of a point P on the unit circle $y = \sin x$, where x is a real number in radians or degrees. If $x > 0$, the rotation is counterclockwise. If $x < 0$, the rotation is clockwise. A complete rotation is 2π or 360°.

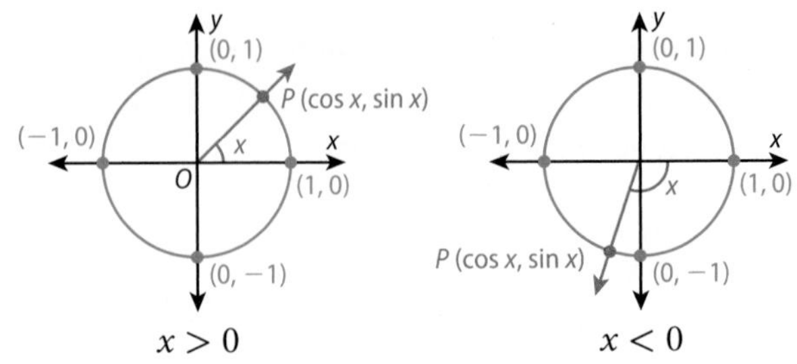

The table below show values of sin x for given values of x in radians from 0 to 2π.

x	0	$\frac{\pi}{4}$	$\frac{\pi}{2}$	$\frac{3\pi}{4}$	π	$\frac{5\pi}{4}$	$\frac{3\pi}{2}$	$\frac{7\pi}{4}$	2π
sin x	0	≈ 0.7	1	≈ 0.7	0	≈ −0.7	−1	≈ −0.7	0

Plotting these points and drawing a smooth curve through them results in part of the graph of $y = \sin x$. This is called a sine wave or sinusoidal curve and has these properties:

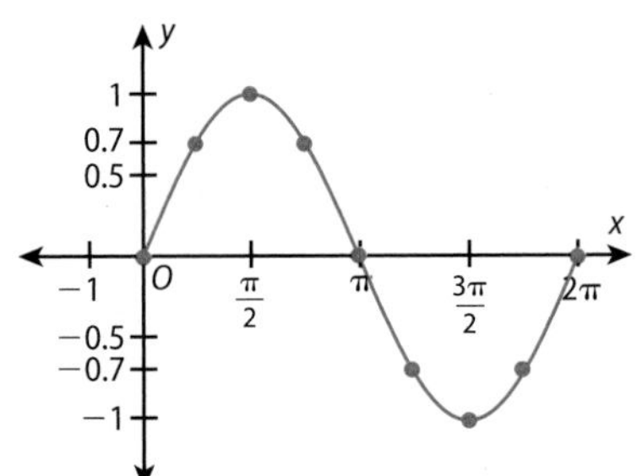

- the domain is all real numbers, $[-\infty, \infty]$.
- the range is $-1 \leq \sin x \leq 1$, or $[-1, 1]$.
- the period is 2π, where $\sin x = \sin(x + 2\pi)$.
- the x-intercepts are at $k\pi$, where k is an integer.
- the y-intercept is at 0.
- the **amplitude** $|a|$ is 1, where $a = \frac{1}{2}(\sin x_{max} - \sin x_{min})$.

Watch Out!

Remember: rotations can be expressed in degrees or radians. Radians can be converted into degrees by multiplying the number of degrees by $\frac{180°}{\pi}$. Here are three equivalences:

$\frac{\pi}{2}$ radians = 90°

π radians = 180°

2π radians = 360°

EXAMPLE 1

What are the amplitude, period, and x-intercepts of $y = 2\sin x$ shown in red in the graph? The graph of $y = \sin x$ is in blue.

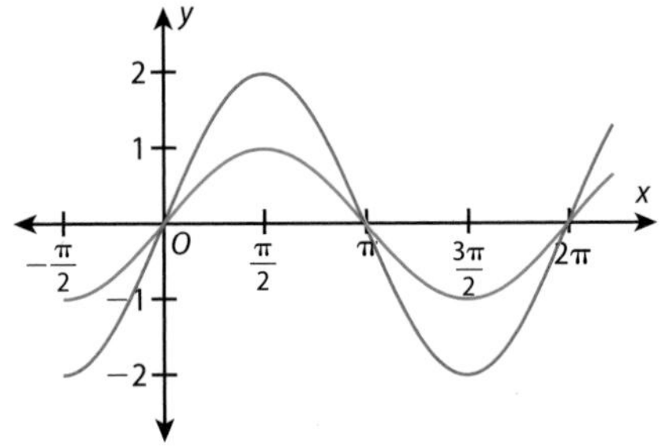

The coefficient of sin x is a, the amplitude of the function, whose maximum and minimum values are 2 and −2, respectively. So, $a = \frac{1}{2}(2-(-2)) = \frac{1}{2}(4) = 2$.

The period is 2π. The x-intercepts are integer multiples of π.

EXAMPLE 2

What is the equation of this sine wave shown in red? The graph of $y = \sin x$ is in blue.

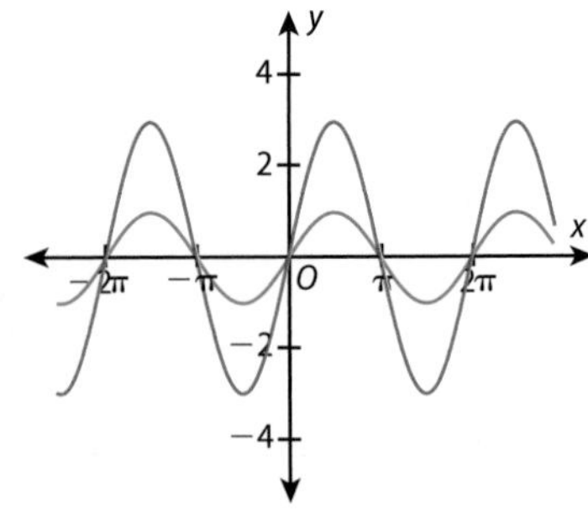

The maximum of the function in red is 3 and the minimum is 3.

Its amplitude is $a = \frac{1}{2}(3-(-3)) = \frac{1}{2}(6) = 3$.

So, the equation is $y = 3\sin x$.

SEARCH

To see step-by-step videos of these problems, enter the page number into the SWadvantage.com Search Bar.

EXAMPLE 3

What are the amplitude, period, and x-intercepts of $y = \frac{1}{2}\sin x$ shown in red on this graph? The graph of $y = \sin x$ is shown in blue.

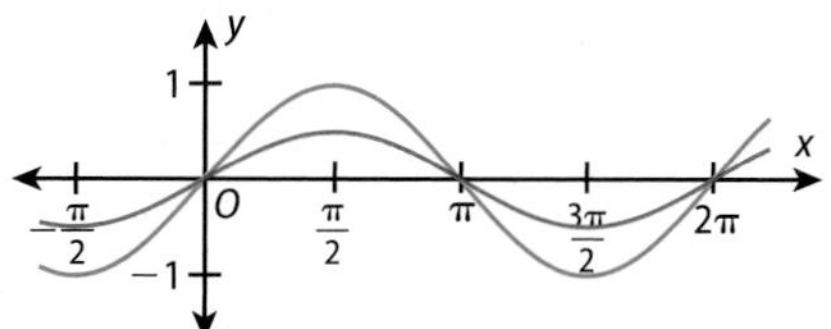

STEP 1 The coefficient of $\sin x$ is a, $\frac{1}{2}$. Therefore, the amplitude is $\left|\frac{1}{2}\right| = \frac{1}{2}$. This function is half as tall as the function $y = \sin x$.

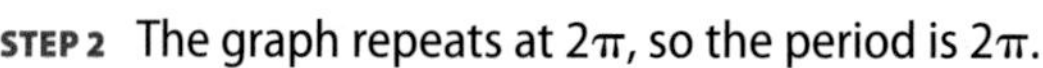

STEP 2 The graph repeats at 2π, so the period is 2π.

STEP 3 The x-intercepts are integer multiples of π.

Need More HELP

Remember: The period of a function is the smallest interval along the x-axis in which the graph of a function repeats.

Graphs of $y = \sin(bx)$

If $b = 1$, the period of the function $y = \sin bx$ is 2π. If $b \neq 1$, then the period of $y = \sin(bx)$ is $\frac{2\pi}{b}$, where $b > 0$. The amplitude is 1 because $a = 1$.

- If $0 < b < 1$, the graph of the function is stretched horizontally, and the period is greater than 2π.
- If $b > 1$, the graph of the function is compressed horizontally, and the period is less than 2π.

EXAMPLE 4

What are the amplitude and period of $y = \sin 2x$ in red on this graph? The graph of $y = \sin x$ is in blue.

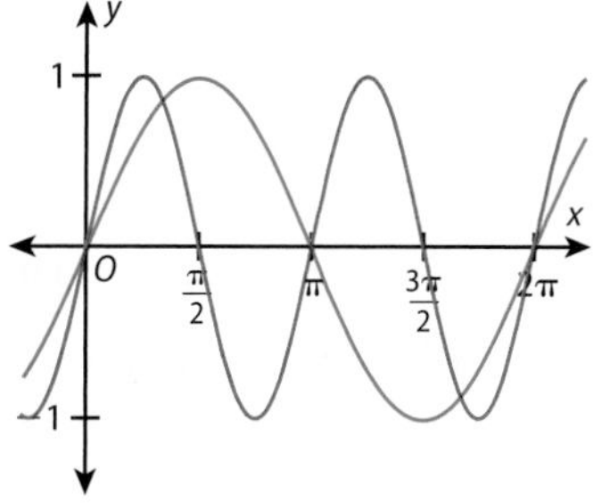

The coefficient a of $\sin 2x$ is 1, so the amplitude is 1.

The value of b is 2, so $\frac{2\pi}{2} = \pi$. Therefore, the period of this function is π. That is, the graph of this function completes one period over the interval $[0, \pi]$, rather than $[0, 2\pi]$. The graph is compressed horizontally so that two complete periods of this function are completed between 0 and 2π.

Need More HELP

The use of brackets in the notation $[0, \pi]$ represents a closed interval that includes all values of x between 0 and π, and both 0 and π. Intervals can be open $(0, \pi)$, or partially open and closed: $(0, \pi]$ and $[0, \pi)$.

EXAMPLE 5

What are the amplitude, period, and x-intercepts of $y = \sin \frac{1}{3}x$ in red on this graph? The graph of $y = \sin x$ is in blue.

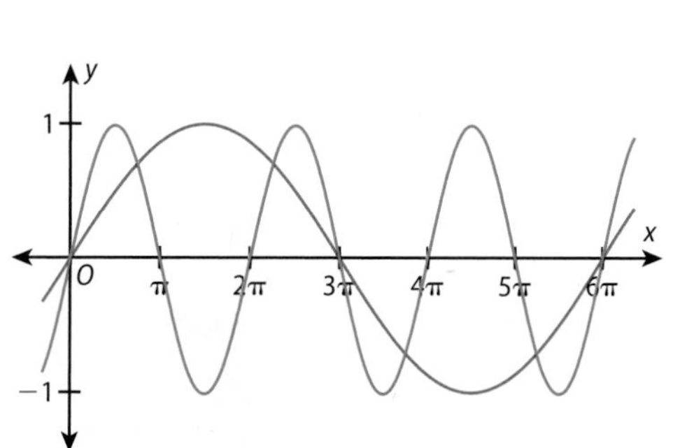

The coefficient of $\sin \frac{1}{3}x$ is 1, so the amplitude is 1.

The value of b is $\frac{1}{3}$, so the period of this function is $\frac{2\pi}{\left(\frac{1}{3}\right)} = 2\pi \cdot 3 = 6\pi$.

The graph of this function is stretched horizontally and completes one period over the interval $[0, 6\pi]$. That is, only $\frac{1}{3}$ of one period of this function is completed between 0 and 2π. Its x-intercepts occur at $x = 3k\pi$, where k is an integer.

Graphs of $y = a \sin(bx)$

If $a \neq 1$ and $b \neq 0$, then the amplitude, period, and x-intercepts of the sine function change.

Watch Out!

The x-intercepts of the normal sine function occur at $x = 2k\pi$. If $b \neq 1$, then they occur at intervals of $\frac{2k\pi}{b}$.

EXAMPLE 6

What are the amplitude, period, and x-intercepts of $y = 3 \sin 4x$ shown in red on this graph? The graph of $y = \sin x$ is in blue.

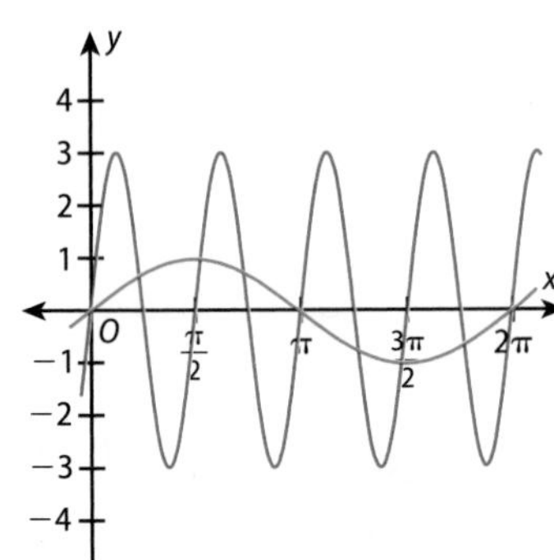

STEP 1 The coefficient of $\sin 4x$ is a, the amplitude. So, for this function, $a = 3$.

STEP 2 The coefficient of x in the argument of the sine is b. The period of the sine function is $\frac{2\pi}{b}$, so the period of this sine wave is $\frac{2\pi}{4} = \frac{\pi}{2}$. The graph completes one period over the interval $\left[0, \frac{\pi}{2}\right]$, and four complete periods between 0 and 2π.

STEP 3 The x-intercepts are at $\frac{k\pi}{4}$, where k is an integer.

Try It This Way

To verify the x-intercepts of the sine function when $b = 1$, make a table.

k	$k\pi$
−2	-2π
−1	$-\pi$
0	0
1	π
2	2π

EXAMPLE 7

What are the amplitude, period, and x-intercepts of $y = \frac{1}{2} \sin \frac{x}{4}$ shown in blue on this graph? The graph of $y = \sin x$ is in red.

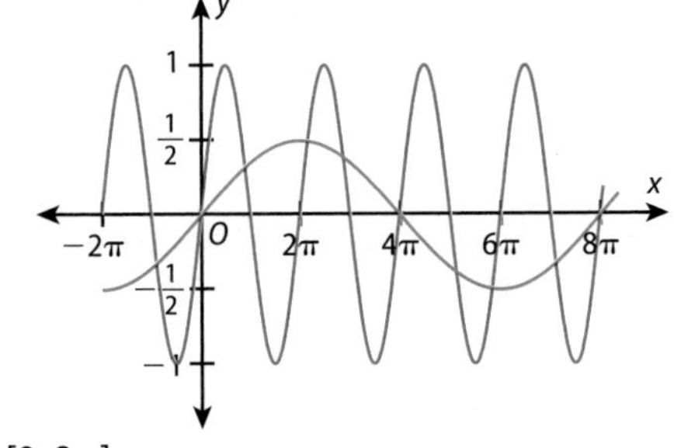

STEP 1 The amplitude is $\frac{1}{2}$.

STEP 2 The period of this sine wave is

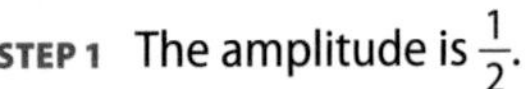

$$\frac{2\pi}{\left(\frac{1}{4}\right)} = \frac{2\pi}{\left(\frac{1}{4}\right)} \cdot \frac{4}{4} = 8\pi.$$

The graph completes one period over the interval $[0, 8\pi]$.

STEP 3 The x-intercepts are at $4k\pi$, where k is an integer.

GOT TO KNOW!

The Sine Function

Function	$y = \sin x$	$y = a \sin(bx)$
Domain	$[-\infty, \infty]$	$[-\infty, \infty]$
Range	$[-1, 1]$	$[-a, a]$

Period	2π	$\frac{2\pi}{b}, b > 0$
Amplitude	1	$\lvert a \rvert = a$ if $a > 0$; $= -a$, if $a < 0$
x-intercepts	$k\pi$, k is an integer	$\frac{k\pi}{b}$, k is an integer

Graphs of $y = a\cos(x)$

The definition of the cosine can be expressed in terms of the x-coordinate of a point P on the unit circle $y = \sin x$, where x is a real number. The table below show values of $\sin x$ for given values of x from 0 to 2π. Values of $\cos x$ repeat in intervals of 2π or 360°.

x	0	$\frac{\pi}{4}$	$\frac{\pi}{2}$	$\frac{3\pi}{4}$	π	$\frac{5\pi}{4}$	$\frac{3\pi}{2}$	$\frac{7\pi}{4}$	2π
$\cos x$	1	≈ 0.7	0	≈ -0.7	-1	≈ -0.7	0	0.7	1

Plotting these points and drawing a smooth curve through them results in a portion of the graph of $y = \cos x$. This is also a sinusoidal curve with the following properties:

- the domain is all real numbers, $[-\infty, \infty]$.
- the range is $-1 \leq \cos x \leq 1$, or $[-1, 1]$.
- the period is 2π, where $\cos x = \cos(x + 2\pi)$.
- the x-intercepts are at $\frac{\pi(2k+1)}{2}$, where k is an integer.
- the y-intercept is at 1.
- the amplitude $|a|$ is 1, where $a = \frac{1}{2}(\cos x_{max} - \cos x_{min})$.

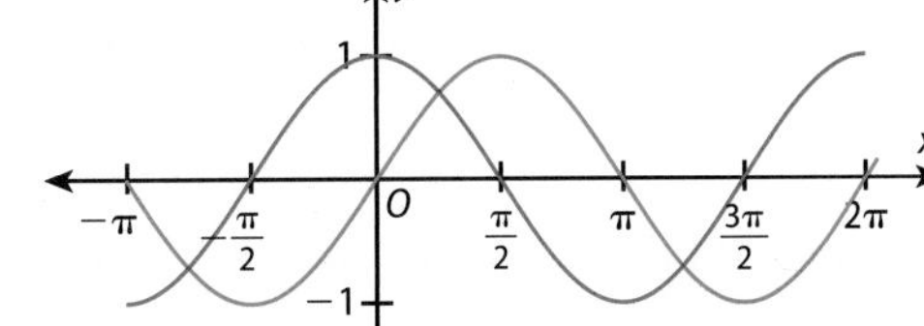

$y = \sin x$ is in blue.
$y = \cos x$ is in red.

The graph of $y = \cos x$ is like that of $y = \sin x$, but translated horizontally by $\frac{\pi}{2}$.

EXAMPLE 8

What are the amplitude, period, and x-intercepts of $y = 0.5\cos x$ shown in red on this graph? The graph of $y = \cos x$ is in blue.

The coefficient of $\cos x$ is a, the amplitude of the function. That is, the maximum and minimum values are 0.5 and -0.5 respectively. So, $a = \frac{1}{2}$.

The period is 2π.

The x-intercepts are integer multiples of $\frac{\pi}{2}$.

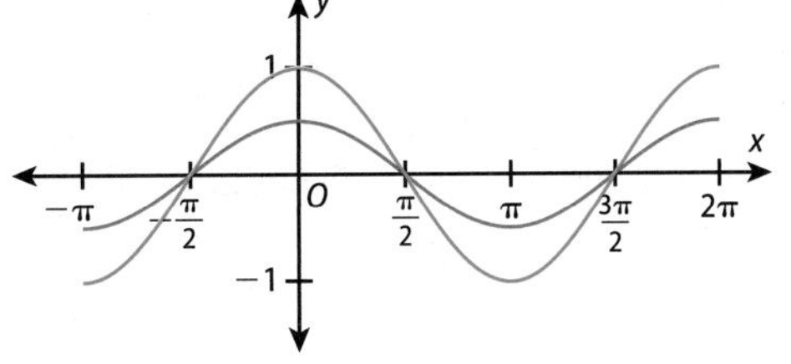

EXAMPLE 9

What is the equation of this cosine function shown in red? The graph of $y = \cos x$ is in blue.

The maximum of the function is 4, and the minimum is -4. Therefore, the amplitude $a = \frac{1}{2}(4-(-4)) = \frac{1}{2}(8) = 4$. So, the equation of this function is $y = 4\cos x$.

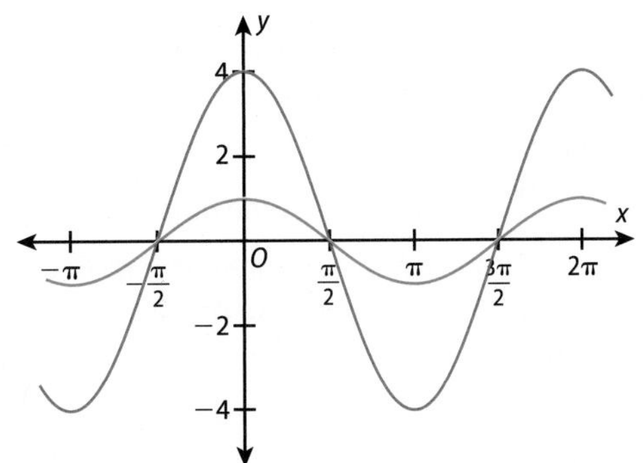

Need More HELP

To use a calculator to find $\cos\frac{\pi}{4}$, set the mode to radians and then press:

COS (2nd ^ ÷ 4) ENTER

Need More HELP

The maximum of a function is the greatest value of y for the function; the minimum is the least value of y for the function.

SEARCH

To see step-by-step videos of these problems, enter the page number into the SWadvantage.com Search Bar.

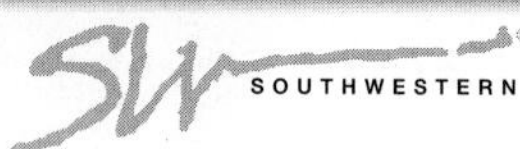

Graphs of $y = \cos(bx)$

If $b = 1$, the period of the function $y = \cos bx$ is 2π. If $b \neq 1$, then the period of $y = \cos(bx)$ is $\frac{2\pi}{b}$, where $b > 0$. The amplitude of $y = \cos(bx)$ is 1 because $a = 1$.

- If $0 < b < 1$, the graph of the function is stretched horizontally, and the period is greater than 2π.
- If $b > 1$, the graph of the function is compressed horizontally, and the period is less than 2π.

The cosine function is out of phase with the sine function by $\frac{\pi}{2}$. The x-intercepts of $y = \sin x$ occur at $k\pi$, where k is an integer. This means that the x-intercepts of $y = \cos x$ lie at $k\pi + \frac{\pi}{2}$, which equals $\frac{2k\pi + \pi}{2} = \frac{\pi(2k + 1)}{2}$, where k is an integer.

Watch Out !

If k is an integer, then $2k$ is an even integer, and $2k + 1$ is an odd integer.

SEARCH

To see step-by-step videos of these problems, enter the page number into the SWadvantage.com Search Bar.

EXAMPLE 10

What is the period of $y = \cos\left(\frac{1}{2}x\right)$ shown in red?

The coefficient of x in the argument of $\cos\left(\frac{1}{2}x\right)$ is $\frac{1}{2}$, so b is $\frac{1}{2}$. Therefore, the period of this function is $\frac{2\pi}{\left(\frac{1}{2}\right)} = \frac{2\pi}{\left(\frac{1}{2}\right)} \cdot \frac{2}{2} = 4\pi$. That is, the graph is stretched and completes one period in twice the interval of 2π.

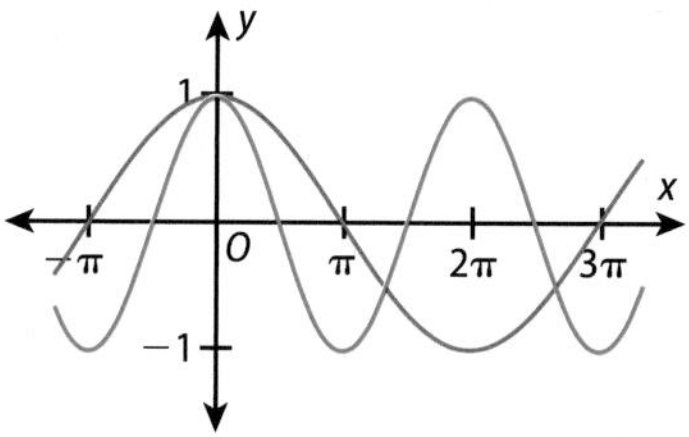

EXAMPLE 11

What are the equation and x-intercepts of the cosine function shown in red?

Between 0 and 2π, the graph has four periods. This means that the graph has been compressed, so the value of $b = 4$ and the period is $\frac{\pi}{2}$. Its amplitude, a, is 1, so its equation is $y = \cos 4x$. The x-intercepts are at $\frac{\pi(2k + 1)}{2} \div 4 = \frac{\pi(2k + 1)}{8}$.

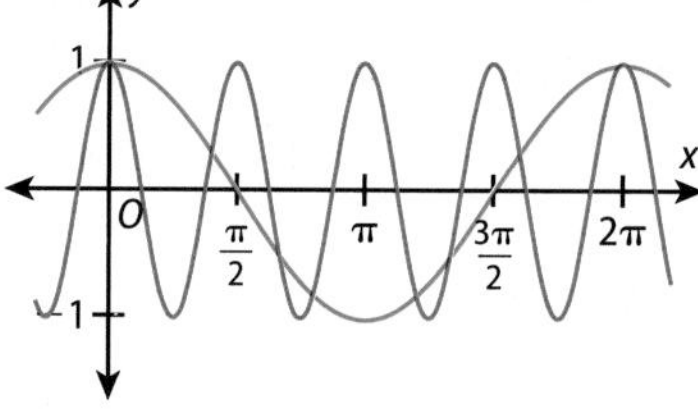

EXAMPLE 12

What are the amplitude, period, and x-intercepts of $y = \cos 3x$, shown in red?

The constant b is 3, so the period of this function is $\frac{2\pi}{b} = \frac{2\pi}{3}$. This means that the graph is compressed horizontally and completes three periods in the interval of length 2π rather than one period in an interval of length 2π.

The amplitude is 1 because $a = 1$.

The x-intercepts are at $\frac{\pi(2k + 1)}{2} \div b$, or $\frac{\pi(k + 1)}{6}$, where k is an integer.

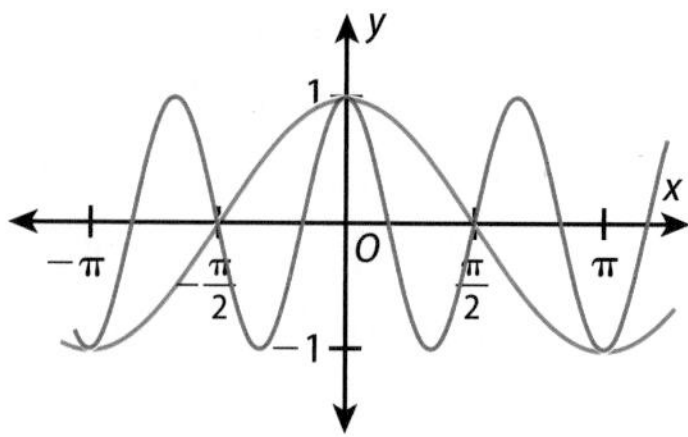

Need More HELP

Remember: if $b = 1$, the x-intercepts of the normal cosine function are at $x = \frac{\pi(2k + 1)}{2}$, where k is an integer, $2k$ is an even integer, and $2k + 1$ is an odd integer.

Graphs of $y = a\cos(bx)$

As with the sine function, changing the constants a and b affect the amplitude and period of the cosine function, and the values of the x-intercepts.

EXAMPLE 13

What are the amplitude, period, and x-intercepts of $y = 2\cos\left(\frac{x}{2}\right)$?

STEP 1 The coefficient of $2\cos\left(\frac{1}{2}\pi\right)$ is a, the amplitude. Here, $a = 2$.

STEP 2 The coefficient of x in the argument of the cosine is $\frac{1}{2}$. The period is $\frac{2\pi}{b}$, so the period of this function is $\frac{2\pi}{\left(\frac{1}{2}\right)} = 4\pi$. The graph is stretched, completing one period in 4π units, rather than 2π.

STEP 3 The x-intercepts are at $\frac{\pi(2k+1)}{2} \div \frac{1}{2}$, or $\pi(2k + 1)$, with k an integer.

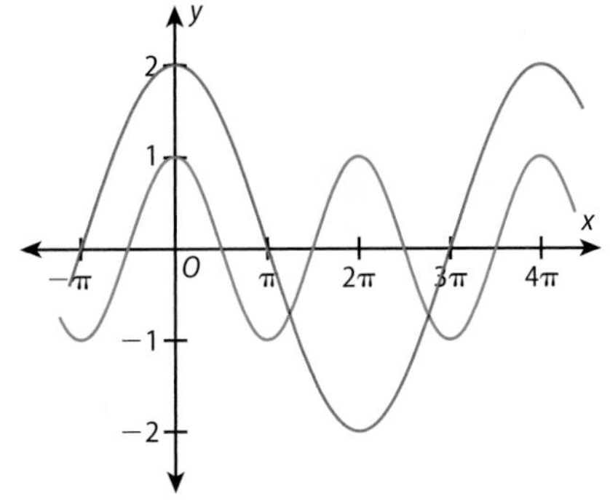

Need More HELP

Compare the period of $y = \cos\left(\frac{1}{2}\pi\right)$ and $y = \cos 2x$. Notice that when $0 < b < 1$, the graph is stretched in a horizontal direction; when $b > 0$, the graph is compressed in a horizontal direction.

EXAMPLE 14

What are the amplitude, period, and x-intercepts of $y = \frac{1}{4}\cos(2x)$?

STEP 1 The coefficient of $\cos(2x)$ is the amplitude, which is $\frac{1}{4}$.

STEP 2 The coefficient of x in the argument is 2, so the period is therefore $\frac{2\pi}{2} = \pi$. The graph is compressed and completes one period in an interval of π rather than 2π.

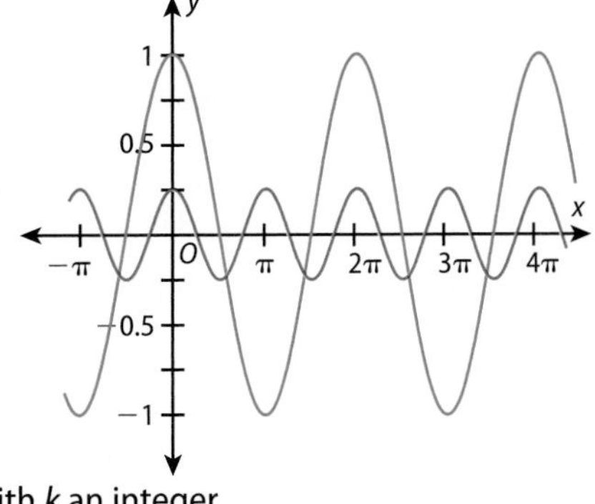

STEP 3 The x-intercepts are at $\frac{\pi(2k+1)}{2} \div 2 = \frac{\pi(2k+1)}{4}$, with k an integer.

GOT TO KNOW!

The Cosine Function

Function	$y = \cos x$	$y = a\cos(bx)$
Domain	$[-\infty, \infty]$	$[-\infty, \infty]$
Range	$[-1, 1]$	$[-a, a]$
Period	2π	$\frac{2\pi}{b}, b > 0$
Amplitude	1	$\lvert a\rvert = a$ if $a > 0$; $= -a$, if $a < 0$
x-intercepts	$\frac{\pi(2k+1)}{2}$, k is an integer	$\frac{\pi(2k+1)}{2} \div b$, k is an integer

Using a Graphing Calculator

Graphing $y = \sin(x)$

You can use handheld graphing calculators to graph functions and analyze their properties. Trigonometric graphs can be displayed in degrees or radians. The five major keys to use lie directly below the viewing window. These are Y=, WINDOW, ZOOM, TRACE, and GRAPH.

Watch Out!

The argument of a function is the variable or expression on which the function operates. For $y = \sin(x)$, the argument is x. For $y = \sin(x + 2)$, the argument is $x + 2$.

Need More HELP

Remember—the graph of $y = \sin x$ is a sinusoidal curve. Its amplitude is 1, and its period is 2π. Its x-intercepts occur at even multiples of π.

Watch Out!

If you graph the sine in DEGREE mode, the x-interval is from $-352.5°$ to $352.5°$, marked at intervals of 90°.

EXAMPLE 1

Use a graphing calculator to graph $y = \sin x$, where x is in radians.

STEP 1 Press the MODE key and use the arrow keys to set the mode to RADIAN.

STEP 2 Press the Y= key. At the blinking cursor next to \Y1=, press the SIN key. Then press the X,T,θ,n key. Press) to close the argument for sin(x). The display reads $\backslash Y_1 = \sin(X)$.

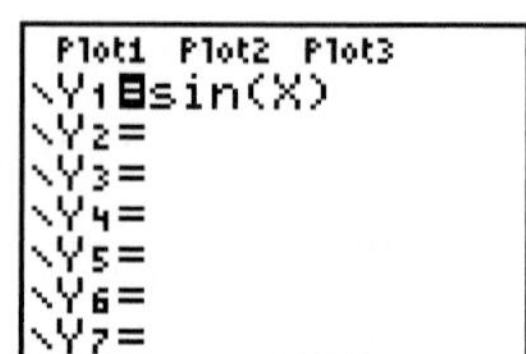

STEP 3 To display the graph in the interval $[-2\pi, 2\pi]$, press the ZOOM key. Then, press the down arrow key and select the 7th option, shown as 7↓ZTRIG, and press ENTER.

STEP 4 Some calculators graph the function as soon as you press ENTER from the ZOOM menu. Because x is in radians, this graph shows two periods of the graph in the interval $[-2\pi, 2\pi]$. The scale along the horizontal axis is marked in intervals of $\frac{\pi}{2}$.

The vertical axis is marked in units of 1 in the interval $(-4, 4)$.

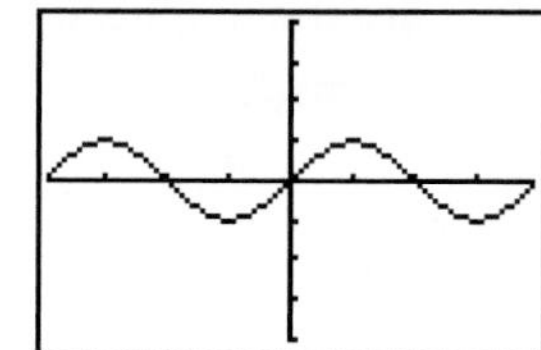

STEP 5 To see the coordinates of a point on the graph, press TRACE. Press the right or left arrows to move the point along the curve. The x- and y-coordinates of the point on the graph in the viewing window appear below the graph.

STEP 6 To see a table of values for this function, press 2nd and GRAPH. Use the down arrow to scroll through the list of values.

Changing the Viewing Window

There are times when you may want to examine different portions of a graph. You can do this by changing the intervals to be displayed on the axes that appear in the viewing window.

EXAMPLE 2

Show the graph of $y = \sin x$ in the intervals $[0, \pi]$ and $(-1, 1)$.

STEP 1 Press WINDOW. The Xmin and Xmax values that appear are $-6.1522856\ldots$ and $6.1522856\ldots$, which are approximations for -2π and 2π, respectively. These represent the domain of the function in the viewing window.

- At the blinking cursor next to Xmin, set the minimum to 0.
- At the blinking cursor at Xmax, set the maximum to π.

STEP 2 The Ymin and Ymax values are -4 and 4. These represent the range of the function in the viewing window. Change Ymin to -1 and Ymax to 1. Then press enter.

STEP 3 Press GRAPH to view the graph. The period of $y = \sin x$ is 2π. So, the interval from 0 to π only displays one-half of the period of the normal sine curve. The amplitude is 1, so the max and min are correct.

Watch Out !

Always choose an interval on the y-axis that will include the amplitude of the function.

Graphing $y = a\sin(bx)$

To graph $y = a\sin(bx)$ when a and/or b are not equal to 1, be sure to enter the function correctly on the calculator.

EXAMPLE 3

Graph the function $y = 3\sin\left(\frac{1}{2}x\right)$ from $[0, 4\pi]$, where x is in radians.

STEP 1 Press Y= to enter the function. If necessary, press CLEAR to erase any function that may have been entered previously.

STEP 2 Next to \Y1=, enter 3 and press SIN. The display reads \Y1=3sin(.

STEP 3 To enter $\frac{1}{2}$, enter either .5 or press 1 ÷ 2 .Then press X,T,θ,n. The display reads either \$Y_1$= 3sin(.5X or \$Y_1$=3sin(1/2 x.

STEP 4 Press the) key to close the argument. The display reads \$Y_1$=3sin(.5X) or \$Y_1$=3sin(1/2X), depending how you entered $\frac{1}{2}$.

STEP 5 Press WINDOW to change the Xmin, Xmax, Ymin and Ymax values of the graph.

- Next to Xmin, enter 0 .
- Next to Xmax, first enter 4 , then press 2nd and ^ (for π).
- Next to Ymin, enter (−) 4 .
- Next to Ymax, press 4 .

STEP 6 Press GRAPH. The amplitude a is 3. The period b is $\frac{2\pi}{\left(\frac{1}{2}\right)} = 4\pi$. So, in this interval, the graph shows two full periods. Click TRACE or 2nd GRAPH to verify values of x and y.

SEARCH

To see step-by-step videos of these problems, enter the page number into the SWadvantage.com Search Bar.

Need More HELP

Remember—For $y = 3\sin\left(\frac{1}{2}x\right)$, the amplitude is $|3|$, and the period is $\frac{2\pi}{b}$, which equals 4π.

Graphing $y = \cos(x)$

Graphing the cosine function is similar to the steps in graphing the sine function. Again, the five major keys to use to graph the trigonometric functions are below the viewing window: Y=, WINDOW, ZOOM, TRACE, and GRAPH.

The graph of $y = \cos x$ is like that of $y = \sin x$, but is out of phase horizontally by $\frac{\pi}{2}$.

Need More HELP

Remember—The graph of $y = \cos x$ is a sinusoidal curve. Its amplitude is 1, and its period is 2π.

EXAMPLE 4

Use a graphing calculator to graph $y = \cos x$, where x is in radians.

STEP 1 Press the MODE key and use the arrow keys to set the mode to RADIAN.

STEP 2 Press Y=. This displays a Plot window and next to the blinking cursor press the COS key. Then press the X,T,θ,*n* key. Press) to close the argument for cos(*x*). The display reads \Y_1= cos(X).

STEP 3 To display the graph in the interval $[-2\pi, 2\pi]$, press the ZOOM key. Then, press the down arrow key and select the 7th option that reads 7↓ZTRIG and press ENTER.

STEP 4 To see the graph, press GRAPH. The graph shows two periods of the cosine graph in the interval $[-2\pi, 2\pi]$. The scale along the horizontal axis is marked in intervals of $\frac{\pi}{2}$. The vertical axis is marked in units of 1 in the interval $(-4, 4)$.

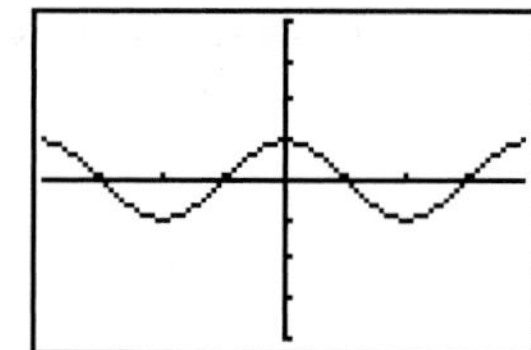

STEP 5 To see the coordinates of a point on the graph, press TRACE. Press the right or left arrows to move the point along the curve. The *x*- and *y*-coordinates of the point along the graph in the viewing window are reported below the graph.

STEP 6 To see a table of values for this function, press 2nd and GRAPH. Use the down arrow to scroll through the list of values.

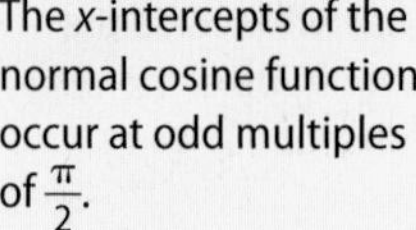

Watch Out

The *x*-intercepts of the normal cosine function occur at odd multiples of $\frac{\pi}{2}$.

SEARCH

To see step-by-step videos of these problems, enter the page number into the SWadvantage.com Search Bar.

Graphing $y = a\cos(bx)$

Like that of the graph of $y = a \sin(bx)$, the amplitude of the graph of $y = a \cos(bx)$ is $|a|$, and its period is $\frac{2\pi}{b}$, where $b > 0$. You can use WINDOW and/or ZOOM to change the intervals along the axes on which the graphs will appear. See Example 2.

EXAMPLE 5

Graph the function $y = \frac{1}{4}\cos(3x)$ from $[-\pi, \pi]$, where x is in radians.

STEP 1 Press Y= to enter the function. If necessary, press CLEAR to erase any function that may have been entered previously.

STEP 2 Next to \Y1=, use the number keys to enter 0.25 or 1 ÷ 4 and press COS. The display reads \Y1=.25 cos(or \Y=1/4 cos(, depending on how you entered $\frac{1}{4}$.

STEP 3 Then enter 3 and press X,T,θ,n. The display reads \Y1=.25 cos(3X or \Y1=1/4 cos(3X. Press the) key to close the argument.

STEP 4 Press WINDOW to change the Xmin, Xmax, Ymin and Ymax values for this graph.

- Next to Xmin, enter (–) and 2nd and ^.
- Next to Xmax, press 2nd and ^.
- Next to Ymin, enter (–) and 1.5.
- Next to Ymax, enter 1.5.

STEP 5 Press GRAPH. The amplitude a is $\frac{1}{4}$. The period b is $\frac{2\pi}{3}$, which means that in an interval of 2π along the x-axis, there are three periods. Click TRACE and/or 2nd GRAPH to verify values of x and y.

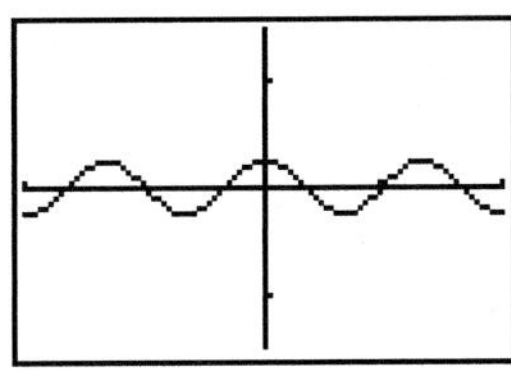

Need More HELP

The value of a in the equation is $\frac{1}{4}$, so the amplitude of this function is $\frac{1}{4}$. The period of this function is $\frac{2\pi}{b}$, where $b = 3$. So, the period is $\frac{2\pi}{3}$.

GOT TO KNOW!

Graphing the Sine and Cosine Functions

You can use these basic steps to graph $y = a \sin(bx)$ and $y = a \cos(bx)$ using a handheld graphing calculator.

1. Press MODE to choose whether x is in radians or degrees.
2. Choose Y=, enter a and press SIN or COS.
3. Enter b, then press X,T,θ,n. Press) to close the argument.
4. Press ZOOM and choose option 7 to automatically set the intervals in the viewing window; or press WINDOW to manually enter the x- and y-intervals on the axes.
5. Press GRAPH to see the graph.
6. Press TRACE to move a point along the curve and see its coordinates.
7. Press TABLE to display coordinates of points on the graph of the function.

Horizontal Translations of the Sine and Cosine Functions

A horizontal translation is a shift, or displacement, of the graph of a basic function along the x-axis. The graph of a function of the form $y = \sin(x - d)$ is a horizontal translation of the graph of $y = \sin x$, where d is the amount of translation. A horizontal translation of a trigonometric function, such as the sine, is also called a **phase shift**.

- If $d > 0$, the phase shift is d units to the right.
- If $d < 0$, the phase shift is d units to the left.

The expression $(x - d)$ is called the **argument** of the function. It is the expression on which the function operates. If the equation is of the form $y = \sin(x + d)$, rewrite the argument as a subtraction equation, $y = \sin(x - (-d))$, to determine the correct direction of the displacement.

Need More HELP

In a transformation, the original figure is called the pre-image. The resulting figure after a transformation is called the image. The symbol x' represents the image of the value of x in the pre-image.

SEARCH

To see step-by-step videos of these problems, enter the page number into the SWadvantage.com Search Bar.

Watch Out

Adding $\frac{\pi}{3}$ to each critical value of x generates the corresponding image point x', which is out of phase $\frac{\pi}{3}$ units to the right of the pre-image.

EXAMPLE 1

Graph $y = \sin\left(x - \frac{\pi}{3}\right)$.

METHOD 1

STEP 1 Graph the basic function $y = \sin x$. Its amplitude is 1 and its period is 2π. In the interval $[0, 2\pi]$, the five critical values of x include the x-intercepts of the graph and values of x at its maximum and minimum points. The x-values of these points are $0, \frac{\pi}{2}, \pi, \frac{3\pi}{2}$, and 2π.

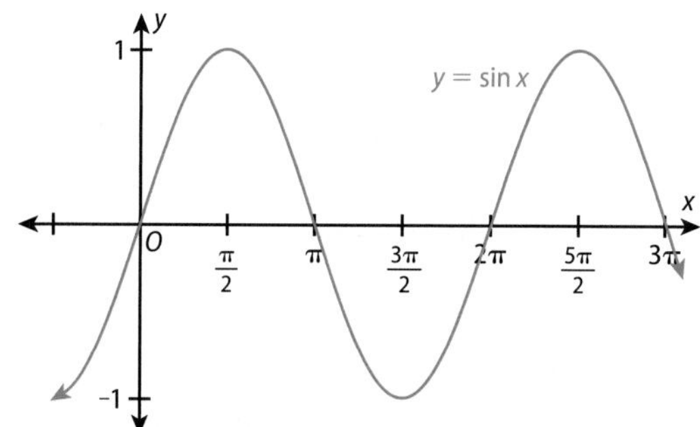

STEP 2 Create a table of values of the image.

In the equation $y = \sin\left(x - \frac{\pi}{3}\right)$, $d = \frac{\pi}{3}$. Because d is positive, the basic function (the pre-image) is translated $\frac{\pi}{3}$ units to the right. So adding $\frac{\pi}{3}$ to each of the critical values of x in the interval $[0, 2\pi]$ yields the following x'-values in the image.

x	0	$\frac{\pi}{2}$	π	$\frac{3\pi}{2}$	2π
x'	$0 + \frac{\pi}{3} = \frac{\pi}{3}$	$\frac{\pi}{2} + \frac{\pi}{3} = \frac{5\pi}{6}$	$\pi + \frac{\pi}{3} = \frac{4\pi}{3}$	$\frac{3\pi}{2} + \frac{\pi}{3} = \frac{11\pi}{6}$	$2\pi + \frac{\pi}{3} = \frac{7\pi}{3}$

STEP 3 Plot each of the critical values of x in the table above to its new value. Then sketch a sinusoidal curve with amplitude 1 connecting the new values of x'.

Here are the graphs of the pre-image $y = \sin x$ and its image $y = \sin\left(x - \frac{\pi}{3}\right)$ under this translation.

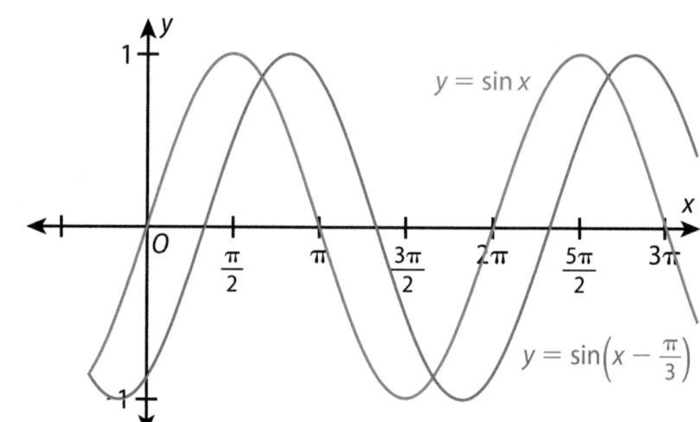

METHOD 2

To complete one period for the sine function, the argument $x - \frac{\pi}{3}$ must assume all values in the closed interval $[0, 2\pi]$. That is, in one period, $0 \le x - \frac{\pi}{3} \le 2\pi$.

STEP 1 Solve the inequality $0 \le x - \frac{\pi}{3} \le 2\pi$ for x.

$$0 \le x - \frac{\pi}{3} \le 2\pi$$

Add $\frac{\pi}{3}$ to both sides of the inequality.

$$0 + \frac{\pi}{3} \le x \le 2\pi + \frac{\pi}{3}$$

Solve for x by simplifying both sides.

$$\frac{\pi}{3} \le x \le \frac{7\pi}{3}$$

STEP 2 There are five critical points for the sine graph in the interval $\left[\frac{\pi}{3}, \frac{7\pi}{3}\right]$. So, to find the corresponding values of x, divide the interval into four equal parts using the Midpoint Formula: $x_m = \frac{1}{2}(x_1 + x_2)$, where x_m is the midpoint between x_1 and x_2. Start by finding the midpoint halfway between the endpoints of the entire interval $\left[\frac{\pi}{3}, \frac{7\pi}{3}\right]$. The midpoint $\frac{4\pi}{3}$ includes one-half of the period of the sine curve whose length is 2π.

$$x_m = \frac{1}{2}\left(\frac{\pi}{3} + \frac{7\pi}{3}\right) = \frac{1}{2}\left(\frac{8\pi}{3}\right) = \frac{4\pi}{3}$$

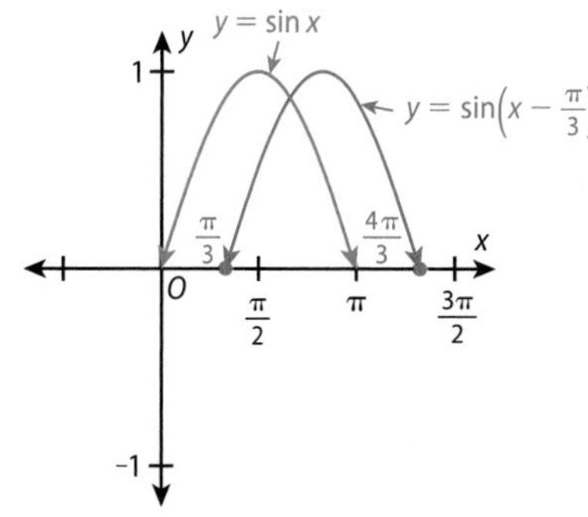

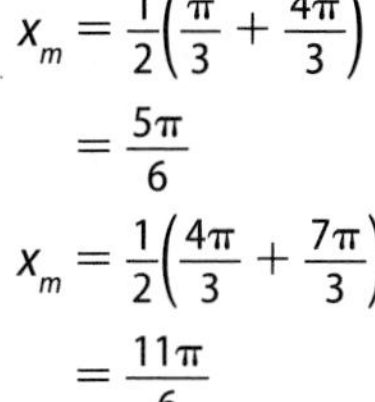

STEP 3 Next, find the midpoints of the intervals $\left[\frac{\pi}{3}, \frac{4\pi}{3}\right]$ and $\left[\frac{4\pi}{3}, \frac{7\pi}{3}\right]$. Each represents $\frac{1}{4}$ of an interval whose length is 2π.

Therefore, the x-values of the five critical points for this function are $\frac{\pi}{3}, \frac{5\pi}{6}, \frac{4\pi}{3}, \frac{11\pi}{6}$ and $\frac{7\pi}{3}$.

$$x_m = \frac{1}{2}\left(\frac{\pi}{3} + \frac{4\pi}{3}\right) = \frac{5\pi}{6}$$

$$x_m = \frac{1}{2}\left(\frac{4\pi}{3} + \frac{7\pi}{3}\right) = \frac{11\pi}{6}$$

STEP 4 Plot these points along the x-axis and draw the sinusoidal curve through them. The graph of $y = \sin\left(x - \frac{\pi}{3}\right)$ is out of phase of the graph of $y = \sin x$ by $\frac{\pi}{3}$. Its period is 2π and its amplitude is 1. Both graphs are shown for comparison.

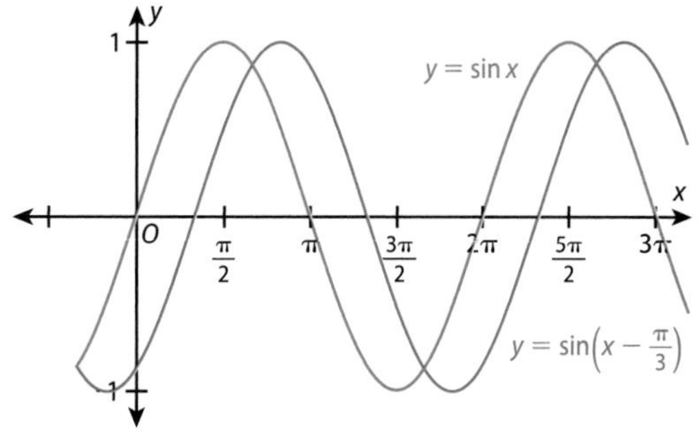

Solving a compound inequality such as $0 \le x \le 2$ is equivalent to solving two simple inequalities: $0 \le x$ and $x \le 2$.

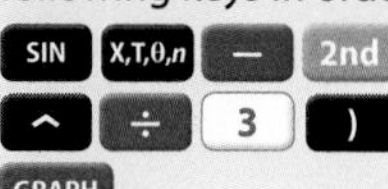

To graph $y = \sin\left(x - \frac{\pi}{3}\right)$, press MODE and choose RADIAN. Then press Y= and the following keys in order.

SIN X,T,θ,n − 2nd ^ ÷ 3) GRAPH

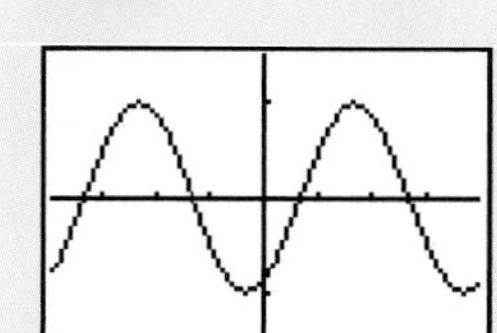

EXAMPLE 2

Graph $y = \cos\left(x + \frac{\pi}{4}\right)$.

METHOD 1

STEP 1 Graph the basic function $y = \cos x$. Its amplitude is 1 and its period is 2π. In the interval $[0, 2\pi]$, the five critical values of x include its two x-intercepts and three values of x at its maximum and minimum points. The five critical points of the cosine function in the interval $[0, 2\pi]$, are $0, \frac{\pi}{2}, \pi, \frac{3\pi}{2}$, and 2π.

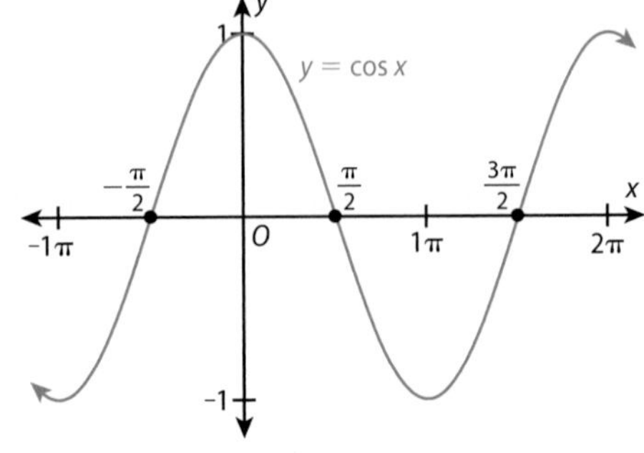

STEP 2 Create a table of values of the image.

Rewrite the argument $\left(x + \frac{\pi}{4}\right)$ as $\left(x - \left(-\frac{\pi}{4}\right)\right)$, where $d = -\frac{\pi}{4}$. Since d is negative, the basic cosine function is translated $\frac{\pi}{4}$ units to the left. Shifting each of the critical values $\frac{\pi}{4}$ units to the left yields the following x'-values:

x	0	$\frac{\pi}{2}$	π	$\frac{3\pi}{2}$	2π
x'	$0 - \frac{\pi}{4} = -\frac{\pi}{4}$	$\frac{\pi}{2} - \frac{\pi}{4} = \frac{\pi}{4}$	$\pi - \frac{\pi}{4} = \frac{3\pi}{4}$	$\frac{3\pi}{2} - \frac{\pi}{4} = \frac{5\pi}{4}$	$2\pi - \frac{\pi}{4} = \frac{7\pi}{4}$

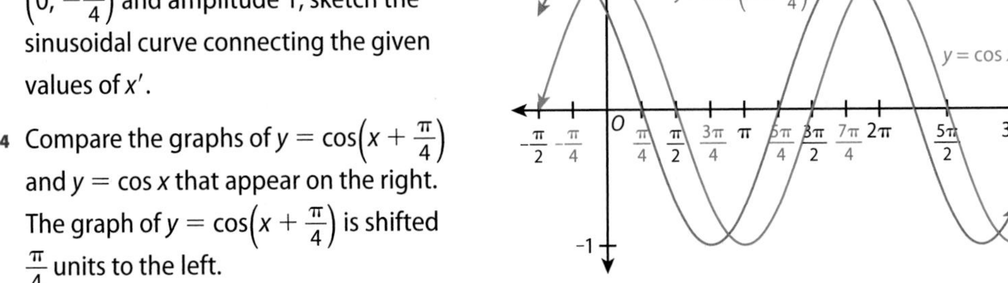

STEP 3 Plot each of the critical values of x' along the x-axis. Then starting at $\left(0, -\frac{\pi}{4}\right)$ and amplitude 1, sketch the sinusoidal curve connecting the given values of x'.

STEP 4 Compare the graphs of $y = \cos\left(x + \frac{\pi}{4}\right)$ and $y = \cos x$ that appear on the right. The graph of $y = \cos\left(x + \frac{\pi}{4}\right)$ is shifted $\frac{\pi}{4}$ units to the left.

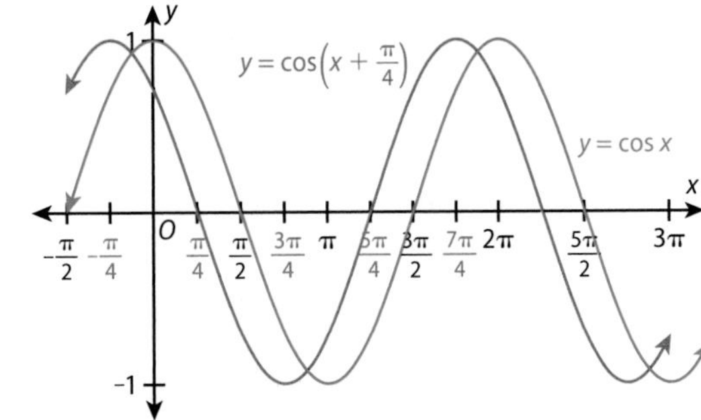

Need More HELP

Remember—the x-intercepts of $y = \cos x$ occur at odd multiples of $\frac{\pi}{2}$. The minimum and maximum values of the cosine function are -1 and 1, respectively.

SEARCH

To see step-by-step videos of these problems, enter the page number into the SWadvantage.com Search Bar.

METHOD 2

To complete one period for the cosine function, the argument $x + \frac{\pi}{4}$ must assume all values in the closed interval $[0, 2\pi]$. That is, in one period, $0 \le x + \frac{\pi}{4} \le 2\pi$.

STEP 1 Solve the inequality $0 \le x + \frac{\pi}{4} \le 2\pi$.

$$0 \le x - \frac{\pi}{4} \le 2\pi$$

Subtract $\frac{\pi}{4}$ from both sides of the inequality.

$$0 - \frac{\pi}{4} \le x \le 2\pi - \frac{\pi}{4}$$

Solve for x by simplifying both sides.

$$-\frac{\pi}{4} \le x \le \frac{7\pi}{4}$$

STEP 2 There are five critical points for the cosine graph in the closed interval $\left[-\frac{\pi}{4}, \frac{7\pi}{4}\right]$. So, to find the corresponding values of x', divide this interval into four equal parts. The midpoint of the interval $\left[-\frac{\pi}{4}, \frac{7\pi}{4}\right]$ is $\frac{3\pi}{4}$.

$$x_m = \frac{1}{2}\left(-\frac{\pi}{4} + \frac{7\pi}{4}\right) = \frac{3\pi}{4}$$

STEP 3 The midpoints of the intervals $\left[-\frac{\pi}{4}, \frac{3\pi}{4}\right]$ and $\left[\frac{3\pi}{4}, \frac{7\pi}{4}\right]$ are $\frac{\pi}{4}$ and $\frac{5\pi}{4}$. Therefore, the x'-values of the five critical points in one period of this function are $-\frac{\pi}{4}, \frac{\pi}{4}, \frac{3\pi}{4}, \frac{5\pi}{4}$, and $\frac{7\pi}{4}$.

$$x_m = \frac{1}{2}\left(-\frac{\pi}{4} + \frac{3\pi}{4}\right) = \frac{\pi}{4}$$

$$x_m = \frac{1}{2}\left(\frac{3\pi}{4} + \frac{7\pi}{4}\right) = \frac{5\pi}{4}$$

STEP 4 Plot these points along the x-axis and draw the sinusoidal curve through them starting at $\left(0, -\frac{\pi}{4}\right)$. The graph of $y = \cos\left(x + \frac{\pi}{4}\right)$ is out of phase of the graph of $y = \cos x$ by $\frac{\pi}{4}$. Its period is 2π and its amplitude is 1. Both graphs are shown for comparison.

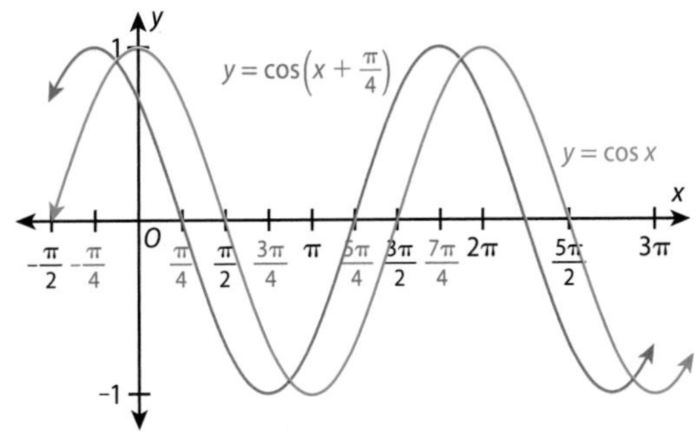

Try It This Way

To graph $y = \cos\left(x + \frac{\pi}{4}\right)$, press

and choose RADIAN. Then press Y= and the following keys in order.

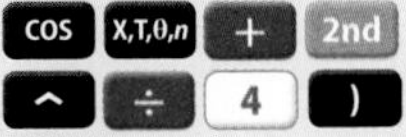

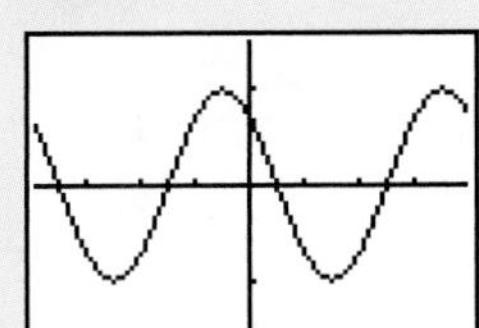

GOT TO KNOW!

Horizontal Translations of the Sine and Cosine

- A horizontal translation of the sine and cosine graphs is a left or right phase shift of the basic functions along the x-axis.
- The equations $y = \sin(x - d)$ and $y = \cos(x - d)$ represent translations of the graphs of $y = \sin x$ and $y = \cos x$, respectively, where d is the amount of translation.
- If $d > 0$, the shift is to the right; if $d < 0$, the shift is to the left.

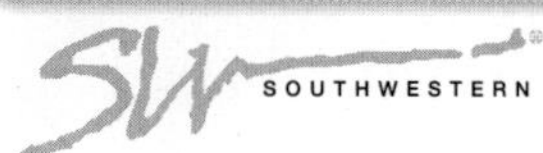

Vertical Translations of the Sine and Cosine Functions

A vertical translation is a shift of the graph of a basic function along the y-axis. The graphs of functions of the form $y = c + \sin x$ and $y = c + \cos x$ are therefore vertical translations of the graph of $y = \sin x$ and $y = \cos x$, where c is the amount of translation.

- If $c > 0$, the graph is translated c units up.
- If $c < 0$, the graph is translated $|c|$ units down.

Watch Out!

The amplitude of the graph of $y = 2 + \sin 3x$ is still 1. The vertical translation does not affect its amplitude.

EXAMPLE 3

Graph $y = 2 + \sin 3x$.

STEP 1 In this equation $c = 2$, so the graph of $y = \sin 3x$ is to be translated vertically 2 units up. Therefore, to graph this function, first graph $y = \sin 3x$.

- The value of a is 1, so its amplitude is 1.
- The value of b is 3, so its period is $\frac{2\pi}{3}$. This means that one period of this function is one-third the period of the basic sine function.

STEP 2 Since the period of this function is $\frac{2\pi}{3}$, you can calculate the critical values of x' in the interval $\left[0, \frac{2\pi}{3}\right]$. These values of x represent the three x-intercepts of the sine function and the two values of x when y is a maximum and a minimum. One critical point is at 0, where $y = \sin 3x$ is 1. The remaining four values can be found by finding the midpoints of the three intervals between 0 and $\frac{2\pi}{3}$.

- One-half of one period from 0 to $\frac{2\pi}{3}$ is $\frac{1}{2} \times \frac{2\pi}{3}$ or $\frac{\pi}{3}$.
- One-half of the interval between 0 and $\frac{\pi}{3}$ is $\frac{\pi}{6}$.
- One half of the interval between $\frac{\pi}{3}$ and $\frac{2\pi}{3}$ is $\frac{\pi}{2}$.

So, the five critical points have x'-values of $0, \frac{\pi}{6}, \frac{\pi}{3}, \frac{\pi}{2}, \frac{2\pi}{3}$. Plot these points along the x-axis and draw the graph of $y = \sin 3x$.

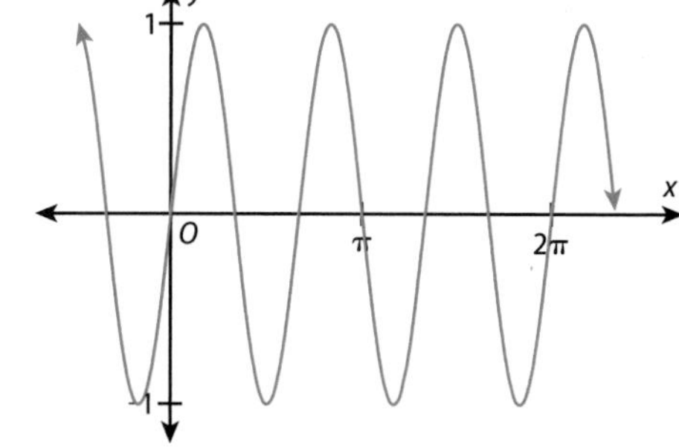

STEP 3 The values of y in the equation $y = 2 + \sin 3x$ are 2 units greater than those in $y = \sin 3x$. Therefore, the graph of $y = \sin 3x$ is translated 2 units up. The amplitude and period of the image $y = 2 + \sin 3x$ are the same as those in the pre-image $y = \sin 3x$. Here are the two graphs together on the right.

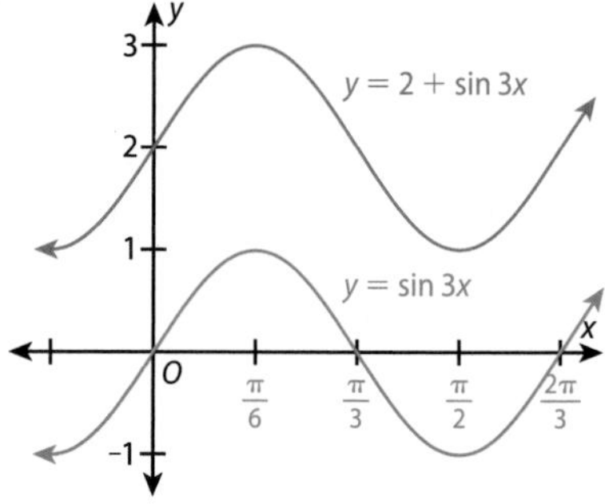

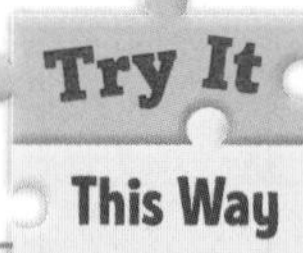

To use a graphing calculator to graph $y = 2 + \sin(3x)$ press MODE and choose RADIAN. Then press Y= and the following keys in order. 2 + SIN 3 X,T,θ,n) GRAPH

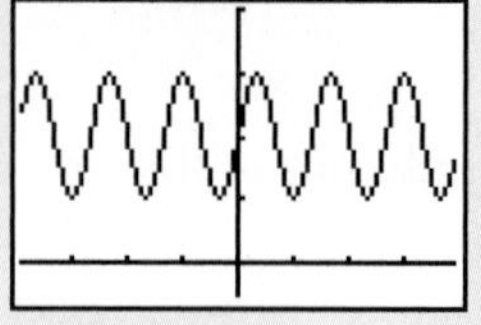

EXAMPLE 4

Graph $y = -1 + 2\cos\frac{1}{2}x$.

STEP 1 The graph of $y = 2\cos\frac{1}{2}x$ has an amplitude of 2 and a period of $\frac{2\pi}{\left(\frac{1}{2}\right)}$, or 4π. Its graph appears on the right.

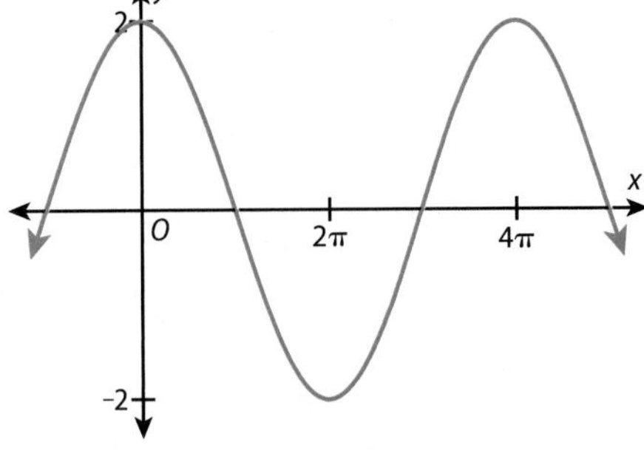

STEP 2 The value of c in $y = -1 + 2\cos\frac{1}{2}x$ is -1. So the graph is translated $|-1|$ unit below the graph of $y = 2\cos\frac{1}{2}x$. Its amplitude and period remain as 2 and 4π.

The graphs of both functions appear on the right.

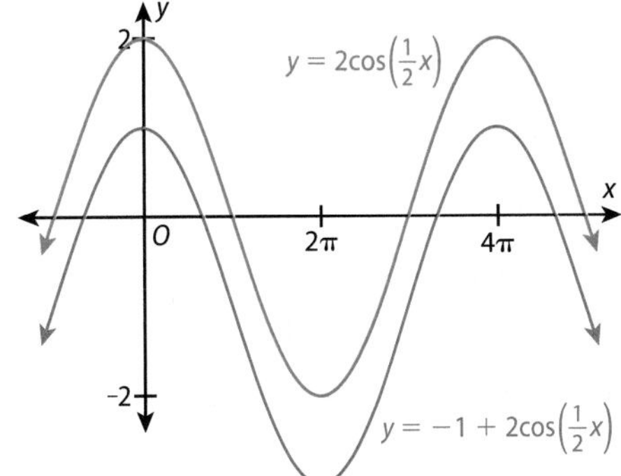

Try It This Way

To graph $y = -1 + 2\cos\frac{1}{2}x$ press MODE and choose RADIAN. Then press Y= and the following keys in order.

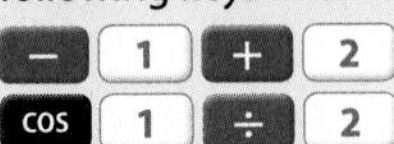

or . 5 X,T,θ,n) GRAPH

EXAMPLE 5

Graph $y = 3 + \frac{1}{2}\sin\left(\frac{x}{2} + \pi\right)$.

STEP 1 Factor $\left(\frac{x}{2} + \pi\right)$ to rewrite it the form of $(x - d)$, where d is the horizontal displacement of the function. The phase shift d is 2π, which is positive. So, the graph of $y = 3 + \frac{1}{2}\sin\frac{1}{2}(x + 2\pi)$ is translated 2π units to the right.

$$\left(\frac{x}{2} + \pi\right) = \frac{1}{2}(x + 2\pi)$$

STEP 2 The amplitude a of the pre-image $y = 3 + \frac{1}{2}\sin\frac{1}{2}(x + 2\pi)$ is $\frac{1}{2}$. Its period is $\frac{2\pi}{\left(\frac{1}{2}\right)}$, which equals 4π.

STEP 3 The value of c in the image $y = 3 + \frac{1}{2}\sin\frac{1}{2}(x + 2\pi)$ is 3, which means that the graph is translated 3 units up. Here are the graphs of $y = \frac{1}{2}\sin\left(\frac{x}{2} + \pi\right)$ and $y = 3 + \frac{1}{2}\sin\left(\frac{x}{2} + \pi\right)$.

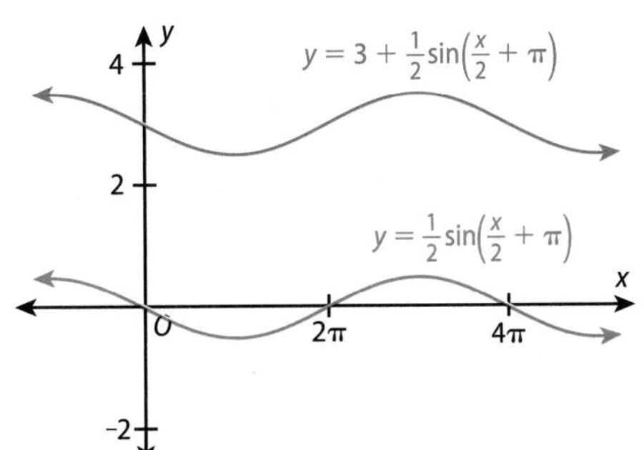

GOT TO KNOW!

Vertical Translations of the Sine and Cosine

- A vertical translation of the sine and cosine functions is an up or down displacement of the basic functions along the y-axis.
- The basic equations $y = c + \sin x$ and $y = c + \cos x$ represent vertical translations, where c is the amount of translation.
- If $c > 0$, the displacement is c units up; if $c < 0$, the displacement is $|c|$ units down.

Graphs of the Tangent and Cotangent Functions

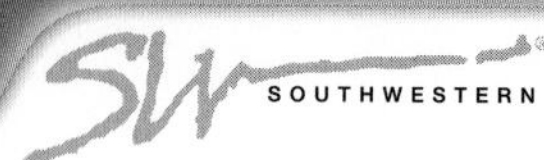

Graphs of the Tangent Function

Need More HELP

The period of the tangent function is the distance between two adjacent undefined values: for example, $\left|\frac{\pi}{2} - \left(-\frac{\pi}{2}\right)\right| = \pi$.

The tangent function (tan) is defined as the ratio $\frac{\sin x}{\cos x}$. This means that tan x is undefined when cos x equals zero. These undefined values occur at the x-intercepts of the cosine function at $x = \frac{\pi}{2} + k\pi$, where k is an integer. For example, when $k = -1, 0,$ and 1, x equals $-\frac{\pi}{2}, \frac{\pi}{2}$, and $\frac{3\pi}{2}$, respectively. This means that $y = \tan x$ is not continuous, and as x increases from left to right, tan x increases for all values of x in its domain.

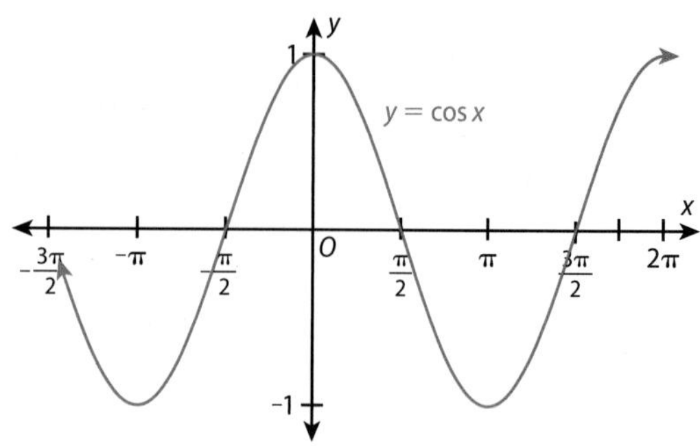

The properties of $y = \tan x$ are listed below.

- The domain is all real numbers: $x \neq \frac{\pi}{2} + k\pi$.
- The range is all real numbers, $(-\infty, \infty)$
- The period is π, where $\tan x = \tan(x + \pi)$.
- The x-intercepts are $k\pi$, where k is an integer.
- The y-intercept is 0.

To graph the function $y = \tan x$, use a graphing calculator or a trig table to determine values of tan x for given values of x closest to the origin between $-\frac{\pi}{2}$ and $\frac{\pi}{2}$.

x	$-\frac{\pi}{2}$	$-\frac{\pi}{3}$	$-\frac{\pi}{4}$	$-\frac{\pi}{6}$	0	$\frac{\pi}{6}$	$\frac{\pi}{4}$	$\frac{\pi}{3}$	$\frac{\pi}{2}$
tan x	∞	−1.732	−1	−0.577	0	0.577	1	1.732	∞

Watch Out !

Remember—Although the asymptotes are usually drawn when graphing the tangent function, they are not part of the graph of the tangent function.

Graph the points in the table and draw a smooth curve through them. This produces the graph of one period of the function $y = \tan x$.

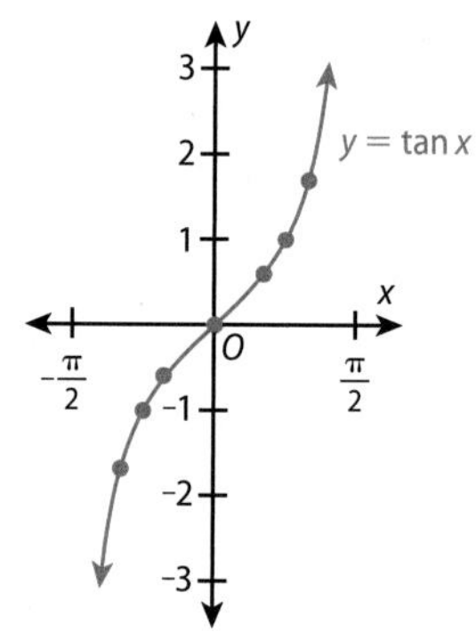

Because the range of the tangent function is all real numbers, this function has no amplitude.

Vertical lines through the values of x where tan x is undefined are called **asymptotes**. As values of x approach these undefined values, the tangent curve gets closer and closer to the line but never touches it. On either side of an asymptote, the graph of $y = \tan x$ increases without limit.

When graphing $y = \tan x$, lines are usually included to indicate the asymptotes.

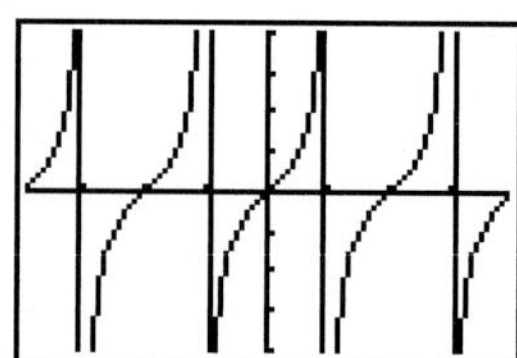

A graphing calculator displays the graph of $y = \tan x$ as shown on the right. It includes the graph of the function and its four asymptotes in the interval $[-2\pi, 2\pi]$.

EXAMPLE 1

Graph $y = \tan x$ over the interval $[-\pi, \pi]$.

The graph of $y = \tan x$ has a period of π. Therefore, in the interval $[-\pi, \pi]$, there are two periods.

- The x-intercepts are $-\pi$, 0, and π.
- Asymptotes are $x = -\frac{\pi}{2}$ and $x = \frac{\pi}{2}$.

You can use the values in the preceding table and a calculator or trig table to find other values of $\tan x$ between its asymptotes. Then plot $y = \tan x$ in the interval $[-\pi, \pi]$. Include the asymptotes in this interval.

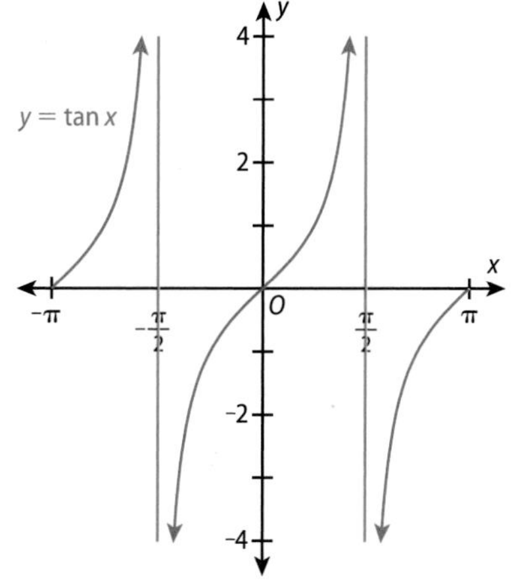

x	$-\frac{2\pi}{3}$	$-\frac{3\pi}{4}$	$-\frac{5\pi}{6}$	$\frac{2\pi}{3}$	$\frac{3\pi}{4}$	$\frac{5\pi}{6}$
$\tan x$	1.732	1	0.577	−1.732	−1	−0.577

Watch Out !

Most values of $\tan x$ are irrational numbers, so most of the values of $\tan x$ in the tables are approximations.

In an equation of the form $y = a \tan x$, the constant a does not represent the amplitude of the function. Rather, it means that the values of $\tan x$ are each multiplied by a.

EXAMPLE 2

Graph $y = 2\tan x$ over the interval $\left[-\pi, \frac{3\pi}{2}\right)$.

STEP 1 Use a calculator or trig table and identify the critical values of x in the desired interval. Then create a table of values for $\tan x$ and $2\tan x$.

x	$-\pi$	$-\frac{3\pi}{4}$	$-\frac{\pi}{2}$	$-\frac{\pi}{4}$	0	$\frac{\pi}{4}$	$\frac{\pi}{2}$	$\frac{3\pi}{4}$	$\frac{3\pi}{2}$
$\tan x$	0	1	∞	−1	0	1	∞	−1	∞
$2\tan x$	0	2	∞	−2	0	2	∞	−2	∞

STEP 2 Sketch the asymptotes of the function: $x = -\frac{\pi}{2}$ and $x = \frac{\pi}{2}$.

STEP 3 Plot the x-intercepts of $y = 2\tan x$ within the given intervals.

STEP 4 Draw a smooth curve through the points between adjacent asymptotes.

Compare the graphs of $y = 2\tan x$ and $y = \tan x$ on the right to see how they differ.

- The two graphs have the same asymptotes and the same x-intercepts.
- Both functions are discontinuous and increase from left to right for all values of x in their domain.

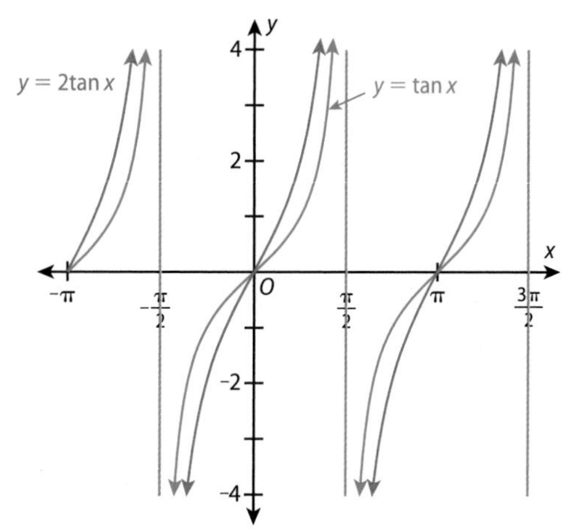

Try It This Way

To graph $y = 2\tan x$, be sure the calculator is in radian mode. Set the window to graph within the interval $\left[-\pi, \frac{3\pi}{2}\right)$.

Then press Y= 2 TAN X,T,θ,n) and GRAPH.

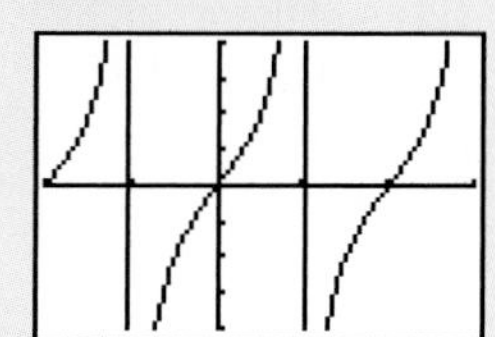

Graphs of the Cotangent Function

The tangent and cotangent are reciprocal functions. Therefore, when x equals positive and negative odd multiples of $\frac{\pi}{4}$, $\cot x = \tan x$, which equal 1 and -1, respectively.

The cotangent function (cot) is defined as the ratio $\frac{\cos x}{\sin x}$. It is also the reciprocal of the tangent ratio: $\cot x = \frac{1}{\tan x}$. The function $y = \cot x$ is undefined when either $\sin x$ or $\tan x$ equals zero. These values occur at the x-intercepts of the sine function at $x = \pi k$, where k is an integer. For example, when $k = -1, 0,$ and 1, x equals $-\pi$, 0, and π, respectively.

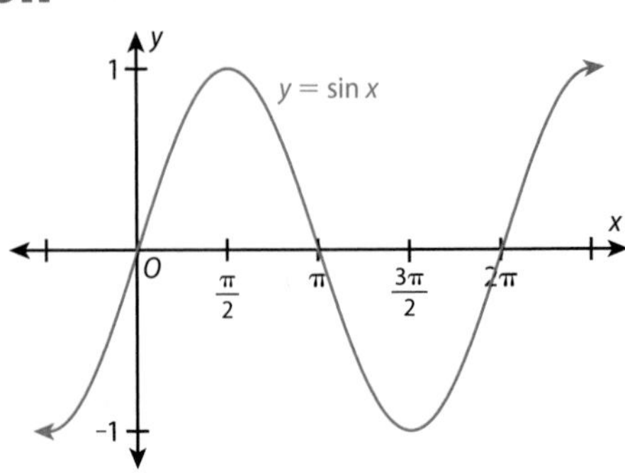

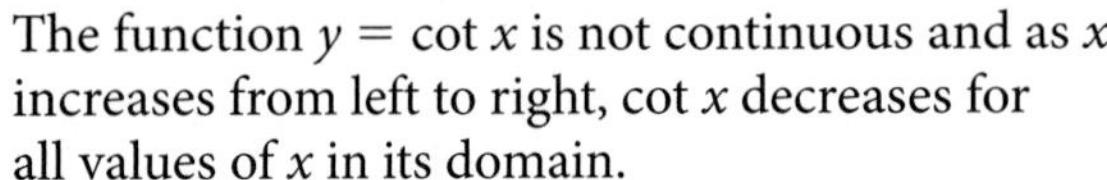

The function $y = \cot x$ is not continuous and as x increases from left to right, $\cot x$ decreases for all values of x in its domain.

The properties of $y = \cot x$ are listed below.

- The domain is all real numbers: $x \neq k\pi$.
- The range is all real numbers, $(-\infty, \infty)$.
- The period is π, where $\cot x = \cot(x + \pi)$.
- The x-intercepts are $\frac{\pi}{2} + k\pi$, where k is an integer.
- The y-intercept is 0.

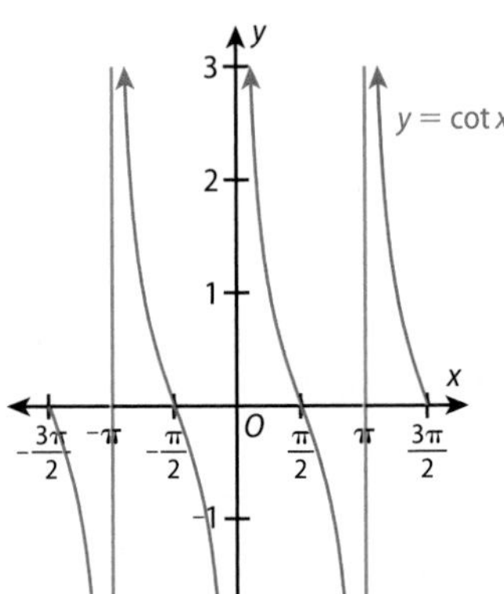

Need More HELP

To find a value such as $\cot\frac{\pi}{3}$ on a calculator, press 1 ÷ TAN. Then press the following keys: 2nd ^ ÷ 3).

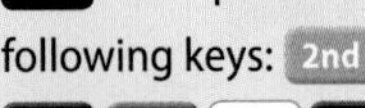

You can use a calculator or a trig table to find values of $\cot x$. However, most calculators do not have a cotangent key. Therefore, to use a calculator to determine values of $\cot x$, you will need to use one of the identities: $\cot x = \frac{1}{\tan x}$ or $\cot x = \frac{\cos x}{\sin x}$.

EXAMPLE 3

Graph $y = \cot x$ in the interval $(-\pi, \pi)$.

STEP 1 To graph this function, calculate values of $\cot x$ in the desired open interval between $-\pi$ and π.

x	$-\pi$	$-\frac{\pi}{2}$	$-\frac{\pi}{3}$	$-\frac{\pi}{4}$	$-\frac{\pi}{6}$	0	$\frac{\pi}{6}$	$\frac{\pi}{4}$	$\frac{\pi}{3}$	$\frac{\pi}{2}$	π
$\cot x$	∞	0	-0.577	-1	-1.732	∞	1.732	1	0.577	0	∞

STEP 2 Sketch the asymptotes for this function: $x = -\pi$, $x = 0$, and $x = \pi$. Then between each pair of adjacent asymptotes, plot the points for $(x, \cot x)$ in the table.

STEP 3 Draw smooth curves through each set of points. Have each curve approach an asymptote as y decreases.

The graphs of $y = \cot x$ and its three asymptotes in this interval are shown at the right.

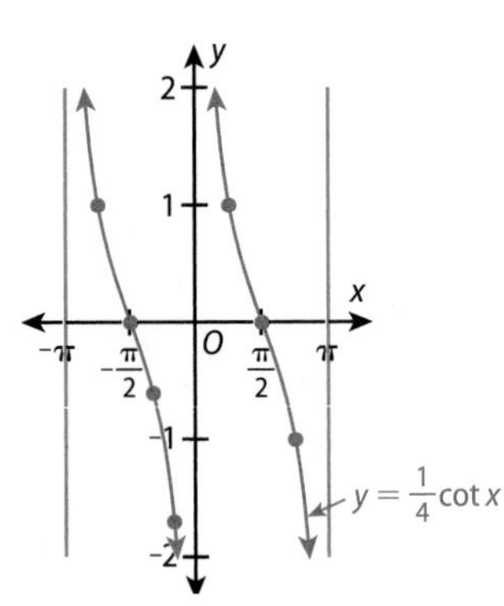

SEARCH

To see step-by-step videos of these problems, enter the page number into the SWadvantage.com Search Bar.

EXAMPLE 4

Graph $y = \frac{1}{4}\cot x$ in the interval $(0, 2\pi)$.

STEP 1 Determine critical values of $\cot x$ in the given interval.

x	0	$\frac{\pi}{4}$	$\frac{\pi}{2}$	$\frac{3\pi}{4}$	π	$\frac{5\pi}{4}$	$\frac{3\pi}{2}$	$\frac{7\pi}{4}$	2π
$\cot x$	∞	1	0	-1	∞	1	0	-1	∞
$\frac{1}{4}\cot x$	∞	$\frac{1}{4}$	0	$-\frac{1}{4}$	∞	$\frac{1}{4}$	0	$-\frac{1}{4}$	∞

STEP 2 To find $\frac{1}{4}\cot x$, multiply each critical value of $\cot x$ by $\frac{1}{4}$.

STEP 3 Draw the three asymptotes in this interval: $x = 0, x = \pi$, and $x = 2\pi$. Plot the points in the table and sketch the cotangent curve.

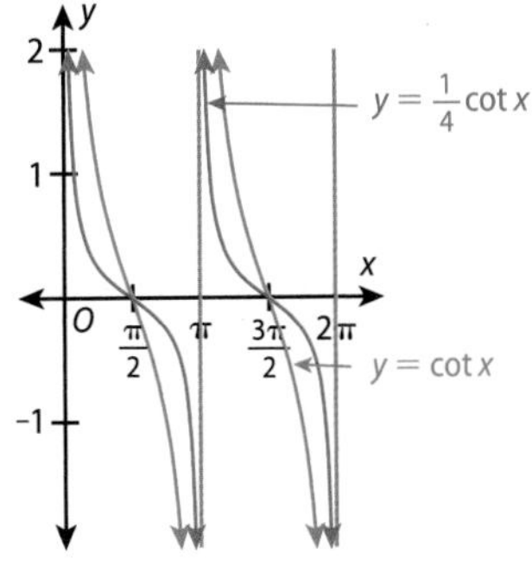

Compare the graphs of $y = \frac{1}{4}\cot x$ and $y = \cot x$.

- Both have the same asymptotes and x-intercepts.
- Both are decreasing, discontinuous functions.

Need More HELP

To complete the table, find the reciprocals of $\tan x$ for each defined value of x. That is, if $\tan x = \frac{1}{2}$, then $\cot x = 2$. Remember, if $\tan x = 0$, then $\cot x = \infty$ and vice versa.

EXAMPLE 5

Graph $y = \cot x$ and $y = \tan x$ together in the interval $(0, \pi)$.

The asymptotes of $y = \cot x$ are $x = 0$ and $x = \pi$. The asymptote of $y = \tan x$ is $x = \frac{\pi}{2}$. Plot the points for each function when $x = 0, \frac{\pi}{4}, \frac{\pi}{2}, \frac{3\pi}{2}$, and π. Then sketch the curves. Note that:

- from 0 to π, the cotangent decreases.
- from 0 to $\frac{\pi}{2}$, $\tan x$ increases from 0 to ∞; from $\frac{\pi}{2}$ to π, $\tan x$ increases from $-\infty$ to 0.

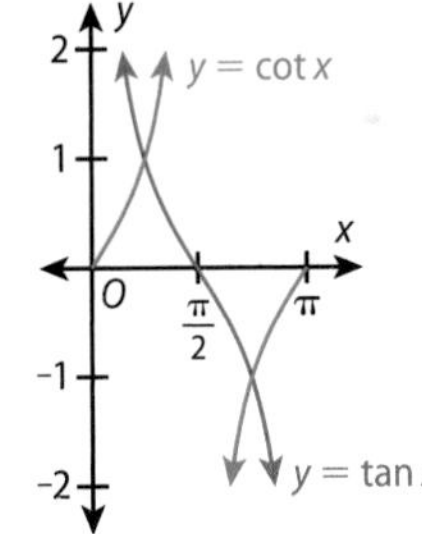

Need More HELP

In this interval, the intersection of $y = \tan x$ and $y = \cot x$ is $\left(\frac{\pi}{4}, 1\right)$.

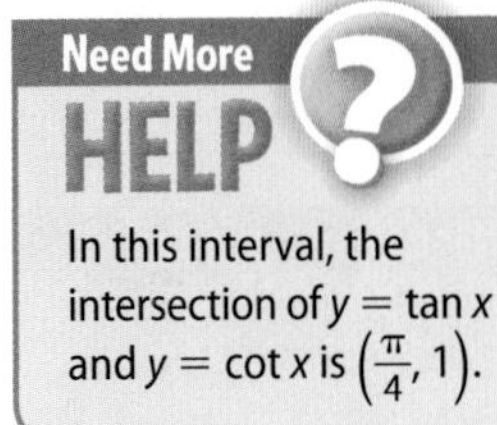

Graphing the Tangent and Cotangent Functions

	$y = \tan x$	$y = \cot x$
Domain	All real numbers, except $x = \frac{\pi}{2} + k\pi$, where k is an integer	All real numbers, except $x = k\pi$, where k is an integer
Range	All real numbers: $(-\infty, \infty)$	All real numbers: $(-\infty, \infty)$
Period	π	π
Amplitude	None	None
Asymptotes	$x = \frac{\pi}{2} + k\pi$	$x = k\pi$
Behavior	Increasing and discontinuous	Decreasing and discontinuous

Graphs of the Secant and the Cosecant Functions

Graphing the Secant Function

Need More HELP

For a review of the cosine function, its features, and its graph, see pp. 955–957.

Recall the following features of the cosine function.

- If x is any real number, then $-1 \le \cos x \le 1$.
- The period of the cosine is 360°, or 2π.
- The amplitude of the cosine function is 1.
- The cosine function is continuous. That is, its graph is unbroken.
- The equation $\cos x = 0$ has infinitely many solutions. They are $90°n$, or $\frac{\pi n}{2}$, where n is any odd integer.

SEARCH

To see step-by-step videos of these problems, enter the page number into the SWadvantage.com Search Bar.

The graph of the cosine function over the interval $-360° \le x \le 360°$, or $-2\pi \le x \le 2\pi$, is shown at the right. The graph shows two cycles. The features mentioned above are reflected in the graph.

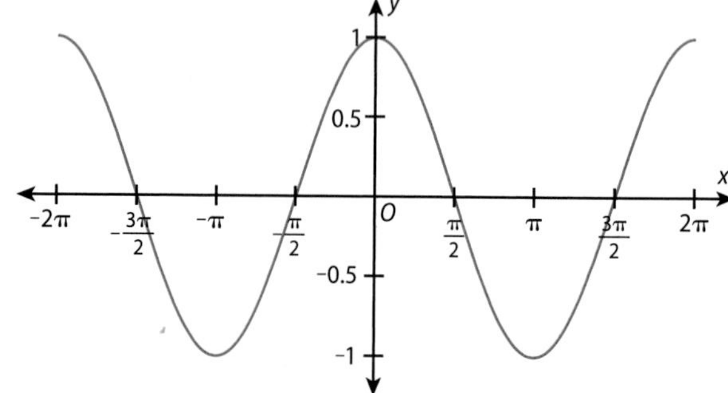

These facts about the cosine function will become important in any analysis of the secant function.

Finally, recall that the secant function is the reciprocal of the cosine function: $\sec x = \frac{1}{\cos x}$.

EXAMPLE 1

a. Find all values of x for which $\sec x = 1$.

Use the reciprocal relationship.

$$\sec x = 1$$
$$\frac{1}{\cos x} = 1$$
$$\cos x = 1$$
$$x = 360°n, \text{ or } 2\pi n, \text{ where } n \text{ is an integer}$$

Therefore, $\sec x = 1$, if $x = 360°n$, or $2\pi n$, where n is an integer.

b. Find all values of x for which $\sec x = y$ is undefined.

Use the reciprocal relationship. $\frac{1}{\cos x} = \sec x$

STEP 1 Recall that division by 0 is not possible.

$\frac{5}{0}$ not possible $\quad \frac{-1}{0}$ not possible $\quad \frac{a}{0}$ not possible

STEP 2 Find the values of x for which $\cos x = 0$.

If $x = 90°n$, or $x = \frac{\pi n}{2}$, where n is any odd integer, then $\cos x = 0$.

Thus, $\sec x = y$ is undefined when $x = 90°n$, or $\frac{\pi n}{2}$, where n is any odd integer.

Need More HELP

To find values of x for which $\cos x = 1$ and $\cos x = 0$, you can simply read them from the graph of the cosine function. The values of x for which $\cos x = 1$ are those values of x which give the highest point on the graph. The values of x for which $\cos x = 0$ are those values of x for which the graph crosses the x-axis.

Recall that an asymptote of a graph is a line that a curve approaches but does not intersect.

EXAMPLE 2

Use a table of values to explore the behavior of $y = \sec x$ in each situation.

a. y as x approaches $\frac{\pi}{2}$ from values of x less than $\frac{\pi}{2}$ (approaches from the left)

x	0	$\frac{\pi}{16}$	$\frac{\pi}{8}$	$\frac{3\pi}{16}$	$\frac{\pi}{4}$	$\frac{5\pi}{16}$	$\frac{3\pi}{8}$	$\frac{7\pi}{16}$
y	1	1.01959	1.08239	1.20269	1.41421	1.79995	2.61313	5.12583

As x approaches $\frac{\pi}{2}$ from the left, y increases without bound.

b. y as x approaches $\frac{\pi}{2}$ from values of x greater than $\frac{\pi}{2}$ (approaches from the right)

x	π	$\frac{15\pi}{16}$	$\frac{7\pi}{8}$	$\frac{13\pi}{16}$	$\frac{3\pi}{4}$	$\frac{11\pi}{16}$	$\frac{5\pi}{8}$	$\frac{9\pi}{16}$
y	−1	−1.01959	−1.08239	−1.20269	−1.41421	−1.79995	−2.61313	−5.12583

As x approaches $\frac{\pi}{2}$ from the right, y decreases without bound.

c. Make a diagram to show the behavior discovered in Part (a) and Part (b).

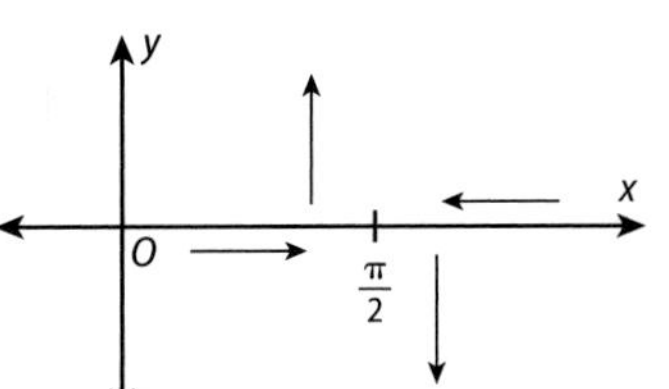

The horizontal arrows show x approaching $\frac{\pi}{2}$ from the left and the right. The vertical arrows show the corresponding behavior of y.

- The graph of $y = \sec x$ slopes up to the right with $x = \frac{\pi}{2}$ as an asymptote when x is less than but close to $\frac{\pi}{2}$.
- The graph of $y = \sec x$ slopes down to the left with $x = \frac{\pi}{2}$ as an asymptote when x is greater than but close to $\frac{\pi}{2}$.

Watch Out!

Detection of a trend can often be useful. Use a graphing calculator to confirm the trend in in Part (a) and in Part (b).

An auxiliary diagram like the one in Part (c) can help give an intuitive idea of what to expect.

EXAMPLE 3

Graph $y = \sec x$ over the interval $-2\pi \le x \le 2\pi$.

STEP 1 Use the result of Example 2 Part (a) and Part (b). Draw dashed lines where the asymptotes will be in the specified interval. These occur for undefined values.

$$x = -\frac{3\pi}{2}, -\frac{\pi}{2}, \frac{\pi}{2}, \text{ and } \frac{3\pi}{2}$$

STEP 2 Draw U shapes with maximum values of −1 and minimum values of 1 as shown. Use the result of Example 2 Part (c) to complete the graph using the asymptotic nature of the function.

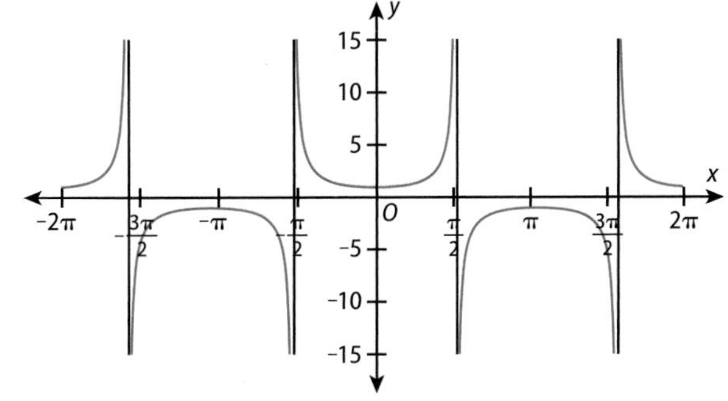

Ways to REMEMBER

The U shapes in the graph of $y = \sec x$ are determined by the values of x for which $\cos x = 0$. Picture the graph of $y = \cos x$, and the graph of $y = \sec x$ will come to mind.

Graphing the Cosecant Function

Recall the following features of the sine function.

- If x is any real number, then $-1 \leq \sin x \leq 1$.
- The period of the sine is 360°, or 2π.
- The amplitude of the sine function is 1.
- The sine function is continuous. That is, its graph is unbroken.
- The equation $\sin x = 0$ has infinitely many solutions. They are $180°n$, or πn, where n is any integer.

Need More HELP

For a review of the sine function, its features, and its graph, see pp. 952–954.

The graph of the sine function over the interval $-360° \leq x \leq 360°$, or $-2\pi \leq x \leq 2\pi$, is shown at the right. The graph shows two cycles. The features mentioned above are reflected in the graph. These facts about the sine function will become important in any analysis of the cosecant function.

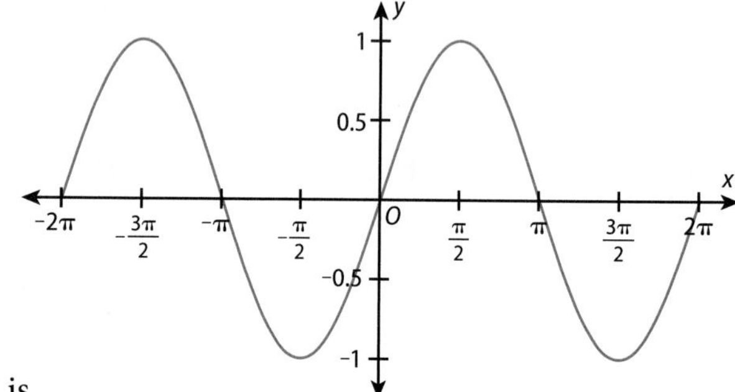

Finally, recall that the cosecant function is the inverse of the sine function: $\csc x = \frac{1}{\sin x}$.

EXAMPLE 4

a. Find all values of x for which $\csc x = 1$.

$$\csc x = 1$$

Use the reciprocal relationship. $$\frac{1}{\sin x} = 1$$

$$\sin x = 1$$

$$x = 90° + 360°n, \text{ or } \frac{\pi}{2} + 2\pi n, \text{ where } n \text{ is an integer}$$

Therefore, $\csc x = 1$, if $x = 90° + 360°n$, or $\frac{\pi}{2} + 2\pi n$, where n is an integer.

b. Find all values of x for which $\csc x = y$ is not defined.

Use the reciprocal relationship. $\frac{1}{\sin x} = \csc x$

Recall that division by 0 is not possible.

Find the values of x for which $\sin x = 0$.

If $x = 360°n$ or $x = 2\pi n$, where n is any integer, then $\sin x = 0$.

Thus, $\csc x = y$ is not defined when $x = 360°n$ or $2\pi n$, where n is an integer.

c. What is the range of $\csc x = y$?

Since $|\sin x| \leq 1$, and $\csc x = \frac{1}{\sin x}$, $|\csc x| \geq 1$.

The range is all real numbers greater than or equal to 1 or less than or equal to -1.

Need More HELP

Find all values of x in the interval $0° \leq x \leq 360°$ for which $\sin x = 1$ and all other such values can be obtained by using the period of the sine function. The same is true for values of x for which $\sin x = 0$.

SEARCH

To see step-by-step videos of these problems, enter the page number into the SWadvantage.com Search Bar.

The graph of $y = \csc x$ has asymptotes similar to that of the graph of $y = \sec x$, but not at the same values of x.

EXAMPLE 5

Use a table of values to explore the behavior of $y = \csc x$ in each situation.

a. Identify the asymptotes of the graph of $y = \csc x$.

The asymptotes occur at the values excluded from the domain of the function. They are $x = \pi n$, where n is an integer.

b. y on the interval $0 < x < \pi$

x	$\frac{\pi}{8}$	$\frac{\pi}{4}$	$\frac{3\pi}{8}$	$\frac{\pi}{2}$	$\frac{5\pi}{8}$	$\frac{3\pi}{4}$	$\frac{7\pi}{8}$
y	2.61313	1.41421	1.08239	1	1.08239	1.41421	2.61313

On the interval $0 < x < \pi$, y decreases from infinity to a minimum of 1, then increases without bound.

c. y on the interval $\pi < x < 2\pi$

x	$\frac{15\pi}{8}$	$\frac{7\pi}{4}$	$\frac{13\pi}{8}$	$\frac{3\pi}{2}$	$\frac{11\pi}{8}$	$\frac{5\pi}{4}$	$\frac{9\pi}{8}$
y	−2.61313	−1.41421	−1.08239	−1	−1.08239	−1.41421	−2.61313

On the interval $\pi < x < 2\pi$, y increases from negative infinity to a maximum of -1, then decreases without bound.

d. Make a diagram to show the behavior discovered in Part (a) and in Part (b).

Between 0 and π, the graph shows a U shape opening upward. Its lowest point is $\left(\frac{\pi}{2}, 1\right)$. Between π and 2π, the graph shows a U shape opening downward. Its highest point is $\left(\frac{3\pi}{2}, -1\right)$.

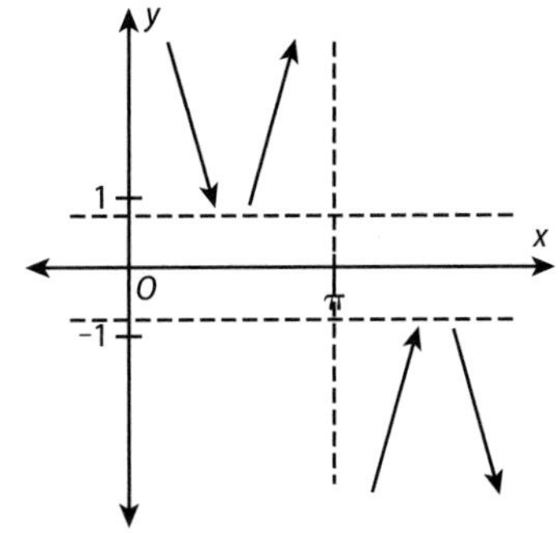

Try It This Way

If x is positive and increases, then the value of the reciprocal of x decreases. Therefore, since $\sin x$ increases as x increases from 0 to $\frac{\pi}{2}$, its reciprocal decreases. Since $\sin x$ decreases as x increases from $\frac{\pi}{2}$ to π, its reciprocal increases. This would explain the U shape discovered in Part (b).

EXAMPLE 6

Graph $y = \csc x$ over the interval $-2\pi \leq x \leq 2\pi$.

STEP 1 Use the result of Example 5 Part (a). Draw dashed lines for the asymptotes in the specified interval:

$$x = -2\pi, -\pi, 0, \pi, \text{ and } 2\pi$$

STEP 2 Draw U shapes with maximum values of -1 and minimum values of 1 as shown. Use the result of Example 5 Part (b) and Part (c) to complete the graph.

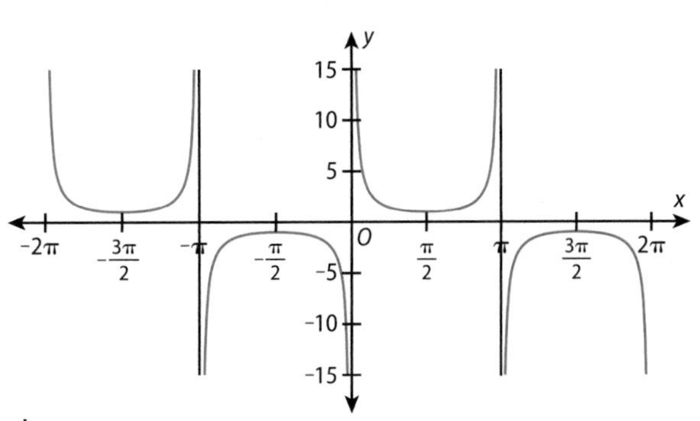

Shift the graph of $y = \sec x$ left or right $\frac{\pi}{2}$ units.

Ways to REMEMBER

The U shapes in the graph of $y = \csc x$ are determined by the values of x for which $\sin x = 0$. Picture the graph of $y = \sin x$, and the graph of $y = \csc x$ will come to mind.

Other Transformations

Graphing Translations, Reflections, and Scalings

Knowledge of basic, or parent, functions is important in analyzing and graphing more complicated functions.

Watch Out !

Some might think that when a number is subtracted from x, the translation is to the left. This is not so. The translation is to the right.

EXAMPLE 1

Graph each function on the interval $0 \leq x \leq 2\pi$.

a. $f(x) = \tan\left(x - \frac{\pi}{2}\right)$

The graph of f is the translation $\frac{\pi}{2}$ units to the right of the graph of $y = \tan x$. The graph is shown at the left below.

b. $g(x) = \tan x + 2$

The graph of g is the translation 2 units up of the graph of $y = \tan x$. The graph is shown in the center below.

c. $h(x) = \tan\left(x + \frac{\pi}{2}\right) - 1$

The graph of h is the translation $\frac{\pi}{2}$ units to the left of the graph of $y = \tan x$ followed by the translation of the result down 1 unit. The graph is shown at the right below.

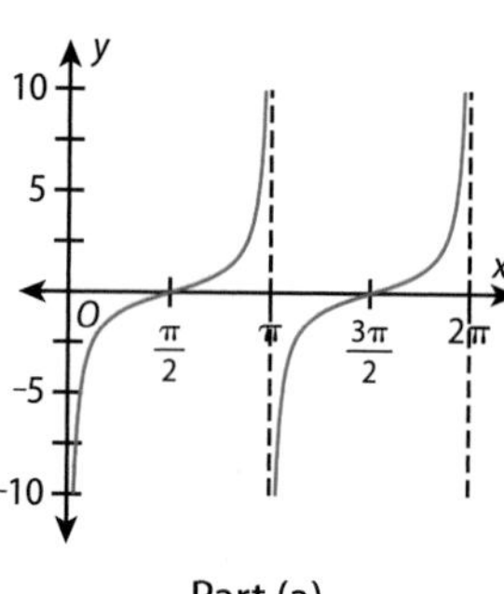

Part (a)

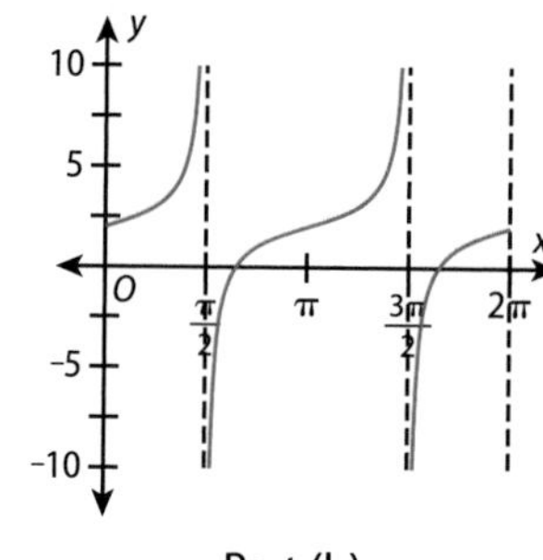

Part (b)

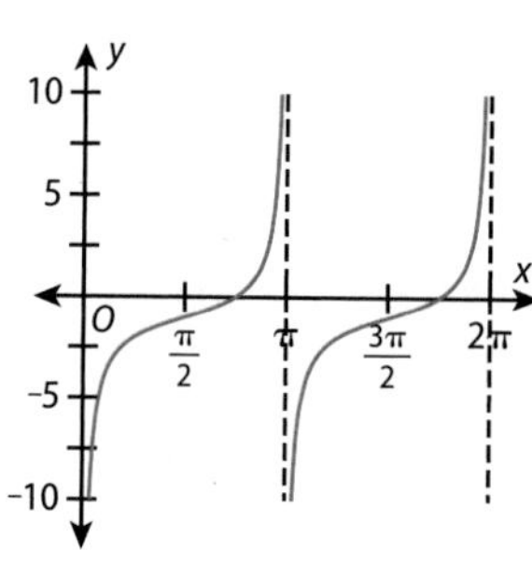

Part (c)

EXAMPLE 2

Graph $f(x) = -2\tan(-x)$ on the interval $0 \leq x \leq 2\pi$.

STEP 1 Analyze f. Since the tangent function is an odd function, $-\tan(-x) = \tan x$.

$$-\tan(-x) = -\frac{\sin(-x)}{\cos(-x)}$$
$$= -\frac{-\sin x}{\cos x}$$
$$= \frac{\sin x}{\cos x} = \tan x$$

STEP 2 Graph $f(x) = 2\tan x$.

The graph is shown at the right. Notice that it is the graph of $y = \tan x$ stretched by a factor of 2 vertically.

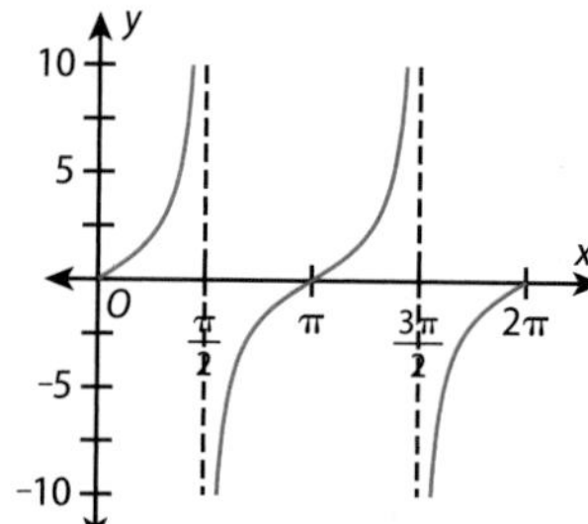

In many situations, a trigonometric function is affected by multiple transformations.

EXAMPLE 3

Let $f(x) = 3\sin(2x)$.

a. Describe how to obtain the graph of f from the graph of $y = \sin x$.

STEP 1 The period of $y = \sin x$ is 2π. The period of $y' = \sin(2x)$ is one half that, or π. One cycle of the graph occurs on the interval $0 \leq x \leq \pi$.

STEP 2 The amplitude of $y = \sin x$ and $y' = \sin(2x)$ is 1.

$$-1 \leq \sin(2x) \leq 1$$

$$3(-1) \leq 3\sin(2x) \leq (3)1$$

The amplitude of $f(x) = 3\sin(2x)$ is 3.

STEP 3 Scale the graph of $y = \sin x$ by a factor of 0.5 horizontally and by a factor of 3 vertically.

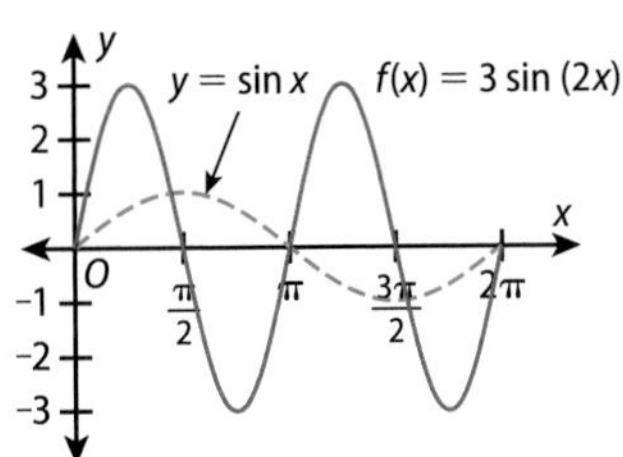
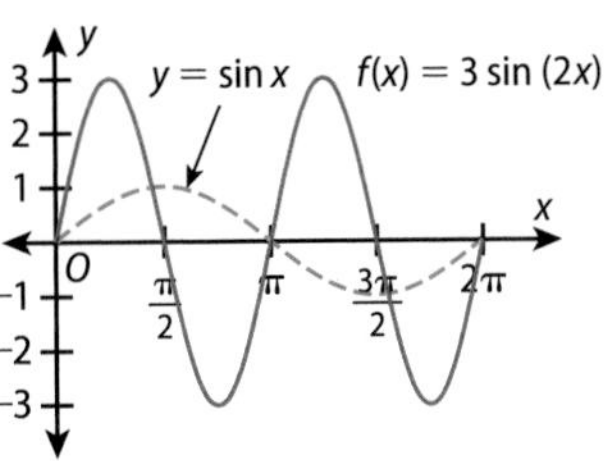

b. Graph $y = \sin x$ and $f(x) = 3\sin(2x)$ on the same set of axes using the interval $0 \leq x \leq 2\pi$.

The graph of $y = \sin x$ is shown as a dashed curve. The graph of $f(x) = 3\sin(2x)$ is shown as a solid curve. Notice that one cycle of $f(x) = 3\sin(2x)$ spans the interval that shows one-half of a cycle of $y = \sin x$.

Try It This Way

Transformations are performed one after another. The graph of f can be obtained in one of two orders.

First deal with the coefficient of x, 2. Then deal with the multiplier 3. Alternatively, graph $y = 3\sin x$, then compress the result by using the coefficient 2.

EXAMPLE 4

Let $f(x) = \csc x$.

a. Construct a function g such that the range of g is $|g(x)| \geq 2$ and the asymptotes of g are the lines $x = \pi n$, where n is an integer.

The range of f is $|f(x)| \geq 1$. The asymptotes of the graph of f are the lines $x = \pi n$, where n is an integer.

Let $g(x) = 2\csc x$.

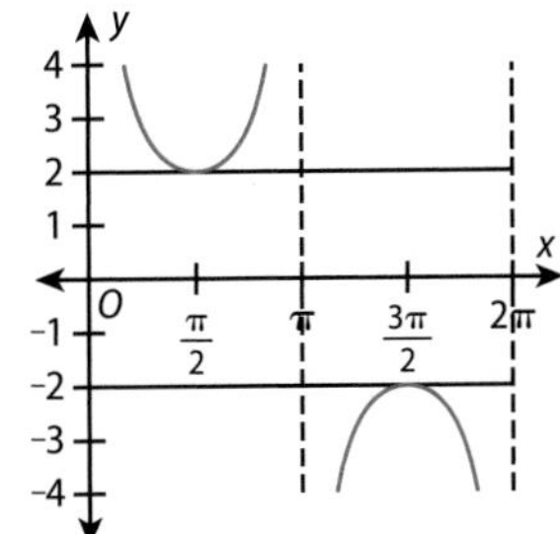

b. Graph g on the interval $0 \leq x \leq 2\pi$. Confirm that g meets the requirements of the problem.

The graph is shown at the right along with the graphs of $y = -2$ and $y = 2$. This confirms the range and the asymptotes.

SEARCH

To see step-by-step videos of these problems, enter the page number into the SWadvantage.com Search Bar.

The graphs of $y = \sin x$ and $y = \cos x$ over the interval $0 \leq x \leq \pi$ reveal some interesting facts that can be useful in dealing with translations.

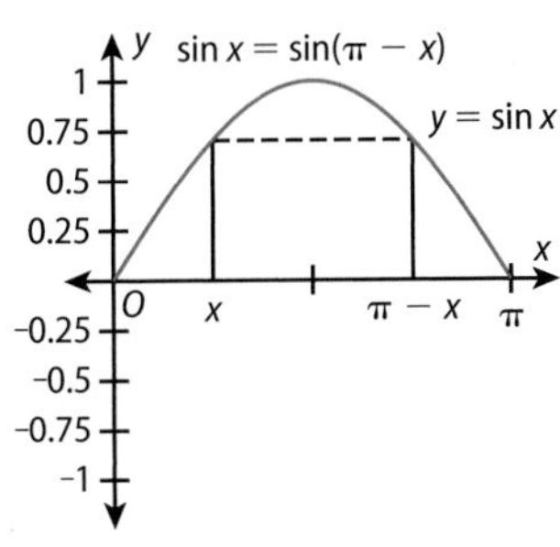

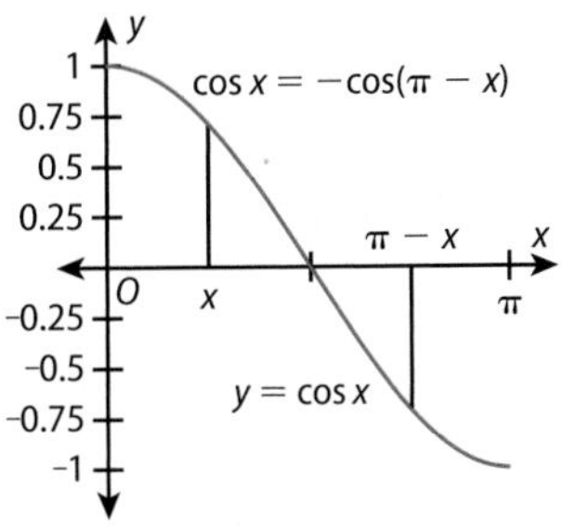

Constructing Functions That Involve Transformations

EXAMPLE 5

Need More HELP

Recall the graph of $y = \cos x$ over the interval $0 \leq x \leq \pi$. The cosine of an angle is the opposite of the cosine of its supplement.

Let $f(x) = \sec x$. Write an equation for g, the translation of the graph of f to the right π units and up 3 units. Write the equation for g in simplest form.

$$g(x) = \sec(x - \pi) + 3$$
$$= \frac{1}{\cos(x - \pi)} + 3$$
$$g(x) = \frac{1}{-\cos x} + 3$$

Therefore, $g(x) = -\sec x + 3$.

EXAMPLE 6

Let $f(x) = \sin x$.

a. Construct a function g that has asymptotes at those values of x for which $\sin x = 0$ and is a reflection of the graph of f in the x-axis.

The reciprocal function, $\csc x$, has asymptotes at those values of x for which $\sin x = 0$.

$$y = \csc x$$

To reflect this graph in the x-axis, replace y with $-y$.

$$-y = \csc x$$
$$y = -\csc x$$

Let $g(x) = -\csc x$.

b. Graph f and g on the interval $0 \leq x \leq 2\pi$.

The graphs of f and g are shown at the right. The y-axis and the dashed lines $y = \pi$ and $y = 2\pi$ show asymptotes at the values of x for which $\sin x = 0$.

$g(x) = -\csc x$

$f(x) = \sin x$

Need More HELP

The values of x for which $\sin x = 0$ give asymptotes for its reciprocal, the cosecant function.

EXAMPLE 7

SEARCH

To see step-by-step videos of these problems, enter the page number into the SWadvantage.com Search Bar.

Let $f(x) = \tan x$. Write an equation for g, the translation of f to the right π units, up 2 units followed by a reflection in the y-axis.

STEP 1 Use the periodicity of the tangent function.

$$\tan(x - \pi) = \tan x$$

STEP 2 Apply the vertical translation.

$$\tan(x - \pi) + 2 = \tan x + 2$$

STEP 3 Apply the reflection.

To reflect a graph in the y-axis, replace x with $-x$. Then use the fact that the tangent is an odd function.

$$\tan(-x - \pi) + 2 = \tan(-x) + 2$$

Therefore, $g(x) = -\tan x + 2$.

You can use your knowledge of transformations to help you write an equation for a given graph. The key to discovering a valid equation is the recognition of similarities with a parent graph.

EXAMPLE 8

Write an equation for the graph shown below. Point *P* has coordinates $P\left(\frac{\pi}{2}, 1\right)$.

The graph resembles a translation of the graph of the tangent function.

Let $y = \tan(x - h) + k$ for some real numbers h and k. Let $h = \frac{\pi}{2}$ and $k = 1$.

Then $y = \tan\left(x - \frac{\pi}{2}\right) + 1$.

It is easy to see that when $x = \frac{\pi}{2}$, then $y = 1$.

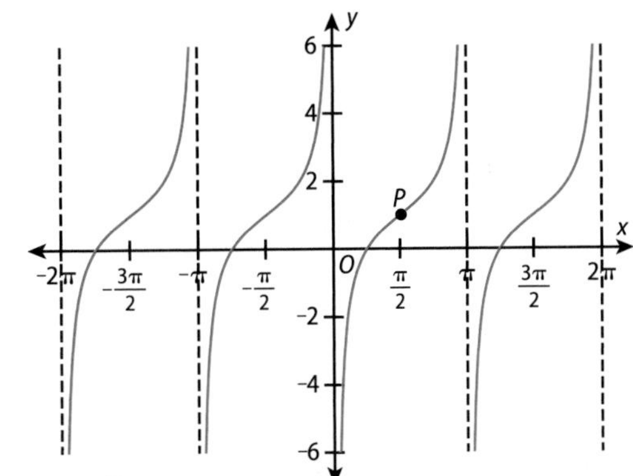

GOT TO KNOW!

Summary of Transformations

Let f be a function.

Translations:

The equation $y = f(x - h) + k$ represents a translation of the graph of f.

If $h > 0$, the translation is to the **right** h units.

If $h < 0$, the translation is to the **left** $|h|$ units.

If $k > 0$, the translation is **up** k units.

If $k < 0$, the translation is **down** $|k|$ units.

Reflections:

The reflection of the graph of $y = f(x)$ in the **x-axis** is the graph of $y = -f(x)$.

The reflection of the graph of $y = f(x)$ in the **y-axis** is the graph of $y = f(-x)$.

The reflection of the graph of $y = f(x)$ in the **origin** is the graph of $y = -f(-x)$.

Dilations (Scaling):

Let a be a positive real number.

$0 < a < 1$ The graph of $y = af(x)$ is a **vertical compression** of the graph of $y = f(x)$.

The graph of $y = f(ax)$ is a **horizontal stretch** of the graph of $y = f(x)$.

$a > 1$ The graph of $y = af(x)$ is a **vertical stretch** of the graph of $y = f(x)$.

The graph of $y = f(ax)$ is a **horizontal compression** of the graph of $y = f(x)$.

Using a Rotation of Axes

Ways to REMEMBER

Both sets of rotation equations involve the sine, s, and the cosine, c.

From xy to $x'y'$

x': +c −s

y': +s +c

From $x'y'$ to xy

x: +c +s

y: −s +c

Both sets of rotation equations involve + and −.

From xy to $x'y'$

x': +c −s

y': +s +c

From $x'y'$ to xy

x: +c +s

y: −s +c

A point in the plane has a designated location when a pair of coordinate axes is imposed on the plane. A given point, therefore, can have different coordinates if there are multiple coordinate axes on the same plane.

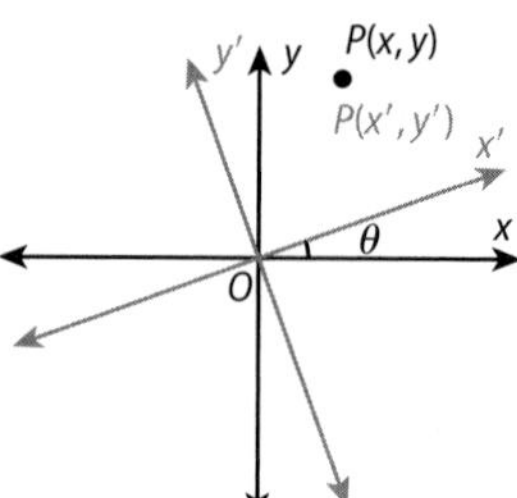

The diagram at the right shows point P in the xy-plane. In that system, the coordinates are $P(x, y)$. It also shows the $x'y'$-plane with the same origin as the xy-plane. In that system, P has coordinates $P(x', y')$. The $x'y'$-coordinate system is a rotation of the xy-coordinate system through an angle θ.

The equations that relate the coordinates of P' to those of P are called the rotation of axes equations and are stated below.

From x and y to x' and y' $\quad x' = x\cos\theta - y\sin\theta$ and $y' = x\sin\theta + y\cos\theta$

From x' and y' to x and y $\quad x = x'\cos\theta + y'\sin\theta$ and $y = -x'\sin\theta + y'\cos\theta$

EXAMPLE 9

The xy-coordinate system is rotated 30° counterclockwise to create the $x'y'$-coordinate system. The coordinates of P in the xy-coordinate system are $P(3, 5)$. Find the coordinates of P in the $x'y'$-coordinate system.

STEP 1 Write the rotation equations. Choose equations that give x' and y' from x and y.

$$x' = x\cos\theta - y\sin\theta \text{ and } y' = x\sin\theta + y\cos\theta$$

STEP 2 Substitute.

$x = 3$ and $y = 5$ $\quad x' = 3\cos 30° - 5\sin 30°$ and $y' = 3\sin 30° + 5\cos 30°$

STEP 3 Simplify.

$\cos 30° = \frac{\sqrt{3}}{2}$ $\quad x' = 3\left(\frac{\sqrt{3}}{2}\right) - 5\left(\frac{1}{2}\right)$ and $y' = 3\left(\frac{1}{2}\right) + 5\left(\frac{\sqrt{3}}{2}\right)$

$\sin 30° = \frac{1}{2}$ $\quad x' = \frac{3\sqrt{3} - 5}{2}$ and $y' = \frac{3 + 5\sqrt{3}}{2}$

Therefore, the coordinates of P in the $x'y'$-coordinate system are $P\left(\frac{3\sqrt{3} - 5}{2}, \frac{3 + 5\sqrt{3}}{2}\right)$.

The equation below is the general form of a second-degree equation in x and y.

$$Ax^2 + Bxy + Cy^2 + Dx + Ey + F = 0$$

Ellipses, hyperbolas, and parabolas are equation types covered by this equation. An easy way to tell what type of curve is determined by the coefficients is the test below.

- The equation represents an ellipse if $B^2 - 4AC < 0$.
- The equation represents a hyperbola if $B^2 - 4AC > 0$.
- The equation represents a parabola if $B^2 - 4AC = 0$.

For instance, the equation $4x^2 + 9y^2 - 36 = 0$ represents an ellipse as $A = 4$, $B = 0$, $C = 9$ and $0^2 - 4(4)(9) < 0$.

By using a suitable rotation of axes, an equation in which $B \neq 0$ can be transformed into an equation where $B = 0$. Once that is done, a graph of the original equation can be obtained.

EXAMPLE 10

In the *xy*-coordinate system, a curve has equation $x^2 + xy + y^2 - 6 = 0$. Write an equation in the $x'y'$-coordinate system resulting from rotating the original system 45° clockwise.

STEP 1 Write a strategy.

Use rotation equations that give x and y in terms of x' and y'.

$x = x' \cos\theta + y' \sin\theta$ and $y = -x' \sin\theta + y' \cos\theta$

STEP 2 Identify θ.

$\theta = -45°$ since the rotation is 45° clockwise.

STEP 3 Apply the rotation equations.

$x = x' \cos(-45°) + y' \sin(-45°)$ and $y = -x' \sin(-45°) + y' \cos(-45°)$

$$x = x'\left(\frac{\sqrt{2}}{2}\right) + y'\left(-\frac{\sqrt{2}}{2}\right) \quad \text{and } y = -x'\left(-\frac{\sqrt{2}}{2}\right) + y'\left(\frac{\sqrt{2}}{2}\right)$$

$$x = \left(\frac{\sqrt{2}}{2}\right)(x' - y') \quad \text{and } y = \left(\frac{\sqrt{2}}{2}\right)(x' + y')$$

STEP 4 Substitute into the original equation.

$$\left(\left(\frac{\sqrt{2}}{2}\right)(x' - y')\right)^2 + \left(\frac{\sqrt{2}}{2}\right)(x' - y')\left(\frac{\sqrt{2}}{2}\right)(x' + y') + \left(\left(\frac{\sqrt{2}}{2}\right)(x' + y')\right)^2 - 6 = 0$$

STEP 5 Multiply and simplify.

$$\left(\left(\frac{\sqrt{2}}{2}\right)(x' - y')\right)^2 = \frac{(x')^2}{2} - xy + \frac{(y')^2}{2}$$

$$\left(\frac{\sqrt{2}}{2}\right)(x' - y')\left(\frac{\sqrt{2}}{2}\right)(x' + y') = \frac{(x')^2}{2} - \frac{(y')^2}{2}$$

$$\left(\left(\frac{\sqrt{2}}{2}\right)(x' + y')\right)^2 = \frac{(x')^2}{2} + xy + \frac{(y')^2}{2}$$

$$\frac{3(x')^2}{2} + \frac{(y')^2}{2} - 6 = 0$$

STEP 6 Write the final result. The curve is an ellipse.

$$\frac{(x')^2}{4} + \frac{(y')^2}{12} = 1$$

The given equation involves x and y. The objective is to get an equation that involves x' and y', coordinates in a new coordinate system.

SEARCH

To see step-by-step videos of these problems, enter the page number into the SWadvantage.com Search Bar.

Often, the angle needed to eliminate the *xy*-term in $Ax^2 + Bxy + Cy^2 + Dx + Ey + F = 0$ is unknown. To calculate it, use $\tan(2\theta) = \frac{B}{C - A}$.

Combining Trigonometric Functions

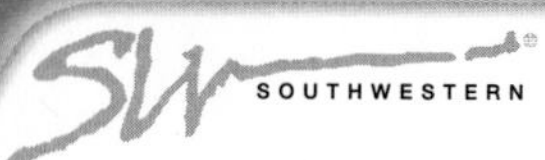

Graphing Sums and Differences of Functions

If f and g are functions, then the functions $f + g$ and $f - g$ are defined as follows.

$$(f + g)(x) = f(x) + g(x) \qquad (f - g)(x) = f(x) - g(x)$$

The graphs of $f + g$ and $f - g$ are obtained from the graphs of f and g by addition or subtraction of y-coordinates.

Need More HELP

A small sampling of domain values may be enough to see a pattern but not identify it. The tables in Example 1 suggest a quadratic pattern because there are two x-intercepts. It is true, however, that the sum of a linear function and a quadratic function will be another quadratic function.

EXAMPLE 1

Let $f(x) = 2x$ and $g(x) = x^2$.

a. Make a table to find the values of $f + g$ for $x = -3, -2, -1, 0, 1, 2,$ and 3.

x	−3	−2	−1	0	1	2	3
f(x)	−6	−4	−2	0	2	4	6
g(x)	9	4	1	0	1	4	9
f(x) + g(x)	3	0	−1	0	3	8	15

b. Make a table to find the values of $f - g$ for $x = -3, -2, -1, 0, 1, 2,$ and 3.

x	−3	−2	−1	0	1	2	3
f(x)	−6	−4	−2	0	2	4	6
g(x)	9	4	1	0	1	4	9
f(x) − g(x)	−15	−8	−3	0	1	0	−3

SEARCH

To see step-by-step videos of these problems, enter the page number into the SWadvantage.com Search Bar.

EXAMPLE 2

Let $f(x) = \sin x$ and $g(x) = \cos x$.

a. Make a table to find the values of $f + g$ for $x = -2\pi, -\frac{3\pi}{2}, -\pi, -\frac{\pi}{2}, 0, \frac{\pi}{2}, \pi, \frac{3\pi}{2},$ and 2π.

x	-2π	$-\frac{3\pi}{2}$	$-\pi$	$-\frac{\pi}{2}$	0	$\frac{\pi}{2}$	π	$\frac{3\pi}{2}$	2π
f(x)	0	1	0	−1	0	1	0	−1	0
g(x)	1	0	−1	0	1	0	−1	0	1
f(x) + g(x)	1	1	−1	−1	1	1	−1	−1	1

b. Make a table to find the values of $f - g$ for $x = -2\pi, -\frac{3\pi}{2}, -\pi, -\frac{\pi}{2}, 0, \frac{\pi}{2}, \pi, \frac{3\pi}{2},$ and 2π.

x	-2π	$-\frac{3\pi}{2}$	$-\pi$	$-\frac{\pi}{2}$	0	$\frac{\pi}{2}$	π	$\frac{3\pi}{2}$	2π
f(x)	0	1	0	−1	0	1	0	−1	0
g(x)	1	0	−1	0	1	0	−1	0	1
f(x) − g(x)	−1	1	1	−1	−1	1	1	−1	−1

EXAMPLE 3

Let $f(x) = \sin x$ and $g(x) = \cos x$. Let $-2\pi \leq x \leq 2\pi$. Graph each function.

a. $f + g$

This is the function in Example 2 Part (a). Both f and g are periodic with period 2π. Thus, $f + g$ is also periodic with period 2π. To get an idea of the graph, plot the values from the table. This is shown in the graph at the left below. Since the sketch may not show a pattern, use a graphing calculator or computer software to plot many points. The graph is shown at the right below.

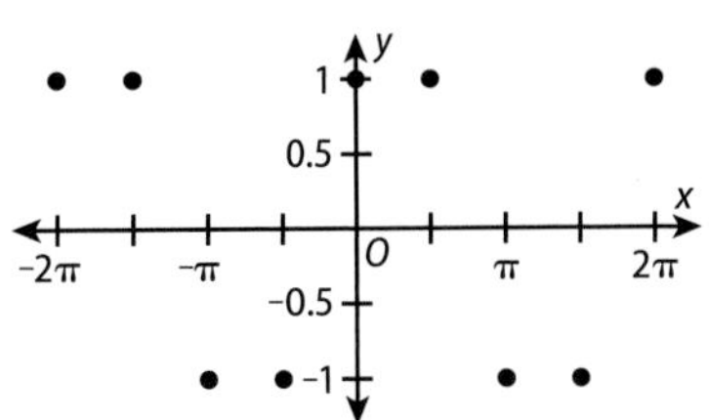

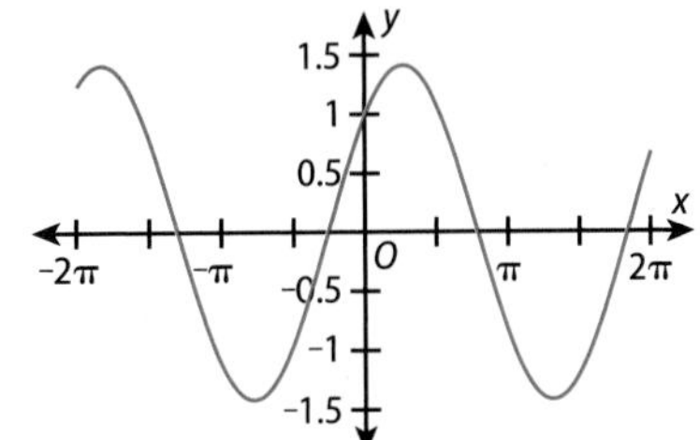

b. $f - g$

This is the function in Example 2 Part (b). Both f and g are periodic with period 2π. Thus, $f - g$ is also periodic with period 2π. To get an idea of the graph, plot the values from the table. As in Part (a), this sampling does not show the graph adequately. Use a graphing calculator or computer software to get a more representative picture. The resulting graph is shown at the right below.

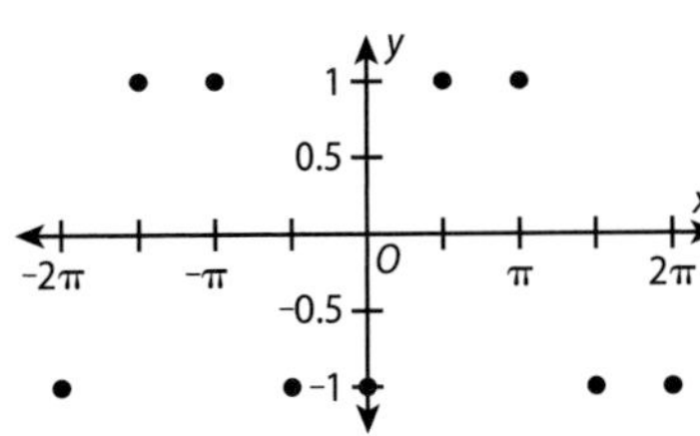

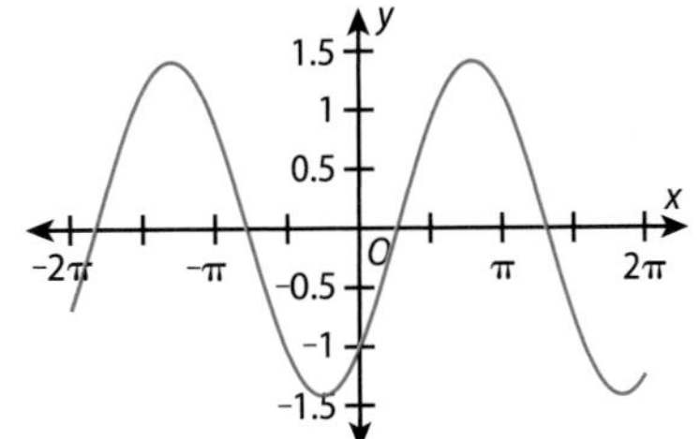

Watch Out

None of the points in the scatter plot are maximums or minimums. The local maxima and local minima occur between successive pairs of points. This is seen in the continuous graph at the left.

EXAMPLE 4

Let $f(x) = \sin x$, $g(x) = \csc x$, $h(x) = \cos x$, and $m(x) = \sec x$. Let $-2\pi \leq x \leq 2\pi$. Graph each function.

a. $f + g$

To graph $f + g$, note that $\csc x = \frac{1}{\sin x}$. Use a graphing calculator or computer software. The graph is shown below.

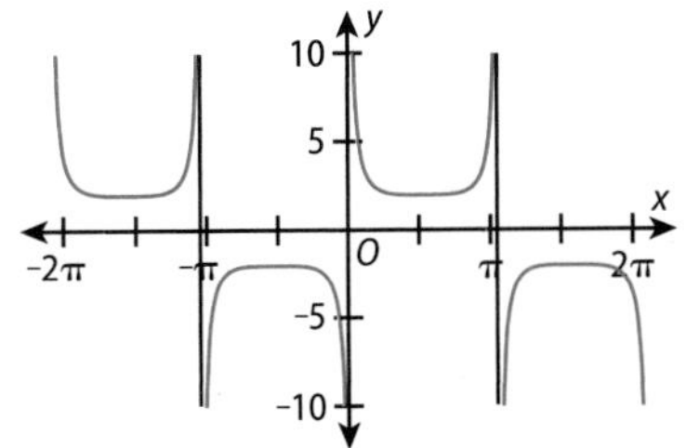

b. $h - m$

To graph $h - m$, note that $\sec x = \frac{1}{\cos x}$. Use a graphing calculator or computer software. The graph is shown below.

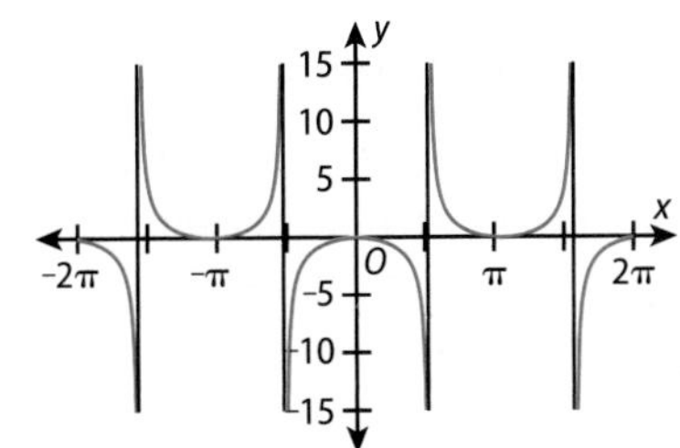

Watch Out

While the graphs resemble the graphs of $y = \csc x$ and $y = \sec x$, they are not equivalent.

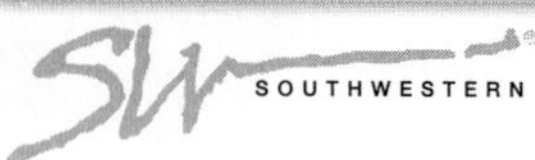

Graphing Products and Quotients of Functions

In some cases, it is possible to predict the behavior of a sum or difference of two functions. It is often very difficult to predict what results from multiplying two functions or dividing them. Let f and g be functions.

$$(fg)(x) = f(x)g(x) \qquad \left(\frac{f}{g}\right)(x) = \frac{f(x)}{g(x)},\ g(x) \neq 0$$

EXAMPLE 5

Let $f(x) = x + 2$ and $g(x) = 2x - 3$. Classify f, g, and fg.

Both f and g are linear functions.

$$f(x)g(x) = (x + 2)(2x - 3)$$
$$= 2x^2 + x - 6$$

The product function, fg, is a quadratic function.

EXAMPLE 6

Let $f(x) = \sin x$ and $g(x) = \csc x$.

a. Write an expression for fg.

$$(fg)(x) = f(x)g(x) = \sin x \frac{1}{\sin x} = 1$$

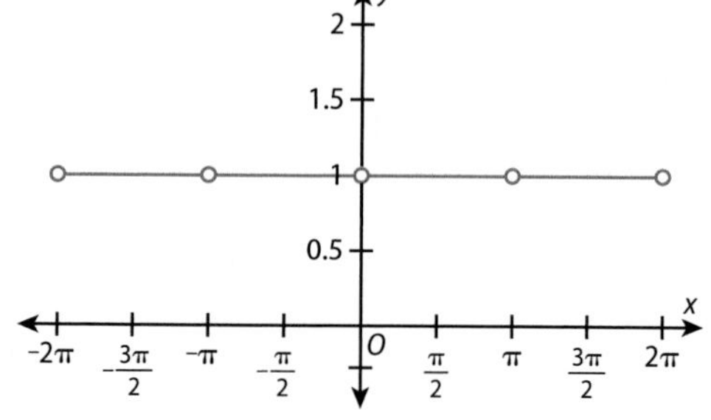

b. State any restrictions on the domain.

The product fg is defined for all real numbers except multiples of π.

c. What features might a graphing calculator display not show?

A calculator display probably will not show holes at $x = n\pi$, where n is an integer.

d. Graph fg on the interval $-2\pi \leq x \leq 2\pi$.

The graph is shown at the right above. Open circles indicate points where the function is not defined.

> **Watch Out !**
>
> Be careful about excluded values from the domain. In Examples 6 and 7, functions g and n have infinitely many excluded values. These excluded values play a role in the product functions.

EXAMPLE 7

Let $m(x) = \cos x$ and $n(x) = \sec x$. Compare the graph of mn with that of fg in Example 6.

$$(mn)(x) = m(x)n(x) = \cos x \frac{1}{\cos x} = 1$$

As in Example 6, the graph of mn is the horizontal line $y = 1$ with holes in it. However, the holes are not at the multiples of π. The holes occur where x is an integer multiple of $\frac{\pi}{2}$.

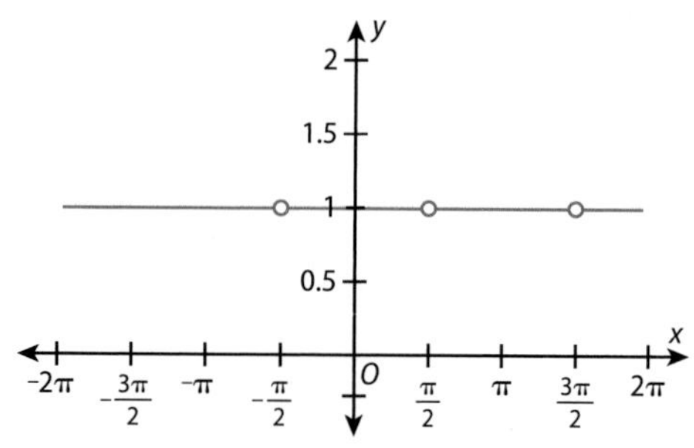

> **SEARCH**
>
> To see step-by-step videos of these problems, enter the page number into the SWadvantage.com Search Bar.

In many applications, a product of two functions may involve an algebraic function and a trigonometric function.

EXAMPLE 8

Let $f(x) = x$ and $g(x) = \sin x$.

Analyze fg for nonnegative values of x. Then graph fg over a suitable interval for x.

STEP 1 Look for bounding conditions.

$$-1 \le \sin x \le 1$$

$x \ge 0$ $$-1(x) \le x \sin x \le 1(x)$$

$$-x \le x \sin x \le x$$

If $x \ge 0$, the graph of $(fg)(x) = x \sin x$ is bounded by the graphs of $y = x$ and $y = -x$.

STEP 2 Examine the behavior of fg at values of x for which $\sin x = 1$ or $\sin x = -1$. Make a table.

x	$\frac{\pi}{2}$	$\frac{3\pi}{2}$	$\frac{5\pi}{2}$	$\frac{7\pi}{2}$
$(fg)(x)$	1.57	−4.71	7.85	−10.00

x	$\frac{9\pi}{2}$	$\frac{11\pi}{2}$	$\frac{13\pi}{2}$	$\frac{15\pi}{2}$
$(fg)(x)$	14.1	−17.28	20.42	−23.56

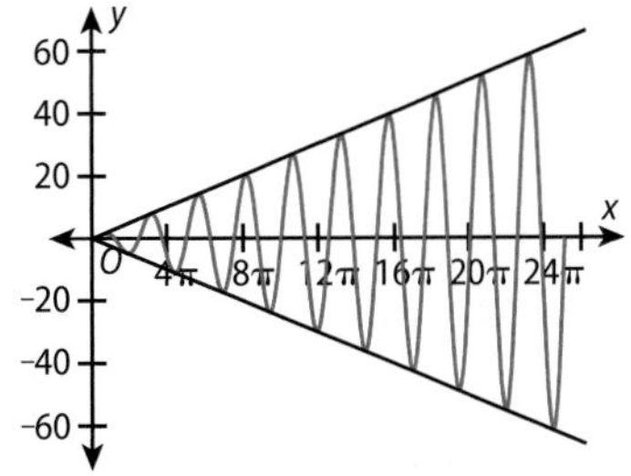

As x increases, the values of fg increase in absolute value. That is, the distances between high points and low points increase. The graph is shown at the right above. The interval for x is $0 \le x \le 24\pi$. The graph also shows the graphs of $y = x$ and $y = -x$ for nonnegative values of x.

Need More HELP

Function f causes the maximums and minimums to be greater and greater. Function g causes the product to fluctuate up and down. These factors lead to a graph that becomes taller and taller and yet exhibits a sine-like pattern.

Quotients of predictable functions can also produce unpredictable results. A rational function, for example, is the quotient of two polynomial functions. Polynomial functions are continuous. However, the quotient probably is not. As a simple example, let $f(x) = 1$ and $g(x) = x$. The quotient function $\left(\frac{f}{g}\right)(x) = \frac{1}{x}$ is a pair of branches that are not connected to one another. This function is one of the simplest rational functions, the reciprocal function.

EXAMPLE 9

Let $f(x) = \sin x$ and $g(x) = \cos x$. Analyze $\frac{f}{g}$. Then graph the quotient.

- Both $f(x) = \sin x$ and $g(x) = \cos x$ are continuous functions with period 2π.
- The denominator, $\cos x$, equals 0, when $x = \frac{\pi n}{2}$ and n is an odd integer.

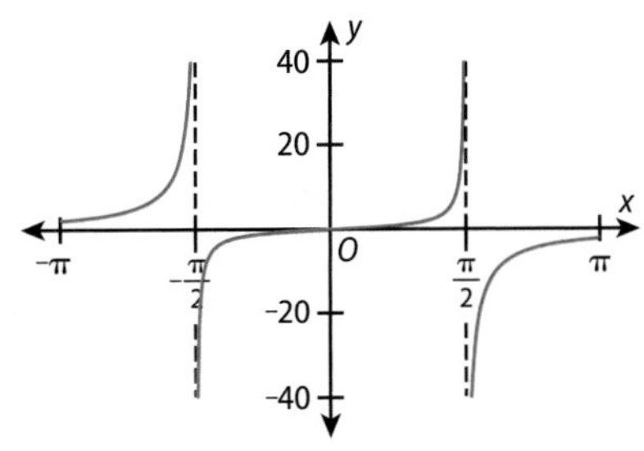

The graph is shown here and it is the graph of the tangent function. Notice that the graph of the quotient is not continuous.

Harmonic Motion

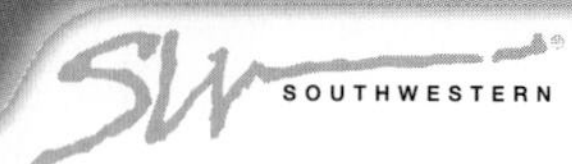

Exploring Simple Harmonic Motion

Many natural phenomena exhibit periodic motion. A pendulum clock is a common example, as shown by the diagram on the left below. The pendulum swings back and forth at regular time intervals. As a second example, a weight on a spring bobs up and down when pulled down from its resting position. This is illustrated at the right below. In each case, the motion is predictable. Of course, each of the situations is ideal. That is, other forces, such as resistance, are neglected.

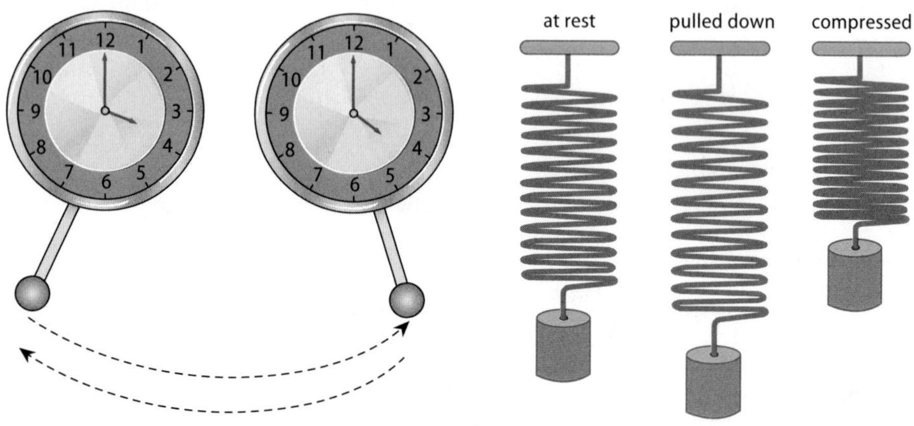

EXAMPLE 1

A small mass is suspended from a small spring. At time $t = 0$, the weight is pulled down 3 centimeters and then released. It takes 4 seconds for the weight to reach its maximum height above its equilibrium point and return to its original distance below the equilibrium point when it was released.

a. Draw a diagram to illustrate the height above the equilibrium point after 0 seconds, 1 second, 2 seconds, 3 seconds, and 4 seconds.

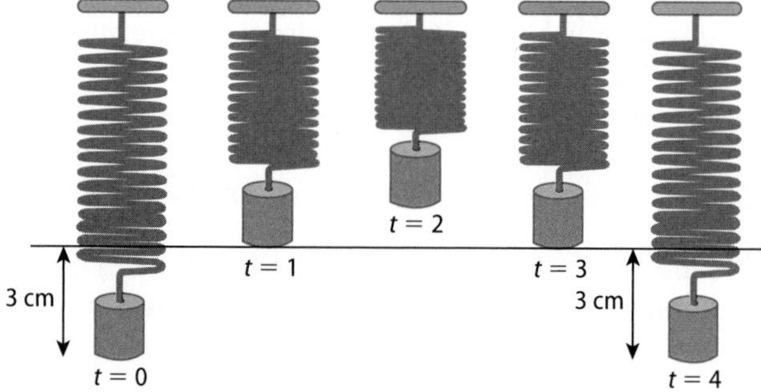

b. Write an equation using either the sine or the cosine function to represent the vertical displacement y of the mass as a function of elapsed time.

Consider a cosine function of the form $y = a\cos(bt)$, where a and b are real numbers. Consider an amplitude of 3 and period that is one fourth of 2π. Since the mass is 3 centimeters below the equilibrium point at $t = 0$, a will be a negative number.

$$y = -3\cos\left(\frac{\pi t}{2}\right)$$

c. Confirm the equation in Part (b) with a table of values.

t	0	1	2	3	4
y	-3	0	3	0	-3

Try It This Way

The period in Example 1 is 4. The period is calculated using the expression $\frac{2\pi}{b}$. In the equation $y = -3\cos\left(\frac{\pi t}{2}\right)$, $b = \frac{\pi}{2}$. The period equals $\frac{2\pi}{\frac{\pi}{2}} = 2\pi\left(\frac{2}{\pi}\right) = 4$.

Motion back and forth in a regular fashion can be represented by a trigonometric function. This diagram shows movement along $\overline{AB}$. Velocity is constant over time.

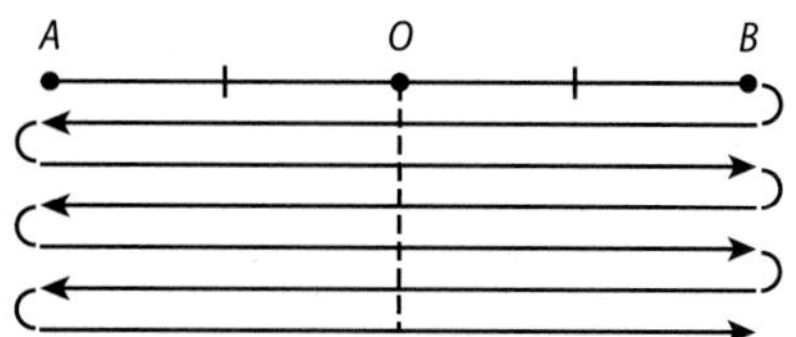

Need More HELP

The motion can be represented either by a sine or a cosine function. The choice of function is partly a matter of convenience and partly determined by the diagram.

EXAMPLE 2

Line segment *AB* is 16 centimeters long. A particle moves back and forth along $\overline{AB}$ starting from the point specified. Use a diagram to show the periodic motion of that point along $\overline{AB}$.

a. It takes 10 seconds to go from *A* to *B* and back to *A*.

The motion is shown at the left below.

b. It takes 12 seconds to go from *O* to *B* to *A* and back to *O*.

The motion is shown at the center below.

c. It takes 8 seconds to go from *B* to *A* and back to *B*.

The motion is shown at the right below.

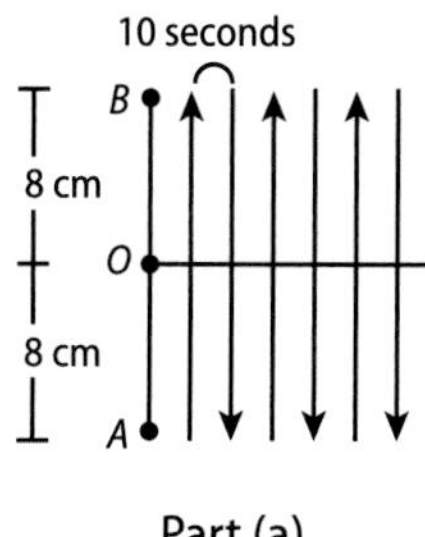

Part (a)

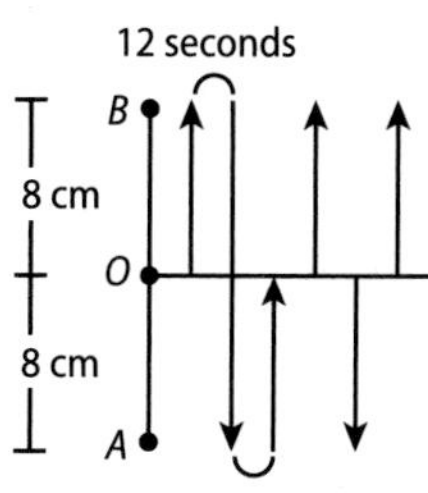

Part (b)

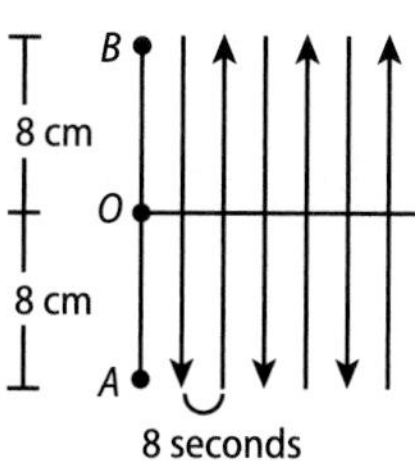

Part (c)

SEARCH

To see step-by-step videos of these problems, enter the page number into the SWadvantage.com Search Bar.

EXAMPLE 3

Write an equation for each motion. Let *t* represent time.

a. the motion in Part (a) in Example 2

Use a variation on the sine function. $y = -8\sin\frac{2\pi t}{10}$ $y = -8\sin\frac{\pi t}{5}$

b. the motion in Part (b) in Example 2

Use a variation on the sine function. $y = 8\sin\frac{2\pi t}{12}$ $y = 8\sin\frac{\pi t}{6}$

c. the motion in Part (c) in Example 2

Use a variation on the cosine function. $y = 8\cos\frac{2\pi t}{8}$ $y = 8\cos\frac{\pi t}{4}$

GOT TO KNOW!

Simple Harmonic Motion

If a particle moves in simple harmonic motion, then its displacement from a center point can be represented by $y = a\sin(bt)$ or $y = a\cos(bt)$, where a and b depend on the initial conditions.

Exploring Harmonic Motion with Damping

A function f is an increasing function if the following condition is met.

If $x_1 < x_2$ on an interval, then $f(x_1) < f(x_2)$.

A function f is a decreasing function if this condition is met.

If $x_1 < x_2$ on an interval, then $f(x_1) > f(x_2)$.

Need More HELP

Think of increasing and decreasing functions in simple terms. A linear function is increasing if its slope is positive. A linear function is decreasing if its slope is negative.

An exponential function $y = b^x$ is an increasing function if $b > 1$. An exponential function $y = b^x$ is decreasing if $0 < b < 1$.

EXAMPLE 4

Describe each function as increasing or decreasing.

a. $y = 2^x$

METHOD 1

Use a table of values.
As x increases, y increases.
The function is an increasing function.

x	1	5	10	20	30
y	2	32	1,024	1,048,576	1,073,741,824

METHOD 2

Use a graph.

The graph shows a curve that slopes up to the right as you read the x-axis from left to right. So, $y = 2^x$ is an increasing function.

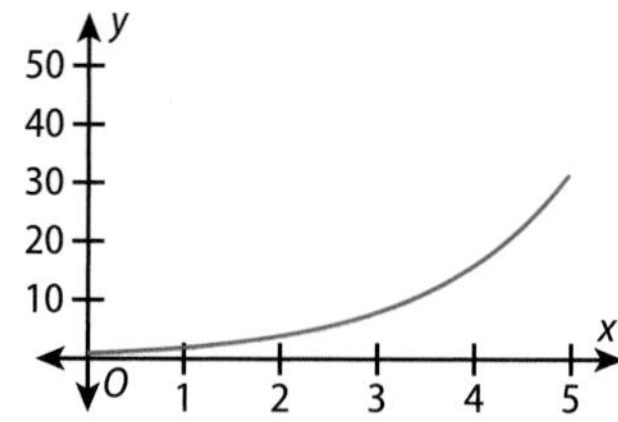

b. $y = 2^{-x}$

METHOD 1

Use a table of values.
As x increases, y decreases.
The function is a decreasing function.

x	1	5	10	20	30
y	$\frac{1}{2}$	$\frac{1}{32}$	$\frac{1}{1,024}$	$\frac{1}{1,048,576}$	$\frac{1}{1,073,741,824}$

METHOD 2

Use a graph.

The graph shows a curve that slopes down to the right as you read the x-axis from left to right. So, $y = 2^{-x}$ is a decreasing function.

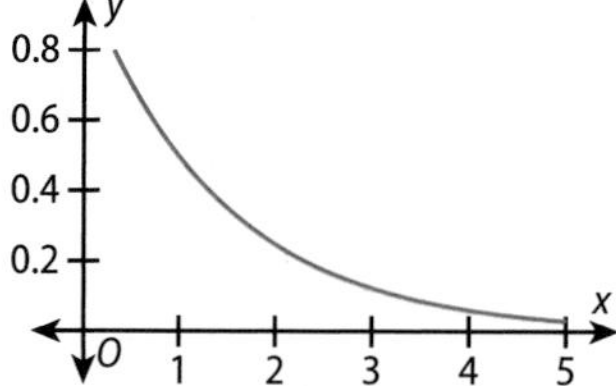

Watch Out!

The function $y = 2^{-x}$ is a decreasing function even though the base appears to be 2. Recall that $2^{-x} = \left(\frac{1}{2}\right)^x$. Therefore, $y = 2^{-x}$ is really $y = 0.5^x$.

A mass on a spring does not bob up and down achieving its least and greatest distances from the equilibrium point indefinitely. Forces at work retard or damp displacement.

The diagram illustrates that over time, the mass on a spring will come to rest. Forces acting on the mass will eventually stop its upward and downward displacement from the equilibrium point.

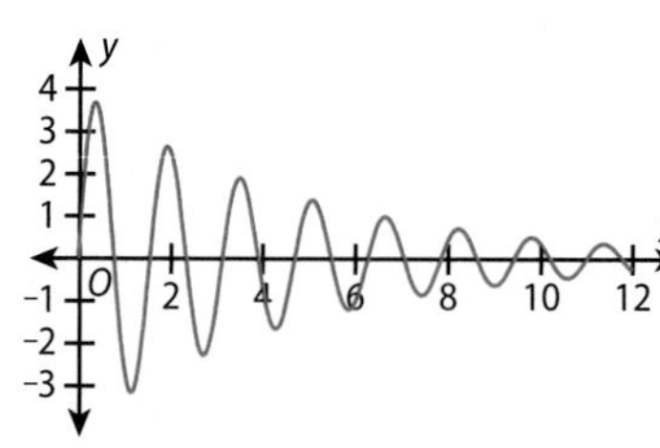

A more realistic model for the motion of a mass on a spring involves an exponential function that shows decay and a trigonometric function.

The function $y = e^{-x}$ represents the natural exponential decay function. This function coupled with the functions $y = \sin x$ or $y = \cos x$ is a natural choice for modeling the slow decline in displacement of a mass on a spring. An equation of the form shown below can be used to model many mass and spring problems.

$$y = Ce^{-at}\sin(bt + c)$$

EXAMPLE 5

Use a graphing calculator to graph each equation in which a mass on a spring tends to come to rest. Use the given range for *t*.

a. $\mathbf{y = 10e^{-0.1t}\sin(4t)}$ **over the interval** $\mathbf{0 \le t \le 20}$

The graphs of $y_1, y_2 = 10e^{-0.1t}$, and $y_3 = -10e^{-0.1t}$ are shown at the left below.

b. $\mathbf{y = 10e^{-0.2t}\sin(4t)}$ **over the interval** $\mathbf{0 \le t \le 20}$

The graphs of $y_1, y_2 = 10e^{-0.2t}$, and $y_3 = -10e^{-0.2t}$ are shown at the center below.

c. $\mathbf{y = 10e^{-0.4t}\sin(4t)}$ **over the interval** $\mathbf{0 \le t \le 20}$

The graphs of $y_1, y_2 = 10e^{-0.4t}$, and $y_3 = -10e^{-0.4t}$ are shown at the right below.

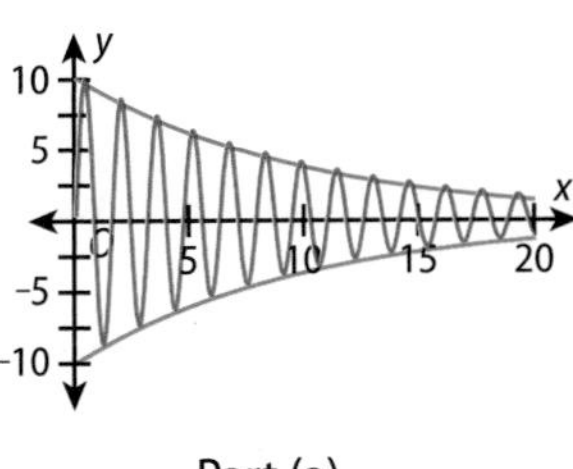

Part (a)

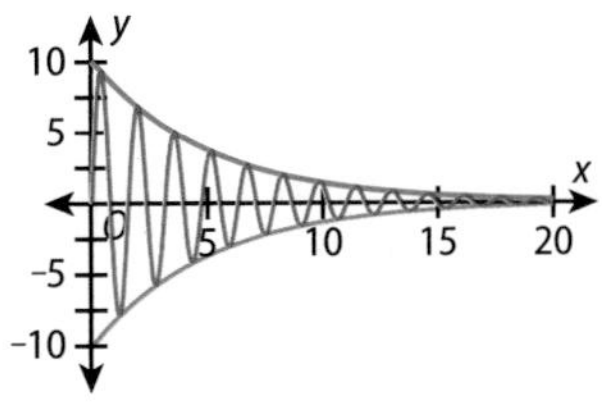

Part (b)

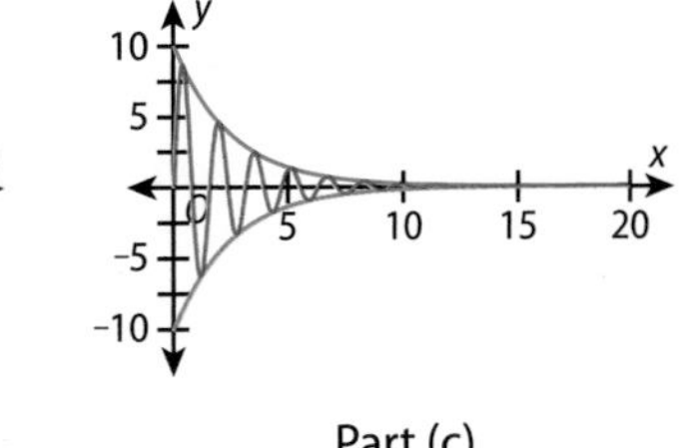

Part (c)

SEARCH

To see step-by-step videos of these problems, enter the page number into the SWadvantage.com Search Bar.

The diagrams above suggest that the speed at which a mass on a spring comes to rest depends in great part on the value of a in $y = Ce^{-at}\sin(bt + c)$, given that all other parameters are constant.

EXAMPLE 6

Compare the damping effect, in informal terms, of $\mathbf{a = 0.05}$ **in** $\mathbf{y = 10e^{-at}\sin(4t)}$ **as compared to that of** $\mathbf{a = 0.1}$ **in the same equation.**

Given the graphs in Example 5, one would expect the damping effect for $a = 0.05$ to be less than that in the case where $a = 0.1$. That is, the reduction in the peaks and valleys in the graph for $a = 0.05$ would be less than those in the case where $a = 0.1$. The graph of $y = 10e^{-0.05t}\sin(4t)$ is shown at the right.

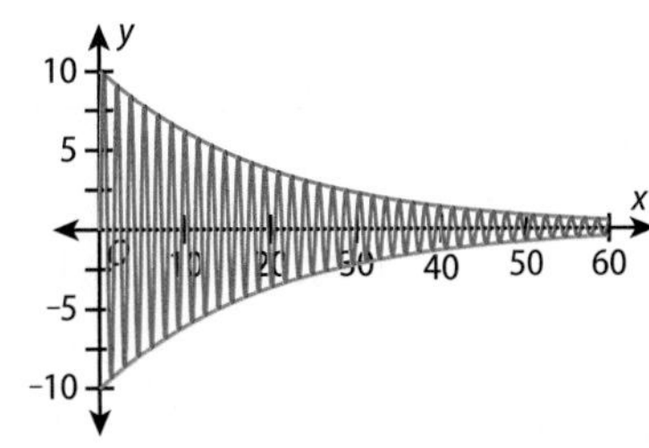

The graph illustrates that if a is reduced, it will take longer for the displacement to tend to 0.

Modeling with Trigonometric Functions

Modeling Ferris Wheel Motion

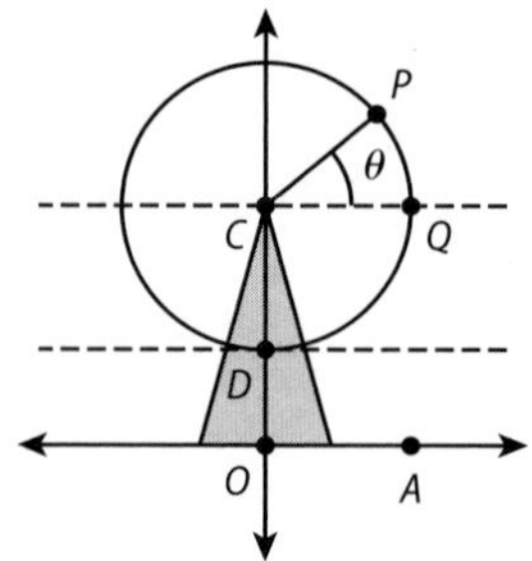

An amusement park features a Ferris wheel ride. The diagram at the right shows a Ferris wheel and point P, a seat that revolves in the ride.

The radius of the wheel is CP.

The distance between the entry platform, $\overline{OA}$, and the seat at the start of the ride is DO.

The seat revolves around the circle centered at C in a counterclockwise fashion. The diagram shows θ, the angle $\overline{CP}$ makes with the horizontal. **Use this diagram for Examples 1–4.**

EXAMPLE 1

Let $\overleftrightarrow{OA}$ be the x-axis in a rectangular coordinate system. Let $\overleftrightarrow{CO}$ be the y-axis in that system. Let O be the origin. Write the coordinates of point $P(x, y)$.

STEP 1 Suppose that C is the center of the rectangular coordinate system. Then:

$$P'(x, y) = P'(CP\cos\theta, CP\sin\theta)$$

STEP 2 Use a translation to write the coordinates of P given that O is the origin of the coordinate system.

$$P(x, y) = P(CP\cos\theta, DO + CP\sin\theta)$$

SEARCH

To see step-by-step videos of these problems, enter the page number into the SWadvantage.com Search Bar.

EXAMPLE 2

The Ferris wheel makes one complete revolution in 2 minutes. The radius of the Ferris wheel is 30 feet. Write θ as a function of time t in minutes.

Solve a proportion. $\quad \dfrac{\text{time}}{\text{arc length}} \quad \dfrac{t}{2} = \dfrac{\theta}{2\pi}$

Therefore, $\theta = \pi t$.

EXAMPLE 3

Riders board the Ferris wheel seats 3 feet above the platform. That is, $DO = 3$. Write the coordinates of P as a function of time.

From Example 1, $P(x, y) = P(CP\cos\theta, DO + CP\sin\theta)$.
From Example 2, $\theta = \pi t$.
In addition, $CP = 30$ and $DO = 3$.

Therefore, $P(x, y) = P(30\cos(\pi t), 3 + 30\sin(\pi t))$.

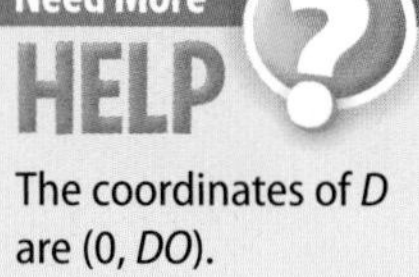

The coordinates of D are $(0, DO)$.

EXAMPLE 4

How high above $\overleftrightarrow{OA}$ will a rider be after 30 seconds on the Ferris wheel ride?

Let $t = 0.5$ minutes $\quad 3 + 30\sin(\pi t) \quad 3 + 30\sin(\pi(0.5)) = 33$ feet

After 30 seconds, a rider will be at the top of the wheel, or 33 feet above the entry platform.

Modeling Double Circular Motion

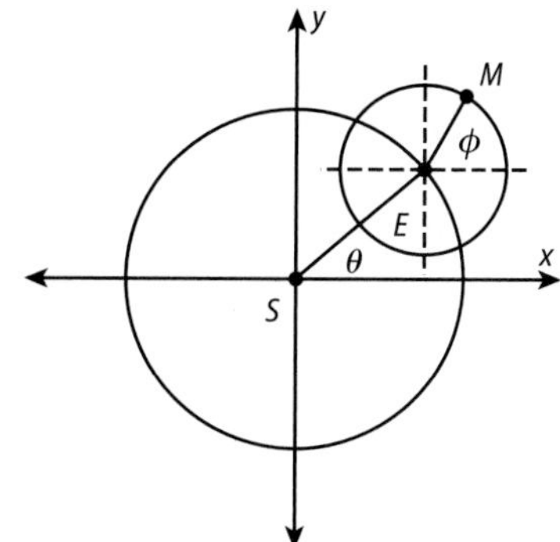

The diagram at the right shows the Moon, M, orbiting Earth, E, while Earth orbits the sun, S. The position of Earth forms the angle θ with the x-axis, and the position of the Moon forms the angle ϕ with the x-axis. The diagram shows a body revolving around a point that, in turn, revolves around a fixed point.

Assume that the orbit of Earth around the sun is a circle whose radius is 93,000,000 miles.

Assume that the orbit of the moon around Earth is a circle whose radius is 240,000 miles.

EXAMPLE 5

a. Write coordinates for the orbit of Earth, E, around the sun, S.

Let S be the origin of a rectangular coordinate system. Let $E(x, y)$ represent the coordinates of Earth.

$SE = 9.3 \times 10^7$ $\quad$ $E(9.3 \times 10^7 \cos\theta, 9.3 \times 10^7 \sin\theta)$

b. Write coordinates for the orbit of the moon, M, around Earth, E.

Suppose that E is the origin of a rectangular coordinate system. Let $M(x', y')$ represent the coordinates of the moon.

$ME = 2.4 \times 10^5$ $\quad$ $M(2.4 \times 10^5 \cos\phi, 2.4 \times 10^5 \sin\phi)$

c. Write coordinates for the orbit of the moon, M, around the sun, S.

$M(x + x', y + y')$

Use a translation. $\quad$ $M(9.3 \times 10^7 \cos\theta + 2.4 \times 10^5 \cos\phi, 9.3 \times 10^7 \sin\theta + 2.4 \times 10^5 \sin\phi)$

For a review of scientific notation, see p. 588.

EXAMPLE 6

An amusement park ride is illustrated at the right. The disk at S with radius 25 feet revolves at 30 revolutions per minute. The disk at E with radius 5 feet revolves at 20 revolutions per minute. At the start of the ride both disks begin spinning counterclockwise.

Model the motion of M about point S as a function of time t in minutes.

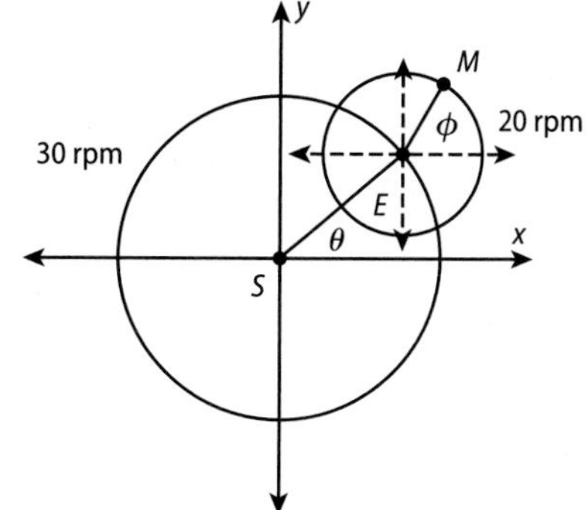

STEP 1 Use the model of planetary motion as a guide.

Identify the radii and write functions for θ and ϕ in terms of time t.

$SE = 25$ and $EM = 5$

$\theta = \frac{2\pi t}{30}$ and $\phi = \frac{2\pi t}{20}$

STEP 2 Write the model.

$$M\left(25\cos\left(\frac{\pi t}{15}\right) + 5\cos\left(\frac{\pi t}{10}\right), 25\sin\left(\frac{\pi t}{15}\right) + 5\sin\left(\frac{\pi t}{10}\right)\right)$$

Watch Out !

The number of revolutions per minute is not the period of the model.

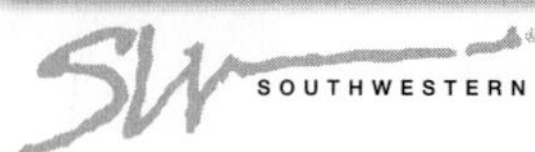

Modeling Daylight Hours

SEARCH

To see step-by-step videos of these problems, enter the page number into the SWadvantage.com Search Bar.

Everyone knows that when spring comes the number of daylight hours increases. When summer arrives, the number of daylight hours achieves its maximum. As fall arrives, the number of daylight hours decreases. Then in winter, the days get shorter and the nights get longer. The diagram below illustrates this somewhat periodic phenomenon. Note that the diagram is a simplified version of actuality.

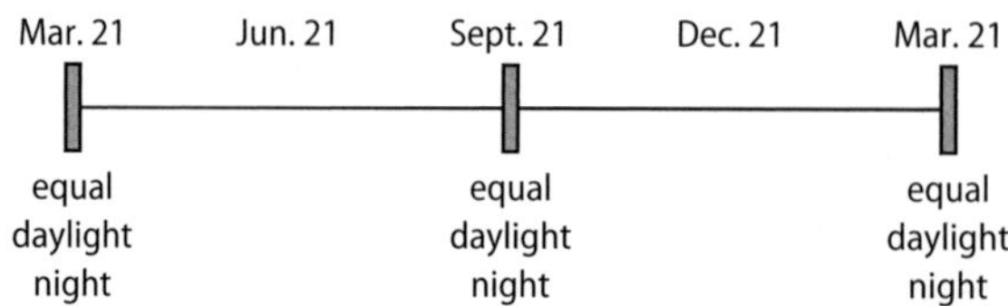

A sine curve can be used to model the number of hours of daylight in a day for a particular location. Of course, data for the location will depend on the location's position on Earth. Regardless of location, one year is 365 days. The needed model for $h(t)$ in terms of t, the number of days after January 1, is shown at the right.

$$h(t) = a\sin\left(\frac{2\pi}{365}t + b\right) + c$$

EXAMPLE 7

In one location, the number of daylight hours reaches its maximum on June 21. That number is 15 hours. The number of daylight hours reaches its minimum on December 21. That number is 10 hours.

Write a model for the number $h(t)$ of daylight hours for this location as a function of t.

STEP 1 Determine a, the amplitude of the function.

$a = \frac{\text{max} - \text{min}}{2}$ $\qquad a = \frac{15 - 10}{2} = 2.5$ $\qquad a = 2.5$

STEP 2 Determine c.

Average the maximum and minimum. $\qquad \frac{15 + 10}{2} = 12.5$ $\qquad c = 12.5$

STEP 3 Write the model developed so far.

$$h(t) = 2.5\sin\left(\frac{2\pi}{365}t + b\right) + 12.5$$

STEP 4 Use the fact that June 21st is the 171st day of the year to determine the value of b.

Obtain data. $\qquad h(171) = 15$ and $t = 171$

Substitute. $\qquad 15 = 2.5\sin\left(\frac{2\pi}{365}(171) + b\right) + 12.5$

Simplify. $\qquad \sin\left(\frac{2\pi}{365}(171) + b\right) = \frac{15 - 12.5}{2.5}$

Isolate b and use a calculator. $\qquad \sin(2.9 + b) = 1$

$$b = \sin^{-1}(1) - 2.9$$

$$b \approx -1.33$$

STEP 5 Write the model. $\qquad h(t) = 2.5\sin\left(\frac{2\pi}{365}t - 1.33\right) + 12.5$

Need More HELP

The parameters a and c both depend on the maximum and minimum hours of daylight. The value of b is found by using a particular data point, here (171, 15).

Watch Out!

The value of b is not found by solving $2.9 + b = 1$. To find it, use a calculator and the inverse of the sine. Be sure to set the calculator in radian mode.

Modeling Tidal Behavior

The orbit of the moon around Earth affects the tides. People who enjoy going to the beach know the difference between high and low tide. During high tide, there is less beach to enjoy. During low tide, more of the beach is available. The diagram below shows the difference between high tide and low tide.

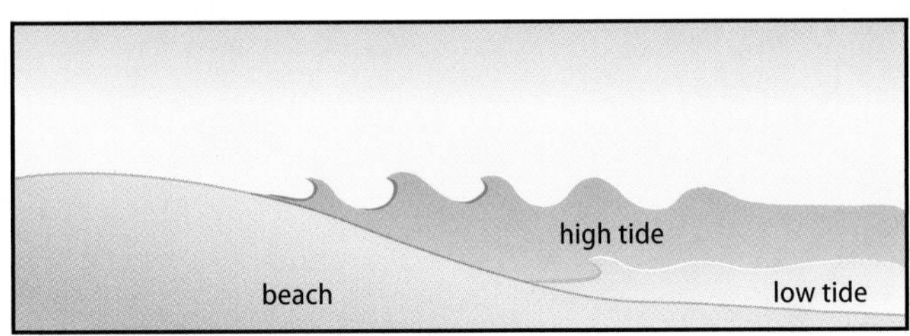

Because of the phases of the moon, tidal behavior is somewhat periodic. Therefore, a trigonometric function can be used to model its behavior. These equations may be candidates for suitable models.

$$w(t) = a \sin(bt + c) + d \qquad w(t) = a \cos(bt + c) + d$$

EXAMPLE 8

A student determined that high tide at a shore near his home occurred at midnight on February 10th. He measured the water level at that time to be 10 feet. Later, he measured the water level at low tide and found it to be 1 foot. At this shore, the time difference between successive high tides is 12 hours.

Determine a model using either a sine or cosine function to model the water depth, $w(t)$, in feet as a function of time t, hours after midnight.

STEP 1 Since maximum water height is achieved at midnight, when $t = 0$, a cosine function is a suitable choice. This implies that $c = 0$.

$w(t) = a\cos(bt) + d$

STEP 2 Determine a, the amplitude of the function.

$a = \frac{\max - \min}{2}$ $\qquad a = \frac{10 - 1}{2} = 4.5$ $\qquad a = 4.5$

STEP 3 Determine d.

Average the maximum and minimum. $\qquad \frac{10 + 1}{2} = 5.5$ $\qquad d = 5.5$

STEP 4 Write the model developed so far.

$w(t) = 4.5\cos(bt) + 5.5$

STEP 5 Determine b.

two high tides in one day $\qquad b = \frac{2\pi}{12} = \frac{\pi}{6}$

STEP 6 Write a model.

$w(t) = 4.5\cos\left(\frac{\pi}{6}t\right) + 5.5$

When $t = 0, 6, 12, 18$, and 24, $w(t) =$ 10 feet, 1 foot, 10 feet, 1 foot, and 10 feet.

Need More HELP

Both sine and cosine can be used as models. However, a basic knowledge of the graph of the cosine function suggests that the cosine function is the more appropriate choice. This choice also makes the value of $c = 0$.

Trigonometric Identities

What Came Before?

- Trigonometric ratios
- Geometric proofs

What's This About?

- Rewriting trigonometric ratios
- Verifying Identities
- Using sum, difference, half-angle and double-angle identities

Practical Apps

- Identities are used to determine the intensity of light coming through a polarized lens.
- Physicists use identities to simplify projectile motion calculations.

just for FUN!

Loan agent to the trig function couple:

Sine, please sign here ____. And cosine, you can cosign here ____.

CONTENTS UPLOAD DOWNLOAD

Trigonometry

You can find more practice problems online by visiting:
www.SWadvantage.com

Reciprocal and Quotient Identities

Trigonometric identities are trigonometric equations involving trigonometric functions that are true for all occurring values of the variables. See the *Got To Know!* box for the reciprocal and quotient identities. These identities can be proved using the definition of the functions.

You can use these identities to simplify complicated expressions that are difficult to graph or calculate.

SEARCH

To see step-by-step videos of these problems, enter the page number into the SWadvantage.com Search Bar.

EXAMPLE 1

Simplify $\sin\theta\sec\theta$.

Use a reciprocal identity. Substitute $\sec\theta$ with $\frac{1}{\cos\theta}$. $\quad \sin\theta\sec\theta = \sin\theta \cdot \frac{1}{\cos\theta}$

Multiply. $\quad = \frac{\sin\theta}{\cos\theta}$

Use a quotient identity. Substitute $\frac{\sin\theta}{\cos\theta}$ with $\tan\theta$. $\quad = \tan\theta$

Therefore, $\sin\theta\sec\theta = \tan\theta$.

You can also derive identities from the fundamental identities. Prove identities by rewriting one or both sides of the equation to make both sides of the equation equal.

EXAMPLE 2

Prove $\sin\theta\csc\theta = 1$.

Write the original identity. $\quad \sin\theta\csc\theta = 1$

Substitute using the reciprocal identity $\sin\theta = \frac{1}{\csc\theta}$. $\quad \left(\frac{1}{\csc\theta}\right)\csc\theta = 1$

Simplify. $\quad 1 = 1$

Because the right side of the identity simplifies to equal the left side, then the identity $\sin\theta\csc\theta = 1$ is true.

Thus, the three reciprocal identities can be written as $\sin\theta \cdot \csc\theta = 1$, $\cos\theta \cdot \sec\theta = 1$, and $\tan\theta \cdot \cot\theta = 1$.

GOT TO KNOW!

Reciprocal Identities

$\sin\theta = \frac{1}{\csc\theta}$ $\quad \cos\theta = \frac{1}{\sec\theta}$ $\quad \tan\theta = \frac{1}{\cot\theta}$

$\csc\theta = \frac{1}{\sin\theta}$ $\quad \sec\theta = \frac{1}{\cos\theta}$ $\quad \cot\theta = \frac{1}{\tan\theta}$

Quotient Identities

$\tan\theta = \frac{\sin\theta}{\cos\theta}$ $\quad \cot\theta = \frac{\cos\theta}{\sin\theta}$

Negative Identities

You can find the trigonometric values of negative angles if you know the relationship between the trigonometric functions of negative angles and the trigonometric functions of positive angles.

Notice that $\sin(-240°) = \frac{\sqrt{3}}{2}$ and

$-\sin(240°) = -\left(-\frac{\sqrt{3}}{2}\right) = \frac{\sqrt{3}}{2}$.

In general, $\sin(-\theta) = -\sin\theta$.

This is one of the negative identities. See the *Got To Know!* box for the six negative identities. You can use these identities to find the trigonometric values of negative angles.

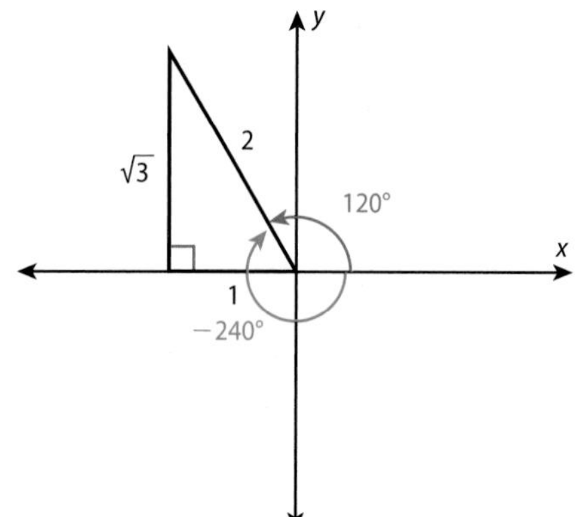

GOT TO KNOW!

Negative Identities

$\sin(-\theta) = -\sin\theta$

$\cos(-\theta) = \cos\theta$

$\tan(-\theta) = -\tan\theta$

$\csc(-\theta) = -\csc\theta$

$\sec(-\theta) = \sec\theta$

$\cot(-\theta) = -\cot\theta$

EXAMPLE 3

If $\sin(-\theta) = -\frac{2}{3}$ and $\tan\theta = -\frac{2\sqrt{5}}{5}$, find the values of the other trigonometric functions of θ.

Use the given equation and $-\sin\theta = \sin(-\theta)$.	If $\sin(-\theta) = -\frac{2}{3}$, then $-\sin\theta = -\frac{2}{3}$
Multiply both sides by −1.	$\sin\theta = -\left(-\frac{2}{3}\right) = \frac{2}{3}$, so $\sin\theta = \frac{2}{3}$
Use a reciprocal identity.	$\csc\theta = \frac{1}{\sin\theta} = \frac{1}{\frac{2}{3}} = \frac{3}{2}$, so $\csc\theta = \frac{3}{2}$
Use a reciprocal identity.	$\cot\theta = \frac{1}{\tan\theta} = \frac{1}{-\frac{2\sqrt{5}}{5}} = -\frac{\sqrt{5}}{2}$, so $\cot\theta = -\frac{\sqrt{5}}{2}$
Start with a quotient identity.	$\tan\theta = \frac{\sin\theta}{\cos\theta}$
Multiply both sides by $\cos\theta$.	$\cos\theta \cdot \tan\theta = \sin\theta$
Divide both sides by $\tan\theta$.	$\cos\theta = \frac{\sin\theta}{\tan\theta}$
Substitute in known values.	$\frac{\sin\theta}{\tan\theta} = \frac{\frac{2}{3}}{-\frac{2\sqrt{5}}{5}} = -\frac{\sqrt{5}}{3}$, so $\cos\theta = -\frac{\sqrt{5}}{3}$
Use a reciprocal identity.	$\sec\theta = \frac{1}{\cos\theta} = -\frac{3}{\sqrt{5}} = -\frac{3\sqrt{5}}{5}$, so $\sec\theta = -\frac{3\sqrt{5}}{5}$

A value was found for each of the six trigonometric functions using the two given functions and reciprocal, quotient, and negative identities.

Need More HELP

The reciprocal of $-\frac{2\sqrt{5}}{5}$ is $-\frac{5}{2\sqrt{5}}$.

Rationalize the denominator.

$-\frac{5}{2\sqrt{5}} \cdot \frac{\sqrt{5}}{\sqrt{5}} = -\frac{5\sqrt{5}}{10}$

Simplify. $-\frac{\sqrt{5}}{2}$

Remember the unit circle.

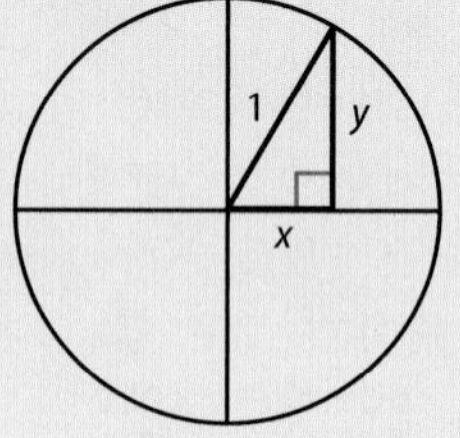

Pythagorean Identity

By applying the Pythagorean theorem to the reference triangle in the unit circle formed by x, y, and r where r is 1, you can derive the following identity.

$$x^2 + y^2 = r^2$$

$$x^2 + y^2 = 1$$

$$\cos^2\theta + \sin^2\theta = 1$$

Not surprisingly, this is called the **Pythagorean identity**. There are two other forms of this identity which are derived in the following two examples.

EXAMPLE 4

Derive the identity $\tan^2\theta + 1 = \sec^2\theta$.

Write the Pythagorean identity.	$\cos^2\theta + \sin^2\theta = 1$
Divide each term by $\cos^2\theta$.	$\frac{\cos^2\theta}{\cos^2\theta} + \frac{\sin^2\theta}{\cos^2\theta} = \frac{1}{\cos^2\theta}$
Simplify using equivalent identities.	$1 + \tan^2\theta = \sec^2\theta$
Use the commutative property.	$\tan^2\theta + 1 = \sec^2\theta$

SEARCH

To see step-by-step videos of these problems, enter the page number into the SWadvantage.com Search Bar.

EXAMPLE 5

Derive the identity $\cot^2\theta + 1 = \csc^2\theta$.

Write the Pythagorean identity.	$\cos^2\theta + \sin^2\theta = 1$
Divide each term by $\sin^2\theta$.	$\frac{\cos^2\theta}{\sin^2\theta} + \frac{\sin^2\theta}{\sin^2\theta} = \frac{1}{\sin^2\theta}$
Simplify using equivalent identities.	$\cot^2\theta + 1 = \csc^2\theta$

You can use the rules of algebra to write these identities in a number of different ways.

EXAMPLE 6

Show that $\sin^2\theta = 1 - \cos^2\theta$.

Use a Pythagorean identity.	$\sin^2\theta + \cos^2\theta = 1$
Subtract $\cos^2\theta$ from both sides.	$\sin^2\theta + \cos^2\theta - \cos^2\theta = 1 - \cos^2\theta$
Simplify.	$\sin^2\theta = 1 - \cos^2\theta$

Pythagorean Identities

$\cos^2\theta + \sin^2\theta = 1$

$\tan^2\theta + 1 = \sec^2\theta$

$\cot^2\theta + 1 = \csc^2\theta$

The fundamental identities may be used to simplify trigonometric expressions and to convert expressions into forms that can be evaluated efficiently. You can write the same expression in different ways by using factoring, common denominators, and the same simplifying techniques used to simplify algebraic expressions.

EXAMPLE 7

Simplify $\frac{\sin^2\theta}{\sec^2\theta - 1}$.

Substitute $\sec^2\theta$ with a Pythagorean identity. $\frac{\sin^2\theta}{\sec^2\theta - 1} = \frac{\sin^2\theta}{(\tan^2\theta + 1) - 1}$

Simplify. $= \frac{\sin^2\theta}{\tan^2\theta}$

Substitute $\frac{\sin^2\theta}{\cos^2\theta}$ for $\tan^2\theta$. $= \frac{\sin^2\theta}{\frac{\sin^2\theta}{\cos^2\theta}}$

Divide. $= \cos^2\theta$

Therefore, $\frac{\sin^2\theta}{\sec^2\theta - 1} = \cos^2\theta$.

Watch Out!

Always make sure that you are substituting using equivalent expressions when simplifying or proving trigonometric identities.

Pythagorean identities are sometimes used in radical form, such as $\csc\theta = \pm\sqrt{1 + \cot^2\theta}$. The sign of the radical will depend on the quadrant in which θ is located.

EXAMPLE 8

Use the Pythagorean identities to find $\csc\theta$ if $\tan\theta = -5$ and $\sin\theta > 0$.

Uses a Pythagorean identity. $\csc^2\theta = 1 + \cot^2\theta$

Take the square root of both sides of the equation. $\csc\theta = \pm\sqrt{1 + \cot^2\theta}$

Use the definition of cotangent to find a value for $\cot\theta$. $\cot\theta = \frac{1}{\tan\theta} = \frac{1}{-5}$

Substitute in the given value. $= \pm\sqrt{1 + \left(\frac{1}{-5}\right)^2}$

Simplify. $= \pm\sqrt{\frac{26}{25}}$

Since $\tan\theta < 0$ and $\sin\theta > 0$, θ is in Quadrant II. Cosecant is positive in Quadrant II.

Therefore, $\csc\theta = \frac{\sqrt{26}}{5}$.

Pythagorean Identities in Radical Form

$\sin\theta = \pm\sqrt{1 - \cos^2\theta}$ $\sec\theta = \pm\sqrt{1 + \tan^2\theta}$ $\csc\theta = \pm\sqrt{1 + \cot^2\theta}$

Complementary Cofunctions

Remember that two angles are *complementary* when the sum of their measures is 90°.

Recall that in a right triangle, where C is the right angle, angle A + angle $B = 90°$. The figure on the right shows that $\sin A = \cos B$. Since $B = 90° - A$, then $\sin A = \cos(90° - A)$. The sin and cosine functions are cofunctions.

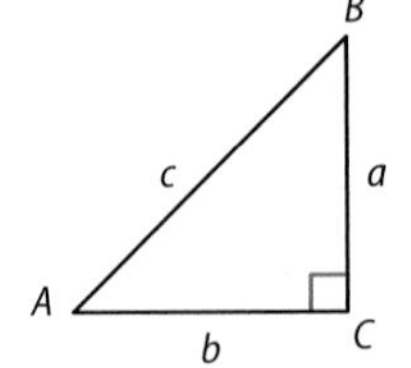

Since $\sin A = \frac{a}{c}$ and $\cos B = \frac{a}{c}$,
$\sin A = \cos B$.

The value of any defined trigonometric function of an acute angle is equal to the value of the cofunction of its complement.

For example, $\sin 30° = \cos 60° = \frac{1}{2}$.

The six trigonometric functions form three pairs of cofunctions: sine and cosine, tangent and cotangent, secant and cosecant.

You can use the cofunction identities to simplify trigonometric expressions.

SEARCH

To see step-by-step videos of these problems, enter the page number into the SWadvantage.com Search Bar.

EXAMPLE 9

Simplify the following expressions.

a. $\dfrac{\sin(90° - \theta)}{\cos(90° - \theta)}$

Use a cofunction identity. $\dfrac{\sin(90° - \theta)}{\cos(90° - \theta)} = \dfrac{\cos\theta}{\sin\theta}$

Use a quotient identity. $= \cot\theta$

Therefore, $\dfrac{\sin(90° - \theta)}{\cos(90° - \theta)} = \cot\theta$.

b. $\dfrac{\cos^2(90° - \theta)}{\cos\theta}$

Use a cofunction identity. $\dfrac{\cos^2(90° - \theta)}{\cos\theta} = \dfrac{\sin^2\theta}{\cos\theta}$

$= \dfrac{\sin\theta\sin\theta}{\cos\theta}$

Use a quotient identity. $= \sin\theta\tan\theta$

Therefore, $\dfrac{\cos^2(90° - \theta)}{\cos\theta} = \sin\theta\tan\theta$.

GOT TO KNOW!

Cofunction Identities

$\sin\theta = \cos(90° - \theta)$ $\tan\theta = \cot(90° - \theta)$ $\sec\theta = \csc(90° - \theta)$

$\cos\theta = \sin(90° - \theta)$ $\cot\theta = \tan(90° - \theta)$ $\csc\theta = \sec(90° - \theta)$

These fundamental identities are used to simplify trigonometric expressions, to find the value of trigonometric functions, to write expressions in terms of other trigonometric functions, and to verify identities. Sometimes you will use algebraic factoring.

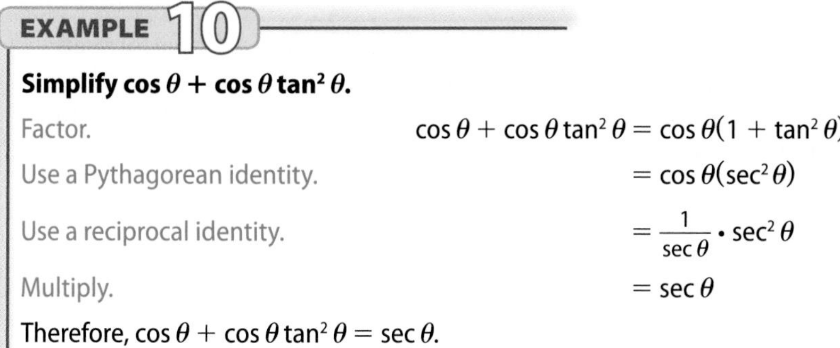

EXAMPLE 10

Simplify $\cos\theta + \cos\theta\tan^2\theta$.

Factor.	$\cos\theta + \cos\theta\tan^2\theta = \cos\theta(1 + \tan^2\theta)$
Use a Pythagorean identity.	$= \cos\theta(\sec^2\theta)$
Use a reciprocal identity.	$= \frac{1}{\sec\theta} \cdot \sec^2\theta$
Multiply.	$= \sec\theta$

Therefore, $\cos\theta + \cos\theta\tan^2\theta = \sec\theta$.

Sometimes you will operate on fractions.

EXAMPLE 11

Add $\frac{\cos\theta}{1 + \sin\theta} + \frac{1 + \sin\theta}{\cos\theta}$.

Find a common denominator.	$\frac{\cos\theta}{1 + \sin\theta} + \frac{1 + \sin\theta}{\cos\theta} = \frac{\cos\theta}{1 + \sin\theta} \cdot \frac{\cos\theta}{\cos\theta} + \frac{1 + \sin\theta}{\cos\theta} \cdot \frac{1 + \sin\theta}{1 + \sin\theta}$
Multiply each of the numerators. Keep the denominator in factored form.	$= \frac{\cos^2\theta}{(1 + \sin\theta)\cos\theta} + \frac{1 + 2\sin\theta + \sin^2\theta}{\cos\theta(1 + \sin\theta)}$
Combine numerators.	$= \frac{\cos^2\theta + 1 + 2\sin\theta + \sin^2\theta}{(1 + \sin\theta)\cos\theta}$
Use the Pythagorean identity $\cos^2\theta + \sin^2\theta = 1$ to simplify.	$= \frac{2 + 2\sin\theta}{(1 + \sin\theta)\cos\theta}$
Factor.	$= \frac{2(1 + \sin\theta)}{(1 + \sin\theta)\cos\theta}$
Cancel.	$= \frac{2}{\cos\theta}$
Use a reciprocal identity to simplify.	$= 2\sec\theta$

Therefore, $\frac{\cos\theta}{1 + \sin\theta} + \frac{1 + \sin\theta}{\cos\theta} = 2\sec\theta$.

You will use all of these techniques to verify identities in the next lessons.

Verifying Trigonometric Identities

Proofs of Trigonometric Identities

Previously, you rewrote trigonometric expressions in equivalent forms. Now you will prove or verify trigonometric identities using the fundamental identities and the rules of algebra. Unlike solving an equation, there is no set of rules to follow. However, there are some guidelines you may follow.

Identities, although they contain an equal sign, are *not* equations. You may *not* perform an operation such as multiplying, adding, or taking square roots on both sides of the equal sign. One approach to verifying an identity is to work with one side of the equal sign and attempt to show that it is equivalent to the other side.

EXAMPLE 1

Verify the identity:

$$\frac{\csc^2\theta - 1}{\tan\theta} = \cot^3\theta$$

Simplify the expression on the left side of the equal sign. It is more complicated.

Begin with the left side.	$\frac{\csc^2\theta - 1}{\tan\theta}$
Use the Pythagorean identity $\csc^2\theta - 1 = \cot^2\theta$.	$= \frac{\cot^2\theta}{\tan\theta}$
Write as a multiplication expression.	$= \cot^2\theta\left(\frac{1}{\tan\theta}\right)$
Use the reciprocal identity $\frac{1}{\tan\theta} = \cot\theta$.	$= \cot^2\theta(\cot\theta)$
Multiply.	$= \cot^3\theta$

Because the left side of the identity simplifies to equal the right side, the identity $\frac{\csc^2\theta - 1}{\tan\theta} = \cot^3\theta$ is true.

Need More HELP

You should not "work across" the equal sign when trying to verify an identity. To do so assumes that what is being proved is already true.

GOT TO KNOW!

General Strategies for Verifying Identities

- Simplify the more complicated side of the identity until it is identical to the other side.
- Transform both sides of the identity into the same expression.

Another approach to verifying an identity is to work on both sides of the equal sign until both sides are equivalent expressions.

EXAMPLE 2

Verify the identity:

$$\sin \theta(1 + \cot^2 \theta) = \csc \theta$$

Transform both sides of the equation to the same expression.

$$\sin \theta(1 + \cot^2 \theta) = \csc \theta$$

Use the Pythagorean identity $1 + \cot^2 \theta = \csc^2 \theta$ on the left side.

$$\sin \theta(\csc^2 \theta) = \csc \theta$$

Use the Reciprocal identities $\csc^2 \theta = \frac{1}{\sin^2 \theta}$ and $\csc \theta = \frac{1}{\sin \theta}$ on both sides.

$$\sin \theta\left(\frac{1}{\sin^2 \theta}\right) = \frac{1}{\sin \theta}$$

Multiply.

$$\frac{1}{\sin \theta} = \frac{1}{\sin \theta}$$

Because both sides of the identity are equivalent to the same expression, the identity $\sin \theta(1 + \cot^2 \theta) = \csc \theta$ is true.

SEARCH

To see step-by-step videos of these problems, enter the page number into the SWadvantage.com Search Bar.

Sometimes it is practical to work with each side separately, to obtain one common form equivalent to both sides.

EXAMPLE 3

Verify the identity:

$$\frac{\cot^2 \theta}{1 + \csc \theta} = \frac{1 - \sin \theta}{\sin \theta}$$

STEP 1 Work with the left side.

$$\frac{\cot^2 \theta}{1 + \csc \theta}$$

Use the Pythagorean identity $\cot^2 \theta = \csc^2 \theta - 1$.

$$= \frac{\csc^2 \theta - 1}{1 + \csc \theta}$$

Factor.

$$= \frac{(\csc \theta - 1)\cancel{(\csc \theta + 1)}}{\cancel{1 + \csc \theta}}$$

Simplify.

$$= \csc \theta - 1$$

STEP 2 Work with the right side.

$$\frac{1 - \sin \theta}{\sin \theta}$$

Distribute the denominator.

$$= \frac{1}{\sin \theta} - \frac{\sin \theta}{\sin \theta}$$

Use the reciprocal identity $\frac{1}{\sin \theta} = \csc \theta$.

$$= \csc \theta - 1$$

Because both sides of the identity equal $\csc \theta - 1$, the identity $\frac{\cot^2 \theta}{1 + \csc \theta} = \frac{1 - \sin \theta}{\sin \theta}$ is true.

Specific Strategies

The basic rules of arithmetic can be applied to trigonometric functions.

EXAMPLE 4

Verify the identity:

$$\frac{\sin\theta + \tan\theta}{\cos\theta + \csc\theta} = \sin\theta\tan\theta$$

Transform both sides of the identity into the same expression. It helps to draw a vertical line between each expression as you work on each side.

Step	Left side	Right side
	$\frac{\sin\theta + \tan\theta}{\cos\theta + \csc\theta}$	$\sin\theta\tan\theta$
Change both sides to sines and cosines.	$\frac{\sin\theta + \frac{\sin\theta}{\cos\theta}}{\frac{\cos\theta}{\sin\theta} + \frac{1}{\sin\theta}}$	$\sin\theta\frac{\sin\theta}{\cos\theta}$
Add the fractions on the left. Multiply on the right.	$\frac{\frac{\sin\theta\cos\theta + \sin\theta}{\cos\theta}}{\frac{\cos\theta + 1}{\sin\theta}}$	$\frac{\sin^2\theta}{\cos\theta}$
Rewrite the fraction as a division expression.	$\frac{\sin\theta\cos\theta + \sin\theta}{\cos\theta} \div \frac{\cos\theta + 1}{\sin\theta}$	$\frac{\sin^2\theta}{\cos\theta}$
To divide, multiply by the reciprocal.	$\frac{\sin\theta\cos\theta + \sin\theta}{\cos\theta} \cdot \frac{\sin\theta}{\cos\theta + 1}$	$\frac{\sin^2\theta}{\cos\theta}$
Factor and cancel.	$\frac{\sin\theta\cancel{(\cos\theta + 1)}}{\cos\theta} \cdot \frac{\sin\theta}{\cancel{\cos\theta + 1}}$	$\frac{\sin^2\theta}{\cos\theta}$
Multiply the fractions. Cancel if possible.	$\frac{\sin^2\theta}{\cos\theta} =$	$\frac{\sin^2\theta}{\cos\theta}$

Because both sides of the identity equal $\frac{\sin^2\theta}{\cos\theta}$, the identity $\frac{\sin\theta + \tan\theta}{\cos\theta + \csc\theta} = \sin\theta\tan\theta$ is true.

SEARCH

To see step-by-step videos of these problems, enter the page number into the SWadvantage.com Search Bar.

GOT TO KNOW!

Specific Strategies for Verifying Identities

- Express functions in terms of sines and cosines.
- Perform the indicated algebraic operations such as adding, subtracting, multiplying, and dividing fractions.
- Factor.
- Multiply binomials.
- Multiply a fraction by a useful equivalent of 1.

Sometimes you will need to multiply binomials to arrive at a Pythagorean identity.

EXAMPLE 5

Verify the identity:

$$(\tan^2\theta + 1)(\cos^2\theta - 1) = 1 - \sec^2\theta$$

The left side of the equal sign is more complicated than the right side. Try to change the left side so that it is the same expression as the one on the right side. Begin by multiplying the binomials.

	$(\tan^2\theta + 1)(\cos^2\theta - 1)$
Multiply the binomials. Use the FOIL method.	$= \tan^2\theta\cos^2\theta - \tan^2\theta + \cos^2\theta - 1$
Use the Quotient identity $\tan^2\theta = \frac{\sin^2\theta}{\cos^2\theta}$.	$= \frac{\sin^2\theta}{\cos^2\theta}(\cos^2\theta) - \tan^2\theta + \cos^2\theta - 1$
Multiply.	$= \sin^2\theta - \tan^2\theta + \cos^2\theta - 1$
Use the Commutative Property and factor out -1.	$= (\sin^2\theta + \cos^2\theta) - (\tan^2\theta + 1)$
Use the Pythagorean identities $\sin^2\theta + \cos^2\theta = 1$; $\tan^2\theta + 1 = \sec^2\theta$.	$= 1 - \sec^2\theta$

Because the left side of the identity simplifies to equal the right side, the identity is true.

Need More HELP

Remember: FOIL means to first multiply the First terms, then multiply the Outer terms, next multiply the Inner terms, and last multiply the Last terms.

You can use the same technique you used to rationalize the denominator to create a Pythagorean identity.

EXAMPLE 6

Verify the identity:

$$\frac{1 - \cos\theta}{\sin\theta} = \frac{\sin\theta}{1 + \cos\theta}$$

METHOD 1

Begin with the left side.	$\frac{1 - \cos\theta}{\sin\theta}$
Multiply by 1 in the form of $\frac{1 + \cos\theta}{1 + \cos\theta}$.	$= \frac{(1 - \cos\theta)(1 + \cos\theta)}{\sin\theta(1 + \cos\theta)}$
Multiply. Use the FOIL method.	$= \frac{1 - \cos^2\theta}{\sin\theta(1 + \cos\theta)}$
Use the Pythagorean identity $\sin^2\theta = 1 - \cos^2\theta$.	$= \frac{\sin^2\theta}{\sin\theta(1 + \cos\theta)}$
Simplify.	$= \frac{\sin\theta}{(1 + \cos\theta)}$

Because the left side of the identity simplifies to equal the right side, the identity is true.

A second method for verifying this identity is on the next page.

Watch Out!

Be careful. Do *not* cross multiply. To do so means you assume the identity is true *before* you prove it to be true.

There can be more than one way to verify an identity. Here is another way to verify the identity in Example 6.

Verify the identity:

$$\frac{1-\cos\theta}{\sin\theta}=\frac{\sin\theta}{1+\cos\theta}$$

METHOD 2

Begin with the right side.	$\frac{\sin\theta}{1+\cos\theta}$
Multiply by 1 in the form of $\frac{1-\cos\theta}{1-\cos\theta}$.	$=\frac{\sin\theta(1-\cos\theta)}{1+\cos\theta(1-\cos\theta)}$
Multiply the binomial.	$=\frac{\sin\theta(1-\cos\theta)}{1-\cos^2\theta}$
Use the Pythagorean identity $\sin^2\theta=1-\cos^2\theta$.	$=\frac{\sin\theta(1-\cos\theta)}{\sin^2\theta}$
Simplify.	$=\frac{1-\cos\theta}{\sin\theta}$

Because the right side of the identity simplifies to equal the left side, the identity is true.

SEARCH

To see step-by-step videos of these problems, enter the page number into the SWadvantage.com Search Bar.

Sometimes you need only apply a strategy to part of an identity.

EXAMPLE 7

Verify the identity:

$$\tan^2\theta+\csc^2\theta-\cot^2\theta=\sec^2\theta$$

Begin on the left side. You might want to write all of the terms in sine and cosine. But since the right side of the identity is $\sec^2\theta$, leave the $\tan^2\theta$ alone.

	$\tan^2\theta+\csc^2\theta-\cot^2\theta$
Write the last two terms in sines and cosines.	$=\tan^2\theta+\frac{1}{\sin^2\theta}-\frac{\cos^2\theta}{\sin^2\theta}$
Add the fractions.	$=\tan^2\theta+\frac{1-\cos^2\theta}{\sin^2\theta}$
Use the Pythagorean identity $\sin^2\theta=1-\cos^2\theta$.	$=\tan^2\theta+\frac{\sin^2\theta}{\sin^2\theta}$
Simplify.	$=\tan^2\theta+1$
Use the Pythagorean identity $\sec^2\theta=\tan^2\theta+1$.	$=\sec^2\theta$

Because the left side of the identity simplifies to equal the right side, the identity is true.

You can use a graphing calculator to see if an equation *may* be an identity. First graph the left side of the identity. Then, without clearing the screen, graph the right side. If the graphs coincide, there is a strong indication that the equation is an identity. You can then verify the identity algebraically.

EXAMPLE 8

Verify the identity:

$$\frac{\sin\theta}{\csc\theta} = \sin^2\theta$$

METHOD 1

Verify the identity graphically.

STEP 1 Graph $y = \frac{\sin\theta}{\csc\theta}$.

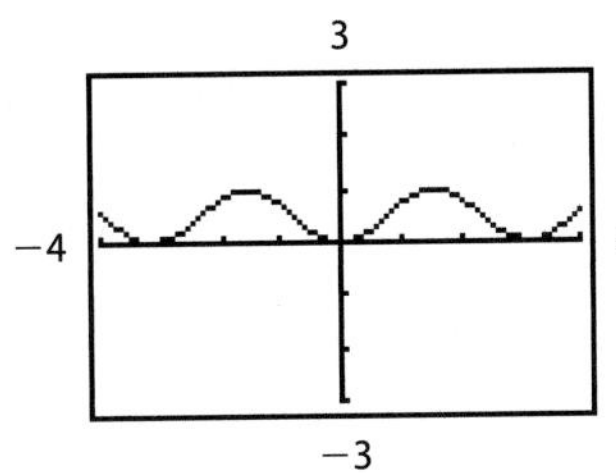

STEP 2 Graph $y = \sin^2\theta$.

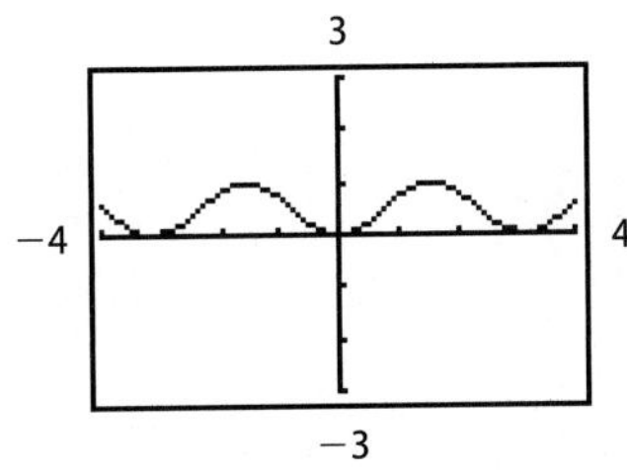

STEP 3 Compare the graphs.

The graphs are the same. If you place them on the same screen, they will coincide.

Since the graphs are the same, there is a strong indication that the identity is true.

METHOD 2

Verify the identity algebraically.

Begin with the left side. $\frac{\sin\theta}{\csc\theta}$

Use the reciprocal identity $\csc\theta = \frac{1}{\sin\theta}$. $= \frac{\sin\theta}{\frac{1}{\sin\theta}}$

To divide, multiply by the reciprocal. $= \sin\theta \cdot \frac{\sin\theta}{1}$

Multiply. $= \sin^2\theta$

Because the left side of the identity simplifies to equal the right side, the identity is true.

Try It This Way

Use a graphing calculator to graph both sides of the equation on the same screen. If only one curve appears, this is a strong indication (but not proof) that the equation is an identity.

Sum and Differences Identities I

Identities for Cosine

Certain tasks in surveying, astronomy, navigation, and mathematics require finding the *exact* value of the sine, cosine, or tangent of an angle. Tables or calculators only give us approximations. We can use the exact values we know of the special angles in a sum or difference identity to find the exact value of a trigonometric function of some angles.

Watch Out!

You cannot use the distributive property to evaluate the sum of two angles.
$\cos(30° + 45°) \neq \cos 30° + \cos 45°$

EXAMPLE 1

Find the exact value of cos 75°.

Write 75° as the sum of two special angles.	$75° = 30° + 45°$
Write the cosine as a sum of angles.	$\cos 75° = \cos(30° + 45°)$
Use the sum identity for cosine.	$\cos 75° = \cos 30° \cos 45° - \sin 30° \sin 45°$
Substitute the exact values for the cosine and sine of the special angles.	$= \frac{\sqrt{3}}{2}\left(\frac{\sqrt{2}}{2}\right) - \frac{1}{2}\left(\frac{\sqrt{2}}{2}\right)$
Simplify.	$= \frac{\sqrt{6} - \sqrt{2}}{4}$

EXAMPLE 2

Find the exact value of $\cos \frac{\pi}{12}$.

Write $\frac{\pi}{12}$ as the difference of two special angles.	$\frac{\pi}{12} = \frac{\pi}{3} - \frac{\pi}{4}$
Write the cosine as a sum of angles.	$\cos \frac{\pi}{12} = \cos\left(\frac{\pi}{3} - \frac{\pi}{4}\right)$
Use the difference identity for cosine.	$\cos \frac{\pi}{12} = \cos \frac{\pi}{3} \cos \frac{\pi}{4} + \sin \frac{\pi}{3} \sin \frac{\pi}{4}$
Substitute the exact values for the cosine and sine of the special angles.	$= \frac{1}{2}\left(\frac{\sqrt{2}}{2}\right) + \left(\frac{\sqrt{3}}{2}\right)\left(\frac{\sqrt{2}}{2}\right)$
Simplify.	$= \frac{\sqrt{2} + \sqrt{6}}{4}$

GOT TO KNOW!

Sum and Difference Identities for Cosine

$\cos(\alpha + \beta) = \cos \alpha \cos \beta - \sin \alpha \sin \beta$

$\cos(\alpha - \beta) = \cos \alpha \cos \beta + \sin \alpha \sin \beta$

You can use sum and difference identities in some applications.

EXAMPLE 3

A camera is mounted on a wall outside a bank. The camera is 12 feet above the ground. It can sense an object 13 feet away in one direction and 20 feet away in the other direction. Find the exact value of the cosine of the angle between these two lines of sight.

Use the angle sum identity for cosine to find the sum of the angles.

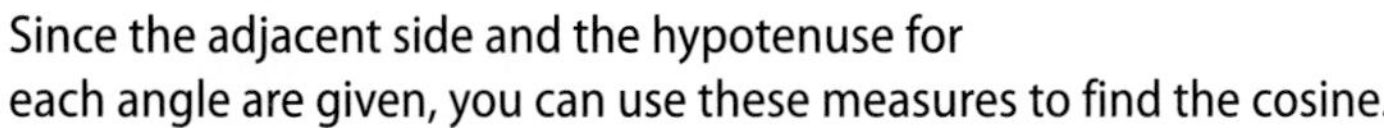

Since the adjacent side and the hypotenuse for each angle are given, you can use these measures to find the cosine.

To find the sine, you need to find the measure of the opposite side of each angle in the triangles.

Use the Pythagorean Theorem.	$x^2 + 12^2 = 13^2$	$y^2 + 12^2 = 20^2$
Square each term.	$x^2 + 144 = 169$	$y^2 + 144 = 400$
Subtract.	$x^2 = 25$	$y^2 = 256$
Take the square root of both sides.	$x = 5$	$y = 16$
Use the cosine sum identity.	$\cos(\alpha + \beta) = \cos\alpha\cos\beta - \sin\alpha\sin\beta$	
Substitute the values into the identity.	$= \frac{12}{13} \cdot \frac{12}{20} - \frac{5}{13} \cdot \frac{16}{20}$	
Simplify.	$= \frac{36}{65} - \frac{20}{65} = \frac{16}{65}$	

The cosine of the angle between the two lines of sight is $\frac{16}{65}$.

SEARCH

To see step-by-step videos of these problems, enter the page number into the SWadvantage.com Search Bar.

You can also use the sum and difference formulas to verify the cofunction identities.

EXAMPLE 4

Verify the identity:

$$\cos\left(\frac{\pi}{2} - \theta\right) = \sin\theta$$

Use the difference identity for cosine.	$\cos\left(\frac{\pi}{2} - \theta\right) = \cos\frac{\pi}{2}\cos\theta + \sin\frac{\pi}{2}\sin\theta$
Substitute the exact values for the cosine and sine of $\frac{\pi}{2}$.	$= (0)\cos\theta + (1)\sin\theta$
Simplify.	$= \sin\theta$

Because the left side of the identity simplifies to equal the right side, then the identity is true.

Sum and Difference Identities II

Identities for Sine and Tangent

Recall that sine and cosine are cofunctions of complementary angles. You can use the difference identity for cosine to prove the sum identity for sine.

Need More HELP

Remember the cofunction identities:

$\sin\theta = \cos(90° - \theta)$

(See p. 1000.)

EXAMPLE 1

Prove the identity:

$\mathbf{\sin(\alpha + \beta) = \sin\alpha\cos\beta + \cos\alpha\sin\beta}$

Begin with the left side of the identity.	$\sin(\alpha + \beta)$
Use a cofunction identity: $\sin\theta = \cos(90° - \theta)$.	$= \cos[90° - (\alpha + \beta)]$
Regroup after distributing the -1.	$= \cos[(90° - \alpha) - \beta]$
Use the difference identity for cosine.	$= \cos(90° - \alpha)\cos\beta + \sin(90° - \alpha)\sin\beta$
Use a cofunction identity.	$= \sin\alpha\cos\beta + \cos\alpha\sin\beta$

Because the left side can be shown to equal the right side, then the identity is true.

You can use the sum and difference identities to verify other identities.

EXAMPLE 2

Verify the identity:

$\mathbf{\sin(\alpha + \beta)\sin(\alpha - \beta) = \sin^2\alpha - \sin^2\beta}$

Begin with the left side of the identity.	$\sin(\alpha + \beta)\sin(\alpha - \beta)$
Use the sum and difference identities for sine.	$= (\sin\alpha\cos\beta - \cos\alpha\sin\beta)(\sin\alpha\cos\beta + \cos\alpha\sin\beta)$
Multiply the binomials. Use FOIL.	$= \sin^2\alpha\cos^2\beta - \cos^2\alpha\sin^2\beta$
Use the Pythagorean identity $\cos^2\theta = 1 - \sin^2\theta$.	$= \sin^2\alpha(1 - \sin^2\beta) - (1 - \sin^2\alpha)\sin^2\beta$
Use the distributive property.	$= \sin^2\alpha - \sin^2\alpha\sin^2\beta - \sin^2\beta + \sin^2\alpha\sin^2\beta$
Combine like terms.	$= \sin^2\alpha - \sin^2\beta$

Because the left side of the identity simplifies to equal the right side, then the identity is true.

GOT TO KNOW!

Sum and Difference Identities for Sine

$\sin(\alpha + \beta) = \sin\alpha\cos\beta + \cos\alpha\sin\beta$

$\sin(\alpha - \beta) = \sin\alpha\cos\beta - \cos\alpha\sin\beta$

You can also use the sum identity for sine to find the exact value of the sine of some angles that are not special angles.

EXAMPLE 3

Find the exact value of sin 105°.

Write 105° as the sum of two special angles. $105° = 60° + 45°$

Write the sine as a sum of angles. $\sin 105° = \sin(60° + 45°)$

Use the sum identity for sine. $= \sin 60° \cos 45° + \cos 60° \sin 45°$

Substitute the exact values for the sine and cosine of the special angles. $= \frac{\sqrt{3}}{2}\left(\frac{\sqrt{2}}{2}\right) + \left(-\frac{1}{2}\right)\left(\frac{\sqrt{2}}{2}\right)$

Simplify. $= \frac{\sqrt{6}}{4} - \frac{\sqrt{2}}{4}$

Therefore, $\sin 105° = \frac{\sqrt{6}}{4} - \frac{\sqrt{2}}{4}$

Try It This Way

For Example 3, a difference of two special angles can also be found. The same exact value can be found by using the difference identity for sine such as sin(105°) = sin(135° − 30°).

The sum and difference identities for tangent are derived by using the identities for sine and cosine. You can use a sum or difference identity for tangent to find the exact value of the tangent of an angle that is not a special angle.

EXAMPLE 4

Find the exact value of tan 255°.

Write 255° as the sum of two special angles. $255° = 210° + 45°$

Write the tangent as a sum of angles. $\tan 255° = \tan(210° + 45°)$

Use the sum identity for tangent. $= \frac{\tan 210° + \tan 45°}{1 - \tan 210° \tan 45°}$

Substitute the exact values for the tangents. $= \frac{\frac{\sqrt{3}}{3} + 1}{1 - \frac{\sqrt{3}}{3}(1)}$

Simplify. $= 2 + \sqrt{3}$

Therefore, $\tan 255° = 2 + \sqrt{3}$

Need More HELP

To simplify a complex fraction like the one in Example 4, first add the fractions in both the numerator and denominator of the fraction.

For more help, go to *Complex Fractions* (Book 2, p. 1990).

GOT TO KNOW!

Sum and Difference Identities for Tangent

$$\tan(\alpha + \beta) = \frac{\tan\alpha + \tan\beta}{1 - \tan\alpha\tan\beta} \qquad \tan(\alpha - \beta) = \frac{\tan\alpha - \tan\beta}{1 + \tan\alpha\tan\beta}$$

Double-Angle Identities

Verifying Double-Angle Identities

The double-angle formulas can be used to find the values of the trigonometric functions at 2α from their values at α.

You can easily derive the double-angle identities from the angle sum identities. Substitute α for β in the identities for $\sin(\alpha + \beta)$ and $\cos(\alpha + \beta)$.

$$\begin{aligned} \sin 2\alpha &= \sin(\alpha + \alpha) \\ &= \sin\alpha\cos\alpha + \cos\alpha\sin\alpha \\ &= \sin\alpha\cos\alpha + \sin\alpha\cos\alpha \\ \sin 2\alpha &= 2\sin\alpha\cos\alpha \end{aligned}$$

$$\begin{aligned} \cos 2\alpha &= \cos(\alpha + \alpha) \\ &= \cos\alpha\cos\alpha - \sin\alpha\sin\alpha \\ \cos 2\alpha &= \cos^2\alpha - \sin^2\alpha \end{aligned}$$

Using the Pythagorean identity, you can derive two other identities for $\cos 2\alpha$. Once you have derived these identities, you can then use them to verify other identities.

SEARCH

To see step-by-step videos of these problems, enter the page number into the SWadvantage.com Search Bar.

EXAMPLE 1

Verify the identity:

$$\frac{\cos\theta + \sin\theta}{\cos 2\theta} = \frac{1}{\cos\theta - \sin\theta}$$

Begin with the left side of the identity. $\frac{\cos\theta + \sin\theta}{\cos 2\theta}$

Use the double-angle identity $\cos 2\theta = \cos^2\theta - \sin^2\theta$. $= \frac{\cos\theta + \sin\theta}{\cos^2\theta - \sin^2\theta}$

Factor the denominator and cancel. $= \frac{\cancel{\cos\theta + \sin\theta}}{\cancel{(\cos\theta + \sin\theta)}(\cos\theta - \sin\theta)}$

Simplify. $= \frac{1}{\cos\theta - \sin\theta}$

Because the left side of the identity simplifies to equal the right side, then the identity is true.

You can derive the double-angle identity for the tangent function by using the angle sum identity for tangent, $\tan(\alpha + \beta)$. Try this on your own.

GOT TO KNOW!

Double-Angle Identities

$\sin 2\alpha = 2\sin\alpha\cos\alpha$

$\cos 2\alpha = \cos^2\alpha - \sin^2\alpha$

$\cos 2\alpha = 1 - 2\sin^2\alpha$

$\cos 2\alpha = 2\cos^2\alpha - 1$

$\tan^2\alpha = \frac{2\tan\alpha}{1 - \tan^2\alpha}$

You can evaluate trigonometric functions by using the double-angle identities.

EXAMPLE 2

$\cos\theta = -\frac{4}{5}$ and $\pi < \theta < \frac{3\pi}{2}$. Find the exact value of $\sin 2\theta$, $\cos 2\theta$, and $\tan 2\theta$.

Draw a diagram. θ is in Quadrant III.

From the diagram, you can find $\sin\theta$ and $\tan\theta$.

$$\sin\theta = -\frac{3}{5} \qquad \tan\theta = \frac{3}{4}$$

Substitute the values you know into each of the double-angle identities. Use the given value for cosine.

$$\sin 2\theta = 2\sin\theta\cos\theta \qquad \cos 2\theta = 2\cos^2\theta - 1 \qquad \tan 2\theta = \frac{2\tan\theta}{1-\tan^2\theta}$$

$$= 2\left(-\frac{3}{5}\right)\left(-\frac{4}{5}\right) = \frac{24}{25} \qquad = 2\left(-\frac{4}{5}\right)^2 - 1 = \frac{7}{25} \qquad = \frac{2\left(\frac{3}{4}\right)}{1-\left(\frac{3}{4}\right)^2} = \frac{24}{7}$$

Need More HELP

If you have a choice, use a given value for your calculations. In Example 2 you are given the value of $\cos\theta$. You may have made a mistake finding the value for $\sin\theta$. So, for $\cos 2\theta$, use the identity involving cosine rather than sine.

Double-angle identities are sometimes used in surveying.

EXAMPLE 

A pole casts a shadow of 30 feet at a certain time of day and a shadow of 10 feet at a later time when the angle of elevation is twice as large. What is the height of the pole, to the nearest foot?

Use tangent.

Find the tangent of each angle. $\tan\alpha = \frac{h}{30}$

$\tan 2\alpha = \frac{h}{10}$

Use the double-angle identity. $\tan 2\alpha = \frac{2\tan\alpha}{1-\tan^2\alpha}$

$$\frac{h}{10} = \frac{2\left(\frac{h}{30}\right)}{\frac{900-h^2}{900}}$$

Substitute in for $\tan\alpha$ and $\tan 2\alpha$.

$$\frac{h}{10} = \frac{60h}{900-h^2}$$

Cross multiply. $600h = h(900 - h^2)$

Divide both sides by h. $600h = 900 - h^2$

Subtract 900 from both sides. $-300 = -h^2$

Multiply both sides by -1. $300 = h^2$

Take the square root of both sides. $17 \approx h$

The pole is about 17 feet tall.

Half-Angle Identities

Deriving Half-Angle Identities

The half-angle identities can be easily derived from the double-angle identities. To prove the half-angle identities for cosine, let $\theta = \frac{\alpha}{2}$.

$$\cos 2\left(\frac{\alpha}{2}\right) = 1 - 2\sin^2\left(\frac{\alpha}{2}\right) \qquad \cos 2\left(\frac{\alpha}{2}\right) = 2\cos^2\left(\frac{\alpha}{2}\right) - 1$$

$$\cos\alpha = 1 - 2\sin^2\left(\frac{\alpha}{2}\right) \qquad \cos\alpha = 2\cos^2\left(\frac{\alpha}{2}\right) - 1$$

$$2\sin^2\left(\frac{\alpha}{2}\right) = 1 - \cos\alpha \qquad 2\cos^2\left(\frac{\alpha}{2}\right) = 1 + \cos\alpha$$

$$\sin^2\left(\frac{\alpha}{2}\right) = \frac{1-\cos\alpha}{2} \qquad \cos^2\left(\frac{\alpha}{2}\right) = \frac{1+\cos\alpha}{2}$$

$$\sin\left(\frac{\alpha}{2}\right) = \pm\sqrt{\frac{1-\cos\alpha}{2}} \qquad \cos\frac{\alpha}{2} = \pm\sqrt{\frac{1+\cos\alpha}{2}}$$

The values of the half angles are positive or negative depending on the quadrant in which $\frac{\alpha}{2}$ lies.

EXAMPLE 1

Determine the exact value of sin 15°.

Write 15° as half of a special angle. $\quad 15° = \frac{30°}{2}$

Write the sine as a quotient of angles. $\quad \sin 15° = \sin\frac{30°}{2}$

Use the identity for $\sin\frac{\alpha}{2}$. Choose the positive sign, since 15° is in the first quadrant. $\quad = \sqrt{\frac{1-\cos 30°}{2}}$

Substitute $\frac{\sqrt{3}}{2}$ for cos 30° and simplify. $\quad = \sqrt{\frac{1-\frac{\sqrt{3}}{2}}{2}} = \sqrt{\frac{1}{2} - \frac{\sqrt{3}}{4}} = \frac{\sqrt{2-\sqrt{3}}}{2}$

Need More HELP

Remember the trigonometric values of the angles in special right triangles. For help, go to pages 898–901.

There are three half-angle identities for tangent. You may want to prove these on your own.

GOT TO KNOW!

Half-Angle Identities

$$\sin\frac{\alpha}{2} = \pm\sqrt{\frac{1-\cos\alpha}{2}} \qquad \tan\frac{\alpha}{2} = \pm\sqrt{\frac{1-\cos\alpha}{1+\cos\alpha}},\ \cos\alpha \neq -1$$

$$\cos\frac{\alpha}{2} = \pm\sqrt{\frac{1+\cos\alpha}{2}} \qquad \tan\frac{\alpha}{2} = \frac{1-\cos\alpha}{\sin\alpha},\ \sin\alpha \neq 0$$

$$\tan\frac{\alpha}{2} = \frac{\sin\alpha}{1+\cos\alpha},\ \cos\alpha \neq -1$$

You can double an angle and then use a half-angle identity to find the exact trigonometric values of some angles.

EXAMPLE 2

Determine the exact value of tan(−22.5°).

An angle that measures −22.5° is in Quadrant IV. So, the sign of sin(−22.5°) will be negative and the sign of cos(−22.5) will be positive.

Write −22.5° as half of a special angle. $-22.5° = -\frac{45°}{2}$

Write the tangent as a quotient of angles. $\tan(-22.5°) = \tan\left(-\frac{45°}{2}\right)$

Use an identity for $\tan\frac{\alpha}{2}$. $= \frac{\sin(-45°)}{1 + \cos(-45°)}$

Use negative identities. $= \frac{-\sin 45°}{1 + \cos 45°}$

Substitute $\frac{\sqrt{2}}{2}$ for sin 45° and cos 45°. $= \frac{-\frac{\sqrt{2}}{2}}{1 + \frac{\sqrt{2}}{2}}$

Simplify. $= \frac{-\frac{\sqrt{2}}{2}}{\frac{2+\sqrt{2}}{2}} = -\frac{\sqrt{2}}{2+\sqrt{2}}$

$= \frac{2 - 2\sqrt{2}}{2} = 1 - \sqrt{2}$

Half-angle identities can be used to prove other identities.

EXAMPLE 3

Verify the identity:

$$-\cos\theta = 2\sin^2\frac{\theta}{2} - 1$$

Begin with the right side. $2\sin^2\frac{\theta}{2} - 1$

Use the half-angle identity for sine. $= 2\left(\pm\sqrt{\frac{1-\cos\theta}{2}}\right)^2 - 1$

Square the square root. $= 2\left(\frac{1-\cos\theta}{2}\right) - 1$

Multiply. $= 1 - \cos\theta - 1$

Simplify. $= -\cos\theta$

Because the right side of the identity simplifies to equal the left side, then the identity is true.

SEARCH

To see step-by-step videos of these problems, enter the page number into the SWadvantage.com Search Bar.

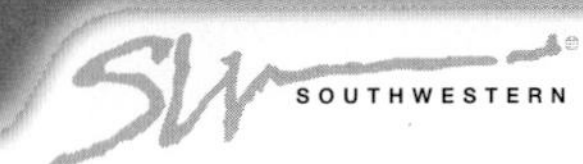

Product-to-Sum Identities

Recall that in algebra, the distributive property connects addition and multiplication. A product may be written as a sum and a sum may be written as a product. The product-to-sum identities connect addition and multiplication in trigonometry. These identities are used in higher mathematics, such as calculus.

There are four product-to-sum identities. Each of these identities is found by adding or subtracting the sum and difference identities for sine or cosine. We will derive the identity for $\cos\alpha\cos\beta$ and $\sin\alpha\sin\beta$ below.

First:

Add $\cos(\alpha+\beta)$ to $\cos(\alpha-\beta)$.

$$\begin{aligned} \cos\alpha\cos\beta + \sin\alpha\sin\beta &= \cos(\alpha-\beta) \\ \cos\alpha\cos\beta - \sin\alpha\sin\beta &= \cos(\alpha+\beta) \\ \hline 2\cos\alpha\cos\beta &= \cos(\alpha-\beta) + \cos(\alpha+\beta) \end{aligned}$$

You may use the identity in this form or you may divide both sides by 2.

$$\cos\alpha\cos\beta = \frac{1}{2}[\cos(\alpha-\beta)+\cos(\alpha+\beta)]$$

Next:

Subtract $\cos(\alpha+\beta)$ from $\cos(\alpha-\beta)$.

$$\begin{aligned} \cos\alpha\cos\beta + \sin\alpha\sin\beta &= \cos(\alpha-\beta) \\ -[\cos\alpha\cos\beta - \sin\alpha\sin\beta &= \cos(\alpha+\beta)] \\ \hline 2\sin\alpha\sin\beta &= \cos(\alpha-\beta) - \cos(\alpha+\beta) \end{aligned}$$

You may use the identity in this form or you may divide both sides by 2.

$$\sin\alpha\sin\beta = \frac{1}{2}[\cos(\alpha-\beta)-\cos(\alpha+\beta)]$$

You can use the product-to-sum identities to rewrite trigonometric functions.

Watch Out!

You can use the product-to-sum identity with the constant 2 multiplied by $\sin\alpha\cos\beta$ or the constant $\frac{1}{2}$ multiplied by $\sin(\alpha+\beta)+\sin(\alpha-\beta)$, but you cannot have both constants in use at the same time.

EXAMPLE 1

Express 2 sin 60° cos 60° as a sum. Then, evaluate the sum.

Use a product-to-sum identity.

$2\sin\alpha\cos\beta = \sin(\alpha+\beta)+\sin(\alpha-\beta)$ $\quad 2\sin 60^\circ\cos 60^\circ = \sin(60^\circ+60^\circ)+\sin(60^\circ-60^\circ)$

Simplify. $\quad = \sin(120^\circ)+\sin(0^\circ)$

Substitute values for sine and simplify. $\quad = \frac{\sqrt{3}}{2}+0=\frac{\sqrt{3}}{2}$

GOT TO KNOW!

Product-to-Sum Identities

$\cos\alpha\cos\beta = \frac{1}{2}[\cos(\alpha-\beta)+\cos(\alpha+\beta)]$ $\quad \sin\alpha\cos\beta = \frac{1}{2}[\sin(\alpha+\beta)+\sin(\alpha-\beta)]$

$\sin\alpha\sin\beta = \frac{1}{2}[\cos(\alpha-\beta)-\cos(\alpha+\beta)]$ $\quad \cos\alpha\sin\beta = \frac{1}{2}[\sin(\alpha+\beta)-\sin(\alpha-\beta)]$

EXAMPLE 2

Express sin 15° sin 45° as a difference. Then, evaluate the difference.

Use a product-to-sum identity.

$\sin\alpha\sin\beta = \frac{1}{2}[\cos(\alpha-\beta) - \cos(\alpha+\beta)]$ $\quad \sin 15°\sin 45° = \frac{1}{2}[\cos(15° - 45°) - \cos(15° + 45°)]$

Simplify. $\quad = \frac{1}{2}[\cos(-30°) - \cos 60°]$

Substitute values for cosine and simplify. $\quad = \frac{1}{2}\left(\frac{\sqrt{3}}{2} - \frac{1}{2}\right)$

$$= \frac{\sqrt{3}-1}{4}$$

SEARCH

To see step-by-step videos of these problems, enter the page number into the SWadvantage.com Search Bar.

You can also use the product-to-sum identities to write sums or differences as products.

EXAMPLE 3

Express cos 15° + cos 75° as a product. Then, evaluate the product.

Notice that the product-to-sum identities involve adding and subtracting two angles.

Let $\alpha + \beta = 75°$ and $\alpha - \beta = 15°$. This is a simple system of equations.

Add the two equations and solve for α.

$$\begin{aligned} \alpha + \beta &= 75° \\ + \alpha - \beta &= 15° \\ \hline 2\alpha \quad &= 90° \\ \alpha \quad &= 45° \end{aligned}$$

Substitute 45° for α and solve for β.

$$\begin{aligned} 45° + \beta &= 75° \\ \beta &= 30° \end{aligned}$$

Next use the product-to-sum identity.

$\cos\alpha\cos\beta = \frac{1}{2}[\cos(\alpha-\beta) + \cos(\alpha+\beta)]$ $\quad \cos 45°\cos 30° = \frac{1}{2}[\cos(45° - 30°) + \cos(45° + 30°)]$

Multiply both sides of the equation by 2. $\quad 2\cos 45°\cos 30° = \cos(45° - 30°) + \cos(45° + 30°)$

Use the commutative property. $\quad \cos(45° - 30°) + \cos(45° + 30°) = 2\cos 45°\cos 30°$

Substitute the values for cos 45° and cos 30°. $\quad = 2\cdot\frac{\sqrt{2}}{2}\cdot\frac{\sqrt{3}}{2}$

Simplify. $\quad = \frac{\sqrt{6}}{2}$

Need More HELP

Think of cos 15° as cos(45° − 30°). Think of cos 75° as cos(45° + 30°). These expressions can then be used in the product-to-sum identity.

On the next pages, you will see how to derive sum-to-product identities where the value of the angle does not have to be rewritten as a sum or a difference.

Sum-to-Product Identities

Sometimes it is useful to change a sum or difference of trigonometric functions to a product. This is done in some applications in physics since calculating a product is easier than calculating a sum or difference. The sum-to-product identities can be obtained from the product-to-sum identities just covered.

Let: $x = \alpha + \beta$ and $y = \alpha - \beta$

Then:

$$\alpha = \frac{x+y}{2} \quad \text{and} \quad \beta = \frac{x-y}{2}$$

Substitute these values for α and β in the identity.

$\sin\alpha\cos\beta = \frac{1}{2}[\sin(\alpha+\beta) + \sin(\alpha-\beta)]$ $\quad$ $\sin\left(\frac{x+y}{2}\right)\cos\left(\frac{x-y}{2}\right) = \frac{1}{2}(\sin x + \sin y)$

Multiply both sides of the equation by 2. $\quad$ $2\sin\left(\frac{x+y}{2}\right)\cos\left(\frac{x-y}{2}\right) = \sin x + \sin y$

Rewrite the equation using the Commutative property. $\quad$ $\sin x + \sin y = 2\sin\left(\frac{x+y}{2}\right)\cos\left(\frac{x-y}{2}\right)$

In a similar way, you can derive each of the sum-to-product identities. Now you can write a sum or difference of a trigonometric function as a product.

EXAMPLE 4

Express cos 195° − cos 105° as a product. Then, evaluate the product.

Use a sum-to-product identity.

$\cos x - \cos y = -2\sin\left(\frac{x+y}{2}\right)\sin\left(\frac{x-y}{2}\right)$ $\quad$ $\cos 195° - \cos 105° = -2\sin\left(\frac{195° + 105°}{2}\right)\sin\left(\frac{195° - 105°}{2}\right)$

Simplify. $\quad$ $= -2\sin 150° \sin 45°$

Substitute values for sine and simplify. $\quad$ $= -2\left(\frac{1}{2}\right)\left(\frac{\sqrt{2}}{2}\right) = -\frac{\sqrt{2}}{2}$

SEARCH

To see step-by-step videos of these problems, enter the page number into the SWadvantage.com Search Bar.

GOT TO KNOW!

Sum-to-Product Identities

$\sin x + \sin y = 2\sin\left(\frac{x+y}{2}\right)\cos\left(\frac{x-y}{2}\right)$ $\quad$ $\cos x + \cos y = 2\cos\left(\frac{x+y}{2}\right)\cos\left(\frac{x-y}{2}\right)$

$\sin x - \sin y = 2\cos\left(\frac{x+y}{2}\right)\sin\left(\frac{x-y}{2}\right)$ $\quad$ $\cos x - \cos y = -2\sin\left(\frac{x+y}{2}\right)\sin\left(\frac{x-y}{2}\right)$

You can also use these identities for angles in radian measure.

EXAMPLE 5

Express $\sin\frac{3\pi}{4} - \sin\frac{\pi}{4}$ as a product. Then, evaluate the product.

Use a sum-to-product identity. $\sin\frac{3\pi}{4} - \sin\frac{\pi}{4} = 2\cos\left(\frac{\frac{3\pi}{4}+\frac{\pi}{4}}{2}\right)\sin\left(\frac{\frac{3\pi}{4}-\frac{\pi}{4}}{2}\right)$

Simplify. $= 2\cos\left(\frac{\frac{4\pi}{4}}{2}\right)\sin\left(\frac{\frac{2\pi}{4}}{2}\right) = 2\cos\left(\frac{\pi}{2}\right)\sin\left(\frac{\pi}{4}\right)$

Evaluate. $= 2(0)\left(\frac{\sqrt{2}}{2}\right) = 0$

Sometimes the measure of an angle is a simple algebraic expression.

EXAMPLE 6

Express $\sin 3x + \sin 5x$ as a product.

Use a sum-to-product identity. $\sin 3x + \sin 5x = 2\sin\left(\frac{3x+5x}{2}\right)\cos\left(\frac{3x-5x}{2}\right)$

Simplify. $= 2\sin\left(\frac{8x}{2}\right)\cos\left(\frac{-2x}{2}\right)$

$= 2\sin 4x\cos(-x)$

Use a negative identity, $\cos(-\theta) = \cos\theta$. $= 2\sin 4x\cos x$

You can use the sum-to-product identities to verify other identities.

EXAMPLE 

Verify the identity:

$$\frac{\sin t + \sin 3t}{\cos t + \cos 3t} = \tan 2t$$

Begin with the left side. $\frac{\sin t + \sin 3t}{\cos t + \cos 3t}$

Use sum-to-product identities. $= \frac{2\sin\left(\frac{t+3t}{2}\right)\cos\left(\frac{t-3t}{2}\right)}{2\cos\left(\frac{t+3t}{2}\right)\cos\left(\frac{t-3t}{2}\right)}$

Simplify. $= \frac{\sin 2t}{\cos 2t}$

Use a quotient identity. $= \tan 2t$

Inverse Trigonometric Functions and Trigonometric Equations

What Came Before?

- Graphing trigonometric functions
- Using identities to simplify trigonometric expressions

What's This About?

- Finding the measure of an angle that has a known trigonometric ratio
- Solving trigonometric equations and inequalities
- Graphing inverse trigonometric functions

Practical Apps

- Hydraulics used in robotics make use of trigonometric functions in motors that result in movement.
- Trigonometric equations are used to calculate the distance from Earth to planets and their moons.

Just for FUN!

Q: How did archaeologists find out about trigonometric Noah?

A: They found an ark sign.

CONTENTS | UPLOAD | DOWNLOAD | *Trigonometry*

You can find more practice problems online by visiting:
www.SWadvantage.com

Inverse Sine Function

The Inverse Sine Relation and Function

Need More HELP

$y = \sin x$
domain: all real numbers
range: $[-1, 1]$

$y = \sin^{-1} x$
domain: $[-1, 1]$
range: all real numbers

The inverse of $y = \sin x$ is a relation but not a function. For each value of y, there are infinitely many values of x.

The diagram at the right shows the graph $y = \sin x$ over the interval from -2π to 2π. It also shows the graph of $y = 0.5$. The diagram illustrates that the sine function is not one-to-one. The inverse of $y = \sin x$ is a relation but not a function.

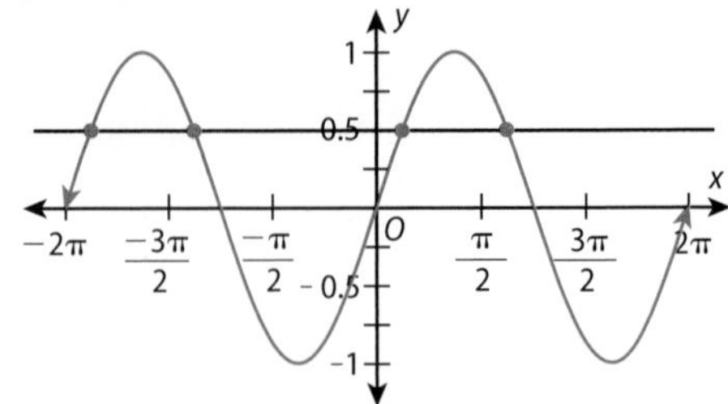

EXAMPLE 1

a. Find all values of x over the interval from -2π to 2π for which $\sin x = 0$.

Make a table using the graph as a guide.

x	-2π	$-\pi$	0	π	2π
$\sin x$	0	0	0	0	0

If x is any multiple of π, then $\sin x = 0$. If n is an integer, then $x = n\pi$.

b. Find all values of x over the interval from -2π to 2π for which $\sin x = 1$.

When $x = \frac{\pi}{2}$, $\sin \frac{\pi}{2} = 1$ and when $x = -\frac{3\pi}{2}$, $\sin\left(-\frac{3\pi}{2}\right) = 1$.

The sine function is periodic with period 2π. Therefore, $x = 2\pi n + \frac{\pi}{2}$.

If you restrict the domain of the sine function to the interval $\left[-\frac{\pi}{2}, \frac{\pi}{2}\right]$, then the restricted function is one-to-one and its inverse is a function. The restricted domain, $\left[-\frac{\pi}{2}, \frac{\pi}{2}\right]$, is the set of **principal values** for the sine function. For the definition of the sine with its principal values and the inverse sine function, see the *Got to Know!* box.

Need More HELP

The equation $\sin x = 0.55$ can also be written $x = \sin^{-1} 0.55$.

EXAMPLE 2

Estimate a principal value for which $\sin x = 0.55$.

Set the calculator to radian mode. $\sin 0.58$ is about 0.5480. $\sin 0.59$ is about 0.5564.

Both 0.58 and 0.59 are reasonable estimates of x.

GOT TO KNOW!

The Sine Function

$y = \text{Sin } x$ if and only if $y = \sin x$ and $-\frac{\pi}{2} \leq x \leq \frac{\pi}{2}$.

The Inverse Sine Function

$y = \text{Sin}^{-1} x$ if and only if x is in $\left[-\frac{\pi}{2}, \frac{\pi}{2}\right]$ and $x = \sin y$.

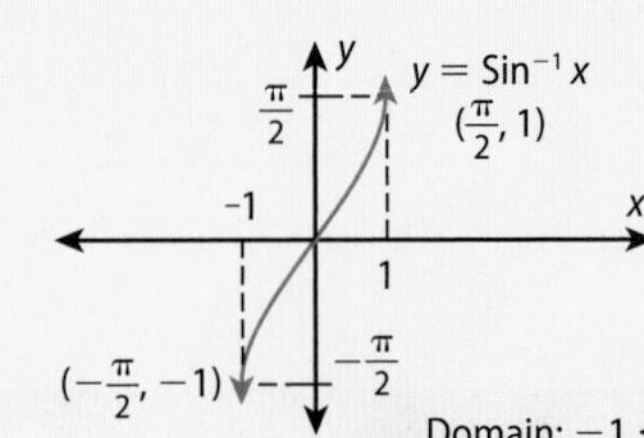

Domain: $-1 \leq x \leq 1$
Range: $-\frac{\pi}{2} \leq y \leq \frac{\pi}{2}$

EXAMPLE 3

Find the value of x between 0° and 90° for which $\sin x = \frac{\sqrt{2}}{2}$.

Use what you know about the sines of special angles. The angle whose sine is $\frac{\sqrt{2}}{2}$ is 45°. Sketch and label an isosceles right triangle as shown to check.

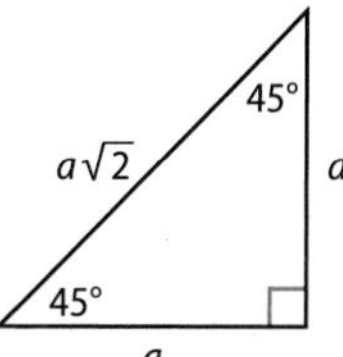

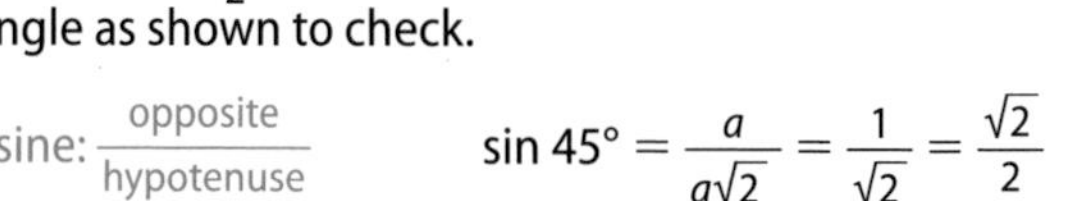

sine: $\frac{\text{opposite}}{\text{hypotenuse}}$ $\qquad \sin 45° = \frac{a}{a\sqrt{2}} = \frac{1}{\sqrt{2}} = \frac{\sqrt{2}}{2}$

Thus, $x = 45°$.

SEARCH

To see step-by-step videos of these problems, enter the page number into the SWadvantage.com Search Bar.

Using a Calculator to Evaluate the Inverse Sine

In many applications, you will need to use a calculator to evaluate the inverse sine.

EXAMPLE 4

a. If $\sin x = 0.7$ and $0° < x° < 90°$, find x in degrees to the nearest tenth.

MODE Degrees 2nd SIN 0 . 7 ENTER

$x \approx 44.4°$

b. If $\sin x = 0.7$ and $0 < x < \frac{\pi}{2}$, find x in radians to the nearest tenth.

MODE Radians 2nd SIN 0 . 7 ENTER

$x \approx 0.8$

c. If $\sin x = -0.7$ and $-\frac{\pi}{2} < x < 0$, find x in radians to the nearest tenth.

MODE Radians 2nd SIN (−) 0 . 7 ENTER

$x \approx -0.8$

Watch Out!

Decide for each situation whether you need to be in degree mode or in radian mode.

Using the Inverse Sine in Right Triangles

To find the measure of an angle in a right triangle, you can use an inverse trigonometric function.

EXAMPLE 5

In right triangle ABC, find the measure of $\angle A$ to the nearest degree.

sine: $\frac{\text{opposite}}{\text{hypotenuse}}$ $\qquad \sin A = \frac{5}{13}$

Solve for $m\angle A$. $\qquad m\angle A = \text{Sin}^{-1}\left(\frac{5}{13}\right)$

Use degree mode. $\qquad m\angle A \approx 23°$.

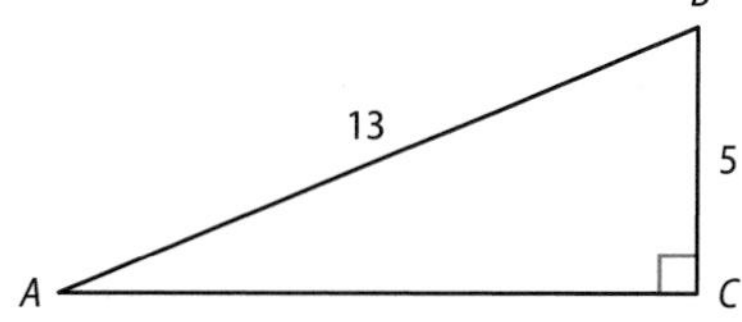

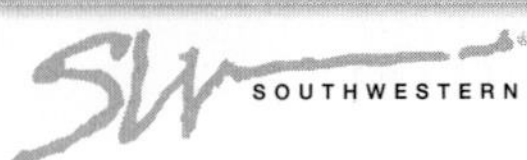

Using the Composition of a Function with an Inverse

The application of the inverse of a function f to the function f gives the identify function x. If f is a function whose inverse is a function, then $f(f^{-1}(x)) = f^{-1}(f(x)) = x$.

SEARCH

To see step-by-step videos of these problems, enter the page number into the SWadvantage.com Search Bar.

EXAMPLE 6

Find $\sin\left(\text{Sin}^{-1}\left(\frac{3}{5}\right)\right)$.

Sketch a right triangle.

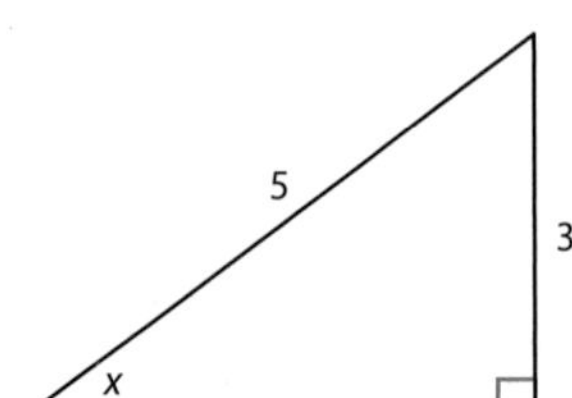

Let $x = \text{Sin}^{-1}\left(\frac{3}{5}\right)$. Then $\sin x = \frac{3}{5}$.

So, $\sin\left(\text{Sin}^{-1}\left(\frac{3}{5}\right)\right) = \frac{3}{5}$.

EXAMPLE 7

Find the measures of all angles such that $\sin^{-1}(\sin 30°)$.

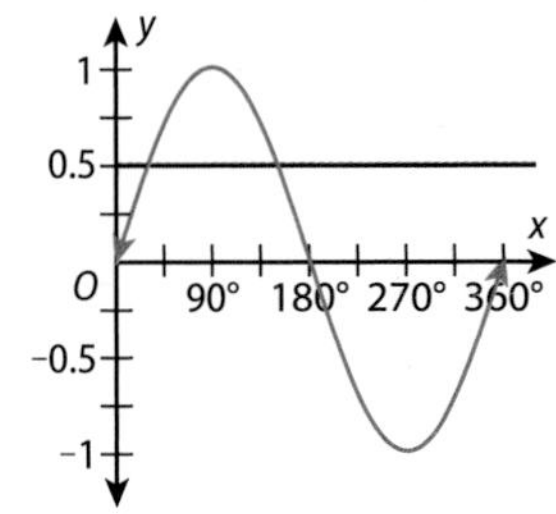

METHOD 1

Use a graph. Because $\sin 30° = 0.5$, sketch $y = \sin x$ and $y = 0.5$.

Use the graph.	$\sin 30° = 0.5$ and $\sin 150° = 0.5$
Extend the pattern.	$360°n + 30°$ and $360°n + 150°$

METHOD 2

STEP 1 Sketch a coordinate diagram that shows a right triangle in each quadrant, each with a 30° angle as shown.

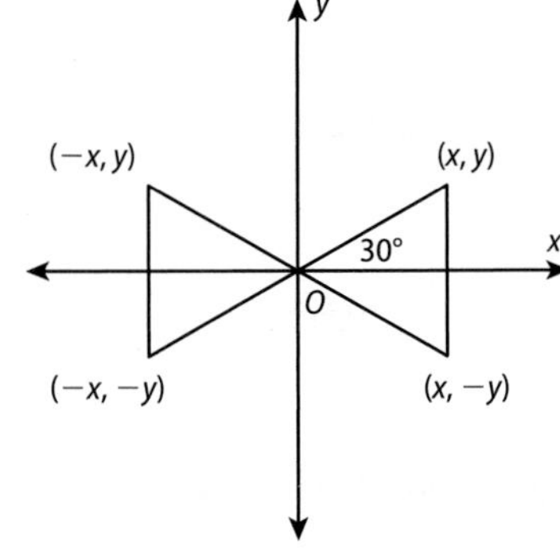

STEP 2 For the triangles in the third and fourth quadrants, the sine is negative because y is negative.

Because $\sin 30°$ is positive, eliminate $180° + 30°$ and $360° - 30°$ from consideration.

STEP 3 Extend the pattern.

Use coterminal angles.	$360°n + 30°$ and $360°n + 150°$

By either method, $\sin^{-1}(\sin 30°)$ is the set of angles whose measures are $360°n + 30°$ or $360°n + 150°$, where n is an integer.

EXAMPLE 8

Evaluate $\sin\left(\text{Sin}^{-1}\frac{\sqrt{3}}{2}\right)$.

Use definition of inverse sine.	If $x = \text{Sin}^{-1}\frac{\sqrt{3}}{2}$, then $x = 60°$ or $\frac{\pi}{3}$. Therefore, $\sin 60° = \sin\frac{\pi}{3} = \frac{\sqrt{3}}{2}$.

So, $\sin\left(\text{Sin}^{-1}\frac{\sqrt{3}}{2}\right) = \frac{\sqrt{3}}{2}$.

Using sin *x*, Sin *x*, and $\text{Sin}^{-1}x$ Together

In some problems, sin *x*, Sin *x*, and $\text{Sin}^{-1}x$ appear together with their inverses.

EXAMPLE 9

a. Calculate $\sin(\text{Sin}^{-1}1 + \text{Sin}^{-1}0)$.

$\text{Sin}^{-1}1 = \frac{\pi}{2}$ and $\text{Sin}^{-1}0 = 0$

$\sin(\text{Sin}^{-1}1 + \text{Sin}^{-1}0) = \sin\left(\frac{\pi}{2} + 0\right) = \sin\frac{\pi}{2} = 1$

b. Calculate $\text{Sin}^{-1}\left(\sin\frac{\pi}{2} + \sin\frac{3\pi}{2}\right)$.

$\sin\frac{\pi}{2} = 1$ and $\sin\frac{3\pi}{2} = -1$

$\text{Sin}^{-1}\left(\sin\frac{\pi}{2} + \sin\frac{3\pi}{2}\right) = \text{Sin}^{-1}(1 + (-1)) = \text{Sin}^{-1}0 = 0$

c. Calculate $\text{Sin}^{-1}\left(\sin\frac{\pi}{2} - \sin\frac{3\pi}{2}\right)$.

$\sin\frac{\pi}{2} = 1$ and $\sin\frac{3\pi}{2} = -1$

$\text{Sin}^{-1}\left(\sin\frac{\pi}{2} - \sin\frac{3\pi}{2}\right) = \text{Sin}^{-1}(1 - (-1)) = \text{Sin}^{-1}2$

There is no real number whose sine is 2. There is no solution.

Watch Out !

The domain of sin *x* is all real numbers. The domain of Sin *x* is the interval $\left[-\frac{\pi}{2}, \frac{\pi}{2}\right]$.

The domain of $\sin^{-1}x$ is the interval $[-1, 1]$.

The domain of $\text{Sin}^{-1}x$ is also $[-1, 1]$.

EXAMPLE 10

Graph $y = \sin(\text{Sin}^{-1}x)$.

STEP 1 Use composition of functions.

The domain of $\text{Sin}^{-1}x$: $[-1, 1]$

The range of $\text{Sin}^{-1}x$: $\left[-\frac{\pi}{2}, \frac{\pi}{2}\right]$

The domain of $\sin(\text{Sin}^{-1}x)$: $\left[-\frac{\pi}{2}, \frac{\pi}{2}\right]$

The range of $\sin(\text{Sin}^{-1}x)$: $[-1, 1]$

STEP 2 Graph the resulting function $y = x$, using the domain and range found in Step 1.

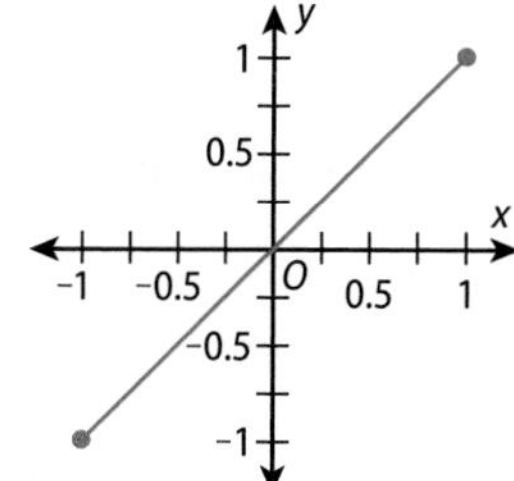

Try It This Way

Make a conjecture based on the composition of a function with its inverse to get $y = x$. Then verify the conjecture analytically or graphically.

Inverse Cosine Function

The Inverse Cosine Relation and Function

The diagram at the right shows the graph $y = \cos x$ over the interval from -2π to 2π. As with the sine function, the cosine function is not one-to-one. The inverse of $y = \cos x$ is a relation but not a function.

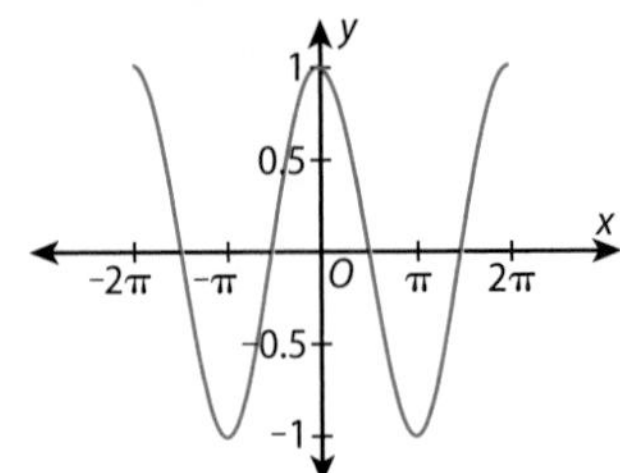

EXAMPLE 1

a. Find all values of x for which $\cos x = -1$.

Make a table using the graph as a guide.

x	-2π	$-\pi$	0	π	2π
$\cos x$	1	-1	1	-1	1

If x is any odd multiple of π, then $\cos x = -1$.

Therefore, if n is an integer, then $x = (2n + 1)\pi$.

b. Find all values of x for which $\cos x = 0$.

When $x = \frac{\pi}{2}$, $\cos \frac{\pi}{2} = 0$.

The cosine function is periodic with period 2π, but has a value of 0 every π units.

Therefore, $x = \pi n + \frac{\pi}{2}$, where n is any integer.

Need More HELP

$y = \cos x$
domain: all real numbers
range: $[-1, 1]$

$y = \cos^{-1} x$
domain: $[-1, 1]$
range: all real numbers.

The inverse of $y = \cos x$ is a relation but not a function. For each value of y, there are infinitely many values of x.

If you restrict the domain of the cosine function to the interval $[0, \pi]$, then the restricted function is one-to-one and its inverse is a function. The restricted domain, $[0, \pi]$, is the set of **principal values** for the cosine function. For the definition of the cosine with its principal values and the inverse cosine function, see the *Got To Know!* box.

EXAMPLE 2

Estimate a principal value in radians for which $\cos x = 0.88$.

The equation $\cos x = 0.88$ can also be written $x = \cos^{-1} 0.88$.

Set the calculator to radian mode. $\cos 0.49$ is about 0.8823. $\cos 0.50$ is about 0.8776.

Both 0.49 and 0.50 are reasonable estimates of x.

GOT TO KNOW!

The Cosine Function

$y = \text{Cos}\, x$ if and only if $y = \cos x$ and $0 \leq x \leq \pi$.

The Inverse Cosine Function

$y = \text{Cos}^{-1} x$ if and only if x is in $[0, \pi]$, and $x = \cos y$.

$(-1, \pi)$ $y = \text{Cos}^{-1} x$ $(1, 0)$

Domain: $-1 \leq x \leq 1$
Range: $0 \leq y \leq \pi$

EXAMPLE 3

Find the value of x between 0° and 90° for which $\cos x = \frac{\sqrt{3}}{2}$.

Sketch and label a 30°-60°-90° right triangle as shown.

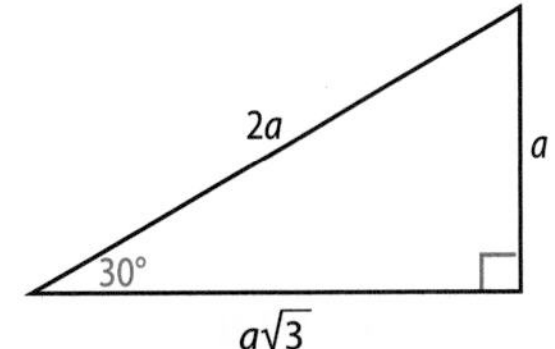

cosine: $\frac{\text{adjacent}}{\text{hypotenuse}}$ $\qquad \cos 30° = \frac{a\sqrt{3}}{2a} = \frac{\sqrt{3}}{2}$

Thus, $x = 30°$.

SEARCH

To see step-by-step videos of these problems, enter the page number into the SWadvantage.com Search Bar.

Using a Calculator to Evaluate the Inverse Cosine

In many applications, you will need to use a calculator to evaluate the inverse cosine.

EXAMPLE 4

a. If $\cos x = 0.2$ and $0° < x° < 180°$, find x to the nearest tenth of a degree.

MODE Degrees 2nd COS 0 . 2) ENTER

$x \approx 78.5°$

b. If $\cos x = 0.2$ and $0 < x < \pi$, find x in radians to the nearest tenth.

MODE Radians 2nd COS 0 . 2) ENTER

$x \approx 1.4$

c. If $\cos x = -0.2$ and $0 < x < \pi$, find x in radians to the nearest tenth.

MODE Radians 2nd COS (−) 0 . 2) ENTER

$x \approx 1.8$

Watch Out !

Decide for each individual situation whether you need to be in degree mode or in radian mode.

Using the Inverse Cosine In Right Triangles

To find the measure of an angle in a right triangle, you can use an inverse trigonometric function.

EXAMPLE 5

In right triangle XYZ, find the measure of $\angle X$ to the nearest degree.

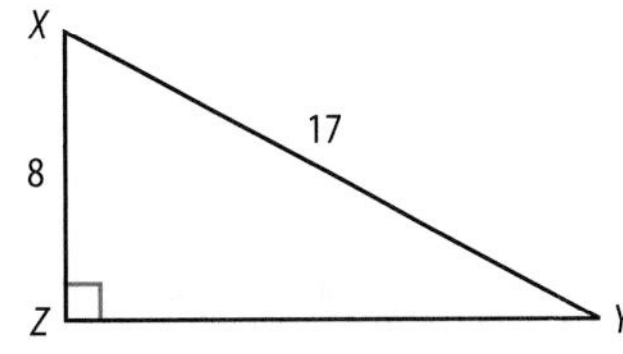

Write $\cos X$. $\qquad \cos X = \frac{8}{17}$

Solve for $m\angle X$. $\qquad m\angle X = \text{Cos}^{-1}\left(\frac{8}{17}\right)$

Use degree mode. $\qquad m\angle X \approx 62°$

Therefore, $m\angle X \approx 62°$.

Using the Composition of a Function with an Inverse

The application of the inverse of a function f to the function f gives the identify function x. If f is a function whose inverse is a function, then $f(f^{-1}(x)) = f^{-1}(f(x)) = x$.

EXAMPLE 6

Find cos (Cos^{-1} 0.8).

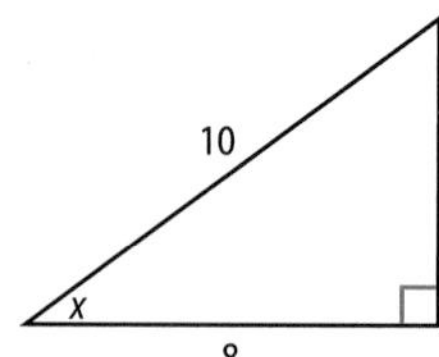

Sketch a right triangle.

Let $x = \text{Cos}^{-1}\left(\frac{8}{10}\right)$.

Then $\cos x = \frac{8}{10}$, or $\frac{4}{5}$.

So, $\cos(\text{Cos}^{-1}\ 0.8) = \frac{4}{5}$.

Need More HELP

Note that $0.8 = \frac{8}{10}$.

EXAMPLE 7

Find the value of $\text{Cos}^{-1}\left(\cos \frac{7\pi}{6}\right)$.

STEP 1 Since $\frac{7\pi}{6} = 210°$, sketch a coordinate diagram showing a right triangle with a 30° angle in the third quadrant as shown.

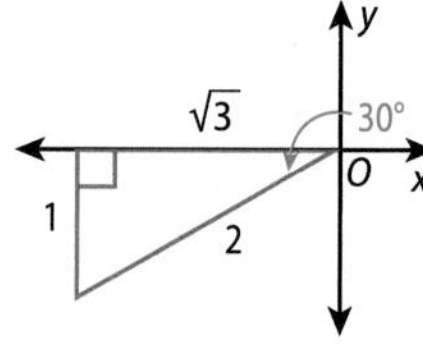

$$\cos \frac{7\pi}{6} = \cos 210° = -\frac{\sqrt{3}}{2}$$

STEP 2 Now draw a second reference angle. The angle should be in the interval [90°, 180°].

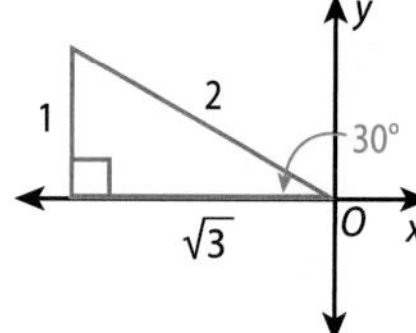

$$\cos 150° = -\frac{\sqrt{3}}{2}$$

STEP 3 The range of $\text{Cos}^{-1} x$ is $[0, \pi]$, or [0°, 180°].

$$\text{Cos}^{-1}\left(-\frac{\sqrt{3}}{2}\right) = 150°, \text{ or } \frac{5\pi}{6}$$

Therefore, $\text{Cos}^{-1}\left(\cos \frac{7\pi}{6}\right) = 150°$, or $\frac{5\pi}{6}$.

CHECK Use a calculator to make an estimate.

$$\text{Cos}^{-1}\left(\cos \frac{7\pi}{6}\right) \approx 2.618 \text{ and } \frac{5\pi}{6} \approx 2.618$$

Watch Out !

$\frac{7\pi}{6}$ is not a principal value of $y = \text{Cos}\, x$.

EXAMPLE 8

Under what conditions on x will $\text{Cos}^{-1}(\cos x) = x$?

Use the definition of $\text{Cos}^{-1} x$. The range of $\text{Cos}^{-1} x$ is $[0, \pi]$, or [0°, 180°].

For $\text{Cos}^{-1}(\cos x)$ to equal x, the restricted domain for $\cos x$ must be $[0, \pi]$, or [0°, 180°].

Using Various Trigonometric Functions and Inverses Together

In some problems, sin *x*, cos *x*, and inverses appear together in combination.

EXAMPLE 9

a. Calculate $\sin\left(\text{Cos}^{-1}\left(-\frac{1}{2}\right) - \text{Sin}^{-1}\frac{1}{2}\right)$.

Use principal values. $\text{Cos}^{-1}\left(-\frac{1}{2}\right) = \frac{2\pi}{3}$ $\quad \text{Sin}^{-1}\frac{1}{2} = \frac{\pi}{6}$

Substitute and subtract. $\text{Cos}^{-1}\left(-\frac{1}{2}\right) - \text{Sin}^{-1}\frac{1}{2} = \frac{2\pi}{3} - \frac{\pi}{6}$

$= \frac{\pi}{2}$

$\sin\left(\text{Cos}^{-1}\left(-\frac{1}{2}\right) - \text{Sin}^{-1}\frac{1}{2}\right) = \sin\frac{\pi}{2} = 1$

b. Calculate $\cos\left(\text{Sin}^{-1}\frac{1}{2} + \text{Cos}^{-1}\frac{1}{2}\right)$.

Use principal values. $\text{Sin}^{-1}\frac{1}{2} = \frac{\pi}{6}$ $\quad \text{Cos}^{-1}\frac{1}{2} = \frac{\pi}{3}$

Substitute and subtract. $\text{Sin}^{-1}\frac{1}{2} + \text{Cos}^{-1}\frac{1}{2} = \frac{\pi}{6} + \frac{\pi}{3}$

$= \frac{\pi}{2}$

$\cos\left(\text{Sin}^{-1}\frac{1}{2} + \text{Cos}^{-1}\frac{1}{2}\right) = \cos\frac{\pi}{2} = 0$

Watch Out !

The domain of cos *x* is all real numbers.

The domain of Cos *x* is the interval $[0, \pi]$.

The domain of $\cos^{-1} x$ is the interval $[-1, 1]$.

The domain of $\text{Cos}^{-1} x$ is also $[-1, 1]$.

EXAMPLE 10

Write $\sin(\text{Cos}^{-1} x)$ in terms of *x*.

STEP 1 Sketch a right triangle diagram.

Let $A = \text{Cos}^{-1} x$.

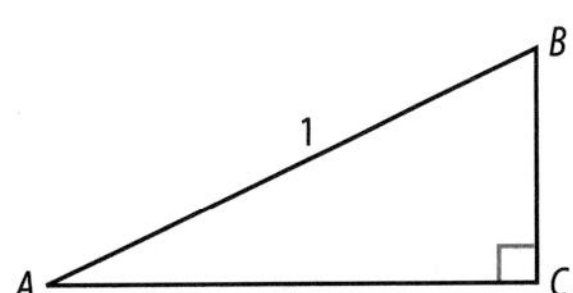

STEP 2 Write an expression for *BC*, the length of the side opposite $\angle A$.

$BC = \sqrt{1 - x^2}$

STEP 3 Use the definition of sine.

$\sin A = \frac{\sqrt{1 - x^2}}{1} = \sqrt{1 - x^2}$

Therefore, $\sin(\text{Cos}^{-1} x) = \sqrt{1 - x^2}$.

SEARCH

To see step-by-step videos of these problems, enter the page number into the SWadvantage.com Search Bar.

The Inverse Tangent Function

Evaluating the Inverse Tangent Function

Ways to REMEMBER

An easy way to remember the principal values for the tangent function is to recall that the graph has asymptotes at $x = -\frac{\pi}{2}$ and at $x = \frac{\pi}{2}$.

Like the sine and cosine functions, the tangent function, $y = \tan x$, is not a one-to-one function. The domain can be restricted to the interval $-\frac{\pi}{2} < x < \frac{\pi}{2}$, or $-90° < x < 90°$, which is its set of principal values. The restricted function, $y = \text{Tan}\, x$, is one-to-one and has an inverse that is a function. For the definition of the tangent function with its principal values and the inverse tangent function, see the *Got To Know!* box.

EXAMPLE 1

a. Find all values of x for which $\tan x = 1$.

Sketch a right triangle whose legs have length 1.

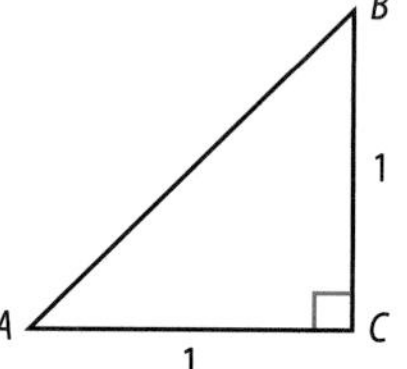

Set up the equation. $\tan x = \frac{\text{opposite}}{\text{adjacent}} = \frac{1}{1} = 1$

Solve. $x = 45°$

Since the tangent has period 180°, then $x = (180°)n + 45°$.

b. Evaluate $\text{Tan}^{-1}\left(-\sqrt{3}\right)$.

Use a reference angle in the fourth quadrant.

$\tan x < 0$ when $-90° < x \leq 0°$ $\text{Tan}^{-1}\left(-\sqrt{3}\right) = -60°$

Try It This Way

You can use your calculator's TAN^{-1} feature to solve for x in $\tan x = 1$.

Enter 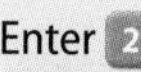  ) ENTER.

EXAMPLE 2

A hot air balloon rises at the rate of 120 feet per minute. An observer watches this from 500 feet away from the point where the balloon begins its ascent. To the nearest degree, at what angle of elevation will the observer see the balloon after 6 minutes?

Sketch a right triangle showing the altitude after 6 minutes.

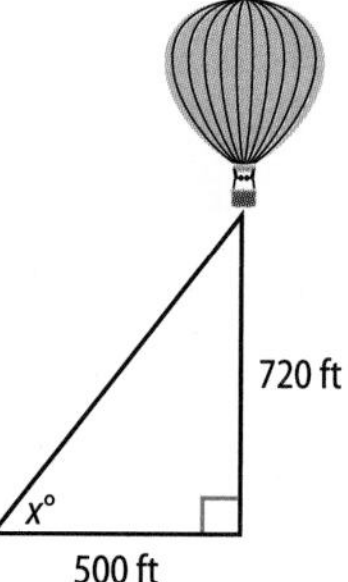

Use $d = rt$ to find the height of the balloon. $d = (120)(6) = 720$

Set up and solve the equation. $x° = \text{Tan}^{-1}\left(\frac{720}{500}\right) \approx 55°$

So, the observer will see the balloon at an approximate angle of elevation of 55°.

GOT TO KNOW!

The Tangent Function

$y = \text{Tan}\, x$ if and only if $y = \tan x$ and $-\frac{\pi}{2} < x < \frac{\pi}{2}$.

The Inverse Tangent Function

$y = \text{Tan}^{-1} x$ if and only if $x = \tan y$ and $-\frac{\pi}{2} < y < \frac{\pi}{2}$.

Using Inverse Functions and Composition

EXAMPLE 3

Evaluate $\cos\left(\text{Tan}^{-1}\left(-\frac{4}{3}\right)\right)$.

STEP 1 Sketch a reference triangle in the fourth quadrant.

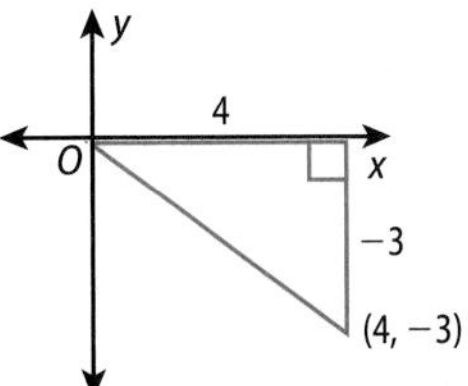

STEP 2 Apply the Pythagorean Theorem to find the length of the hypotenuse.

$$\sqrt{3^2 + 4^2} = 5$$

STEP 3 Use the cosine ratio to evaluate the function.

$\cos\left(\text{Tan}^{-1}\left(-\frac{4}{3}\right)\right) = \frac{3}{5}$, or 0.6.

Watch Out !

Use a calculator set to radian mode.

If the calculator shows a decimal close to but not equal to 0.6, then use another method to verify that $\cos\left(\text{Tan}^{-1}\left(-\frac{4}{3}\right)\right)$.

EXAMPLE 4

Verify that $\cos\left(\text{Tan}^{-1}\left(\frac{1}{x}\right)\right) = \frac{\sqrt{x^2+1}}{x^2+1}$ if $x = 1$.

Evaluate the expression on the left side for $x = 1$. $\cos\left(\text{Tan}^{-1}\left(\frac{1}{1}\right)\right) = \cos\left(\frac{\pi}{4}\right) = \frac{\sqrt{2}}{2}$

Evaluate the expression on the right side for $x = 1$. $\frac{\sqrt{1^2+1}}{1^2+1} = \frac{\sqrt{2}}{2}$

Both sides are equal to $\frac{\sqrt{2}}{2}$, so the equation is true when $x = 1$.

Inverse Functions and Reciprocal Functions

The definition of the inverse cotangent is stated below. Notice that it is defined in terms of the cotangent, the reciprocal of the tangent.

$$y = \text{Cot}^{-1} x \text{ if and only if } \cot y = x \text{ and } 0 < y < \pi.$$

EXAMPLE 5

Let $x > 0$. Derive a relationship between $\text{Cot}^{-1} x$ and $\text{Tan}^{-1}\left(\frac{1}{x}\right)$.

Sketch a reference triangle in the first quadrant since $x > 0$.

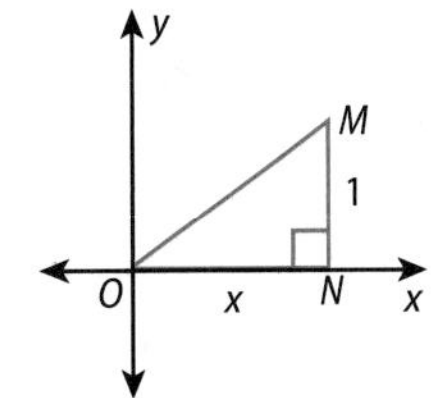

$\text{Tan}^{-1}\left(\frac{1}{x}\right) = m\angle MON$

Since $\text{Cot}\,(m\angle MON) = \frac{x}{1} = x$, then $\text{Cot}^{-1} x = m\angle MON$.

Therefore, $\text{Cot}^{-1} x = \text{Tan}^{-1}\left(\frac{1}{x}\right)$.

SEARCH

To see step-by-step videos of these problems, enter the page number into the SWadvantage.com Search Bar.

Solving Trigonometric Equations I

Exploring Trigonometric Equations

A **trigonometric equation** is an equation that involves at least one trigonometric function. The solution to a trigonometric equation is any number for which the equation is true.

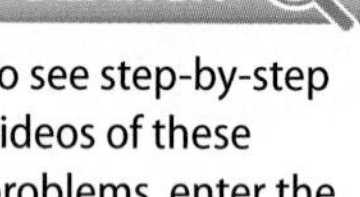

SEARCH

To see step-by-step videos of these problems, enter the page number into the SWadvantage.com Search Bar.

Watch Out !

The graph of $y = \sin x$ is bounded by the horizontal lines $y = -1$ and $y = 1$.

If $\sin x = a$, then a must be between -1 and 1 for the equation to have a solution.

EXAMPLE 1

How many solutions does each equation have?

a. $\sin x = \sqrt{2}$

METHOD 1

Since $-1 \leq \sin x \leq 1$ and $\sqrt{2} > 1$, this equation has no solution.

METHOD 2

Solving by calculator gives an error message. There is no solution.

b. $\tan x = \sqrt{3}$ **if** $0° < x < 90°$

The graph of $y = \tan x$ on the interval $-90° < x < 90°$ is one-to-one and continuous. Every horizontal line intersects the graph in exactly one point. The equation has exactly one solution.

c. $\cos x = \frac{\sqrt{2}}{2}$

Since $-1 \leq \frac{\sqrt{2}}{2} \leq 1$ and $y = \cos x$ is continuous, there is at least one solution. On the interval $0 < x < 2\pi$, any horizontal line with equation $y = a$, where $-1 \leq a \leq 1$, will intersect the graph in exactly two points. Because the function is periodic with period 2π, there are infinitely many solutions.

There are many ways to find exact and approximate solutions of trigonometric equations.

EXAMPLE 2

Solve each equation.

a. $\cos x = 0.85$ **given that** $0 \leq x \leq \pi$

Use a calculator.

MODE Radian 2nd COS . 8 5) ENTER

To the nearest hundredth, x is approximately 0.55.

Need More HELP

A reference triangle is often a useful aid in determining solutions. Be attentive to the sign of the value of the given trigonometric function.

b. $\sin x = -\frac{\sqrt{3}}{2}$ **given that** $180° \leq x \leq 270°$

Sketch a 30°–60°–90° triangle as a reference triangle in the third quadrant.

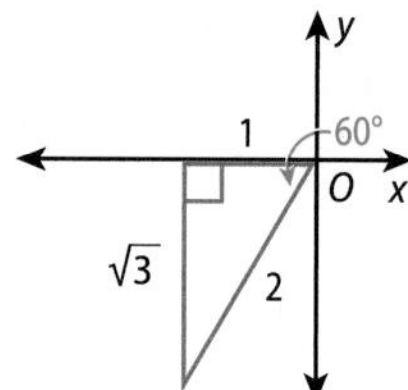

$$x = 60° + 180°$$

$$x = 240°$$

Therefore, $\sin x = -\frac{\sqrt{3}}{2}$ when $x = 240°$.

Solving Trigonometric Equations Using Properties

The properties of equality can be used to solve trigonometric equations.

EXAMPLE 3

Find all solutions to $\sin(x - 30°) - 4 = -3$.

	$\sin(x - 30°) - 4 = -3$
Add 4 to both sides.	$\sin(x - 30°) = 1$
Evaluate $\sin^{-1}1$.	$x - 30° = 90°$
Add 30° to both sides.	$x = 120°$
$y = \sin x$ has period 360°.	$x = 120° + 360°n$, n an integer

$\sin(x - 30°) = 1$

$(x - 30°) = \sin^{-1} 1$

$x - 30° = 90°$

EXAMPLE 4

Find all solutions to $\cos(2x) = 0.5$ in the interval $0 \le x \le \pi$.

	$\cos(2x) = 0.5$
Evaluate $\cos^{-1}0.5$.	$2x = \frac{\pi}{3}$
Solve for x.	$x = \frac{\pi}{6}$
Sketch a graph.	In $0 \le x \le \pi$, $x = \frac{\pi}{6}$ or $\frac{5\pi}{6}$.

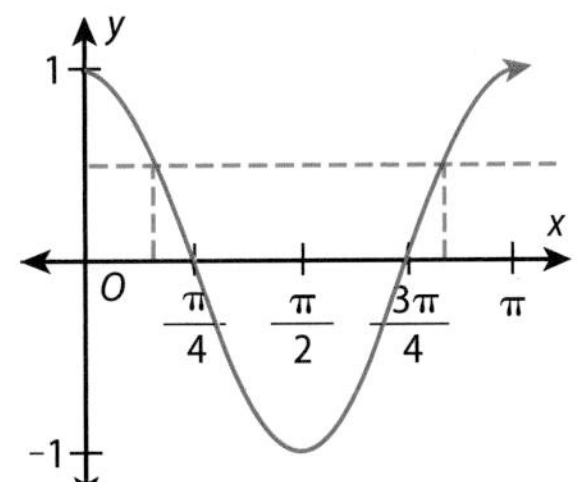

Watch Out

Not every trigonometric function has period 2π. The period of $y = \cos(2x)$ is π, not 2π.

EXAMPLE 5

Find all solutions to $2 \sin x + 3 = 4$.

	$2 \sin x + 3 = 4$
Apply properties of equality.	$\sin x = 0.5$
Solve.	$x = 30°$ or $150°$, or $\frac{\pi}{6}$ or $\frac{5\pi}{6}$

In general, the solution is $x = 30° + 360°n$ or $x = 150° + 360°n$, or $x = \frac{\pi}{6} + 2\pi n$ or $x = \frac{5\pi}{6} + 2\pi n$, where n is any integer.

Watch Out

Use a graph to predict or check. The graph and dashed line indicate that there are 4 solutions.

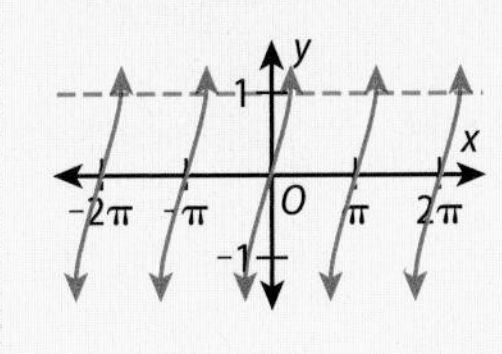

EXAMPLE 6

Find all solutions to $\sin x - \cos x = 0$ in the interval $-2\pi \le x \le 2\pi$.

	$\sin x - \cos x = 0$
Add $\cos x$ to each side.	$\sin x = \cos x$
Divide each side by $\cos x$.	$\frac{\sin x}{\cos x} = 1$
Substitute: $\tan x = \frac{\sin x}{\cos x}$	$\tan x = 1$
Solve.	$x = -\frac{7\pi}{4}, -\frac{3\pi}{4}, \frac{\pi}{4}$ or $\frac{5\pi}{4}$.

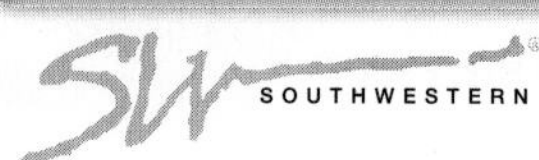

Solving Quadratic Trigonometric Equations

Just as you can solve an algebraic equation such as $x^2 - x = 0$ by factoring, you can also solve many trigonometric equations by factoring.

Watch Out

There are two square roots of a positive number.

EXAMPLE 7

Solve $(\cos x)^2 = \frac{3}{4}$ given that $0° \leq x \leq 360°$.

Find the square root of both sides. $(\cos x)^2 = \frac{3}{4}$

Solve two equations. $\cos x = \frac{\sqrt{3}}{2}$ or $\cos x = -\frac{\sqrt{3}}{2}$

$x = 30°, 150°, 210°,$ or $330°$

Need More HELP

When the problem does not have restrictions on the domain, the solution should be written as a general solution.

EXAMPLE 8

Solve $2\cos^2 x - 7\cos x + 3 = 0$.

Let $u = \cos x$. $2u^2 - 7u + 3 = 0$

Factor. $(2u - 1)(u - 3) = 0$

Apply the Zero-Product Property. $u = 0.5$ or $u = 3$

Substitute $\cos x$ for u. $\cos x = 0.5$ or $\cos x = 3$

Solve. $\cos x = 3$ has no solution. $\cos x = 0.5$ when $x = 60° + 360°n$

or $x = 300° + 360°n$

Therefore, if n is any integer, $x = 60° + 360°n$ or $x = 300° + 360°n$.

Need More HELP

For a review of using the quadratic formula, go to *The Quadratic Formula* in *Algebra* (Book 2, p. 1710).

EXAMPLE 9

Solve $\cos^2 x - 2\cos x - 1 = 0$ in the interval $0° \leq x \leq 180°$.

Let $u = \cos x$. $u^2 - 2u - 1 = 0$

Apply the quadratic formula. $u = \frac{-(-2) \pm \sqrt{(-2)^2 - 4(1)(-1)}}{2(1)}$

$u = 1 \pm \sqrt{2}$

$u \approx -0.4142$ or 2.4142

Replace u with $\cos x$. $\cos x \approx -0.4142$ or $\cos x \approx 2.4142$

Use a calculator in degree mode. $\cos x \approx 2.4142$ has no solution.

If $\cos x \approx -0.4142$, then $x \approx 114.47°$

Use a graph to confirm that $y = \cos x$ has exactly one solution in the interval $0° \leq x \leq 180°$.

Therefore, $\approx 114.47°$.

Solve $\cos^2 x - \sin^2 x = 0$.

METHOD 1

STEP 1 Use properties of equality and square roots.

$$\cos^2 x - \sin^2 x = 0$$

$$\cos^2 x = \sin^2 x$$

$\sqrt{x^2} = |x|$

$$|\cos x| = |\sin x|$$

$$\cos x = \pm \sin x$$

$$\cos x = \sin x \text{ or } \cos x = -\sin x$$

STEP 2 On one set of axes, graph $y = \cos x$ and $y = \sin x$. On another set of axes, graph $y = \cos x$ and $y = -\sin x$.

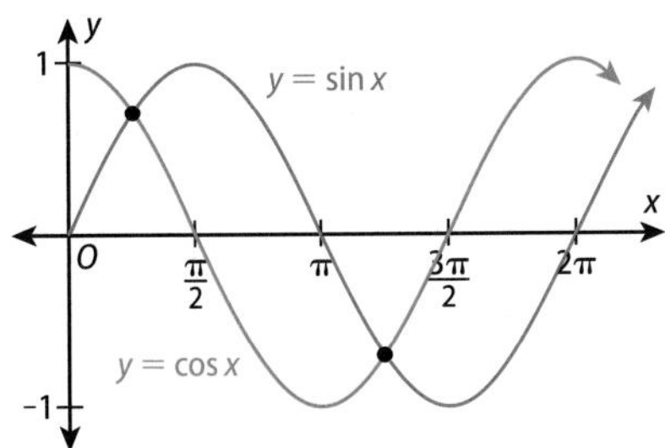

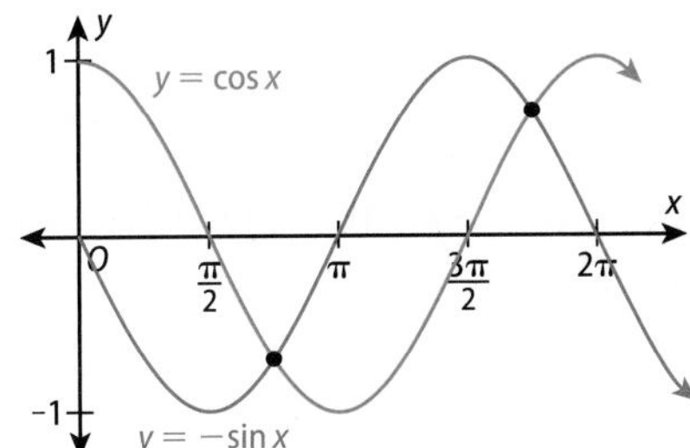

The graphs indicate that there are four solutions in the interval $0 \leq x \leq 2\pi$.

STEP 3 Solve the two equations. Write the general solution.

$$\cos x = \sin x \qquad \cos x = -\sin x$$

$$x = \frac{\pi}{4} \text{ or } \frac{5\pi}{4} \qquad x = \frac{3\pi}{4} \text{ or } \frac{7\pi}{4}$$

$x = \frac{\pi}{4} + 2\pi n, \frac{3\pi}{4} + 2\pi n, \frac{5\pi}{4} + 2\pi n,$ or $\frac{7\pi}{4} + 2\pi n$, where n is any integer.

METHOD 2

Factor the difference of two squares.

$$\cos^2 x - \sin^2 x = 0$$

$a^2 - b^2 = (a + b)(a - b)$

$$(\cos x + \sin x)(\cos x - \sin x) = 0$$

Apply the Zero-Product Property.

$$\cos x + \sin x = 0 \text{ or } \cos x - \sin x = 0$$

$$\cos x = \sin x \text{ or } \cos x = -\sin x$$

$$\frac{\sin x}{\cos x} = 1 \text{ or } \frac{\sin x}{\cos x} = -1$$

$\tan x = \frac{\sin x}{\cos x}$

$$\tan x = 1 \text{ or } \tan x = -1$$

In general, $x = \frac{\pi}{4} + 2\pi n, \frac{3\pi}{4} + 2\pi n, \frac{5\pi}{4} + 2\pi n,$ or $\frac{7\pi}{4} + 2\pi n$.

Try It This Way

It is common that a given problem can be solved in a variety of ways. Try graphing $y = \cos^2 x - \sin^2 x$ on a calculator. Then look for the x-intercepts of the graph using a trace feature. However, a decimal solution rather than an exact solution will be found.

SEARCH

To see step-by-step videos of these problems, enter the page number into the SWadvantage.com Search Bar.

Watch Out

If you solve a problem by means of one method and find the solution to differ from that found by a second method, then either there are two equivalent forms of the solution or there is an error.

Solving Trigonometric Equations II

Recall that equations that are true for all allowable values of the variables are identities.

Exploring the Use of Identities to Solve Equations

Some trigonometric equations involve only one trigonometric function. There are many trigonometric equations that involve multiple functions. The use of a trigonometric identity can simplify solving such equations.

EXAMPLE 1

Solve $\csc\theta \sin\theta = 1$. State any restrictions on θ.

$$\csc\theta\sin\theta = 1$$

Use the definition of $\csc\theta$. $\quad \frac{1}{\sin\theta}\cdot\sin\theta = 1$

Simplify. $\quad 1 = 1$

The equation is true for all real numbers except those for which $\sin\theta = 0$. Therefore θ is any real number except for the multiples of π.

There are no values of x for which $\cos x = 2$ because $-1 \le \cos x \le 1$. The equation has no solution.

EXAMPLE 2

Solve $\cos^2 x - \sin^2 x = 2$. State any restrictions on x.

Use a double angle identity. $\quad \cos^2 x - \sin^2 x = 2$

$\cos^2 x - \sin^2 x = \cos(2x)$ $\quad \cos(2x) = 2$

Evaluate $\cos^{-1} 2$. $\quad 2x = \cos^{-1} 2$

There is no solution.

SEARCH

To see step-by-step videos of these problems, enter the page number into the SWadvantage.com Search Bar.

EXAMPLE 3

Solve $\cos^2 x - \sin^2 x - 1 = \frac{\sqrt{2}}{2}$ on the interval $0 \le x \le \frac{\pi}{2}$.

METHOD 1

Find an algebraic solution. $\quad \cos^2 x - \sin^2 x - 1 = \frac{\sqrt{2}}{2}$

Use a double angle identity: $\cos^2 x - \sin^2 x = \cos(2x)$. $\quad \cos(2x) - 1 = \frac{\sqrt{2}}{2}$

Add 1 to both sides. $\quad \cos(2x) = \frac{\sqrt{2}}{2} + 1$

Evaluate $\cos^{-1}\left(\frac{\sqrt{2}}{2} + 1\right)$. $\quad \cos(2x) = \text{no solution}$

There are no values of x for which $\cos x = \left(\frac{\sqrt{2}}{2} + 1\right)$ because $-1 \le \cos x \le 1$. The equation has no solution.

METHOD 2

Sketch the graph of $y = \cos^2 x - \sin^2 x - 1 - \frac{\sqrt{2}}{2}$.

Since the graph has no x-intercepts, there are no solutions.

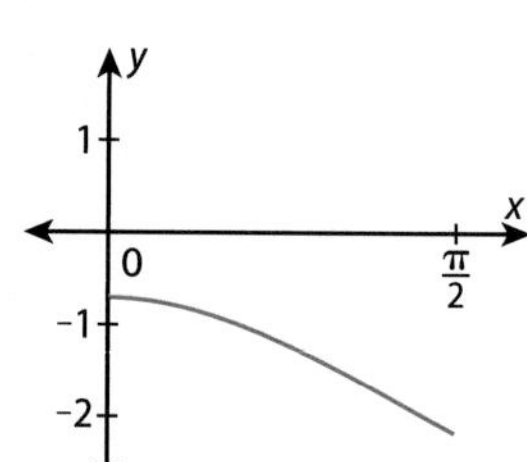

Using Reciprocal Identities to Solve Equations

When reciprocal functions are involved in a trigonometric equation, one of the reciprocal identities can be used to write an equation involving only one function.

EXAMPLE 4

Solve $\cos x - \sec x = 0$.

$$\cos x - \sec x = 0$$

Add $\sec x$ to both sides. $\quad \cos x = \sec x$

Use $\sec x = \frac{1}{\cos x}$. $\quad \cos x = \frac{1}{\cos x}$

Multiply both sides by $\cos x$. $\quad \cos^2 x = 1$

Subtract 1 from both sides. $\quad \cos^2 x - 1 = 0$

Factor. $\quad \cos x = 1$ or $\cos x = -1$

$$x = 0 + 2\pi n \text{ or } x = \pi + 2\pi n$$

So, all solutions are $x = \pi n$, where n is an integer.

Watch Out!

Numbers for which a denominator is 0 must be excluded from consideration of solutions. There are no solutions when $\cos x = 0$, that is, when x is a multiple of $\frac{\pi}{2}$.

EXAMPLE 5

Solve $2 \sin x + \csc x = 3$ on the interval $0 \le x \le 2\pi$.

STEP 1 Use identities to write the equation so that it involves just one trigonometric function, and then simplify.

$$2 \sin x + \csc x = 3$$

$\csc x = \frac{1}{\sin x}$ $\quad 2 \sin x + \frac{1}{\sin x} = 3$

$$2 \sin^2 x + 1 = 3 \sin x$$

$$2 \sin^2 x - 3 \sin x + 1 = 0$$

STEP 2 Use substitution to write and solve an algebraic equation.

Let $u = \sin x$. $\quad 2u^2 - 3u + 1 = 0$

Factor. $\quad (2u - 1)(u - 1) = 0$

Solve. $\quad u = \frac{1}{2}$ or $u = 1$

STEP 3 Use substitution again to write and solve two trigonometric equations.

$$\sin x = \frac{1}{2} \text{ or } \sin x = 1$$

If $\sin x = \frac{1}{2}$ and $0 \le x \le 2\pi$, then $x = \frac{\pi}{6}$ or $\frac{5\pi}{6}$.

If $\sin x = 1$ and $0 \le x \le 2\pi$, then $x = \frac{\pi}{2}$.

Therefore, $x = \frac{\pi}{6}, \frac{\pi}{2}$, or $\frac{5\pi}{6}$.

Need More HELP?

Review the three reciprocal identities.

$\csc \theta = \frac{1}{\sin \theta}$

$\sec \theta = \frac{1}{\cos \theta}$

$\cot \theta = \frac{1}{\tan \theta}$

Using Pythagorean, Cofunction, and Negative-Angle Identities to Solve Equations

The occurrence of the square of sin x, cos x, or tan x might suggest the use of a Pythagorean identity. Other clues might suggest the use of a cofunction identity or negative-angle identity.

Review the three Pythagorean Identities.

$\sin^2 x + \cos^2 x = 1$
$1 + \cot^2 x = \csc^2 x$
$1 + \tan^2 x = \sec^2 x$

EXAMPLE 6

Solve $\tan^2 x + \sec^2 x = 1$.

	$\tan^2 x + \sec^2 x = 1$
$1 + \tan^2 x = \sec^2 x$	$\tan^2 x + (1 + \tan^2 x) = 1$
Simplify.	$2\tan^2 x = 0$
Simplify.	$\tan x = 0$

The tangent function has period π. Therefore, $x = n\pi$, where n is an integer.

The cofunction identities are symbolic ways of saying that the sine and cosine functions are translations of one another.

$\sin x = \cos(90° - x)$
$\cos x = \sin(90° - x)$

EXAMPLE 7

Solve $\cos(90° - x) + \sin x = \sqrt{3}$ on the interval $0° \leq x \leq 360°$.

	$\cos(90° - x) + \sin x = \sqrt{3}$
$\cos(90° - x) = \sin x$	$\sin x + \sin x = \sqrt{3}$
Simplify.	$\sin x = \frac{\sqrt{3}}{2}$

In the interval $0° \leq x \leq 360°$, $x = 60°$ or $120°$.

EXAMPLE 8

Solve $(1 + \sin^2(-\theta)) + 2(1 - \cos\theta) = 5$. Use a graph to confirm.

	$(1 + \sin^2(-\theta)) + 2(1 - \cos\theta) = 5$
$\sin(-\theta) = -\sin\theta$	$(1 - \sin^2\theta) + 2(1 - \cos\theta) = 5$
$\cos^2\theta = 1 - \sin^2\theta$	$\cos^2\theta + 2(1 - \cos\theta) = 5$
Simplify.	$\cos^2\theta - 2\cos\theta - 3 = 0$
Let $u = \cos\theta$.	$u^2 - 2u - 3 = 0$
Factor.	$(u - 3)(u + 1) = 0$
Apply the Zero-Product Property.	$u = 3$ or $u = -1$
Let $\cos\theta = u$.	$\cos\theta = 3$ or $\cos\theta = -1$

The equation $\cos\theta = 3$ has no solution.

If $\cos\theta = -1$, then $\theta = (2n + 1)\pi$, where n is any integer.

The graph at the right confirms the results. It shows the graphs of $y = (1 + \sin^2(-\theta)) + 2(1 - \cos\theta)$ and $y = 5$. The graphs intersect where $x = -\pi$ and π.

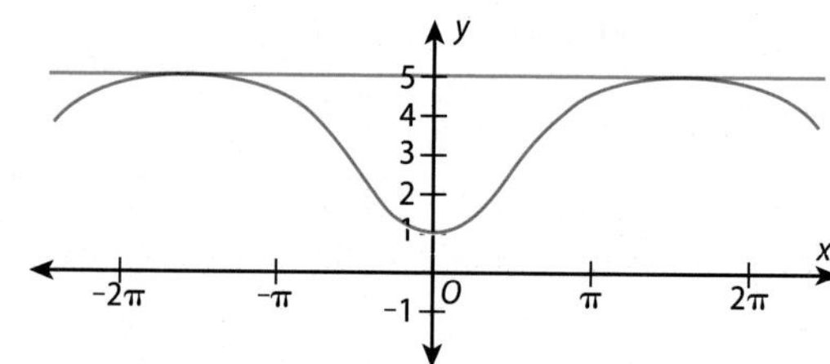

Using Addition, Double-, and Half-Angle Identities

In many equations, sum and difference identities, double-angle identities, and half-angle identities play a role in the solution process.

EXAMPLE 9

Solve $\sin(\theta + 30°) = \cos\theta$ in the interval $0 < \theta < 90°$.

$$\sin(\theta + 30°) = \cos\theta$$

Use an addition formula. $$\sin\theta\cos 30° + \cos\theta\sin 30° = \cos\theta$$

Evaluate cos 30° and sin 30°. $$\sqrt{3}\sin\theta + \cos\theta = 2\cos\theta$$

Simplify. $$\sqrt{3}\sin\theta = \cos\theta$$

$$\frac{\sqrt{3}}{3} = \frac{\sin\theta}{\cos\theta}$$

$\tan\theta = \frac{\sin\theta}{\cos\theta}$ $$\tan\theta = \frac{\sqrt{3}}{3}$$

Thus, in the interval $0 < \theta < 90°$, $\theta = 30°$.

EXAMPLE 10

Find all solutions to $\sin 2x - \sin x = 0$. Use a graph to confirm.

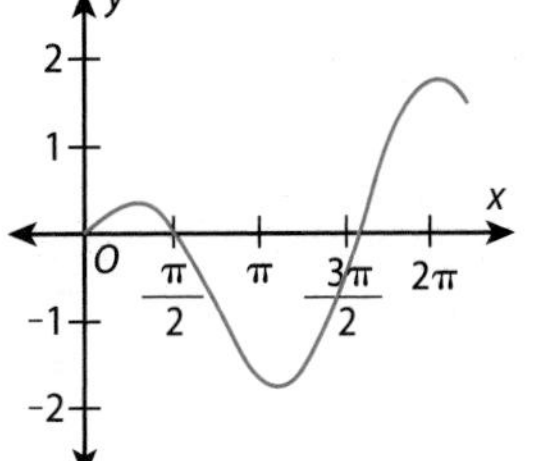

$$\sin 2x - \sin x = 0$$

$\sin 2x = 2\sin x\cos x$ $$2\sin x\cos x - \sin x = 0$$

Factor. $$\sin x(2\cos x - 1) = 0$$

$$\sin x = 0 \text{ or } \cos x = 0.5$$

$x = 180°n, 60° + 360°n$, or $300° + 360°n$, n an integer.

EXAMPLE 11

Solve $\cos\frac{x}{2} = 2\sin\frac{x}{2}$ given $0 \le x \le 2\pi$. Use a graph to confirm.

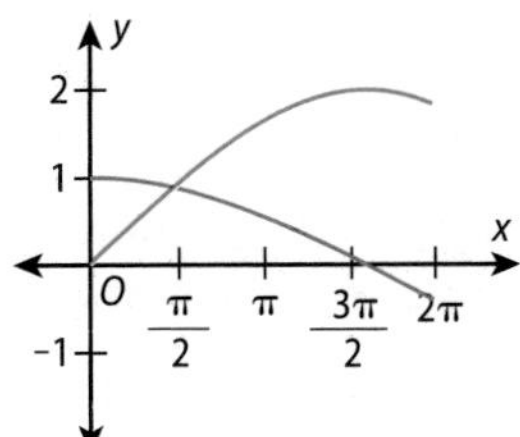

$$\cos\frac{x}{2} = 2\sin\frac{x}{2}$$

Use half-angle identities. $$\pm\sqrt{\frac{1+\cos x}{2}} = \pm 2\sqrt{\frac{1-\cos x}{2}}$$

Square each side. $$\frac{1+\cos x}{2} = 4\left(\frac{1-\cos x}{2}\right)$$

Multiply both sides by 2. $$1 + \cos x = 4(1 - \cos x)$$

Solve for x. $$\cos x = 0.6$$

$$x \approx 0.9273$$

In the interval $0 \le x \le 2\pi$, $x \approx 0.9273$ as the graph suggests.

Need More HELP

Review the sum and difference identities.

$\sin(x \pm y) = \sin x\cos y \pm \cos x\sin y$

$\cos(x \pm y) = \cos x\cos y \pm \sin x\sin y$

Review the double-angle identities.

$\sin 2x = 2\sin x\cos x$

$\cos 2x = \cos^2 x - \sin^2 x = 2\cos^2 x - 1 = 1 - 2\sin^2 x$

Review the half-angle identities.

$\sin\frac{x}{2} = \pm\sqrt{\frac{1-\cos x}{2}}$

$\cos\frac{x}{2} = \pm\sqrt{\frac{1+\cos x}{2}}$

SEARCH

To see step-by-step videos of these problems, enter the page number into the SWadvantage.com Search Bar.

Solving Trigonometric Inequalities

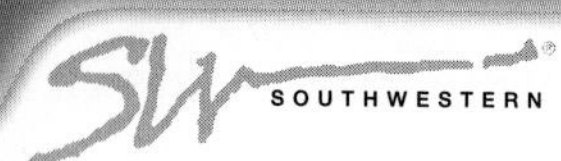

Exploring Trigonometric Inequalities

A **trigonometric inequality** is an inequality that involves trigonometric functions.

There are significant similarities and differences between trigonometric inequalities and algebraic inequalities, both with regard to method and solution possibilities.

SEARCH

To see step-by-step videos of these problems, enter the page number into the SWadvantage.com Search Bar.

EXAMPLE 1

Determine all solutions to $\sin x > 1$.

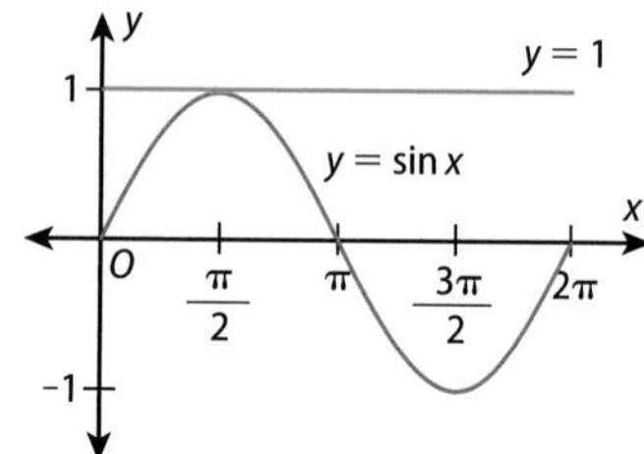

METHOD 1

Use analysis.

Since the range of the sine function is all real numbers between -1 and 1 inclusive, there are no solutions.

METHOD 2

Graph $y = \sin x$ and $y = 1$.

Analyze the graph. Although the graphs intersect, the point of intersection does not produce a solution.

By either method, the inequality has no solution.

Need More HELP

The sine and cosine functions are bounded functions. All range values for $y = \sin x$ and $y = \cos x$ lie in a horizontal band. The band is determined by $y = -1$ and $y = 1$.

EXAMPLE 2

Determine all solutions to $|\cos x| \le 1$.

The inequality $|\cos x| \le 1$ gives a compound inequality.

If $|a| \le b$ and $b > 0$, then $-b \le a \le b$. $\quad -1 \le \cos x \le 1$

The compound inequality is true for all values of x since the range of the cosine function is the band between -1 and 1 inclusive.

Therefore, $|\cos x| \le 1$ is true for all real numbers.

Need More HELP

Draw a right triangle and label the sides to help you correctly write the tangent ratio.

EXAMPLE 3

An observer standing 400 feet from the point where a hot air balloon begins its ascent watches the balloon ascend to an altitude of 900 feet. To the nearest degree, from what angles of elevation does the observer watch the balloon rise?

Let x represent the angle of elevation in degrees.

The goal is to find all values of x in the interval $0° \le x < 90°$ for which $0 \le \tan x < \frac{900}{400}$.

From moment of ascent to an altitude of 900 feet, the angle of view varies from 0° to the degree measure for which $0 \le \tan x < \frac{900}{400}$.

Use a calculator in degree mode.

MODE Degrees 2nd TAN 9 0 0 ÷ 4 0 0) ENTER

$x \approx 66°$

The angle of elevation ranges from 0° to about 66°.

Solving Simple Trigonometric Inequalities

Many of the methods used to solve trigonometric inequalities are similar to those used to solve algebraic inequalities. Both analytical and graphical methods can be useful in solving a trigonometric inequality.

EXAMPLE 4

Find all values of x for which $\tan x > 1$.

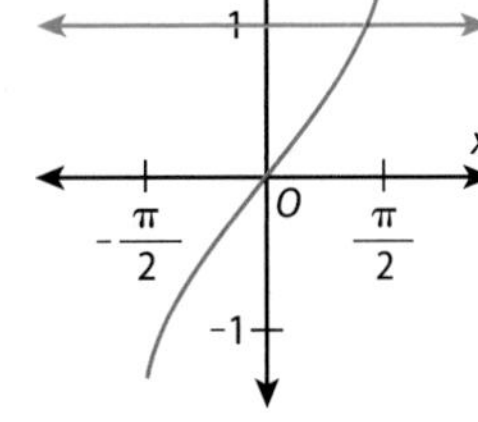

STEP 1 Sketch the graph of $y = \tan x$ on the interval $-\frac{\pi}{2} < x < \frac{\pi}{2}$ since the tangent function has period π. Also sketch the graph of $y = 1$.

STEP 2 Find the value of x on the interval $-\frac{\pi}{2} < x < \frac{\pi}{2}$ for which $\tan x = 1$. Use either a right triangle diagram or the TRACE feature of a graphing calculator. By either method:

$x = 45°$, or $\frac{\pi}{4}$

STEP 3 Write the solution on the interval $-\frac{\pi}{2} < x < \frac{\pi}{2}$.

$45° < x < 90°$, or $\frac{\pi}{4} < x < \frac{\pi}{2}$

STEP 4 Write the general, or complete, solution.

$45° + 180°n < x < 90° + 180°n$, or $\frac{\pi}{4} + \pi n < x < \frac{\pi}{2} + \pi n$, where n is any integer.

EXAMPLE 5

Find all values of x for which $\sin x > 0.2x - 1$.

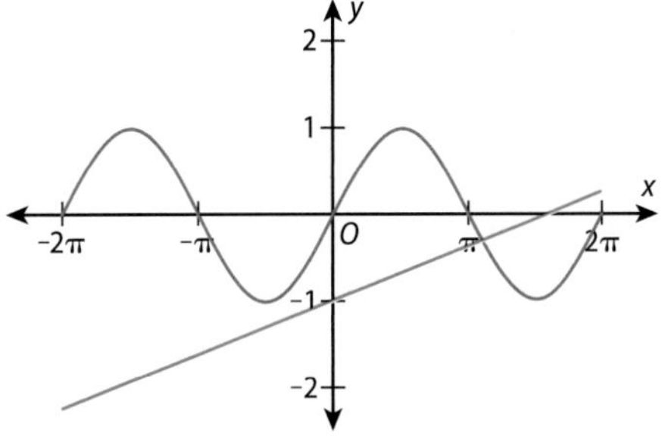

This inequality involves a trigonometric function and a linear function. Use a graphing calculator to graph two equations on the interval $-2\pi \le x \le 2\pi$.

Graph $y = \sin x$ and $y = 0.2x - 1$.

The inequality $\sin x > 0.2x - 1$ is true for those values of x for which the graph of $y = \sin x$ is above the graph of $y = 0.2x - 1$.

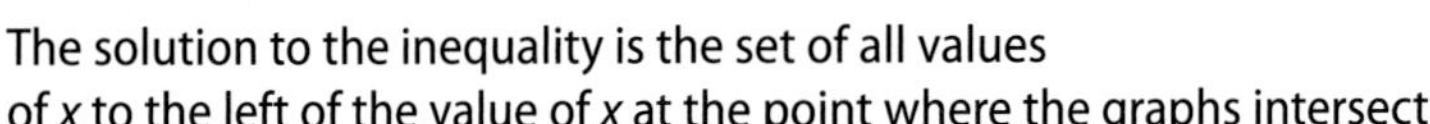

The solution to the inequality is the set of all values of x to the left of the value of x at the point where the graphs intersect.

To find the x-coordinate of the point of intersection, solve $\sin x = 0.2x - 1$.

Use the TRACE function to approximate the x-coordinate of the point where the graphs intersect.

$x \approx 3.4555$

The approximate solution is the set of all x such that $x < 3.4555$. Notice that the symbol $<$ is used rather than $\le$ because the x-coordinate of the point of intersection is not a solution.

Need More HELP

In addition to using the trace function on a graphing calculator, you can also use the INTERSECT function to find the point(s) of intersection of two graphs.

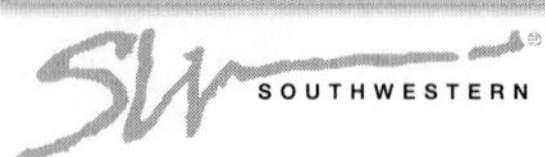

Solving More Complicated Trigonometric Inequalities

Many techniques used to solve algebraic inequalities can also be used to solve trigonometric inequalities.

EXAMPLE 6

Solve $2\cos^2 x - 3\cos x + 1 \leq 0$ on the interval $0 \leq x \leq 2\pi$.

STEP 1 Use substitution. Let $u = \cos x$. Solve the algebraic inequality.

$$2u^2 - 3u + 1 \leq 0$$

Factor. $\quad (2u - 1)(u - 1) \leq 0$

$ab \leq 0$, a and b have opposite signs. $\quad u \leq 0.5$ and $u \geq 1$ or $u \geq 0.5$ and $u \leq 1$

$u \leq 0.5$ and $u \geq 1$ has no solution. The solution to $u \geq 0.5$ and $u \leq 1$ is $0.5 \leq u \leq 1$.

STEP 2 Use substitution again. Let $u = \cos x$.

$$0.5 \leq \cos x \leq 1$$

Graph $y = 0.5$, $y = \cos x$, and $y = 1$.

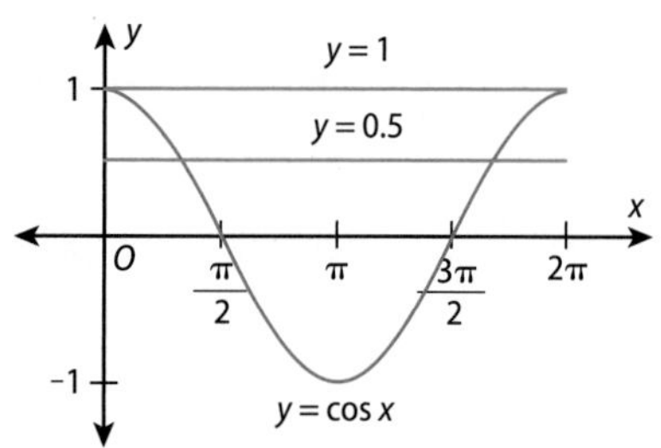

STEP 3 Determine the x-coordinates of the points where the graph of $y = \cos x$ intersects the horizontal lines. Write the solution.

$$0 \leq x \leq \frac{\pi}{3} \text{ or } \frac{5\pi}{3} \leq x \leq 2\pi$$

A trigonometric identity may often be useful or even necessary to solve a trigonometric inequality.

EXAMPLE 7

Watch Out!

Check the period of functions involved.

$y = 4\sin x\cos x$ has period π, not 2π, because $4\sin x\cos x$ equals $2\sin 2x$, which has period π.

Solve $4\sin x\cos x < \sqrt{3}$.

Start by simplifying the left side of the equation so it involves one trigonometric function instead of two.

$$4\sin x\cos x < \sqrt{3}$$

Substitute $\sin 2x$ for $2\sin x\cos x$. $\quad 2(2\sin x\cos x) < \sqrt{3}$

$$2(\sin 2x) < \sqrt{3}$$

Solve for $\sin 2x$. $\quad \sin 2x < \frac{\sqrt{3}}{2}$

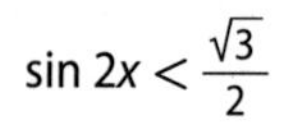

Sketch the graphs of $y = \sin 2x$ and $y = \frac{\sqrt{3}}{2}$ on the same set of axes.

The boundary points of the inequality occur where $\sin 2x = \frac{\sqrt{3}}{2}$.

Solve for x. $\quad \sin 2x = \frac{\sqrt{3}}{2}$

Divide by 2. $\quad 2x = \frac{\pi}{3} + 2n\pi \quad$ or $\quad 2x = \frac{2\pi}{3} + 2n\pi$

$$x = \frac{\pi}{6} + n\pi \quad \text{or} \quad x = \frac{\pi}{3} + n\pi$$

The graph shows that one interval for which the graph of $y = \sin 2x$ is below the graph of $y = \frac{\sqrt{3}}{2}$ is $\frac{\pi}{3} < x < \frac{7\pi}{6}$. The general form for all the intervals is $\frac{\pi}{3} + n\pi < x < \frac{7\pi}{6} + n\pi$.

Solving Systems of Trigonometric Inequalities

A **system of trigonometric equations** is a collection of trigonometric equations in the same variables. A **system of trigonometric inequalities** is a collection of trigonometric inequalities in the same variables. A solution to such a system is any ordered pair that makes each equation or inequality in the system true. For example, the value of x on the interval $0 \le x \le \pi$ for which $\begin{cases} y = \sqrt{3}\sin x \\ y = \cos x \end{cases}$ is true is $\frac{\pi}{6}$, as this graph suggests. For a system of equations, the solution is a set of discrete points. The solution set for a system of trigonometric inequalities may be a collection of intervals.

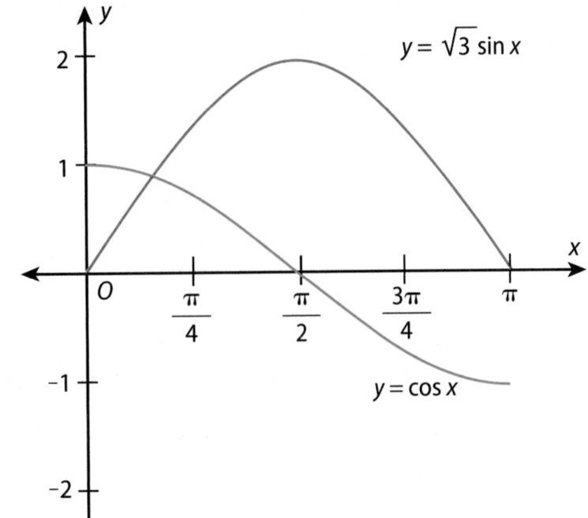

EXAMPLE 8

Solve $\begin{cases} \sin x \ge 0.5 \\ \cos x \ge 0.5 \end{cases}$ on the interval $0 \le x \le 2\pi$.

STEP 1 Graph $y = \sin x$, $y = \cos x$, and $y = 0.5$ on the same set of axes.

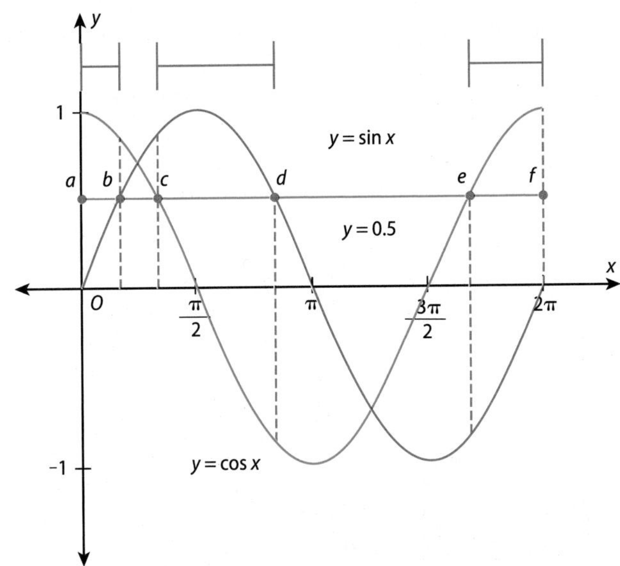

STEP 2 Look at the graph to find the points where the graphs of both $y = \sin x$ and $y = \cos x$ are above the graph of $y = 0.5$. These points are between the boundary points b and c.

STEP 3 Find the coordinates of the required boundary points.

At point b, $\sin x = 0.5$, so $x = \frac{\pi}{6}$. At point c, $\cos x = 0.5$, so $x = \frac{\pi}{3}$.

The solution to the system is $\frac{\pi}{6} \le x \le \frac{\pi}{3}$.

SEARCH

To see step-by-step videos of these problems, enter the page number into the SWadvantage.com Search Bar.

Try It This Way

Use sketching a graph or diagram as a problem solving strategy. A graph can help determine the number of points of intersection and the number of boundary points. In this problem, there are six boundary points and four points of intersection.

Inverse Trigonometric Functions and Equations

For each trigonometric function, there is an inverse trigonometric function. For a list of the definitions of the six inverse trigonometric functions, see the *Got To Know!* box.

Watch Out !

When using a calculator, the answer may not be exact. For example, 1.0472 is a display that might occur. This is an approximation to $\frac{\pi}{3}$. If an exact answer is required, then a calculator may not be the more useful approach. Instead, draw and label a special right triangle to solve the equation.

EXAMPLE 1

Solve each equation. Give an exact or an approximate solution.

a. $\mathbf{Cos^{-1}\,x = 0.5}$ **given that x is in radians.**

If $\text{Cos}^{-1}\,x = 0.5$, then $x = \frac{\pi}{3}$.

b. $\mathbf{Sin^{-1}\,\theta \approx 0.4152}$ **given that θ is in degrees.**

Use a calculator in degree mode.

If $\text{Sin}^{-1}\,\theta \approx 0.4152$, then $\theta \approx 24.5°$.

EXAMPLE 2

a. Show that $x = \frac{\sqrt{2}}{2}$ **is not a solution to** $\text{Sin}^{-1}\,x = 135°$**.**

Although $\sin 135° = \frac{\sqrt{2}}{2}$, 135° is not in the interval $-90° \le x \le 90°$, the range of $\text{Sin}^{-1}\,x$.

b. Show that $x = -\frac{\sqrt{2}}{2}$ **is a solution to** $\text{Cos}^{-1}\,x = 135°$**.**

Since $\cos 135° = -\frac{\sqrt{2}}{2}$ and 135° is in the interval $0° \le x \le 180°$, then $-\frac{\sqrt{2}}{2}$ is the solution to $\text{Cos}^{-1}\,x = 135°$.

Try It This Way

Use a calculator to find cos 135° and an approximation to $-\frac{\sqrt{2}}{2}$. If the decimal approximations are close then it is likely that $-\frac{\sqrt{2}}{2}$ is a solution.

GOT TO KNOW!

Inverse Trigonometric Functions

Inverse sine	$y = \text{Sin}^{-1}\,x$ if and only if x is in $\left[-\frac{\pi}{2}, \frac{\pi}{2}\right]$ and $x = \sin y$.
Inverse cosine	$y = \text{Cos}^{-1}\,x$ if and only if x is in $[0, \pi]$, and $x = \cos y$.
Inverse tangent	$y = \text{Tan}^{-1}\,x$ if and only if $x = \tan y$ and $-\frac{\pi}{2} < y < \frac{\pi}{2}$.
Inverse secant	$\text{Sec}^{-1}\,x = \text{Cos}^{-1}\,\frac{1}{x}$ if $\lvert x\rvert \ge 1$.
Inverse cosecant	$\text{Csc}^{-1}\,x = \text{Sin}^{-1}\,\frac{1}{x}$ if $\lvert x\rvert \ge 1$.
Inverse cotangent	$y = \text{Cot}^{-1}\,x$ if and only if $\cot y = x$ and $0 < y < \pi$.

The solution to an equation may involve composition of a function with its inverse. Keep in mind, the solution may have restrictions.

EXAMPLE 3

Solve $\text{Sin}^{-1} x = -60°$.

$$\text{Sin}^{-1} x = -60°$$

Apply composition. $$\sin(\text{Sin}^{-1} x) = \sin(-60°)$$

$f(f^{-1}(x)) = x$ $$x = \sin(-60°)$$

$$x = -\frac{\sqrt{3}}{2}$$

If $\text{Sin}^{-1} x = -60°$, then $x = -\frac{\sqrt{3}}{2}$.

SEARCH

To see step-by-step videos of these problems, enter the page number into the SWadvantage.com Search Bar.

In some problems, you may need to use composition and a trigonometric identity.

EXAMPLE 4

Solve $\text{Cos}^{-1} x = \frac{\pi}{12}$. Give an exact solution.

$$\text{Cos}^{-1} x = \frac{\pi}{12}$$

Apply composition. $$\cos(\text{Cos}^{-1} x) = \cos\frac{\pi}{12}$$

$f(f^{-1}(x)) = x$ $$x = \cos\frac{\pi}{12}$$

$$x = \cos\left(\frac{1}{2} \times \frac{\pi}{6}\right)$$

Since $\frac{\pi}{12}$ is in the interval $0 \le x \le \frac{\pi}{2}$, $x \ge 0$.

Use a half-angle formula. $$x = \sqrt{\frac{1 + \cos\left(\frac{\pi}{6}\right)}{2}}$$

$\cos\frac{\pi}{6} = \frac{\sqrt{3}}{2}$ $$= \sqrt{\frac{1 + \frac{\sqrt{3}}{2}}{2}}$$

Simplify the radical expression. $$= \sqrt{\frac{\frac{2 + \sqrt{3}}{2}}{2}}$$

$$= \frac{\sqrt{2 + \sqrt{3}}}{2}$$

If $\text{Cos}^{-1} x = \frac{\pi}{12}$, then $x = \frac{\sqrt{2 + \sqrt{3}}}{2}$.

Watch Out !

Whether to use + or − in the half-angle formula depends on the quadrant in which $\frac{\pi}{12}$ lies.

Oblique Triangles and Vectors

What Came Before?

- Solving right triangles
- Congruence and similarity theorems

What's This About?

- Using the Law of Sines and Law of Cosines to solve oblique triangles
- Finding the area of triangles by using formulas
- Performing operations with and graphing vectors

Practical Apps

- Land surveyors use the Law of Sines and the Law of Cosines when finding measures that are not associated with a right triangle.
- Air traffic controllers use vectors to project the paths of aircraft.

just for FUN!

Q: What did the vector say to the scalar?

A: You just need more direction in your life.

CONTENTS UPLOAD DOWNLOAD

Trigonometry

You can find more practice problems online by visiting:
www.SWadvantage.com

The Law of Sines

Using Congruence Criteria

Recall that two triangles are congruent if and only if corresponding angles and corresponding sides are congruent. The triangles at the right are congruent. The congruence is written as $\triangle ABC \cong \triangle XYZ$.

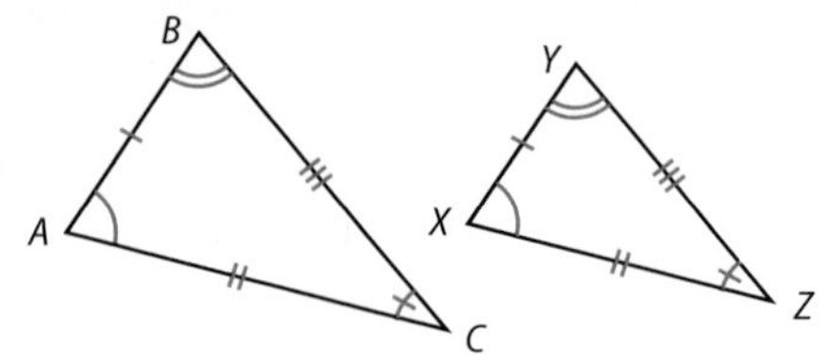

It is not necessary to identify and then verify six congruence relationships in order to determine whether two triangles are congruent. There are special criteria that can be used. For a summary of congruence criteria, see the *Got To Know!* box.

Need More HELP

For a review of triangle congruence criteria, see p. 768 for the SSS and SAS situations and see p. 772 for the ASA and AAS situations.

EXAMPLE 1

Identify the congruence criterion by which $\triangle ABC$ and $\triangle XYZ$ above are congruent.

a. $\overline{AB} \cong \overline{XY}, \overline{AC} \cong \overline{XZ}$, **and** $\angle A \cong \angle X$

The hypotheses of the SAS congruence criterion are satisfied. Therefore, $\triangle ABC \cong \triangle XYZ$.

b. $\overline{AB} \cong \overline{XY}, \overline{AC} \cong \overline{XZ}$, **and** $\overline{BC} \cong \overline{YZ}$

The hypotheses of the SSS congruence criterion are satisfied. Therefore, $\triangle ABC \cong \triangle XYZ$.

c. $\angle A \cong \angle X, \angle C \cong \angle Z$, **and** $\overline{AC} \cong \overline{XZ}$

The hypotheses of the ASA congruence criterion are satisfied. Therefore, $\triangle ABC \cong \triangle XYZ$.

SEARCH

To see step-by-step videos of these problems, enter the page number into the SWadvantage.com Search Bar.

EXAMPLE 2

The triangles at the right are congruent, $\triangle KLM \cong \triangle RST$. To show the congruence by using the ASA congruence criterion, what congruences would need to be verified?

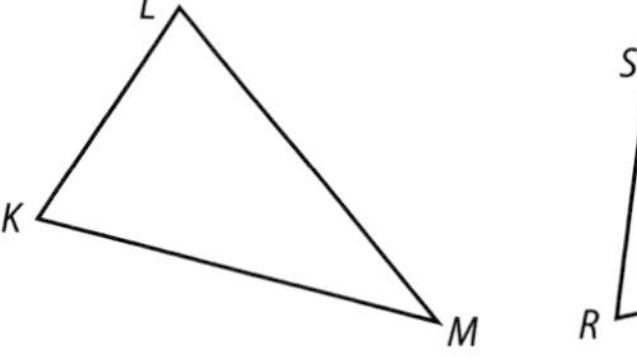

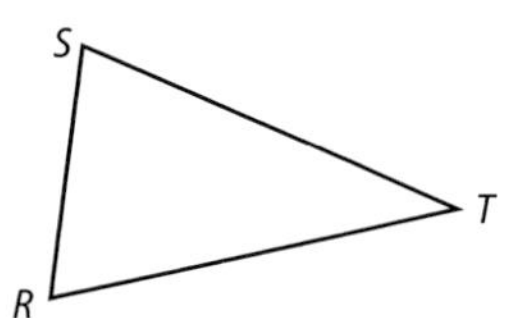

The congruence of two angles and the included side would need to be verified.

$\angle K \cong \angle R, \angle M \cong \angle T$, and $\overline{KM} \cong \overline{RT}$, or

$\angle L \cong \angle S, \angle K \cong \angle R$, and $\overline{LK} \cong \overline{SR}$, or

$\angle L \cong \angle S, \angle M \cong \angle T$, and $\overline{LM} \cong \overline{ST}$

Triangle Congruence Criteria

SAS If two sides and the included angle of one triangle are congruent to two sides and the included angle of another triangle, then the triangles are congruent.

SSS If three sides of one triangle are congruent to the three sides of another triangle, then the triangles are congruent.

ASA If two angles and the included side of one triangle are congruent to two angles and the included side of another triangle, then the triangles are congruent.

Proving the Law of Sines

There is an important trigonometric relationship among the lengths of the sides of a triangle and the measures of its angles. It is known as the law of sines. For a statement of the law of sines, see the *Got To Know!* box.

To prove the law of sines, use the diagram below. The diagrams show $\angle A$ in standard position. Notice that both acute and obtuse triangles are shown for $\angle A$. In the acute case, the altitude, or height, is contained in the interior of the triangle. In the obtuse case, the altitude is outside the triangle.

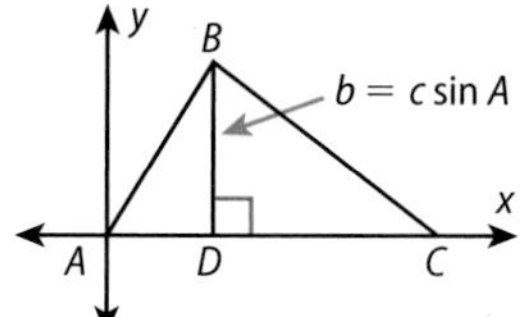

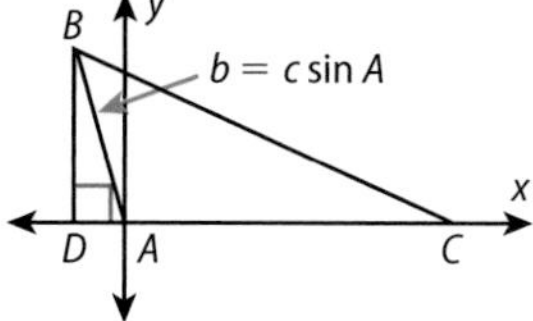

Consider $\overline{AC}$ with length b to be the base and $\overline{BD}$ to be the height.

$$\text{Area } \triangle ABC = \frac{1}{2} \times bc \sin A$$

The triangle can be positioned with $\angle B$ in standard position. If this is done, another calculation of area can be made.

$$\text{Area } \triangle ABC = = \frac{1}{2} \times ac \sin B$$

The triangle can be positioned with $\angle C$ in standard position. If this is done, a third calculation of area results.

$$\text{Area } \triangle ABC = = \frac{1}{2} \times ab \sin C$$

Now there are three measures of area for the same triangle.

$$\frac{1}{2} \times bc \sin A = \frac{1}{2} \times ac \sin B = \frac{1}{2} \times ab \sin C$$

Multiply by 2. $bc \sin A = ac \sin B = ab \sin C$

Divide by *abc*. $\frac{\sin A}{a} = \frac{\sin B}{b} = \frac{\sin C}{c}$

Need More HELP

Recall that the area of a triangle is dependent on two measures, the length of the base and the length of the height.

$A = \frac{1}{2} \times \text{base} \times \text{height}$

For a review of trigonometric ratios and right triangles, see p. 902.

Ways to REMEMBER

Each ratio in the law of sines involves the same letter, once as a capital letter and once as a lowercase letter. Each type of letter occurs in the same part of the ratio, either numerator or denominator.

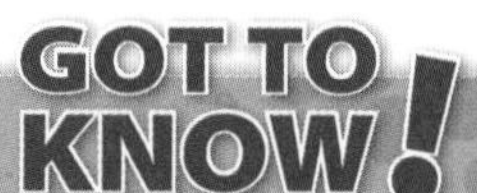

The Law of Sines

In $\triangle ABC$ whose sides have length a, b, and c, $\frac{\sin A}{a} = \frac{\sin B}{b} = \frac{\sin C}{c}$.

Applying the Law of Sines

The law of sines can be used to prove theorems from geometry.

Prove that the base angles of an isosceles triangle are congruent.

The diagram at the right shows an isosceles triangle with two sides congruent. The base angles are $\angle A$ and $\angle B$. Since $AC = BC$, then $a = b$.

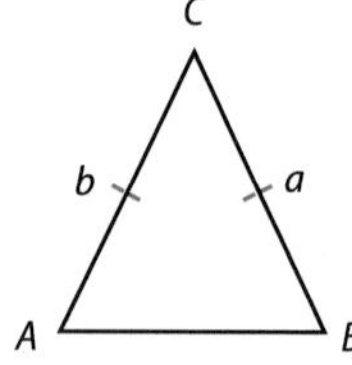

Apply the law of sines.	$\frac{\sin A}{a} = \frac{\sin B}{b}$
$a = b$	$\sin A = \sin B$
$\sin x$ is one-to-one on $0° \leq x \leq 90°$.	$m\angle A = m\angle B$

Therefore, $\angle A \cong \angle B$.

Need More HELP

The definition of an isosceles triangle together with two pieces of numerical information is sufficient to prove all triangular measures.

EXAMPLE 4

Given the diagram at the right, find $m\angle Q$. Give your answer to the nearest degree.

The diagram shows PQ, the measure of the angle opposite $\overline{PQ}$ and PR.

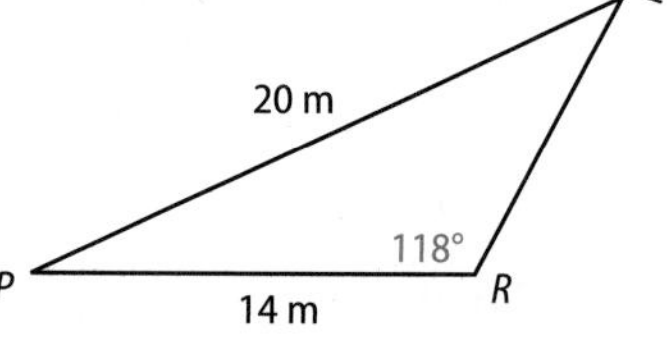

SEARCH

To see step-by-step videos of these problems, enter the page number into the SWadvantage.com Search Bar.

STEP 1 Write a proportion that involves the law of sines. This will involve three pieces of given information and one unknown measure.

$$\frac{\sin R}{PQ} = \frac{\sin Q}{PR}$$

$PQ = 20$, $PR = 14$, and $m\angle R = 118°$ $\qquad \frac{\sin 118°}{20} = \frac{\sin Q}{14}$

STEP 2 Solve the proportion for $\sin Q$.

Use cross products. $\qquad \sin Q = \frac{14(\sin 118°)}{20}$

Use a calculator. $\qquad \sin Q \approx 0.6181$

STEP 3 Use an inverse to find $m\angle Q$.

Use a calculator set to degree mode.

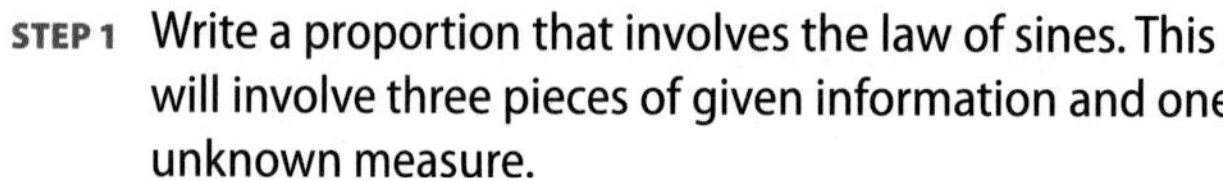

$m\angle Q \approx 38°$

EXAMPLE 5

Given $\triangle GMN$ at the right, find MN to the nearest whole number of feet.

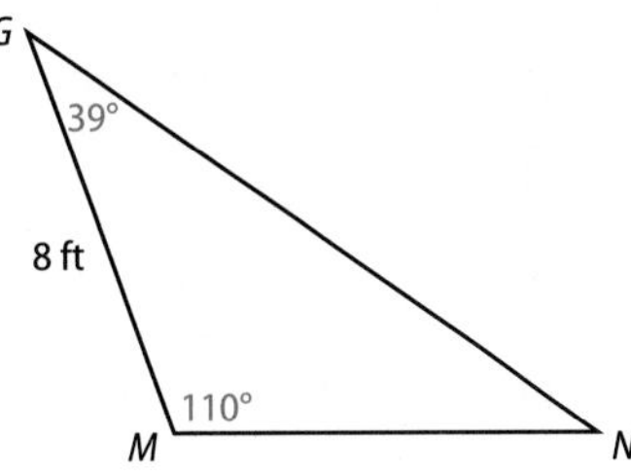

STEP 1 Write a proportion using the law of sines that involves MN.

$$\frac{\sin G}{MN} = \frac{\sin N}{GM}$$

Substitute known measurements. Use the triangle sum theorem to find $m\angle N$.

$$\frac{\sin 39°}{MN} = \frac{\sin N}{8} \qquad m\angle N = 180° - (39° + 110°) = 31° \qquad \frac{\sin 39°}{MN} = \frac{\sin 31°}{8}$$

STEP 2 Solve the proportion for MN.

$$MN = \frac{8 \cdot \sin 39°}{\sin 31°} \approx 9.7751$$

Therefore, MN is about 10 feet.

Need More HELP

ASA information assures that there is a unique solution to a problem that involves the law of sines.

EXAMPLE 6

The diagram shows a proposed park for land bounded by three streets. Find XY to the nearest whole number of feet.

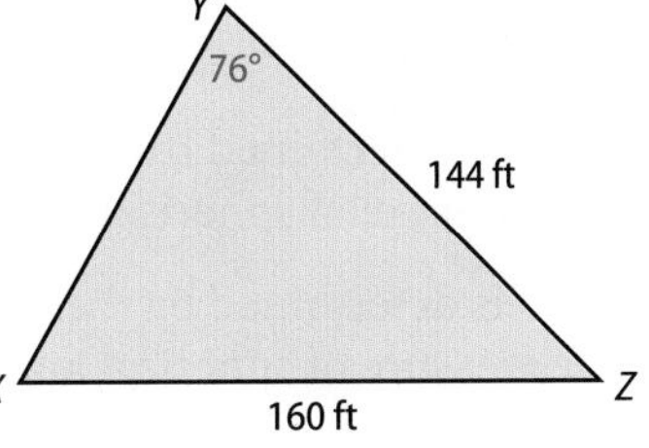

STEP 1 Use the law of sines to find $m\angle Y$.

$$\frac{\sin X}{YZ} = \frac{\sin Y}{XZ} \qquad \frac{\sin X}{144} = \frac{\sin 76°}{160}$$

$$\sin X \approx 0.8733$$

Thus, $m\angle X \approx 61°$.

STEP 2 Calculate $m\angle Z$. $\quad m\angle Z \approx 180° - (61° + 76°) = 43°$

STEP 3 Use the law of sines again with the new information that $m\angle Z \approx 43°$.

$$\frac{\sin Z}{XY} = \frac{\sin X}{YZ} \qquad \frac{\sin 43°}{XY} = \frac{\sin 61°}{144} \qquad XY = \frac{144 \sin 43°}{\sin 61°} \approx 112$$

The side of the park that is $\overline{XY}$ is about 112 feet.

Watch Out!

In using the law of sines, be sure that data is entered correctly into the ratios chosen. Check that correct substitutions are made.

EXAMPLE 7

Show that if the angles in $\triangle ABC$ have the same measure, then the sides have the same length.

Write the law of sines. $\qquad \frac{\sin A}{a} = \frac{\sin B}{b} = \frac{\sin C}{c}$

$m\angle A = m\angle B = m\angle C \qquad \frac{\sin A}{a} = \frac{\sin B}{b} = \frac{\sin C}{c} \rightarrow \frac{1}{a} = \frac{1}{b} = \frac{1}{c}$

Therefore $a = b = c$.

The Law of Sines on a Sphere

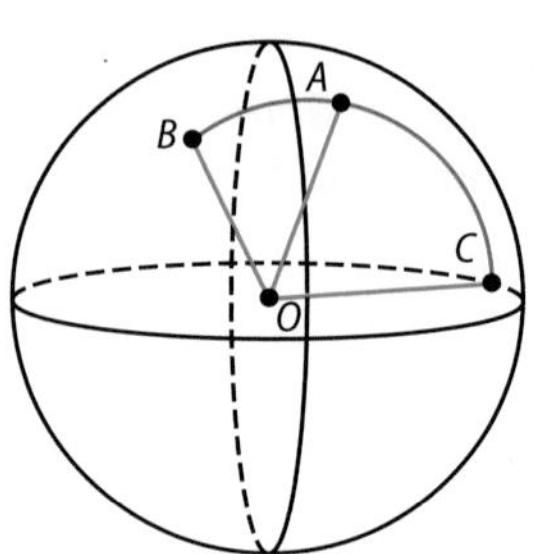

The diagram at the right shows a **sphere**. A sphere is the set of all points in three-dimensional space that is a fixed distance, the **radius**, from a fixed point, the **center**. In the diagram, O is the center and $\overline{OA}$, $\overline{OB}$, and $\overline{OC}$ are radii. The three points shown determine a **spherical angle**. The sides of the angle contain $\overline{AB}$ and $\overline{AC}$, both portions of a great circle. A **great circle** is the intersection of a plane and the sphere and its center.

EXAMPLE 8

Two radii of a sphere with a radius of 1,350 miles form an angle that measures 120°. Find the length of the arc determined by the endpoints of the radii that lie on the sphere.

Calculate the fraction of the circumference.	$\frac{120°}{360°} = \frac{1}{3}$
Apply the length of arc formula.	$\frac{1}{3} \times 1{,}350 \times 2\pi = 900\pi$

The arc has a length of 900π miles.

The diagram at the right shows a somewhat special spherical triangle determined by points O, A, B, and C.

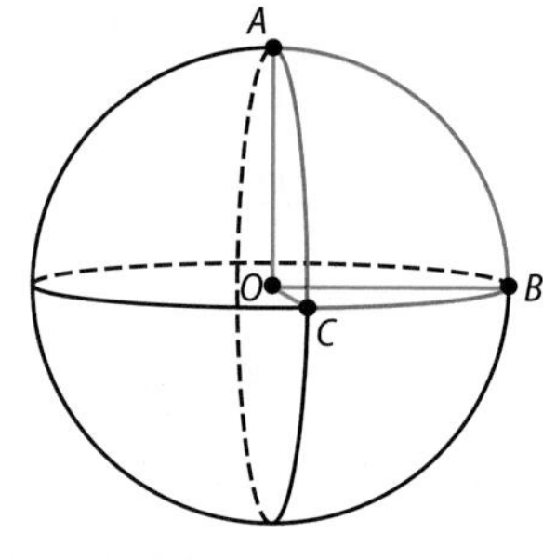

$m\overparen{AC}$ is determined by the radius, $\overline{OA}$ or $\overline{OC}$, and $m\angle AOC$. The measure of spherical angle A is determined by $m\angle BOC$.

$m\overparen{AB}$ is determined by the radius, $\overline{OA}$ or $\overline{OB}$ and $m\angle AOB$. The measure of spherical angle B is determined by $m\angle AOC$.

$m\overparen{BC}$ is determined by the radius, $\overline{OB}$ or $\overline{OC}$ and $m\angle BOC$. The measure of spherical angle C is determined by $m\angle AOB$.

EXAMPLE 9

Is it possible for a spherical triangle to have angles whose sum is 270°?

Yes, consider a sphere with center at the origin of a three-dimensional coordinate system. The coordinate axes divide the sphere into 8 spherical triangles, each having angles whose measures are 90°. The sum of three angles each measuring 90° is 270°.

EXAMPLE 10

Sketch a spherical triangle that has one vertex at the North pole and a central angle along the equator that measures 120°. Explain your reasoning.

A section of a sphere that is one third of a hemisphere is a spherical triangle that meets the specified conditions.

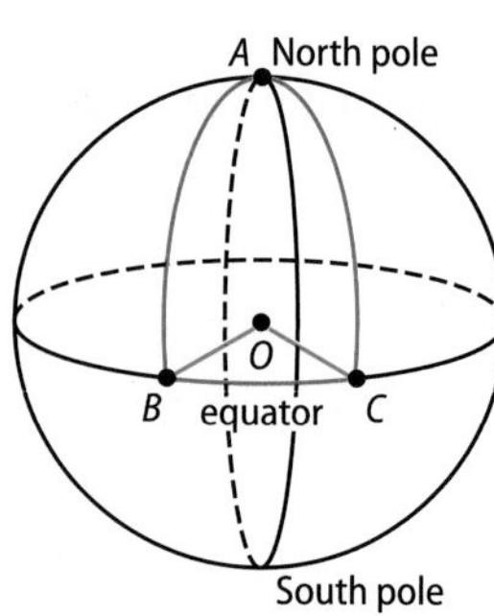

Need More HELP

For a review of circles and parts of circles, see p. 162.

For a review of spheres, see p. 176.

A sphere is a surface of revolution. For a review of solids of revolution, see p. 716.

For a review of radian measure, see p. 936.

For a review of radian measure as applied to arc length, see p. 940.

Practice using spatial visualization by drawing diagrams. Recall that dashed line segments and arcs indicate features not visible from the vantage point shown.

To see step-by-step videos of these problems, enter the page number into the SWadvantage.com Search Bar.

The two endpoints of a diameter of a sphere can be considered the North pole and the South pole of the sphere. The intersection of the plane perpendicular to the line containing the poles and containing the center of the sphere is the equator.

EXAMPLE 11

Refer to the diagram at the right and the information below.

- **Point *A* is at the North pole of the sphere. Points *B* and *C* lie along the equator.**
- **The radius of the sphere is 5,347 miles.**
- **$m\angle BOC = 30°$**

Find the measures of all the sides and angles in the triangle. Verify the law of sines for the sphere.

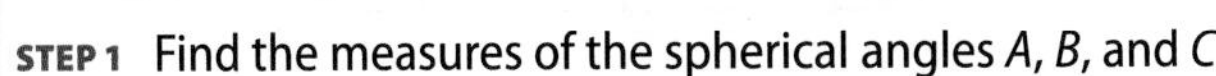

STEP 1 Find the measures of the spherical angles *A*, *B*, and *C*.

The plane containing *A*, *O*, and *C* is perpendicular to the plane containing the equator, so $m\angle C = 90°$.

The plane containing *A*, *O*, and *B* is perpendicular to the plane containing the equator, so $m\angle B = 90°$.

Finally, $m\angle CAB = 30°$. Therefore, $m\angle A = 30°$.

STEP 2 Find the lengths of the sides $m\widehat{AC}$, $m\widehat{AB}$, and $m\widehat{BC}$.

Use the arc length formula.

$$a = m\widehat{BC} = \frac{30°}{360°} \times 2\pi \times 5{,}347 = \frac{5{,}347\pi}{6}$$

$$b = m\widehat{AC} = \frac{90°}{360°} \times 2\pi \times 5{,}347 = \frac{5{,}347\pi}{2}$$

$$c = m\widehat{AB} = \frac{90°}{360°} \times 2\pi \times 5{,}347 = \frac{5{,}347\pi}{2}$$

STEP 3 Calculate ratios.

$$\frac{\sin A}{\sin a} \rightarrow = \frac{\sin 30°}{\sin\left(\frac{5{,}347\pi}{6}\right)} \approx -0.5 \qquad \frac{\sin B}{\sin b} \rightarrow = \frac{\sin 90°}{\sin\left(\frac{5{,}347\pi}{2}\right)} \approx -1$$

$$\frac{\sin C}{\sin C} \rightarrow = \frac{\sin 90°}{\sin \frac{5{,}347\pi}{2}} \approx -1$$

Need More HELP

Points on Earth are located by angle measures.

For example, the latitude of Washington, D.C. is 38°53′42.4″ N, and the latitude of Ottawa is 45°22′00″ N. Latitude is the angle measured either north or south of the equator.

The longitude of Washington, D.C. is 77°02′12.0″ W. The longitude of Ottawa is 75°43′00″ W. Longitude is the angle measured east or west of the great circle containing the poles and Greenwich, England.

GOT TO KNOW!

The Law of Sines on a Sphere

Let $\triangle ABC$ be a spherical triangle with vertices *A*, *B*, and *C*.

A, *B*, and *C* represent the measures of the central angles with vertices *A*, *B*, and *C*.

a, *b*, and *c* represent the radius times the measures of the angles that determine *A*, *B*, and *C*.

Then $\frac{\sin A}{\sin a} = \frac{\sin B}{\sin b} = \frac{\sin C}{\sin c}$.

The Ambiguous Case

The SSA Triangle Situation

Knowing the lengths of two sides of a triangle and the measure of one angle that is not an included angle is not always sufficient to determine the measures of all the other parts of a triangle. In fact, it is possible that SSA information does not guarantee the existence of a triangle at all.

Watch Out !

A common mistake is to believe that every problem with given information has a solution. The information given here is sufficient to draw a correct conclusion. However, that conclusion shows that a triangle does not exist.

EXAMPLE 1

Determine if the given measures form a triangle: Given $AB = 16$, $m\angle DAB = 29°$, and $BC = 5$.

STEP 1 Draw a sketch with some precision.

Draw $\overrightarrow{AD}$.

Draw $\angle DAB$ with measure 29°.

Mark point B on $\overrightarrow{AB}$ so that AB is 16 units long.

At B, draw $\overline{BC}$ 5 units long.

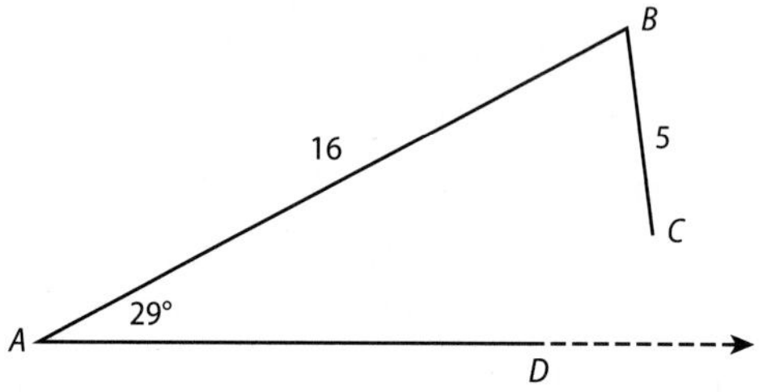

STEP 2 Interpret the diagram.

Since no measure for $\angle ABC$ is given, $\overline{BC}$ is allowed to swing from point B. No matter what angle measure is chosen for $\angle ABC$, there is no way that $\overline{BC}$ will intersect $\overrightarrow{AD}$ because $\overline{BC}$ is too short.

Therefore, the given measures do not form a triangle.

Watch Out !

Another common mistake is to believe that every problem with given information has a unique solution. As above, the information given here is sufficient to draw a correct conclusion. However, that conclusion shows that the solution is not unique.

EXAMPLE 2

Determine if the given measures form a triangle: Given $AB = 16$, $m\angle DAB = 29°$, and $BC = 8$.

As in Example 1, a precise sketch is a useful first step.

STEP 1 Draw a sketch with some precision.

Draw $\overrightarrow{AD}$.

Draw $\angle DAB$ with measure 29°.

Mark point B on $\overrightarrow{AB}$ so that AB is 16 units long.

At B, draw $\overline{BC}$ 8 units long.

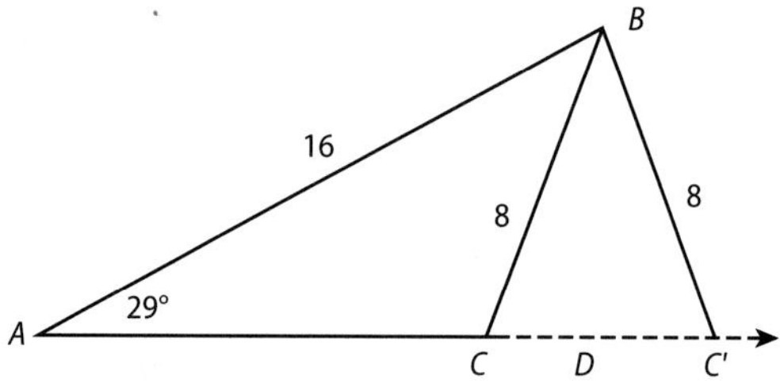

STEP 2 Interpret the diagram.

Since no measure for $\angle ABC$ is given, $\overline{BC}$ is allowed to swing from point B. There are two angles for $\angle ABC$ for which $\overline{BC}$ will intersect $\overrightarrow{AD}$. Two distinct triangles are possible: $\triangle ABC$ and $\triangle ABC'$.

Two triangles are possible with this given information.

To see step-by-step videos of these problems, enter the page number into the SWadvantage.com Search Bar.

There are other problem scenarios possible. These will also be explored in the examples. For a summary of solution possibilities, see the *Got To Know!* box.

EXAMPLE 3

Given $a = 18$, $c = 16$, and $m\angle C = 42°$, use the law of sines to determine how many triangles are possible.

STEP 1 Use the law of sines to find $m\angle A$.

$$\frac{\sin A}{a} = \frac{\sin C}{c}$$

$$\frac{\sin A}{18} = \frac{\sin 42°}{16}$$

$$\sin A \approx 0.7528$$

$$m\angle A_1 \approx 49° \text{ or } m\angle A_2 \approx 131°$$

If you add either $m\angle A$ to the given angle, 42°, the sum does not exceed 180°.

STEP 2 Interpret the result.

Two triangles can be drawn using the given information.

Need More HELP

Problem solving requires decision making. Some choices you make are not helpful. For instance, choosing $\frac{\sin A}{a} = \frac{\sin B}{b}$ is not helpful because it involves too many unknowns.

$\frac{\sin 29°}{5} = \frac{\sin B}{b}$

Both $m\angle B$ and b are unknown.

EXAMPLE 4

Given $AB = 16$, $m\angle AB = 29°$, and $BC = 5$, use the law of sines to determine how many triangles are possible. (This is the data from Example 1.)

STEP 1 Use the law of sines to find $m\angle A$.

$$\frac{\sin A}{a} = \frac{\sin C}{c}$$

$$\frac{\sin 29°}{5} = \frac{\sin C}{16}$$

$$\sin A \approx 1.5514$$

Since $-1 \leq \sin A \leq 1$, $\sin A \approx 1.5514$ has no solution.

STEP 2 Interpret the result.

No triangle can be drawn using the given information.

Need More HELP

To better understand this summary chart, review the basic trigonometry of a right triangle. See page 902.

Solution Possibilities for the Law of Sines

Using the diagrams that helped to prove the law of sines, it is possible to identify the different solution possibilities.

$\angle A$ is acute.

no solution	$a < b \sin A$
one solution	$a = b \sin A$ or $a \geq b$
two solutions	$b \sin A < a < b$

$\angle A$ is a right angle.

one solution	$b = a \sin B$

$\angle A$ is obtuse.

no solution	$a \leq b$
one solution	$a > b$

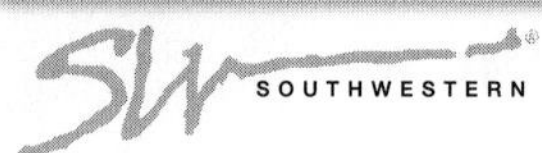

Using the Law of Sines in Multiple Situations

The law of sines is useful in different mathematical contexts and in real-world contexts.

SEARCH

To see step-by-step videos of these problems, enter the page number into the SWadvantage.com Search Bar.

EXAMPLE 5

In isosceles triangle $\triangle KLM$, the vertex angle measures 53°. The base of the triangle is 7 units long. How long are the other sides of the triangle?

Draw and label a sketch.

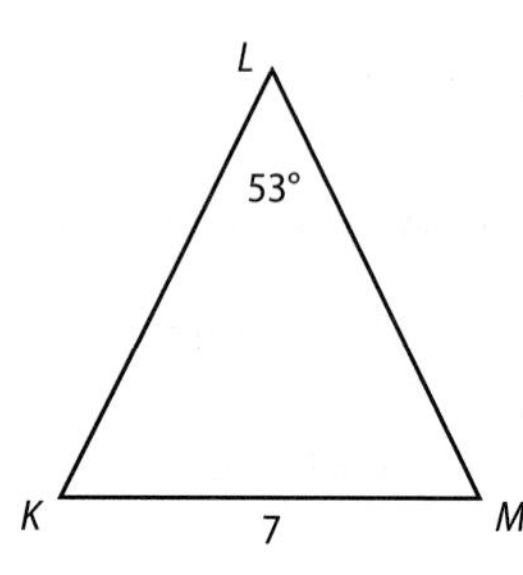

Since the triangle is isosceles, base angles are congruent.

$$m\angle K = m\angle M = \frac{1}{2}(180° - 53°) = 63.5°$$

$$\frac{\sin L}{KM} = \frac{\sin K}{LM} \qquad \frac{\sin 53°}{7} = \frac{\sin 63.5°}{LM}$$

$$LM = \frac{7 \sin 63.5°}{\sin 53°}$$

$$LM \approx 7.8$$

The congruent sides of the triangle are about 7.8 units long.

EXAMPLE 6

Need More HELP

In this problem, choosing $\frac{\sin Y}{XZ} = \frac{\sin X}{YZ}$ is not helpful because it involves too many unknowns.

$\frac{\sin 66°}{1{,}601} = \frac{\sin X}{YZ}$

Both $m\angle X$ and YZ are unknown.

The diagram represents a park bounded by three streets. How far is it along Oak Street from its intersections with Ash Street and Elm Street?

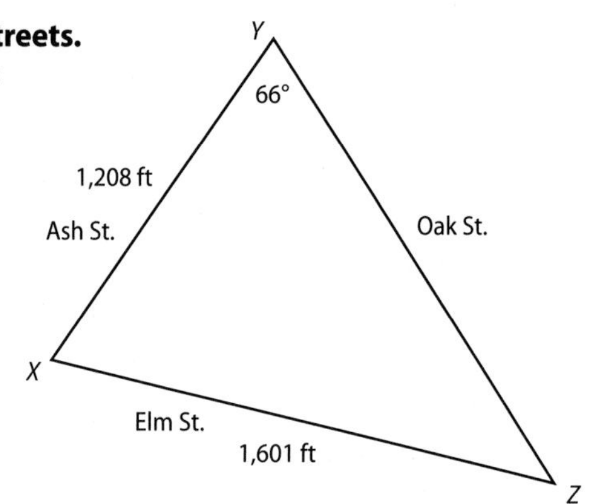

STEP 1 Find the measure of $\angle Z$.

$$\frac{\sin Y}{XZ} = \frac{\sin Z}{XY} \qquad \frac{\sin 66°}{1{,}601} = \frac{\sin Z}{1{,}208}$$

$$\sin Z = \frac{1{,}208 \sin 66°}{1{,}601}$$

$$m\angle Z \approx 44°$$

STEP 2 Find the measure of $\angle X$.

$$m\angle X = 180° - (66° + 44°) = 70°$$

STEP 3 Apply the law of sines again.

$$\frac{\sin Y}{XZ} = \frac{\sin X}{YZ} \qquad \frac{\sin 66°}{1{,}601} = \frac{\sin 70°}{YZ}$$

$$YZ = \frac{1{,}601 \sin 70°}{\sin 66°}$$

$$YZ \approx 1{,}647$$

The specified distance is about 1,647 feet.

When approaching a triangle problem that involves SSA information, first try to determine how many solutions are possible. The most complicated situation occurs when there are two solutions.

EXAMPLE 7

If possible, find all the measures of the sides and angles of a triangle given that $b = 23$, $c = 15$, and $m\angle C = 37°$. If it is not possible, state that there is no solution.

STEP 1 Determine how many solutions there are.

Choose the two ratios in the law of sines that involve letter pairs. Here the pairs are b, c, $\angle B$, and $\angle C$.

$$\frac{\sin B}{b} = \frac{\sin C}{c} \qquad \frac{\sin B}{23} = \frac{\sin 37°}{15}$$

$$\sin B \approx 0.9228$$

There are two values of x for which $\sin x = 0.9228$ on the interval $0° \leq x \leq 180°$.

There are two triangles possible.

STEP 2 Find the two possible measures for $\angle B$.

If $\sin B \approx 0.9228$, then $m\angle B \approx 67°$ or $m\angle B \approx 113°$.

STEP 3 Solve the triangle using the given information and $m\angle B \approx 67°$.

Determine the measure of the third angle.

$$m\angle A = 180° - (37° + 67°) = 76°$$

$$\frac{\sin A}{a} = \frac{\sin C}{c} \qquad \frac{\sin 76°}{a} = \frac{\sin 37°}{15}$$

$$a = \frac{15 \sin 76°}{\sin 37°}$$

$$a \approx 24$$

As a check, verify that $\frac{\sin 76°}{24} \approx \frac{\sin 67°}{23} \approx \frac{\sin 37°}{15}$.

STEP 4 Solve the triangle using the given information and $m\angle B \approx 113°$.

Determine the measure of the third angle.

$$m\angle A = 180° - (37° + 113°) = 30°$$

$$\frac{\sin A}{a} = \frac{\sin C}{c} \qquad \frac{\sin 30°}{a} = \frac{\sin 37°}{15}$$

$$a = \frac{15 \sin 30°}{\sin 37°}$$

$$a \approx 12$$

As a check, verify that $\frac{\sin 30°}{12} \approx \frac{\sin 113°}{23} \approx \frac{\sin 37°}{15}$.

In $\triangle ABC$, $a \approx 24$, $b = 23$, $c = 15$, $m\angle A = 76°$, $m\angle B = 67°$, and $m\angle C = 37°$, or $a \approx 12$, $b = 23$, $c = 15$, $m\angle A = 30°$, $m\angle B = 113°$, and $m\angle C = 37°$.

Need More HELP

If $0 \leq y < 1$, then there are two values of x within $0° \leq x \leq 180°$, for which $\sin x = y$. Look at the graph of $y = \sin x$ to confirm this. For a review of the graph of the sine function, see p. 952.

Watch Out!

A common error is failing to check answers for reasonableness. The solutions in this example involve many calculations. Use the law of sines with all six numerical values to see if the three ratios give the same approximate decimal.

The Law of Cosines

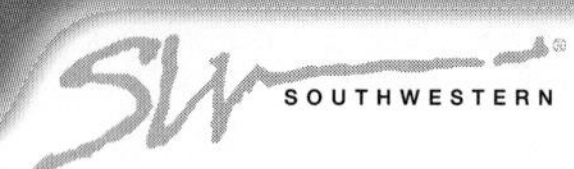

Need More **HELP**

There are many inequality theorems from geometry that are useful. For a review of these theorems, see p. 664.

Exploring Triangle Inequalities

In geometry, there are many theorems that involve a triangle and inequalities. Some of these are listed below.

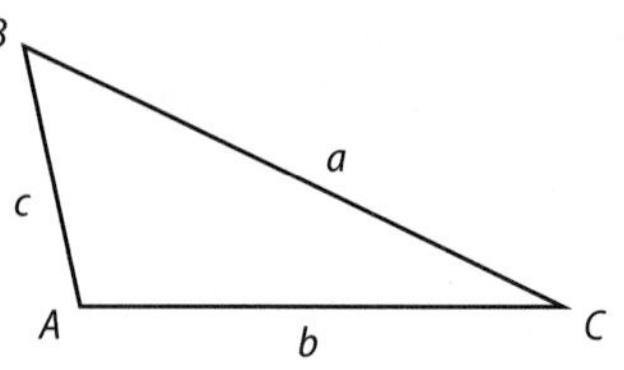

- If one side of a triangle is longer than a second side of the triangle, then the angle opposite the longer side has a greater measure than the angle opposite the shorter side. In the diagram at the right, if $AC > AB$, then $m\angle B > m\angle C$.
- If one angle of a triangle has a greater measure than a second angle of the triangle, then the side opposite the greater angle is longer than the side opposite the lesser angle. In the diagram at the right above, if $m\angle B > m\angle C$, then $AC > AB$.
- (The triangle inequality theorem) The sum of the lengths of any two sides of a triangle is greater than the length of the third side. For example, $AB + AC > BC$.

SEARCH

To see step-by-step videos of these problems, enter the page number into the SWadvantage.com Search Bar.

EXAMPLE 1

Jason and Ralph live 8 miles apart along a straight road. Frankie lives 6 miles from Jason along a straight road. Determine the minimum and maximum distances between where Frankie and Ralph live. Write an inequality that shows all possible distances between the homes of Ralph and Frankie.

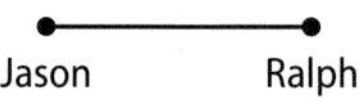

STEP 1 Sketch a diagram that assumes that all three people live along the same road, but order them differently.

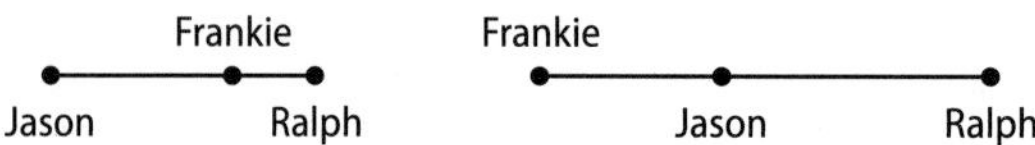

STEP 2 Analyze and interpret the diagram.

minimum: 8 miles − 6 miles = 2 miles   maximum: 8 miles + 6 miles = 14 miles

If x represents the specified distance, then $2 \le x \le 14$.

EXAMPLE 2

Is it possible to construct a triangle whose sides are 20 units, 15 units and 42 units long?

A triangle like $\triangle ABC$ shown above can be useful. Label the sides using measurements given from least to greatest. The longest side is opposite the angle with the greatest measure. The shortest side is opposite the angle with the least measure.

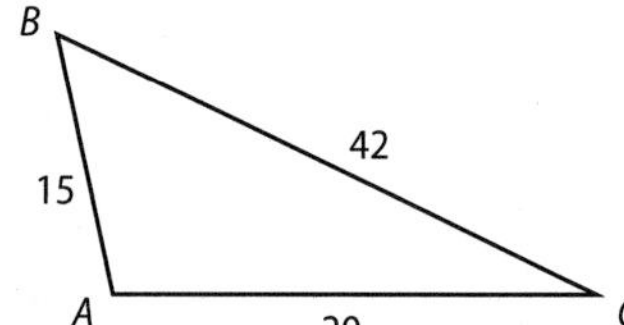

Use the triangle inequality to check that its conditions are met.

$AB + BC > AC$? $15 + 42 = 57 > 20$ ✔

$AC + BC > AB$? $20 + 42 = 62 > 15$ ✔

$AB + AC > BC$? $15 + 20 = 35 > 42$ ✗

One of the three inequalities that must be true to satisfy the triangle inequality is not true. Therefore, a triangle with sides of 20 units, 15 units, and 42 units cannot be constructed.

Deriving the Law of Cosines

The diagrams below show $\triangle ABC$ with $\angle C$ in standard position on a coordinate system. One diagram shows $\angle C$ as an acute angle. The other diagram shows $\angle C$ as an obtuse angle. The proof of the law of cosines is a coordinate proof heavily dependent on the distance formula in the plane applied to find AB.

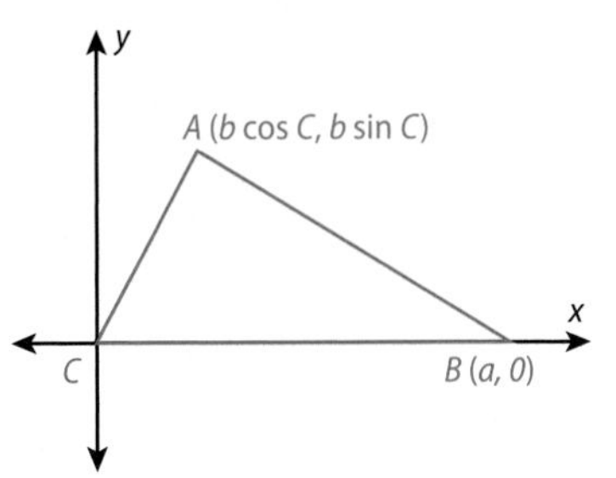

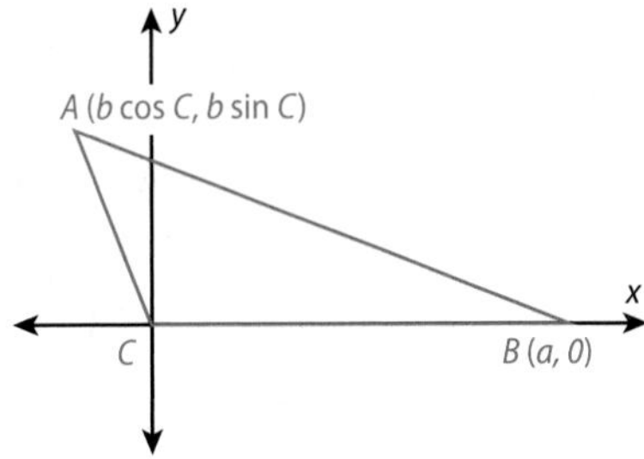

$$\begin{aligned}(AB)^2 = c^2 &= (b \cos C - a)^2 + (b \sin C - 0)^2 \\ &= a^2 - 2ab \cos C + b^2 \cos^2 C + b^2 \sin^2 C \\ &= (b^2 \cos^2 C + b^2 \sin^2 C) + a^2 - 2ab \cos C \\ &= b^2(\cos^2 C + \sin^2 C) + a^2 - 2ab \cos C \\ \cos^2 C + \sin^2 C = 1 \qquad &= b^2 + a^2 - 2ab \cos C\end{aligned}$$

Therefore, $c^2 = a^2 + b^2 - 2ab \cos C$.

By following the same reasoning with $\angle A$ and then $\angle B$ in standard position, two other forms of the law of cosines will result. For a full statement of the law of cosines, see the *Got To Know!* box.

The Pythagorean theorem is a special case of the law of cosines. If $\triangle ABC$ is a right triangle with right angle at C, then $m\angle C = 90°$ and c is the length of the hypotenuse.

$$\begin{aligned}c^2 &= a^2 + b^2 - 2ab \cos C \\ &= a^2 + b^2 - 2ab \cos 90° \\ &= a^2 + b^2 - 2ab(0) \\ &= a^2 + b^2\end{aligned}$$

Need More HELP

For a review of the distance formula and its uses, see p. 818.

For a review of how to write coordinate proofs, see p. 828.

Ways to REMEMBER

The letter by itself on one side of the equation has the matching capital letter to the right of "cos." The other two lowercase letters make up the sum of squares and the product to the left of "cos."

EXAMPLE 3

Derive a formula for the length of the base of isosceles triangle $\triangle ABC$ with vertex angle $\angle C$.

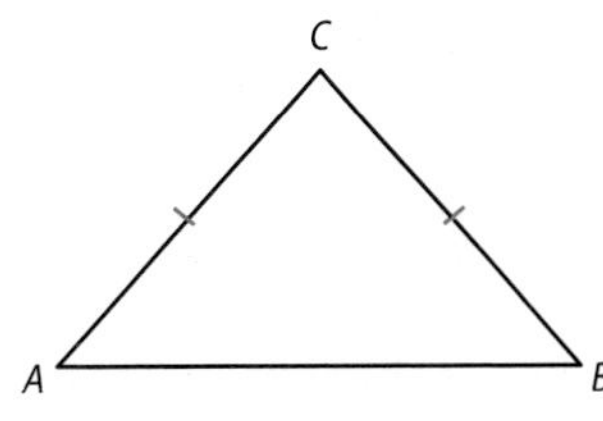

$$\begin{aligned}(AB)^2 &= (AC)^2 + (BC)^2 - 2(AC)(BC) \cos C \\ AC = BC \qquad &= 2(AC)^2 - 2(AC)^2 \cos C \\ &= (AC)^2(2 - 2 \cos C)\end{aligned}$$

Therefore, base AB is given by $AB = (AC\sqrt{2})\sqrt{1 - \cos C}$.

GOT TO KNOW!

The Law of Cosines

In any triangle $\triangle ABC$:

$a^2 = b^2 + c^2 - 2bc \cos A$ $\qquad b^2 = a^2 + c^2 - 2ac \cos B$ $\qquad c^2 = a^2 + b^2 - 2ab \cos C$

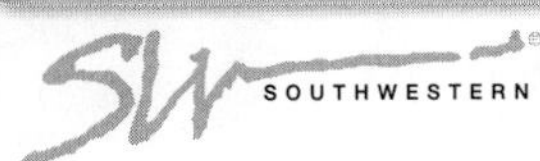

Applying the Law of Cosines

The law of cosines is an appropriate solution method in an SAS situation.

EXAMPLE 4

In $\triangle KLM$, $KL = 24$ meters, $KM = 30$ meters, and $m\angle K = 55°$. Approximate LM to the nearest tenth of a meter.

The given information involves lengths of two sides and the measure of the included angle.

Apply the law of cosines.	$(LM)^2 = (KL)^2 + (KM)^2 - 2(KL)(KM)\cos K$
Substitute known values.	$(LM)^2 = (24)^2 + (30)^2 - 2(24)(30)\cos 55°$
Simplify.	$(LM)^2 = 650.05$
Take the square root.	$LM \approx 25.5$

In $\triangle KLM$, LM is about 25.5 meters.

Need More HELP

Many times a problem without a diagram is given. To help assure an accurate solution, sketch a diagram of your own. The diagram will show an SAS condition. Then it is clear that the law of cosines will yield the solution.

SEARCH

To see step-by-step videos of these problems, enter the page number into the SWadvantage.com Search Bar.

Recall that a triangle can be classified as acute, right, or obtuse.

EXAMPLE 5

Use the law of cosines to classify $\triangle XYZ$ as acute, right, or obtuse. Sketch a diagram to help.

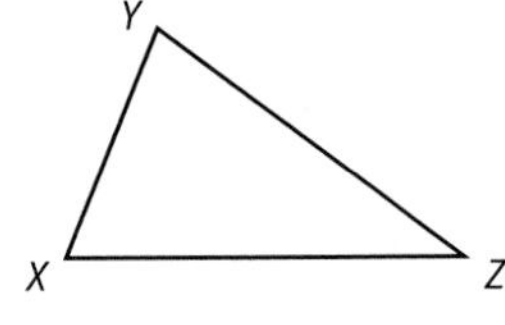

a. $XY = 6$, $YZ = 8$, and $XZ = 12$

$$12^2 = 6^2 + 8^2 - 2(6)(8)\cos Y$$
$$\cos Y \approx -0.4583$$
$$m\angle Y \approx 117°$$

The triangle is obtuse since it has an obtuse angle.

b. $XY = 6$, $YZ = 8$, and $XZ = 10$

$$10^2 = 6^2 + 8^2 - 2(6)(8)\cos Y$$
$$\cos Y = 0$$
$$m\angle Y \approx 90°$$

The triangle is a right triangle since it has a right angle.

c. $XY = 6$, $YZ = 8$, and $XZ = 8$

$$8^2 = 6^2 + 8^2 - 2(6)(8)\cos Y$$
$$\cos Y \approx 0.375$$
$$m\angle Y \approx 68°$$

The triangle is an isosceles triangle since two sides have the same length. $m\angle X = m\angle Y$. Therefore, $m\angle Z \approx 180° - 68° - 68° = 44°$. The triangle is acute since all of the angles are acute.

Based on the results of Example 5:

If $m\angle A > 90°$ in $\triangle ABC$, then $a^2 < b^2 + c^2$.
If $m\angle A = 90°$ in $\triangle ABC$, then $a^2 = b^2 + c^2$.
If $m\angle A < 90°$ in $\triangle ABC$, then $a^2 > b^2 + c^2$.

EXAMPLE 6

Use the diagram at the right. Find the length of *VY* to the nearest tenth of a unit.

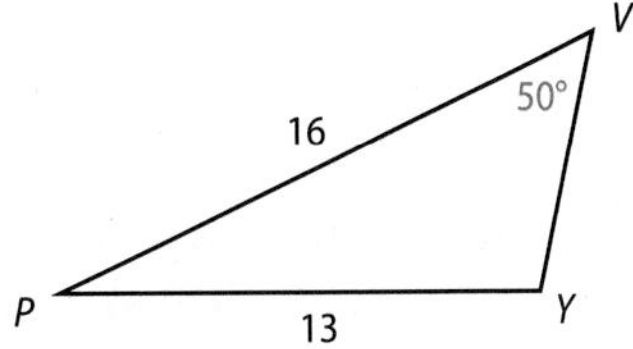

Notice that the information in the diagram gives two sides and an angle, in that order, making it an ambiguous case. There could be two triangles or no triangle with these measures.

STEP 1 Use the law of sines to find the measure of $\angle Y$, if possible.

$$\frac{\sin Y}{PV} = \frac{\sin V}{PY}$$

$$\frac{\sin Y}{16} = \frac{\sin 50°}{13}$$

$$\sin Y = \frac{16 \sin 50°}{13}$$

$m\angle Y \approx 71°$ or $m\angle Y \approx 109°$

There are two possible triangles with the given measures.

STEP 2 Find the corresponding possible measures of $\angle P$.
Case 1: $m\angle Y \approx 71°$. Then $m\angle P \approx 180° - (50° + 71°) = 59°$
Case 2: $m\angle Y \approx 109°$. Then $m\angle P \approx 180° - (50° + 109°) = 21°$

STEP 3 Use the law of sines again to find the corresponding possible lengths of $\overline{VY}$. Use the ratio $\frac{VY}{\sin P} = \frac{PV}{\sin Y}$

Case 1:

$$\frac{VY}{\sin 59°} = \frac{16}{\sin 71°}$$

$$VY = \frac{16 \sin 59°}{\sin 71°}$$

$$VY \approx 14.5$$

Case 2:

$$\frac{VY}{\sin 21°} = \frac{16}{\sin 109°}$$

$$VY = \frac{16 \sin 21°}{\sin 109°}$$

$$VY \approx 6.1$$

The length of $\overline{VY}$ could be either 14.5 or 6.1.

Need More HELP

For more about the ambiguous case in solving triangles, see page 1020.

Try It This Way

In Step 3, you could use the law of cosines to find the length of $\overline{VY}$ instead of the law of sines.

EXAMPLE 7

Derive a formula for the length, *BD*, of the shorter diagonal of parallelogram *ABCD*.

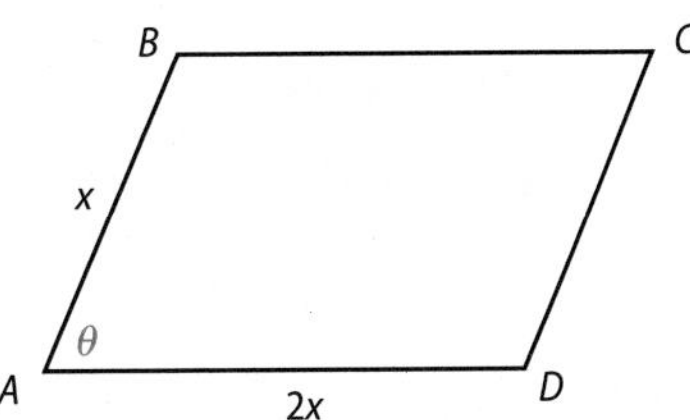

Use the law of cosines. $(BD)^2 = (AB)^2 + (AD)^2 - 2(AB)(AD) \cos \theta$

Substitute. $(BD)^2 = (x)^2 + (2x)^2 - 2(x)(2x) \cos \theta$

Simplify. $(BD)^2 = 5x^2 - 4x^2 \cos \theta$

Take the square root. $BD = \sqrt{5x^2 - 4x^2 \cos \theta}$

Since $x > 0$, $\sqrt{x^2} = x$. Therefore, $BD = x\sqrt{5 - 4\cos \theta}$.

Need More HELP

For a review of parallelograms and their properties, see p. 638.

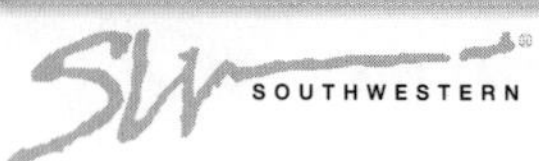

Solving Navigation Problems

The law of cosines often plays a significant role in solving navigation problems.

EXAMPLE 8

A ship departs port at point *O*. It sails along a course that is 30° east of north at a speed of 18 knots for 3 hours. It then changes direction and sails 50° south of east at a speed of 20.25 knots for 2 hours. At that time, the ship is at location *B*. To the nearest tenth of a nautical mile, how far, along a straight line, is the ship from port?

STEP 1 Analyze the problem and gather data.

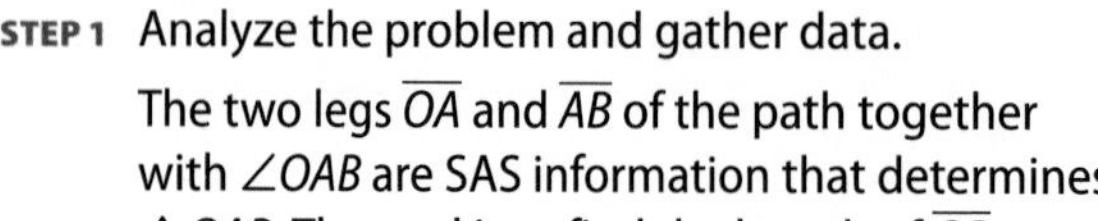

The two legs $\overline{OA}$ and $\overline{AB}$ of the path together with $\angle OAB$ are SAS information that determines $\triangle OAB$. The goal is to find the length of $\overline{OB}$.

STEP 2 Find *OA* and *OB* by using the equation below.

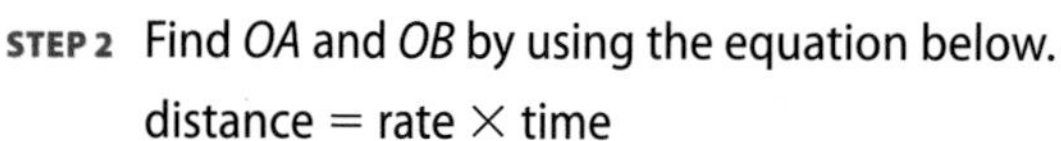

distance = rate × time

$$OA = \frac{18 \text{ nautical miles}}{\text{hour}} \times 3 \text{ hours} = 54 \text{ nautical miles}$$

$$AB = \frac{20.25 \text{ nautical miles}}{\text{hour}} \times 2 \text{ hours} = 40.5 \text{ nautical miles}$$

Find $m\angle OAB$ by using theorems about parallel lines.

given	$m\angle 1 = 30°$ and $m\angle 2 = 50°$
alternate interior angles	$m\angle 3 = m\angle 1 = 30°$
complementary angles	$m\angle 4 = 90° - m\angle 2 = 90° - 50° = 40°$

$$\angle OAB = m\angle 3 + m\angle 4 = 30° + 40° = 70°$$

STEP 3 Apply the law of cosines.

Use the law of cosines.	$(OB)^2 = (OA)^2 + (AB)^2 - 2(OA)(AB)\cos(\angle OAB)$
Substitute.	$(OB)^2 = 54^2 + 40.5^2 - 2(54)(40.5)\cos 70°$
Simplify.	$(OB)^2 = 3{,}060.25$
Take the square root.	$OB \approx 55.3$

To the nearest tenth of a nautical mile, the distance of $\overline{OB}$ is 55.3 nautical miles.

Need More HELP

In the diagram, the two north-south lines are parallel. This makes it possible to relate the measure of $\angle 1$ to $\angle 3$. For a review of parallel lines and transversals, see p. 630.

EXAMPLE 9

Use the information from Example 8. To the nearest tenth of a degree, what is the measure, *x*°, of the angle formed by $\overline{OB}$ and due north?

By the law of sines, $\sin x° = \frac{40.5 \sin 70°}{55.3}$. Therefore, $\sin x° \approx 0.6882$.

Thus, to the nearest tenth of a degree, $x° = 43.5° + m\angle 1 = 43.5° + 30° = 73.5°$.

Exploring the Law of Cosines on the Sphere

Just as there is a law of sines for spheres, there is a law of cosines for spheres.

EXAMPLE 10

Sketch the sphere and spherical triangle described below.

Vertex *A* is at the north pole of the sphere with center *O*. Vertex *B* is determined by *O*, *A*, and *B* on the equator. Vertex *C* is determined by *O*, *A*, and *C* on the equator. The measure of $\angle BOC$ is 120°.

The description given implies that the central angles have the following measures.

$m\angle AOB = 90°$

$m\angle AOC = 90°$

$m\angle BOC = 120°$

The diagram shows the triangle with its defining angles labeled.

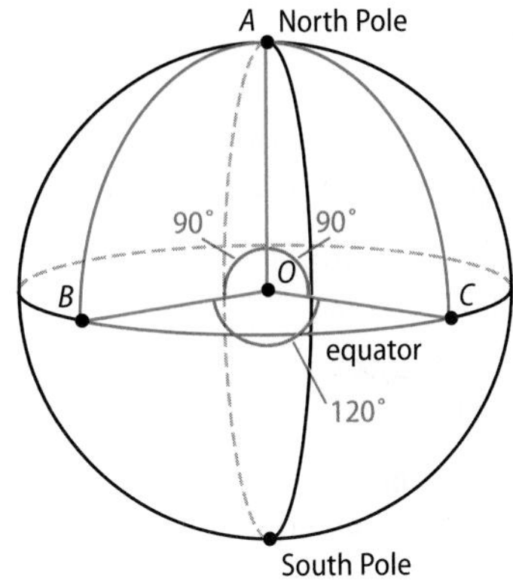

Need More HELP

For a review of three-dimensional surfaces and the sphere in particular, see pp. 716 and 1052.

EXAMPLE 11

The sphere in Example 10 has a radius of 1 unit. Find the measures of the angles and the lengths of its triangle's three sides.

$a = m\widehat{BC} = \frac{2\pi}{3}$ $\quad b = m\widehat{AC} = \frac{\pi}{2}$ $\quad c = m\widehat{AB} = \frac{\pi}{2}$

$m\angle A = 120°$ $\quad m\angle B = 90°$ $\quad m\angle C = 90°$

SEARCH

To see step-by-step videos of these problems, enter the page number into the SWadvantage.com Search Bar.

EXAMPLE 12

For the spherical triangle in Examples 10 and 11, verify the law of cosines for *a*.

Write the law of cosines for *a*.	$\cos a = \cos b \cos c + \sin b \sin c \cos A$
Substitute for *a*.	$\cos \frac{2\pi}{3} = -0.5$
Substitute for *b*, *c*, and *A*.	$\cos \frac{\pi}{2} \cos \frac{\pi}{2} + \sin \frac{\pi}{2} \sin \frac{\pi}{2} \cos 120° = -0.5$

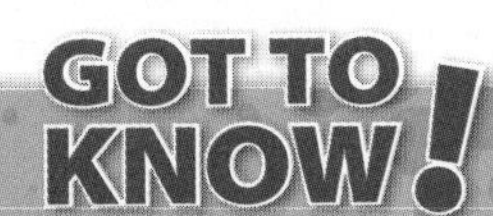

The Law of Cosines for the Sphere

Let $\triangle ABC$ be a spherical triangle with vertices *A*, *B*, and *C*.

A, *B*, and *C* represent the measures of the central angles with vertices *A*, *B*, and *C*.

a, *b*, and *c* represent the radius times the measures of the angles that determine *A*, *B*, and *C*.

Central Angles $\quad \cos a = \cos b \cos c + \sin b \sin c \cos A$

Similar formulas can be written for cos *b* and cos *c*.

Surface Angles $\quad \cos A = -\cos B \cos C + \sin B \sin C \cos a$

Similar formulas can be written for cos *B* and cos *C*.

Area of a Triangle

Selecting and Using Area Formulas

There are many formulas for the area of a triangle. The simplest of these is stated below.

$$\text{Area} = \frac{1}{2} \times \text{base} \times \text{height}$$

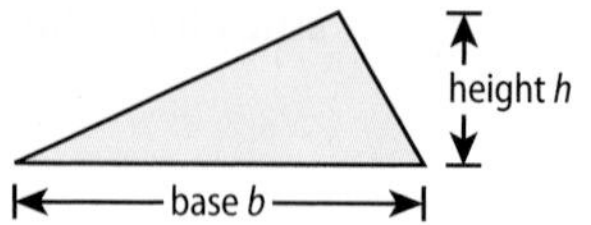

Using trigonometry, it is possible to derive triangle area formulas that involve SAS, ASA, or SSS information. For a summary of formulas that give the area of a triangle, see the *Got To Know!* box.

Need More HELP

If you initially choose a formula that does not fit the given data, rethink the choice and choose another formula. In this example, the expression $\frac{1}{2}bc \sin A$ would not be suitable because the measure of $\angle A$ is not given and it cannot easily be found.

EXAMPLE 1

In $\triangle XYZ$, $XY = 13$, $XZ = 18$, and $YZ = 8$. To the nearest tenth of a square unit, find the area of $\triangle XYZ$.

STEP 1 Select an area formula appropriate to the information given. Since the lengths of the sides are given and no angle measurements are given, select Heron's formula.

STEP 2 Apply Heron's formula.

$$s = \frac{1}{2}(13 + 18 + 8) = 19.5 \qquad \text{Area} = \sqrt{19.5(19.5 - 13)(19.5 - 18)(19.5 - 8)}$$
$$= \sqrt{2{,}186.44} \approx 46.7594$$

To the nearest tenth of a square unit, the area is about 46.8 square units.

Ways to REMEMBER

In the area formula such as $\frac{1}{2}bc \sin A$, the capital letter to the right of "sin" is the letter not found in the product to the left of "sin".

EXAMPLE 2

The area of $\triangle PQR$ is 2,560 square feet. $PR = 140$ feet and $PQ = 40$ feet. Find the measure of $\angle P$ to the nearest whole number of degrees.

Make a sketch as a guide.

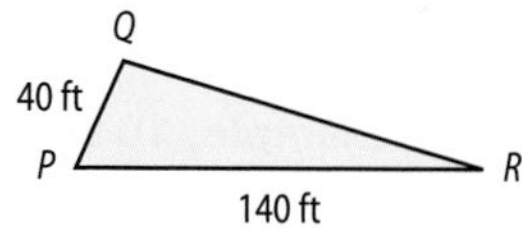

$$\text{Area} = \frac{1}{2}(PQ)(PR) \sin P$$

Solve for $m\angle P$. $\quad 2{,}560 = \frac{1}{2}(40)(140) \sin P$

$$\sin P \approx 0.9143$$

Therefore, $m\angle P$ is about 66°.

EXAMPLE 3

Derive formulas for the area of an equilateral triangle whose sides have length a.

Heron's formula: $s = 1.5a$

Area: $\sqrt{1.5a(1.5a - a)(1.5a - a)(1.5a - a)} = \sqrt{\frac{3a^4}{16}} = \frac{a^2\sqrt{3}}{4}$

Sine formula:

Area: $\frac{1}{2}(a)(a) \sin 60° = \frac{a^2\sqrt{3}}{4}$

EXAMPLE 4

In isosceles triangle $\triangle DEF$, $m\angle D = m\angle F = 50°$ and the area of the triangle is 172 square meters. To the nearest tenth, find the length of the base of the triangle.

STEP 1 Since $m\angle E = 180° - (50° + 50°) = 80°$, select an area formula that involves all three angles and only one side length.

$$\text{Area} = \frac{1}{2}(DF)^2 \frac{\sin D \sin F}{\sin E}$$

STEP 2 Write and solve an equation to find DF, the length of the base.

$$172 = \frac{1}{2}(DF)^2 \frac{\sin 50° \sin 50°}{\sin 80°}$$

$$DF = \sqrt{2(172)\left(\frac{\sin 80°}{\sin 50° \sin 50°}\right)} \approx 24.0271$$

The base of the triangle is about 24.0 meters long.

Watch Out!

You might think that because only two angle measures are given, then $\frac{1}{2}(DF)^2 \frac{\sin D \sin F}{\sin E}$ cannot be used. Since the measures of two angles are given, the measure of the third angle can easily be found.

EXAMPLE 5

Find the area of the parallelogram at the right. The parallelogram represents a part of a larger design.

L M
8 in.
60°
K 10 in. N

STEP 1 Find the area of $\triangle LKN$.

area of $\triangle LKN = \frac{1}{2}(KL)(KN) \sin K = \frac{1}{2}(8)(10) \sin 60° = 20\sqrt{3}$

STEP 2 Find the area of parallelogram $KLMN$.

The parallelogram is divided into congruent triangles: $\triangle LKN \cong \triangle NML$

area of parallelogram $KLMN = 2(20\sqrt{3}) = 40\sqrt{3}$

The area of the parallelogram is $40\sqrt{3}$ square inches.

SEARCH 

To see step-by-step videos of these problems, enter the page number into the SWadvantage.com Search Bar.

GOT TO KNOW!

Area Formulas for a Triangle

Given $\triangle ABC$ whose sides have length a, b, and c:

$$\text{Area} = \frac{1}{2}bc \sin A = \frac{1}{2}ac \sin B = \frac{1}{2}ab \sin C$$

$$\text{Area} = \frac{1}{2}a^2 \frac{\sin B \sin C}{\sin A} = \frac{1}{2}b^2 \frac{\sin A \sin C}{\sin B} = \frac{1}{2}c^2 \frac{\sin A \sin B}{\sin C}$$

Heron's Formula

Let s represent the semiperimeter.

$$s = \frac{1}{2}(a + b + c) \qquad \text{Area} = \sqrt{s(s-a)(s-b)(s-c)}$$

Vectors

Exploring Vectors

If two motorists are driving along the same straight road, then speed can help describe how far apart they are over time. Speed by itself is not adequate to describe location over time. Both speed and direction are needed. The diagram at the right represents a motorist traveling northeast at a speed of 55 miles per hour. After 2 hours, the motorist will be 110 miles northeast of point *O*. After 3 hours, the motorist will be 165 miles northeast of point *O*.

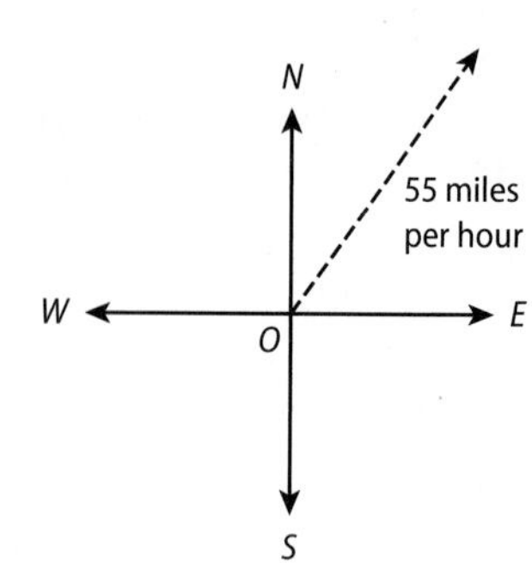

A **vector** is a quantity with both magnitude and direction. A vector is also described as a directed line segment. To denote a vector, write its initial point, then its terminal point, then a half arrow above the two letters. A bold lowercase letter such as **v** is also used to denote a vector. The diagram at the right illustrates vector $\overrightarrow{AB}$ with initial point *A* and terminal point *B*. If a directed line segment represents a vector, then its length is the **magnitude** of the vector. **Equivalent vectors** are vectors with the same magnitude and direction.

$\overrightarrow{AB}$

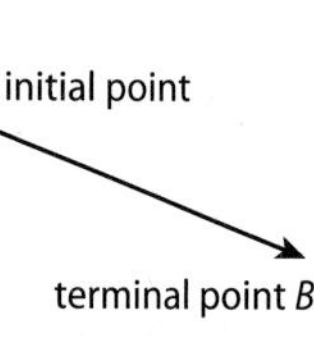

A vector in the plane with initial point (0, 0) and terminal point (*x*, *y*) is like a two-dimensional number. A real number can be thought of as a one-dimensional number, related to a point along the real number line. In the context of vectors, a **scalar** is a real number.

Need More **HELP**

A horizontal or vertical translation of a vector will produce an equivalent vector. For a review of translations, see p. 834.

EXAMPLE 1

a. On a grid, sketch a vector $\overrightarrow{ST}$ with initial point $S(-1, 1)$ that is equivalent to the vector shown.

From point $S(-1, 1)$, move to the right 6 units, then up 3 units to arrive at *T*. By the Pythagorean theorem, $\overrightarrow{ST}$ and the given vector have the same magnitude.

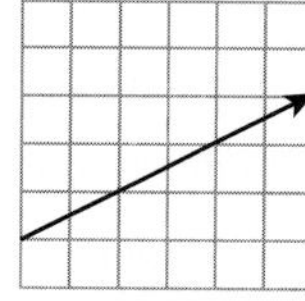

b. On the same grid, sketch a vector $\overrightarrow{XY}$ with initial point $X(8, 3)$ in the opposite direction that has the same magnitude as the one shown.

From point $X(8, 3)$, move to the left 6 units, then down 3 units to arrive at *Y*. By the Pythagorean theorem, $\overrightarrow{XY}$ and the given vector have the same magnitude. Their directions are opposite because the initial (terminal) point of one is the terminal (initial) point of the other.

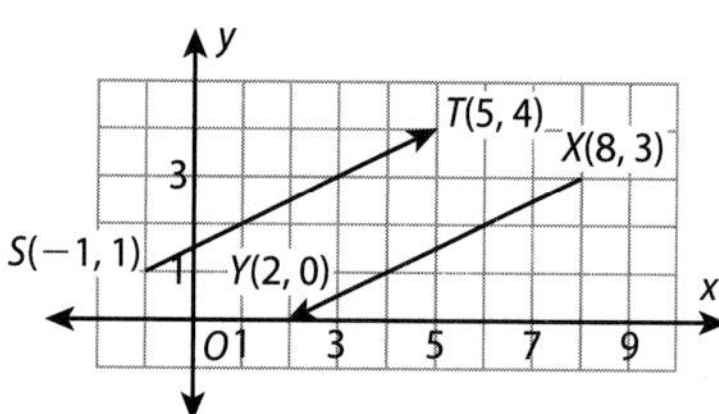

Ways to **REMEMBER**

The magnitude of a vector is the distance between its tip and tail.

GOT TO KNOW!

Magnitude of a Vector in the Plane

If $P(x_1, y_1)$ represents the initial point and $Q(x_2, y_2)$ represents the terminal point of $\overrightarrow{PQ}$, then the magnitude of $\overrightarrow{PQ}$, denoted by $\| \ \|$ is given by $\|\overrightarrow{PQ}\| = \sqrt{(x_2 - x_1)^2 + (y_2 - y_1)^2}$.

If a vector is represented in the *xy*-plane, then its direction is often expressed as the measure of the angle formed by the positive *y*-axis and the vector in a clockwise fashion.

EXAMPLE 2

Find the magnitude and direction of the vector whose initial point is the origin and whose terminal point is *A*(3, 2).

The diagram at the right below shows the situation. The angle indicating direction is labeled α.

$$\|\overrightarrow{OA}\| = \sqrt{(3-0)^2 + (2-0)^2}$$
$$= \sqrt{13}$$

$$\tan(90° - \alpha) = \frac{\text{opposite}}{\text{adjacent}} \text{ or } \frac{\text{rise}}{\text{run}} = \frac{2}{3}$$

$$(90° - \alpha) \approx 34° \qquad \alpha \approx 56°$$

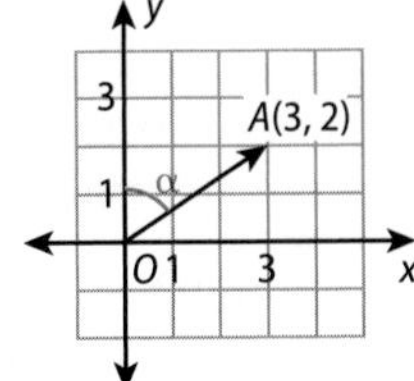

Watch Out !

In many contexts, an angle is measured counterclockwise with its initial side along the positive *x*-axis.

Consider two vectors **u** and **v** such that the initial point of **v** is the terminal point of **u**. The **resultant** of **u** and **v** is the vector whose initial point is the initial point of **u** and whose terminal point is the terminal point of **v**. Addition notation is used to indicate the resultant.

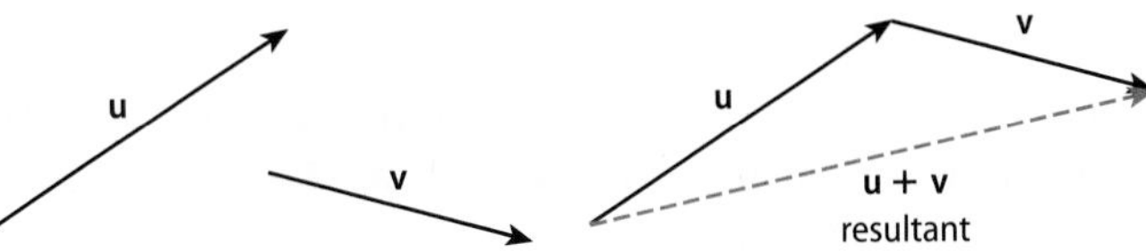

The diagrams above show the triangle method for sketching the resultant. The diagrams below show what is called the parallelogram method.

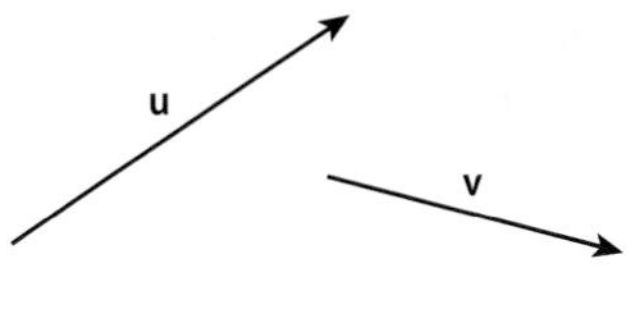

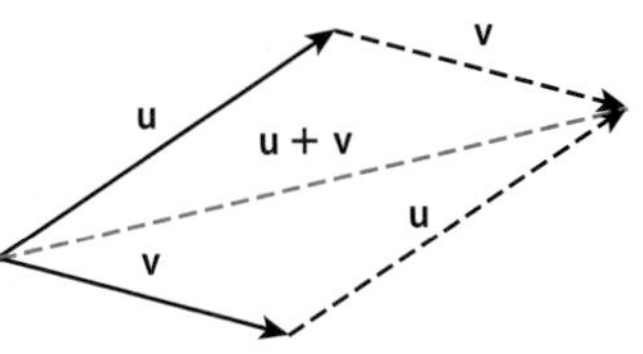

Try It This Way

There are several correct ways to arrange the vectors to get the resultant. The outcomes will only differ in location in the plane.

EXAMPLE 3

Sketch the resultant of u and v shown at the right.

METHOD 1

Use a triangle.

Place equivalent vectors tail to tip.

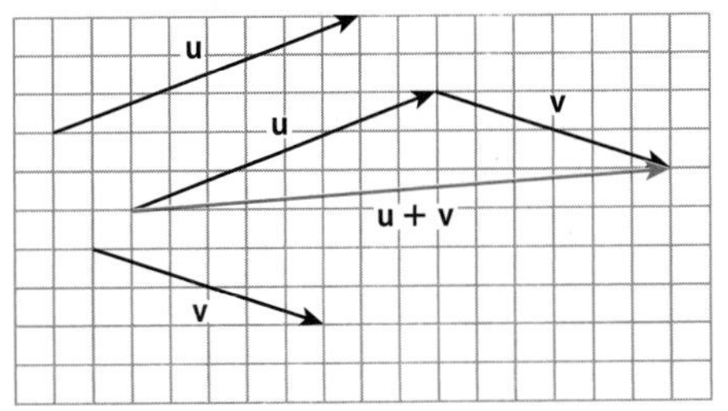

METHOD 2

Use a parallelogram.

Place equivalent vectors tail to tail.

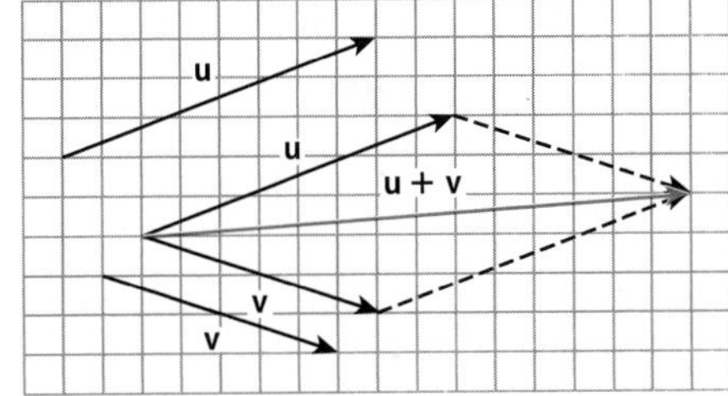

By either method, the resultants are the same.

SEARCH

To see step-by-step videos of these problems, enter the page number into the SWadvantage.com Search Bar.

Using Laws of Trigonometry with Vectors

The translation of a vector in the plane to another location results in an equivalent vector. A translation using coordinates can be useful in solving resultant problems with coordinates.

Need More HELP

For a review of the Pythagorean theorem, see p. 678. For a review of the distance formula, see p. 818.

EXAMPLE 4

Let u be the vector with initial point at the origin and terminal point at (6, 4) and let v be the vector with initial point at the origin and terminal point at (3, −3). Find the magnitude of the resultant.

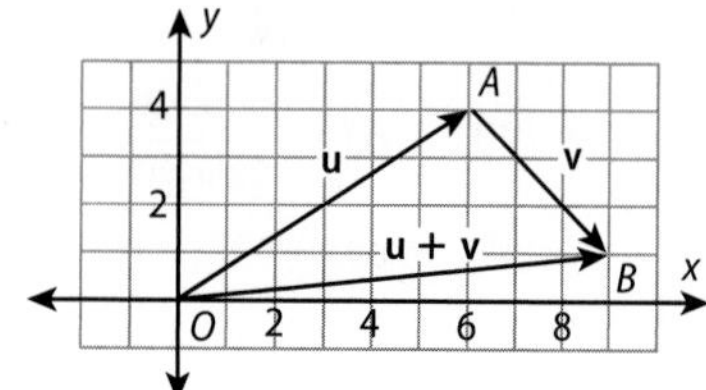

STEP 1 Sketch a diagram that shows **u** and the translation of **v** so that the initial point of **v** is at the terminal point of **u**.

STEP 2 The initial point of **u** + **v** is (0, 0) and the terminal point of **u** + **v** is (9, 1). Use (0, 0) and (9, 1) to find $\|\mathbf{u} + \mathbf{v}\|$.

STEP 3 Use the distance formula.

$$\|\mathbf{u} + \mathbf{v}\| = \sqrt{(9 - 0)^2 + (1 - 0)^2} = \sqrt{82}$$

EXAMPLE 5

Let u be the vector with initial point at the origin and terminal point at (6, 4) and let v be the vector with initial point at the origin and terminal point at (3, −3). Find the measure clockwise from the positive *y*-axis to the resultant.

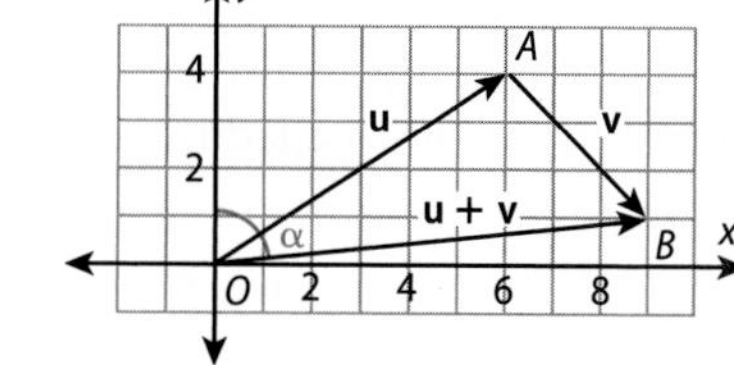

STEP 1 Sketch a diagram like the one used in Example 4. Include labels that help find $m\angle\alpha$.

STEP 2 Solve an equation involving the tangent. The initial point of **u** + **v** is (0, 0) and the terminal point is (9, 1).

Use $\frac{\text{rise}}{\text{run}}$. $\quad \tan(90° - \alpha) = \frac{1}{9}$

$$(90° - \alpha) \approx 6.3 \qquad \alpha \approx 83.7°$$

EXAMPLE 6

Use the diagram and the data below to approximate $\|\mathbf{b}\|$ to the nearest tenth of a unit.

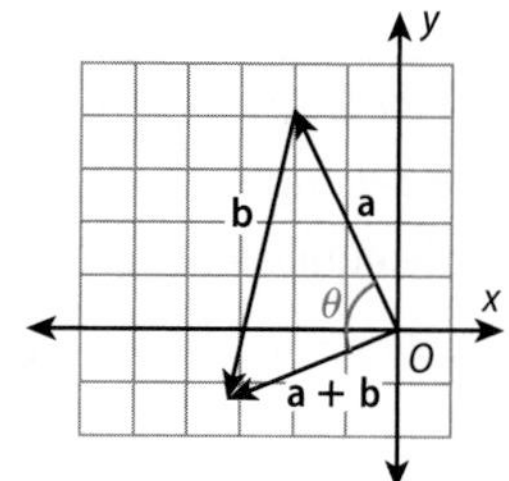

$\|\mathbf{a}\| = 24$ **direction from the *y*-axis clockwise to a: 330°**

$\|\mathbf{a} + \mathbf{b}\| = 20$ **direction from the *y*-axis clockwise to a + b: 235°**

The measure of the angle θ between **a** and **a** + **b** is 330° − 235° = 95°.

$$\|\mathbf{b}\|^2 = \|\mathbf{a}\|^2 + \|\mathbf{a} + \mathbf{b}\|^2 - 2\|\mathbf{a}\| \cdot \|\mathbf{a} + \mathbf{b}\| \cos\theta$$

$$\|\mathbf{b}\|^2 = 24^2 + 20^2 - 2(24)(20)\cos 95°$$

$$\|\mathbf{b}\|^2 \approx 1{,}059.67$$

$$\|\mathbf{b}\| \approx 32.5526$$

The magnitude of **b** is about 32.6 units.

EXAMPLE 7

In the diagram at the right, $\overrightarrow{OB}$ is the resultant of $\overrightarrow{OA}$ and $\overrightarrow{AB}$.

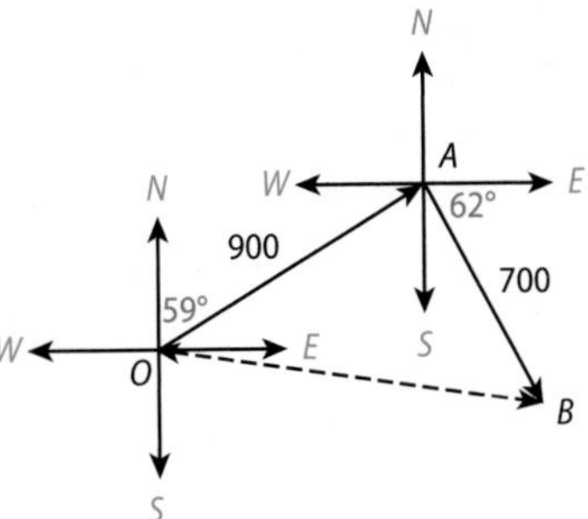

a. Find $\|\overrightarrow{OB}\|$ to the nearest whole number.

STEP 1 Find $m\angle OAB$.

$m\angle OAS = 59°$ and $m\angle BAS = 90° - 62° = 28°$

$m\angle OAB = m\angle OAS + m\angle BAS$

$m\angle OAB = 59° + 28° = 87°$

STEP 2 Use the law of cosines.

$\|\overrightarrow{OB}\|^2 = 900^2 + 700^2 - 2(900)(700)\cos 87°$

$\|\overrightarrow{OB}\| \approx 1{,}111$

To the nearest whole number, the magnitude of $\overrightarrow{OB}$ is 1,111 units.

b. Find the measure of the angle measured clockwise from the north-south line to $\overrightarrow{OB}$ to the nearest whole number of degrees.

STEP 1 Identity data that can be used by the law of sines or cosines.

SSS information $\quad OA = 900$, $AB = 700$, and $OB = 1{,}111$

STEP 2 Use the law of cosines.

Use the law of cosines. $\quad \|\overrightarrow{AB}\|^2 = \|\overrightarrow{OA}\|^2 + \|\overrightarrow{OB}\|^2 - 2\,\|\overrightarrow{OA}\| \cdot \|\overrightarrow{OB}\| \cos\angle AOB$

Substitute. $\quad 700^2 = 900^2 + 1{,}111^2 - 2(900)(1{,}111)\cos\angle AOB$

Simplify. $\quad \cos\angle AOB \approx 0.7772$

$m\angle AOB \approx 39°$

Use the remote exterior angle sum theorem. To the nearest degree, the angle between the north-south line and $\overrightarrow{OB}$ is $39° + 59° = 98°$.

Watch Out !

Many problems involving course and direction will involve the four basic compass directions. North-south lines are parallel and east-west lines are also parallel.

EXAMPLE 8

In the diagram, $\overrightarrow{OA}$ and $\overrightarrow{OB}$ determine θ, the angle between them. They also create a parallelogram. Use vectors to derive a formula for the longer diagonal of the parallelogram.

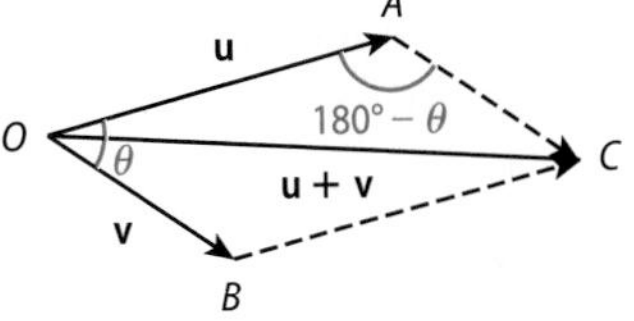

In $\triangle OAC$, $m\angle OAC = 180° - \theta$ since consecutive angles in a parallelogram are supplementary.

Apply the law of cosines in $\triangle OAC$.

$\|\mathbf{u} + \mathbf{v}\|^2 = \|\mathbf{u}\|^2 + \|\mathbf{v}\|^2 - 2\|\mathbf{u}\| \cdot \|\mathbf{v}\| \cos(180° - \theta)$

$\cos(180° - \theta) = -\cos\theta \quad = \|\mathbf{u}\|^2 + \|\mathbf{v}\|^2 - 2\|\mathbf{u}\| \cdot \|\mathbf{v}\| (-\cos\theta)$

$\|\mathbf{u} + \mathbf{v}\| = \sqrt{\|\mathbf{u}\|^2 + \|\mathbf{v}\|^2 + 2\|\mathbf{u}\| \cdot \|\mathbf{v}\| \cos\theta}$

SEARCH

To see step-by-step videos of these problems, enter the page number into the SWadvantage.com Search Bar.

Components of a Vector

Exploring the Resolution of a Vector

Recall that you find the resultant of two vectors by completing a triangle for which the resultant is the sum of the two given vectors. The resolution of a vector into components is the reverse process. To resolve a vector into components, find two more basic vectors from which you can acquire the given vector as the resultant.

In the coordinate plane, for every vector, there is a vector that has its initial point at the origin and is equivalent to the given vector. Because of this, a vector in the plane can be represented by an ordered pair $\mathbf{v} = (x, y)$. To distinguish a vector from a point, the notation $\mathbf{v} = \langle x, y \rangle$ is often used.

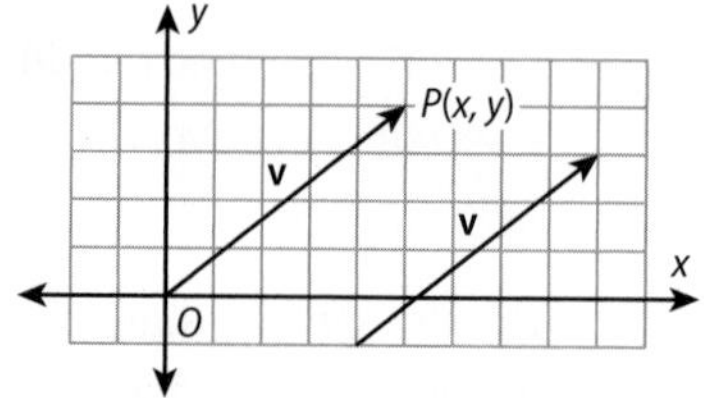

EXAMPLE 1

Write each vector v as an ordered pair using the directions given.

a. From the origin, move right 7 units, then up 4 units.

$\mathbf{v} = (7, 4)$

b. From the origin, move left 7 units, then down 4 units.

$\mathbf{v} = (-7, -4)$

c. From the origin, move right 7 units, then down 4 units.

$\mathbf{v} = (7, -4)$

d. From the origin, move left 7 units, then up 4 units.

$\mathbf{v} = (-7, 4)$

SEARCH

To see step-by-step videos of these problems, enter the page number into the SWadvantage.com Search Bar.

The **horizontal component** of the vector $v = (x, y)$ is the x-coordinate of the point representing the vector. The **vertical component** of the vector $v = (x, y)$ is the y-coordinate of the point representing the vector. Resolution of a vector in the plane can be accomplished by using right triangle trigonometry. The direction of a vector is the angle measured counterclockwise from the positive x-axis to the vector.

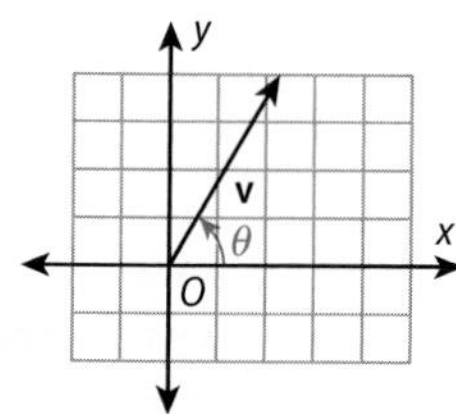

EXAMPLE 2

A vector v has magnitude 6 units and direction angle $\theta = 140°$. Find the horizontal and vertical components of v.

STEP 1 Sketch a diagram to find the quadrant of the terminal point of **v**. The terminal point is in Quadrant II. Thus, $x < 0$ and $y > 0$.

STEP 2 To find the horizontal component, use the cosine ratio. To find the vertical component, use the sine ratio.

$$\cos(180° - \theta) = \frac{OQ}{QP} \qquad \sin(180° - \theta) = \frac{PQ}{OP}$$

$\cos(180° - \theta) = -\cos\theta$

$$-\cos 40° = \frac{x}{6} \qquad \sin 40° = \frac{y}{6}$$

$$x = -6\cos 40° \qquad y = 6\sin 40°$$

The horizontal component is $x = -6\cos 40°$. The vertical component is $y = 6\sin 40°$.

Watch Out !

The lengths of the sides of any triangle are always positive numbers. However, the x- and y-coordinates of a point can be positive or negative.

In many problems, it is necessary to solve triangle problems before being able to find the components of a resultant.

EXAMPLE 3

Find the horizontal and the vertical components of the resultant, u + v, given the information about u and v below.

u: magnitude 230 miles; direction 24° **v: magnitude 210 miles; direction 300°**

STEP 1 Draw a sketch of the given situation.

STEP 2 Make a plan to find the magnitude and direction angle of the resultant.

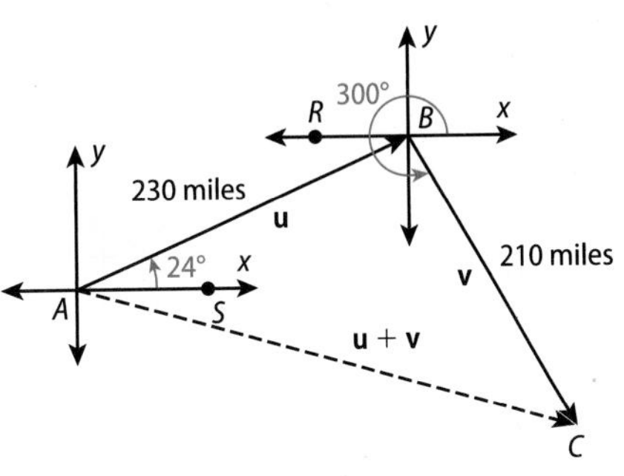

Use the law of cosines to find $\|\mathbf{u} + \mathbf{v}\|$ and to find $m\angle BAC$.

To find $\|\mathbf{u} + \mathbf{v}\|$, first find $m\angle ABC$.

Alternate interior angles gives: $m\angle RBA = 24°$

$m\angle ABC = 300° - (180° + 24°) = 96°$

$$\|\mathbf{u} + \mathbf{v}\|^2 = \|\mathbf{u}\|^2 + \|\mathbf{v}\|^2 - 2\|\mathbf{u}\| \cdot \|\mathbf{v}\| \cos(\angle ABC)$$
$$= 230^2 + 210^2 - 2(230)(210) \cos 96°$$
$$= 107{,}097$$
$$\|\mathbf{u} + \mathbf{v}\| \approx 327.3$$

Use the law of sines to find $m\angle BAC$.

$$\frac{\sin(\angle BAC)}{\|\mathbf{v}\|} = \frac{\sin(\angle ABC)}{\|\mathbf{u} + \mathbf{v}\|}$$
$$\frac{\sin(\angle BAC)}{210} = \frac{\sin 96°}{327.3}$$
$$\sin(\angle BAC) = \frac{210 \sin 96°}{327.3}$$
$$m(\angle BAC) \approx 40°$$

STEP 3 Use the information gathered along with a sketch to complete the solution.

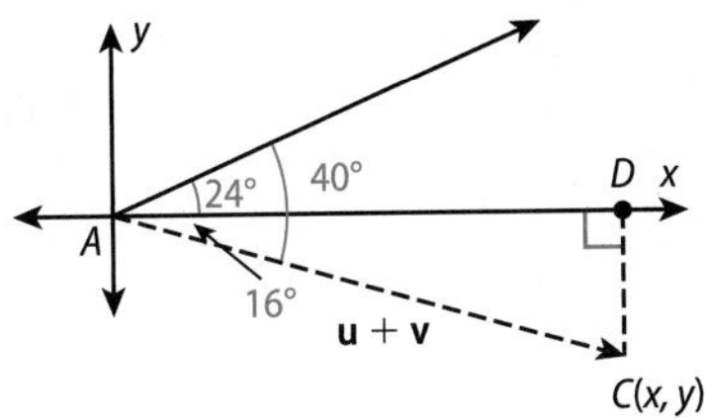

In $\triangle ADC$:

$$\cos 16° = \frac{CD}{\|\mathbf{u} + \mathbf{v}\|} \text{ and } \sin 16° = \frac{AD}{\|\mathbf{u} + \mathbf{v}\|}$$
$$CD = 327.3 \cos 16° \text{ and } AD = 327.3 \sin 16°$$

Therefore, $CD \approx 314.6$ and $AD \approx 90.2$.

Since $C(x, y)$ is in the fourth quadrant, the x component of $\|\mathbf{u} + \mathbf{v}\|$ is about 314.6 and the y component of $\|\mathbf{u} + \mathbf{v}\|$ is about -90.2.

Need More HELP

At the initial points of **u** and **v**, sketch small sets of axes to help measure angles correctly.

Try It This Way

Once $\|\mathbf{u} + \mathbf{v}\|$ has been found, the law of cosines could also be used to find $m\angle BAC$.

Watch Out!

Trying to put too much data on one diagram can increase the margin of error. Sketch a second diagram with only the information needed to take the next step.

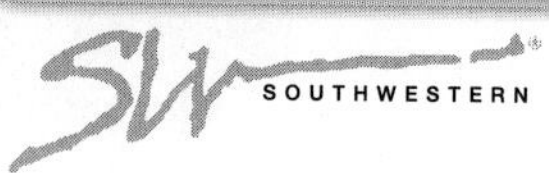

Using Vectors in Three-Dimensional Space

Just as an ordered pair specifies a vector in the *xy*-plane with initial point at the origin, an ordered triple specifies a vector in three dimensions. The diagram below illustrates the representation of a point in a three-dimensional coordinate system and the associated vector.

Let α, β, and γ represent the angles that a vector $\mathbf{v} = \langle x, y, z \rangle$ makes with the positive *x*-axis, the positive *y*-axis, and the positive *z*-axis, respectively. These are the **direction angles** for **v**. See the diagram below. These angles determine what are called the direction cosines for **v**. For the definitions of the direction cosines, see the *Got To Know!* box.

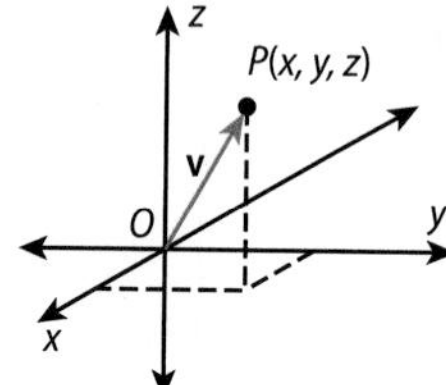

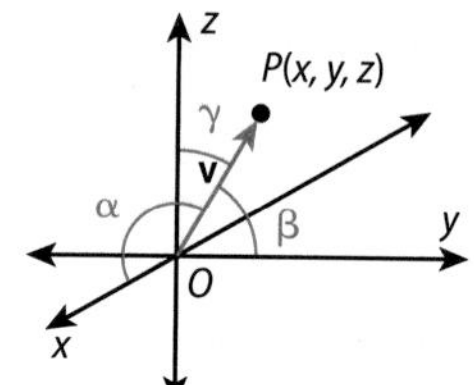

Need More HELP

The *xy*-plane is like a table top. Unlike the two-dimensional system, in the three-dimensional system, the *y*-axis is oriented horizontally and the *x*-axis is pictured as slanted at an angle. The *z*-axis always rises up from and falls below the *xy*-plane.

EXAMPLE 4

The direction angles for $\mathbf{v} = \langle x, y, z \rangle$ are $\alpha = 30°$, $\beta = 60°$, and $\gamma = 45°$ and $\|\mathbf{v}\| = 10$. Find *x*, *y*, and *z*.

Use direction cosines.

$\|\mathbf{v}\| = \sqrt{x^2 + y^2 + z^2}$

$$\cos\alpha = \frac{x}{\sqrt{x^2 + y^2 + z^2}} \qquad \cos\beta = \frac{y}{\sqrt{x^2 + y^2 + z^2}}$$

$$\cos 30° = \frac{x}{10} \qquad \cos 60° = \frac{y}{10}$$

$$x = 10\cos 30° \qquad y = 10\cos 60°$$

$$x = 5\sqrt{3} \qquad y = 5$$

$$\cos\gamma = \frac{z}{\sqrt{x^2 + y^2 + z^2}}$$

$$\cos 45° = \frac{z}{10}$$

$$z = 10\cos 45°$$

$$z = 5\sqrt{2}$$

Ways to REMEMBER

α ⟶ *x*-coordinate
β ⟶ *y*-coordinate
γ ⟶ *z*-coordinate

All ratios have the same denominator, the magnitude of the vector.

GOT TO KNOW!

Direction Cosines

Let $\mathbf{v} = \langle x, y, z \rangle$ and let α, β, and γ represent the direction angles for **v**. The direction cosines are defined as below.

$$\cos\alpha = \frac{x}{\sqrt{x^2 + y^2 + z^2}} \qquad \cos\beta = \frac{y}{\sqrt{x^2 + y^2 + z^2}} \qquad \cos\gamma = \frac{z}{\sqrt{x^2 + y^2 + z^2}}$$

In addition, $\cos^2\alpha + \cos^2\beta + \cos^2\gamma = 1$.

The three coordinate planes divide three-dimensional space into eight octants. In the octant where all three coordinates are positive, the direction angles α, β, and γ are all acute.

If $x > 0$, then $0° < \alpha < 90°$. If $y > 0$, then $0° < \beta < 90°$. If $z > 0$, then $0° < \gamma < 90°$.

EXAMPLE 5

Let v = ⟨3, 4, 7⟩. Find the direction angles for v.

Given $x = 3, y = 4$, and $z = 7$.

Distance formula $\|\mathbf{v}\| = \sqrt{3^2 + 4^2 + 7^2} = \sqrt{74}$

Use direction cosines. $\cos\alpha = \frac{3}{\sqrt{74}}$ $\cos\beta = \frac{4}{\sqrt{74}}$ $\cos\gamma = \frac{7}{\sqrt{74}}$

$\alpha \approx 69.6°$ $\beta \approx 62.3°$ $\gamma \approx 35.5°$

Try It This Way

You can make a quick sketch that locates $P(3, 4, 7)$ as an aid to see that α, β, and γ are acute.

EXAMPLE 6

Describe vectors u and v as perpendicular or not perpendicular.

a. u = ⟨0, 1, 1⟩ and v = ⟨0, −1, 1⟩

Both **u** and **v** lie in the *yz*-plane.

In $\triangle QOQ'$, $\cos(\angle QOQ') = \frac{1}{\|\mathbf{u}\|} = \frac{1}{\sqrt{2}}$

In $\triangle POP'$, $\cos(\angle POP') = \frac{1}{\|\mathbf{v}\|} = \frac{1}{\sqrt{2}}$

Therefore, $m\angle QOQ' = m\angle QOQ' = 45°$.

Let γ and γ' be the direction cosines for **u** and **v**, respectively. Measured counterclockwise from the *z*-axis, $\gamma = 315°$ and $\gamma' = 45°$. The angle between **u** and **v** is 90°. The vectors are perpendicular.

b. u = ⟨1, 0, 1⟩ and v = ⟨1, 0, 2⟩

Both **u** and **v** lie in the *xz*-plane. Let γ and γ' be the direction cosines with regard to the *z*-axis for **u** and **v**, respectively. Then γ is $\angle POP'$ and γ' is $\angle QOQ'$.

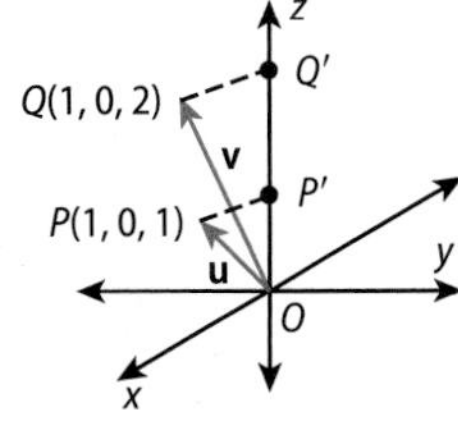

In $\triangle QOQ'$, $\cos\gamma = \frac{1}{\sqrt{2}}$. Thus, $\gamma = 45°$.

In $\triangle POP'$, $\cos\gamma' = \frac{2}{\sqrt{5}}$. Thus, $\gamma' \approx 27°$.

Since $|\gamma - \gamma'| \neq 90°$, vectors **u** and **v** are not perpendicular.

Need More HELP

If one coordinate in an ordered triple is 0, then the point lies in a coordinate plane.

$P(a, b, 0) \longrightarrow$ *xy*-plane

$P(a, 0, b) \longrightarrow$ *xz*-plane

$P(0, a, b) \longrightarrow$ *yz*-plane

SEARCH

To see step-by-step videos of these problems, enter the page number into the SWadvantage.com Search Bar.

Applying Addition and Subtraction in the Plane

Addition is the process of finding the total number of items when two or more groups of items are joined. As you know, one vector can be combined with another to produce a third vector, the resultant. This underlies the concept of vector addition. Like addition of numbers, vector addition is a binary operation. That is, addition applies to a pair of objects. As with addition of numbers, vector addition is commutative.

EXAMPLE 1

Using the vectors below, illustrate that vector addition is commutative.

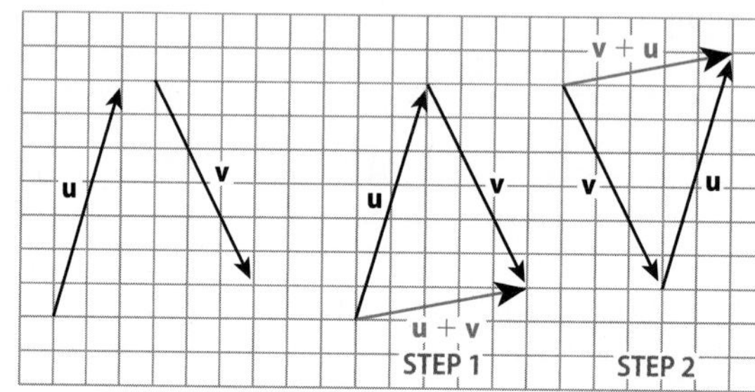

STEP 1 To sketch **u** + **v**, begin with **u**. Place the initial point of **v** at the terminal point of **u**. Sketch the vector whose initial point is the initial point of **u** and whose terminal point is the terminal point of **v**. This vector is **u** + **v**.

STEP 2 To sketch **v** + **u**, begin with **v**. Place the initial point of **u** at the terminal point of **v**. Sketch the vector whose initial point is the initial point of **v** and whose terminal point is the terminal point of **u**. This vector is **v** + **u**.

STEP 3 Compare outcomes. The vector **u** + **v** is represented by the translation 5 units right and 1 unit up. The vector **v** + **u** is also represented by the translation 5 units right and 1 unit up. Although **u** + **v** and **v** + **u** are in different locations, **u** + **v** = **v** + **u**. That is, addition is commutative.

Need More HELP

Much can be learned about addition and subtraction by using translations in the plane. For a review of translations, see p. 834.

Vector addition is also associative.

EXAMPLE 2

Using the vectors at the left below, illustrate (u + v) + r = u + (v + r).

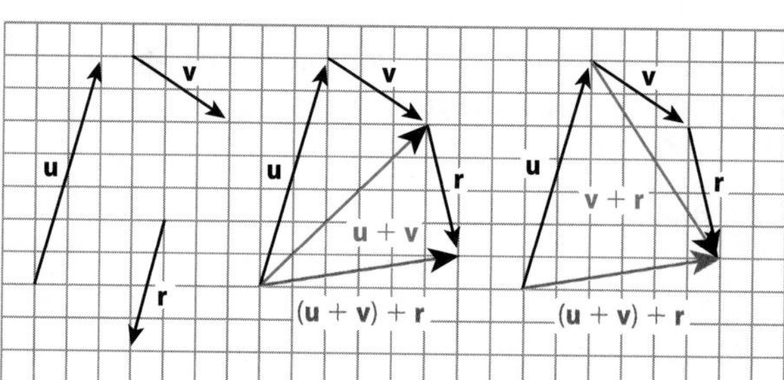

The middle diagram shows **r** added to **u** + **v** and the right diagram shows the sum **v** + **r** added to **u**. Both (**u** + **v**) + **r** and **u** + (**v** + **r**) are represented by the translation 6 units to the right and 1 unit up. Thus, (**u** + **v**) + **r** = **u** + (**v** + **r**).

SEARCH

To see step-by-step videos of these problems, enter the page number into the SWadvantage.com Search Bar.

The zero vector, denoted $\mathbf{0}$, is the vector whose initial and terminal points are the same. It is the vector with magnitude 0 and not assigned a direction. Think of the zero vector as a point.

$$\mathbf{u} + \mathbf{0} = \mathbf{u}$$

Every nonzero vector u has an additive inverse, denoted $-\mathbf{u}$. The additive inverse of $\mathbf{u}$ is the vector whose magnitude is the same as that of $\mathbf{u}$ but whose direction is the opposite of the direction of $\mathbf{u}$. The notation $-\mathbf{u}$ is shorthand for $(-1)\mathbf{u}$. The zero vector is its own additive inverse.

$$\mathbf{u} + (-\mathbf{u}) = \mathbf{0} \qquad \mathbf{u} - \mathbf{u} = \mathbf{0}$$

The fact that $-(\mathbf{u} + \mathbf{v}) = -\mathbf{u} + (-\mathbf{v})$ is a very useful property of vector addition.

Watch Out!

Since the number 0 and the zero vector are different, the zero vector is distinguished by bold type. In handwritten work, a half arrow above 0 can be used instead of bold type.

EXAMPLE 3

The diagram at the right shows two legs, $\overrightarrow{AB}$, then $\overrightarrow{BC}$ of a trip. Find the magnitude and direction of the return trip, $\overrightarrow{CA}$. $\overrightarrow{CA}$ is the additive inverse of the resultant $\overrightarrow{AC}$.

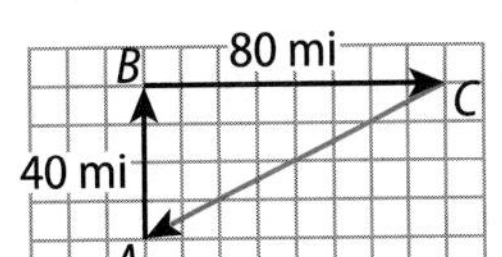

Use the Pythagorean theorem. $\|\overrightarrow{AC}\| = \sqrt{40^2 + 80^2} \approx 89.4$

Use trigonometry. $\tan(\angle BCA) = \frac{40}{80} = 0.5$

$m\angle BCA \approx 26.6°$

The direction of $\overrightarrow{CA}$ is $180° + 26.6° = 206.6°$.

Thus, $\overrightarrow{CA}$ has magnitude 89.4 miles and direction 206.6°.

Watch Out!

The difference between $\overrightarrow{AC}$ and $\overrightarrow{CA}$ is the order in which the letters are written. The terminal point of the vector is the letter written under the half arrowhead.

To subtract an integer b from an integer a, add the opposite of b to a. Vector subtraction is defined much the same way. For vectors $\mathbf{u}$ and $\mathbf{v}$, $\mathbf{u} - \mathbf{v} = \mathbf{u} + (-\mathbf{v})$.

EXAMPLE 4

Show that $-(\mathbf{u} + \mathbf{v}) + \mathbf{u} + \mathbf{v} = \mathbf{0}$.

$-(\mathbf{u} + \mathbf{v}) = -\mathbf{u} + (-\mathbf{v})$	$-(\mathbf{u} + \mathbf{v}) + \mathbf{u} + \mathbf{v} = -\mathbf{u} + (-\mathbf{v}) + \mathbf{u} + \mathbf{v}$
Apply the commutative property.	$= -\mathbf{u} + \mathbf{u} + (-\mathbf{v}) + \mathbf{v}$
Use the associative property.	$= (-\mathbf{u} + \mathbf{u}) + (-\mathbf{v}) + \mathbf{v})$
Apply the additive inverse.	$= \mathbf{0} + \mathbf{0}$
Apply the additive vector identity.	$= \mathbf{0}$

Therefore, $-(\mathbf{u} + \mathbf{v}) + \mathbf{u} + \mathbf{v} = \mathbf{0}$.

Basic Vector Addition Properties

Addition is commutative.	$\mathbf{u} + \mathbf{v} = \mathbf{v} + \mathbf{u}$
Addition is associative.	$(\mathbf{u} + \mathbf{v}) + \mathbf{r} = \mathbf{u} + (\mathbf{v} + \mathbf{r})$
Vector addition has an identity.	$\mathbf{u} + \mathbf{0} = \mathbf{u}$
Every vector $\mathbf{u}$ has an inverse, $-\mathbf{u}$.	$\mathbf{u} + (-\mathbf{u}) = \mathbf{0}$

Using Vector Addition and Subtraction with Coordinates

When a vector **u** is positioned in the coordinate plane or in three-dimensional space, it can be represented by an ordered pair or an ordered triple.

xy-plane: $\mathbf{u} = \langle x, y\rangle$ xyz-space: $\mathbf{u} = \langle x, y, z\rangle$

Addition can be carried out using addition of coordinates.

If $\mathbf{u} = \langle x_1, y_1\rangle$ and $\mathbf{v} = \langle x_2, y_2\rangle$, then

$\mathbf{u} + \mathbf{v} = \langle x_1 + x_2, y_1 + y_2\rangle$.

If $\mathbf{u} = \langle x_1, y_1, z_1\rangle$ and $\mathbf{v} = \langle x_2, y_2, z_2\rangle$, then

$\mathbf{u} + \mathbf{v} = \langle x_1 + x_2, y_1 + y_2, z_1 + z_2\rangle$.

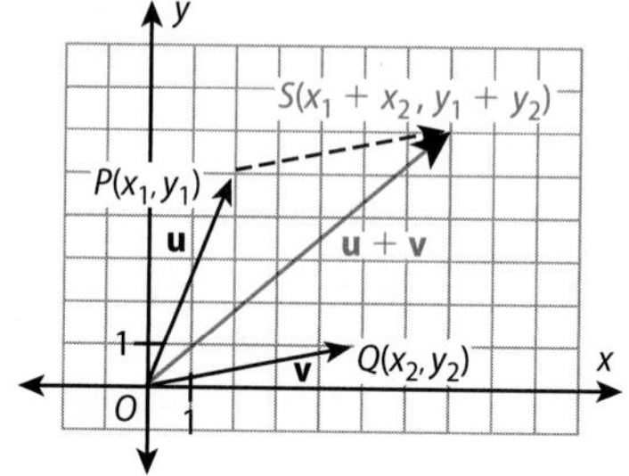

Ways to REMEMBER

Addition and subtraction are carried out coordinate-wise. Line up the ordered pairs to assure that corresponding coordinates are added.

(first, second)
(first, second)

(first ± first,
second ± second)

EXAMPLE 5

Let $\mathbf{u} = \langle -3, 4\rangle$, $\mathbf{v} = \langle 6, -5\rangle$, and $\mathbf{r} = \langle 0, -2\rangle$. Find $\mathbf{u} + \mathbf{v} + \mathbf{r}$.

$$\begin{aligned}
\mathbf{u} + \mathbf{v} + \mathbf{r} &= (\mathbf{u} + \mathbf{v}) + \mathbf{r} \\
&= (\langle -3, 4\rangle + \langle 6, -5\rangle) + \langle 0, -2\rangle \\
&= \langle -3 + 6, 4 + (-5)\rangle + \langle 0, -2\rangle \\
&= \langle 3, -1\rangle + \langle 0, -2\rangle \\
&= \langle 3 + 0, -1 + (-2)\rangle \\
&= \langle 3, -3\rangle
\end{aligned}$$

Therefore, $\mathbf{u} + \mathbf{v} + \mathbf{r} = \langle 3, -3\rangle$.

Watch Out!

Carefully examine vector expressions that are given. If they can be simplified, do that first. The risk of error is reduced and less work is involved when you simplify expressions before you carry out subsequent steps.

Subtraction can be carried out by subtracting coordinates.

If $\mathbf{u} = \langle x_1, y_1\rangle$ and $\mathbf{v} = \langle x_2, y_2\rangle$, then $\mathbf{u} - \mathbf{v} = \langle x_1 - x_2, y_1 - y_2\rangle$.

EXAMPLE 6

Let $\mathbf{u} = \langle -3, 4\rangle$, $\mathbf{v} = \langle 6, -5\rangle$, and $\mathbf{r} = \langle 0, -2\rangle$. Find $\mathbf{u} - \mathbf{r} - (\mathbf{v} - \mathbf{r})$.

STEP 1 Simplify the expression $\mathbf{u} - \mathbf{r} - (\mathbf{v} - \mathbf{r})$.

$$\begin{aligned}
\mathbf{u} - \mathbf{r} - (\mathbf{v} - \mathbf{r}) &= \mathbf{u} - \mathbf{r} - \mathbf{v} + \mathbf{r} \\
&= \mathbf{u} - \mathbf{v}
\end{aligned}$$

STEP 2 Find $\mathbf{u} - \mathbf{v} = \langle -3, 4\rangle - \langle 6, -5\rangle$.

$$\begin{aligned}
\langle -3, 4\rangle - \langle 6, -5\rangle &= \langle -3 - 6, 4 - (-5)\rangle \\
&= \langle -9, 9\rangle
\end{aligned}$$

Therefore, $\mathbf{u} - \mathbf{r} - (\mathbf{v} - \mathbf{r}) = \langle -9, 9\rangle$.

EXAMPLE 7

A motorist completes a trip in three parts as indicated below. Determine how far east or west and how far north or south he is from his starting point when the trip is completed.

Part A: east 240 miles south 38 miles

Part B: west 180 miles south 40 miles

Part C: west 250 miles north 50 miles

STEP 1 Set up an *xy*-coordinate system with the four compass directions as the axes and the starting point at the origin.

STEP 2 Represent each part of the trip as a vector determined by translations.

Part A: $\langle 240, -38\rangle$ Part B: $\langle -180, -40\rangle$ Part C: $\langle -250, 50\rangle$

STEP 3 Calculate the resultant using vector addition.

$$\langle 240, -38\rangle + \langle -180, -40\rangle + \langle -250, 50\rangle = \langle -190, -28\rangle$$

At the end of the trip, the motorist is 190 miles west and 28 miles south of his starting point.

Try It This Way

You can draw a diagram to help you visualize a given situation. A diagram for Example 7 would show a vector pointing to the right and up, followed by a vector pointing left and down. The third vector would point left and upward.

EXAMPLE 8

Let $\mathbf{u} = \langle -7, 12\rangle$ and $\mathbf{v} = \langle 4x - 3, -2y + 5\rangle$. Find v such that $\mathbf{u} + \mathbf{v} = \langle -2x + 1, y\rangle$.

$$\mathbf{u} + \mathbf{v} = \langle -7 + (4x - 3), 12 + (-2y + 5)\rangle$$
$$= \langle 4x - 10, -2y + 17\rangle$$

If $\mathbf{u} + \mathbf{v} = \langle -2x + 1, y\rangle$, then $\langle 4x - 10, -2y + 17\rangle = \langle -2x + 1, y\rangle$.

Set corresponding coordinates equal to each other. Then solve for x and for y.

$4x - 10 = -2x + 1$ and $-2y + 17 = y$

$$x = \frac{11}{6} \text{ and } y = \frac{17}{3}$$

$$\mathbf{v} = \langle 4x - 3, -2y + 5\rangle = \left\langle 4 \cdot \frac{11}{6} - 3, -2 \cdot \frac{17}{3} + 5\right\rangle = \left\langle \frac{13}{3}, -\frac{19}{3}\right\rangle$$

SEARCH

To see step-by-step videos of these problems, enter the page number into the SWadvantage.com Search Bar.

EXAMPLE 9

Let $\mathbf{u} = \langle x - y, x + y\rangle$ and $\mathbf{v} = \langle 3, 2\rangle$. Find x and y such that $\mathbf{u} - \mathbf{v} = \langle 2, 1\rangle$.

STEP 1 Write a system of equations by using subtraction and equating corresponding coordinates.

$$\begin{cases} x - y - 3 = 2 \\ x + y - 2 = 1 \end{cases} \rightarrow \begin{cases} x - y = 5 \\ x + y = 3 \end{cases}$$

STEP 2 Solve the system of equations.

$$\begin{cases} x - y = 5 \\ x + y = 3 \end{cases} \rightarrow 2x = 8 \rightarrow x = 4$$

If $x = 4$, then substitute 4 into one of the equations: $4 + y = 3 \rightarrow y = -1$

Therefore, $x = 4$ and $y = -1$.

Need More HELP

Remember that substitution and elimination are two of the methods used to solve a system of equations. All methods should result in the same answers.

Multiplication by a Scalar

Exploring Scalar Multiplication

In arithmetic, multiplication is introduced as repeated addition. In algebra, monomials are introduced as sums of the same variable expression.

$$4(3) = 3 + 3 + 3 + 3 \text{ and } 5x^2 = x^2 + x^2 + x^2 + x^2 + x^2$$

The development of the concept of the multiple of a vector **v** with a scalar is similar. The diagrams below show the scalar multiples 2**v** and 3**v**.

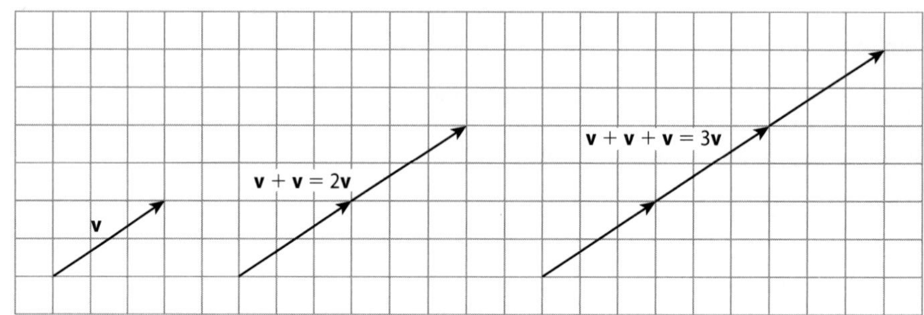

If **v** is a vector and a is a scalar, the **scalar multiple** $a\mathbf{v}$ is the vector with magnitude $|a| \cdot \|\mathbf{v}\|$ and the same direction as **v** if $a > 0$ and direction opposite to **v** if $a < 0$. If $a = 0$, then $a\mathbf{v} = \mathbf{0}$. For the properties of scalar multiplication, see the *Got To Know!* box.

Need More HELP

To demonstrate that $-\mathbf{u}$ has direction opposite that of **u**, sketch several vectors. Use translations like "4 units right and 2 units up." Then sketch the vectors that carry out the translations that undo the instructions that formed the original vectors.

4 units right, 2 units up

4 units left, 2 units down

EXAMPLE 1

Find the magnitude of v. State whether the direction of v is the same or opposite that of the specified vector.

a. $\mathbf{u} = \langle -2, 5\rangle$; $\mathbf{v} = 2.5\mathbf{u}$; **u**

$$\|\mathbf{v}\| = 2.5\|\mathbf{u}\| = 2.5\sqrt{(-2)^2 + 5^2} = 2.5\sqrt{29}$$

Since $2.5 > 0$, the direction of **v** is the same as that of **u**.

b. $\mathbf{u} = \langle 6, 12\rangle$; $\mathbf{v} = -2.5\mathbf{u}$; **u**

$$\|\mathbf{v}\| = 2.5\|\mathbf{u}\| = 2.5\sqrt{6^2 + 12^2} = 2.5\sqrt{180} = 15\sqrt{5}$$

Since $-2.5 \leq 0$, the direction of **v** is opposite that of **u**.

c. $\mathbf{u} = \langle -2, 5\rangle$ and $\mathbf{r} = \langle 3, 4\rangle$; $\mathbf{v} = 3(\mathbf{u} + \mathbf{r})$; $\mathbf{u} + \mathbf{r}$

Add.	$\mathbf{u} + \mathbf{r} = \langle 1, 9\rangle$
Find the magnitude of $\|\mathbf{u} + \mathbf{r}\|$.	$\|\mathbf{u} + \mathbf{r}\| = \sqrt{1^2 + 3^2} = \sqrt{10}$
Find the magnitude of $3\|\mathbf{u} + \mathbf{r}\|$.	$\|3(\mathbf{u} + \mathbf{r})\| = 3\sqrt{10}$

Since $3 > 0$, the direction of **v** is the same as that of $\mathbf{u} + \mathbf{r}$.

Properties of Scalar Multiplication

Let **u** and **v** be vectors and let a and b be scalars.

$a(\mathbf{u} + \mathbf{v}) = a\mathbf{u} + a\mathbf{v}$ $\quad (a + b)\mathbf{u} = a\mathbf{u} + b\mathbf{u}$ $\quad a(b\mathbf{u}) = (ab)\mathbf{u}$ $\quad 1\mathbf{u} = \mathbf{u}$ $\quad (-1)\mathbf{u} = -\mathbf{u}$

EXAMPLE 2

The diagram at the right shows the position of a moving particle after 1 unit of time.

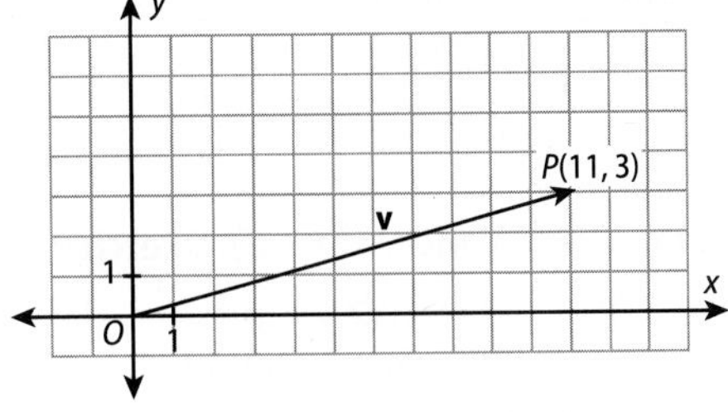

a. Write a vector to describe position after *t* units of time.

$t\mathbf{v} = t\langle 11, 3\rangle = \langle 11t, 3t\rangle$

b. Find the distance from *O* to the particle's position after 8 units of time.

METHOD 1

Find $\|\mathbf{v}\|$. $\|\mathbf{v}\| = \sqrt{11^2 + 3^2} = \sqrt{130}$

Multiply by 8. distance: $8\sqrt{130}$

METHOD 2

Find $\|t\mathbf{v}\|$. $\|t\mathbf{v}\| = \sqrt{(11t)^2 + (3t)^2} = \sqrt{130t^2} = t\sqrt{130}$

Substitute 8 for t. distance: $8\sqrt{130}$

Need More HELP

Multiplication of a vector by a positive scalar is closely related to enlargement and reduction as studied in dilations and similar figures. For a review of similar figures, see p. 790. For a review of dilations, see p. 850.

The multiplication of a vector by a positive scalar affects the magnitude of the result.

EXAMPLE 3

In each set of conditions placed on *a*, compare the magnitude of *a*u with that of u.

a. $0 < a < 1$

Let $\|\mathbf{u}\|$ be the magnitude of **u**.

$$\|\mathbf{u}\| \cdot 0 < \|\mathbf{u}\| \cdot a < \|\mathbf{u}\| \cdot 1$$

$$0 < a\|\mathbf{u}\| < \|\mathbf{u}\|$$

The magnitude of a**u** is less than the magnitude of **u**.

b. $a > 1$

Let $\|\mathbf{u}\|$ be the magnitude of **u**.

$$\|\mathbf{u}\| \cdot a > \|\mathbf{u}\| \cdot 1$$

$$a\|\mathbf{u}\| > \|\mathbf{u}\|$$

The magnitude of a**u** is greater than the magnitude of **u**.

SEARCH

To see step-by-step videos of these problems, enter the page number into the SWadvantage.com Search Bar.

EXAMPLE 4

Find *x* and *y* such that $\mathbf{u} = \langle x, y\rangle$ has the same direction as $\mathbf{v} = \langle 5, 12\rangle$ but has magnitude 1.

Find the magnitude of **v**. $\|\mathbf{v}\| = \sqrt{5^2 + 12^2} = 13$

Let $x = \frac{5}{13}$ and let $y = \frac{12}{13}$.

Then: $\mathbf{u} = \left\langle \frac{5}{13}, \frac{12}{13}\right\rangle$, or $\frac{1}{13}\langle 5, 12\rangle$, has magnitude 1 and the same direction as **v**.

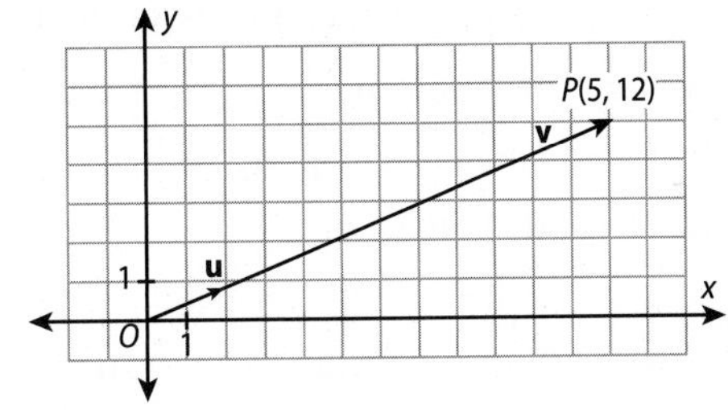

Try It This Way

Think of reducing the magnitude of **v** by its own length. This thinking suggests a multiplier a that is equivalent to $\frac{1}{\|\mathbf{v}\|}$.

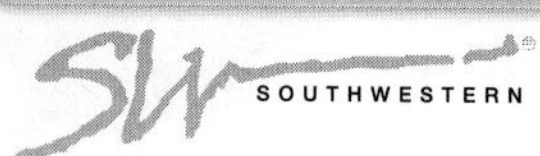

Using Linear Combinations

A **linear combination** of vectors **u** and **v** is any expression of the form $a\mathbf{u} + b\mathbf{v}$, where a and b are scalars.

Need More HELP

Remember that when a vector is represented by a pair of numbers, it is assumed that the initial point is at the origin.

EXAMPLE 5

Let u = ⟨3, 1⟩ and v = ⟨2, 2⟩. Sketch u, v, and 3u + 2v.

STEP 1 Plot (3, 1) and (2, 2). These are the terminals points of **u** and **v**.

STEP 2 Find and sketch 3**u** and 2**v**.

$3\mathbf{u} = 3\langle 3, 1\rangle = \langle 9, 3\rangle$

$2\mathbf{v} = 2\,\langle 2, 2\rangle = \langle 4, 4\rangle$

STEP 3 Find and sketch 3**u** + 2**v**.

METHOD 1

Use the parallelogram method.

METHOD 2

Find and plot (9 + 4, 3 + 4), or (13, 7).

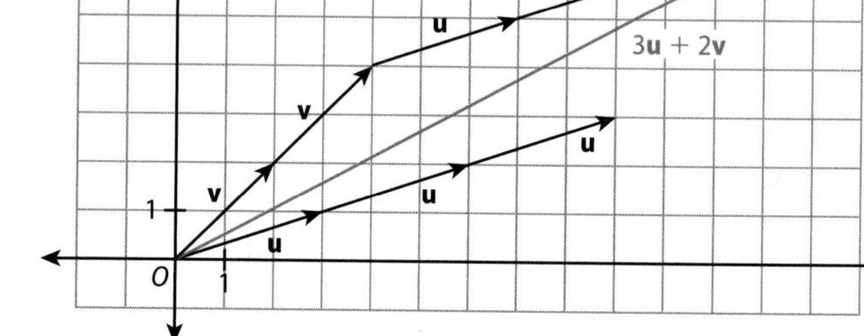

Watch Out !

Remember that when you multiply a vector by a number a, you should multiply each coordinate by a.

$a\langle x, y\rangle \neq \langle ax, y\rangle$

A mistake like this is similar to the mistake shown below in using the distributive property.

$a(b + c) \neq ab + c$

EXAMPLE 6

Let u = ⟨−3, 7⟩ and v = ⟨2, 5⟩. Write −4u + 5v as a single vector.

	$-4\mathbf{u} + 5\mathbf{v} = -4\langle -3, 7\rangle + 5\langle 2, 5\rangle$
scalar multiplication	$= \langle (-4)(-3), (-4)(7)\rangle + \langle 5(2), 5(5)\rangle$
	$= \langle 12, -28\rangle + \langle 10, 25\rangle$
vector addition	$= \langle 12 + 10, -28 + 25\rangle$
	$= \langle 22, -3\rangle$

Therefore, $-4\mathbf{u} + 5\mathbf{v} = \langle 22, -3\rangle$.

EXAMPLE 7

Let u and v be vectors in the plane. Simplify 3(u + v) − 5(u − v).

Use $a(\mathbf{u} + \mathbf{v}) = a\mathbf{u} + a\mathbf{v}$.	$3(\mathbf{u} + \mathbf{v}) - 5(\mathbf{u} - \mathbf{v}) = 3\mathbf{u} + 3\mathbf{v} - 5\mathbf{u} + 5\mathbf{v}$
Use the commutative property.	$= 3\mathbf{u} - 5\mathbf{u} + 3\mathbf{v} + 5\mathbf{v}$
Use $(a + b)\mathbf{u} = a\mathbf{u} + b\mathbf{u}$.	$= (3 - 5)\mathbf{u} + (3 + 5)\mathbf{v}$
	$= -2\mathbf{u} + 8\mathbf{v}$

Therefore, $3(\mathbf{u} + \mathbf{v}) - 5(\mathbf{u} - \mathbf{v}) = -2\mathbf{u} + 8\mathbf{v}$.

In many problems that involve linear combinations of vectors, systems of linear equations are needed to find solutions.

EXAMPLE 8

Let u = ⟨3, 1⟩, v = ⟨5, 2⟩, and r = ⟨19, 7⟩. Find scalars *a* and *b* such that *a*u + *b*v = r.

STEP 1 Use the representations for **u**, **v**, and **r**.

$$a\langle 3, 1\rangle + b\langle 5, 2\rangle = \langle 19, 7\rangle$$

STEP 2 Write and solve a system of equations.

$$\begin{cases} 3a + 5b = 19 \\ a + 2b = 7 \end{cases}$$

Use substitution. $3(-2b + 7) + 5b = 19$

$b = 2$

Use substitution. $a + 2(2) = 7$

$a = 3$

STEP 3 CHECK

$$3\langle 3, 1\rangle + 2\langle 5, 2\rangle = \langle 9, 3\rangle + \langle 10, 4\rangle = \langle 9 + 10, 3 + 4\rangle = \langle 19, 7\rangle$$

Therefore, $a = 3$ and $b = 2$.

Try It This Way

An alternate arrangement of the vector equation is shown here.

$a\langle 3, 1\rangle$

$b\langle 5, 2\rangle$

equals

$\langle 19, 7\rangle$

This vertical arrangement might help assure that corresponding components are equated.

EXAMPLE 9

Let u = ⟨*x*, *y*⟩, v = ⟨*y*, −*x*⟩, and r = ⟨3, 7⟩. Find *x* and *y* such that 2u + 3v = −4r.

STEP 1 Write 2**u** + 3**v** and −4**r** as single vectors.

$$2\mathbf{u} + 3\mathbf{v} = 2\langle x, y\rangle + 3\langle y, -x\rangle = \langle 2x + 3y, -3x + 2y\rangle$$

$$-4\mathbf{r} = -4\langle 3, 7\rangle = \langle -12, -28\rangle$$

STEP 2 Set components equal to write a system of equations.

$$\begin{cases} 2x + 3y = -12 \\ -3x + 2y = -28 \end{cases}$$

STEP 3 Solve the system of equations for *x* and *y*.

Multiply the first equation by 2.

Multiply the second equation by −3.

$$\begin{cases} 2x + 3y = -12 \\ -3x + 2y = -28 \end{cases} \rightarrow \begin{cases} 4x + 6y = -24 \\ 9x - 6y = 84 \end{cases}$$

Add the resulting equations. $13x = 60$

$x = \frac{60}{13}$

Substitute to find *y*. $2 \times \frac{60}{13} + 3y = -12$

$y = -\frac{92}{13}$

Therefore, $x = \frac{60}{13}$ and $y = -\frac{92}{13}$.

Watch Out !

Multiplying the first equation by 2 is shorthand for multiplying each side of the equation by 2. Remember that the left side of the equation consists of two terms. Be sure to multiply each term by 2.

The Dot Product

SOUTHWESTERN

Defining the Dot Product

An important theorem from geometry states the following.

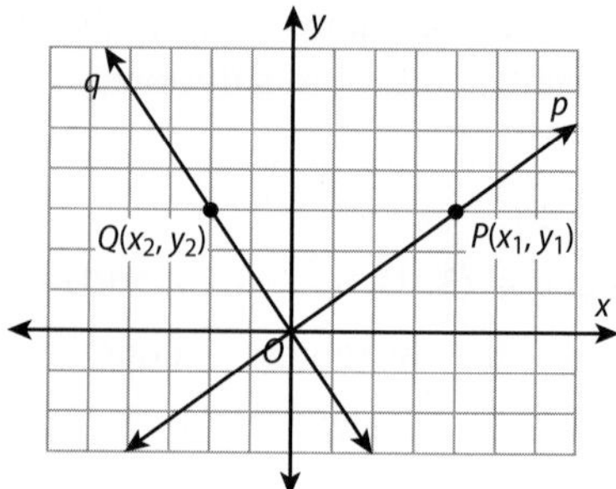

Two nonvertical lines in the coordinate plane are perpendicular if and only if the product of their slopes is -1.

Lines p and q in the graph have slopes $\frac{y_1}{x_1}$ and $\frac{y_2}{x_2}$.

p and q are perpendicular if and only if $\frac{y_1}{x_1} \cdot \frac{y_2}{x_2} = -1$.

That is, lines p and q are perpendicular if and only if $x_1x_2 + y_1y_2 = 0$.

EXAMPLE 1

Lines *p* and *q* have equations of the form $y = mx$. Point *P* is on line *p* and point *Q* is on line *q*. Determine whether *p* and *q* are perpendicular.

a. $P(5, 3)$ and $Q(-3, 5)$

Since $(5)(-3) + (3)(5) = 0$, lines p and q are perpendicular.

b. $P(-3, 7)$ and $Q(4, 6)$

Since $(-3)(4) + (7)(6) \neq 0$, lines p and q are not perpendicular.

Watch Out!

The properties of the dot product are not the same as the properties that apply to the multiplication of real numbers.

An important vector operation is the dot product. For statements of the definition and properties of the dot product, see the *Got To Know!* box.

EXAMPLE 2

Let $\mathbf{u} = \langle x_1, y_1 \rangle$ and $\mathbf{v} = \langle x_2, y_2 \rangle$. Find each dot product.

a. $\mathbf{u} = \langle -11, 4 \rangle$ and $\mathbf{v} = \langle -4, -11 \rangle$

$\mathbf{u} \cdot \mathbf{v} = (-11)(-4) + (4)(-11) = 0$

b. $\mathbf{u} = \langle 3, 7 \rangle$ and $\mathbf{v} = \langle 6, 14 \rangle$

$\mathbf{u} \cdot \mathbf{v} = (3)(6) + (7)(14) = 116$

GOT TO KNOW!

Definition and Properties of the Dot Product

Let $\mathbf{u} = \langle x_1, y_1 \rangle$, $\mathbf{v} = \langle x_2, y_2 \rangle$, and $\mathbf{r}$ represent vectors and a and b represent scalars.

The **dot product** of $\mathbf{u}$ and $\mathbf{v}$, denoted $\mathbf{u} \cdot \mathbf{v}$, is defined as $\mathbf{u} \cdot \mathbf{v} = x_1x_2 + y_1y_2$.

$\mathbf{u} \cdot \mathbf{v} = \mathbf{v} \cdot \mathbf{u}$	$a(\mathbf{u} \cdot \mathbf{v}) = (a\mathbf{u} \cdot \mathbf{v})$	$\mathbf{r} \cdot (\mathbf{u} + \mathbf{v}) = \mathbf{r} \cdot \mathbf{u} + \mathbf{r} \cdot \mathbf{v}$
$\mathbf{u} \cdot \mathbf{u} = \lVert\mathbf{u}\rVert^2$	$\mathbf{0} \cdot \mathbf{0} = 0$	$\mathbf{r} \cdot (a\mathbf{u} + b\mathbf{v}) = a(\mathbf{r} \cdot \mathbf{u}) + b(\mathbf{r} \cdot \mathbf{v})$

The dot product has many uses in geometry and trigonometry. The following example illustrates that two vectors are perpendicular if and only if the dot product equals 0.

Need More HELP

A rotation leaves magnitude unchanged but changes the direction of a vector. The image of a vector under a rotation does not yield an equivalent vector. For a review of rotations, see p. 842.

EXAMPLE 3

Let $\mathbf{u} = \langle x, y \rangle$. Its rotation 90° counterclockwise is $\mathbf{v} = \langle -y, x \rangle$. Show that $\mathbf{u} \cdot \mathbf{v} = 0$.

$$\mathbf{u} \cdot \mathbf{v} = (x)(-y) + y(x)$$
$$= -xy + xy = 0$$

For the formula used to find the angle between two vectors, see the *Got to Know!* box.

EXAMPLE 4

Let $\mathbf{u} = \langle 4, 1 \rangle$ and $\mathbf{v} = \langle 5, 8 \rangle$. Find the measure of the angle between u and v.

STEP 1 Calculate magnitudes and the dot product.

$\|\mathbf{u}\| = \sqrt{(-4)^2 + 1^2} = \sqrt{17}$ $\quad \|\mathbf{v}\| = \sqrt{5^2 + 8^2} = \sqrt{89}$ $\quad \mathbf{u} \cdot \mathbf{v} = (-4)(5) + (1)(8) = -12$

STEP 2 Write and solve $\mathbf{u} \cdot \mathbf{v} = \|\mathbf{u}\| \, \|\mathbf{v}\| \cos \theta$.

$\mathbf{u} \cdot \mathbf{v} = \|\mathbf{u}\| \, \|\mathbf{v}\| \cos \theta$ $\quad -12 = \sqrt{17}\,\sqrt{89} \cos \theta$

$$\cos \theta = \frac{-12}{\sqrt{17}\,\sqrt{89}} \approx 108°$$

The angle between **u** and **v** measures about 108°.

EXAMPLE 5

Let $\mathbf{u} = \langle 5, 2 \rangle$ and $\mathbf{v} = \langle -6, 5 \rangle$. Use the dot product to determine whether the triangle formed is acute, right, or obtuse.

Calculate $\mathbf{u} \cdot \mathbf{v}$, $\|\mathbf{u}\|$, and $\|\mathbf{v}\|$. $\quad \mathbf{u} \cdot \mathbf{v} = (5)(-6) + (2)(5) = -20$

$\|\mathbf{u}\| = \sqrt{5^2 + 2^2} = \sqrt{29}$ and $\|\mathbf{v}\| = \sqrt{(-6)^2 + 5^2} = \sqrt{61}$

Write an expression for $\cos \theta$. $\quad \cos \theta = \dfrac{-20}{\sqrt{29}\,\sqrt{61}}$

Since $\dfrac{-20}{\sqrt{29}\,\sqrt{61}} < 0$, then $90° < \theta < 180°$.

Therefore, the triangle determined by **u** and **v** is an obtuse triangle.

SEARCH

To see step-by-step videos of these problems, enter the page number into the SWadvantage.com Search Bar.

GOT TO KNOW!

The Angle Between Two Vectors

If **u** and **v** are vectors and θ $(0° \le \theta \le 180°)$ is the angle between them, then $\mathbf{u} \cdot \mathbf{v} = \|\mathbf{u}\| \, \|\mathbf{v}\| \cos \theta$.

Watch Out!

The bold Roman letter **i** represents a vector. Do not confuse this notation with the italic *i* that represents $\sqrt{-1}$.

$\mathbf{i} = \langle 1, 0 \rangle$

$i = \sqrt{-1}$

Using Basis Vectors

In the *xy*-plane, there are two special vectors, **i** and **j**.

$\mathbf{i} = \langle 1, 0 \rangle$ and $\mathbf{j} = \langle 0, 1 \rangle$

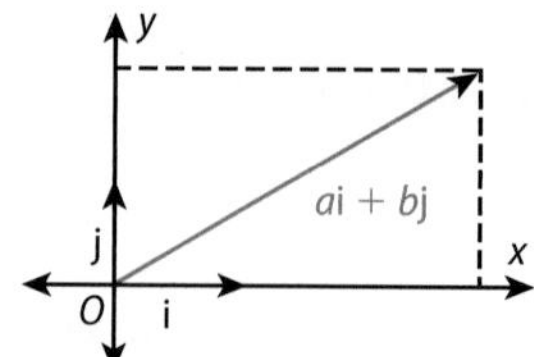

Using **i** and **j**, every vector **u** can be written as a linear combination of them.

If $\mathbf{u} = \langle a, b \rangle$, then for scalars a and b, $\mathbf{u} = a\mathbf{i} + b\mathbf{j}$.

This is shown in the diagram above. The vectors **i** and **j** form a basis for the set of all vectors in the *xy*-plane. Each vector **i** and **j** is a **unit vector**; a vector with magnitude 1.

Notice that **i** lies along the *x*-axis and that **j** lies along the *y*-axis. Thus, the vectors **i** and **j** are perpendicular. In general, two vectors **u** and **v** are perpendicular, or **orthogonal**, if their dot product equals 0. (The zero vector and any vector are also considered to be orthogonal.)

$\mathbf{u} \cdot \mathbf{v} = 0$ if and only if **u** and **v** are orthogonal.

The vectors **i** and **j** form an orthogonal basis for all vectors in the *xy*-plane.

EXAMPLE 6

Represent $\mathbf{u} = \langle -3, 7 \rangle$, $\mathbf{v} = \langle 7.82, 0 \rangle$, and $\mathbf{w} = \langle 0, 3.75 \rangle$ as linear combinations of i and j.

$\mathbf{u} = (-3)\mathbf{i} + 7\mathbf{j}$ $\quad$ $\mathbf{v} = 7.82\mathbf{i}$ $\quad$ $\mathbf{w} = 3.75\mathbf{j}$

If $u = a\mathbf{i} + b\mathbf{j}$, then $a\mathbf{i}$ and $b\mathbf{j}$ are called the projections of **u** onto **i** and **j**. Using the formula for the angle between two vectors, you can find the projection of a vector onto another vector.

Ways to REMEMBER

When sketching a projection, drop a perpendicular from the terminal point of the vector to be projected onto the other vector. Think of creating a right triangle.

EXAMPLE 7

Let $\overrightarrow{OA} = \langle 4, 3 \rangle$. Find w, the projection of $\overrightarrow{OA}$ onto $\overrightarrow{OB} = \langle 8, 2 \rangle$.

STEP 1 Sketch vectors $\overrightarrow{OA}$, $\overrightarrow{OB}$, and θ, the angle between them.

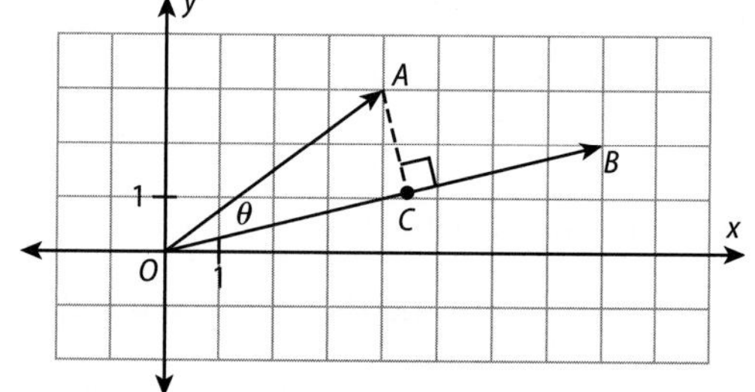

STEP 2 Find θ. Use $\overrightarrow{OA} \cdot \overrightarrow{OB} = \|\overrightarrow{OA}\| \cdot \|\overrightarrow{OB}\| \cos \theta$.

$\overrightarrow{OA} \cdot \overrightarrow{OB} = 38$, $\|\overrightarrow{OA}\| = 5$, and $\|\overrightarrow{OB}\| = 2\sqrt{17}$

Therefore, $38 = 10\sqrt{17} \cos \theta$.

$\theta \approx 23°$.

STEP 3 In $\triangle OAC$, find OC.

Since $\cos 23° = \frac{OC}{5}$, then $OC = 5 \cos 23°$. Therefore, $OC \approx 4.6$.

STEP 4 Write **w** in terms of $\overrightarrow{OB}$.

$\mathbf{w} = \frac{OC}{OB} \cdot \overrightarrow{OB}$. Since $OC \approx 4.6$ and $OB = 2\sqrt{17}$, then $\mathbf{w} = \frac{2.3}{\sqrt{17}} \overrightarrow{OB}$.

Every vector **r** in the *xy*-plane can be written as some combination of noncollinear vectors **u** and **v**. If, for example, $\mathbf{u} = \langle 3, 1\rangle$, $\mathbf{v} = \langle 5, 2\rangle$, and $\mathbf{r} = \langle 19, 7\rangle$, then $\mathbf{r} = 3\mathbf{u} + 2\mathbf{v}$. Refer to Example 8 on page 1081.

Every vector **w** in the *xy*-plane can be written as the linear combination of a given unit vector **u** and a unit vector **v** orthogonal to **u**. In the diagram at the right, $\mathbf{w} = 3\mathbf{u} + 2\mathbf{v}$.

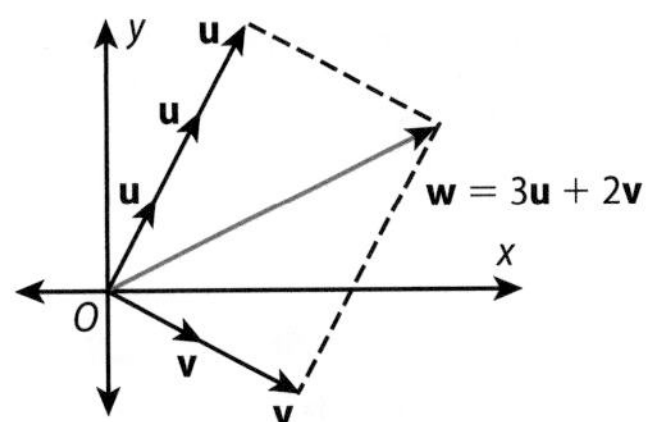

EXAMPLE 8

Let $\mathbf{u} = \left\langle \frac{\sqrt{2}}{2}, \frac{\sqrt{2}}{2} \right\rangle$ and $\mathbf{r} = \langle 4, 7\rangle$. Write r as a linear combination of u and a unit vector v orthogonal to u.

STEP 1 Choose a unit vector orthogonal to **u**.

Since $\|\mathbf{u}\| = \sqrt{\left(\frac{\sqrt{2}}{2}\right)^2 + \left(\frac{\sqrt{2}}{2}\right)^2} = \sqrt{\frac{2}{4} + \frac{2}{4}} = 1$, **u** is a unit vector.

Let $\mathbf{v} = \left\langle -\frac{\sqrt{2}}{2}, \frac{\sqrt{2}}{2} \right\rangle$.

Since $\sqrt{\left(\frac{\sqrt{2}}{2}\right)^2 + \left(\frac{\sqrt{2}}{2}\right)^2} = \sqrt{\frac{2}{4} + \frac{2}{4}} = 1$, **v** is a unit vector.

STEP 2 Make a rough sketch to see the situation. Then find the projections of **r** onto **u** and **v**.

Find θ for $m\angle ROU$.

Use $\overrightarrow{OR} \cdot \mathbf{u} = \|\overrightarrow{OR}\| \cdot \|\mathbf{u}\| \cos\theta$.

$$\overrightarrow{OR} \cdot \mathbf{u} = \frac{\sqrt{2}}{2} \cdot 4 + \frac{\sqrt{2}}{2} \cdot 7 = \frac{11\sqrt{2}}{2}$$

$$\|\overrightarrow{OR}\| = \sqrt{65} \text{ and } \|\mathbf{u}\| = 1$$

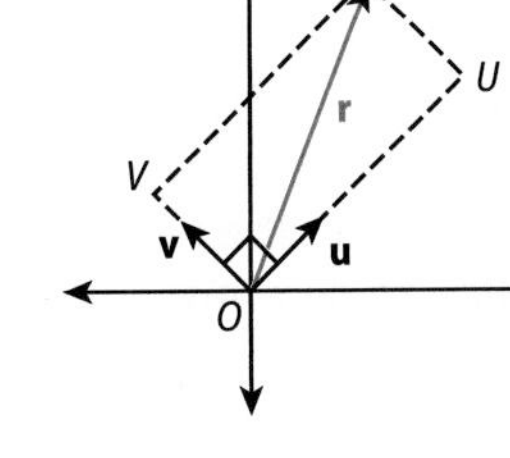

Therefore, $\frac{11\sqrt{2}}{2} = \sqrt{65}\cos\theta$

$$\cos\theta = \frac{11\sqrt{2}}{2\sqrt{65}}$$

$$\theta \approx 15°$$

STEP 3 Use $\triangle ROU$ to complete finding the projections of **r** onto **u** and **v**.

$$\cos\theta = \frac{OU}{OR} \qquad \sin\theta = \frac{RU}{OR}$$

$$\cos 15° = \frac{OU}{\sqrt{65}} \qquad \sin 15° = \frac{RU}{\sqrt{65}}$$

Therefore, $OU = \sqrt{65}\cos 15°$ and $RU = \sqrt{65}\sin 15°$.

STEP 4 Write the linear combination.

$\mathbf{r} = (\sqrt{65}\cos 15°)\mathbf{u} + (\sqrt{65}\sin 15°)\mathbf{v}$

SEARCH

To see step-by-step videos of these problems, enter the page number into the SWadvantage.com Search Bar.

Need More HELP

When dealing with a complicated solution to a problem, step back and consider the underlying solution strategy. The goal is to use **u** and **v** to create a rectangle for which **r** is a diagonal.

Applications of Vectors

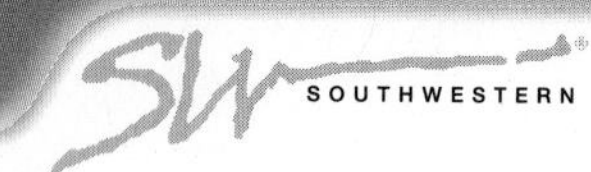

Applying Vectors in Navigation

Travel often requires some way to tell direction and distance. Vectors can provide help determining where an object is after a succession of course settings.

SEARCH

To see step-by-step videos of these problems, enter the page number into the SWadvantage.com Search Bar.

EXAMPLE 1

A delivery-truck driver travels along four legs of a trip. From point O, he drives to location A. From there, he drives to location B, and so on. To the nearest tenth of a mile, how far from the starting point is the driver at the end of the last leg of the trip?

A: west 150 miles north 15 miles **B: west 40 miles south 60 miles**

C: east 120 miles south 35 miles **D: east 120 miles north 70 miles**

STEP 1 Use vector addition to determine where the driver is relative to the starting point when the last delivery is made.

For signs for coordinates, use the compass directions here.

E $+$ W $-$ N $+$ S $-$

For the first leg of the route: west 250 becomes -250 and north 15 becomes $+15$.

Use vector addition: $\langle -150, 15\rangle + \langle -40, -60\rangle + \langle 120, -35\rangle + \langle 120, 70\rangle = \langle 50, -10\rangle$

STEP 2 Calculate magnitude.

$$\|\langle 50, -10\rangle\| = \sqrt{50^2 + (-10)^2} \approx 51$$

STEP 3 Interpret the result.

After the last delivery, the driver is about 51 miles from the starting point.

EXAMPLE 2

Two ships leave port at the same time. Use the information about location from port after 3 hours of sailing to determine the measure of the angle between their courses.

Ship A: 56 miles east and 18 miles north **Ship B: 46 miles east and 15 miles south**

STEP 1 Draw a sketch of the situation. The sketch does not need to be to scale.

STEP 2 Calculate θ using the dot product.

$$\overrightarrow{OA} \cdot \overrightarrow{OB} = \|\overrightarrow{OA}\| \cdot \|\overrightarrow{OB}\| \cos(\angle AOB)$$

$$\cos(\angle AOB) = \frac{\overrightarrow{OA} \cdot \overrightarrow{OB}}{\|\overrightarrow{OA}\| \cdot \|\overrightarrow{OB}\|}$$

$$= \frac{56 \cdot 46 + 18 \cdot (-16)}{\sqrt{56^2 + 18^2} \cdot \sqrt{46^2 + (-16)^2}}$$

$$\approx 0.7987$$

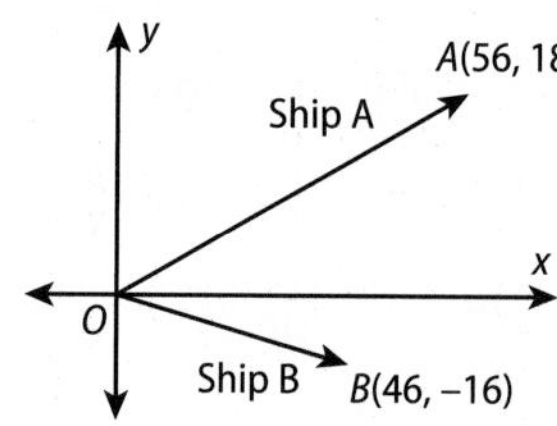

Use the inverse cosine. $\text{Cos}^{-1}(0.7987) \approx 37°$

The courses of ships A and B form an angle of about 37°.

One way to remember how to find the cosine of the angle between two vectors is this ratio.

$$\frac{\text{dot prod}}{\text{prod of mags}}$$

It helps to write the dot product over the product of the magnitudes.

In some vector problems, **v** is given but the solution depends on using **−v**.

$$\text{If } \mathbf{v} = \langle x, y \rangle, \text{ then } -\mathbf{v} = \langle -x, -y \rangle.$$

It may also be necessary to rewrite a vector given the coordinates of its endpoints.

If $P(x_1, y_1)$ is initial point of **v** and $Q(x_2, y_2)$ is the terminal point of **v**, then the vector below is equivalent to **v**.

$$\langle x_2 - x_1, y_2 - y_1 \rangle$$

EXAMPLE 3

A rescue boat leaves port to respond to an incident. A second rescue boat leaves a dock on an island 31 miles east and 6 miles north of port at the same time. The boats meet 19 miles east and 1 mile south of port. To the nearest whole number of degrees, find the measure of the angle between the paths of the boats.

STEP 1 Make a rough sketch to picture departure points, courses, and the point where they meet.

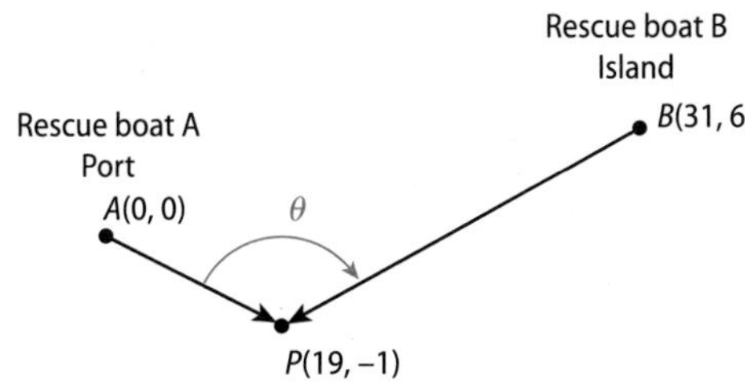

STEP 2 Analyze the data. The goal is to find the measure of $\angle APB$. Use the formula for the angle between two vectors, $\overrightarrow{PA}$ and $\overrightarrow{PB}$, the additive inverses, or opposites, of $\overrightarrow{AP}$ and $\overrightarrow{BP}$.

STEP 3 Represent $\overrightarrow{PA}$ and $\overrightarrow{PB}$ using coordinates.

$\overrightarrow{PA} = -\langle 19 - 0, -1 - 0 \rangle = \langle -19, 1 \rangle$ and $\overrightarrow{PB} = -\langle 19 - 31, -1 - 6 \rangle = \langle 12, 7 \rangle$

STEP 4 Calculate measures needed to find θ, the required angle.

$$\overrightarrow{PA} \cdot \overrightarrow{PB} = \|\overrightarrow{PA}\| \cdot \|\overrightarrow{PB}\| \cos \theta$$

To use the formula, calculate $\overrightarrow{PA} \cdot \overrightarrow{PB}$, $\|\overrightarrow{PA}\|$, and $\|\overrightarrow{PB}\|$.

Calculate the dot product. $\overrightarrow{PA} \cdot \overrightarrow{PB} = (-19)(12) + (1)(7)$

Calculate magnitudes. $\|\overrightarrow{PA}\| = \sqrt{(-19)^2 + 1^2}$ $\|\overrightarrow{PB}\| = \sqrt{12^2 + 7^2}$

STEP 5 Perform the calculations to find θ.

METHOD 1

Make a calculator-ready expression. $\text{Cos}^{-1} \dfrac{(-19)(12) + (1)(7)}{\sqrt{(-19)^2 + 1^2} \cdot \sqrt{12^2 + 7^2}} \approx 146.7°$

METHOD 2

Approximate as you go. $\text{Cos}^{-1}\theta \approx -0.8361$. Thus, $\theta \approx 146.7°$.

By either method, the boats approach one another at about a 146.7° angle.

Need More HELP

Recall that when the coordinates of two vectors are given, subtraction of corresponding coordinates produces an equivalent vector needed to apply to a formula.

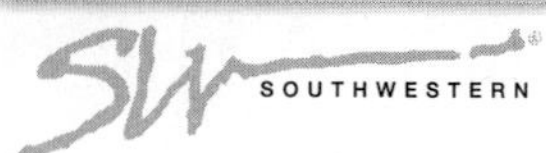

Applying Vectors to Force Problems

Every vector **w** in the plane can be written as some linear combination of two noncollinear vectors **u** and **v**. In particular, if **u** and **v** are perpendicular, then **w** will be the diagonal of a rectangle. This idea plays an important role in problems involving forces. In the example below, notice that **w** is the diagonal of the rectangle formed by **u** and **v**.

Need More HELP

The vector **w** is the vector whose magnitude and direction are known. The vector **u** is the vector of interest. To achieve a rectangle with **u** as one side and **w** as the diagonal, bring in vector **v**, perpendicular to **u**. This vector helps to resolve **w** into a linear combination of two perpendicular vectors. The magnitude and direction of **v** do not really come into play. It is a helping vector.

EXAMPLE 4

The diagram at the right shows a weight on an inclined plane. The force w exerted by gravity is 980 N (newtons, the basic unit of force in the metric system). Find the component u of force in the direction of the ramp.

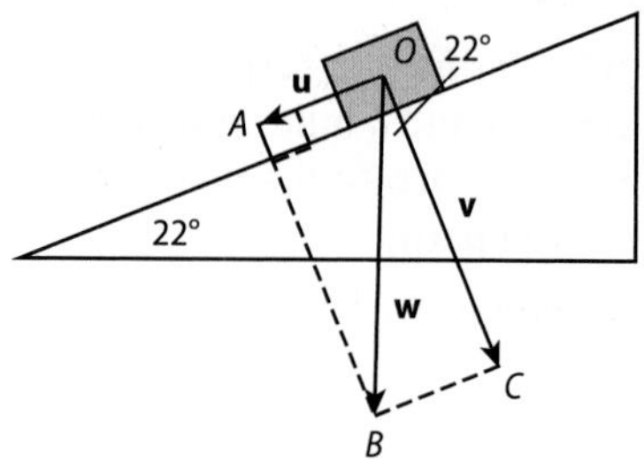

The diagram shows **w** as the sum of **u** and **v**, the components of **w** in the direction of the inclined plane and the direction perpendicular to the inclined plane. The magnitude of **w** is 980 N.

In $\triangle OBC$, $\sin(\angle BOC) = \dfrac{BC}{\|\mathbf{w}\|}$

$$\sin 22° = \frac{BC}{\|\mathbf{w}\|}$$

$$\|\overrightarrow{BC}\| = \|\overrightarrow{OA}\|\ \frac{BC}{OB} = \frac{OA}{980};\ \sin 22° = \frac{OA}{980}$$

$$OA = 980 \sin 22° \approx 367$$

The force in the direction of the ramp is about 367 N.

EXAMPLE 5

The diagram in Example 4 shows a weight on an inclined plane. Suppose that the angle of inclination is increased by 5°. By how many newtons does the component u of force in the direction of the ramp change from that found when the angle measures 22°?

The solution follows the same line of reasoning as above except that 27° replaces 22°.

$$OA = 980 \sin 27° \approx 445$$

The force in the direction of the ramp is about 445 N. This is a clear increase of about 78 N.

EXAMPLE 6

The diagram in Example 4 shows a weight on an inclined plane. For what angle of inclination will the component of force in the direction of the ramp be greater than 500 N?

Let θ be the required angle of inclination for the ramp. Solve $980 \sin \theta > 500$.

$$980 \sin \theta > 500$$

$$\sin \theta > \frac{500}{980}$$

$$30.7° < \theta < 90°$$

If the angle is approximately 30.7° or more, up to a limit of 90°, the force will exceed 500 N.

SEARCH

To see step-by-step videos of these problems, enter the page number into the SWadvantage.com Search Bar.

Force applied to move an object from one place to a different place is called *work*. The diagrams below show two situations.

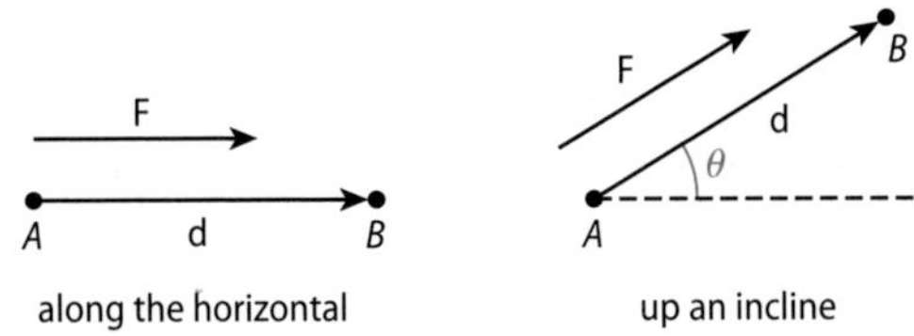

If the force and displacement vectors have the same direction, then work W is the product of the magnitude of the force, $\|\mathbf{F}\|$, and the magnitude of the displacement, $\|\mathbf{d}\|$.

$$W = \|\mathbf{F}\| \, \|\mathbf{d}\|$$

If the force and displacement have formed an angle θ, then work W is the product of the magnitude of the force in the direction of $\mathbf{d}$, $\|\mathbf{F}\| \cos \theta$, and the magnitude of the displacement, $\|\mathbf{d}\|$.

$$W = \|\mathbf{F}\| \, \|\mathbf{d}\| \cos \theta = \mathbf{F} \cdot \mathbf{d}$$

A basic unit of work is the joule, the amount of work needed to move 1 kilogram a distance of 1 meter in the direction of the force.

EXAMPLE 7

Find the work done in each situation.

a. $\|\mathbf{F}\| = 400$ **N,** $\mathbf{d} = \langle 5, 0 \rangle$ **and** $\theta = 0°$

The force and displacement have the same direction since $\theta = 0°$.

$W = \|\mathbf{F}\| \, \|\mathbf{d}\| = 400 \times 5 = 2{,}000$

b. $\mathbf{F} = \langle 1, 4 \rangle, \mathbf{d} = \langle 5, 3 \rangle$

The force and displacement do not have the same direction.

$W = \mathbf{F} \cdot \mathbf{d} = \langle 1, 4 \rangle \cdot \langle 5, 3 \rangle = (1)(5) + (4)(3) = 17$

c. $\|\mathbf{F}\| = 1{,}200$ **N,** $\mathbf{d} = \langle 5, 3 \rangle$**, and** $\theta = 30°$

The force and displacement do not have the same direction.

Use $W = \|\mathbf{F}\| \, \|\mathbf{d}\| \cos \theta$. $W = 1{,}200 \sqrt{5^2 + 3^2} \cos 30° \approx 6{,}059.7$

EXAMPLE 8

A force represented by $\mathbf{F} = 5\mathbf{i} + 6\mathbf{j}$ is applied to an object initially at $A(3, 4)$ to move it to $B(10, 8)$. Find the amount of work involved.

Write an equivalent vector, $\overrightarrow{OP}$, for $\overrightarrow{AB}$ with initial point at the origin. Write **F** in coordinate form.

$$\overrightarrow{OP} = \langle 10 - 3, 8 - 4 \rangle = \langle 7, 4 \rangle \text{ and } \mathbf{F} = \langle 5, 6 \rangle$$

Apply the dot product. $\mathbf{F} \cdot \mathbf{d} = \langle 5, 6 \rangle \cdot \langle 7, 4 \rangle = (5)(7) + (6)(4) = 59$

The action accomplishes 59 units of work.

Watch Out !

When given a vector's initial point and terminal point, find an equivalent vector with initial point at the origin before applying a formula.

Polar Coordinates and the Complex Plane

What Came Before?

- Graphing vectors
- Operations with complex numbers

What's This About?

- Converting rectangular coordinates to polar coordinates
- Graphing polar and parametric equations
- Representing complex numbers in polar form

Practical Apps

- The recording patterns of microphone pickups are represented as polar graphs.
- The path of the moon around the earth can be modeled by a polar equation.

just for FUN!

Q: What's a polar bear?

A: A rectangular bear after a coordinate transformation.

CONTENTS | UPLOAD | DOWNLOAD

Trigonometry

You can find more practice problems online by visiting:
www.SWadvantage.com

Polar Coordinates

Representing Vectors Using Circles

There are many different ways to represent a vector. One approach is to use an ordered pair (x, y) of real numbers. This is illustrated in the diagram at the left below. A magnitude r and a direction θ can also be used to represent a vector. This is illustrated in the diagram at the right below.

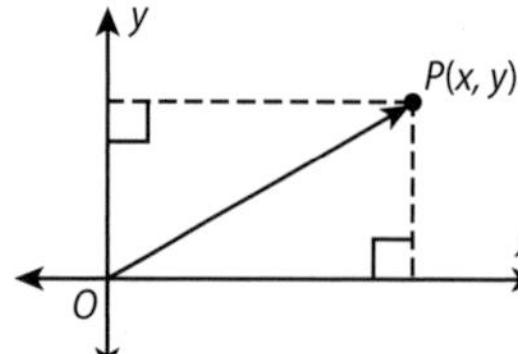

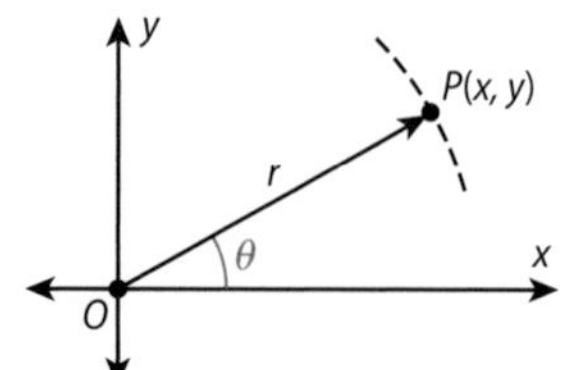

A coordinate system in which circles centered at the origin are used to locate points is an important alternative to the rectangular coordinate system.

Refer to the diagram at the right.

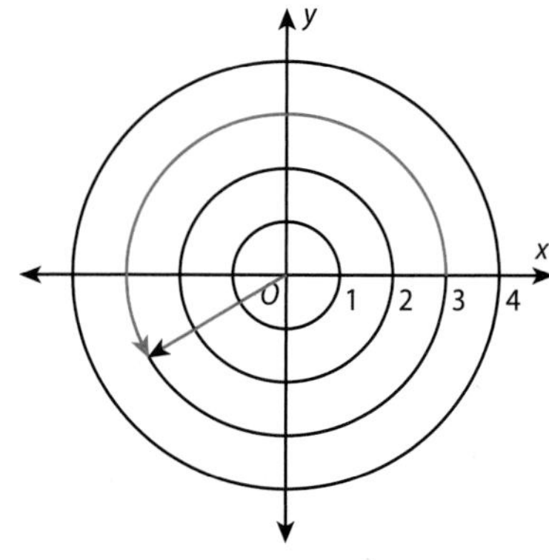

a. Determine the radius of the circle on which the terminal point of the vector shown lies.

The terminal point of the vector lies on a circle of radius 3.

b. Estimate the measure of the angle the vector makes with the positive x-axis measured counterclockwise.

The arc shown is more than 180° and less than 270°.
A reasonable estimate of the measure is 210°.

Ways to REMEMBER

To measure angles using the correct orientation, think of clock directions.

Go back in time:

positive

Go forward in time:

negative

This is the opposite of what seems intuitive.

EXAMPLE 2

Let vector v be defined as having magnitude 4 and angle $\theta = 45°$, where θ is measured counterclockwise from the positive x-axis.

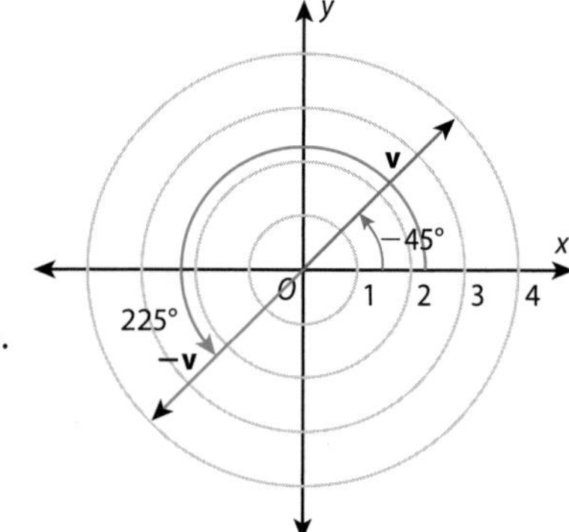

a. Sketch v.

Sketch the vector with initial point at the origin, lying along the positive x-axis, and having length 4. Rotate this vector 45° from the positive x-axis in the counterclockwise direction.

b. Sketch −v.

Both $-\mathbf{v}$ and $\mathbf{v}$ are additive inverses of one another.

$$\mathbf{v} + (-\mathbf{v}) = \mathbf{0}$$

Therefore, $-\mathbf{v}$ has the same magnitude, 4, and its direction is opposite that of $\mathbf{v}$. Place the initial point of $-\mathbf{v}$ at the origin and the terminal point of $-\mathbf{v}$ on the circle with radius 4. The angle $-\mathbf{v}$ makes with the positive x-axis is 225°.

c. How are the angles that determine v and −v related?

The angles that determine $\mathbf{v}$ and $-\mathbf{v}$ differ by 180°.

Defining the Polar Coordinate System

The **polar coordinate** system is that system in the plane determined by a point, the **pole**, and the **polar axis**, a ray that has the pole as its endpoint. Typically, the polar axis is shown as a ray pointing to the right. Every point in the plane has a pair of **polar coordinates**, the ordered pair (r, θ), where r is a real number and θ is an angle measure. Notice that there is no requirement that r be nonnegative and there is no requirement that θ be measured from the polar axis in any particular orientation.

EXAMPLE 3

Graph each point on the same polar coordinate system.

a. ***R*(4, 135°)**

Since θ is positive, rotate a ray with endpoint at the pole 135° counterclockwise from the polar axis. Point *R* will lie along the circle with radius 4.

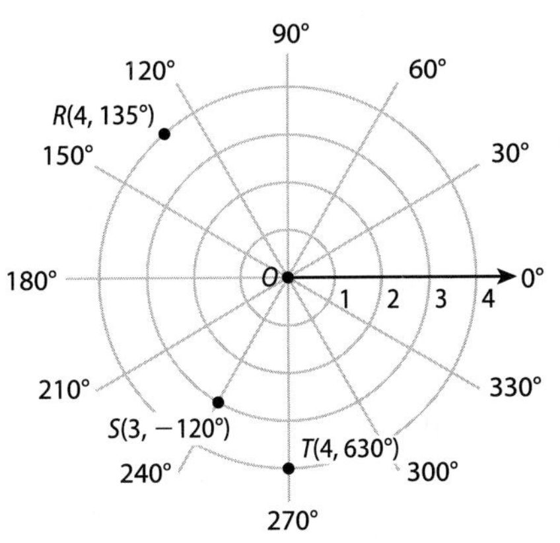

b. ***S*(3, −120°)**

Since θ is negative, rotate a ray with endpoint at the pole 120° clockwise from the polar axis. Point *S* will lie along the circle with radius 3.

c. ***T*(4, 630°)**

Since θ is positive, the rotation of a ray will be counterclockwise. Since 630° = 360° + 270°, the rotation will be one full revolution and three-quarters of a second revolution. Point *T* will lie on the circle with radius 4.

Example 3 illustrates that a point in the polar coordinate system can have more than one representation. The ordered pairs below give further illustration of this. All the representations shown here are the same as $C(4, 20°)$.

$$(4, 380°) \text{ and } (4, -340°)$$

Given *M*(2.5, 110°), write a representation of *M* using an angle measure greater than 360° and another representation of *M* using a negative angle.

Add 360° to 110°.	(2.5, 110° + 360°) = (2.5, 470°)
Subtract 360° from 110°.	(2.5, 110° − 360°) = (2.5, −250°)

In the polar coordinate system, r can be a negative number. For example, the coordinates (−4, 20°) name the point that is on the ray opposite to the ray produced by rotating a ray along the polar axis 20° counterclockwise. To plot (−4, 20°), first plot (4, 20°). Then rotate that point about the origin 180° either clockwise or counterclockwise. The point (−4, 20°) could also be represented by an ordered pair in which both numbers are negative. The coordinates (−4, −160°) also represent the point (−4, 20°).

(4, 20°)
180°
polar axis
(−4, 20°)

SEARCH

To see step-by-step videos of these problems, enter the page number into the SWadvantage.com Search Bar.

For a review of transformations, in particular, rotations and reflections, see p. 838 for reflections and p. 842 for rotations.

Using Multiple Representations

Geometry problems can be studied in the polar coordinate system as well as in the rectangular coordinate system.

EXAMPLE 5

Let $A(3, 30°)$, $B(-3, 300°)$, $C(3, -150°)$, and $D(-3, -240°)$ be points in the polar coordinate system.

a. Plot *A*, *B*, *C*, and *D*.

Use positive values of r and θ.

$A(3, 30°) = A(3, 30°)$

$B(-3, 300°) = B(3, 120°)$

$C(3, -150°) = C(3, 210°)$

$D(-3, -240°) = D(3, 300°)$

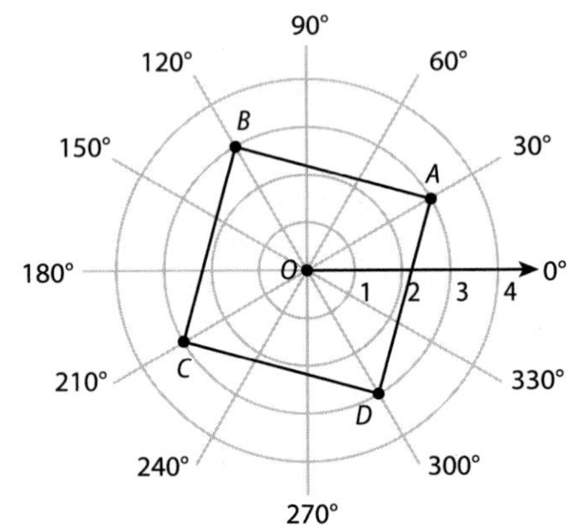

b. Describe polygon *ABCD*.

Points *A*, *B*, *C*, and *D* determine a square.

c. Justify your description.

If the diagonals of a quadrilateral are congruent and perpendicular, then the quadrilateral is a square.

Need More HELP

Congruence and perpendicularity of diagonals of a quadrilateral are sufficient conditions to assure that a quadrilateral is a square. For a review of the properties of special quadrilaterals, see p. 650.

EXAMPLE 6

Describe each shaded region.

a. the region shaded red using $r > 0$ and positive values of θ

The points in the region shaded red all lie within or on the circles with radii 2 and 4. Therefore, $2 \le r \le 4$.

The radii making 30° and 60° angles with the polar axis bound the region shaded red. Therefore, $30° \le \theta \le 60°$. To describe all points in the shaded region, add a nonnegative multiple of 360°.

$2 \le r \le 4$ and $30° + n360° \le \theta \le 60° + n360°$, where n is a nonnegative integer

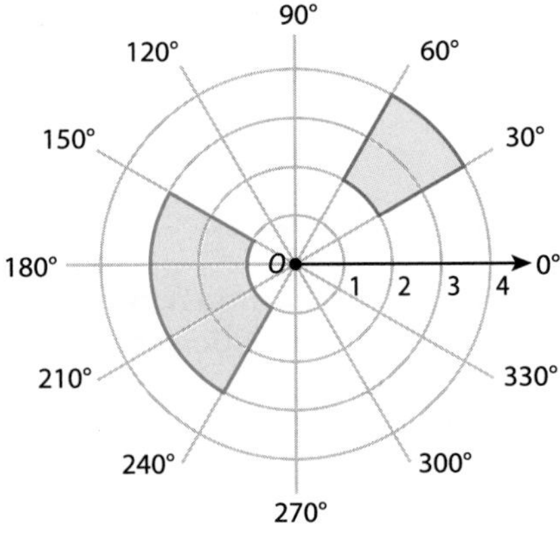

b. the region shaded blue using $r > 0$ and negative values of θ

The points in the region shaded blue all lie within or on the circles with radii 1 and 3. Therefore, $1 \le r \le 3$. The radii making 150° and 240° angles with the polar axis bound the region shaded blue. Therefore, $150° \le \theta \le 240°$. To describe all points in the shaded region, add a nonpositive multiple of 360°.

$1 \le r \le 3$ and $150° + n360° \le \theta \le 240° + n360°$, where n is a nonpositive integer

Alternatively, use $-120°$ instead of 240° and $-210°$ instead of 150°.

$1 \le r \le 3$ and $-210° + n360° \le \theta \le -120° + n360°$, where n is a nonpositive integer

Some surprising conclusions result from the fact that a single point in the polar coordinate system has multiple representations.

EXAMPLE 7

Use a diagram to show that $P(r, \theta) = Q(-r, \theta + 180°)$.

STEP 1 Sketch $P(r, \theta)$.

STEP 2 Sketch $P'(r, \theta + 180°)$, the rotation of $P(r, \theta)$ counterclockwise 180°.

STEP 3 To plot $Q(-r, \theta + 180°)$, reflect $P'(r, \theta + 180°)$ in the origin. The image after the reflection is $P(r, \theta)$.

STEP 4 Draw the conclusion. $P(r, \theta) = Q(-r, \theta + 180°)$

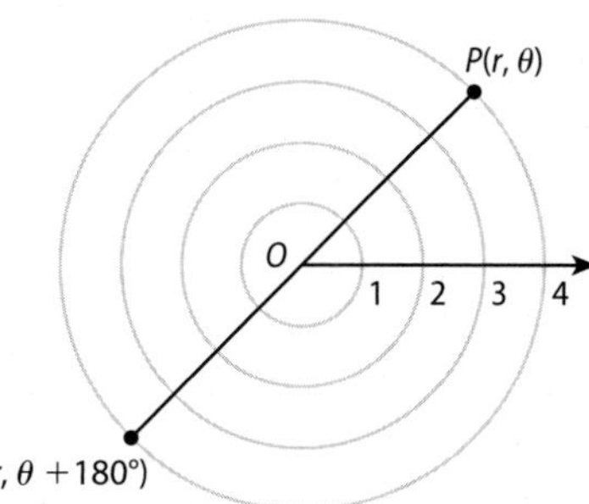

EXAMPLE 8

Let $P(r, \theta)$ and $Q(r, \phi)$ be points in the polar coordinate system such that $\overrightarrow{OP}$ and $\overrightarrow{OQ}$ are perpendicular. Write an equation that relates θ and ϕ.

Rotate $\overrightarrow{OP}$ counterclockwise 90°. The image is $P(r, \theta + 90°)$. Thus, $\phi = \theta + 90° + 360°n$.

Rotate $\overrightarrow{OP}$ clockwise 90°. The image is $P(r, \theta - 90°)$. Thus, $\phi = \theta - 90° + 360°n$.

Therefore: $\phi - \theta - 360°n = 90°$ or $\phi - \theta - 360°n = -90°$

Putting these equations together, $|\phi - \theta - 360°n| = 90°$.

Recall that if $|x| = a$, then $x = a$ or $x = -a$.

Furthermore, if $x = a$ or $x = -a$, then $|x| = a$.

EXAMPLE 9

Using positive and negative values of r and θ, write several other representations of $P(r, \theta)$.

Draw a sketch that shows a location for $P(r, \theta)$.

Rotate P counterclockwise 360°. $P(r, \theta) = P(r, \theta + 360°)$

Rotate P clockwise 360°. $P(r, \theta) = P(r, \theta - 360°)$

Rotate P 180°. Then reflect in the origin. $P(r, \theta) = P(-r, \theta + 180°)$

$P(r, \theta) = P(-r, \theta - 180°)$

Addition of $360°n$ will give additional representations.

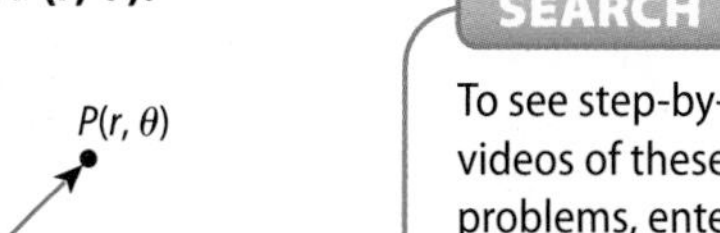

SEARCH

To see step-by-step videos of these problems, enter the page number into the SWadvantage.com Search Bar.

EXAMPLE 10

Find negative values of r and θ, where $(-720° \leq \theta \leq -360°)$, such that $X(r, \theta) = P(5, 120°)$.

Rotate $P(5, 120°)$ clockwise 180° to get $P'(5, -60°)$.

Reflect $P'(5, -60°)$ in the origin to get $P''(-5, -60°)$.

Rotate $P''(-5, -60°)$ clockwise 360° to get $P'''(-5, -420°)$.

Addition of $360°n$ will give additional representations.

Thus, $P'''(-5, -420°) = P(5, 120°)$.

Polar and Rectangular Coordinates

Converting Points Across Coordinate Systems

The diagram at the right shows point P in the plane. It is located in two coordinate systems, each having O as the origin. The polar axis in the polar coordinate system coincides with the positive x-axis in the rectangular coordinate system. There is a relationship, or correspondence, between the two representations.

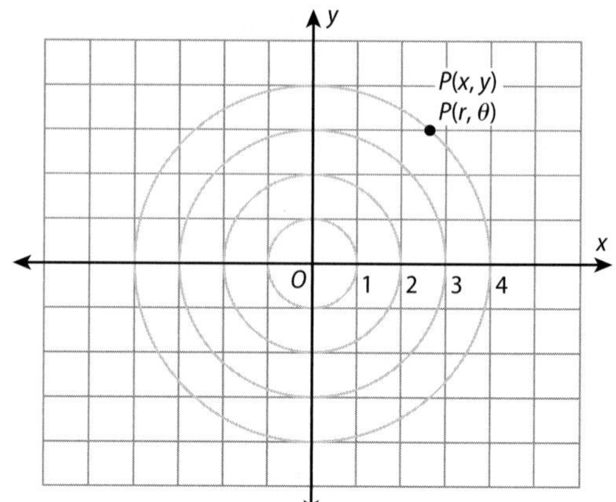

$$P(x, y) \leftrightarrow P(r, \theta)$$

Right-triangle trigonometry provides a way to write algebraic conversion equations. For the equations that relate the two systems of coordinates, see the *Got To Know!* box.

Need More HELP

A point can have two representations in two coexistent coordinate reference systems. Example 1 shows two different sets of coordinates for point P.

EXAMPLE 1

In the rectangular coordinate system, P has coordinates $P\left(-\frac{\sqrt{2}}{2}, \frac{\sqrt{2}}{2}\right)$. Write the corresponding coordinates in the polar coordinate system. Use a positive value of r and a positive value of θ.

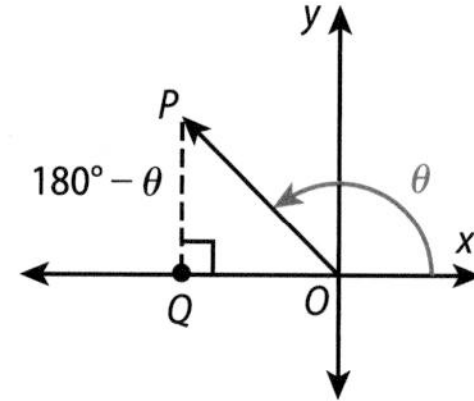

STEP 1 In rectangular coordinates, P is in the second quadrant.

STEP 2 In the sketch for Step 1, show a reference triangle, $\triangle OPQ$.

STEP 3 In $\triangle OPQ$, find OP and $m\angle POQ$.

$x = -\frac{\sqrt{2}}{2}; y = \frac{\sqrt{2}}{2}$ $\qquad OP = \left(-\frac{\sqrt{2}}{2}\right)^2 + \left(\frac{\sqrt{2}}{2}\right)^2 = 1$

In $\triangle OPQ$: $\qquad \sin(180° - \theta) = \frac{y}{r} = \frac{PQ}{OP} = \frac{\sqrt{2}}{2}$

$$180° - \theta = 45°$$

Therefore, $r = 1$ and $\theta = 135°$. Thus, $P\left(-\frac{\sqrt{2}}{2}, \frac{\sqrt{2}}{2}\right) = P(1, 135°)$.

GOT TO KNOW!

Conversion Formulas for Rectangular and Polar Coordinate Systems

From rectangular coordinates to polar coordinates:

If P has coordinates $P(x, y)$, then $r = \pm\sqrt{x^2 + y^2}$ and $\cos\theta = \frac{x}{r}$ and $\sin\theta = \frac{y}{r}$.

From polar coordinates to rectangular coordinates:

If P has coordinates $P(r, \theta)$, then $x = r\cos\theta$ and $y = r\sin\theta$.

EXAMPLE 2

In the polar coordinate system, *T* has coordinates *T*(4, −120°). Write the corresponding coordinates in the rectangular coordinate system.

STEP 1 Identify r and θ.

$r = 4$ and $\theta = -120°$

STEP 2 Apply the conversion equations.

$x = r\cos\theta$ and $y = r\sin\theta$

$x = 4\cos(-120°)$ and $y = 4\sin(-120°)$

$x = -2$ and $y = -2\sqrt{3}$

STEP 3 Write the rectangular coordinates.

$T(4, -120°) = T\left(-2, -2\sqrt{3}\right)$

Need More HELP

Picture θ as a rotation clockwise. The terminal side of the angle generated is in the third quadrant where both coordinates are negative.

Given coordinates of a point $P(x, y)$ in the rectangular coordinate system, you can tell in advance what to expect for a value of θ by noting the quadrant in which $P(x, y)$ lies. For example, if $P(x, y)$ is in the second quadrant in the rectangular coordinate system, then the terminal side of the angle shown at the right is an obtuse angle. This can serve as a check on the calculation of θ when using the conversion formulas.

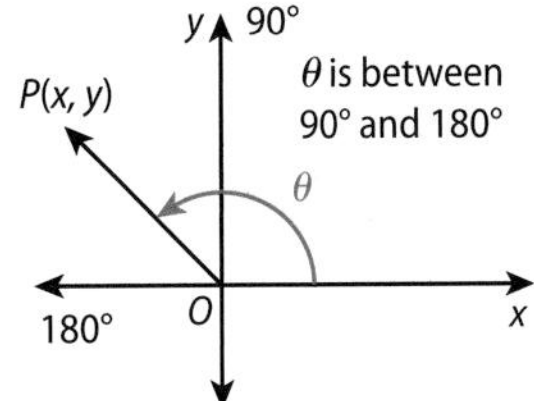

SEARCH

To see step-by-step videos of these problems, enter the page number into the SWadvantage.com Search Bar.

EXAMPLE 3

In the rectangular coordinate system, *N* has coordinates *N*(−4, 5). Write polar coordinates for this point.

STEP 1 Identify x and y.

$x = -4$ and $y = 5$

STEP 2 Find r.

Let $r > 0$.

$$r = \sqrt{x^2 + y^2} = \sqrt{(-4)^2 + 5^2} = \sqrt{41}$$

STEP 3 Find θ.

$$\cos\theta = \frac{x}{r} \text{ and } \sin\theta = \frac{y}{r}$$

$$\cos\theta = \frac{-4}{\sqrt{41}} \text{ and } \sin\theta = \frac{5}{\sqrt{41}}$$

Choose a value of θ between 90° and 180° since $\cos\theta < 0$ and $\sin\theta > 0$ when $90° < \theta < 180°$.

$\theta \approx 129°$

Polar coordinates for $N(-4, 5)$ are $\left(\sqrt{41}, 129°\right)$. Other representations are possible.

Ways to REMEMBER

Keep a mental picture of a simple right triangle diagram in mind like the one below.

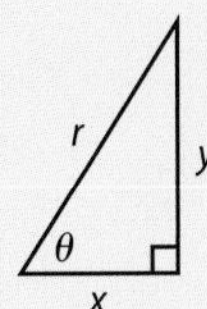

It shows x, y, r, and θ, all of the ingredients used in the conversion equations. Such a diagram can help you remember the conversion equations.

Rewriting Equations Across Coordinate Systems

In the rectangular coordinate system, the equation of a line and the equation of a circle have these forms.

line: $y = mx + b$ circle centered at the origin: $x^2 + y^2 = r^2$

In the polar coordinate system, a line and a circle have very simple equations.

line: $r = \theta$ circle centered at the origin: $r = a$

For a line, the angle of the line is fixed and the value of r can be any real number. For a circle, the radius is fixed and the angle can be any real number or degree measure.

Using the equations for conversion from one system to the other, an equation can be represented in each system.

EXAMPLE 4

The equation $x^2 + y^2 = 16$ represents the circle with radius 4 and center at the origin. Show that $r = 4$ is the corresponding equation in the polar coordinate system.

Use the conversion equations.	$x = r\cos\theta$ and $y = r\sin\theta$
Substitute.	$(r\cos\theta)^2 + (r\sin\theta)^2 = 16$
Simplify.	$r^2\cos^2\theta + r^2\sin^2\theta = 16$
Factor.	$r^2(\cos^2\theta + \sin^2\theta) = 16$
Use an identity, $\cos^2\theta + \sin^2\theta = 1$.	$r^2 = 16$
Take the square root.	$r = \pm 4$

Both $r = 4$ and $r = -4$ represent the specified equation.

Need More HELP

Transforming an equation in rectangular coordinates to one in polar coordinates may require the use of fundamental trigonometric identities. For a review of simple trigonometric identities, see p. 996.

EXAMPLE 5

Write a polar equation for $x^2 - y^2 = 1$.

Use the conversion equations.	$x = r\cos\theta$ and $y = r\sin\theta$
Substitute.	$(r\cos\theta)^2 - (r\sin\theta)^2 = 1$
Simplify.	$r^2(\cos^2\theta - \sin^2\theta) = 1$
Use an identity, $\cos^2\theta - \sin^2\theta = \cos(2\theta)$.	$r^2\cos(2\theta) = 1$
Divide.	$r^2 = \frac{1}{\cos(2\theta)}$
Use an identity, $\sec\theta = \frac{1}{\cos\theta}$.	$r^2 = \sec(2\theta)$
Take the square root.	$r = \pm\sqrt{\sec(2\theta)}$

If $x^2 - y^2 = 1$, then $r = \pm\sqrt{\sec(2\theta)}$.

To get the complete representation both + and − solutions are needed.

EXAMPLE 6

Write an equation in terms of x and y, an equation in the rectangular coordinate system, for the polar equation $r(1 - \sin\theta) = 5$.

STEP 1 Write the conversion equations.

$$r = \pm\sqrt{x^2 + y^2} \text{ and } \cos\theta = \frac{x}{y} \text{ and } \sin\theta = \frac{y}{r}$$

STEP 2 Multiply.

$$r(1 - \sin\theta) = 5 \quad \rightarrow \quad r - r\sin\theta = 5$$

STEP 3 Use the conversion formulas.

$$\pm\sqrt{x^2 + y^2} - y = 5$$

STEP 4 Simplify.

$$\pm\sqrt{x^2 + y^2} = y + 5$$
$$x^2 + y^2 = (y + 5)^2$$
$$x^2 + y^2 = y^2 + 10y + 25$$
$$x^2 - 10y - 25 = 0$$

Therefore, $x^2 - 10y - 25 = 0$ represents $r(1 - \sin\theta) = 5$.

Need More HELP

If you need more help writing an equation of a circle by completing the square, see pp. 824–827.

EXAMPLE 7

Write an equation in terms of x and y, an equation in the rectangular coordinate system, for the polar equation $r = 2\cos\theta$.

$$r = 2\cos\theta$$

Use the conversion equations.

$$r = \pm\sqrt{x^2 + y^2} \text{ and } \cos\theta = \frac{x}{r}$$
$$\pm\sqrt{x^2 + y^2} = 2\left(\frac{x}{\pm\sqrt{x^2 + y^2}}\right)$$

Multiply each side by $\pm\sqrt{x^2 + y^2}$.

$$\left(\pm\sqrt{x^2 + y^2}\right)^2 = 2x$$
$$x^2 + y^2 = 2x$$

Simplify. Complete the square.

$$x^2 - 2x + 1 + y^2 = 1$$
$$(x - 1)^2 + y^2 = 1$$

Therefore, in the rectangular coordinate system, $(x - 1)^2 + y^2 = 1$ represents $r = 2\cos\theta$.

SEARCH

To see step-by-step videos of these problems, enter the page number into the SWadvantage.com Search Bar.

The graph of the equation $(x - 1)^2 + y^2 = 1$ is the circle with center at $(1, 0)$ and radius 1. In the next topic, graphs of polar equations will be discussed. There it can be seen that the graph of $r = 2\cos\theta$ is indeed a circle.

An equation in the rectangular coordinate system for $r = 2\sin\theta$ is $x^2 + (y - 1)^2 = 1$. The graph of this equation is also a circle. Its radius is also 1. The center of the circle is $(0, 1)$.

Graphs of Polar Equations

Analyzing Polar Equations

A polar equation makes it possible to create intricate designs that would be very difficult to create using an equation in rectangular coordinates. The designs below are the graphs of $r = \sin(3\theta)$, $r = \sin(5\theta)$, $r = \sin(7\theta)$, and $r = \sin(9\theta)$, respectively. Each of them is called a rose. The number of petals is related to the coefficient of θ in the polar equations. Replacing sine with cosine will produce similar roses.

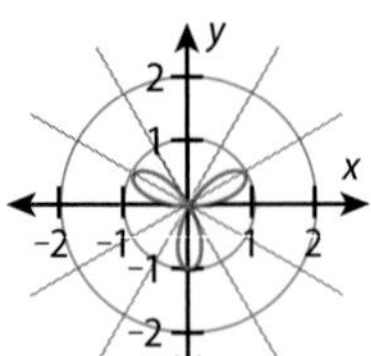

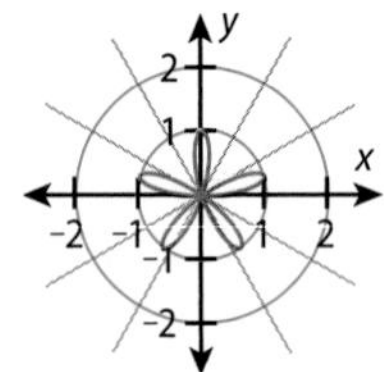

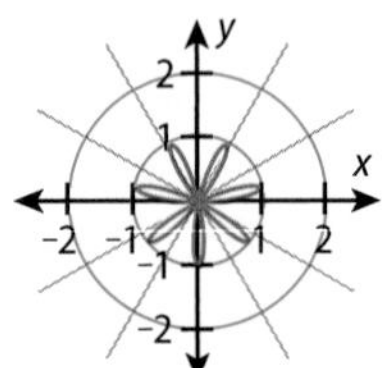

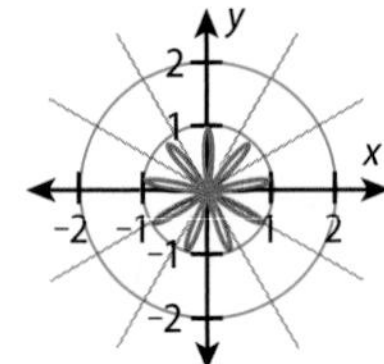

EXAMPLE 1

Analyze $r = \sin(3\theta)$. Graph the equation.

STEP 1 Make basic observations.

Since $-1 \leq \sin\theta \leq 1$, the graph is contained in $|r| \leq 1$.

STEP 2 Make a table to see how r varies when $0 \leq \theta \leq \frac{\pi}{3}$.

The table suggests a path from (0, 0) to $\left(1, \frac{\pi}{6}\right)$, then back to the origin, $\left(0, \frac{\pi}{3}\right)$, a continuous loop.

$\theta = 0$	$\theta = \frac{\pi}{6}$	$\theta = \frac{\pi}{3}$
$r = 0$	$r = 1$	$r = 0$

Make a table to see how r varies when $\frac{\pi}{3} \leq \theta \leq \frac{2\pi}{3}$.

This suggests a path from $\left(0, \frac{\pi}{3}\right)$ to $\left(-1, \frac{\pi}{2}\right)$, then back to $\left(0, \frac{2\pi}{3}\right)$, a continuous loop.

$\theta = \frac{\pi}{3}$	$\theta = \frac{\pi}{2}$	$\theta = \frac{2\pi}{3}$
$r = 0$	$r = -1$	$r = 0$

Finally, make a table to see how r varies when $\frac{2\pi}{3} \leq \theta \leq \pi$. The table suggests a path from $\left(0, \frac{2\pi}{3}\right)$ to $\left(1, \frac{5\pi}{6}\right)$, then back to the origin, $(0, \pi)$, a third continuous loop.

$\theta = \frac{2\pi}{3}$	$\theta = \frac{5\pi}{6}$	$\theta = \pi$
$r = 0$	$r = 1$	$r = 0$

STEP 3 Interpret the tables.

The graph shows three loops in all. These loops intersect only at the pole. Piece them together to get the graph shown here. Notice that the pole has multiple polar coordinate representations.

$(0, 0), \left(0, \frac{\pi}{3}\right), \left(0, \frac{2\pi}{3}\right), (0, \pi)$

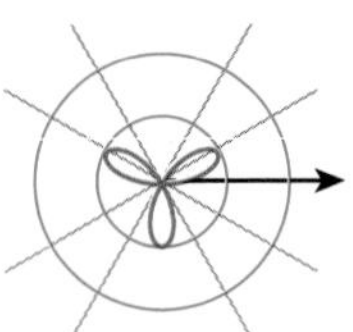

Need More HELP

As part of the analysis, look for values of θ for which r is 0 or maximum. These values are key values.

SEARCH

To see step-by-step videos of these problems, enter the page number into the SWadvantage.com Search Bar.

Frequently, a polar graph is a continuous closed curve. It can be thought of as a path.

Graphing Roses and Cardioids

Equations of the form $r = \sin(n\theta)$ and $r = \cos(n\theta)$, where $n \geq 2$, form a family of polar graphs, the family of **roses**.

Watch Out!

A graphing calculator can guide the analysis at the start of the solution. However, if the range for θ is not large enough, the graph that results will be misleading.

EXAMPLE 2

Analyze $r = \cos(2\theta)$. Graph the equation.

STEP 1 Make basic observations. Since $-1 \leq \cos\theta \leq 1$, the graph is contained in $|r| \leq 1$.

STEP 2 Make a table that lists key values of r and θ. Divide the interval $0 \leq \theta \leq 2\pi$ into eight subintervals. Evaluate $\cos(2\theta)$ for the endpoints of the intervals.

$\theta = 0$	$\theta = \frac{\pi}{4}$	$\theta = \frac{\pi}{2}$	$\theta = \frac{3\pi}{4}$	$\theta = \pi$	$\theta = \frac{5\pi}{4}$	$\theta = \frac{3\pi}{2}$	$\theta = \frac{7\pi}{4}$	$\theta = 2\pi$
$r = 1$	$r = 0$	$r = -1$	$r = 0$	$r = 1$	$r = 0$	$r = -1$	$r = 0$	$r = 1$

STEP 3 Use the table of values to draw conclusions that help graph the equation.

The graph will have four loops. Each loop is intersected equally by the line containing the polar axis and the line $\theta = \frac{\pi}{2}$.

The graph is shown at the right. Notice that even though the multiplier of θ is 2, there are four loops. The graph is called a **four-leafed rose**.

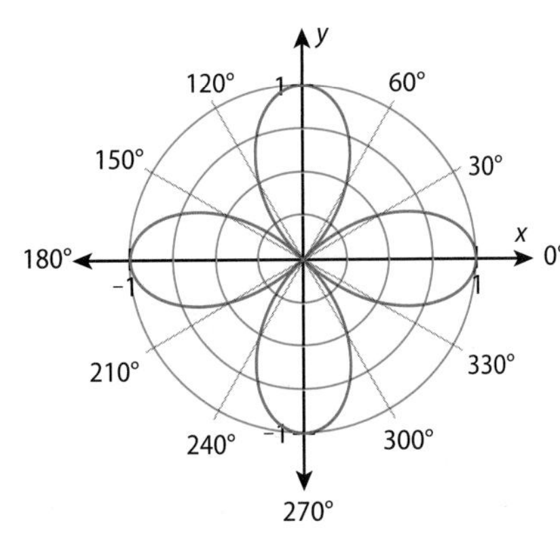

Watch Out!

Although the period of $\cos(2\theta)$ is π, the interval $0 \leq \theta \leq \pi$ is not sufficient to obtain the entire graph.

EXAMPLE 3

Analyze $r = 1 + \cos\theta$. Graph the equation.

STEP 1 Make basic observations. Since $-1 \leq \cos\theta \leq 1$, the graph is contained in $|r| \leq 1$. The function $1 + \cos\theta$ has period 2π.

STEP 2 Make a table that lists key values of r and θ. Divide the interval $0 \leq \theta \leq 2\pi$ into four subintervals. Evaluate $\cos\theta$ for the endpoints of the intervals.

$\theta = 0$	$\theta = \frac{\pi}{2}$	$\theta = \pi$	$\theta = \frac{3\pi}{2}$	$\theta = 2\pi$
$r = 2$	$r = 1$	$r = 0$	$r = 1$	$r = 2$

STEP 3 Sketch the graph interval by interval.

$0 \leq \theta \leq \frac{\pi}{2}$ $\quad \frac{\pi}{2} \leq \theta \leq \pi$ $\quad \pi \leq \theta \leq \frac{3\pi}{2}$ $\quad \frac{3\pi}{2} \leq \theta \leq 2\pi$

This diagram shows the four sections, each determined by the interval for θ that is indicated above. The graph is called a **cardioid**.

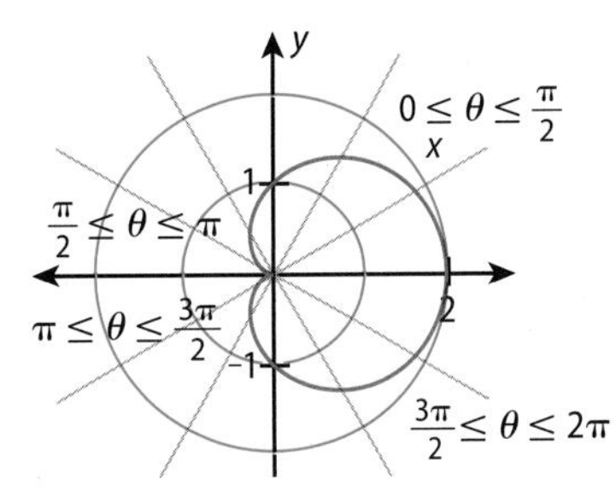

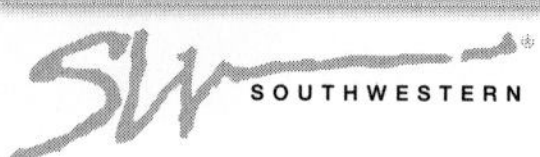

Graphing Lemniscates and Spirals

In many situations, an expression is given for r. In many other situations, an expression is given for r^2.

EXAMPLE 4

Analyze $r^2 = 4\sin(2\theta)$. Graph the equation.

STEP 1 Because the equation contains r^2, write a pair of equations for r by taking the square root.

$$\begin{cases} r = 2\sqrt{\sin(2\theta)} \\ r = -2\sqrt{\sin(2\theta)} \end{cases}$$

Notice that θ may not take on any values for which $\sin(2\theta)$ is negative. Consider analyzing each equation for the interval $0 \le \theta \le \pi$.

STEP 2 Make a table of values using key values of θ.

It is only necessary to use the interval $0 \le \theta \le \frac{\pi}{2}$. This interval is sufficient to obtain each loop.

$r = 2\sqrt{\sin(2\theta)}$		
$\theta = 0$	$\theta = \frac{\pi}{4}$	$\theta = \frac{\pi}{2}$
$r = 0$	$r = 2$	$r = 0$

$r = -2\sqrt{\sin(2\theta)}$		
$\theta = 0$	$\theta = \frac{\pi}{4}$	$\theta = \frac{\pi}{2}$
$r = 0$	$r = -2$	$r = 0$

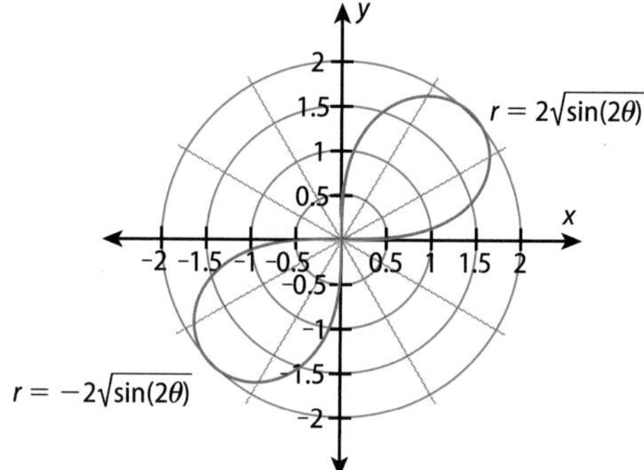

STEP 3 The graph consists of two loops as shown at the right above.

This graph is called a **lemniscate**.

Need More HELP

Use a graphing calculator to check your work as you go. First use the upper equation and graph on the interval $0 \le \theta \le \frac{\pi}{2}$. The display should confirm the loop in the upper right. Then use the lower equation and graph on the same interval. The display should confirm the loop in the lower left.

EXAMPLE 5

Analyze $r = \frac{1}{\theta}$. Graph the equation.

STEP 1 Make observations about the allowable values of r and θ.

r cannot equal 0 and θ cannot equal 0.

However, $\lim_{\theta \to \infty} r = 0$ and $\lim_{\theta \to 0} r = \infty$.

STEP 2 Interpret Step 1.

The graph begins at infinity and spirals in toward the pole. The pole is not part of the graph, shown at the right.

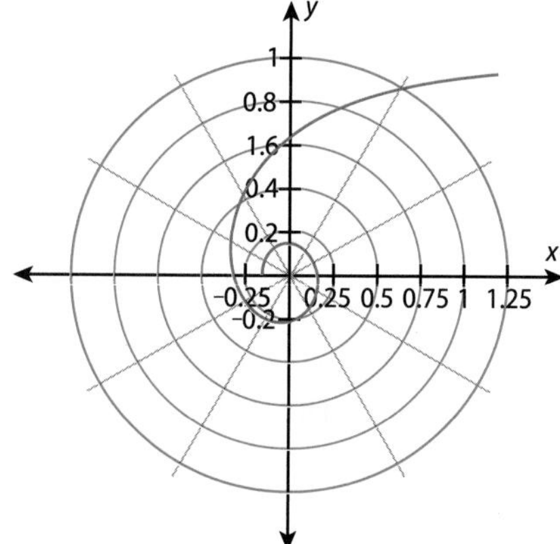

Watch Out!

The equation $r = \frac{1}{\theta}$ looks like the equation $y = \frac{1}{x}$. The graph of the polar equation is a continuous curve. The graph of the rectangular equation is discontinuous.

Using Tests for Symmetry

Just as a graph of an equation in rectangular coordinates may be symmetric, the graph of a polar equation may exhibit symmetry. There are tests that can be used to determine whether a polar graph has symmetry. For statements of the symmetry tests for polar graphs, see the *Got To Know!* box.

In applying tests for symmetry it is often useful to recall that the sine function is an odd function and that the cosine function is an even one. In addition:

$$\cos(\pi - \theta) = -\cos\theta$$

EXAMPLE 6

Test the polar equation $r = 1 + \cos\theta$ for symmetry in its graph. Use a graph to confirm.

Let (r, θ) be on the graph of $r = 1 + \cos\theta$.

Symmetry about the polar axis:

Test $(r, -\theta)$. $\quad r = 1 + \cos(-\theta) = 1 + \cos\theta$

Since $(r, -\theta)$ is on the graph whenever (r, θ) is on the graph, the graph has polar axis symmetry.

Symmetry about the line $\theta = 90°$ or $\frac{\pi}{2}$:

Test $(-r, -\theta)$. $\quad -r = -(1 + \cos(-\theta)) = -1 - \cos(-\theta) = -1 + \cos\theta \neq 1 + \cos\theta$

Test $(r, \pi - \theta)$ $\quad 1 + \cos(\pi - \theta) = 1 - \cos\theta \neq 1 + \cos\theta$

Since neither $(-r, -\theta)$ nor $(r, \pi - \theta)$ is on the graph whenever (r, θ) is on the graph, the graph does not have symmetry in the line $\theta = 90°$ or $\frac{\pi}{2}$.

Symmetry about the pole:

Test $(-r, \theta)$. $\quad -r = -(1 + \cos\theta) = -1 - \cos\theta \neq 1 + \cos\theta$

Since $(-r, \theta)$ is not on the graph whenever (r, θ) is on the graph, the graph does not have symmetry about the pole.

The equation $r = 1 + \cos\theta$ is the equation in Example 3. The graph shown there confirms the conclusions about symmetry.

SEARCH

To see step-by-step videos of these problems, enter the page number into the SWadvantage.com Search Bar.

Watch Out!

The test for symmetry about the line $\theta = 90°$ or $\frac{\pi}{2}$ contains two parts.

$(r, \pi - \theta)$ or $(-r, -\theta)$

Each of these must be checked before a conclusion is drawn.

GOT TO KNOW!

Symmetry Tests for Polar Graphs

Symmetry about the polar axis: A polar graph has symmetry about the polar axis if whenever (r, θ) is on the graph, then $(r, -\theta)$ or $(-r, \pi - \theta)$ is also on the graph.

Symmetry about the line $\theta = 90°$ or $\frac{\pi}{2}$: A polar graph has symmetry about the line $\theta = 90°$ or $\frac{\pi}{2}$ if whenever (r, θ) is on the graph, then $(r, \pi - \theta)$ or $(-r, -\theta)$ is also on the graph.

Symmetry about the pole: A polar graph has symmetry about the pole if whenever (r, θ) is on the graph, then $(-r, \theta)$ or $(r, \pi + \theta)$ is also on the graph.

Watch Out!

The italic letter *e* is used to indicate the eccentricity. Do not confuse this use of *e* with the base of the natural exponential and logarithmic functions.

Graphing Polar Equations of Conics

One of the frequently used definitions of a conic section is the one based on a fixed point, the focus *F*, and a fixed line, the directrix *d*. The conic is defined as the set of all points in the plane such that the ratio of distance from the focus to a point on the curve, *FP*, to the distance from the point on the curve to the directrix, *PD*, is a constant, *e*. This is illustrated in the diagram at the right. The distance between the focus and the directrix is $|p|$.

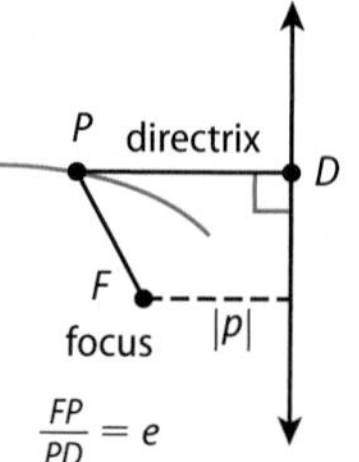

Of all the conic sections, the three you will use most often are the ellipse, the hyperbola, and the parabola. (The circle is a special case of the ellipse.) For each of these conic sections, there is a rectangular equation and a polar equation.

The equations below represent polar equations for the ellipse, the hyperbola, and the parabola.

$$r = \frac{ep}{1 + e\cos\theta} \qquad r = \frac{ep}{1 - e\cos\theta} \qquad r = \frac{ep}{1 + e\sin\theta} \qquad r = \frac{ep}{1 - e\sin\theta}$$

The value of *e* is the way to distinguish one type of conic from another.

$0 < e < 1$ ellipse $\qquad e = 1$ parabola $\qquad e > 1$ hyperbola

The eccentricity of the conic section is denoted *e*.

EXAMPLE 7

Identify each conic section from its equation.

a. $r = \dfrac{6}{1 + 2\cos\theta}$

hyperbola because $e = 2$ and $2 > 1$

b. $r = \dfrac{3}{2 - \cos\theta}$

$$r = \frac{3}{2 - \cos\theta} = \frac{3}{2(1 - 0.5\cos\theta)} = \frac{1.5}{1 - 0.5\cos\theta}$$

ellipse because $e = 0.5$ and $0 < 0.5 < 1$

c. $r = \dfrac{2}{1 + \cos\theta}$

parabola because $e = 1$

Need More HELP

For help on conic sections see pp. 1910–1919, see pp. 1920–1927 for circles, see pp. 1928–1931 for ellipses, and see pp. 1932–1935 for hyperbolas.

The following summary helps explain the four different equations above.

$1 + e\cos\theta$ vertical directrix to the right of the pole

$1 - e\cos\theta$ vertical directrix to the left of the pole

$1 + e\sin\theta$ horizontal directrix above the pole

$1 - e\sin\theta$ horizontal directrix below the pole

In Part (a) of Example 7, the directrix is vertical and to the right of the pole.

Before graphing a polar equation of a conic section, analyze the equation. The analysis provides information about the type of conic and its orientation. In particular, the analysis indicates whether an ellipse or hyperbola spreads out horizontally or vertically.

EXAMPLE 8

Analyze $r = \frac{6}{3 - 1.5\cos\theta}$. Then graph the equation.

STEP 1 Write the equation in one of the specified forms.

$$r = \frac{6}{3 - 1.5\cos\theta} = \frac{12 \times 0.5}{3(1 - 0.5\cos\theta)} = \frac{4 \times 0.5}{1 - 0.5\cos\theta}$$

STEP 2 Read data from the equation.

Using $r = \frac{ep}{1 - e\cos\theta}$, $p = 4$ and $e = 0.5$.

The conic is an ellipse and the distance between the focus and the directrix is 4. The directrix is vertical and to the left of the focus.

STEP 3 Graph the equation. The graph shows an ellipse with some elongation horizontally. Yet it almost looks somewhat circular also.

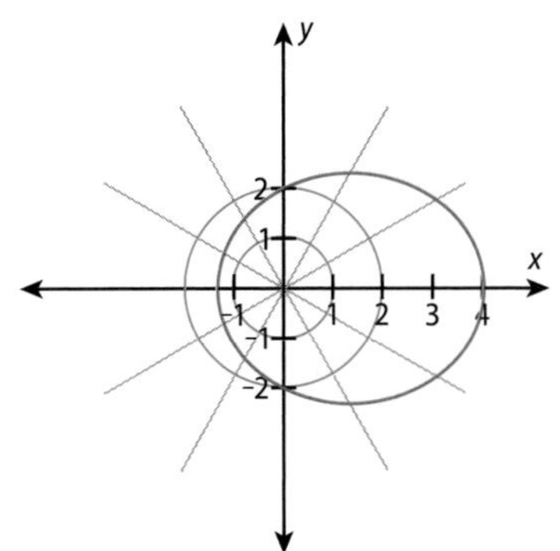

Watch Out !

A given equation may have a very simple graph type but have an equation that does not show it. Follow the algebraic steps that are needed to write an equation in the appropriate form. Then follow the process that discriminates one type of graph from another.

EXAMPLE 9

Analyze $r = \frac{6}{3 - 4\sin\theta}$. Then graph the equation.

STEP 1 Write the equation in one of the specified forms.

$$r = \frac{6}{3 - 4\sin\theta} = \frac{6}{3\left(1 - \frac{4}{3}\sin\theta\right)} = \frac{\frac{4}{3} \times \frac{3}{2}}{1 - \frac{4}{3}\sin\theta}$$

STEP 2 Read data from the equation.

Using $r = \frac{ep}{1 - e\sin\theta}$, $p = \frac{3}{2}$ and $e = \frac{4}{3}$.

The conic is a hyperbola and the distance between the focus and the directrix is $\frac{3}{2}$. The directrix is horizontal and below the pole. This follows because the denominator of $r = \frac{ep}{1 - e\sin\theta}$ contains the sine and subtraction.

STEP 3 Graph the equation. The hyperbola opens up and down as seen in the graph at the right.

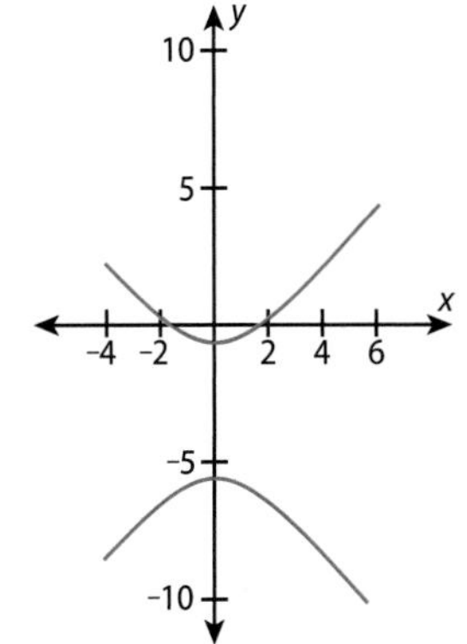

SEARCH

To see step-by-step videos of these problems, enter the page number into the SWadvantage.com Search Bar.

Parametric Equations

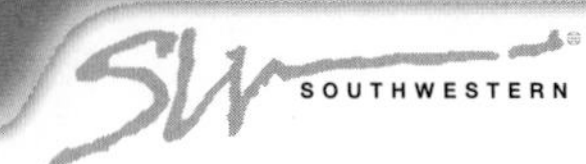

Defining Parametric Equations

Both diagrams below show the position of a point $P(x, y)$ on a curve C. However, the diagrams have one significant difference, the inclusion of the variable t in the diagram at the right below. In that diagram, the x- and y-coordinates are both functions of t. The diagram could represent the position of a point as a function of elapsed time, t.

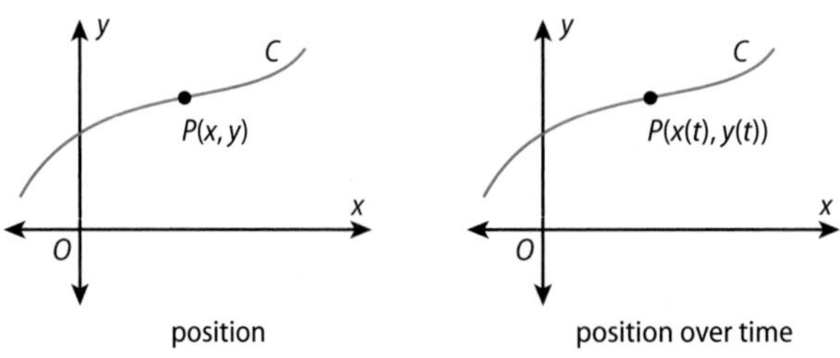

Equations in a variable like t, called a **parameter**, that determine the x-coordinate and y-coordinate of a point in the plane are called **parametric equations**. If, for example, $x(t) = x^2$ and $y(t) = 2x + 1$, then these equations are parametric equations of the curve determined.

SEARCH

To see step-by-step videos of these problems, enter the page number into the SWadvantage.com Search Bar.

EXAMPLE 1

Let $x(t) = t^2$ and $y(t) = 2t + 1$. Make a table of values for $(x(t), y(t))$ given $t = 0, 1, 2, 3, 4$, and 5.

t	0	1	2	3	4	5
$x(t)$	$0^2 = 0$	$1^2 = 1$	$2^2 = 4$	$3^2 = 9$	$4^2 = 16$	$5^2 = 25$
$y(t)$	$2(0) + 1 = 1$	$2(1) + 1 = 3$	$2(2) + 1 = 5$	$2(3) + 1 = 7$	$2(4) + 1 = 9$	$2(5) + 1 = 11$

To graph a pair of parametric equations, $x(t)$ and $y(t)$), evaluate each function for a sampling of values of t. Then graph the ordered pairs (x, y).

Watch Out !

When using a graphing calculator or computer software, be careful to evaluate the reasonableness of the graph resulting from data entry. A linear expression for x and a quadratic expression for y should produce a parabola or part of one.

EXAMPLE 2

Let $0 \le t \le 5$. Graph the points (x, y) determined by $x(t) = t^2$ and $y(t) = 2t + 1$.

METHOD 1

Set up a table of values as in Example 1. Plot the points obtained, then sketch a continuous curve.

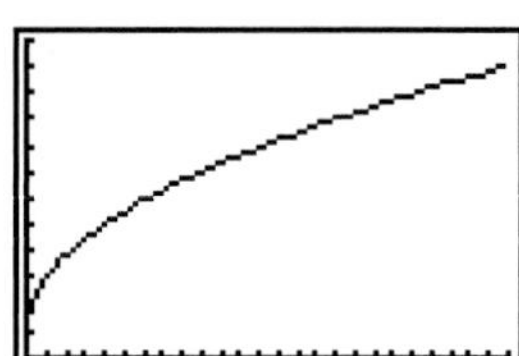

METHOD 2

Enter the functions into a graphing calculator or computer software. Specify the range for t.

By either method, the graph will look something like the graph at the right.

In Example 2, the specified range for t is $0 \le t \le 5$. However, the actual range for x is $0 \le x \le 25$. It is often the case that the ranges for t and x will not be the same.

An ellipse can be represented as a rectangular equation, a polar equation, or a pair of parametric equations.

EXAMPLE 3

Graph $x(t) = 3 \cos t$ and $y(t) = 2 \sin t$. Identify the graph.

STEP 1 Choose a range for t. Since the sine and cosine functions are periodic with period 2π, let the range for t be $0 \leq t \leq 2\pi$.

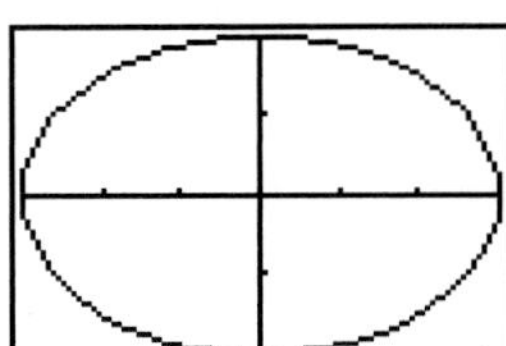

STEP 2 Enter the function definitions into a graphing calculator or computer software. Use the range already chosen for t. The graph is shown at the right.

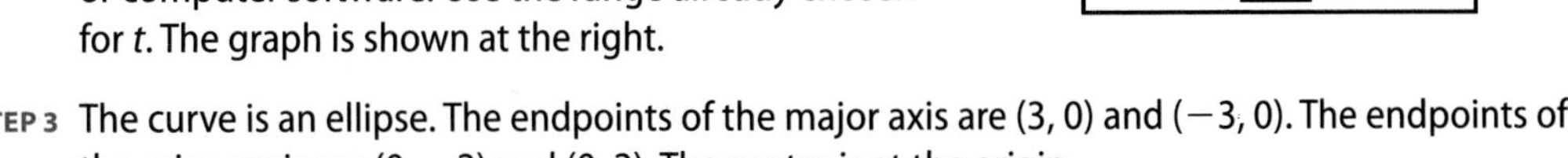

STEP 3 The curve is an ellipse. The endpoints of the major axis are (3, 0) and (−3, 0). The endpoints of the minor axis are (0, −2) and (0, 2). The center is at the origin.

Watch Out !

The selection of the range for t is critical. An interval that is too short will produce an incomplete graph. To see this, graph the equations over the interval $0 \leq t \leq \pi$. Over this interval, only the top half of the ellipse will be shown.

One of the commonplace applications of parametric equations in the plane is that of projectile motion. For the parametric equations related to projectile motion, see the *Got To Know!* box.

EXAMPLE 4

A projectile is launched upward at a 45° angle with the horizontal and given an initial velocity of 400 feet per second.

a. Write parametric equations for position.

$x(t) = (400 \cos 45°)t = 200\sqrt{2t}$ and $y(t) = (400 \sin 45°)t - \frac{1}{2}(16)t^2 = 200\sqrt{2t} - 8t^2$

b. Graph the path of the projectile.

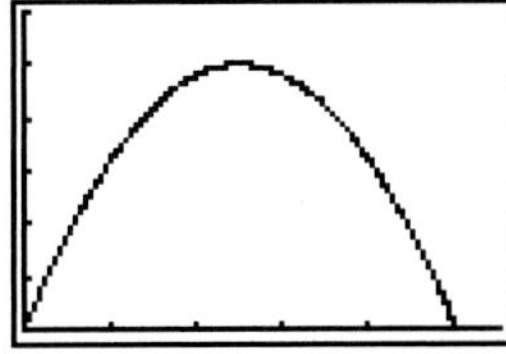

The lower limit for t is $t = 0$, the moment of launch. The upper limit for t is the time it takes for the projectile to hit the ground.

Solve $200\sqrt{2t} - 8t^2 = 0$ to find that value of t.

If $200\sqrt{2t} - 8t^2 = 0$, then $t \approx 35.4$

For the graphing interval use $0 \leq t \leq 35.4$.

The graph is shown at the right. Notice the graph is a parabola.

GOT TO KNOW!

Parametric Equations for Projectile Motion

Let v_0 be the initial velocity of a projectile launched at a launch angle θ with the horizontal. Then position $P(x(t), y(t))$ is given by the equations below. The value of g in the metric system is 9.8 meters per second per second. In the U. S. Customary system it is 16 feet per second per second.

$$x(t) = (v_0 \cos \theta)t \text{ and } y(t) = (v_0 \sin \theta)t - \frac{1}{2}gt^2$$

Transforming Parametric and Rectangular Equations

It is often possible to transform a pair of parametric equations for a curve into a single rectangular equation for that curve. The reverse process is often possible as well.

EXAMPLE 5

Write a single rectangular equation for the curve whose parametric equations are $x(t) = 2t + 1$ and $y(t) = 2t^2 - 3t$.

STEP 1 Write a strategy.

Replace t in the equation for y with an expression for it from the equation for x.

STEP 2 Carry out the strategy. Use x in place of $x(t)$ and y in place of $y(t)$.

$$x = 2t + 1 \longrightarrow t = \frac{x-1}{2}$$

Write the equation for y. $\quad y = 2t^2 - 3t$

Substitute. $\quad = 2\left(\frac{x-1}{2}\right)^2 - 3\left(\frac{x-1}{2}\right)$

Simplify. $\quad = \frac{x^2}{2} - x + \frac{1}{2} - \frac{3x}{2} + \frac{3}{2}$

$$y = \frac{1}{2}x^2 - \frac{5}{2}x + 2$$

Therefore, $y = \frac{1}{2}x^2 - \frac{5}{2}x + 2$ represents $x(t) = 2t + 1$ and $y(t) = 2t^2 - 3t$.

SEARCH

To see step-by-step videos of these problems, enter the page number into the SWadvantage.com Search Bar.

A given rectangular equation can have several different parametrizations. The following example illustrates this fact.

EXAMPLE 6

Write parametric equations for $y = (2x + 3)^2 - 5(2x + 3)$ using the parametrization specified.

a. Use t for $x(t)$.

Let $t = x(t)$.

Then $x(t) = t$ and $y(t) = (2t + 3)^2 - 5(2t + 3)$.

b. Use an expression of the form mt for $x(t)$.

Let $t = 2x(t)$.

Then $x(t) = \frac{t}{2}$ and $y(t) = (t + 3)^2 - 5(t + 3)$.

c. Use an expression of the form $mt + b$ for $x(t)$.

Let $t = 2x(t) + 3$.

Then $x(t) = \frac{t-3}{2}$ and $y(t) = t^2 - 5t$.

Using Parametric Equations to Create Designs

Many attractive patterns can be created with parametric equations. The sine and cosine functions often play a role in the creation. To be successful, technology in the form of a graphing calculator or computer is virtually essential.

EXAMPLE 7

Graph each set of parametric equations. Describe the pattern.

a. $x(t) = \cos t + t$ **and** $y(t) = \sin t + t$

Choose a suitable range for t. The interval $0 \le t \le 8\pi$ will give sufficient detail. The graph is shown at the left below. It appears to show soft steps.

b. $x(t) = t\cos t$ **and** $y(t) = t\sin t$

Choose a suitable range for t. The interval $0 \le t \le 8\pi$ will give sufficient detail. The graph is shown at the right below. It appears to show an elliptical spiral starting at the origin and spiraling outward.

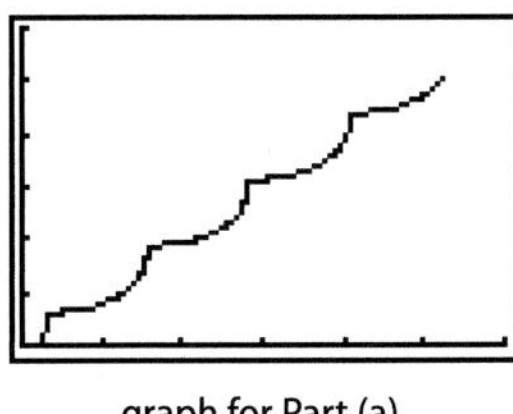

graph for Part (a)

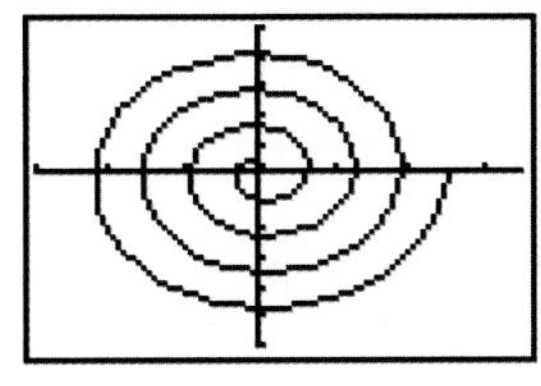

graph for Part (b)

Watch Out !

If the range for t is short, it is possible that only a small portion of the graph will be displayed. It might be wise to make a second attempt with a longer interval for t. By doing so, more of the pattern may be visible.

If the graphing interval in Example 7 is lengthened to $0 \le t \le 100\pi$, for example, then the number of steps would increase and the spiral would show many more "rings."

EXAMPLE 8

Graph each set of parametric equations. Describe the pattern.

a. $x(t) = \cos(3t)$ **and** $y(t) = \sin(4t)$ **on** $0 \le t \le 2\pi$

The graph is shown at the left below. It appears to look like a tightly wound bow.

b. $\begin{cases} x(t) = 3\cos t + 2\cos(6t) \\ y(t) = 3\sin t - 2\sin(6t) \end{cases}$ **on** $0 \le t \le 2\pi$

The graph is shown at the right below. It appears to look like a flower with seven petals.

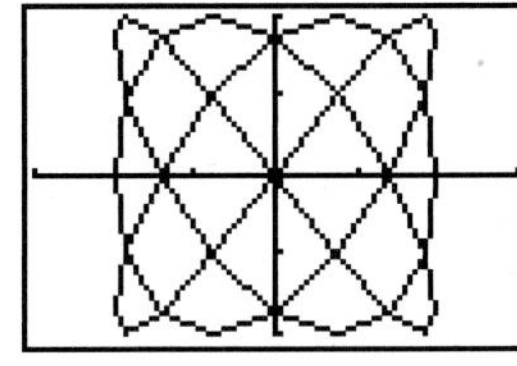

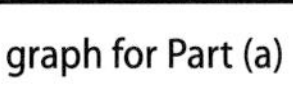

graph for Part (a)

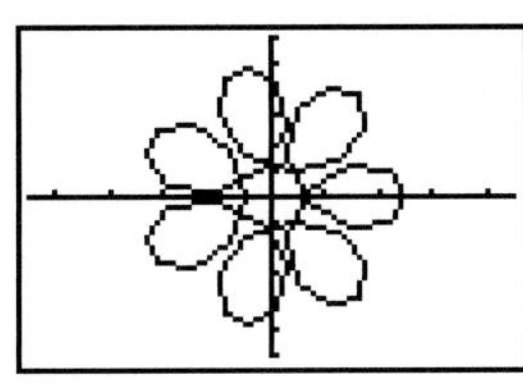

graph for Part (b)

Watch Out !

Be careful about predicting a design or pattern before graphing a pair of parametric equations. Even a small change in coefficients can produce a totally different graph. The graph of
$x(t) = \cos(3t)$
$y(t) = \sin(4t)$
is shown in Example 8. Change the coefficient 3 to 4 and the result will simply be a circle, a completely different curve.

Complex Roots of Equations

Reviewing Roots of Polynomial Equations

A graphing calculator can confirm that every equation of the form $x^2 + a = 0$, where $a > 0$, has no real solutions. The graph of $y = x^2 + a$ has no x-intercepts.

Recall the following definitions and theorems about roots of polynomial equations, $P(x) = 0$.

$P(x) = a_n x^n + a_{n-1} x^{n-1} + \cdots + a_1 x^1 + a_0$, where the coefficients are real.

A **root** of $P(x) = 0$ is any number x for which $P(x) = 0$.

An important theorem from the theory of equations states the following:

> If $P(x)$ is a polynomial in x with real coefficients, then $P(x)$ can be written as a product of linear factors with real coefficients and quadratic factors with real coefficients.

As an example:

> If $P(x) = x^5 - x^4 + 5x^3 - 5x^2 + 4x - 4$, then $P(x) = (x - 1)(x^2 + 1)(x^2 + 4)$.

The equations $x^2 + 1 = 0$ and $x^2 + 4 = 0$ have no real solutions. The solutions are imaginary numbers. The **imaginary unit**, denoted i, is defined as $i = \sqrt{-1}$.

A **complex number** is any number of the form $a + bi$, where a and b are real numbers and i is the imaginary unit. The number a is called the **real part** of $a + bi$ and b is called the **imaginary part** of $a + bi$. If $a = 0$, then bi is called an **imaginary number**.

EXAMPLE 1

Find the roots of each polynomial equation.

a. $P(x) = x^2 + 1 = 0$

$$(x - \sqrt{-1})(x + \sqrt{-1}) = 0$$

$x = i$ or $x = -i$

b. $P(x) = x^2 + 8 = 0$

$$(x - \sqrt{-8})(x + \sqrt{-8}) = 0$$

$x = \sqrt{-8}\ i = 2\sqrt{2}\ i$ or $x = -\sqrt{-8} = -2i\sqrt{2}$

EXAMPLE 2

Use the quadratic formula to find the roots of $P(x) = x^2 - 4x + 5 = 0$.

Substitute values in the quadratic formula. $\quad x = \dfrac{-(-4) \pm \sqrt{(-4)^2 - 4(1)(5)}}{2(1)}$

Simplify. $\quad x = 2 \pm i$

The roots of $x^2 - 4x + 5 = 0$ are $2 + i$ and $2 - i$.

Exploring the Fundamental Theorem of Algebra

The fundamental theorem of algebra is one of the most important theorems in algebra. The theorem makes it possible to solve any polynomial equation in one variable.

Solve $x^3 - 6x^2 + 13x = 0$

STEP 1 Factor.

$$x^3 - 6x^2 + 13x = 0$$
$$x(x^2 - 6x + 13) = 0$$

STEP 2 Apply the quadratic formula to $x^2 - 6x + 13 = 0$.

Substitute values in the quadratic formula. $x = \dfrac{-(-6) \pm \sqrt{(-6)^2 - 4(1)(13)}}{2(1)}$

Simplify. $= \dfrac{6 \pm \sqrt{-16}}{2} = \dfrac{6 \pm 4i}{2} = 3 \pm 2i$

The roots of $x^3 - 6x^2 + 13x = 0$ are 0, $3 + 2i$, and $3 - 2i$.

Factoring is a technique that goes hand in hand with the zero product property. It states that if $ab = 0$, then $a = 0$ or $b = 0$.

EXAMPLE 4

Solve $P(x) = (x^2 + x - 6)(x^2 - 10x + 34) = 0$.

STEP 1 Apply the zero-product property.

$x^2 + x - 6 = 0$ or $x^2 - 10x + 34 = 0$

STEP 2 Solve each quadratic equation.

METHOD 1

Use factoring to solve $x^2 + x - 6 = 0$.

$$(x - 2)(x + 3) = 0$$
$$x = 2 \text{ or } x = -3$$

METHOD 2

Use the quadratic formula to solve $x^2 - 10x + 34 = 0$.

$$x = \frac{-(-10) \pm \sqrt{(-10)^2 - 4(1)(34)}}{2(1)} = \frac{10 \pm \sqrt{-36}}{2} = 5 \pm 6i$$

Therefore, the roots of $P(x) = (x^2 + x - 6)(x^2 - 10x + 34) = 0$ are $-3, 2, 5 + 6i$, and $5 - 6i$.

SEARCH

To see step-by-step videos of these problems, enter the page number into the SWadvantage.com Search Bar.

The Fundamental Theorem of Algebra

If $P(x) = 0$ is a polynomial equation in x with real coefficients and degree n, then $P(x) = 0$ has at least one complex root.

$P(x) = 0$ has exactly n complex roots occurring in complex conjugate pairs.

Using Synthetic Division and Other Methods

Many times, a polynomial equation is given and the goal is to find all of its roots, but there is no guidance as to how to find the roots. In those cases, it is necessary to try a variety of methods.

Watch Out!

A graphing calculator display might indicate that roots are integers. However, they should be verified by evaluation as shown in Example 5. It would be risky to assume that if the display shows that a number is a root, then it must be a root.

EXAMPLE 5

Determine the nature of the roots of $x^4 - 9x^3 + 31x^2 - 9x - 50 = 0$. Find the real roots.

STEP 1 Analyze the equation.

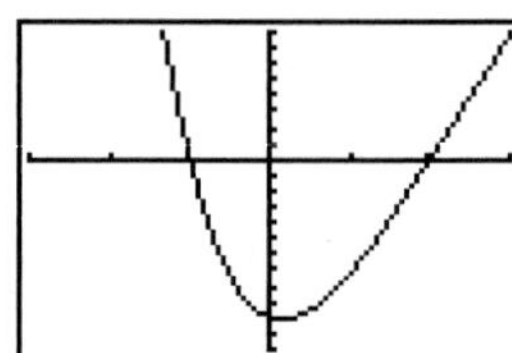

By the fundamental theorem of algebra, there are four roots because the degree of the polynomial is 4. There are four real roots, four complex roots, or two real roots and two complex roots.

STEP 2 Graph the equation. The diagram at the right shows that there are two real roots. They appear to be -1 and 2. Test these numbers.

$(-1)^4 - 9(-1)^3 + 31(-1)^2 - 9(-1) - 50 = 0$

$2^4 - 9(2)^3 + 31(2)^2 - 9(2) - 50 = 0$

There are two real roots and they are -1 and 2.

Recall the factor theorem. It is stated below.

> If a is a root of $P(x) = 0$, then $x - a$ is a factor of $P(x)$ and $P(x) = (x - a)Q(x)$, where $Q(x)$ is a polynomial of degree one less than that of $P(x)$.

In Example 5, 2 is a root of $x^4 - 9x^3 + 31x^2 - 9x - 50 = 0$ and $x - 2$ is a factor of it. Therefore, $x^4 - 9x^3 + 31x^2 - 9x - 50 = (x - 2)Q(x)$ for some polynomial $Q(x)$. Synthetic division is a method that can be used to find $Q(x)$. The next example shows how this can be done.

Ways to REMEMBER

Synthetic division is a division shortcut.

- Coefficients in order
- Bring down leading.
- Multiply, then add.
- Write sum below.
- Repeat as you go.

The bottom row has the coefficients of the quotient.

EXAMPLE 6

For $P(x) = x^4 - 9x^3 + 31x^2 - 9x - 50 = 0$ the expression $x - 2$ is a factor. Find the quotient when $P(x)$ is divided by $x - 2$.

STEP 1 Write the coefficients of $P(x)$ and 2 as shown at the right. Bring the leading coefficient, 1, down.

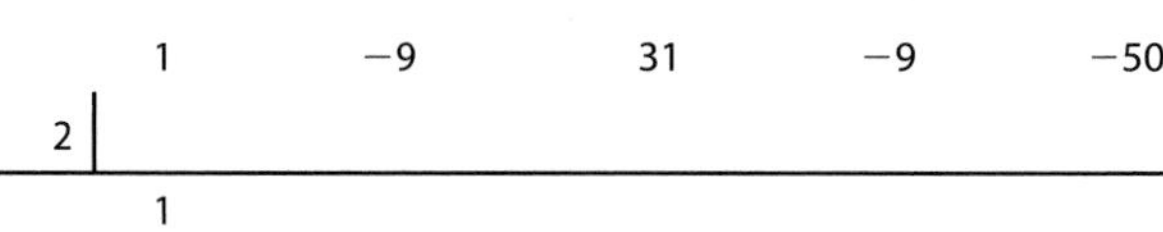

	1	−9	31	−9	−50
2					
	1				

STEP 2 Multiply by 2 and add as shown at the right.

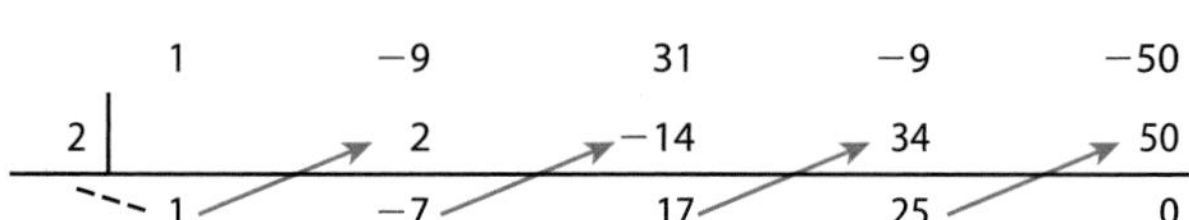

	1	−9	31	−9	−50
2		2	−14	34	50
	1	−7	17	25	0

STEP 3 Read the bottom line as the quotient. It is a polynomial of degree 3 with leading coefficient 1.

$$Q(x) = x^3 - 7x^2 + 17x + 25$$

When $x^4 - 9x^3 + 31x^2 - 9x - 50$ is divided by $x - 2$, the quotient, $Q(x)$, is $x^3 - 7x^2 + 17x + 25$.

The array showing the coefficients of $P(x)$ and a along with the multiplication and addition resulting in a bottom row of numbers is called synthetic division. This is how the factor theorem can be implemented.

The real roots of $P(x) = x^4 - 9x^3 + 31x^2 - 9x - 50 = 0$ are -1 and 2 as Example 5 showed. The synthetic division in Example 6 showed that $P(x) = (x - 2)(x^3 - 7x^2 + 17x + 25)$.

EXAMPLE 7

Use synthetic division to find the quotient when $Q(x) = x^3 - 7x^2 + 17x + 25$ is divided by $x + 1$.

STEP 1 Write the coefficients of $Q(x)$ and -1 as shown at the right. Bring the leading coefficient, 1, down.

	1	−7	17	25
−1				

The factor theorem requires a divisor of the form $x - a$. Write $x - (-1)$ for $x + 1$. In synthetic division, use -1.

STEP 2 Multiply by -1 and add as shown in the next diagram.

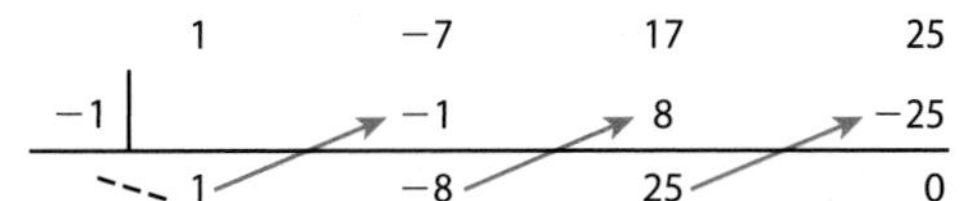

STEP 3 Read the bottom line as the quotient, $Q_1(x)$. It is a polynomial of degree 2 with leading coefficient 1.

$$Q_1(x) = x^2 - 8x + 25$$

> **Watch Out !**
>
> Synthetic division is a process that can be repeated. Once it has been used and a polynomial of degree one less is obtained, it is then used on the polynomial found to be the quotient, not the original polynomial.

EXAMPLE 8

Solve $P(x) = x^4 - 9x^3 + 31x^2 - 9x - 50 = 0$. Show an organized approach to the solution.

STEP 1 From Example 5, there are two real roots, -1 and 2, verified by using a graphing calculator,

STEP 2 From Example 6, $P(x) = x^4 - 9x^3 + 31x^2 - 9x - 50 = (x - 2)Q(x)$

$$P(x) = (x - 2)(x^3 - 7x^2 + 17x + 25)$$

STEP 3 From Example 7, $P(x) = x^4 - 9x^3 + 31x^2 - 9x - 50 = (x - 2)(x + 1)Q_1(x)$.

$$P(x) = (x - 2)(x + 1)(x^2 - 8x + 25)$$

STEP 4 Solve $x^2 - 8x + 25 = 0$ to determine the complex roots.

Use the quadratic formula. $x = \dfrac{-(-8) \pm \sqrt{(-8)^2 - 4(1)(25)}}{2(1)} = \dfrac{8 \pm \sqrt{-36}}{2}$

$$= 4 \pm 3i$$

Therefore, the roots of $P(x) = x^4 - 9x^3 + 31x^2 - 9x - 50 = 0$ are $-1, 2, 4 + 3i$, and $4 - 3i$.

> **SEARCH**
>
> To see step-by-step videos of these problems, enter the page number into the SWadvantage.com Search Bar.

EXAMPLE 9

Solve $P(x) = x^4 - 1 = 0$.

STEP 1 By the fundamental theorem of algebra, there are four roots to be found.

STEP 2 Observe: $P(x)$ is the difference of two squares, $(x^2)^2$ and $(1^2)^2$.

Factor. $P(x) = (x^2)^2 - (1^2)^2 = (x^2 - 1)(x^2 + 1)$

STEP 3 Use the zero product property to solve.

$x^2 - 1 = 0$ or $x^2 + 1 = 0$ $\qquad x = \pm 1$ or $x = \pm i$

The roots of $x^4 - 1 = 0$ are $-1, 1, i$, and $-i$.

Polar Form of Complex Numbers

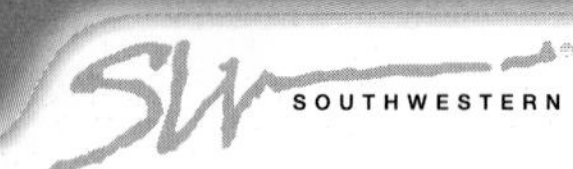

For a review of the connection between the rectangular coordinate system and the polar coordinate system, see p. 1096.

Representing Complex Numbers in the Plane

Every point in the plane can be represented as an ordered pair in the rectangular coordinate system and in the polar coordinate system. The diagrams below show the coordinates of point P in each system.

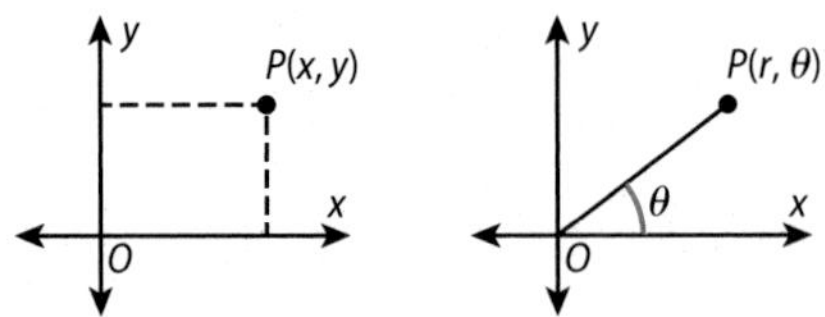

Every complex number z can be represented as a point P in each coordinate system. For the representations of z in each coordinate system, see the *Got To Know!* box. The **absolute value**, or **modulus**, of z is r. The **amplitude**, or **argument**, of z is θ.

Need More HELP

The identities $\cos(180° - \theta) = -\cos\theta$ and $\sin(180° - \theta) = \sin\theta$ are so useful, they should be committed to memory.

EXAMPLE 1

Let $z = -5 + 3i$. Write the polar form of z.

STEP 1 Sketch a diagram to get an idea of the value of θ.

STEP 2 Determine the value of r.

$$r = \sqrt{(-5)^2 + 3^2} = \sqrt{34}$$

STEP 3 Use a reference triangle to determine the value of θ.

In $\triangle OPQ$,

$$\cos(180° - \theta) = \frac{OQ}{OP}$$

$$\cos\theta = -\frac{5}{\sqrt{(-5)^2 + 3^2}}$$

$$= -\frac{5}{\sqrt{34}}$$

$$\theta \approx 149°$$

STEP 4 Write the polar form.

In polar form, $-5 + 3i$ is represented as $\sqrt{34}(\cos 149° + i \sin 149°)$.

Example 1 shows that the process of writing a complex number given in rectangular form is similar to the process of writing polar coordinates given the point in rectangular coordinates.

GOT TO KNOW!

Rectangular and Polar Forms of a Complex Number

Let z be a complex number.

In the rectangular coordinate system: (x, y) $\quad z = x + yi$

In the polar coordinate system: (r, θ) $\quad z = r\cos\theta + (r\sin\theta)i$

$$= r(\cos\theta + i\sin\theta)$$

EXAMPLE 2

Let $z = 10\left(\cos\frac{5\pi}{6} + \left(\sin\frac{5\pi}{6}\right)i\right)$. Write the rectangular form of z.

METHOD 1

Use identities.

$$\cos\frac{5\pi}{6} = -\cos\left(\pi - \frac{5\pi}{6}\right)$$
$$= -\cos\frac{\pi}{6}$$
$$= -\frac{\sqrt{3}}{2}$$
$$\sin\frac{5\pi}{6} = \sin\left(\pi - \frac{5\pi}{6}\right)$$
$$= \sin\frac{\pi}{6}$$
$$= \frac{1}{2}$$

Therefore, $z = -10\frac{\sqrt{3}}{2} + 10\left(\frac{1}{2}\right)i$, or $-5\sqrt{3} + 5i$.

METHOD 2

Use a calculator.

$$10\left(\cos\frac{5\pi}{6} + \left(\sin\frac{5\pi}{6}\right)i\right) = 10\cos\frac{5\pi}{6} + \left(10\sin\frac{5\pi}{6}\right)i$$

$$10\cos\frac{5\pi}{6} \approx -8.6603 \text{ and } 10\sin\frac{5\pi}{6} = 5$$

Therefore, $z \approx -8.6603 + 5i$.

Watch Out!

Both exact values and approximate values have their usefulness. Make sure you pay attention to which value is most appropriate for the problem you are working on.

SEARCH

To see step-by-step videos of these problems, enter the page number into the SWadvantage.com Search Bar.

The additive inverse of $x + yi$ is $-x - yi$. The additive inverse has a patterned polar form.

EXAMPLE 3

Let $z = x + yi$. Write a formula for the polar form of $-z$.

STEP 1 The point representing $-z$ is the rotation of the point representing z about the origin 180°. The diagram illustrates this.

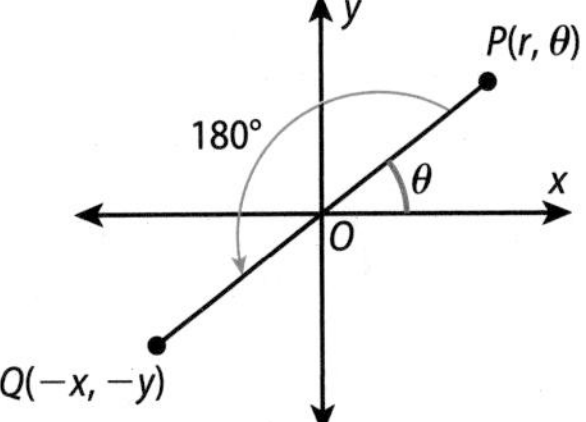

STEP 2 Write the representation of $-z$.

METHOD 1

$$-z = r\cos(180° + \theta) + (r\sin(180° + \theta))i$$
$$-z = r(-\cos\theta) + r(-\sin\theta)i$$
$$z = -r\cos\theta - (r\sin\theta)i$$

METHOD 2

$$x = r\cos\theta \text{ and } y = r\sin\theta$$
$$-x = -r\cos\theta \text{ and } -y = -r\sin\theta$$

Therefore, $-x - yi = -r\cos\theta - (r\sin\theta)i$.

Need More HELP?

Objects in the plane can have many interpretations:

- rotation of a point 180°
- additive inverse of a vector
- additive inverse of a complex number

These interpretations have meaning in two coordinate systems: rectangular and polar

Exploring the Polar Form of a Complex Number Further

A set of related complex numbers often creates a regular polygon.

Watch Out!

The real number 1 is a complex number whose value of θ is 0°.

EXAMPLE 4

Describe the polygon determined by these three complex numbers. Verify the conclusion.

$$z_1 = 1 \qquad z_2 = \cos 120° + (\sin 120°)i \qquad z_3 = \cos 240° + (\sin 240°)i$$

STEP 1 Write each complex number in rectangular form.

$$z_1 = 1 \qquad z_2 = -\frac{1}{2} + \frac{\sqrt{3}}{2}i \qquad z_3 = -\frac{1}{2} - \frac{\sqrt{3}}{2}i$$

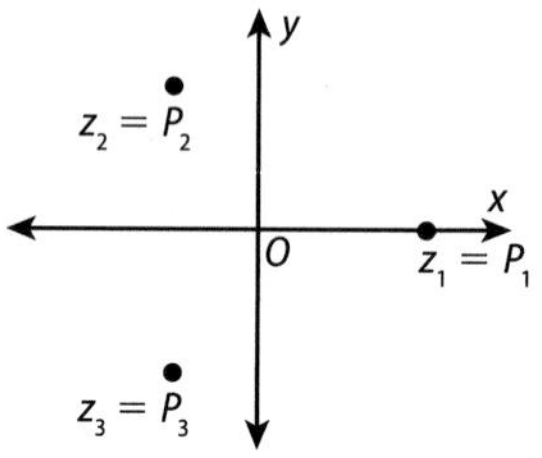

STEP 2 Make a quick sketch. Label the points representing z_1, z_2, and z_3.

STEP 3 Use the distance formula to calculate P_1P_2, P_2P_3, and P_3P_1.

$$P_1P_2 = \sqrt{\left(1 - \left(-\frac{1}{2}\right)\right)^2 + \left(0 - \frac{\sqrt{3}}{2}\right)^2} = \sqrt{\frac{9}{4} + \frac{3}{4}} = \sqrt{3}$$

$$P_2P_3 = \sqrt{\left(-\frac{1}{2} - \left(-\frac{1}{2}\right)\right)^2 + \left(\frac{\sqrt{3}}{2} - \left(-\frac{\sqrt{3}}{2}\right)\right)^2} = \sqrt{0 + 3} = \sqrt{3}$$

$$P_3P_1 = \sqrt{\left(-\frac{1}{2} - 1\right)^2 + \left(-\frac{\sqrt{3}}{2} - 0\right)^2} = \sqrt{\frac{9}{4} + \frac{3}{4}} = \sqrt{3}$$

Watch Out!

It is easy to omit or neglect a symbol indicating a negative coordinate. Also recall that $-(-x) = x$.

STEP 4 Draw the conclusion.

Since $P_1P_2 = P_2P_3 = P_3P_1$, the polygon formed is an equilateral triangle. The vertices are on the circle with radius 1 and center at the origin.

EXAMPLE 5

Find the roots of $z^3 - 1 = 0$.

STEP 1 Factor $z^3 - 1$.

$$z^3 - 1 = (z - 1)(z^2 + z + 1)$$

STEP 2 Apply the zero product property.

$$z - 1 = 0 \text{ or } z^2 + z + 1 = 0$$

STEP 3 Apply the quadratic formula to solve $z^2 + z + 1 = 0$.

$$z = \frac{-(1) \pm \sqrt{1^2 - 4(1)(1)}}{2(1)}$$

$$z = -\frac{1}{2} + \frac{\sqrt{3}}{2}i \text{ or } z = -\frac{1}{2} - \frac{\sqrt{3}}{2}i$$

The roots of $z^3 - 1 = 0$ are 1, $-\frac{1}{2} + \frac{\sqrt{3}}{2}i$, and $z = -\frac{1}{2} - \frac{\sqrt{3}}{2}i$.

Try It This Way

As an alternative to relying on the factor form for the difference of two cubes, graph $y = x^3 - 1$ on a graphing calculator to confirm that 1 is a root. Then use synthetic division to obtain $z^2 + z + 1$.

EXAMPLE 6

Write the roots of $z^3 - 1 = 0$ as complex numbers in polar form.

From Example 5, the roots of $z^3 - 1 = 0$ are 1, $-\frac{1}{2} + \frac{\sqrt{3}}{2}i$, and $z = -\frac{1}{2} - \frac{\sqrt{3}}{2}i$.

For each complex number, $r = 1$. For each complex number, find θ.

z_1: $\cos\theta = 1$ and $\sin\theta = 0$ Therefore, $\theta = 0°$.

z_2: $\cos\theta = -\frac{1}{2}$ and $\sin\theta = \frac{\sqrt{3}}{2}$ Therefore, $\theta = 120°$.

z_3: $\cos\theta = -\frac{1}{2}$ and $\sin\theta = -\frac{\sqrt{3}}{2}$ Therefore, $\theta = 240°$.

In polar form, the roots of $z^3 - 1 = 0$ are $\cos 0° + (\sin 0°)i$, $\cos 120° + (\sin 120°)i$, and $\cos 240° + (\sin 240°)i$.

Need More HELP

Angle measures whose sines and cosines are $\pm\frac{1}{2}$ and $\frac{\sqrt{3}}{2}$ are some of the special angles and are worth memorizing.

Graphically, the third roots of 1 are the vertices of an equilateral triangle whose vertices are on the circle with center at the origin and radius 1.

Let z be a complex number defined by $z = \frac{t}{t+1}(\cos t + (\sin t)i)$, where t is a variable. The table below shows how the real and imaginary parts of z change as t increases. However, it is difficult to see any pattern.

SEARCH

To see step-by-step videos of these problems, enter the page number into the SWadvantage.com Search Bar.

t	1	2	5	10	20	50
x	0.2702	−0.2774	0.2364	−0.7628	0.3886	0.9460
y	0.4207	0.6062	−0.7991	−0.4946	0.8695	−0.2572

Parametric equations might help discern a pattern.

EXAMPLE 7

Let z be a complex number defined by $z = \frac{t}{t+1}(\cos t + (\sin t)i)$. Describe what happens as t is allowed to increase without bound.

Let $z = x + yi$. Write functions for x and y in terms of t.

$$x(t) = \frac{t}{t+1}\cos t \text{ and } y(t) = \frac{t}{t+1}\sin t$$

Graph $(x(t), y(t))$ using parametric equations. The graph is shown at the right.

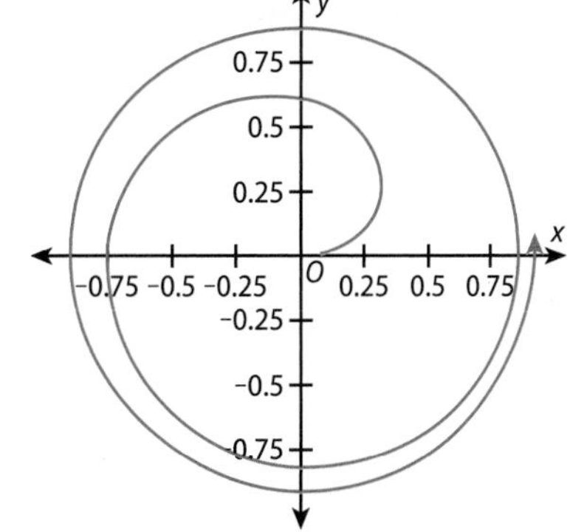

As t increases without bound, the curve approximates the circle centered at the origin with radius 1 more and more. The unit circle is a limiting curve.

Watch Out!

Analysis of the parametric equations may well be a good first step. A graphing calculator should be used to confirm or deny initial predictions.

The limiting behavior shown in Example 7 is explained by the fact that the unit circle has coordinates $(\cos t, \sin t)$ and $\frac{t}{t+1}$ approaches 1 as t increases without bound.

Product and Quotient Theorems

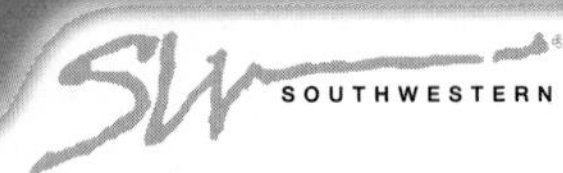

Multiplying Complex Numbers in Polar Form

There is a simple formula for multiplying complex numbers in polar form. Its proof depends on the use of the addition formulas for the sine and the cosine. For a statement of the product formula, see the *Got To Know!* box.

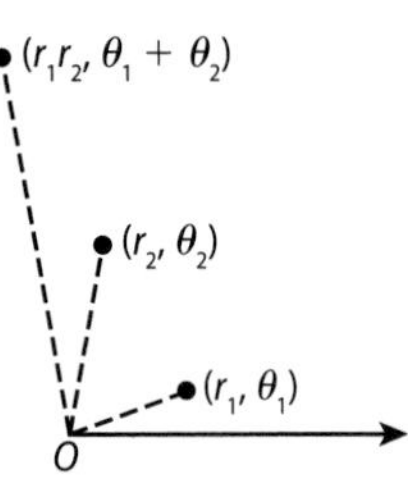

The diagram at the right illustrates the product formula in the case where r_1 and r_2 are both greater than 1. The point representing the product is the rotation and dilation of the two factors in it.

Ways to REMEMBER

To multiply one complex number by another, multiply values of r and add values of θ.

EXAMPLE 1

Let $z_1 = 3\cos 45° + (3\sin 45°)i$ and $z_2 = 4\cos 90° + (4\sin 90°)i$. Write the polar and rectangular forms of z_1z_2.

$z_1z_2 = r_1r_2(\cos(\theta_1 + \theta_2) + \sin(\theta_1 + \theta_2)i) = (3)(4)(\cos(45° + 90°) + \sin(45° + 90°)i)$

polar form $= 12(\cos 135° + (\sin 135°)i)$

rectangular form $= 12\left(-\frac{1}{\sqrt{2}} + \frac{1}{\sqrt{2}}i\right) = -6\sqrt{2} + \left(6\sqrt{2}\right)i$

Therefore, $z_1z_2 = 12(\cos 135° + (\sin 135°)i) = -6\sqrt{2} + \left(6\sqrt{2}\right)i$.

EXAMPLE 2

Interpret the multiplication in Example 1 in terms of transformations.

Rotate the vector associated with z_1 counterclockwise 90°. Then scale the result by a factor of 4. Rotate the vector associated with z_2 counterclockwise 45°. Then scale the result by a factor of 3.

Need More HELP

Work backward from a pair of compound inequalities to the required values of r_2 and θ_2. The concentric circles are used to write an inequality for r_2. The spokes are used to write an inequality for θ_2.

EXAMPLE 3

Let $z_1 = 10(\cos 30° + (\sin 30°)i$ and z_2 be a complex number for which $r_2 > 0$ and $0° \le \theta_2 \le 360°$. Find r_2 and θ_2 such that the graph of z_1z_2 is in the shaded region.

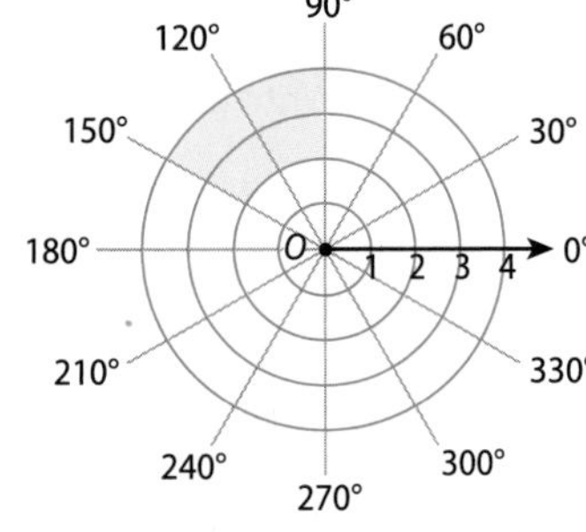

For z_1: $r_1 = 10$ and $\theta_1 = 30°$.

$2 \le r_1r_2 \le 4 \qquad 90° \le \theta_1 + \theta_2 \le 150°$

$2 \le 10r_2 \le 4 \qquad 90° \le 30° + \theta_2 \le 150°$

Then $0.2 \le r_2 \le 0.4$ and $60° \le \theta_2 \le 120°$.

GOT TO KNOW!

The Product Formula for Complex Numbers in Polar Form

Let $z_1 = r_1 \cos \theta_1 + (r_1 \sin \theta_1)i$ and $z_2 = r_2 \cos \theta_2 + (r_2 \sin \theta_2)i$. Then:

$$z_1z_2 = r_1r_2 \cos(\theta_1 + \theta_2) + (r_1r_2 \sin(\theta_1 + \theta_2))i = r_1r_2(\cos(\theta_1 + \theta_2) + \sin(\theta_1 + \theta_2)i)$$

Dividing Complex Numbers in Polar Form

The **conjugate**, $\bar{z}$, of $z = x + yi$ is $x - yi$. For any z, $z\bar{z} = x^1 + y^1$. To derive a formula for the quotient of two complex numbers, z_1 and z_2, use this fact and the difference formulas for sine and cosine. For a statement of the quotient formula, see the *Got To Know!* box.

$$\frac{z_1}{z_2} = \frac{r_1(\cos\theta_1 + (\sin\theta_1))i}{r_2(\cos\theta_2 + (\sin\theta_2))i} = \frac{r_1}{r_2}\,\frac{\cos\theta_1 + (\sin\theta_1)i}{\cos\theta_2 + (\sin\theta_2)i} \cdot \frac{r_2}{r_2}\,\frac{\cos\theta_2 - (\sin\theta_2)i}{\cos\theta_2 - (\sin\theta_2)i}$$

$$= \frac{r_1}{r_2}(\cos\theta_1 + (\sin\theta_1)i)(\cos\theta_2 - (\sin\theta_2)i)$$

Use difference formulas.

$$= \frac{r_1}{r_2}((\cos\theta_1\cos\theta_2 + \sin\theta_1\sin\theta_2) + (\sin\theta_1\cos\theta_2 - \cos\theta_1\sin\theta_2)i)$$

$$\frac{z_1}{z_2} = \frac{r_1}{r_2}(\cos(\theta_1 - \theta_2) + (\sin(\theta_1 - \theta_2))i)$$

EXAMPLE 4

Write $\frac{z_1}{z_2} = \frac{28(\cos 30° + (\sin 30°)i)}{4(\cos 300° + (\sin 300°)i)}$ in polar form.

Apply the quotient formula. $\frac{z_1}{z_2} = \frac{28}{4} \cdot (\cos(30° - 300°) + (\sin(30° - 300°)i)$

Simplify. $= 7(\cos(-270°) + (\sin(-270°)i)$

$= 7i$

Ways to REMEMBER

To divide one complex number by another, divide values of r and subtract values of θ.

EXAMPLE 5

Simplify $\frac{\cos\theta + (\sin\theta)i}{\cos(\theta + 90°) + (\sin(\theta + 90°))i}$.

Apply the quotient formula. $\frac{\cos\theta + (\sin\theta)i}{\cos(\theta + 90°) + (\sin(\theta + 90°))i} = \cos(-90°) + (\sin(-90°))i$

$= -i$

SEARCH

To see step-by-step videos of these problems, enter the page number into the SWadvantage.com Search Bar.

The conclusion in Example 5 is based on some assumptions. It assumes that both numerator and denominator have the same modulus. In addition, if 90° is replaced by 180°, then the expression equals -1 not $-i$.

GOT TO KNOW!

Quotient Formula for Complex Numbers in Polar Form

Let $z_1 = r_1\cos\theta_1 + (r_1\sin\theta_1)i$ and $z_2 = r_2\cos\theta_2 + (r_2\sin\theta_2)i$. Then:

$$\frac{z_1}{z_2} = \frac{r_1}{r_2}(\cos(\theta_1 - \theta_2) + \sin(\theta_1 - \theta_2)i)$$

DeMoivre's Theorem

Finding Powers of Complex Numbers

A simple application of the product formula for complex numbers in polar form is the formula for the square of a complex number.

$$\text{If } z = r\cos\theta + (r\sin\theta)i, \text{ then } z^2 = r^2\cos(2\theta) + (r^2\sin(2\theta))i.$$

DeMoivre's theorem generalizes this. It provides a way to find the nth power of any complex number, where n is a positive integer. For the statement of DeMoivre's theorem, see the *Got To Know!* box.

Iteration occurs often. Recall that $x^2 = x \cdot x$, that $x^3 = x^2 \cdot x^1$, and that $x^4 = x^3 \cdot x^1$. DeMoivre's theorem is based on the idea that $x^n = x^{n-1} \cdot x^1$.

EXAMPLE 1

Let $z = \frac{3}{2} + \frac{3\sqrt{3}}{2}i$. Find z^4 in polar form and rectangular form.

STEP 1 Represent z as a complex number in polar form.

$$z = \frac{3}{2} + \frac{3\sqrt{3}}{2}i = 3\left(\frac{1}{2} + \frac{\sqrt{3}}{2}\right)i$$

Since $\cos\frac{\pi}{3} = \frac{1}{2}$ and $\sin\frac{\pi}{3} = \frac{\sqrt{3}}{2}$:

$$z = 3\cos\frac{\pi}{3} + \left(3\sin\frac{\pi}{3}\right)i = 3\left(\cos\frac{\pi}{3} + \left(\sin\frac{\pi}{3}\right)i\right)$$

STEP 2 Apply DeMoivre's theorem.

$$z^4 = 3^4\left(\cos\frac{4\pi}{3} + \left(\sin\frac{4\pi}{3}\right)i\right)$$

STEP 3 Simplify.

Since $\cos\frac{4\pi}{3} = -\frac{1}{2}$ and $\sin\frac{4\pi}{3} = -\frac{\sqrt{3}}{2}$:

$$z^4 = 81\left(-\frac{1}{2} - \frac{\sqrt{3}}{2}i\right)$$

Therefore, $z^4 = 3^4\left(\cos\frac{4\pi}{3} + \left(\sin\frac{4\pi}{3}\right)i\right) = -\frac{81}{2} - \frac{81\sqrt{3}}{2}i$.

Ways to REMEMBER

nth power of z

nth power of r

nth multiple of θ

The nth power of a complex number can be represented as a pair of parametric equations. Let $z = r\cos\theta + (r\sin\theta)i$.

$$x(n) = r^n\cos(n\theta) \text{ and } x(n) = r^n\cos(n\theta)$$

GOT TO KNOW!

DeMoivre's Theorem

Let $z = r\cos\theta + (r\sin\theta)i$ and let n be a positive integer. Then $z^n = r^n\cos(n\theta) + (r^n\sin(n\theta))i$.

EXAMPLE 2

Let $z = r\cos 30° + (r\sin 30°)i$. Describe the pattern in the nth powers of z for each value of r.

a. $r = 1.07$

Since $r > 1$, r^n increases without bound as n increases without bound. The sequence begins at $\left(\frac{1.07\sqrt{3}}{2}, \frac{1.07}{2}\right)$ and spirals outward.

b. $r = 1$

$r = 1$. All the powers of z lie along the unit circle. The sequence begins at $\left(\frac{\sqrt{3}}{2}, \frac{1}{2}\right)$. When the points are joined in order, they form a regular dodecagon since $12 \times \frac{\pi}{6} = 2\pi$.

c. $r = 0.93$

Since $r < 1$, r^n decreases with 0 as a limit as n increases without bound. The sequence begins at $\left(\frac{0.93\sqrt{3}}{2}, \frac{0.93}{2}\right)$ and spirals inward.

The graphs are shown below.

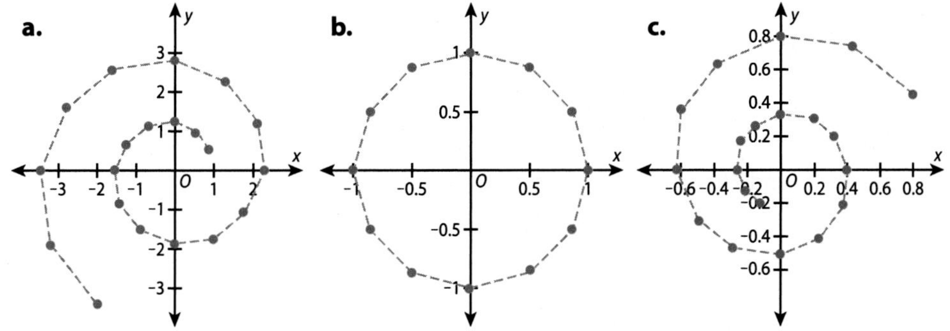

EXAMPLE 3

Let $z = \cos 120° + (\sin 120°)i$ and n be a positive integer. Describe repeating patterns in z^n.

STEP 1 Observe the pattern relating n to the argument θ of $z^n = \cos(n\theta) + (\sin(n\theta))i$.

n	1	2	3	4	5	6	7
$n\theta$	120°	240°	360°	480°, 120°	600°, 240°	720°, 360°	840°, 120°

STEP 2 Write a relationship between n and powers of z.

$n = 1, 4, 7, \ldots \rightarrow z^n = z^1$ $\quad$ $n = 2, 5, 8, \ldots \rightarrow z^n = z^2$ $\quad$ $n = 3, 6, 9, \ldots \rightarrow z^n = z^3$

STEP 3 Divide n by 3. The remainder, 0, 1, or 2, indicates which of z^1, z^2, or z^3 equals z^n.
For example, let $n = 53$.
The quotient of $53 \div 3$ has remainder 2. Therefore, $z^{53} = z^2$.

Need More HELP

A geometric sequence of real numbers involves three cases.
In the case of $r > 1$, the sequence increases.
In the case of $0 < r < 1$, the sequence decreases.
If $r = 1$, the sequence is constant.

SEARCH

To see step-by-step videos of these problems, enter the page number into the SWadvantage.com Search Bar.

Try It This Way

Look for three linear relationships.

$n = 1, 4, 7, \ldots$
$3n - 2$

$n = 2, 5, 8, \ldots$
$3n - 1$

$n = 3, 6, 9, \ldots$
$3n$

The value of the expression indicates which of z^1, z^2, or z^3 equals z^n.

Roots of Complex Numbers

Finding Roots of Complex Numbers

The square root of a complex number is another complex number. That is, the set of complex numbers is closed under the operation of taking a square root. Using polar form, it is possible to find the *n*th roots of a given complex number. For a statement of the necessary formula, see the *Got To Know*! box.

EXAMPLE 1

a. Find the square roots of *i*.

METHOD 1

Use rectangular form. Let $z = x + yi$, where x and y are real numbers, be a square root of i. Then:

$z^2 = (x + yi)^2 = x^2 - y^2 + 2xyi$ and $z^2 = i$

Equate real and imaginary parts. $x^2 - y^2 = 0$ and $2xy = 1$

Solve the system for x and y. $x = \frac{\sqrt{2}}{2}$ and $y = \frac{\sqrt{2}}{2}$ or $x = -\frac{\sqrt{2}}{2}$ and $y = -\frac{\sqrt{2}}{2}$

The square roots of i are $\frac{\sqrt{2}}{2} + \frac{\sqrt{2}}{2}i$ and $-\frac{\sqrt{2}}{2} - \frac{\sqrt{2}}{2}i$.

METHOD 2

Use polar form. Write i as $i = \cos 90° + (\sin 90°)i$.

Let $z = r \cos \theta + (r \sin \theta)i$ be a square root of i.

Apply DeMoivre's theorem. $z^2 = r^2 \cos(2\theta) + (r^2 \sin(2\theta))i = \cos 90° + (\sin 90°)i$

Therefore, $r^2 = 1$ and $2\theta = 90°$.

$r = \pm 1$ and $\theta = 45°$

The square roots, z_1 and z_2, of i are $\cos 45° + (\sin 45°)i$ and $-\cos 45° - (\sin 45°)i$.

b. Show the square roots of *i* in a graph.

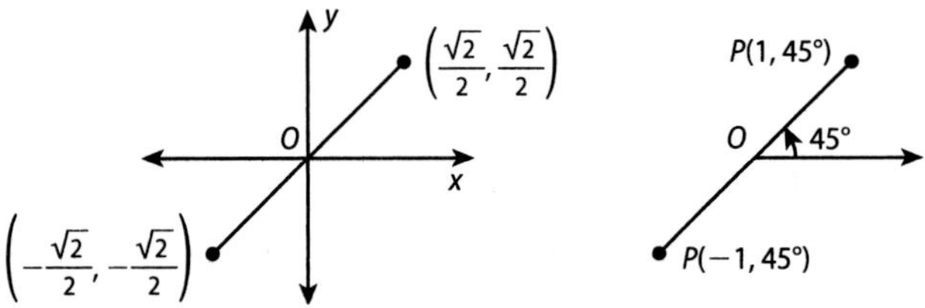

Watch Out!

Be sure to verify or check solutions before claiming that they are found.

Watch Out!

Recall that when you encounter a negative value of r, the direction to take in graphing is the opposite of the direction you would take for a positive value of r.

GOT TO KNOW!

Roots of Complex Numbers

Let $z = r \cos \theta + (r \sin \theta)i$ and let n be a positive integer. Then the nth roots of z, $z_1, z_2, \ldots, z_{n-1}$, and z_n. are given by the formula below.

$$z_k = r^{\frac{1}{n}}\left(\cos\left(\frac{\theta}{n} + \frac{360° k}{n}\right) + \left(\sin\left(\frac{\theta}{n} + \frac{360° k}{n}\right)\right)i\right), \text{ where } k = 1, 2, \ldots, n - 1, \text{ and } n$$

EXAMPLE 2

Find the cube roots of $z = 8(\cos 120° + (\sin 120°)i)$.

Let the three roots of z be represented by z_1, z_2, and z_3. Make a list using $k = 1, 2$, and 3.

$k = 1$ $\quad z_1 = 8^{\frac{1}{3}}\left(\cos\left(\frac{120°}{3} + \frac{360°(1)}{3}\right) + \left(\sin\left(\frac{120°}{3} + \frac{360°(1)}{3}\right)\right)i\right)$

$= 2(\cos 160° + (\sin 160°)i)$

$k = 2$ $\quad z_2 = 8^{\frac{1}{3}}\left(\cos\left(\frac{120°}{3} + \frac{360°(2)}{3}\right) + \left(\sin\left(\frac{120°}{3} + \frac{360°(2)}{3}\right)\right)i\right)$

$= 2(\cos 280° + (\sin 280°)i)$

$k = 3$ $\quad z_3 = 8^{\frac{1}{3}}\left(\cos\left(\frac{120°}{3} + \frac{360°(3)}{3}\right) + \left(\sin\left(\frac{120°}{3} + \frac{360°(3)}{3}\right)\right)i\right)$

$= 2(\cos 400° + (\sin 400°)i)$

The cube roots are $2(\cos 160° + (\sin 160°)i)$, $2(\cos 280° + (\sin 280°)i)$, and $2(\cos 400° + (\sin 400°)i)$.

Need More HELP

The key to listing all the roots is first to find $\frac{\theta}{n}$. The argument of each other root is this value plus multiples of $\frac{360°}{n}$.

The product property of exponents and the power of a power property of exponents apply when the base is a complex number as well as a real number.

Product Property: $z^{m+n} = z^m z^n$ Power of a Power Property: $(z^m)^n = z^{mn}$

EXAMPLE 3

Let $z_1, z_2, \ldots, z_5$, and z_6 represent the six roots of 1, with $z_6 = 1$.

a. Write the six roots of 1 as complex numbers in polar form.

In polar form, $1 = \cos 360° + i \sin 360°$. Apply the formula for nth roots with $k = 1, 2, 3, 4, 5$, and 6.

$z_1 = \cos 60° + i \sin 60°$ $\quad z_2 = \cos 120° + i \sin 120°$ $\quad z_3 = \cos 180° + i \sin 180°$

$z_4 = \cos 240° + i \sin 240°$ $\quad z_5 = \cos 300° + i \sin 300°$ $\quad z_6 = \cos 360° + i \sin 360°$

b. Show that $(z_1)^2 = z_2$.

$(z_1)^2 = \cos(2(60°)) + i \sin(2(60°)) = \cos 120° + i \sin 120° = z_2$

c. Show that $(z_1)^4 = z_4$.

Product property of exponents	$(z_1)^4 = (z_1)^2 (z_1)^2$
From Part (b), $(z_1)^2 = z_2$.	$= (\cos 120° + i \sin 120°)(\cos 120° + i \sin 120°)$
	$= \cos 240° + i \sin 240°$
	$(z_1)^4 = z_4$

d. Which of $z_1, z_2, \ldots, z_5$, and z_6 does $(z_2)^{20}$ equal?

Since $z^2 = (z_1)^2$, $(z_2)^{20} = \left((z_1)^2\right)^{20} = (z_1)^{40}$.

Product property of exponents	$(z_1)^{40} = (z_1)^{36} (z_1)^4$
Power of a power property of exponents	$= \left((z_1)^6\right)^6 (z_1)^4$
$(z_1)^6 = 1$ and $1^6 = 1$	$= (1)(z_1)^4$
From Part (c), $(z_1)^4 = z_4$.	$(z_1)^{40} = z_4$

Therefore, $(z_2)^{20} = z_4$.

SEARCH

To see step-by-step videos of these problems, enter the page number into the SWadvantage.com Search Bar.

Watch Out!

Not every sixth root of 1 is some power of z_2. In fact, powers of z_2 will only generate z_2, z_4, and z_6.

Trigonometry

Trigonometric Ratios

$\sin A = \dfrac{\text{leg opposite } \angle A}{\text{hypotenuse}}$	$\cos A = \dfrac{\text{leg adjacent } \angle A}{\text{hypotenuse}}$	$\tan A = \dfrac{\text{leg opposite } \angle A}{\text{leg adjacent } \angle A}$
$\csc A = \dfrac{\text{hypotenuse}}{\text{leg opposite } \angle A}$	$\sec A = \dfrac{\text{hypotenuse}}{\text{leg adjacent } \angle A}$	$\cot A = \dfrac{\text{leg adjacent } \angle A}{\text{leg opposite } \angle A}$

Trigonometric Values of the Special Angles

Degrees	Radians	$\sin\theta$	$\cos\theta$	$\tan\theta$	$\csc\theta$	$\sec\theta$	$\cot\theta$
0	0	0	1	0	undefined	1	undefined
30	$\frac{\pi}{6}$	$\frac{1}{2}$	$\frac{\sqrt{3}}{2}$	$\frac{\sqrt{3}}{3}$	2	$\frac{2\sqrt{3}}{3}$	$\sqrt{3}$
45	$\frac{\pi}{4}$	$\frac{\sqrt{2}}{2}$	$\frac{\sqrt{2}}{2}$	1	$\sqrt{2}$	$\sqrt{2}$	1
60	$\frac{\pi}{3}$	$\frac{\sqrt{3}}{2}$	$\frac{1}{2}$	$\sqrt{3}$	$\frac{2\sqrt{3}}{3}$	2	$\frac{\sqrt{3}}{3}$
90	$\frac{\pi}{2}$	1	0	undefined	1	undefined	0

Conversion Formulas

Degrees to Radians:	$y \text{ radians} = x° \cdot \frac{\pi \text{ radians}}{180°}$	Radians to Degrees:	$y° = x \text{ radians} \cdot \frac{180°}{\pi \text{ radians}}$
Rectangular coordinates to Polar coordinates:		Polar coordinates to Rectangular coordinates:	
$P(x, y)$	$r = \pm\sqrt{x^2 + y^2}$ and $\cos q = \frac{x}{r}$ and $\sin q = \frac{y}{r}$	$P(r, q)$	$x = r\cos q$ and $y = r\sin q$

Rules and Properties

Inverse sine	$y = \sin^{-1} x$ if and only if $x = \sin y$
Inverse cosine	$y = \cos^{-1} x$ if and only if $x = \cos y$
Inverse tangent	$y = \tan^{-1} x$ if and only if $x = \tan y$
Law of Sines	$\frac{\sin A}{a} = \frac{\sin B}{b} = \frac{\sin C}{c}$
Law of Cosines	$a^2 = b^2 + c^2 - 2bc\cos A$ $\quad b^2 = a^2 + c^2 - 2ac\cos B$ $\quad c^2 = a^2 + b^2 - 2ab\cos C$
DeMoivre's Theorem	Let $z = r\cos\theta + (r\sin\theta)i$ and n be a positive integer. $\quad z^n = r^n\cos(n\theta) + (r^n\sin(n\theta))i$
Magnitude of a Vector in the Plane	$\lVert\overrightarrow{PQ}\rVert = \sqrt{(x_2 - x_1)^2 + (y_2 - y_1)^2}$
Angle Between Two Vectors	$\mathbf{u} \cdot \mathbf{v} = \lVert\mathbf{u}\rVert\,\lVert\mathbf{v}\rVert\cos\theta$
Dot Product of Two Vectors	$\mathbf{u} \cdot \mathbf{v} = x_1x_2 + y_1y_2$

Identities

Reciprocal Identities

$\sin\theta = \dfrac{1}{\csc\theta}$	$\cos\theta = \dfrac{1}{\sec\theta}$	$\tan\theta = \dfrac{1}{\cot\theta}$
$\csc\theta = \dfrac{1}{\sin\theta}$	$\sec\theta = \dfrac{1}{\cos\theta}$	$\cot\theta = \dfrac{1}{\tan\theta}$

Quotient Identities

$\tan\theta = \dfrac{\sin\theta}{\cos\theta}$	$\cot\theta = \dfrac{\cos\theta}{\sin\theta}$	

Negative Identities

$\sin(-\theta) = -\sin\theta$	$\cos(-\theta) = \cos\theta$	$\tan(-\theta) = -\tan\theta$
$\csc(-\theta) = -\csc\theta$	$\sec(-\theta) = \sec\theta$	$\cot(-\theta) = -\cot\theta$

Pythagorean Identities

$\cos^2\theta + \sin^2\theta = 1$	$\tan^2\theta + 1 = \sec^2\theta$	$\cot^2\theta + 1 = \csc^2\theta$
$\sin\theta = \pm\sqrt{1 - \cos^2\theta}$	$\sec\theta = \pm\sqrt{1 + \tan^2\theta}$	$\csc\theta = \pm\sqrt{1 + \cot^2\theta}$

Cofunction Identities

$\sin\theta = \cos(90° - \theta)$	$\tan\theta = \cot(90° - \theta)$	$\sec\theta = \csc(90° - \theta)$
$\cos\theta = \sin(90° - \theta)$	$\cot\theta = \tan(90° - \theta)$	$\csc\theta = \sec(90° - \theta)$

Coterminal Identities

$\sin\theta = \sin(360° + \theta)$	$\cos\theta = \cos(360° + \theta)$	$\tan\theta = \tan(360° + \theta)$
$\csc\theta = \csc(360° + \theta)$	$\sec\theta = \sec(360° + \theta)$	$\cot\theta = \cot(360° + \theta)$

Sum and Difference Identities

$\sin(\alpha + \beta) = \sin\alpha\cos\beta + \cos\alpha\sin\beta$	$\sin(\alpha - \beta) = \sin\alpha\cos\beta - \cos\alpha\sin\beta$
$\cos(\alpha + \beta) = \cos\alpha\cos\beta - \sin\alpha\sin\beta$	$\cos(\alpha - \beta) = \cos\alpha\cos\beta + \sin\alpha\sin\beta$
$\tan(\alpha + \beta) = \dfrac{\tan\alpha + \tan\beta}{1 - \tan\alpha\tan\beta}$	$\tan(\alpha - \beta) = \dfrac{\tan\alpha - \tan\beta}{1 + \tan\alpha\tan\beta}$

Double-Angle Identities

$\sin 2\alpha = 2\sin\alpha\cos\alpha$	$\cos 2\alpha = \cos^2\alpha - \sin^2\alpha$ $\cos 2\alpha = 1 - 2\sin^2\alpha$ $\cos 2\alpha = 2\cos^2\alpha - 1$
$\tan 2\alpha = \dfrac{2\tan\alpha}{1 - \tan^2\alpha}$	

Identities (continued)

Half-Angle Identities

$\sin\dfrac{\alpha}{2} = \pm\sqrt{\dfrac{1 - \cos\alpha}{2}}$
$\cos\dfrac{\alpha}{2} = \pm\sqrt{\dfrac{1 + \cos\alpha}{2}}$
$\tan\dfrac{\alpha}{2} = \pm\sqrt{\dfrac{1 - \cos\alpha}{1 + \cos\alpha}}$, $\cos\alpha \neq -1$
$\tan\dfrac{\alpha}{2} = \dfrac{1 - \cos\alpha}{\sin\alpha}$, $\sin\alpha \neq 0$
$\tan\dfrac{\alpha}{2} = \dfrac{\sin\alpha}{1 + \cos\alpha}$, $\cos\alpha \neq -1$

Product-to-Sum Identities

$\cos\alpha\cos\beta = \frac{1}{2}[\cos(\alpha - \beta) + \cos(\alpha + \beta)]$
$\sin\alpha\cos\beta = \frac{1}{2}[\sin(\alpha + \beta) + \sin(\alpha - \beta)]$
$\sin\alpha\sin\beta = \frac{1}{2}[\cos(\alpha - \beta) - \cos(\alpha + \beta)]$
$\cos\alpha\sin\beta = \frac{1}{2}[\sin(\alpha + \beta) - \sin(\alpha - \beta)]$

Sum-to-Product Identities

$\sin x + \sin y = 2\sin\left(\dfrac{x+y}{2}\right)\cos\left(\dfrac{x-y}{2}\right)$
$\cos x + \cos y = 2\cos\left(\dfrac{x+y}{2}\right)\cos\left(\dfrac{x-y}{2}\right)$
$\sin x - \sin y = 2\cos\left(\dfrac{x+y}{2}\right)\sin\left(\dfrac{x-y}{2}\right)$
$\cos x - \cos y = -2\sin\left(\dfrac{x+y}{2}\right)\sin\left(\dfrac{x-y}{2}\right)$

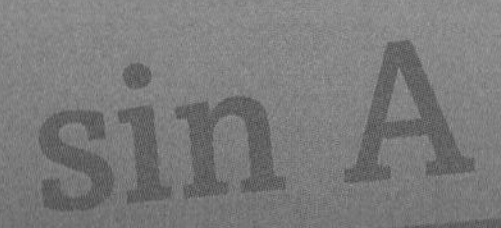

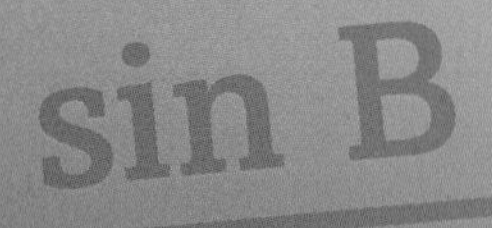

Trigonometric Functions

Angle	Radians	Sine	Cosine	Tangent	Cotangent	Secant	Cosecant		
0°	0.0000	0.0000	1.0000	0.0000	undefined	1.0000	undefined	1.5708	**90°**
1	0.0175	0.0175	0.9998	0.0175	57.2900	1.0002	57.2987	1.5533	**89**
2	0.0349	0.0349	0.9994	0.0349	28.6363	1.0006	28.6537	1.5359	**88**
3	0.0524	0.0523	0.9986	0.0524	19.0811	1.0014	19.1073	1.5184	**87**
4	0.0698	0.0698	0.9976	0.0699	14.3007	1.0024	14.3356	1.5010	**86**
5	0.0873	0.0872	0.9962	0.0875	11.4301	1.0038	11.4737	1.4835	**85**
6	0.1047	0.1045	0.9945	0.1051	9.5144	1.0055	9.5668	1.4661	**84**
7	0.1222	0.1219	0.9925	0.1228	8.1443	1.0075	8.2055	1.4486	**83**
8	0.1396	0.1392	0.9903	0.1405	7.1154	1.0098	7.1853	1.4312	**82**
9	0.1571	0.1564	0.9877	0.1584	6.3138	1.0125	6.3925	1.4137	**81**
10	0.1745	0.1736	0.9848	0.1763	5.6713	1.0154	5.7588	1.3963	**80**
11	0.1920	0.1908	0.9816	0.1944	5.1446	1.0187	5.2408	1.3788	**79**
12	0.2094	0.2079	0.9781	0.2126	4.7046	1.0223	4.8097	1.3614	**78**
13	0.2269	0.2250	0.9744	0.2309	4.3315	1.0263	4.4454	1.3439	**77**
14	0.2443	0.2419	0.9703	0.2493	4.0108	1.0306	4.1336	1.3265	**76**
15	0.2618	0.2588	0.9659	0.2679	3.7321	1.0353	3.8637	1.3090	**75**
16	0.2793	0.2756	0.9613	0.2867	3.4874	1.0403	3.6280	1.2915	**74**
17	0.2967	0.2924	0.9563	0.3057	3.2709	1.0457	3.4203	1.2714	**73**
18	0.3142	0.3090	0.9511	0.3249	3.0777	1.0515	3.2361	1.2566	**72**
19	0.3316	0.3256	0.9455	0.3443	2.9042	1.0576	3.0716	1.2392	**71**
20	0.3491	0.3420	0.9397	0.3640	2.7475	1.0642	2.9238	1.2217	**70**
21	0.3665	0.3584	0.9336	0.3839	2.6051	1.0711	2.7904	1.2043	**69**
22	0.3840	0.3746	0.9272	0.4040	2.4751	1.0785	2.6695	1.1868	**68**
23	0.4014	0.3907	0.9205	0.4245	2.3559	1.0864	2.5593	1.1694	**67**
24	0.4189	0.4067	0.9135	0.4452	2.2460	1.0946	2.4586	1.1519	**66**
25	0.4363	0.4226	0.9063	0.4663	2.1445	1.1034	2.3662	1.1345	**65**
26	0.4538	0.4384	0.8988	0.4877	2.0503	1.1126	2.2812	1.1170	**64**
27	0.4712	0.4540	0.8910	0.5095	1.9626	1.1223	2.2027	1.0996	**63**
28	0.4887	0.4695	0.8829	0.5317	1.8807	1.1326	2.1301	1.0821	**62**
29	0.5061	0.4848	0.8746	0.5543	1.8040	1.1434	2.0627	1.0647	**61**
30	0.5236	0.5000	0.8660	0.5774	1.7321	1.1547	2.0000	1.0472	**60**
31	0.5411	0.5150	0.8572	0.6009	1.6643	1.1666	1.9416	1.0297	**59**
32	0.5585	0.5299	0.8480	0.6249	1.6003	1.1792	1.8871	1.0123	**58**
33	0.5760	0.5446	0.8387	0.6494	1.5399	1.1924	1.8361	0.9948	**57**
34	0.5934	0.5592	0.8290	0.6745	1.4826	1.2062	1.7883	0.9774	**56**
35	0.6109	0.5736	0.8192	0.7002	1.4281	1.2208	1.7434	0.9599	**55**
36	0.6283	0.5878	0.8090	0.7265	1.3764	1.2361	1.7013	0.9425	**54**
37	0.6458	0.6018	0.7986	0.7536	1.3270	1.2521	1.6616	0.9250	**53**
38	0.6632	0.6157	0.7880	0.7813	1.2799	1.2690	1.6243	0.9076	**52**
39	0.6807	0.6293	0.7771	0.8098	1.2349	1.2868	1.5890	0.8901	**51**
40	0.6981	0.6428	0.7660	0.8391	1.1918	1.3054	1.5557	0.8727	**50**
41	0.7156	0.6561	0.7547	0.8693	1.1504	1.3250	1.5243	0.8552	**49**
42	0.7330	0.6691	0.7431	0.9004	1.1106	1.3456	1.4945	0.8378	**48**
43	0.7505	0.6820	0.7314	0.9325	1.0724	1.3673	1.4663	0.8203	**47**
44	0.7679	0.6947	0.7093	0.9657	1.0355	1.3902	1.4396	0.8029	**46**
45°	0.7854	0.7071	0.7071	1.0000	1.0000	1.4142	1.4142	0.7854	**45°**
		Cosine	**Sine**	**Cotangent**	**Tangent**	**Cosecant**	**Secant**	**Radians**	**Angle**

Parent Functions

Sine

$y = \sin x$

period $= 2\pi$; amplitude $= 1$

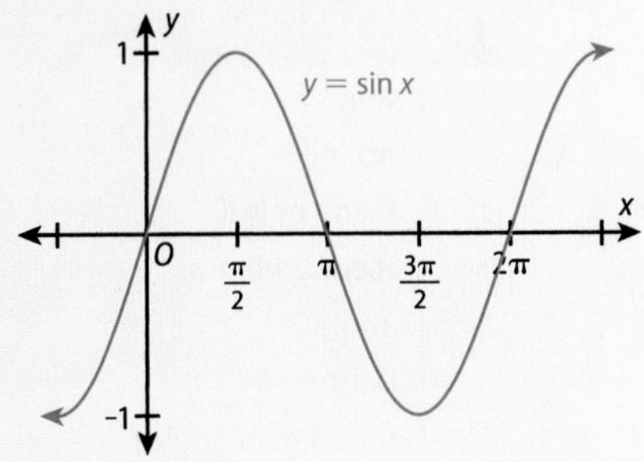

Cosine

$y = \cos x$

period $= 2\pi$; amplitude $= 1$

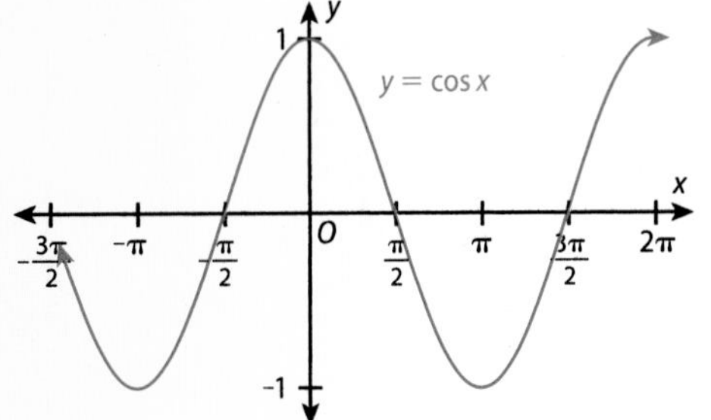

Tangent

$y = \tan x$

period $= \pi$; asymptotes: $x = \frac{\pi}{2} + k\pi$

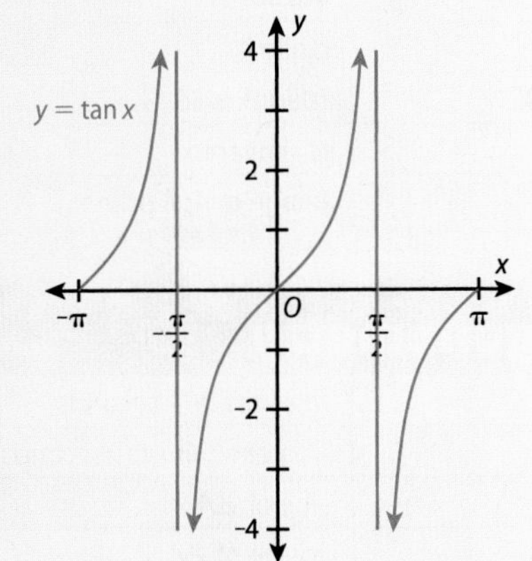

Cotangent

$y = \cot x$

period $= \pi$; asymptotes: $x = k\pi$

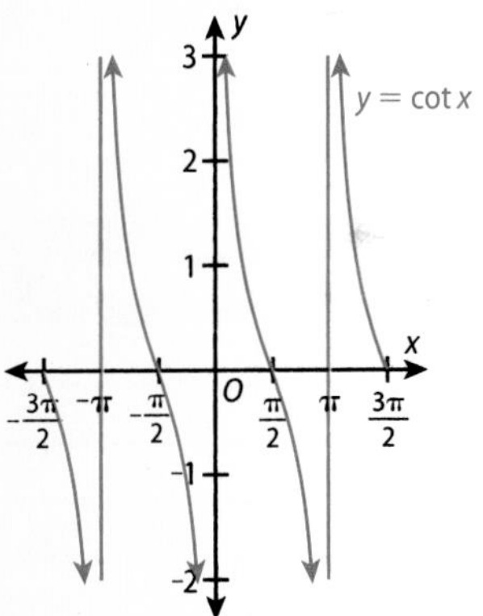

Secant

$y = \sec x$

period $= \pi$; asymptotes: $x = \frac{\pi}{2} + k\pi$

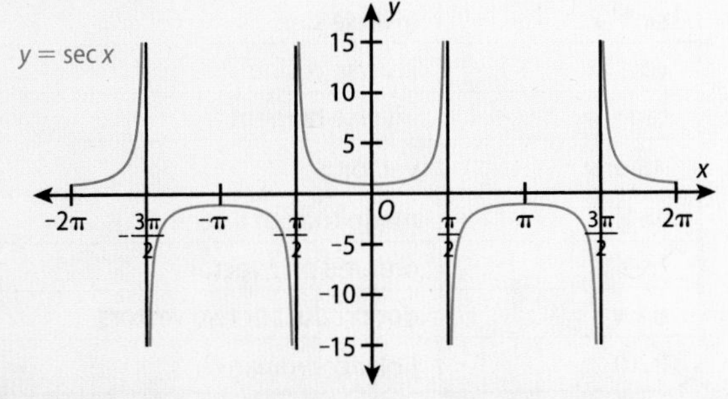

Cosecant

$y = \csc x$

period $= \pi$; asymptotes: $x = k\pi$

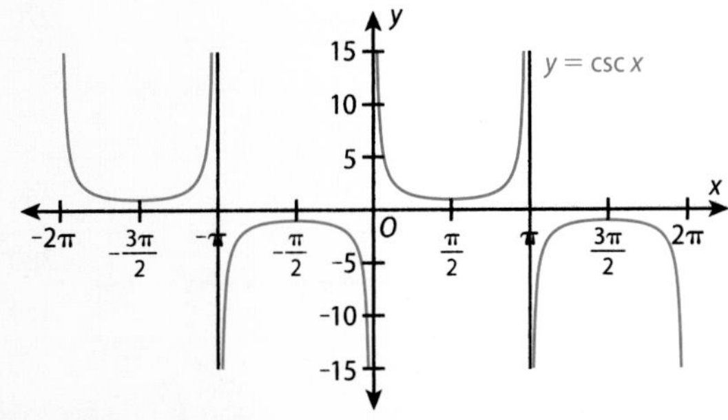

Symbols

Foundations of Mathematics

$>$	is greater than	46
$<$	is less than	46
$=$	is equal to	46
$°$	degrees of an angle	50
$+$	addition	56
$-$	subtraction	62
$\times$	multiplication	68
$\div$	division	74
$\overline{)}$	division	76
10^2	exponent; power of ten	94
$3 \cdot 4; 3(4)$	multiplication	96
$\parallel$	is parallel to	129
$\perp$	is perpendicular to	130
$\overline{AB}$	line segment *AB*	132
AB	length of $\overline{AB}$	132
$\overleftrightarrow{AB}$	line *AB*	132
$\overrightarrow{AB}$	ray *AB*	133
$\angle A$	angle *A*	136
$°$	degrees	137
⌝	right angle symbol	156
$\vert$	tally mark	182
%	percent	196

Numbers and Operations

$\cdot$	decimal point	216
$>$	greater than	222
$<$	less than	222
$=$	equal to	222
R	real numbers	268
Q	rational numbers	268
Z	integers numbers	268
W	whole numbers	268
N	natural numbers	268
$\sqrt{4}$	square root	268
$0.\overline{3}$	repeating decimal; 0.33 . . .	270
3^4	exponent	294
$\frac{1}{a}$	reciprocal	346
$a:b, \frac{a}{b}$	ratio	364
%	percent	380
$\ldots$	and so on	434

Measurement

°F	degrees Fahrenheit	496
°C	degrees Celsius	518
π	pi; $\frac{22}{7}$, about 3.14	544
$\approx$	is approximately equal to	544

Geometry

$\rightarrow$	maps into	612, 834
$\sim p$	not *p*	614
$\leftrightarrow$	if and only if	616
$\cong$	is congruent to	621
$\angle$	angle	621
$°$	degrees	624
$m\angle C$	measure of angle *C*	629
$\parallel$	is parallel to	630
$\overleftrightarrow{AB}$	line *AB*	630
$\perp$	is perpendicular to	633
$\overline{AB}; AB$	line segment *AB*; length of $\overline{AB}$	639
$\overset{\frown}{AB}$	arc *AB*	728
$\odot A$	circle *A*	729
$\triangle ABC$	triangle *ABC*	734
$\sim$	is similar to	790
A'	image of *A*; *A* prime	834

Trigonometry

$'$ $''$	minutes seconds	896
DMS	degrees/minutes/seconds	896
$\sin A$	sine of $\angle A$	902
$\cos A$	cosine of $\angle A$	902
$\tan A$	tangent of $\angle A$	902
θ	theta (angle measure)	903
$\csc A$	cosecant of $\angle A$	904
$\sec A$	secant of $\angle A$	904
$\cot A$	cotangent of $\angle A$	904
$\sin^{-1} x$	inverse sine	915
$\cos^{-1} x$	inverse cosine	915
$\tan^{-1} x$	inverse tangent	915
$\overrightarrow{AB}$ or $\mathbf{v}$	vector	1066
$\Vert\mathbf{a}\Vert$	magnitude of a vector	1066
$\langle x, y \rangle$	ordered pair vector	1070
$\mathbf{u} \cdot \mathbf{v}$	dot product of two vectors	1082
(r, θ)	polar coordinates	1093

Statistics and Probability

P(event)	probability of the event	1232
$n!$	factorial	1245
${}_nP_r$	permutations	1246
${}_nC_r$	combinations	1249
|	tally mark	1260
2 | 6	stem-and-leaf plot key	1276
$\in$	element of a set	1290
$\subset$	subset	1290
$\cap$	intersection of a set	1291
$\cup$	union of a set	1291
~	complement of a set	1291
$\bar{x}$	mean of a set	1324
Σ	sigma: summation	1324
σ	lowercase sigma	1324
μ	mu: mean	1340
$\ddot{p}$	sample proportion	1350
z_c	*z*-score	1350
$P(B \mid A)$	probability of event *B* given event *A*	1360

Algebra

$\|a\|$	absolute value of *a*	1387
$-x$	opposite of *x*	1387
a^b	a = base; b = exponent	1394
$\sqrt{a}$	principal square root	1400
$\pm$	plus or minus	1400
{1, 2, . . .}	set notation	1402
( ), [ ]	for grouping	1419
x	variable or input	1422
x_1, x_2, y_1, y_2	specific values of a variable	1429
(x, y)	ordered pair	1436
y	output variable	1437
$f(x)$	"*f* of *x*", function value at *x*	1450
$=$	is equal to	1458
$\neq$	is not equal to	1458
$\stackrel{?}{=}$	does it equal?	1459
$<$	is less than	1492
$>$	is greater than	1492
$\leq$	is less than or equal to	1492
$\geq$	is greater than or equal to	1492
m	slope	1542
b	*y*-intercept	1542
i	imaginary number, $\sqrt{-1}$	1641

Advanced Algebra

(x, y, z)	ordered triple	1754
$m \times n$	matrix, *m* rows, *n* columns	1772
$\begin{bmatrix} a & b \\ c & d \end{bmatrix}$	matrix	1772
det (M)	determinant	1794
A^{-1}	inverse of matrix *a*	1798
a_n	general term of sequence	1862
S_n	partial sum of sequence	1863
$\sum_{n=1}^{3}$	summation	1864
i	imaginary unit, $\sqrt{-1}$	1894
$a + bi$	complex number	1896
e	eccentricity	1940
$\sqrt[n]{a}$	principal *n*th root	1954
a^n	*n*th power of *a*	1966
a^{-n}	$\frac{1}{a^n}$	1966
$a^{\frac{1}{n}}$	$\sqrt[n]{a}$	1967
$\log b$	common logarithm, base 10	1974
$\ln x$	natural logarithm, $\log_e x$	1975, 2004
e	base for natural log; ≈ 2.718	1975, 2004
$\log_b x$	logarithm of *x*, base *b*	2006
$(a, b], [a, b)$	interval notation	2014
$(f \circ g)(x)$	composition, $f(g(x))$	2063
$f^{-1}(x)$	inverse of a function	2090

Calculus

$\lim_{x \to c} f(x)$	limit	2110
δ, ε	Greek delta, Greek epsilon	2112
$[x]$	greatest integer function	2132
DNE	does not exist	2132
$\infty, -\infty$	infinity, negative infinity	2136
$\therefore$	therefore	2146
$[0, \pi)$	half open interval	2151
Δx	change in *x*	2158
$f'(x)$	derivative of *f*	2159
$\left.\frac{dy}{dx}\right\|_c$	derivative at point *c*	2177
$f''(x)$	second derivative of *f*	2184
$f^{(n)}(x)$	*n*th derivative of *f*	2184
$\int f(x)dx$	integral	2234
$\int_a^b f(x)dx$	definite interval	2246
$F(x)\|_a^b$	endpoints of an interval	2246

Foundations of Mathematics

Basic Addition Facts

+	0	1	2	3	4	5	6	7	8	9	10
0	0	1	2	3	4	5	6	7	8	9	10
1	1	2	3	4	5	6	7	8	9	10	11
2	2	3	4	5	6	7	8	9	10	11	12
3	3	4	5	6	7	8	9	10	11	12	13
4	4	5	6	7	8	9	10	11	12	13	14
5	5	6	7	8	9	10	11	12	13	14	15
6	6	7	8	9	10	11	12	13	14	15	16
7	7	8	9	10	11	12	13	14	15	16	17
8	8	9	10	11	12	13	14	15	16	17	18
9	9	10	11	12	13	14	15	16	17	18	19
10	10	11	12	13	14	15	16	17	18	19	20

Basic Subtraction Facts

−	0	1	2	3	4	5	6	7	8	9	10
0	0										
1	1	0									
2	2	1	0								
3	3	2	1	0							
4	4	3	2	1	0						
5	5	4	3	2	1	0					
6	6	5	4	3	2	1	0				
7	7	6	5	4	3	2	1	0			
8	8	7	6	5	4	3	2	1	0		
9	9	8	7	6	5	4	3	2	1	0	
10	10	9	8	7	6	5	4	3	2	1	0

Basic Addition Facts

0+0=0	1+0=1	2+0=2	3+0=3	4+0=4	5+0=5	6+0=6	7+0=7	8+0=8	9+0=0	10+0=10
0+1=1	1+1=2	2+1=3	3+1=4	4+1=5	5+1=6	6+1=7	7+1=8	8+1=9	9+1=10	10+1=11
0+2=2	1+2=3	2+2=4	3+2=5	4+2=6	5+2=7	6+2=8	7+2=9	8+2=10	9+2=11	10+2=12
0+3=3	1+3=4	2+3=5	3+3=6	4+3=7	5+3=8	6+3=9	7+3=10	8+3=11	9+3=12	10+3=13
0+4=4	1+4=5	2+4=6	3+4=7	4+4=8	5+4=9	6+4=10	7+4=11	8+4=12	9+4=13	10+4=14
0+5=5	1+5=6	2+5=7	3+5=8	4+5=9	5+5=10	6+5=11	7+5=12	8+5=13	9+5=14	10+5=15
0+6=6	1+6=7	2+6=8	3+6=9	4+6=10	5+6=11	6+6=12	7+6=13	8+6=14	9+6=15	10+6=16
0+7=7	1+7=8	2+7=9	3+7=10	4+7=11	5+7=12	6+7=13	7+7=14	8+7=15	9+7=16	10+7=17
0+8=8	1+8=9	2+8=10	3+8=11	4+8=12	5+8=13	6+8=14	7+8=15	8+8=16	9+8=17	10+8=18
0+9=9	1+9=10	2+9=11	3+9=12	4+9=13	5+9=14	6+9=15	7+9=16	8+9=17	9+9=18	10+9=19
0+10=10	1+10=11	2+10=12	3+10=13	4+10=14	5+10=15	6+10=16	7+10=17	8+10=18	9+10=19	10+10=20

Basic Subtraction Facts

0−0=0										
1−0=1	1−1=0									
2−0=2	2−1=1	2−2=0								
3−0=3	3−1=2	3−2=1	3−3=0							
4−0=4	4−1=3	4−2=2	4−3=1	4−4=0						
5−0=5	5−1=4	5−2=3	5−3=2	5−4=1	5−5=0					
6−0=6	6−1=5	6−2=4	6−3=3	6−4=2	6−5=1	6−6=0				
7−0=7	7−1=6	7−2=5	7−3=4	7−4=3	7−5=2	7−6=1	7−7=0			
8−0=8	8−1=7	8−2=6	8−3=5	8−4=4	8−5=3	8−6=2	8−7=1	8−8=0		
9−0=9	9−1=8	9−2=7	9−3=6	9−4=5	9−5=4	9−6=3	9−7=2	9−8=1	9−9=0	
10−0=10	10−1=9	10−2=8	10−3=7	10−4=6	10−5=5	10−6=4	10−7=3	10−8=2	10−9=1	10−10=0

Basic Multiplication Facts

×	0	1	2	3	4	5	6	7	8	9	10
0	0	0	0	0	0	0	0	0	0	0	0
1	0	1	2	3	4	5	6	7	8	9	10
2	0	2	4	6	8	10	12	14	16	18	20
3	0	3	6	9	12	15	18	21	24	27	30
4	0	4	8	12	16	20	24	28	32	36	40
5	0	5	10	15	20	25	30	35	40	45	50
6	0	6	12	18	24	30	36	42	48	54	60
7	0	7	14	21	28	35	42	49	56	63	70
8	0	8	16	24	32	40	48	56	64	72	80
9	0	9	18	27	36	45	54	63	72	81	90
10	0	10	20	30	40	50	60	70	80	90	100

Basic Division Facts

÷	1	2	3	4	5	6	7	8	9	10
1	1	2	3	4	5	6	7	8	9	10
2	2	4	6	8	10	12	14	16	18	20
3	3	6	9	12	15	18	21	24	27	30
4	4	8	12	16	20	24	28	32	36	40
5	5	10	15	20	25	30	35	40	45	50
6	6	12	18	24	30	36	42	48	54	60
7	7	14	21	28	35	42	49	56	63	70
8	8	16	24	32	40	48	56	64	72	80
9	9	18	27	36	45	54	63	72	81	90
10	10	20	30	40	50	60	70	80	90	100

Basic Multiplication Facts

zeros	0 × 0 = 0	1 × 0 = 0	2 × 0 = 0	3 × 0 = 0	4 × 0 = 0	5 × 0 = 0	6 × 0 = 0	7 × 0 = 0	8 × 0 = 0	9 × 0 = 0	10 × 0 = 0
ones	0 × 1 = 0	1 × 1 = 1	2 × 1 = 2	3 × 1 = 3	4 × 1 = 4	5 × 1 = 5	6 × 1 = 6	7 × 1 = 7	8 × 1 = 8	9 × 1 = 9	10 × 1 = 10
twos	0 × 2 = 0	1 × 2 = 2	2 × 2 = 4	3 × 2 = 6	4 × 2 = 8	5 × 2 = 10	6 × 2 = 12	7 × 2 = 14	8 × 2 = 16	9 × 2 = 18	10 × 2 = 20
threes	0 × 3 = 0	1 × 3 = 3	2 × 3 = 6	3 × 3 = 9	4 × 3 = 12	5 × 3 = 15	6 × 3 = 18	7 × 3 = 21	8 × 3 = 24	9 × 3 = 27	10 × 3 = 30
fours	0 × 4 = 0	1 × 4 = 4	2 × 4 = 8	3 × 4 = 12	4 × 4 = 16	5 × 4 = 20	6 × 4 = 24	7 × 4 = 28	8 × 4 = 32	9 × 4 = 36	10 × 4 = 40
fives	0 × 5 = 0	1 × 5 = 5	2 × 5 = 10	3 × 5 = 15	4 × 5 = 20	5 × 5 = 25	6 × 5 = 30	7 × 5 = 35	8 × 5 = 40	9 × 5 = 45	10 × 5 = 50
sixes	0 × 6 = 0	1 × 6 = 6	2 × 6 = 12	3 × 6 = 18	4 × 6 = 24	5 × 6 = 30	6 × 6 = 36	7 × 6 = 42	8 × 6 = 48	9 × 6 = 54	10 × 6 = 60
sevens	0 × 7 = 0	1 × 7 = 7	2 × 7 = 14	3 × 7 = 21	4 × 7 = 28	5 × 7 = 35	6 × 7 = 42	7 × 7 = 49	8 × 7 = 56	9 × 7 = 63	10 × 7 = 70
eights	0 × 8 = 0	1 × 8 = 8	2 × 8 = 16	3 × 8 = 24	4 × 8 = 32	5 × 8 = 40	6 × 8 = 48	7 × 8 = 56	8 × 8 = 64	9 × 8 = 72	10 × 8 = 80
nines	0 × 9 = 0	1 × 9 = 9	2 × 9 = 18	3 × 9 = 27	4 × 9 = 36	5 × 9 = 45	6 × 9 = 54	7 × 9 = 63	8 × 9 = 72	9 × 9 = 81	10 × 9 = 90
tens	0 × 10 = 0	1 × 10 = 10	2 × 10 = 20	3 × 10 = 30	4 × 10 = 40	5 × 10 = 50	6 × 10 = 60	7 × 10 = 70	8 × 10 = 80	9 × 10 = 90	10 × 10 = 100

Basic Division Facts

ones	0 ÷ 1 = 0	1 ÷ 1 = 1	2 ÷ 1 = 2	3 ÷ 1 = 3	4 ÷ 1 = 4	5 ÷ 1 = 5	6 ÷ 1 = 6	7 ÷ 1 = 7	8 ÷ 1 = 8	9 ÷ 1 = 9	10 ÷ 1 = 10
twos	0 ÷ 2 = 0	2 ÷ 2 = 1	4 ÷ 2 = 2	6 ÷ 2 = 3	8 ÷ 2 = 4	10 ÷ 2 = 5	12 ÷ 2 = 6	14 ÷ 2 = 7	16 ÷ 2 = 8	18 ÷ 2 = 9	20 ÷ 2 = 10
threes	0 ÷ 3 = 0	3 ÷ 3 = 1	6 ÷ 3 = 2	9 ÷ 3 = 3	12 ÷ 3 = 4	15 ÷ 3 = 5	18 ÷ 3 = 6	21 ÷ 3 = 7	24 ÷ 3 = 8	27 ÷ 3 = 9	30 ÷ 3 = 10
fours	0 ÷ 4 = 0	4 ÷ 4 = 1	8 ÷ 4 = 2	12 ÷ 4 = 3	16 ÷ 4 = 4	20 ÷ 4 = 5	24 ÷ 4 = 6	28 ÷ 4 = 7	32 ÷ 4 = 8	36 ÷ 4 = 9	40 ÷ 4 = 10
fives	0 ÷ 5 = 0	5 ÷ 5 = 1	10 ÷ 5 = 2	15 ÷ 5 = 3	20 ÷ 5 = 4	25 ÷ 5 = 5	30 ÷ 5 = 6	35 ÷ 5 = 7	40 ÷ 5 = 8	45 ÷ 5 = 9	50 ÷ 5 = 10
sixes	0 ÷ 6 = 0	6 ÷ 6 = 1	12 ÷ 6 = 2	18 ÷ 6 = 3	24 ÷ 6 = 4	30 ÷ 6 = 5	36 ÷ 6 = 6	42 ÷ 6 = 7	48 ÷ 6 = 8	54 ÷ 6 = 9	60 ÷ 6 = 10
sevens	0 ÷ 7 = 0	7 ÷ 7 = 1	14 ÷ 7 = 2	21 ÷ 7 = 3	28 ÷ 7 = 4	35 ÷ 7 = 5	42 ÷ 7 = 6	49 ÷ 7 = 7	56 ÷ 7 = 8	63 ÷ 7 = 9	70 ÷ 7 = 10
eights	0 ÷ 8 = 0	8 ÷ 8 = 1	16 ÷ 8 = 2	24 ÷ 8 = 3	32 ÷ 8 = 4	40 ÷ 8 = 5	48 ÷ 8 = 6	56 ÷ 8 = 7	64 ÷ 8 = 8	72 ÷ 8 = 9	80 ÷ 8 = 10
nines	0 ÷ 9 = 0	9 ÷ 9 = 1	18 ÷ 9 = 2	27 ÷ 9 = 3	36 ÷ 9 = 4	45 ÷ 9 = 5	54 ÷ 9 = 6	63 ÷ 9 = 7	72 ÷ 9 = 8	81 ÷ 9 = 9	90 ÷ 9 = 10
tens	0 ÷ 10 = 0	10 ÷ 10 = 1	20 ÷ 10 = 2	30 ÷ 10 = 3	40 ÷ 10 = 4	50 ÷ 10 = 5	60 ÷ 10 = 6	70 ÷ 10 = 7	80 ÷ 10 = 8	90 ÷ 10 = 9	100 ÷ 10 = 10

Foundations of Mathematics

Place Value

	Billions			Millions			Thousands			Ones		
	hundred billions	ten billions	billions	hundred millions	ten millions	millions	hundred thousands	ten thousands	thousands	hundreds	tens	ones
	2	3	6,	9	1	7,	4	0	5,	3	8	9

Forms of a Number

Standard form	236,917,405,389
Expanded form	200,000,000,000 + 30,000,000,000 + 6,000,000,000 + 900,000,000 + 10,000,000 + 7,000,000 + 400,000 + 5,000 + 300 + 80 + 9
Word form	two hundred thirty-six billion, nine hundred seventeen million, four hundred five thousand, three hundred eighty-nine
Short word form	236 billion, 917 million, 405 thousand, 389

Hints on Memorizing Facts

1. Focus on the ways to memorize facts that are listed on the next page.
2. Memorize the facts by saying the facts aloud.
   - For $3 + 8$, say "Three plus eight equals eleven."
   - For $8 - 3$, say "Eight minus three equals five."
   - For 8×7, say "Eight times seven equals fifty-six."
   - For $56 \div 8$, say "Fifty-six divided by eight equals seven."
3. Memorize a few facts at a time. Work on 2 or 3 facts per day. Start with the easier facts.
4. Practice saying the facts in reverse order, so you don't have to memorize so many facts.
   $8 + 5 = 13, 5 + 8 = 13$ $\quad$ $9 - 4 = 5, 9 - 5 = 4$
5. Memorize one set of times tables at a time. Work on the set until you have mastered it. Then move to another set.
6. Use the relationship of multiplication to division. To remember $10 \div 2 = 5$, think $5 \cdot 2 = 10$.
7. Play fact games.
   - Toss two dice and add the dots that come up. Then have a friend toss two dice and add the dots. Then subtract the smaller sum from the larger sum.
   - Play multiplication facts bingo with some friends.
   - Play "Beat the Clock."
8. Make flash cards and use them on your own or with friends and family. Time how long it takes you to say a set of facts. Try this again the next day and see if you can beat your previous time.
9. Every day, review the facts you know or usually know. Then work on two new facts and play games to practice them.
10. Use a calculator. Enter the fact. Before you press ENTER, say the answer. Then press ENTER to see if you are correct.

Go For It!

Addition Facts: Memorize Fewer Than 121 Facts

There are 121 basic facts, but here are some ways to cut down the task.

- 0 plus any number is that number.
- 1 plus any number is the next number when you count.
- 2 plus any even number is the next even number.
- 2 plus any odd number is the next odd number.
- 10 plus any one-digit number is a teen number with the 1 in the tens place and the one-digit number in the ones place.
- If you know $2 + 3$, you know $3 + 2$. This takes care of half of the 121 facts.
- Once you memorize the doubles, the near doubles are easy to remember.
- Any number plus 9 is one less than that number plus ten.

Subtraction Facts: Memorize Fewer Than 121 Facts

There are 121 basic facts, but here are some ways to cut down the task.

- Any number minus 0 is itself.
- Any number minus itself is 0.
- Any number minus 1 is the previous counting number.
- Any even number minus 2 is the previous even number.
- Any odd number minus 2 is the previous odd number.
- Any teen number minus 10 is the digit in the ones place of the teen number.
- If you know $8 - 3 = 5$, you also know $8 - 5 = 3$. This takes care of half of the subtraction facts.
- Nine minus any number is one less than 10 minus the same number.

Multiplication Facts: Memorize Fewer Than 121 Facts

There are 121 basic facts, but here are some ways to cut down the task.

- Any number times 0 is 0.
- Any number times 1 is itself.
- Any number times 10 is that number with a zero to its right.
- Any number times 2 is the double of that number. For example, $2 \cdot 3 = 3 + 3$, or 6.
- The product of any number times 5 will always have 0 or 5 in the ones place.
- Four times a number is its double times 2. For example, $4 \cdot 3 = 2(2 \cdot 3) = 2(6) = 12$.
- Flip the numbers. If you know $3 \cdot 7 = 21$, you also know that $7 \cdot 3 = 21$.
- Think "one group more" or "one group less." If you know that $3 \cdot 4 = 12$, you know that $4 \cdot 4 = 12 + 4 = 16$.

Division Facts: Memorize Fewer Than 100 Facts

There are 100 facts to remember. Here are some ways to reduce the number of facts you need to memorize.

- Any number divided by 1 is the number itself.
- Any number divided by itself is 1.
- When a number that ends in zero is divided by 10, the quotient is the number without the zero. For example, $50 \div 10 = 5$.
- Pairs of facts are related. If you know that $15 \div 3 = 5$, then you know that $15 \div 5 = 3$.

Foundations of Mathematics

Data Graphs

Pictographs

A *pictograph* uses pictures or symbols to represent data. You can use a pictograph to compare amounts.

Favorite Type of Music

Classical	● ●
Country	● ● ● ● ●
Rap	● ● ●
Rock	● ● ◖
Other	●

Key: ● = 2 votes

Bar Graphs

A *bar graph* is a type of data display that uses bars to organize information. You can compare the information on a bar graph by comparing the lengths of the bars.

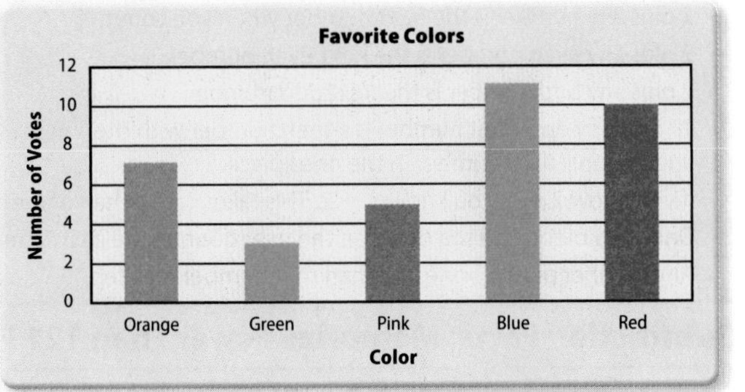

Line Graphs

A *line graph* is a data display that shows information as data points connected by line segments. A line graph usually shows change over time.

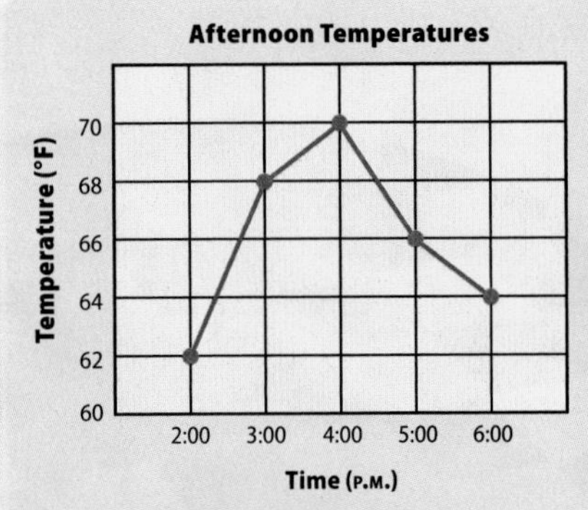

Circle Graphs

A *circle graph* uses sections of a circle to display a set of data as parts of a whole. The whole circle represents 100% of the data.

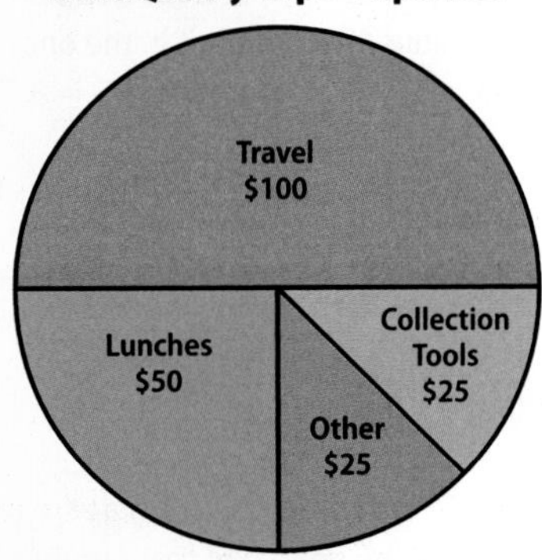

Lines

Points, Lines, Planes

A B a

plane

Line Segment

L M

Ray

V W

Intersecting Lines

Q T S R X

Parallel Lines

L M O P

Perpendicular Lines

right angle symbol

J H I K

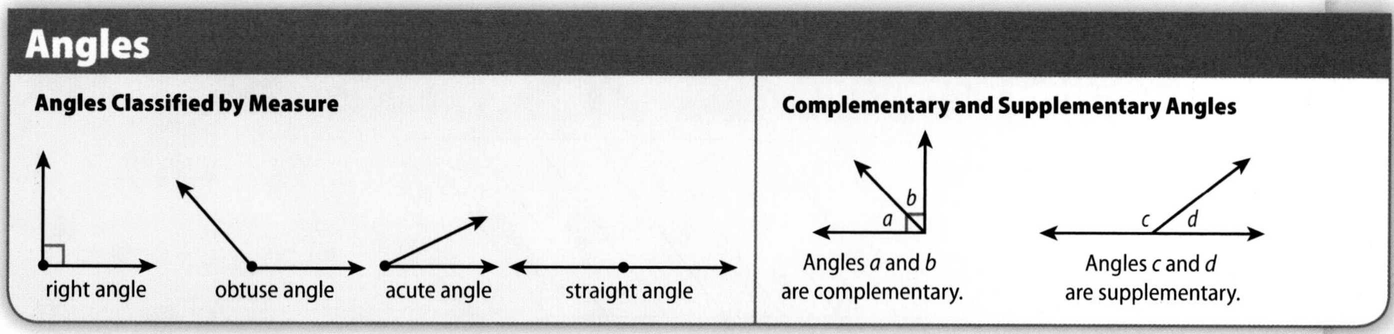

Polygons

Regular Polygons

Triangle

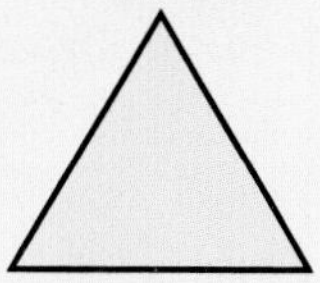

3 sides

Quadrilateral

4 sides

Pentagon

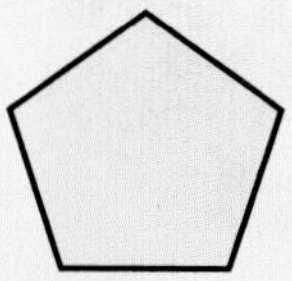

5 sides

Hexagon

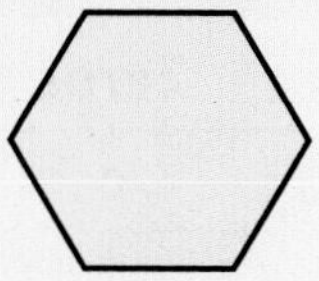

6 sides

Octagon

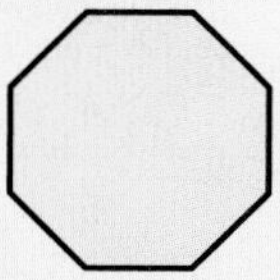

8 sides

Triangles

Equilateral

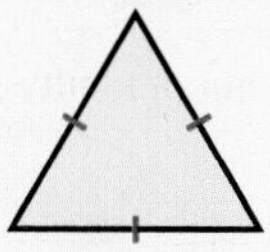

3 equal sides

Isosceles

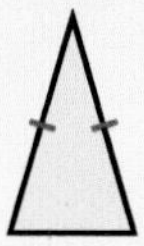

2 equal sides

Scalene

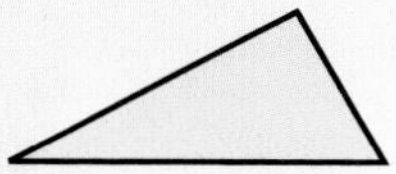

no equal sides

Right

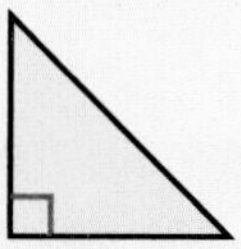

1 right angle

Acute

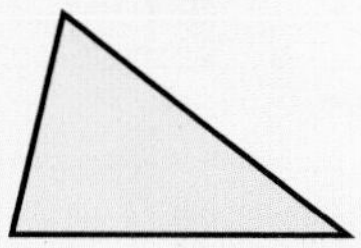

3 acute ($<90°$) angles

Obtuse

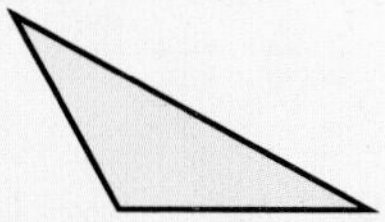

1 obtuse ($>90°$) angle

Quadrilaterals

Trapezoid

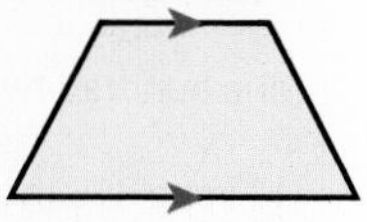

One pair of parallel sides

Parallelogram

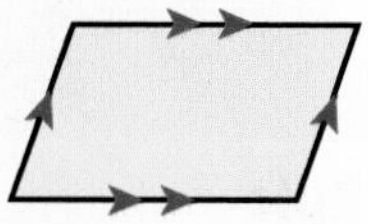

Two pairs of parallel sides

Rhombus

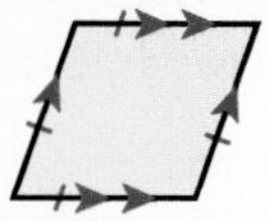

Parallelogram with 4 congruent sides

Rectangle

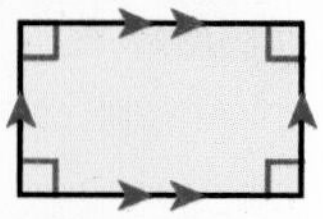

Parallelogram with 4 right angles

Square

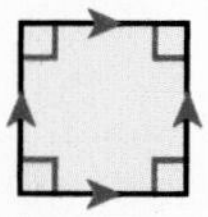

Rectangle with 4 congruent sides

Three-Dimensional Figures

Cube and Prism

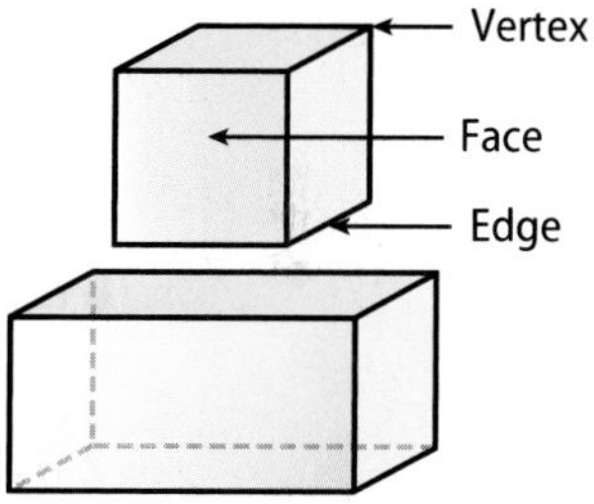

Vertex
Face
Edge

Cylinder

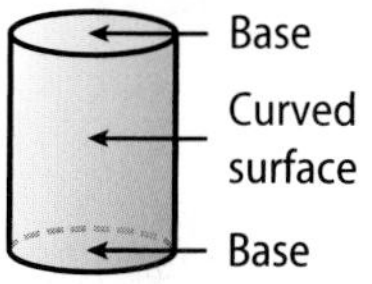

Base
Curved surface
Base

Pyramid

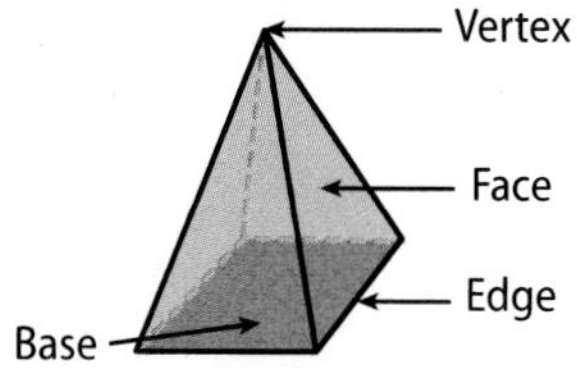

Vertex
Face
Edge
Base

Cone

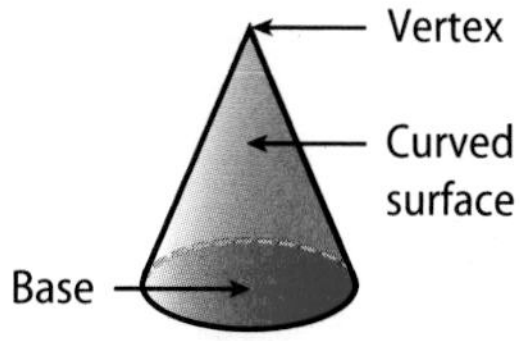

Vertex
Curved surface
Base

Sphere

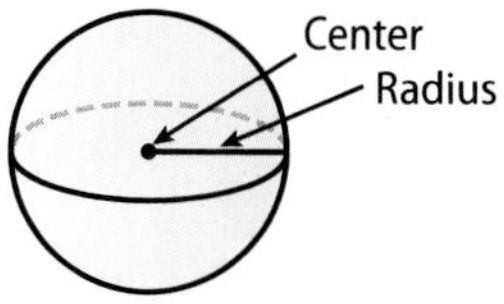

Center
Radius

Numbers and Operations

Decimal Place Value

hundreds	tens	ones		tenths	hundredths	thousandths
1	2	3	.	4	5	6

Forms of a Number

Standard form	123.456
Expanded form	100 + 20 + 3 + 0.4 + 0.05 + 0.006
Word form	one hundred twenty-three and four hundred fifty-six thousandths
Short word form	123 and 456 thousandths
Point form	one twenty-three point four five six

Tests for Divisibility

Divisible by	Rule
2	The digit in the ones place is an even digit: 0, 2, 4, 6, or 8.
3	The sum of the digits is divisible by 3.
4	The number formed by the last two digits is divisible by 4.
5	The digit in the ones place is 0 or 5.
6	The number is divisible by both 2 and 3.
8	The number formed by the last three digits is divisible by 8.
9	The sum of the digits is divisible by 9.
10	The digit in the ones place is 0.

Powers of 10

Power of 10	Value	Zeros
10^0	1	0
10^1	10	1
10^2	100	2
10^3	1,000	3
10^4	10,000	4
10^5	100,000	5
10^6	1,000,000	6
10^7	10,000,000	7

Four-Step Problem Solving Plan

Step 1	**Read**	• Read the problem carefully. You can restate the problem in your own words. • Determine what the problem is asking you to find. • Identify what you know. This is the information given in the problem. • Identify what you need to find out to solve the problem. This is the question asked. You can restate it in your own words.
Step 2	**Plan**	• Plan how to find the answer to the question. • Think about other similar problems you have solved. Think about how the information you know can help you find the answer. • Choose a problem solving strategy.
Step 3	**Solve**	• Solve the problem using your plan. As you work, you can revise your plan if you need to. • Make sure you write a sentence that states your answer.
Step 4	**Check**	• Check your work. • Make sure you have answered the question that was asked. • Make sure your answer makes sense by using another problem solving strategy to check your work.

Formulas, Properties, and Theorems

The Fundamental Theorem of Arithmetic	Every positive integer greater than 1 has exactly one set of prime factors (one prime factorization).
Cross Products Property	The cross products of two fractions are the products of the numerator of one fraction and the denominator of the other fraction. If the cross products of two ratios (fractions) are equal, then the ratios form a proportion.
Percent: Find What Number Is a Given Percent of Another Number	$n = p \times b$ number (n) is a given percent (p) of a given base number (b)
Percent: Find What Percent One Number Is of Another Number	$p = \frac{n}{b}$ percent (p) one number (n) is of another number (b)
Percent: Find a Number When Given a Certain Percent of the Number	$b = \frac{n}{p}$ base number (b) when given a number (n) and the percent (p) the number is of the base number
Percent of Increase	$p\% = \frac{\text{amount of increase}}{\text{original amount}}$ amount of increase = new amount − original amount
Percent of Decrease	$p\% = \frac{\text{amount of decrease}}{\text{original amount}}$ amount of decrease = larger amount − the smaller amount
Simple Interest	$I = prt$ where I is the interest earned or paid, p is the principal amount, r is the interest rate per year, t is the time in years

Numbers and Operations

Ways to Check Answers

Addition

- Reverse the addition order. Add from the bottom of a column to the top of the column, if you had added from top to bottom to solve the problem.
- Use a calculator to enter the computation. Check the calculator result with your answer.
- Use an estimation strategy (*see list below*).

Subtraction

- Reverse the operation. Add the difference (answer) to the subtrahend (number being subtracted).
- Use a calculator to enter the computation. Check the calculator result with your answer.
- Use an estimation strategy (*see list below*).

Multiplication

- Reverse the order of the factors.
- Factor the multiplier, and use the factors to multiply.
- Use a calculator to enter the computation. Check the calculator result with your answer.
- Use an estimation strategy (*see list below*).

Division

- Reverse the operation. Multiply the quotient (answer) by the divisor.
- Factor the divisor and divide each factor separately.
- Use a calculator to enter the computation. Check the calculator result with your answer.
- Use an estimation strategy (*see list below*).

Methods for Estimating

Rounding	• Round numbers so that you can use mental math to perform the computation. • For whole numbers and decimals, add 1 if the digit in the place to the right of the one you're rounding to is greater than or equal to 5. Add 0 if it's less than 5.
Benchmarks	• Rounding to a benchmark instead of a place value sometimes gives you an estimate that is closer to the actual answer. • There are benchmarks for both fractions and decimals.
Compatible Numbers	• Compatible numbers are values that are close to the numbers given in a computation. Choose compatible numbers that make it easy to use mental math. • For division, choose the number for the divisor first. Then find a compatible number for the dividend.
Front-end Estimation	• Use only the whole number parts of decimals or mixed numbers to perform a computation. • You can use the decimal or fraction parts to get a closer estimate.

Benchmarks for Fractions

If the numerator is . . .	Round to . . .
Much less than one-fourth of the denominator	0
About one-fourth of the denominator	$\frac{1}{4}$
About one-half of the denominator	$\frac{1}{2}$
About three-fourths of the denominator	$\frac{3}{4}$
Much greater than three-fourths of the denominator	1

Benchmarks for Decimals

To make addition or subtraction easier, round to ...
0
0.25
0.5
0.75
1

Fraction-Decimal-Percent Equivalents

$\frac{1}{100}$	= 0.01	= 1%	$\frac{8}{16}, \frac{6}{12}, \frac{5}{10}, \frac{4}{8}, \frac{3}{6}, \frac{2}{4}, \frac{1}{2}$	= 0.5	= 50%
$\frac{1}{16}$	= 0.0625	= $6\frac{1}{4}$%	$\frac{5}{9}$	= 0.5555...	= $55\frac{5}{9}$%
$\frac{1}{12}$	= 0.0833...	= $8\frac{1}{3}$%	$\frac{9}{16}$	= 0.5625	= $56\frac{1}{4}$%
$\frac{1}{10}$	= 0.1	= 10%	$\frac{4}{7}$	= 0.571428...	= $57\frac{1}{7}$%
$\frac{1}{9}$	= 0.1111...	= $11\frac{1}{9}$%	$\frac{7}{12}$	= 0.5833...	= $58\frac{1}{3}$%
$\frac{2}{16}, \frac{1}{8}$	= 0.125	= $12\frac{1}{2}$%	$\frac{10}{16}, \frac{5}{8}$	= 0.625	= $62\frac{1}{2}$%
$\frac{1}{7}$	= 0.142857...	= $14\frac{2}{7}$%	$\frac{8}{12}, \frac{6}{9}, \frac{4}{6}, \frac{2}{3}$	= 0.6666...	= $66\frac{2}{3}$%
$\frac{2}{12}, \frac{1}{6}$	= 0.1666...	= $16\frac{2}{3}$%	$\frac{11}{16}$	= 0.6875	= $68\frac{3}{4}$%
$\frac{13}{16}$	= 0.1875	= $18\frac{3}{4}$%	$\frac{7}{10}$	= 0.7	= 70%
$\frac{2}{10}, \frac{1}{5}$	= 0.2	= 20%	$\frac{5}{7}$	= 0.714285...	= $71\frac{3}{7}$%
$\frac{2}{9}$	= 0.2222...	= $22\frac{2}{9}$%	$\frac{12}{16}, \frac{9}{12}, \frac{6}{8}, \frac{3}{4}$	= 0.75	= 75%
$\frac{4}{16}, \frac{3}{12}, \frac{2}{8}, \frac{1}{4}$	= 0.25	= 25%	$\frac{7}{9}$	= 0.7777...	= $77\frac{7}{9}$%
$\frac{2}{7}$	= 0.285714...	= $28\frac{4}{7}$%	$\frac{8}{10}, \frac{4}{5}$	= 0.8	= 80%
$\frac{3}{10}$	= 0.3	= 30%	$\frac{13}{16}$	= 0.8125	= $81\frac{1}{4}$%
$\frac{5}{16}$	= 0.3125	= $31\frac{1}{4}$%	$\frac{10}{12}, \frac{5}{6}$	= 0.8333...	= $83\frac{1}{3}$%
$\frac{4}{12}, \frac{3}{9}, \frac{2}{6}, \frac{1}{3}$	= 0.3333...	= $33\frac{1}{3}$%	$\frac{6}{7}$	= 0.857142...	= $85\frac{5}{7}$%
$\frac{6}{16}, \frac{3}{8}$	= 0.375	= $37\frac{1}{2}$%	$\frac{14}{16}, \frac{7}{8}$	= 0.875	= $87\frac{1}{2}$%
$\frac{4}{10}, \frac{2}{5}$	= 0.4	= 40%	$\frac{8}{9}$	= 0.8888...	= $88\frac{8}{9}$%
$\frac{5}{12}$	= 0.4166...	= $41\frac{2}{3}$%	$\frac{9}{10}$	= 0.9	= 90%
$\frac{3}{7}$	= 0.428571...	= $42\frac{6}{7}$%	$\frac{11}{12}$	= 0.9166...	= $91\frac{2}{3}$%
$\frac{7}{16}$	= 0.4375	= $43\frac{3}{4}$%	$\frac{15}{16}$	= 0.9375	= $93\frac{3}{4}$%
$\frac{4}{9}$	= 0.4444...	= $44\frac{4}{9}$%	$\frac{16}{16}, \frac{12}{12}, \frac{10}{10}, \frac{8}{8}, \frac{6}{6}, \frac{4}{4}, \frac{2}{2}$	= 1.000	= 100%

STAY Focused

Measurement

U.S. Customary System	Metric System
Length	
1 mile (mi) = 1,760 yards = 5,280 feet **1 yard (yd)** = 3 feet = 36 inches **1 foot (ft)** = 12 inches $\frac{1}{36}$ yard = $\frac{1}{12}$ foot = **1 inch (in.)**	**1 kilometer (km)** = 1,000 m 0.001 km = **1 meter (m)** = 100 cm = 1,000 mm 0.01 m = **1 centimeter (cm)** = 10 mm 0.001 m = 0.1 cm = **1 millimeter (mm)**
Area	
1 square mile (mi^2) = 640 acres **1 acre (a)** = 4,840 yd^2 **1 square yard (yd^2)** = 9 ft^2 **1 square foot (ft^2)** = 144 in.^{2} $\frac{1}{144}$ ft^2 = **1 square inch (in.^{2})**	**1 square kilometer (km^2)** = 1,000,000 m^2 **1 square meter (m^2)** = 10,000 cm^2 **1 square centimeter (cm^2)** = 100 mm^2 0.01 cm^2 = **1 square millimeter (mm^2)**
Volume	
1 cubic yard (yd^3) = 27 ft^3 **1 cubic foot (ft^3)** = 1,728 in.^{3} $\frac{1}{1,728}$ ft^3 = **1 cubic inch (in.^{3})**	**1 cubic meter (m^3)** = 1,000,000 cm^3 **1 cubic centimeter (cm^3)** = 1,000 mm^3 0.001 cm^3 = **1 cubic millimeter (mm^3)**
Capacity (Liquid)	
1 gallon (gal) = 4 qt = 8 pt = 16 c = 128 fl oz **1 quart (qt)** = 2 pt = 4 c = 32 fl oz **1 pint (pt)** = 2 c = 16 fl oz **1 cup (c)** = 8 fl oz $\frac{1}{8}$ cup = **1 fluid ounce (fl oz)**	**1 kiloliter (kL)** = 1,000 L 0.001 kL = **1 liter (L)** = 100 cL = 1,000 mL 0.01 L = **1 centiliter (cL)** = 10 mL 0.001 L = 0.1 cL = **1 milliliter (mL)**
Weight	**Mass**
1 ton (t) = 2,000 pounds **1 pound (lb)** = 16 ounces $\frac{1}{16}$ pound = **1 ounce (oz)**	**1 metric ton (t)** = 1,000 kg 0.001 t = **1 kilogram (kg)** = 1,000 g 0.001 kg = **1 gram (g)** = 100 cg = 1,000 mg 0.01 g = **1 centigram (cg)** = 10 mg 0.001 g = 0.1 cg = **1 milligram (mg)**
Temperature	
32°F = freezing point of water 98.6°F = normal body temperature 212°F = boiling point of water $F = \frac{9}{5}C + 32$ or $F = 1.8C + 32$	0°C = freezing point of water 37°C = normal body temperature 100°C = boiling point of water $C = \frac{5}{9}(F - 32)$

Time

60 seconds (s) = **1 minute (min)**	365 days = **1 year (yr)**
60 minutes = **1 hour (h)**	52 weeks (approx.) = 1 year
24 hours = **1 day (d)**	12 months = 1 year
7 days = **1 week (wk)**	10 years = 1 decade
4 weeks (approx.) = **1 month (mo)**	100 years = 1 century

Equivalents

1 acre = 43,560 square feet = 4,840 square yards
1 bushel (U.S.) = 2,150.42 cubic inches
= 32 quarts
1 cord = 128 cubic feet
1 cubic centimeter = 0.061 cubic inch
1 cubic foot = 7.481 gallons = 1,728 cubic inches
1 cubic inch = 0.554 fluid ounce
= 16.387 cubic centimeters
1 cubic meter = 1.308 cubic yards
1 cubic yard = 0.765 cubic meter = 27 cubic feet
1 cup = 8 fluid ounces = 0.5 liquid pint
1 gallon (U.S.) = 231 cubic inches
= 128 U.S. fluid ounces
= 4 liquid quarts
1 liter = 1.057 liquid quarts
1 meter = 39.37 inches = 1.094 yards
1 micron = 0.001 millimeter = 0.00003937 inch
1 mile, nautical = 1.852 kilometers
= 1.151 statute miles
= 6,076.1155 feet
1 milliliter = 0.061 cubic inch
1 pint, dry = 33.600 cubic inches = 0.551 liter
1 pint, liquid = 28.875 inches = 0.473 liter
= 2 cups = 16 fluid ounces
1 pound, avoirdupois = 7,000 grains = 16 ounces
= 453.59237 grams
1 quart, dry (U.S.) = 67.201 cubic inches
= 1.101 liters
1 quart, liquid (U.S.) = 57.75 cubic inches
= 0.946 liter
= 2 pints = 32 fluid ounces
1 square foot = 929 square centimeters
= 144 square inches
1 square inch = 6.45 square centimeters
1 square kilometer = 0.386 square miles
= 247.105 acres
1 square meter = 1.196 square yards
= 10.764 square feet
1 square mile = 640 acres
1 square yard = 0.836 square meter
= 9 square feet
= 1,296 square inches
1 tablespoon = 3 teaspoons = 0.5 fluid ounce
1 ton, metric = 2,204.623 pounds
= 1.102 net tons
1 ton, net or short = 2,000 pounds
= 0.907 metric ton
1 yard = 0.9144 meter = 3 feet = 36 inches

Conversions

To Convert	Into	Multiply By
angstroms	microns	0.0001
centimeters	feet	0.03281
centimeters	inches	0.3937
cubic cm	cubic inches	0.06102
cubic feet	cubic meters	0.02832
days	seconds	86,400.0
degrees (angle)	radians	0.01745
fathoms	feet	6.0
feet	centimeters	30.48
feet	meters	0.3048
feet/min.	cm/sec.	0.5080
feet/sec.	knots	0.5921
feet/sec.	statute mi./hr.	0.6818
furlongs/hr.	statute mi./hr.	0.125
furlongs	feet	660.0
gallons (liq.)	liters	3.785
gal. of water	pounds of water	8.3453
grams	oz. (avoirdupois)	0.03527
grams	pounds	0.002205
hours	days	0.04167
hours	weeks	0.005952
inches	centimeters	2.540
kilograms	pounds	2.205
kilometers	feet	3,280.8
kilometers	mi. (statute)	0.6214
knots	feet/hr.	6080.0
knots	nautical mi./hr.	1.0
knots	statute mi./hr.	1.151
liters	gallons (liq.)	0.2642
liters	pints (liq.)	2.113
meters	feet	3.281
meters	mi. (nautical)	0.0005396
meters	mi. (statute)	0.0006214
microns	meters	0.000001
mi. (nautical)	feet	6,076.115
mi. (statute)	feet	5,280.0
mi. (nautical)	kilometers	1.852
mi. (statute)	kilometers	1.609
mi. (nautical)	mi. (statute)	1.1508
mi. (statute)	mi. (nautical)	0.8684
mi. (statute)/hr.	feet/min.	88.0
millimeters	inches	0.03937
oz. (avoirdupois)	grams	28.3495
oz. (avoirdupois)	lb. (avoirdupois)	0.0625
pints (liq.)	gallons (liq.)	0.125
pints (liq.)	quarts (liq.)	0.5
lb. (avoirdupois)	kilograms	0.4536

Measurement

Length Formulas		Perimeter *P*, Circumference *C*
$P = s_1 + s_2 + s_3$	**Triangle** s_1, s_2, s_3 are lengths of sides	s_1, s_2, s_3
$P = 2\ell + 2w$ or $P = 2(\ell + w)$	**Rectangle** ℓ is length w is width	w, ℓ
$P = 4s$	**Square** s is length of each side	s
$P = 2\ell + 2w$ or $P = 2(\ell + w)$	**Parallelogram** ℓ is length w is width	w, ℓ
$P = ns$	**Regular Polygon** n is number of sides s is length of each side	s
$C = \pi d$ or $C = 2\pi r$	**Circle** π is pi, a number about 3.14 or $\frac{22}{7}$ d is length of diameter r is length of radius	diameter, radius

Area Formulas		Area A, Surface Area SA
$A = \ell w$ or $A = bh$	**Rectangle** ℓ is length; b is length of the base w is width; h is height	w, ℓ
$A = s^2$	**Square** s is length of each side	s
$A = bh$	**Parallelogram** b is length of the base h is height	h, b
$A = \frac{1}{2}bh$	**Triangle** b is length of the base h is height	h, b
$A = \frac{1}{2}ab$	**Right Triangle** a is length of one leg b is length of the other leg	a, b
$A = \frac{s^2}{4}\sqrt{3}$	**Equilateral Triangle** s is length of each side	s
$A = \frac{1}{2}h(b_1 + b_2)$	**Trapezoid** h is height b_1 is length of one parallel side b_2 is length of other parallel side	b_2, h, b_1
$A = \frac{1}{2}ap$	**Regular Polygon** a is length of an apothem p is perimeter of polygon	s, s, a

Table continued on next page

Area Formulas		Area A, Surface Area SA
$A = \frac{1}{2}d_1d_2$	**Kite** d_1 is length of one diagonal d_2 is length of other diagonal	D C d_1 X A d_2 B
$A = \pi r^2$	**Circle** π is pi, a number about 3.14 or $\frac{22}{7}$ r is length of the radius	diameter radius
$SA = 6e^2$	**Cube** e is length of each edge	e
$SA = Ph + 2B$	**Rectangular Prism** P is perimeter of the base h is height B is area of the base	h B w ℓ
$SA = 2\pi rh + 2\pi r^2$ or $SA = 2\pi r(h + r)$	**Right Cylinder** π is pi, a number about 3.14 or $\frac{22}{7}$ r is length of the radius of the base h is height	r h
$SA = \frac{1}{2}P\ell + B$	**Pyramid** P is perimeter of the base ℓ is slant height B is area of the base	ℓ h B
$SA = \pi r\ell + \pi r^2$ or $SA = \pi r(\ell + r)$	**Right Cone** π is pi, a number about 3.14 or $\frac{22}{7}$ r is length of the radius of the base ℓ is slant height	ℓ h r
$SA = 4\pi r^2$	**Sphere** π is pi, a number about 3.14 or $\frac{22}{7}$ r is length of the radius	r

Volume Formulas		Volume V
$V = e^3$	**Cube** e is length of each edge	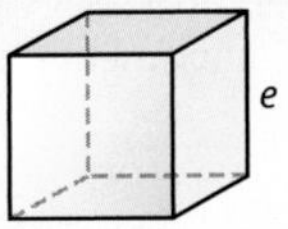 e
$V = \ell wh$	**Rectangular Prism** ℓ is length w is width h is height	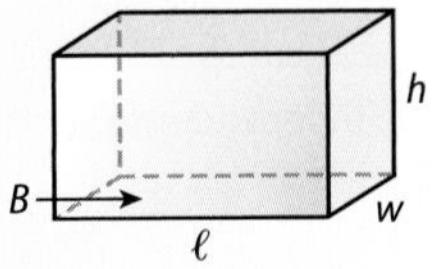 h B w ℓ
$V = Bh$	**Prism** B is area of the base h is height	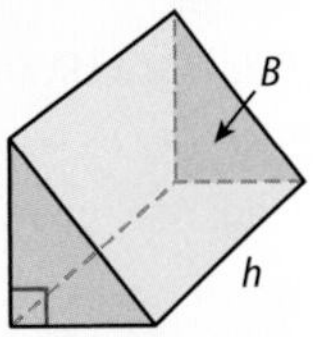 B h
$V = \pi r^2 h$	**Right Cylinder** π is pi, a number about 3.14 or $\frac{22}{7}$ r is length of the radius of the base h is height	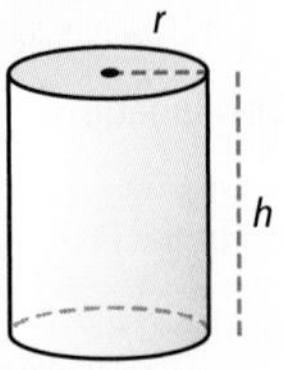 r h
$V = \frac{1}{3}Bh$	**Pyramid** B is area of the base h is height	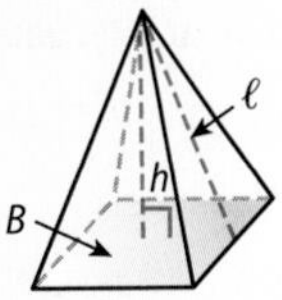 ℓ h B
$V = \frac{1}{3}\pi r^2 h$	**Right Cone** π is pi, a number about 3.14 or $\frac{22}{7}$ r is length of the radius of the base h is height	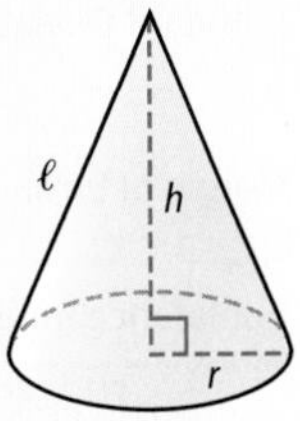 ℓ h r
$V = \frac{4}{3}\pi r^3$	**Sphere** π is pi, a number about 3.14 or $\frac{22}{7}$ r is length of the radius	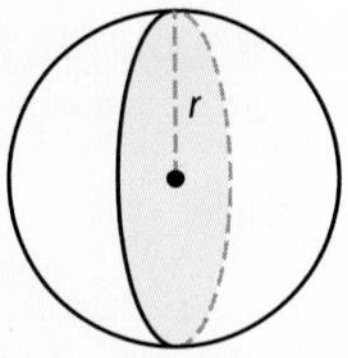 r

Statistics and Probability

Formulas

Probability (theoretical)	$P(\text{event}) = \dfrac{\text{number of favorable outcomes}}{\text{number of total outcomes}}$
Probability (experimental)	$P(\text{event}) = \dfrac{\text{number of times an event occurs}}{\text{number of trials}}$
Complement *C* of an Event *E*	$P(C) = P(\text{not } E)$ $P(C) = 1 - P(E)$ $P(\text{not } E) = 1 - P(E)$ $P(E) + P(\text{not } E) = 1$
Independent Events	$P(A \text{ and } B) = P(A) \cdot P(B)$ $P(A \text{ or } B) = P(A) + P(B) - P(A \text{ and } B)$
Dependent Events	$P(A \text{ and } B) = P(A) \cdot P(B \mid A)$
Odds for an Event	$\text{Odds in favor} = \dfrac{\text{number of favorable outcomes}}{\text{number of unfavorable outcomes}}$
Odds Against an Event	$\text{Odds against} = \dfrac{\text{number of unfavorable outcomes}}{\text{number of favorable outcomes}}$
Permutations	${}_nP_r = \dfrac{n!}{(n-r)!}$
Combinations	${}_nC_r = \dfrac{n!}{r!(n-r)!}$
Binomial Probability	$P(k \text{ successes in } n \text{ trials}) = {}_nC_r \cdot p^k(1-p)^{n-k}$
Outlier	$n < Q1 - 1.5(IQR)$ or $n > Q3 + 1.5(IQR)$
Linear Interpolation and Extrapolation	$y = y_1 + \left(\dfrac{y_2 - y_1}{x_2 - x_1}\right)(x - x_1)$
Variance	$\sigma^2 = \dfrac{\Sigma(x_i - \bar{x})^2}{n}$
Standard Deviation	$\sigma = \sqrt{\dfrac{\Sigma(x_i - \bar{x})^2}{n}}$
Margin of Error	$ME = z_c\sqrt{\dfrac{\hat{p}(1-\hat{p})}{n}}$ $\quad ME = z_c \cdot \dfrac{\sigma}{\sqrt{n}}$
Confidence Interval	$\hat{p} \pm ME$ $\quad \bar{x} \pm ME$

Theorems

Fundamental Counting Principle	If there are *m* ways to choose a first item and *n* ways to choose a second item after the first item has been chosen, then there are $m \times n$ ways to choose both items.
Binomial Theorem	$(a+b)^n = ({}_nC_0)a^n + ({}_nC_1)a^{n-1}b + ({}_nC_2)a^{n-2}b^2 + \ldots + ({}_nC_{n-1})ab^{n-1} + ({}_nC_n)b^n$ $(a+b)^n = \sum_{k=0}^{n} {}_nC_k a^{n-k}b^k$

Data Graphs

Line Plots

A *line plot* displays data along a number line. Each number in the data set is represented by an X or another symbol.

Midterm Scores in Science

			X			
			X	X		
			X	X	X	
X	X	X	X	X	X	
X	X	X	X	X	X	
X	X	X	X	X	X	X
89	**90**	**91**	**92**	**93**	**94**	**95**

Scatter Plots

A *scatter plot* is a graph that shows data points on a coordinate grid. Each data point represents a pair of values.

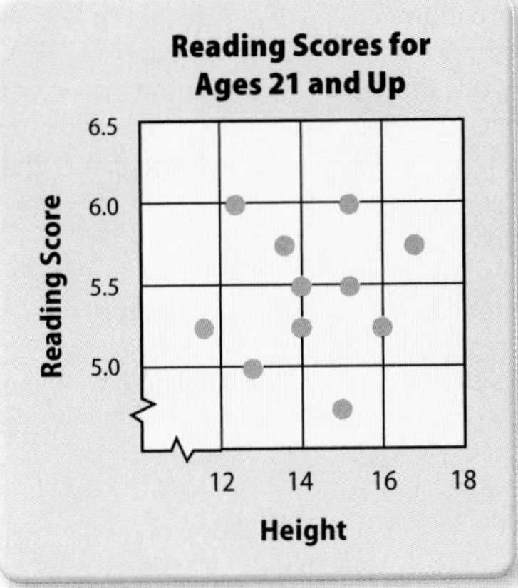

Histograms

A *histogram* displays the frequency of a set of data in equal-size intervals, or ranges, of data.

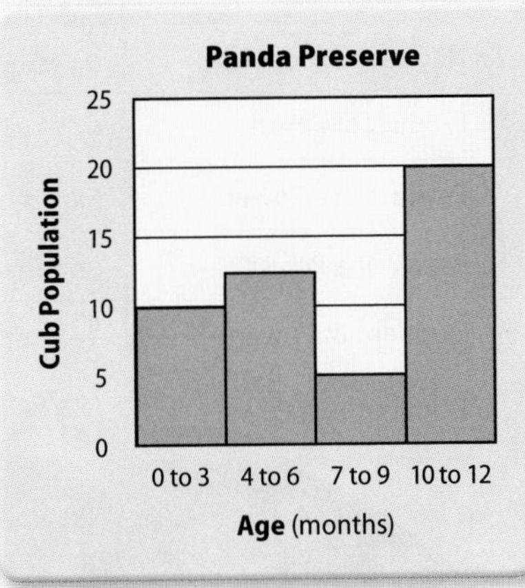

Stem-and-Leaf Plots

A *stem-and-leaf plot* is a data display that can be used to show how data are distributed. The data are in numerical order in two columns.

Cars Parked (Past 10 Days)

Stem	Leaf
0	1 2 3 6
1	0 0 3 6
2	0 9

Key: 2 | 9 = 29

Box-and-Whisker Plots

A *box-and-whisker plot* is a data display that divides a set of data into four equal parts. It shows how the data are distributed among these parts.

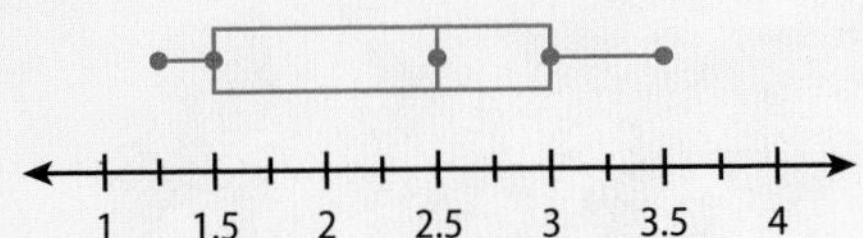

Venn Diagrams

A *Venn diagram* is a graphic display that uses overlapping circles (or squares) to show the relationship between sets and subsets of data.

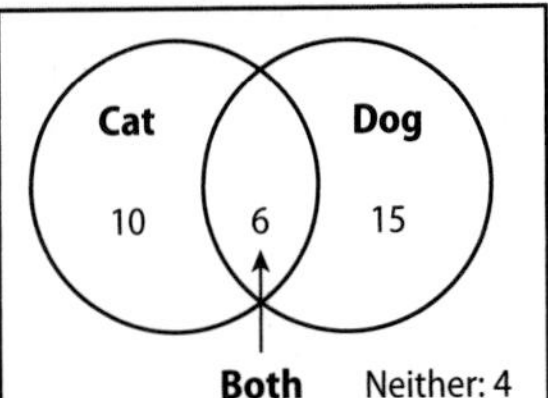

Algebra

Properties of Equality

Addition	If $a = b$, then $a + c = b + c$.
Subtraction	If $a = b$, then $a - c = b - c$.
Multiplication	If $a = b$, then $a \cdot c = b \cdot c$.
Division	If $a = b$ and $c \neq 0$, then $\frac{a}{c} = \frac{b}{c}$.
Reflexive	$a = a$
Symmetric	If $a = b$, then $b = a$.
Transitive	If $a = b$ and $b = c$, then $a = c$.

Properties of Inequality

Addition	If $a < b$, then $a + c < b + c$.
Subtraction	If $a < b$, then $a - c < b - c$.
Multiplication	If $a < b$ and $c > 0$, then $a \cdot c < b \cdot c$. If $a < b$ and $c < 0$, then $a \cdot c > b \cdot c$.
Division	If $a < b$ and $c > 0$, then $\frac{a}{c} > \frac{b}{c}$. If $a < b$ and $c < 0$, then $\frac{a}{c} > \frac{b}{c}$.
Transitive	If $a < b$ and $b < c$, then $a < c$.

These properties are also true for $>$, $\leq$, and $\geq$.

Properties of Real Numbers

Commutative Property	$a + b = b + a$ $a \cdot b = b \cdot a$
Associative Property	$(a + b) + c = a + (b + c)$ $(a \cdot b) \cdot c = a \cdot (b \cdot c)$
Distributive Property	$a(b + c) = ab + ac$ $a(b - c) = ab - ac$
Closure for Addition	$a + b$ is a real number.
Closure for Multiplication	$a \cdot b$ is a real number.
Identity Property	$a + 0 = a$ $a \cdot 1 = a$
Inverse Property	$a + (-a) = 0$ $a \cdot \frac{1}{a} = 1$
Multiplication by 0	$a \cdot 0 = 0$
Multiplication by -1	$a \cdot (-1) = -a$
Zero Product	If $ab = 0$, then $a = 0$, $b = 0$ or both a and $b = 0$.

Properties of Exponents

Zero exponent	$a^0 = 1$
Negative exponent	$a^{-1} = \frac{1}{a}$
Product of Powers	$a^m \times a^n = a^{m+n}$
Product to a Power	$(ab)^n = a^n \times b^n$
Power of a Power	$(a^m)^n = a^{m \cdot n}$
Quotient of Powers	$\frac{a^m}{a^n} = a^{m-n}$
Quotient to a Power	$\left(\frac{a}{b}\right)^n = \frac{a^n}{b^n}$

Translating Word Problems into Algebra

1. Read the problem carefully, and determine what number or numbers need to be found.
2. Represent this unknown number with a variable, for example, x.
3. Identify key words that show what operations are used with the numbers and variables in the problem.
4. Words like *equals* or *is* tell you to write an equation rather than just an expression.
5. Use numbers, variables, operation symbols, and a relationship stated in the problem to write any expression needed.
6. To write an equation, write two expressions and connect them with an equals sign.

Solving Word Problems

Step 1 Read the problem carefully and determine what number or numbers you need to find.

Step 2 Represent one unknown number with a variable.

Step 3 Use a condition stated in the problem to write an expression for a second number.

Step 4 Use a second condition to find two expressions that are equal. Then write these two expressions algebraically and connect them with an equals sign.

Step 5 Solve the equation.

Step 6 Check to make sure the result matches the conditions stated in the problem.

Operations with Signed Numbers

Adding		
If the numbers have the same signs, add the absolute values and use the sign of the numbers.	$5 + 11 = 16$	$-5 + (-11) = -16$
If the numbers have different signs, subtract their absolute values and use the sign of the number with the greater absolute value.	$-7 + 11 = 4$ $7 + (-11) = -4$	$-15 + 6 = -9$ $15 + (-6) = 9$
Subtracting		
To subtract a number, add its opposite.	$8 - 6 = 8 + (-6)$	$-1 - 7 = -1 + (-7)$
Multiplying or Dividing		
If two numbers have the same sign, their product or quotient is positive.	$(+)(+) = (+)$ $(-)(-) = (+)$	$(+) \div (+) = (+)$ $(-) \div (-) = (+)$
If two numbers have different signs, their product or quotient is negative.	$(+)(-) = (-)$ $(-)(+) = (-)$	$(+) \div (-) = (-)$ $(-) \div (+) = (-)$

Algebra

Graphing (x, y) on the Coordinate Plane

Value of x	Value of y	Location of Point
+	+	Quadrant I
−	+	Quadrant II
−	−	Quadrant III
+	−	Quadrant IV
0	+ or −	on the y-axis
+ or −	0	on the x-axis

Formulas

Polynomials

Binomial squares	$(a + b)^2 = a^2 + 2ab + b^2$ $(a - b)^2 = a^2 - 2ab + b^2$
Difference of squares	$a^2 - b^2 = (a + b)(a - b)$
Difference of cubes	$a^3 - b^3 = (a - b)(a^2 + ab + b^2)$
Sum of cubes	$a^3 + b^3 = (a + b)(a^2 - ab + b^2)$

Linear Equations

Slope	$m = \frac{y_2 - y_1}{x_2 - x_1}$
Slope-Intercept Form	$y = mx + b$
Point-Slope Form	$y - y_1 = m(x - x_1)$
Standard Form	$Ax + By = C$

Quadratic Equations and Functions

Standard Form	$ax^2 + bx + c = 0$
Quadratic Formula	$x = \frac{-b \pm \sqrt{b^2 - 4ac}}{2a}$
Discriminant	$b^2 - 4ac$
Vertex Form of a Function	$f(x) = a(x - h)^2 + k$
Line of Symmetry	$x = -\frac{b}{2a}$

Distance

horizontal distance between two points (x_1, y_1) and (x_2, y_2) on the coordinate plane	$\lvert x_2 - x_1 \rvert$
vertical distance between two points (x_1, y_1) and (x_2, y_2) on the coordinate plane	$\lvert y_2 - y_1 \rvert$

Theorems

Rational Zeros Theorem	If the polynomial function has integer coefficients, then every rational zero has this form. p ← a factor of the constant term q ← a factor of the leading coefficient
Rational Roots Theorem	If a polynomial equation $P(x) = 0$ has integer coefficients, then every rational root has this form. p ← a factor of the constant term q ← a factor of the leading coefficient
The Fundamental Theorem of Algebra and Its Corollary	*Theorem:* If $P(x)$ is a polynomial of degree n, then the equation $P(x) = 0$ has at least one root, which is complex. *Corollary:* If $P(x)$ is a polynomial of degree n, then the equation $P(x) = 0$ has exactly n roots when multiplicities are taken into account.
The Remainder Theorem	If a polynomial function $P(x)$ is divided by $x - a$, then the remainder r is equal to $P(a)$.
Descartes' Rule of Signs for Negative Real Zeros	The number of negative real zeros of the polynomial function $P(x)$ is either: • equal to the number of sign changes in $P(-x)$ or • less than the number of sign changes in $P(-x)$ by an even number.
Irrational Zeros Theorem	If $P(x)$ has a zero of the form $a + b\sqrt{c}$, it also has a zero of the form $a - b\sqrt{c}$.

Systems of Two Linear Equations

One Solution	No Solution	Infinitely Many Solutions
consistent system independent system	inconsistent system	consistent system dependent system
intersecting lines	parallel lines	same line
different slopes	same slope different y-intercepts	same slope same y-intercept

Geometry

Formulas

Distance Formula	$d = \sqrt{(x_2 - x_1)^2 + (y_2 - y_1)^2}$	Lateral Area of a Regular Pyramid	$LA = \frac{1}{2}Ps$
Midpoint Formula	$\left(\frac{x_1 + x_2}{2}, \frac{y_1 + y_2}{2}\right)$	Lateral Area of a Regular Cone	$LA = \pi rs$
Slope m	$m = \frac{y_2 - y_1}{x_2 - x_1}$	Euler's Formula	$F + V = E + 2$
Slope-Intercept Form of an Equation for a Line	$y = mx + b$	Length of an Arc	$\ell = 2\pi r\left(\frac{x°}{360°}\right)$
Point-Slope Form of an Equation for a Line	$y - y_1 = m(x - x_1)$	Area of a Sector	$A = \pi r^2\left(\frac{x°}{360°}\right)$
Equation of a Circle	$(x - h)^2 + (y - k)^2 = r^2$ with center (h, k) and radius r		

Perimeter, Area, and Volume

Figure	**Perimeter Formula**	**Area Formula**
Regular Polygon	$P = ns$	$A = \frac{1}{2}ap$
Triangle	$P = s_1 + s_2 + s_3$.	$A = \frac{1}{2}bh$
Square	$P = 4s$	$A = s^2$
Rectangle	$P = 2\ell + 2w$ or $2(\ell + w)$	$A = \ell \cdot w$
Parallelogram	$P = 2(s_1 + s_2)$	$A = b \cdot h$
Trapezoid	$P = s_1 + s_2 + s_3 + s_4$	$A = \frac{1}{2}h(b_1 + b_2)$
Circle	circumference: $C = \pi d$ or $C = 2\pi r$	$A = \pi r^2$
Figure	**Surface Area Formula**	**Volume Formula**
Cube	$SA = 6s^2$	$V = s^3$
Rectangular Prism	$SA = Ph + 2B$	$V = Bh$
Pyramid	$SA = \frac{1}{2}P\ell + B$	$V = \frac{1}{3}Bh$
Cylinder	$SA = 2\pi rh + 2\pi r^2$	$V = \pi r^2 h$
Cone	$SA = \pi r\ell + \pi r^2$	$V = \frac{1}{3}\pi r^2 h$
Sphere	$SA = 4\pi r^2$	$V = \frac{4}{3}\pi r^3$

Congruence Properties

Property	Segments	Angles
Reflexive	$\overline{AB} \cong \overline{AB}$	$\angle X \cong \angle X$
Symmetric	If $\overline{AB} \cong \overline{CD}$, then $\overline{CD} \cong \overline{AB}$.	If $\angle X \cong \angle Y$, then $\angle Y \cong \angle X$.
Transitive	If $\overline{AB} \cong \overline{CD}$ and $\overline{CD} \cong \overline{EF}$, then $\overline{AB} \cong \overline{EF}$.	If $\angle X \cong \angle Y$ and $\angle Y \cong \angle Z$, then $\angle X \cong \angle Z$.

Logic Statements

Statement	In Words	In Symbols
Conditional	If p, then q.	$p \rightarrow q$
Inverse	If not p, then not q.	$\sim p \rightarrow \sim q$
Converse	If q, then p.	$q \rightarrow p$
Contrapositive	If not q, then not p.	$\sim q \rightarrow \sim p$
Biconditional	p if and only if q.	$p \leftrightarrow q$

Truth Table for $p \rightarrow q$

Hypothesis p	Conclusion q	Conditional $p \rightarrow q$	Converse $q \rightarrow p$	Biconditional $p \leftrightarrow q$
T	T	T	T	T
T	F	F	T	F
F	T	T	F	F
F	F	T	T	T

Laws of Logic

The Law of Detachment

If $p \rightarrow q$ is true and p is true, then q is true.

Law of Syllogism

If $p \rightarrow q$ is true and $q \rightarrow r$ is true, then $p \rightarrow r$ must be true.

Types of Reasoning

Deductive Reasoning	• Uses properties, rules, definitions, theorems, given facts, and the laws of logic to arrive at a conclusion. • The conclusion must be true if the hypotheses are true.
Inductive Reasoning	• Uses observations and patterns. • The conclusion is not necessarily true.

Geometry

Angles

Angle Addition Postulate: If point M is in the interior of $\angle JKL$, then $m\angle JKM + m\angle MKL = m\angle JKL$.

Linear Pair Theorem: If two angles form a linear pair, then they are supplementary.

Congruent Supplements Theorem: If two angles are supplementary to the same angle (or to congruent angles), then the angles are congruent.

Congruent Complements Theorem: If two angles are complementary to the same angle (or to congruent angles), then the angles are congruent.

Vertical Angles Theorem: Vertical angles are congruent.

Right Angle Congruence Theorem: All right angles are congruent.

Theorem (p. 628): If two angles are congruent and supplementary, then each angle is a right angle.

Corresponding Angles Postulate: If two parallel lines are cut by a transversal, then corresponding angles are congruent.

Converse of the Corresponding Angles Postulate: If two lines are cut by a transversal and corresponding angles are congruent, then the lines are parallel.

Alternate Interior Angles Theorem: If two parallel lines are cut by a transversal, then alternate interior angles are congruent.

Converse of the Alternate Interior Angles Theorem: If two lines are cut by a transversal and alternate interior angles are congruent, then the lines are parallel.

Alternate Exterior Angles Theorem: If two parallel lines are cut by a transversal, then alternate exterior angles are congruent.

Converse of the Alternate Exterior Angles Theorem: If two lines are cut by a transversal and alternate exterior angles are congruent, then the lines are parallel.

Same-Side Interior Angles Theorem: If two parallel lines are cut by a transversal, then same-side interior angles are supplementary.

Converse of the Same-Side Interior Angles Theorem: If two lines are cut by a transversal and same-side interior angles are supplementary, then the lines are parallel.

Polygons

Polygon Interior Angle-Sum Theorem: The sum of the measures of the interior angles of a polygon with n sides is $(n - 2)180°$.

Polygon Exterior Angle-Sum Theorem: The sum of the measures of the exterior angles of a polygon is 360°.

Parallel and Perpendicular Lines

Theorem (p. 633): In a plane, if two lines are perpendicular to the same line, then they are parallel.

Theorem (p. 814): If two non-vertical lines are parallel, then their slopes are equal.

Theorem (p. 814): If the slopes of two non-vertical lines are equal, then the lines are parallel.

Theorem (p. 816): If two non-vertical lines are perpendicular, then their slopes are negative reciprocals.

Theorem (p. 816): If the slopes of two non-vertical lines are negative reciprocals, then the lines are perpendicular.

Parallel Postulate: Given a line and a point not on the line, there is exactly one line through the point parallel to the line.

Circles

Arc Addition Postulate: The measure of an arc formed by two adjacent arcs is the sum of the measures of the two arcs. $m\widehat{AC} = m\widehat{AB} + m\widehat{BC}$	**Inscribed Angle Theorem:** The measure of an inscribed angle is half the measure of its intercepted arc.
Theorem (p. 728): In the same circle or in congruent circles, two minor arcs are congruent if and only if their central angles are congruent.	**Corollary:** If two inscribed angles intercept the same arc, then they are congruent.
Theorem (p. 734): In the same circle (or in congruent circles), congruent chords have congruent central angles.	**Corollary:** An angle inscribed in a semicircle is a right angle.
Converse of Theorem (p. 734): In the same circle (or in congruent circles), congruent central angles have congruent chords.	**Corollary:** If a quadrilateral is inscribed in a circle, then its opposite angles are supplementary.
Theorem (p. 736): In the same circle (or in congruent circles), congruent arcs have congruent chords.	**Tangent-Chord Angle Theorem:** The measure of an angle whose sides are a tangent and a chord equals half the measure of the intercepted arc.
Converse of Theorem (p. 736): In the same circle (or congruent circles), congruent chords have congruent arcs.	**Tangent-Tangent Angle Theorem:** The measure of the angle formed by two tangents drawn from a point outside a circle equals half the difference of the measures of the intercepted arcs.
Theorem (p. 738): If a diameter (or radius) is perpendicular to a chord, then it bisects the chord and its arc.	**Corollary:** The measure of the angle formed by two tangents drawn from a point outside a circle is 180° minus the measure of the intercepted minor arc.
Theorem (p. 738): If a radius bisects a chord that is not a diameter, then it is perpendicular to the chord.	**Chord-Chord Angle Theorem:** If two chords intersect in a circle, the measure of an angle formed is half the sum of the measures of arcs intercepted by the angle and its vertical angle.
Theorem (p. 738): The perpendicular bisector of a chord passes through the center of the circle.	**Secant-Secant Angle Theorem:** The measure of the angle formed by two secants drawn from a point outside a circle equals half the difference of the measures of the intercepted arcs.
Theorem (p. 739): If two chords of a circle are congruent, then they are equidistant from the center.	**Secant-Tangent Theorem:** The measure of the angle formed by a secant and a tangent drawn from a point in the exterior of a circle equals half the difference of the measures of the intercepted arcs.
Theorem (p. 739): If two chords of a circle are equidistant from the center, then they are congruent.	**Theorem (p. 758):** If two chords intersect inside a circle, then the product of the segment lengths of one chord is equal to the product of the segment lengths of the other.
Theorem (p. 740): If a line is tangent to a circle, then it is perpendicular to the radius drawn to the point of tangency.	**Theorem (p. 760):** If two secants intersect outside a circle, then the product of the lengths of one secant segment and its external segment is equal to the product of the other secant segment and its external segment.
Theorem (p. 740): If a line in the plane of a circle is perpendicular to the radius at a point on the circle, then the line is tangent to the circle.	**Theorem (p. 762):** If a secant and a tangent intersect outside a circle, then the product of the lengths of the secant segment and its external segment is equal to the length of the tangent segment squared.
Two-Tangent Theorem: Two tangent segments drawn from a point not on a circle are congruent.	

Geometry

Quadrilaterals

Theorem (p. 644): If both pairs of opposite sides of a quadrilateral are congruent, then the quadrilateral is a parallelogram.

Theorem (p. 645): If two sides of a quadrilateral are both congruent and parallel, then the quadrilateral is a parallelogram.

Theorem (p. 650): The diagonals of a rectangle are congruent.

Theorem (p. 651): If a parallelogram has one right angle, then it is a rectangle.

Theorem (p. 652): The diagonals of a rhombus are perpendicular.

Theorem (p. 652): The diagonals of a rhombus bisect the angles of the rhombus.

Trapezoid Midsegment Theorem: The midsegment of a trapezoid is parallel to each of the bases, and its length is half the sum of the lengths of the bases.

Theorem (p. 658): The base angles of an isosceles trapezoid are congruent.

Theorem (p. 659): The diagonals of an isosceles trapezoid are congruent.

Theorem (p. 660): If a quadrilateral is a kite, then exactly one pair of opposite angles is congruent.

Theorem (p. 661): The diagonals of a kite are perpendicular.

Triangles

Triangle Inequality Theorem: The sum of the lengths of any two sides of a triangle is always greater than the length of the third side.

Hinge Theorem: If two sides of one triangle are congruent to two sides of another triangle, but their included angles are not congruent, then the side opposite the larger included angle is longer than the side opposite the smaller included angle.

Converse of Hinge Theorem: If two sides of one triangle are congruent to two sides of another triangle, but the third sides are not congruent, then the angle opposite the longer side is larger than the angle opposite the shorter side.

Triangle Angle-Sum Theorem: The sum of the angle measures of a triangle is 180°.

Corollary: The acute angles of a right triangle are complementary.

Corollary: The measure of each angle of an equiangular triangle is 60°.

Exterior Angle Theorem: The measure of an exterior angle of a triangle equals the sum of the measures of its remote interior angles.

Pythagorean Inequality Theorem: Given: a, b, and c are the side lengths of a triangle with c the length of the longest side:
If $c^2 < a^2 + b^2$, then $\triangle ABC$ is acute.
If $c^2 > a^2 + b^2$, then $\triangle ABC$ is obtuse.

Side-Side-Side Congruence Postulate (SSS): If three sides of one triangle are congruent to the corresponding three sides of another triangle, then the triangles are congruent.

Side-Angle-Side Congruence Postulate (SAS): If two sides and the included angle of one triangle are congruent to the corresponding sides and included angle of another triangle, then the triangles are congruent.

Angle-Side-Angle Congruence Postulate (ASA): If two angles and the included side of one triangle are congruent to the corresponding angles and included side of another triangle, then the triangles are congruent.

Angle-Angle-Side Congruence Theorem (AAS): If two angles and a non-included side of one triangle are congruent to the corresponding angles and non-included side of another triangle, then the triangles are congruent.

Angle-Angle Similarity Postulate (AA): If two angles of one triangle are congruent to the corresponding angles of another triangle, then the triangles are similar.

Triangles (continued)

CPCTC: Corresponding Parts of Congruent Triangles are Congruent.

Theorem (p. 784): If two sides of a triangle are congruent, then the angles opposite those sides are congruent.

Theorem (p. 784): If two angles of a triangle are congruent, then the sides opposite those angles are congruent.

Theorem (p. 786): If a triangle is equilateral, it is also equiangular.

Theorem (p. 786): If a triangle is equiangular, it is also equilateral.

Side-Side-Side Similarity Theorem (SSS): If three sides of one triangle are proportional to the corresponding sides of another triangle, then the triangles are similar.

Side-Angle-Side Similarity Theorem (SAS): If two sides of one triangle are proportional to the corresponding sides of another triangle and the included angles are congruent, then the triangles are similar.

Theorem (p. 804): If a segment that is parallel to a side of a triangle intersects the other two sides, then it divides those two sides into proportional segments.

Theorem (p. 804): If a segment divides two sides of a triangle into proportional segments, then it is parallel to the third side.

Theorem (p. 805): An angle bisector of a triangle divides the opposite sides into two segments that are proportional to the other two sides of the triangle.

Theorem (p. 806): A midsegment of a triangle is parallel to one side of the triangle and is half as long as that side.

Theorem (p. 831): The lines that contain the altitudes of a triangle are concurrent.

Right Triangles

Pythagorean Theorem: The sum of the squares of the lengths of the legs of a right triangle equals the square of the length of the hypotenuse.

$a^2 + b^2 = c^2$

Converse of the Pythagorean Theorem: If the sum of the squares of the lengths of two sides of a triangle is equal to the square of the length of the third side, then the triangle is a right triangle.

45°–45°–90° Triangle Theorem: In a 45°–45°–90° triangle, the length of the hypotenuse is $\sqrt{2}$ times the length of a leg.

30°–60°–90° Triangle Theorem: In a 30°–60°–90° triangle, the hypotenuse is twice the length of the shorter leg, and the longer leg is $\sqrt{3}$ times the length of the shorter leg.

Leg-Leg Congruence (LL): If both legs of a right triangle are congruent to the corresponding legs of another right triangle, then the triangles are congruent.

Leg-Angle Congruence (LA): If one leg and an acute angle of a right triangle are congruent to the corresponding leg and acute angle of another right triangle, then the triangles are congruent.

Hypotenuse-Angle Congruence (HA): If the hypotenuse and an acute angle of a right triangle are congruent to the hypotenuse and corresponding acute angle of another right triangle, then the triangles are congruent.

Hypotenuse-Leg Congruence (HL): If the hypotenuse and one leg of a right triangle are congruent to the hypotenuse and corresponding leg of another right triangle, then the triangles are congruent.

Theorem (p. 796): If the altitude is drawn to the hypotenuse of a right triangle, then the two triangles formed are similar to the original triangle and to each other.

Corollary: The length of the altitude drawn to the hypotenuse of a right triangle is the geometric mean of the lengths of the segments into which it divides the hypotenuse.

Corollary: The length of a leg of a right triangle is the geometric mean of the lengths of the hypotenuse and the adjacent segment of the hypotenuse.

Advanced Algebra

Formulas

Conic Sections

Circles	$(x-h)^2+(y-k)^2=r^2$	$\frac{(x-h)^2}{r^2}+\frac{(y-k)^2}{r^2}=1$
	Horizontal Axis	Vertical Axis
Ellipse	$\frac{(x-h)^2}{a^2}+\frac{(y-k)^2}{b^2}=1$	$\frac{(x-h)^2}{b^2}+\frac{(y-k)^2}{a^2}=1$
Hyperbola	$\frac{(x-h)^2}{a^2}-\frac{(y-k)^2}{b^2}=1$	$\frac{(x-h)^2}{b^2}-\frac{(y-k)^2}{a^2}=1$
Parabola	$x-h=\frac{1}{4p}(y-k)^2$	$y-k=\frac{1}{4p}(x-h)^2$

Variation

Inverse Variation	$y=\frac{k}{x}$ or $k=xy$
Direct Variation	$y=kx$, or $k=\frac{y}{x}$
Joint Variation	$y=kxz$ or $k=\frac{y}{xz}$
Power Function	$y=ax^b$

Interest

Simple Interest	$I=Prt$
Compound Interest	$A=P\left(1+\frac{r}{n}\right)^{nt}$

Exponential Models

Growth	$A(t)=a(1+r)^t$
Decay	$A(t)=a(1-r)^t$

Sequences and Series

	Arithmetic	Geometric
First term	a or a_1	a or a_1
Number of terms	n	n
Constant	difference, d	ratio, r
Sequence, explicit	$a_n=a_1+(n-1)d$	$a_n=a_1r^{n-1}$, if $r\neq 0$
Sequence, recursive	$a_n=a_{n-1}+d$	$a_n=r\cdot a_{n-1}$
Partial Sum of Sequence (Sum of finite series)	$S_n=\frac{n(a_1+a_n)}{2}$; $S_n=\frac{n[2a_1+(n-1)d]}{2}$	$S_n=\frac{a_1(1-r^n)}{1-r}$, if $r\neq 1$
Sum of Infinite Series	None	$S=\frac{a_1}{1-r}$, if $\lvert r\rvert<1$
Fibonacci sequence	$a_n=\frac{(1+\sqrt{5})^n-(1-\sqrt{5})^n}{2^n\sqrt{5}}$	

Cramer's Rule

2 equations in 2 variables	$x = \frac{\det(M_x)}{\det(M_c)} = \frac{\begin{vmatrix} c & b \\ f & e \end{vmatrix}}{\begin{vmatrix} a & b \\ d & e \end{vmatrix}}$ and $y = \frac{\det(M_y)}{\det(M_c)} = \frac{\begin{vmatrix} a & c \\ d & f \end{vmatrix}}{\begin{vmatrix} a & b \\ d & e \end{vmatrix}}$	3 equations in 3 variables	$x = \frac{\det(M_x)}{\det(M_c)}, y = \frac{\det(M_y)}{\det(M_c)}, z = \frac{\det(M_z)}{\det(M_c)}$

Properties of Logarithms

	Exponential	For all *b*	Common logs	Natural logs
Zero	$b^0 = 1, b \neq 0$	$\log_b 1 = 0$	$\log 1 = 0$	$\ln 1 = 0$
One	$b^1 = b$	$\log_b b = 1$	$\log 10 = 1$	$\ln e = 1$
Product	$b^x \cdot b^y = b^{x+y}$	$\log_b(xy) = \log_b x + \log_b y$	$\log(xy) = \log x + \log y$	$\ln(xy) = \ln x + \ln y$
Quotient	$b^{\frac{x}{y}} = b^{x-y}, y \neq 0$	$\log_b\left(\frac{x}{y}\right) = \log_b x - \log_b y$	$\log\left(\frac{x}{y}\right) = \log x - \log y$	$\ln\left(\frac{x}{y}\right) = \ln x - \ln y$
Reciprocal	$b^{\frac{1}{y}} = b^{-y}, y \neq 0$	$\log_b\left(\frac{1}{y}\right) = -\log_b y$	$\log\left(\frac{1}{y}\right) = -\log y$	$\ln\left(\frac{1}{y}\right) = -\ln y$
Power	$(b^x)^y = b^{xy}$	$\log_b x^y = y \log_b x$	$\log x^y = y \log x$	$\ln x^y = y \ln x$
Change of Base		$\log_b x = \frac{\log x}{\log b} = \frac{\ln x}{\ln b}$		

Properties of Radicals

Exponents	$a^{\frac{1}{n}} = \sqrt[n]{a}, n \neq 0$	$a^{\frac{m}{n}} = (\sqrt[n]{a})^m = \sqrt[n]{a^m}, n \neq 0$
Product Rule	$\sqrt{a \cdot b} = \sqrt{a} \cdot \sqrt{b}$	$\sqrt[n]{a} \cdot \sqrt[n]{b} = \sqrt[n]{ab}$
Quotient Rule	$\frac{\sqrt{a}}{\sqrt{b}} = \sqrt{\frac{a}{b}}, b \neq 0$	$\frac{\sqrt[n]{a}}{\sqrt[n]{b}} = \sqrt[n]{\frac{a}{b}}, b \neq 0$

Transformations of Functions

Reflections

$g(x) = -f(x)$	over *x*-axis
$g(x) = f(-x)$	over *y*-axis

Dilations

$g(x) = f(cx)$	horizontal $0 < c < 1$: stretch $c > 1$: shrink
$g(x) = c \cdot f(x)$	vertical $0 < c < 1$: shrink $c > 1$: stretch

Translations

$g(x) = f(x - h) + k$ $g(x) = ab^{x-h} + k$ $g(x) = \frac{a}{x-h} + k$ $g(x) = \sqrt{x-h} + k$	$h > 0$: right *h* units $h < 0$: left *h* units $k > 0$: up *k* units $k < 0$: down *k* units

Advanced Algebra

Solving Word Problems

Step 1	Read the problem carefully. Determine what number or numbers need to be found.
Step 2	Represent one unknown number with a suitable variable.
Step 3	Use conditions stated in the problem to write expressions for other numbers.
Step 4	Use additional conditions to find the relationship between expressions. Write the expressions algebraically. Connect them with the appropriate sign ($=$, $<$, $>$, $\leq$, or $\geq$.)
Step 5	Solve the equation or inequality.
Step 6	Check to see if the resulting solution matches the conditions stated in the problem.

Word Problem Formulas

Distance	$d = rt$	d = distance r = rate t = time
Consecutive Number	$A = n + (n + 1)$ $B = n(n + 2)$	n = the first of two consecutive numbers $n + 1$ = the next consecutive number $n + 2$ = the next consecutive odd or even number A = sum of two consecutive numbers B = product of two consecutive odd (or even) numbers
Digit	$A(u + t + h) = u + 10t + 100h$	A = number multiplied by the sum of the digits u = the ones digit of the given number t = the tens digit of the given number h = the hundreds digit of the given number
Coin	$0.25q + 0.1d + 0.05n + 0.01p = A$	q = number of quarters d = number of dimes n = number of nickels p = number of pennies A = total worth
Lever	$\ell_1 w_1 = \ell_2 w_2$	ℓ_1 = length from fulcrum to first weight w_1 = first weight ℓ_2 = length from fulcrum to second weight w_2 = second weight
Work	$\frac{1}{a} + \frac{1}{b} = \frac{1}{n}$	a = length of time it takes person A to complete a task b = length of time it takes person B to complete a task n = length of time it would take A and B to complete the task together

Word Problem Formulas (continued)

Mixture — Use this table format.

Concentration	Volume	Percent Substance	Total Volume Substance
1	V	$a\%$	$0.01(a)(V)$
2	Total – V	$b\%$	$0.01(b)(\text{Total} - V)$
Final	Total	$c\%$	$0.01(c)(\text{Total})$

Parent Functions

Linear (Identity)

$y = x$

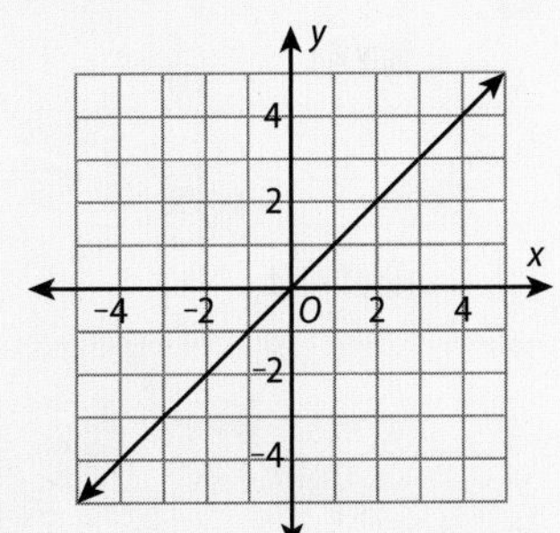

Quadratic (Squared)

$y = x^2$

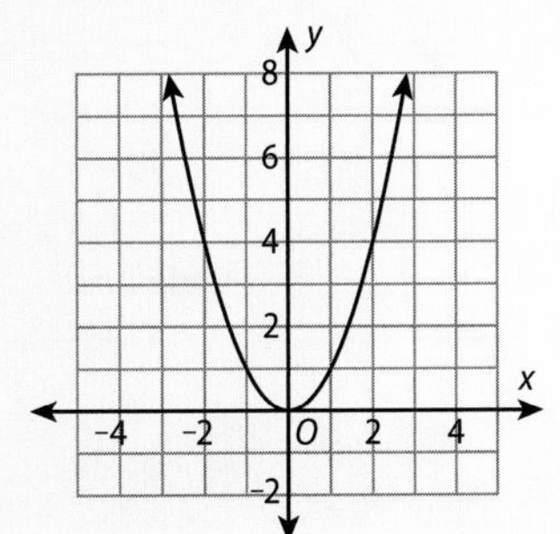

Cubic (Cubed)

$y = x^3$

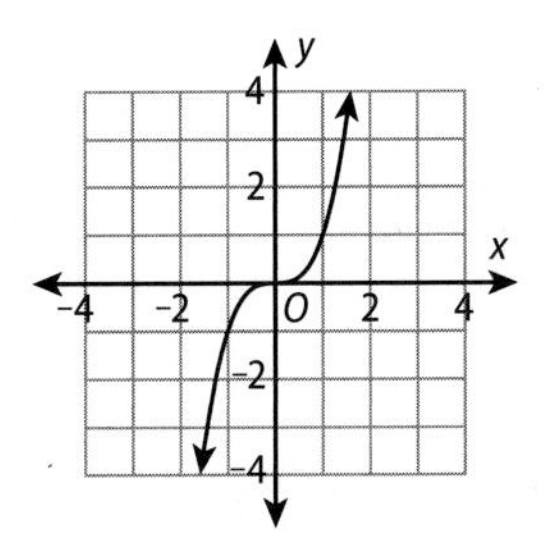

Rational (Reciprocal)

$y = \frac{1}{x}$

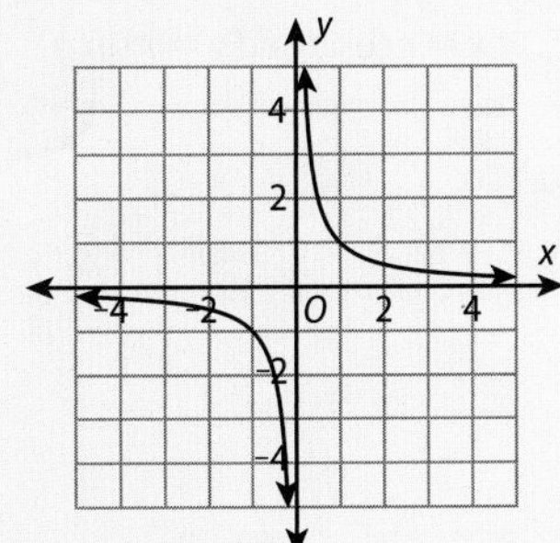

Radical (Square Root)

$y = \sqrt{x}$

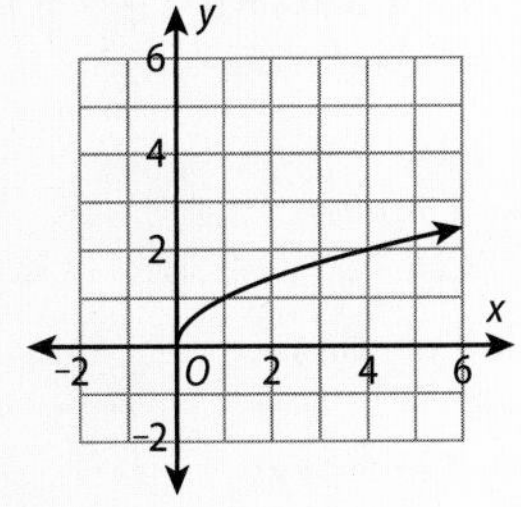

Cube Root

$y = \sqrt[3]{x}$

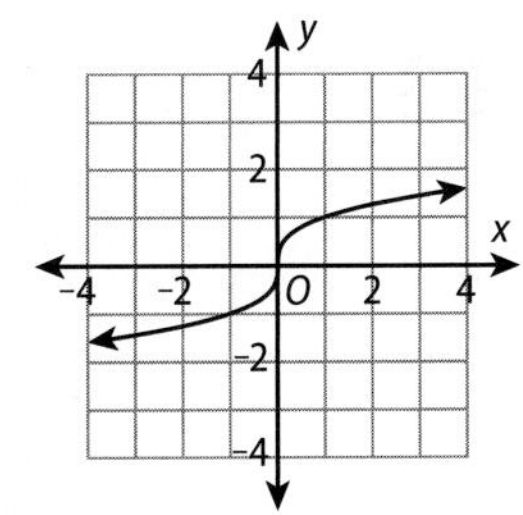

Absolute Value

$y = |x|$

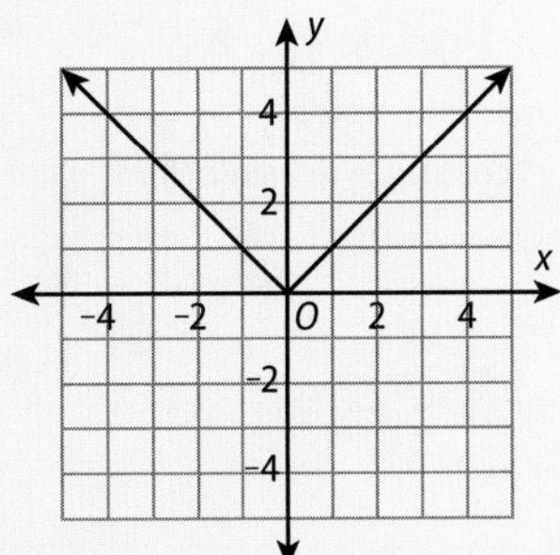

Exponential

$y = e^x$

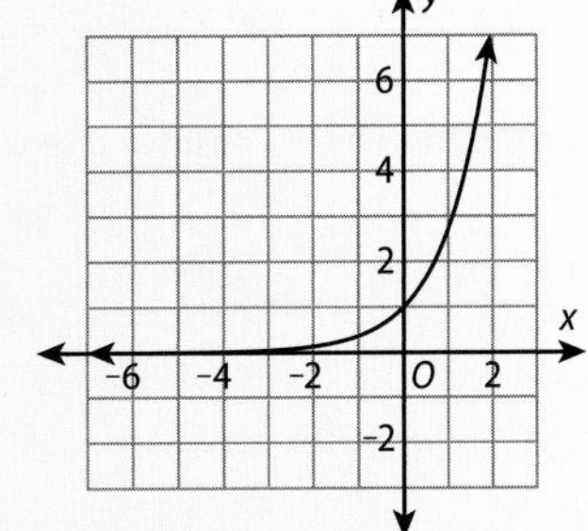

Natural Logarithm

$y = \ln x$

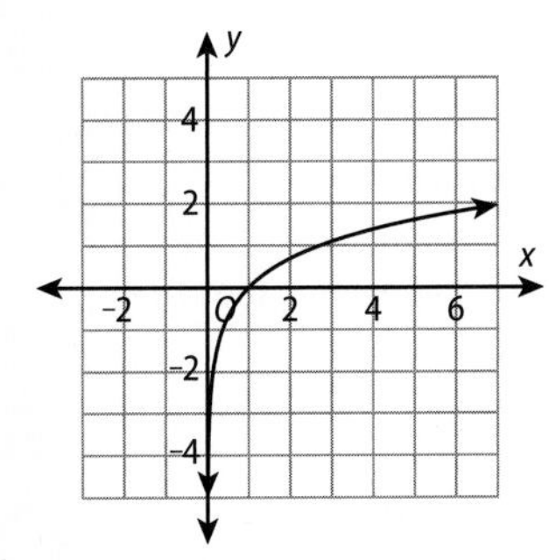

Trigonometry

Trigonometric Ratios

$\sin A = \frac{\text{leg opposite } \angle A}{\text{hypotenuse}}$	$\cos A = \frac{\text{leg adjacent } \angle A}{\text{hypotenuse}}$	$\tan A = \frac{\text{leg opposite } \angle A}{\text{leg adjacent } \angle A}$
$\csc A = \frac{\text{hypotenuse}}{\text{leg opposite } \angle A}$	$\sec A = \frac{\text{hypotenuse}}{\text{leg adjacent } \angle A}$	$\cot A = \frac{\text{leg adjacent } \angle A}{\text{leg opposite } \angle A}$

Trigonometric Values of the Special Angles

Degrees	Radians	$\sin\theta$	$\cos\theta$	$\tan\theta$	$\csc\theta$	$\sec\theta$	$\cot\theta$
0	0	0	1	0	undefined	1	undefined
30	$\frac{\pi}{6}$	$\frac{1}{2}$	$\frac{\sqrt{3}}{2}$	$\frac{\sqrt{3}}{3}$	2	$\frac{2\sqrt{3}}{3}$	$\sqrt{3}$
45	$\frac{\pi}{4}$	$\frac{\sqrt{2}}{2}$	$\frac{\sqrt{2}}{2}$	1	$\sqrt{2}$	$\sqrt{2}$	1
60	$\frac{\pi}{3}$	$\frac{\sqrt{3}}{2}$	$\frac{1}{2}$	$\sqrt{3}$	$\frac{2\sqrt{3}}{3}$	2	$\frac{\sqrt{3}}{3}$
90	$\frac{\pi}{2}$	1	0	undefined	1	undefined	0

Conversion Formulas

Degrees to Radians:	$y \text{ radians} = x° \cdot \frac{\pi \text{ radians}}{180°}$	Radians to Degrees:	$y° = x \text{ radians} \cdot \frac{180°}{\pi \text{ radians}}$
Rectangular coordinates to Polar coordinates:		Polar coordinates to Rectangular coordinates:	
$P(x, y)$	$r = \pm\sqrt{x^2 + y^2}$ and $\cos q = \frac{x}{r}$ and $\sin q = \frac{y}{r}$	$P(r, q)$	$x = r\cos q$ and $y = r\sin q$

Rules and Properties

Inverse sine	$y = \sin^{-1} x$ if and only if $x = \sin y$
Inverse cosine	$y = \cos^{-1} x$ if and only if $x = \cos y$
Inverse tangent	$y = \tan^{-1} x$ if and only if $x = \tan y$
Law of Sines	$\frac{\sin A}{a} = \frac{\sin B}{b} = \frac{\sin C}{c}$
Law of Cosines	$a^2 = b^2 + c^2 - 2bc\cos A$ $b^2 = a^2 + c^2 - 2ac\cos B$ $c^2 = a^2 + b^2 - 2ab\cos C$
DeMoivre's Theorem	Let $z = r\cos\theta + (r\sin\theta)i$ and n be a positive integer. $z^n = r^n\cos(n\theta) + (r^n\sin(n\theta))i$
Magnitude of a Vector in the Plane	$\|\overrightarrow{PQ}\| = \sqrt{(x_2 - x_1)^2 + (y_2 - y_1)^2}$
Angle Between Two Vectors	$\mathbf{u} \cdot \mathbf{v} = \|\mathbf{u}\|\,\|\mathbf{v}\|\cos\theta$
Dot Product of Two Vectors	$\mathbf{u} \cdot \mathbf{v} = x_1x_2 + y_1y_2$

Identities

Reciprocal Identities

$\sin\theta = \frac{1}{\csc\theta}$	$\cos\theta = \frac{1}{\sec\theta}$	$\tan\theta = \frac{1}{\cot\theta}$
$\csc\theta = \frac{1}{\sin\theta}$	$\sec\theta = \frac{1}{\cos\theta}$	$\cot\theta = \frac{1}{\tan\theta}$

Quotient Identities

$\tan\theta = \frac{\sin\theta}{\cos\theta}$	$\cot\theta = \frac{\cos\theta}{\sin\theta}$	

Negative Identities

$\sin(-\theta) = -\sin\theta$	$\cos(-\theta) = \cos\theta$	$\tan(-\theta) = -\tan\theta$
$\csc(-\theta) = -\csc\theta$	$\sec(-\theta) = \sec\theta$	$\cot(-\theta) = -\cot\theta$

Pythagorean Identities

$\cos^2\theta + \sin^2\theta = 1$	$\tan^2\theta + 1 = \sec^2\theta$	$\cot^2\theta + 1 = \csc^2\theta$
$\sin\theta = \pm\sqrt{1-\cos^2\theta}$	$\sec\theta = \pm\sqrt{1+\tan^2\theta}$	$\csc\theta = \pm\sqrt{1+\cot^2\theta}$

Cofunction Identities

$\sin\theta = \cos(90° - \theta)$	$\tan\theta = \cot(90° - \theta)$	$\sec\theta = \csc(90° - \theta)$
$\cos\theta = \sin(90° - \theta)$	$\cot\theta = \tan(90° - \theta)$	$\csc\theta = \sec(90° - \theta)$

Coterminal Identities

$\sin\theta = \sin(360° + \theta)$	$\cos\theta = \cos(360° + \theta)$	$\tan\theta = \tan(360° + \theta)$
$\csc\theta = \csc(360° + \theta)$	$\sec\theta = \sec(360° + \theta)$	$\cot\theta = \cot(360° + \theta)$

Sum and Difference Identities

$\sin(\alpha+\beta) = \sin\alpha\cos\beta + \cos\alpha\sin\beta$	$\sin(\alpha-\beta) = \sin\alpha\cos\beta - \cos\alpha\sin\beta$
$\cos(\alpha+\beta) = \cos\alpha\cos\beta - \sin\alpha\sin\beta$	$\cos(\alpha-\beta) = \cos\alpha\cos\beta + \sin\alpha\sin\beta$
$\tan(\alpha+\beta) = \frac{\tan\alpha + \tan\beta}{1 - \tan\alpha\tan\beta}$	$\tan(\alpha-\beta) = \frac{\tan\alpha - \tan\beta}{1 + \tan\alpha\tan\beta}$

Double-Angle Identities

$\sin 2\alpha = 2\sin\alpha\cos\alpha$	$\cos 2\alpha = \cos^2\alpha - \sin^2\alpha$
$\tan 2\alpha = \frac{2\tan\alpha}{1-\tan^2\alpha}$	$\cos 2\alpha = 1 - 2\sin^2\alpha$ $\cos 2\alpha = 2\cos^2\alpha - 1$

Identities (continued)

Half-Angle Identities

$\sin\frac{\alpha}{2} = \pm\sqrt{\frac{1-\cos\alpha}{2}}$

$\cos\frac{\alpha}{2} = \pm\sqrt{\frac{1+\cos\alpha}{2}}$

$\tan\frac{\alpha}{2} = \pm\sqrt{\frac{1-\cos\alpha}{1+\cos\alpha}}, \cos\alpha \neq -1$

$\tan\frac{\alpha}{2} = \frac{1-\cos\alpha}{\sin\alpha}, \sin\alpha \neq 0$

$\tan\frac{\alpha}{2} = \frac{\sin\alpha}{1+\cos\alpha}, \cos\alpha \neq -1$

Product-to-Sum Identities

$\cos\alpha\cos\beta = \frac{1}{2}[\cos(\alpha-\beta) + \cos(\alpha+\beta)]$

$\sin\alpha\cos\beta = \frac{1}{2}[\sin(\alpha+\beta) + \sin(\alpha-\beta)]$

$\sin\alpha\sin\beta = \frac{1}{2}[\cos(\alpha-\beta) - \cos(\alpha+\beta)]$

$\cos\alpha\sin\beta = \frac{1}{2}[\sin(\alpha+\beta) - \sin(\alpha-\beta)]$

Sum-to-Product Identities

$\sin x + \sin y = 2\sin\left(\frac{x+y}{2}\right)\cos\left(\frac{x-y}{2}\right)$

$\cos x + \cos y = 2\cos\left(\frac{x+y}{2}\right)\cos\left(\frac{x-y}{2}\right)$

$\sin x - \sin y = 2\cos\left(\frac{x+y}{2}\right)\sin\left(\frac{x-y}{2}\right)$

$\cos x - \cos y = -2\sin\left(\frac{x+y}{2}\right)\sin\left(\frac{x-y}{2}\right)$

Trigonometry

Trigonometric Functions

Angle	Radians	Sine	Cosine	Tangent	Cotangent	Secant	Cosecant		
0°	0.0000	0.0000	1.0000	0.0000	undefined	1.0000	undefined	1.5708	90°
1	0.0175	0.0175	0.9998	0.0175	57.2900	1.0002	57.2987	1.5533	89
2	0.0349	0.0349	0.9994	0.0349	28.6363	1.0006	28.6537	1.5359	88
3	0.0524	0.0523	0.9986	0.0524	19.0811	1.0014	19.1073	1.5184	87
4	0.0698	0.0698	0.9976	0.0699	14.3007	1.0024	14.3356	1.5010	86
5	0.0873	0.0872	0.9962	0.0875	11.4301	1.0038	11.4737	1.4835	85
6	0.1047	0.1045	0.9945	0.1051	9.5144	1.0055	9.5668	1.4661	84
7	0.1222	0.1219	0.9925	0.1228	8.1443	1.0075	8.2055	1.4486	83
8	0.1396	0.1392	0.9903	0.1405	7.1154	1.0098	7.1853	1.4312	82
9	0.1571	0.1564	0.9877	0.1584	6.3138	1.0125	6.3925	1.4137	81
10	0.1745	0.1736	0.9848	0.1763	5.6713	1.0154	5.7588	1.3963	80
11	0.1920	0.1908	0.9816	0.1944	5.1446	1.0187	5.2408	1.3788	79
12	0.2094	0.2079	0.9781	0.2126	4.7046	1.0223	4.8097	1.3614	78
13	0.2269	0.2250	0.9744	0.2309	4.3315	1.0263	4.4454	1.3439	77
14	0.2443	0.2419	0.9703	0.2493	4.0108	1.0306	4.1336	1.3265	76
15	0.2618	0.2588	0.9659	0.2679	3.7321	1.0353	3.8637	1.3090	75
16	0.2793	0.2756	0.9613	0.2867	3.4874	1.0403	3.6280	1.2915	74
17	0.2967	0.2924	0.9563	0.3057	3.2709	1.0457	3.4203	1.2714	73
18	0.3142	0.3090	0.9511	0.3249	3.0777	1.0515	3.2361	1.2566	72
19	0.3316	0.3256	0.9455	0.3443	2.9042	1.0576	3.0716	1.2392	71
20	0.3491	0.3420	0.9397	0.3640	2.7475	1.0642	2.9238	1.2217	70
21	0.3665	0.3584	0.9336	0.3839	2.6051	1.0711	2.7904	1.2043	69
22	0.3840	0.3746	0.9272	0.4040	2.4751	1.0785	2.6695	1.1868	68
23	0.4014	0.3907	0.9205	0.4245	2.3559	1.0864	2.5593	1.1694	67
24	0.4189	0.4067	0.9135	0.4452	2.2460	1.0946	2.4586	1.1519	66
25	0.4363	0.4226	0.9063	0.4663	2.1445	1.1034	2.3662	1.1345	65
26	0.4538	0.4384	0.8988	0.4877	2.0503	1.1126	2.2812	1.1170	64
27	0.4712	0.4540	0.8910	0.5095	1.9626	1.1223	2.2027	1.0996	63
28	0.4887	0.4695	0.8829	0.5317	1.8807	1.1326	2.1301	1.0821	62
29	0.5061	0.4848	0.8746	0.5543	1.8040	1.1434	2.0627	1.0647	61
30	0.5236	0.5000	0.8660	0.5774	1.7321	1.1547	2.0000	1.0472	60
31	0.5411	0.5150	0.8572	0.6009	1.6643	1.1666	1.9416	1.0297	59
32	0.5585	0.5299	0.8480	0.6249	1.6003	1.1792	1.8871	1.0123	58
33	0.5760	0.5446	0.8387	0.6494	1.5399	1.1924	1.8361	0.9948	57
34	0.5934	0.5592	0.8290	0.6745	1.4826	1.2062	1.7883	0.9774	56
35	0.6109	0.5736	0.8192	0.7002	1.4281	1.2208	1.7434	0.9599	55
36	0.6283	0.5878	0.8090	0.7265	1.3764	1.2361	1.7013	0.9425	54
37	0.6458	0.6018	0.7986	0.7536	1.3270	1.2521	1.6616	0.9250	53
38	0.6632	0.6157	0.7880	0.7813	1.2799	1.2690	1.6243	0.9076	52
39	0.6807	0.6293	0.7771	0.8098	1.2349	1.2868	1.5890	0.8901	51
40	0.6981	0.6428	0.7660	0.8391	1.1918	1.3054	1.5557	0.8727	50
41	0.7156	0.6561	0.7547	0.8693	1.1504	1.3250	1.5243	0.8552	49
42	0.7330	0.6691	0.7431	0.9004	1.1106	1.3456	1.4945	0.8378	48
43	0.7505	0.6820	0.7314	0.9325	1.0724	1.3673	1.4663	0.8203	47
44	0.7679	0.6947	0.7093	0.9657	1.0355	1.3902	1.4396	0.8029	46
45°	0.7854	0.7071	0.7071	1.0000	1.0000	1.4142	1.4142	0.7854	45°
		Cosine	Sine	Cotangent	Tangent	Cosecant	Secant	Radians	Angle

Parent Functions

Sine

$y = \sin x$

period $= 2\pi$; amplitude $= 1$

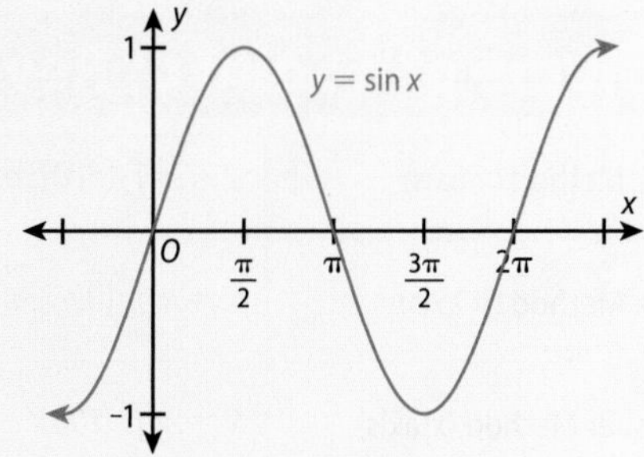

Cosine

$y = \cos x$

period $= 2\pi$; amplitude $= 1$

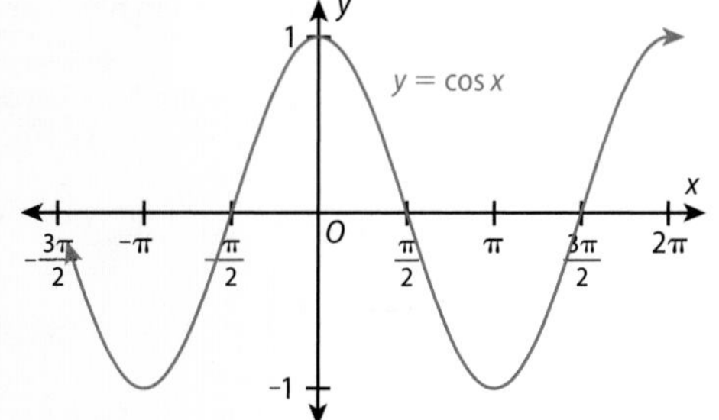

Tangent

$y = \tan x$

period $= \pi$; asymptotes: $x = \frac{\pi}{2} + k\pi$

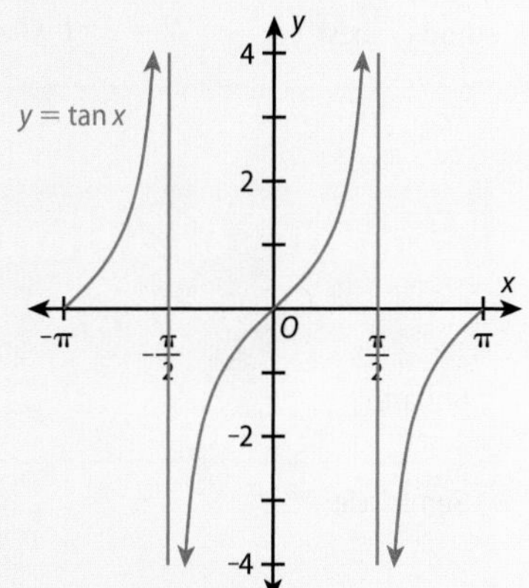

Cotangent

$y = \cot x$

period $= \pi$; asymptotes: $x = k\pi$

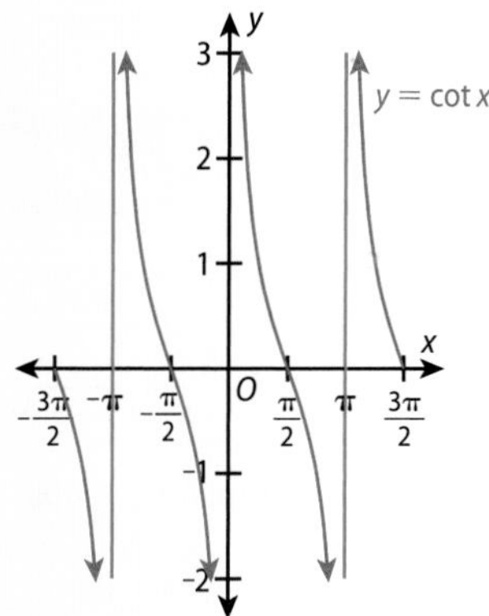

Secant

$y = \sec x$

period $= \pi$; asymptotes: $x = \frac{\pi}{2} + k\pi$

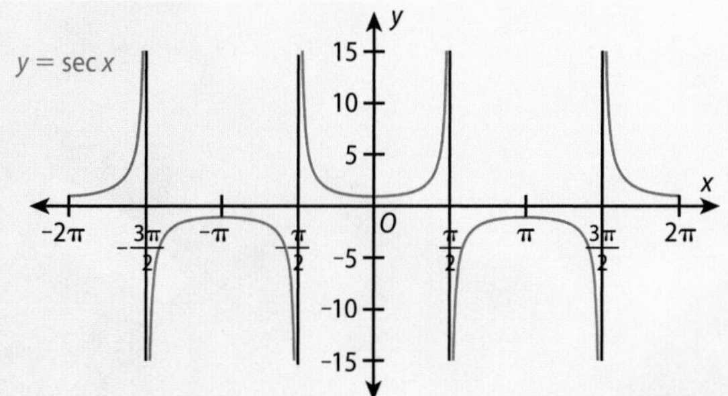

Cosecant

$y = \csc x$

period $= \pi$; asymptotes: $x = k\pi$

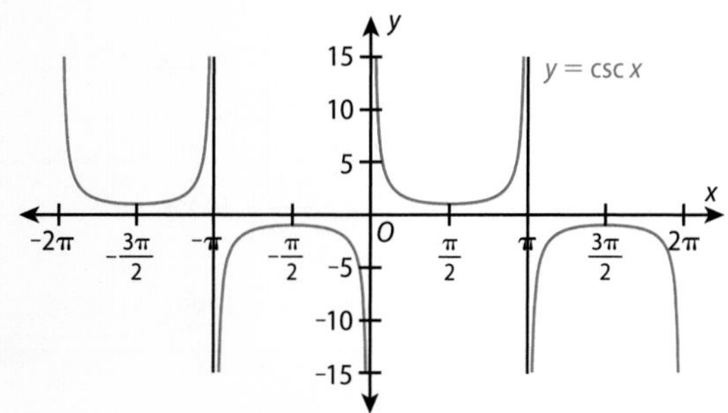

Calculus

Limit Rules

Constant Rule	$\lim_{x \to c} k = k$
Constant Multiplier Rule	$\lim_{x \to c} kf(x) = k \lim_{x \to c} f(x)$
Sum Rule	$\lim_{x \to c} [f(x) + g(x)] = \lim_{x \to c} f(x) + \lim_{x \to c} g(x)$
Difference Rule	$\lim_{x \to c} [f(x) - g(x)] = \lim_{x \to c} f(x) - \lim_{x \to c} g(x)$
Product Rule	$\lim_{x \to c} [f(x) \cdot g(x)] = \lim_{x \to c} f(x) \cdot \lim_{x \to c} g(x)$
Quotient Rule	$\lim_{x \to c} \frac{f(x)}{g(x)} = \frac{\lim_{x \to c} f(x)}{\lim_{x \to c} g(x)}$, if $\lim_{x \to c} g(x) \neq 0$
Power Rule	$\lim_{x \to c} [f(x)]^n = \left[\lim_{x \to c} f(x)\right]^n$
nth Root Rule	$\lim_{x \to c} \sqrt[n]{f(x)} = \sqrt[n]{\lim_{x \to c} f(x)}$, if $\lim_{x \to c} f(x) > 0$
Limits of Radicals	$\lim_{x \to c} \sqrt[n]{x} = \sqrt[n]{c}$, for all c when n is odd, and for $c > 0$ when n is even.
Limits of Composite Functions	If $\lim_{x \to c} g(x) = L$ and $\lim_{x \to c} f(x) = f(L)$, then $f(g(x)) = f\left(\lim_{x \to c} g(x)\right) = f(L)$.

For Derivative Rules, see the table of Derivatives on the next page, or go to pages 2170 and 2172 for constant, sum, difference, power, product, and quotient rules.

For Integral Rules, see the table of Integrals on the next page, or go to page 2234 for constant, constant multiplier, sum, difference, and power rules.

Volume of a Solid of Revolution

Disk Method (x-axis)	$V = \pi \int_a^b [R(x)]^2\, dx$
Disk Method (y-axis)	$V = \pi \int_a^b [R(y)]^2\, dy$
Washer Method (x-axis)	$V = \pi \int_a^b (f(x))^2 - (g(x))^2\, dx$
Washer Method (y-axis)	$V = \pi \int_a^b (f(y))^2 - (g(y))^2\, dy$
Shell Method (x-axis)	$V = 2\pi \int_a^b yf(y)dx$
Shell Method (y-axis)	$V = 2\pi \int_a^b xf(x)dx$

Formulas, Theorems, and Definitions

Special Trigonometric Limits	$\lim_{a \to 0} \frac{\sin a}{a} = 1;\ \lim_{a \to 0} \frac{1 - \cos a}{a} = 0$
Definition of a Derivative	$f'(x) = \lim_{\Delta x \to 0} \frac{f(x + \Delta x) - f(x)}{\Delta x}$
Chain Rule	$\frac{d}{dx}[f(g(x))] = f'(g(x)) \cdot g'(x)$
The Mean Value Theorem	$f'(c) = \frac{f(b) - f(a)}{b - a}$
Area Between Two Curves	$A = \int_a^b f(x)dx - \int_a^b g(x)dx = \int_a^b [f(x) - g(x)]dx$
Fundamental Theorem of Calculus	$\int_a^b f(x)dx = F(b) - F(a)$
Second Fundamental Theorem of Calculus	$\frac{d}{dx}\int_a^x f(t)dt = f(x)$
The Mean Value Theorem for Integrals	$\int_a^b f(x)dx = f(c)(b - a)$
Average Value of a Function	$f(c) = \frac{1}{b - a}\int_a^b f(x)dx$
Integration by Parts	$\int udv = uv - \int vdu$

Volumes of Solids with Known Cross Sections

Square	$V = \int (\text{base})^2\, dx$
Semicircle	$V = \frac{\pi}{8}\int (\text{base})^2\, dx$
Right Isosceles Triangle	$V = \frac{1}{2}\int (\text{base})^2\, dx$
Equilateral Triangle	$V = \frac{\sqrt{3}}{4}\int (\text{base})^2\, dx$

Derivatives

Function, f	Derivative, $\frac{df}{dx}$	Function, f	Derivative, $\frac{df}{dx}$	Function, f	Derivative, $\frac{df}{dx}$
c	0	$\frac{u}{v}$	$\frac{(vu' - uv')}{v^2}$	$\text{arc tan } x$	$\frac{1}{(1 + x^2)}$
x	1	$f[u(x)]$	$\frac{df}{du} \cdot \frac{du}{dx}$	$\text{arc cot } x$	$-\frac{1}{(1 + x^2)}$
kx	k	$\sin x$	$\cos x$	$\text{arc sec } x$	$\frac{1}{\lvert x\rvert\sqrt{x^2 - 1}}$
x^n	nx^{n-1}	$\cos x$	$-\sin x$	$\text{arc csc } x$	$-\frac{1}{\lvert x\rvert\sqrt{x^2 - 1}}$
$k[g(x)]$	$kg'(x)$	$\tan x$	$\sec^2 x$	e^x	e^x
$\frac{1}{x}$	$-\frac{1}{x^2}$	$\cot x$	$-\csc^2 x$	a^x	$a^x \ln a$
$\frac{1}{x^n}$	$-\frac{n}{x^{n+1}}$	$\sec x$	$\sec x \tan x$	$\ln x$	$\frac{1}{x}$
$\sqrt{x}$	$\frac{1}{2\sqrt{x}}$	$\csc x$	$\csc x \cot x$	$\log_a x$	$\frac{1}{x \ln a}$
$u + v$	$u' + v'$	$\text{arc sin } x$	$\frac{1}{\sqrt{1 - x^2}}$	$f^{-1}(x)$	$\frac{1}{\frac{d}{dx}(f(f^{-1}(x)))}$
uv	$uv' + vu'$	$\text{arc cos } x$	$-\frac{1}{\sqrt{1 - x^2}}$		

Integrals

Function, f	Integral, $\int f\,dx$	Function, f	Integral, $\int f\,dx$	Function, f	Integral, $\int f\,dx$
k	kx	e^x	e^x	$\sec^2 x$	$\tan x$
x	$\frac{1}{2}x^2$	$\ln x$	$x \ln x - x$	$\csc^2 x$	$-\cot x$
x^n	$\frac{x^{n+1}}{(n+1)}\quad n \neq -1$	$\sin x$	$-\cos x$	$\sec x \tan x$	$\sec x$
$\frac{1}{x}$	$\ln x$	$\cos x$	$\sin x$	$\csc x \cot x$	$-\csc x$
$\frac{1}{x^n}$	$-\frac{1}{(n-1)x^{n-1}}\quad n \neq 1$	$\tan x$	$\ln \sec x$	$\frac{1}{(ax + b)}$	$\left(\frac{1}{a}\right)\ln(ax + b)$
$\sqrt{x}$	$\frac{2}{3}x^{\frac{3}{2}}$	$\cot x$	$\ln \sin x$	$\frac{1}{(x^2 + a^2)}$	$\left(\frac{1}{a}\right)\text{arc tan}\left(\frac{x}{a}\right)$
$\frac{1}{\sqrt{x}}$	$2\sqrt{x}$	$\sec x$	$\ln(\tan x + \sec x)$	$\frac{1}{(x^2 - a^2)}$	$\left(\frac{1}{2a}\right)\ln\frac{(y - a)}{(x + a)}$
$x^{\frac{n}{r}}$	$\frac{rx^{\left(\frac{n}{r}\right)+1}}{r + n}$	$\csc x$	$\ln(\csc x - \cot x)$	$\frac{1}{\sqrt{(a^2 - x^2)}}$	$\text{arc sin}\left(\frac{x}{a}\right)$
$x^{-\frac{n}{r}}$	$\frac{r}{(r - n)x^{\left(\frac{n}{r}\right)-1}}$	$\sin^2 x$	$\frac{1}{2}x - \frac{1}{2}\sin x \cos x$	$\frac{1}{\sqrt{(x^2 \pm a^2)}}$	$\ln\left(x + \sqrt{(x^2 \pm a^2)}\right)$

Glossary

A

absolute maximum (p. 2202) The highest point on a closed interval.

absolute minimum (p. 2202) The lowest point on a closed interval.

absolute value (p. 1387) The distance of a number from zero on a number line.

absolute value of a complex number (p. 1114) The absolute value of a complex number $a + bi$ is $\sqrt{a^2 + b^2}$.

acre (p. 482) A unit of area equal to 43,560 square feet.

acute angle (pp. 140, 624, 894) An angle with measure greater than 0° and less than 90°.

acute triangle (p. 156) A triangle with three acute angles.

add or subtract from a known fact (p. 70) A way to find the product of two numbers.

addends (p. 82) The numbers that are added to form a sum.

addition (pp. 56, 82) Mathematical operation in which the values of two or more numbers are combined.

addition method (p. 1572) A method of solving a system of equations that involves adding the equations to eliminate a variable.

additive identity (p. 1414) The number zero; the sum of zero and any number is that number.

additive inverse (p. 1415) The opposite of a given number.

adjacent angles (pp. 146, 625) Coplanar angles that share only an endpoint and one side.

adjacent arcs (p. 728) Arcs of the same circle that share exactly one endpoint.

algebraic expression (p. 1422) A mathematical phrase that contains one or more numbers, one or more variables, and one or more arithmetic operations.

algebraic inequality (p. 1492) A mathematical phrase that contains an inequality with a variable.

alternate exterior angles (p. 150) Two non-adjacent exterior angles on opposite sides of a transversal.

alternate interior angles (pp. 150, 630) Two non-adjacent interior angles on opposite sides of a transversal.

altitude of a triangle (pp. 537, 872) The perpendicular distance from a vertex to the line containing the side opposite that vertex.

amplitude (p. 952) The absolute value of half the difference between the maximum and minimum values of a trigonometric function.

angle (pp. 136, 894) A figure formed by two rays with a common endpoint.

angle bisector (p. 868) A ray that divides an angle into two adjacent angles that are congruent.

angle of depression (p. 924) The angle between a horizontal line and the line of sight from an observer to an object at a lower level.

angle of elevation (p. 924) The angle between a horizontal line and the line of sight from an observer to an object at a higher level.

angle of rotation See *rotation*.

angular velocity (p. 942) The number of degrees (radians, or revolutions) per unit time through which a point travels along a circular path.

apothem (p. 690) The distance from the center to a side of a regular polygon.

arc (p. 728) Part of a circle between two points on a circle.

arc of a chord (p. 736) The minor arc cut off by a chord of a circle.

area (pp. 482, 504, 528) The size of the surface of a flat figure or shape.

arithmetic pattern (p. 438) A pattern that grows when the same number is added to each subsequent term.

arithmetic sequence (p. 1859) A sequence in which consecutive terms differ by a constant amount *d*.

arithmetic series (p. 1862) The sum of the terms of an arithmetic sequence.

array (pp. 69, 75) An arrangement of objects in rows and columns where each row has the same number of objects.

asymptote (pp. 968, 1932, 1996, 2020) A line that a graph gets closer and closer to, but never touches or crosses.

average value of a function (p. 2270) If f is a continuous function on $[a, b]$, then the average value $f(c)$ is $f(c) = \frac{1}{b-a}\int_a^b f(x)dx$.

axis of a cone (p. 713) The line segment whose endpoints are the vertex of the cone and the center of the base.

axis of revolution (p. 2278) The line about which a two-dimensional figure revolves that results in a three-dimensional figure, called a *solid of revolution*.

axis of symmetry (pp. 1688, 1910) The line that can be drawn through a parabola so that one side of the parabola is a reflection of the other. It is perpendicular to the directrix and passes through the focus.

B

bar graph (pp. 188, 1270) A graph that uses horizontal or vertical bars to display data in categories.

base angles of a trapezoid (p. 656) Each pair of angles that lie on the same base of a trapezoid.

base angles of an isosceles triangle (p. 784) The two angles adjacent to the base of an isosceles triangle.

base design (p. 706) A drawing that shows the base of a figure made of cubes and the number of cubes in each position.

base of a power (pp. 294, 1396) A number that is used as a factor a given number of times.

base of an isosceles triangle (p. 784) The side that is not a leg, or any side if the triangle is equilateral.

base(s) of a geometric figure See *cone*, *cylinder*, *prism*, *pyramid*, *trapezoid*.

benchmark (p. 316) A reference number such as $0, \frac{1}{2}$, and 1 to which other numbers are compared.

biased sample (p. 1222) A sample that overrepresents or underrepresents some part of the population.

biconditional statement (p. 616) A statement of the form *p if and only if q*. *p* is true if and only if *q* is true.

binomial (pp. 1348, 1600) A polynomial that has two terms.

binomial coefficient (p. 1349) The formula for *n* items taken *k* at a time, ${}_nC_k = \frac{n!}{k!(n-k)!}$.

binomial experiment (p. 1344) An experiment that has exactly two possible outcomes, one of which is called a success.

boundary line (p. 1558) The graph of the related equation in the graph of a linear inequality.

bounded (p. 1590) An area on a graph that is completely enclosed by line segments and forms a polygon.

box-and-whisker plot (p. 1280) A data display that divides a set of data into four equal parts and shows how the data is displayed among these parts.

C

capacity (pp. 484, 506) The measure of the maximum amount of a liquid (or some other substance) a container can hold.

Celsius scale (p. 518) A scale for measuring temperature in which the freezing point of water is 0° and the boiling point is 100°.

center of a circle (pp. 162, 728) The point in the plane of a circle that is the same distance from every point on the circle.

center of a dilation (p. 850) The point about which a figure is dilated.

center of a regular polygon (p. 690) The center of the circumscribed circle.

center of rotation (p. 842) The point about which a figure is rotated.

central angle of a circle (p. 728) An angle whose vertex is the center of a circle.

central angle of a regular polygon (p. 690) An angle formed by two radii of the circumscribed circle.

centroid (p. 866) The intersection of the three medians of a triangle.

chord (pp. 162, 734) A segment whose endpoints are points on a circle.

circle (pp. 162, 728, 1920) The set of points in a plane the same distance from a given point, called the *center*.

circle graph (pp. 194, 1272) A graph that uses a circle to display a set of data as parts of a whole.

circumcenter (p. 876) The point where the perpendicular bisectors of the sides of a triangle intersect.

circumcircle of a polygon (p. 877) A circle that passes through all of the vertices of a polygon.

circumference (p. 162) The distance around a circle.

circumscribed circle (p. 877) A circle that contains all the vertices of a polygon.

closed interval (p. 2151) A set of real numbers that contains its endpoints.

cluster sample (p. 1227) A sample that has a population that is separated into subgroups, which are selected at random.

coefficient (pp. 588, 1422, 1601) The number that is multiplied by the variables of a term.

cofunctions (p. 905) Sine and cosine, secant and cosecant, tangent and cotangent.

combination (p. 1248) An arrangement of items, events, or people from a set without regard to the order.

combinatorial identity (p. 1249) A combination that in general has a value of ${}_nC_n$ that is equal to 1.

common difference (p. 1859) The constant amount by which consecutive terms differ in an arithmetic sequence.

common factor (p. 287) A factor shared by two or more numbers.

common logarithm (p. 1974) A logarithm with base 10 in a logarithmic expression.

common multiple (p. 288) A multiple shared by two or more numbers.

common ratio (p. 1866) The nonzero constant that is the ratio of consecutive terms in a geometric sequence.

common tangent (p. 742) A line (or segment) that is tangent to two coplanar circles.

compatible numbers (pp. 111, 115, 119, 123) Numbers that are easy to add, subtract, multiply, or divide mentally.

complement of an event (pp. 1255, 1291) All of the outcomes different from the favorable outcomes. The sum of the probability of an event and the probability of its complement is 1.

complementary angles (pp. 148, 625, 894) Two angles whose measures total 90°.

complementary events (p. 1255) Two events that make up all the possible outcomes of an experiment.

completing the square (p. 1706) A method for finding real solutions to a quadratic equation by forming an equivalent equation with a perfect trinomial square on one side.

complex conjugate (pp. 1641, 1902) The complex conjugate of the number $a + bi$ is $a - bi$, and vice versa.

complex fraction (p. 1990) A fraction, $\frac{a}{b}$, in which either a or b, or both, are rational expressions.

complex number (pp. 1110, 1896) Any number of the form $a + bi$, where a and b are real numbers and i is the imaginary unit. The number a is called the *real part* and b is called the *imaginary part*. If $a = 0$, then bi is called an *imaginary number*.

composite figure (pp. 552, 582) A figure that is made up of two or more other figures.

composite number (p. 284) A whole number greater than 1 that has more than two factors.

composition (p. 852) A combination of two or more transformations.

compound event (p. 1358) An event made of two or more simple events.

compound inequality (p. 1512) When two simple inequalities are joined by *and* or *or*.

compound interest (pp. 400, 1839, 1999) The interest paid on both the principal and any previously earned interest.

compound locus (p. 721) The set of all points that satisfy several conditions.

compound statement (p. 1512) A statement formed by using the word *and* or *or* to combine two simple statements.

conclusion (p. 612) The part of a conditional statement that follows the word *then*.

concurrent lines (pp. 831, 866) Lines that intersect at the same point, called the *point of concurrency*.

conditional probability (p. 1360) The probability that event B occurs, given that event A has occurred.

conditional statement (p. 612) A statement of the form *if p, then q*.

cone (pp. 174, 568, 576, 713) A geometric solid with a circular base and one vertex, called the *vertex* of the cone. The *height* of a cone is the distance from the vertex to the plane containing the base. See also *right cone*.

confidence interval (p. 1350) An interval, with limits at either end, with a specified probability of including the parameter being estimated.

confidence level (p. 1350) The probability that a result will fall within a confidence interval.

congruent angles (pp. 146, 622) Angles that have equal measures.

congruent arcs (pp. 729, 736) Two arcs in the same circle or in congruent circles that have the same measure.

congruent figures (pp. 622, 766) Figures that have the same shape and size.

congruent segments (p. 622) Segments that have equal lengths.

conjecture (p. 620) A conclusion reached by using inductive reasoning.

conjugate of a real number (p. 1961) For a number written as the sum of two terms, the conjugate of the number is the difference of the terms, and vice versa. $a + b$ and $a - b$ are conjugates.

conjugate of a complex number (pp. 1119, 1641, 1902) The conjugate of $z = x + yi$ is $\bar{z} = x - yi$. See also *complex conjugate.*

conjunction (p. 1513) A compound statement with two statements separated by the word *and.* An inequality using *and* is a conjunction.

consistent system (p. 1580) A system of equations with at least one solution.

constant (p. 1422) A quantity that does not change.

constant differences (p. 2042) The differences in consecutive terms in a sequence are all equal.

constant of proportionality (p. 1842) A constant positive ratio by which two variable quantities are proportionally related.

constraints (p. 1588) In linear programming, the linear inequalities that restrict the solution.

construction (p. 860) A geometric drawing that is made using only a straightedge and a compass.

continuous (p. 2144) If $\lim_{x \to c} f(x) = f(c)$ then f is continuous at $x = c$.

contrapositive of a statement (p. 615) The contrapositive of "if p, then q" is "if not q, then not p."

convenience sample (p. 1228) A sample where the members of the population that are easiest to contact or survey are selected for the sample.

converse of a statement (p. 614) The converse of "if p, then q" is "if q, then p."

conversion factor (p. 492) A ratio of equal quantities measured in different units.

coordinate plane (p. 1442) A plane formed by two number lines that intersect at right angles.

coordinate proof (p. 828) A proof that involves figures in the coordinate plane.

corollary (p. 669) A statement whose proof follows directly from another theorem.

correlation (p. 1313) The strength of the relationship between two variables.

correlation coefficient (p. 1333) Measures the strength of the correlation between the two variables.

corresponding angles (p. 630) Angles that lie in corresponding positions on the same side of a transversal.

cosecant ratio See *trigonometric ratios.*

cosine ratio See *trigonometric ratios.*

cotangent ratio See *trigonometric ratios.*

coterminal angles (pp. 895, 930) Two angles in standard position that have the same terminal side.

count back (p. 64) A strategy for finding the difference of two numbers.

count on (p. 58) A strategy for finding a sum.

counterexample (p. 613) An example that proves a conditional false.

CPCTC (p. 776) An abbreviation for "corresponding parts of congruent triangles are congruent."

critical point (p. 2191) A point on a graph that indicates where the graphical behavior of a function changes.

critical value (p. 2191) When a function f is defined at a point c, and the first derivative of the function at that point is zero or does not exist, then c is a critical value.

cross products (p. 369) The product of the numerator of one fraction and the denominator of another fraction.

cross section (p. 718) The intersection of a three-dimensional figure and a plane.

cube (pp. 166, 178) A rectangular prism all of whose faces are congruent squares.

cumulative frequency (p. 1263) The sum of the frequencies of the data up to a given level.

cumulative frequency distribution (p. 1328) A distribution that shows how many values are less than or equal to any given value in a data set.

cumulative percent frequency table (p. 1328) A distribution that shows the percent of data values less than or equal to a given value.

cylinder (pp. 170, 572) A geometric solid with two congruent parallel circular bases.

D

data (p. 1218) A collection of numbers, measures, or other information.

deductive reasoning (p. 618) The process of using properties, rules, definitions, theorems, and given facts to arrive at a conclusion.

degree of a polynomial (p. 1601) The greatest degree of all the terms in the polynomial.

denominator of a fraction (pp. 302, 304) See *fraction*.

dependent events (p. 1360) The outcome of one event affects the outcome of the other event.

dependent system (p. 1580) A system of linear equations that has infinitely many solutions.

dependent variable (pp. 1438, 1531) The variable, y, when the value of y depends on the value of x.

derivative (p. 2160) The slope of a line tangent to a function at each point of the function.

determinant (p. 1794) In a 2 by 2 matrix, the product of elements in the main diagonal minus the product of the elements in the other diagonal.

deviation from the mean (p. 1324) The difference in value between a data element and the mean of its data set.

diameter (pp. 162, 734) A line segment that contains the center of a circle and whose endpoints are points on the circle, or the length of that segment.

difference (pp. 62, 88) The result of subtraction.

difference of two squares (p. 1616) The product when a binomial of the form $a + b$ is multiplied by a binomial of the form $a - b$.

differential equation (p. 2294) An equation relating a function and one or more of its derivatives.

differentiation (p. 2159) The process of finding a derivative.

dilation (p. 850) A transformation that produces an image similar to the original figure. Also called a *similarity transformation*. For a dilation with *scale factor* r:
If $|r| > 1$, the image is larger than the original. The dilation is an *enlargement*.
If $|r| < 1$, the image is smaller than the original. The dilation is a *reduction*.

dimensional analysis (p. 492) A method of converting from one unit to another within a system of measurement.

dimensions (p. 1772) The number of rows and columns in a matrix.

direct variation (p. 1842) Two variable quantities related proportionally by a constant positive ratio.

direction angles (p. 1072) The angles that a vector $\mathbf{v} = \langle x, y, z \rangle$ makes with the positive x-axis, the positive y-axis, and the positive z-axis, respectively.

directrix (p. 1910) A fixed line associated with a parabola, where each point of the parabola is equidistant from the directrix and the focus.

discontinuous (p. 2144) A function which for certain values or between certain values of the variable does not vary continuously as the variable increases.

discount (p. 397) The difference between the original price of an item and the sale price of the item.

discriminant (p. 1714) The value of $b^2 - 4ac$ in a quadratic equation $ax^2 + bx + c = 0$.

disjunction (p. 1514) A compound statement with two statements separated by the word *or*. An inequality using *or* is a disjunction.

disk (p. 2278) A slice of a solid figure, when the slice is perpendicular to the axis of revolution and is a right circular cylinder.

displacement (pp. 2198, 2272) The change in position over a time interval.

dividend (p. 100) In the quotient $a \div b$, the dividend is a.

divisible (p. 290) A whole number is *divisible* by another whole number if there is no remainder when the first number is divided by the second.

division (pp. 74, 100) Mathematical operation in which the number of equal groups in a total are found. Division is the inverse of *multiplication*.

divisor (p. 100) In the quotient $a \div b$, the divisor is b.

DMS notation (p. 896) Degrees/minutes/seconds notation.

dodecahedron (p. 178) A regular polyhedron with 12 faces that are congruent regular pentagons.

domain (pp. 1436, 1978) The set of all input values x in a relation.

dot product (p. 1082) The quantity $\mathbf{u} \cdot \mathbf{v} = x_1x_2 + y_1y_2$, where $\mathbf{u} = \langle x_1, y_1 \rangle$ and $\mathbf{v} = \langle x_2, y_2 \rangle$.

double stem-and-leaf plot (p. 1286) A plot used to compare two sets of data that shows how data are distributed.

double-bar graph (p. 1284) A graph that uses side-by-side bars to display related data.

double-line graph (p. 1285) A graph that displays the changes of two related sets of data over time.

doubles and near doubles (p. 59) A strategy for finding a sum.

draw a diagram (p. 452) A problem-solving strategy.

E

e (p. 2004) The base for natural logarithms.

eccentricity (p. 1940) A number, represented by e, that describes the "roundness" of a conic section.

edge of a prism (p. 166) The intersection of two faces of a prism.

element (p. 1772) Each number or value in a matrix.

element of a cone (p. 713) Any segment joining the vertex to a point on the circumference of the base.

elimination method (p. 1576) The process of adding equations, or their multiples, to eliminate a variable in a system of equations.

ellipse (pp. 1928, 1941) A type of conic section. For two given points, the *foci*, an ellipse is the set of all points in a plane such that the sum of the distance to each focus is constant.

empirical rule (p. 1340) Provides a quick estimate of the spread of data in a normal distribution given the mean and standard deviation.

enlargement See *dilation*.

equal matrices (p. 1774) Two matrices that have the same dimensions, and corresponding elements have the same value.

equally likely (p. 1232) Two outcomes that have equal probabilities.

equation (pp. 1422, 1458) Two algebraic expressions separated by an equal sign, indicating that the two sides have equal value.

equiangular triangle (pp. 669, 786) A triangle with three congruent angles.

equilateral polygon (p. 676) A polygon in which all the sides are congruent.

equilateral triangle (pp. 156, 538, 786) A triangle with three congruent sides.

equivalent expressions (p. 1406) Expressions that have the same value for any values of the variables.

equivalent fractions (p. 308) Fractions that have the same value.

equivalent ratios (p. 368) Ratios that have the same value.

equivalent vectors (p. 1066) Vectors with the same magnitude and direction.

estimate (pp. 110, 114, 118, 122) A reasonable answer that is close to the exact answer.

evaluate (p. 1422) Substitute a given value for each variable, and then simplify the expression.

even functions (p. 1625) Polynomial functions of degree 2, 4, 6, and so on.

even number (p. 54) A number that is divisible by two.

expanded form (p. 44) The form of a number that expresses the number as the sum of the values of it digits.

experiment (pp. 1236, 1354) An act, operation, or process that can be used to generate outcomes.

experimental probability (p. 1236) The ratio of the number of times a favorable outcome occurs to the total number of trials.

explicit (p. 2208) A relationship between variables in which one variable is solved in terms of the other.

explicit rule (p. 1884) Gives the value of the general term a_n in terms of n.

exponent (pp. 94, 294, 1396) A number that tells how many times a factor is used in a product.

exponential decay function (pp. 2000, 2053) Functions of the form $y = ab^x$ where $0 < b < 1$. If r is the rate of decay, a is the initial amount, and t is time, $y = a(1 - r)^t$.

exponential equations (p. 1978) Equations that contain a variable in an exponent.

exponential functions (p. 1996) Functions that contain a variable in an exponent.

exponential growth function (pp. 1996, 2052) Functions of the form $y = ab^x$, where $b > 1$. If r is the rate of growth, a is the initial amount, and t is time, $y = a(1 + r)^t$.

exponential notation (p. 1396) Expresses multiplication as a power.

exterior angle of a polygon (p. 670) An angle formed by extending one side of a polygon.

extraneous solution (pp. 2013, 2027, 2035, 2038) A solution of a transformed equation that is not in the domain of or a solution of the original equation.

extrapolation (p. 1318) An estimate outside a set of known points.

F

$f(x)$ (p. 1450) The function rule applied to x.

face of a prism (p. 166) Any one of the flat surfaces that make up a prism.

fact family (p. 80) Sets of related facts that use the same numbers.

factor theorem (p. 1646) A polynomial $P(x)$ has a factor of $x - a$ if and only if $P(a) = 0$.

factor tree (p. 296) A diagram that shows how to break a number down into its prime factors.

factorial See n *factorial.*

factoring (p. 1660) Rewriting an expression as the product of its factors.

factors (pp. 96, 286) Numbers that are multiplied to find a product.

Fahrenheit scale (p. 496) A scale for measuring temperature in which the freezing point of water is 32° and the boiling point is 212°.

feasible region (p. 1590) The graph of the solution of the system of linear inequalities that form the constraints.

Fibonacci sequence (p. 1878) A sequence named for Italian mathematician Leonardo of Pisa, also known as Fibonacci. The first two terms of the sequence are 1, and each successive term is the sum of the previous two terms.

finite sequence (p. 1858) A sequence that has a specific number of terms.

finite series (p. 1862) The sum of a finite number of terms.

first quartile (p. 1331) The median of the data that are less than the overall median.

first-order differences (pp. 1690, 2042) The differences between values of y for consecutive values of x. In a linear function, first-order differences are constant for constant change in x.

foci (pp. 1928, 1932, 1941, 1942) Two fixed points used to define an ellipse or hyperbola.

focus (p. 1910) A fixed point used with the directrix to define a parabola.

FOIL (p. 1610) A method of multiplying binomials using the Distributive Property. Its name can help you remember the process: first-outside-inside-last.

formula (p. 527) An equation that shows a relationship between two or more quantities.

45°-45°-90° triangle (pp. 684, 898) An isosceles right triangle.

fractal (p. 809) A self-similar figure made by iteration.

fraction (pp. 302, 304) A number that names a part of a whole or a part of a set; any number written in the form $\frac{a}{b}$, where a and b are integers and $b \neq 0$. The numerator of the fraction is a, and the denominator is b.

frequency (p. 1260) The number of times an event, a number, or a range of events occurs.

frequency polygon (p. 1269) A graph of the data in a frequency table that show the midpoints of the intervals, which can be used to estimate the mean.

frequency table (p. 182) A tally chart or table that includes the frequency of each kind of data.

function (pp. 950, 1439) A relation, or a set of ordered pairs, such that for each element in the domain of the function, there is exactly one element in the range.

function notation (p. 1450) A notation in which a function is named with a letter and the input is shown in parentheses after the function name, such as $f(x)$.

G

general term (p. 1858) The nth term of a sequence.

geometric mean (p. 797) The positive square root of the product of two positive numbers.

geometric pattern (p. 438) A pattern that grows when each subsequent term is multiplied by the same number.

geometric sequence (p. 1866) A sequence in which the ratio of consecutive terms is a non-zero constant.

geometric series (p. 1870) The sum of the terms of a geometric sequence.

glide reflection (p. 852) A composition of a translation (glide) and a reflection over a line that is parallel to the direction of the translation.

golden ratio (p. 1879) A special number approximately equal to 1.6180339887.

golden rectangle (p. 791) A rectangle that can be divided into a square and a rectangle that is similar to the original rectangle.

graph of an inequality (p. 1492) The graph of all solutions of the inequality on a number line.

great circle (p. 1052) The intersection of a sphere and a plane containing the center of the sphere.

greatest common factor (GCF) (p. 287) The greatest factor shared by two or more numbers.

growth factor (pp. 1998, 2003) The quantity $1 + r$ in the exponential growth equation $y = a(1 + r)^x$.

H

half-life (p. 2055) The time it takes a substance to undergo radioactive decay to half of the original amount.

half-open interval (p. 2151) A continuous set of real numbers that contains only one endpoint.

half-plane (pp. 1558, 1936) The region on one side of the line in the graph of an inequality, or on one side of a boundary curve.

half-turn (p. 844) A rotation of 180° or −180°.

hexagonal prism (p. 167) A prism whose base is a hexagon.

higher-order derivative (p. 2184) The derivative of a derivative function.

higher-order equations (p. 1720) Equations of degree 3 or greater.

histogram (p.1267) A graph that displays the frequency of a set of data in equal-size intervals, or ranges, of data.

horizontal component (p. 1070) The x-coordinate of a point representing a vector $\mathbf{v} = (x, y)$.

horizontal translation (p. 1695) Movement of a figure along a horizontal line; $f(x - h)$ translates $f(x)$ horizontally h units.

hyperbola (p. 1932) A type of conic section. The hyperbola is the set of all points in a plane such that the difference of the distances from two fixed points, called the *foci*, is a positive constant.

hypotenuse (p. 678) The side opposite the right angle in a right triangle. It is the longest side.

hypothesis (p. 612) The part of a conditional statement that follows the word *if*.

I

icosahedron (p. 178) A regular polyhedron with 20 faces that are congruent equilateral triangles.

identity matrix for multiplication (p. 1784) A matrix that acts like the number 1 in real-number multiplication.

image See *transformation.*

imaginary number See *complex number.*

imaginary unit *i* (pp. 1110, 1894) The square root of -1.

implicit (p. 2208) A relationship between variables in which one variable is not solved in terms of the other.

implicit differentiation (p. 2208) A method of finding the derivative of both sides of an equation with respect to x and then solving for $\frac{dy}{dx}$.

improper fraction (p. 306) A fraction in which the numerator is greater than the denominator.

incenter (p. 880) The point where the bisectors of the angles of a triangle intersect.

included angle (p. 770) An angle formed by two consecutive sides of a polygon.

included side (p. 772) A side that is shared by two consecutive angles of a polygon.

inconsistent system (p. 1580) A system of equations with no solution.

independent events (p. 1358) The outcome of one event does not influence the outcome of the other event.

independent system (p. 1580) A system of linear equations with exactly one solution.

independent variable (pp. 1438, 1531) A variable whose value determines the value of a dependent variable.

indeterminate form (p. 2124) A rational function in which the limit of the numerator and the denominator both equal zero as x approaches c.

index (p. 1954) The number n in the radical $\sqrt[n]{a}$.

index of summation (p. 1862) Used to indicate the lower and upper limit of the summation, for example $\sum_{k-1}^{3}$.

indirect measurement (p. 800) Using similar triangles to find a length that cannot be measured directly.

inductive reasoning (p. 620) The process of making a conclusion based on observations.

inequality (p. 1492) A mathematical statement that two quantities are not or may not be equal.

infinite geometric series (p. 1874) The sum of the terms of an infinite geometric sequence.

infinite sequence (p. 1858) A sequence that has an infinite number of terms.

infinite series (p. 1862) The sum of an infinite number of terms.

inflection point (pp. 2194, 2204) The point at which a function changes concavity.

initial side of an angle (p. 894) The side that lies on the x-axis. The other side of the angle is the *terminal side.*

initial value (pp. 1998, 2003) For the exponential growth or decay function $y = a(1 \pm r)^x$, a is the initial value.

initial value problem (p. 2295) A problem in which the identity of an unknown function of an independent variable is sought, given the derivative of the function and the value of the function at a specified point.

input (p. 1437) The first number in each ordered pair; the value substituted in an expression or function.

inscribed angle (p. 744) An angle whose vertex is on a circle and whose sides contain chords of the circle.

inscribed circle (p. 883) A circle that is tangent to each side of a polygon.

integers (pp. 268, 1386, 1402) The set of whole numbers and their opposites, $\{\ldots -3, -2, -1, 0, 1, 2, 3, \ldots\}$.

integration (p. 2234) The process of identifying a function from its derivative.

integration by parts (p. 2258) A method to use if an integral includes the product of two functions but does not fit the u-substitution style.

interest (pp. 398, 1838) A fee paid for the use of borrowed money.

interior angle of a polygon (p. 670) An angle determined by two consecutive sides of a polygon.

interquartile range (pp. 1281,1299) The difference between the first quartile and the third quartile of the data.

intersecting lines (p. 129) Lines that share exactly one point.

intersection (p. 1291) The set of elements common to two or more sets.

inverse function (p. 2090) A function that has the range of the original function as its domain and the domain of the original function as its range.

inverse matrix (p. 1798) The matrix which when multiplied by the original matrix gives the identity matrix as the solution.

inverse of a statement (p. 614) The inverse of "if p then q" is "if not p then not q."

inverse operations (pp. 81, 1460) Operations that perform opposite tasks, or that "undo" each other; addition and subtraction are inverse operations; multiplication and division are inverse operations.

inverse variation (p. 1846) A relationship in which one variable quantity increases as the other variable quantity decreases and their product is constant.

irrational number (pp. 268, 1402) A real number that cannot be written as the quotient of two integers.

irregular polygon (p. 154) Any polygon that is not regular.

isometric drawing (p. 698) A drawing that shows three sides of a figure, using triangular isometric dot paper.

isometry (p. 834) A transformation that preserves congruence.

isosceles trapezoid (p. 658) A trapezoid with congruent legs.

isosceles triangle (pp. 156, 784) A triangle with at least two congruent sides.

iteration (p. 808) Repeatedly performing a rule.

joint variation (p. 1850) When a quantity varies directly with the product of two or more quantities.

kite (p. 660) A quadrilateral with exactly two pairs of congruent, consecutive sides.

lateral area of a cone (p. 714) The area of the curved surface.

lateral area of a pyramid (p. 711) The sum of the areas of the lateral faces.

lateral faces See *prism*, *pyramid*.

lateral surface of a cylinder (p. 562) The curved surface of a cylinder.

latus rectum (LR) (p. 1910) The segment that passes through the focus of a parabola and is parallel to the directrix.

Law of Detachment (p. 618) The law that states that if a conditional statement is true and its hypothesis is true, then the conclusion is true.

Law of Syllogism (p. 618) The law that states that if $p \rightarrow q$ is true and $q \rightarrow r$ is true, then $p \rightarrow r$ must be true.

leading coefficient (p. 1624) The coefficient of the term of a polynomial of greatest degree.

leading question (p. 1223) A biased survey question that makes people more or less likely to answer in a particular way.

leading term (p. 1624) The term of a polynomial with the greatest degree.

least common denominator (LCD) (pp. 289, 1986) The least common multiple of the denominators of two or more fractions.

least common multiple (LCM) (p. 288) The common multiple of two or more numbers that has the least value.

legs of a right triangle (p. 678) The two shorter sides that form the right angle in a right triangle.

legs of a trapezoid (p. 656) The sides of a trapezoid that are not the bases.

legs of an isosceles triangle (p. 784) The two congruent sides of an isosceles triangle.

length (pp. 478, 500) The distance between two points.

like fractions (p. 319) Fractions with the same denominator.

like radicals (p. 1958) Radicals that have the same index and the same radicand.

like terms (p. 1412) Terms that contain the same variables raised to the same powers.

limit (pp. 1874, 2010) The sum of an infinite geometric series. The value of a function as its variable approaches a particular value.

line (p. 128) A straight path in a plane that continues without end in two directions. A line has no width.

line graph (pp. 192, 1446) A data display that shows information as data points connected by line segments; often used to display data that change over time.

line of best fit (pp. 1332, 1556) A straight line that most closely follows the trend of data points in a scatter plot.

line of reflection See *reflection.*

line of symmetry (p. 846) A reflection line.

line plot (p. 1321) A graph that displays frequency data as stacks of marks along a number line.

line segment (p. 132) Part of a line consisting of two endpoints on the line and all points between the two endpoints.

line symmetry (p. 846) When there is a reflection over a line that maps a figure onto itself. Also called *reflection symmetry*. See also *line of symmetry*.

linear combination of vectors (p. 1080) Any expression of the form $a\mathbf{u} + b\mathbf{v}$, where a and b are scalars and $\mathbf{u}$ and $\mathbf{v}$ are vectors.

linear combinations (p. 1576) Sum of multiples of equations in a system of equations, used to eliminate a variable.

linear equation (p. 1529) An equation with a graph that is a straight line.

linear function (p. 1451) Any function with a graph that is a straight line.

linear pair (p. 625) Two adjacent angles whose exterior sides lie on a straight line.

linear programming (p. 1588) A useful branch of mathematics that maximizes or minimizes the value of a function, within the restrictions of a system of linear inequalities.

linear velocity (p. 942) The distance per unit time that a point travels along a circular path.

linear-quadratic system (p. 1728) A system of equations that includes a quadratic equation and a linear equation.

local linearity (p. 2169) The linear appearance of a function at a certain point.

local maximum (pp. 1654, 2202) The value of the function at a turning point; any high point on a graph of a function.

local minimum (pp. 1654, 2202) The value of the function at a turning point; any low point on a graph of a function.

location principle (p. 1630) A principle, useful in locating the roots of an equation, stating that if a continuous function has opposite signs for two values of the independent variable, then it is zero for some value of the variable between these two values.

locus (p. 720) The set of all points that satisfy a given condition.

logarithmic function (p. 2006) An equation written in the form $y = \log_b x$, where $b > 0$ and $b \neq 1$. The inverse of an exponential function.

logically equivalent statements (p. 615) Statements that always have the same truth value.

lower extreme (p. 1280) The least data value in a set.

lower quartile (p. 1280) The median of the lower half of the data.

M

magnitude of a vector (p. 1066) The length of a vector.

main diagonal (pp. 1784, 1792) The diagonal of a square matrix drawn from the upper left corner to the lower right corner.

major arc (p. 728) An arc larger than a semicircle.

major axis (p. 1928) The longer of the perpendicular segments through the center of an ellipse, which contains the foci.

make ten (p. 59) A strategy for finding a sum.

margin of error (p. 1350) An interval, or range, around a sample measure that is likely to contain the corresponding population measure.

markup (p. 395) The difference between the price a store pays for an item (wholesale price) and the price a buyer pays for an item (retail price).

mass (p. 510) The measure of the amount of matter in an object.

mathematical induction (p. 1888) The method of proving that a statement is true for all natural numbers.

matrix (p. 1772) A rectangular arrangement of numbers or values.

maximum value (p. 1691) The maximum value(s) of the function over its entire domain; the y-coordinate of the vertex of a quadratic function that opens downward.

mean (pp. 198, 1279, 1294) The sum of the data in a data set divided by the number of items in the set. Also called the *average*.

measure of an arc (p. 728) The measure of a minor arc equals the measure of its central angle. The measure of a major arc is 360° minus the measure of the minor arc with the same endpoints. The measure of a semicircle is 180°.

measures of central tendency (p. 202) Different ways to describe the "center" of a data set.

median (pp. 202, 1278, 1294) The middle number (or the mean of the two middle numbers) when a data set is arranged in order from least to greatest.

median of a triangle (pp. 822, 865) A segment whose endpoints are a vertex of the triangle and the midpoint of the opposite side.

midpoint of a segment (p. 820) A point that divides a segment into two congruent segments.

midsegment of a trapezoid (p. 656) The segment whose endpoints are the midpoints of the legs.

midsegment of a triangle (p. 806) The segment whose endpoints are the midpoints of two sides of a triangle.

midsegment triangle (p. 806) The triangle formed by the three midsegments of another triangle.

minimum value (p. 1691) The minimum value(s) of a function over its entire domain; the y-coordinate of the vertex of a quadratic function that opens upward.

minor (p. 1797) The new, smaller determinant formed after one element is identified in a determinant and then used to form a determinant by deleting the rest of the row and column for that element.

minor arc (p. 728) An arc shorter than a semicircle.

minor axis (p. 1928) The shorter of the perpendicular segments through the center of an ellipse.

minuend (p. 88) The number another number is subtracted from in a difference. In $a - b$, a is the minuend.

minute (p. 896) One-sixtieth of a degree.

mixed number (p. 306) Any number consisting of a whole number and a proper fraction.

mode (pp. 204, 1279, 1295) The number or element in a data set that appears most often in the set.

monomial (pp. 1600, 1982) An algebraic expression consisting of a number or a product of numbers and variables.

multiple (p. 288) The product of a counting number and a positive integer.

multiplicand (p. 96) The first of two numbers in a product.

multiplication (pp. 68, 96) Mathematical operation in which a number of sets of equal size are combined.

multiplicative identity (p. 1414) The number 1; multiplying 1 by any number gives that number.

multiplicative inverse (pp. 1416, 1983) The reciprocal of a number. The product of a number and its multiplicative inverse is 1.

multiplicity (p. 1642) The number of times that $x - r$ is a factor of an equation $P(x) = 0$.

multiplier (p. 96) The second of two numbers in a product.

mutually exclusive events (p. 1366) Two events that cannot happen at the same time.

***n* factorial** (p. 1245) The product in which the factors are descending natural numbers starting with n. The factorial of zero is defined to be 1.

natural logarithm (p. 1975) The logarithm to the base e, where e is called the Euler number and is an irrational constant of about 2.71828.

natural numbers (pp. 268, 1402) The set of counting numbers, $\{1, 2, 3, \ldots\}$.

negation of a statement (p. 614) A statement with the opposite truth value. The negation of p is $\sim p$.

negative angle (p. 895) An angle determined by a clockwise rotation.

negative reciprocals (p. 816) Two numbers whose product is -1.

net (pp. 558, 566, 694) A two-dimensional diagram that you can fold to form a three-dimensional figure.

non-removable discontinuity (p. 2144) A discontinuity that implies that you cannot make the function continuous by any value $f(c)$.

nonresponse (p. 1222) Occurs when some people selected for a sample do not respond to the survey.

normal distribution (p. 1340) A way to describe data that appears as a bell-shaped curve symmetrical around the mean.

normal line (p. 2213) A line that is perpendicular to the tangent line of a curve at the point of tangency.

number pattern (pp. 438, 440) A sequence of numbers that follow a rule.

numerator of a fraction (pp. 302, 304) See *fraction*.

objective function (p. 1592) The function to be maximized or minimized, subject to the constraints of a linear programming problem.

observation (p. 1354) A record or measure of events that occur with no intervention by the researcher.

obtuse angle (pp. 140, 624, 894) An angle with measure greater than 90° and less than 180°.

obtuse triangle (p. 156) A triangle with one obtuse angle.

octagonal prism (p. 167) A prism whose base is an octagon.

octahedron (p. 178) A regular polyhedron with eight faces that are congruent equilateral triangles.

odd functions (p. 1625) Polynomial functions of degree 1, 3, 5, and so on.

odd number (p. 54) A whole number that is not divisible by two.

odds (p. 1254) A comparison of the number of favorable outcomes with the number of unfavorable outcomes in an event.

odometer (p. 478) An instrument used to measure distances in miles.

open interval (p. 2150) A continuous set of real numbers that does not contain its endpoints.

opposites (p. 1386) Numbers that are the same distance from but on opposite sides of zero on a number line. The opposite of a is $-a$, and the sum of opposites is zero.

optimization function (p. 1588) The function that is maximized or minimized in linear programming; the objective function.

order of a differential equation (p. 2294) The power of the highest derivative of an equation.

order of symmetry (p. 847) The number of rotations of the smallest angle greater than 0° and less than or equal to 360° that produces an image that coincides with the original.

ordered pair (p. 1436) A pair of numbers (x, y) used to locate a point on a coordinate plane; the first number tells how far to move horizontally and the second number tells how far to move vertically.

ordered triple (p. 1754) A set of three numbers (x, y, z) that describe a point in a three-dimensional coordinate system.

origin (p. 1442) The point where the coordinate axes intersect.

orthocenter (p. 873) The point where the altitudes of a triangle intersect.

orthogonal vectors (p. 1084) Perpendicular vectors.

orthographic drawing (p. 702) A drawing that shows up to six views of a three-dimensional figure.

outcome (p. 1232) The result of an experiment.

outlier (pp. 1283, 1298) A very large or very small value that is not typical of its data set.

output (p. 1437) The second number in each ordered pair; the value of the expression or function.

overlapping events (p. 1366) Two events that can happen at the same time.

parabola (pp. 1910, 1916) A type of conic section. For a given point, called the *focus*, and a given line not through the focus, called the *directrix*, a parabola is the set of all points such that the distance to the focus equals the distance to the directrix.

paragraph proof (p. 626) A proof that uses complete sentences to explain and justify each step, eventually reaching the desired conclusion.

parallel lines (pp. 129, 630) Coplanar lines that do not intersect.

parallelogram (pp. 158, 532, 638) A quadrilateral with two pairs of parallel sides.

parametric equations (p. 1106) A set of equations that define x and y in terms of another variable, called a *parameter*.

parent functions (pp. 1625, 2098) The most basic form of a number of related graphs with similar features. The related forms are transformations of the parent function.

parent quadratic function (p. 1688) The function $y = x^2$.

partial product (p. 96) A product formed by multiplying the multiplicand by one digit of the multiplier when the multiplier has more than one digit.

partial sum (p. 1863) Sum of the first n terms of a sequence.

Pascal's triangle (p. 1347) An arithmetic triangle that is used to calculate the binomial coefficients of various numbers; used in algebra and probability with the binomial theorem. Each row starts and ends with 1 and each other number is the sum of the two numbers above it.

pattern (p. 432) A sequence that follows a rule.

percent (pp. 196, 277, 380) A ratio that compares a number to 100.

percent of change (increase or decrease) (pp. 394, 396) The ratio of the amount of change to the original quantity expressed as a percent.

percentile rank (p. 1329) The percent of the total number of values less than or equal to a value.

perfect square (pp. 1400, 1952) A number that is the square of a rational number.

perfect-square trinomial (p. 1614) A polynomial that is the result of squaring a binomial.

perimeter (p. 524) The distance around a closed plane figure.

period (p. 40) Each group of three places on a place-value chart.

period of a function (p. 950) The length of the repeating portion of a function.

periodic function (p. 950) A function f such that $f(x) = f(x + np)$, where x is any real number in the domain of f, n is an integer, and p is a positive real number. The smallest value of p is the *period* of the function.

permutation (p. 1244) An arrangement of a group, or set, of objects in a particular order.

perpendicular bisector of a segment (pp. 864, 876) A line, ray, or segment that is perpendicular to the given segment at its midpoint.

perpendicular lines (p. 130) Two lines that intersect to form right angles.

phase shift (p. 962) A horizontal translation of a periodic function.

pictograph (p. 186) A graph that uses symbols to display data.

piecewise function (p. 2076) A function that is defined by two or more equations.

plane (pp. 128, 144) A flat, two-dimensional surface that extends infinitely in all directions.

Platonic solids (p. 178) The five regular polyhedra: tetrahedron, cube, octahedron, dodecahedron, and icosahedron.

point (p. 128) A location in space. A point has no size.

point of concurrency See *concurrent lines.*

point of symmetry (p. 848) The point about which you can rotate a figure 180° so that its image coincides with the original figure.

point of tangency See *tangent to a circle.*

point symmetry (p. 848) 180° rotational symmetry.

polar coordinate system (p. 1092) The coordinate system in a plane determined by a point, called the *pole*, and the *polar axis*, a ray that has the pole as its endpoint.

polar coordinates of a point (p. 1092) The ordered pair (r, θ), where r is a real number and θ is an angle measure.

polygon (p. 154) A closed plane figure with three or more straight sides that intersect only at their endpoints.

polynomial (pp. 1600, 1982) An algebraic expression that is the sum of one or more monomials.

polynomial function (p. 1624) A function of degree n, where n is a nonnegative integer, and the degrees of the terms are decreasing from n to 0.

population (pp. 1218, 1222) The set of individuals or items that represent the data in a data set.

positive angle (p. 895) An angle determined by a counterclockwise rotation.

postulate (p. 624) A statement that is accepted as true without being proven.

power (pp. 294, 1396) A number written as a base with an exponent.

power function (p. 2056) A function in the form $y = ax^b$.

power of ten (pp. 94, 588) The product when 10 is multiplied by itself a given number of times.

pre-image See *transformation.*

prime factorization (p. 296) Writing a number as the product of it prime factors.

prime number (p. 284) A whole number greater than 1 that has exactly two factors, 1 and the number itself.

prime polynomial (p. 1670) A polynomial that cannot be factored.

principal (pp. 398, 1838) The amount of money deposited, invested, or borrowed.

principal square root (pp. 1400, 1952) The nonnegative square root of a number.

principal values of inverse trigonometric functions (pp. 1022, 1026, 1030) The values in the restricted domains of the corresponding trigonometric functions.

prism (pp. 166, 570) A geometric solid with two congruent parallel *bases* that are polygons. The *lateral faces* are parallelograms.

probability (p. 1232) A numerical measure of the likelihood that a given event will occur.

product (pp. 68, 96) The result of multiplication.

proper fraction (p. 306) A fraction in which the numerator is less than the denominator.

proportion (p. 369) An equation that states two ratios are equal.

protractor (p. 137) A tool used to measure angles.

pure imaginary number (p. 1896) Any complex number of the form $a + bi$ for which $a = 0$ and $b \neq 0$.

pyramid (pp. 172, 566, 574, 710) A geometric solid with one *base* that is a polygon and *lateral faces* that are triangles. The common vertex of the triangular faces is the *vertex* of the pyramid. The distance from the vertex to the plane containing the base is the *height* (altitude) of the pyramid. See also *regular pyramid*.

Pythagorean triple (p. 681) Three whole numbers a, b, and c, where $a^2 + b^2 = c^2$.

Q

quadrantal angle (pp. 895, 929) An angle whose terminal side lies on the x-axis or the y-axis.

quadrants (p. 1524) The four regions into which the x- and y-axes divide the coordinate plane.

quadratic function (p. 1688) Any function that can be written in the standard form $y = ax^2 + bx + c$, where $a \neq 0$.

quadratic-quadratic system (p. 1732) A system of equations that consists of two quadratic equations.

quadrilateral (p. 158) A polygon with four sides.

quarter-turn (p. 844) A rotation of 90° or −90°.

quartiles (p. 1331) The four parts that a data set is divided into, each containing an equal number of data values.

quotient (pp. 74, 100) The result of dividing one number by another.

R

radian (p. 936) A measure of a central angle of a circle based on arc length, where 2π radians is equal to 360°.

radical function (p. 2032) A function that contains a variable under a radical symbol.

radical inequality (p. 2036) An inequality that contains a variable under a radical symbol.

radical sign (pp. 1400, 1952, 1954) The designated symbol for the principal square root of a mathematical quantity.

radicand (pp. 1400, 1952, 1954, 2032) The number or expression under the radical sign.

radius of a circle (pp. 162, 728, 1920) A segment whose endpoints are the center of a circle and a point on the circle, or the length of that segment.

radius of a regular polygon (p. 690) A segment whose endpoints are the center and a vertex of the polygon, or the length of that segment.

random sample (p. 1224) A sample for which each member of the identified population is equally likely to be selected.

randomized block design (p. 1354) In the statistical theory of the design of experiments, blocking is the arranging of experimental units in groups (blocks) that are similar to one another.

range (pp. 1436, 1978) The set of all output values y in a relation.

range of a data set (pp. 204, 1278) The difference between the greatest and the least value in a data set.

rate (p. 366) A ratio that compares quantities with different units of measure.

rate of change (p. 1536) A ratio that compares the change in the dependent variable with the change in the independent variable.

rate of decay (p. 2053) The growth rate b in the exponential equation $y = ab^x$, where $0 < b < 1$.

ratio (p. 364) A comparison of two quantities by division.

rational equation (p. 2026) An equation that contains fractional, or rational, expressions.

rational expression (pp. 1986, 1990) The quotient of two polynomials $\frac{a}{b}$, with $b \neq 0$.

rational function (p. 2020) A function of the form $y = \frac{p(x)}{q(x)}$, where $p(x)$ and $q(x)$ are polynomials and $q(x) \neq 0$.

rational number (pp. 268, 1402, 1970) A number that can be written in the form $\frac{p}{q}$ where p and q are integers, and $q \neq 0$.

rationalizing the denominator (p. 1964) The process by which a fraction containing radicals in the denominator is rewritten to have only rational numbers in the denominator.

raw score (p. 1341) An original data value in a normal distribution before conversion to a standard normal z-score.

ray (p. 133) Part of a line consisting of one endpoint and all points of the line on one side of the endpoint.

real numbers (pp. 268, 1402) The combined set of rational numbers and irrational numbers.

reciprocals (pp. 346, 1983) Two numbers whose product is 1.

rectangle (p. 158, 650) A parallelogram with four right angles.

rectangular prism (p. 166) A prism with a rectangular base.

recursive rule (p. 1880) The rule for each term of a sequence written in terms of one or more of the preceding terms.

reduction See *dilation*.

reference angle (pp. 931, 932) The smallest positive acute angle that the terminal side of an angle makes with the x-axis.

reflection (pp. 838, 2086) An isometry that *flips* a figure over a line, called the *line of reflection*.

reflection symmetry See *line symmetry*.

regression (pp. 1332, 1336) A statistical analysis analyzing the association between two variables. It is used to find the relationship between two variables.

regrouping (pp. 84, 90, 228, 233) Organizing a value in a different way in order to rename a number.

regular polygon (pp. 154, 525, 676) A polygon with congruent sides and congruent angles.

regular polyhedron (p. 178) A polyhedron in which all faces are congruent regular polygons and the same number of faces meet at each vertex.

regular pyramid (p. 711) A pyramid with a base that is a regular polygon. The lateral faces are congruent isosceles triangles. The height of each lateral face is the *slant height* of the regular pyramid.

regular tessellation (p. 854) A tessellation consisting of congruent copies of a regular polygon.

related rates (p. 2214) A class of problems in which rates of change are related by means of differentiation.

relation (p. 1436) A set of ordered pairs.

relative frequency (p. 1262) A ratio of the number of times the event occurs and the total number of events.

remainder (pp. 100, 290) The whole number that is left when the divisor does not divide evenly into the dividend.

remote interior angles (p. 670) For each exterior angle of a triangle, the two interior angles that are not adjacent to the exterior angle.

removable discontinuity (p. 2144) A discontinuity that implies that you can make a function continuous by defining or changing the function value $f(c)$.

renaming a measure (pp. 485, 489) Expressing the same quantity using a different unit of measure.

repeated addition (p. 70) A way to find the product of two numbers.

repeated solution (p. 1642) A solution that occurs more than once in a factored equation when using the Zero-Product Property.

repeating decimal (pp. 257, 270) A decimal in which one digit or a block of digits repeats indefinitely.

replication (p. 1355) Observations made under identical conditions.

resultant (p. 1067) The sum of two vectors.

rhombus (pp. 158, 650) A parallelogram with four congruent sides.

Riemann sum (p. 2242) A method of using the areas of rectangles to approximate the total area under a curve on a graph.

right angle (pp. 140, 624, 894) An angle with measure 90°.

right cone (p. 713) A cone whose axis is perpendicular to the base. The *slant height* is the length of a segment whose endpoints are the vertex of the cone and a point on the circumference of the base. An *oblique cone* is any cone that is not a right cone.

right triangle (p. 156) A triangle with one right angle.

rise (p. 1537) The vertical distance between two points on the graph; the change in y.

root of a polynomial (p. 1110) Any solution of a polynomial equation.

root of an equation (p. 1630) A solution to an equation of the form $f(x) = 0$. Roots may be real or complex.

roses (p. 1101) A family of graphs of the polar equations of the form $r = \sin(n\theta)$ and $r = \cos(n\theta)$, where $n \geq 2$.

rotation (p. 842) An isometry that turns a figure about a point, called the *center of rotation*. Rays from the center of rotation to corresponding points on the pre-image and image form the *angle of rotation*.

rotational symmetry (p. 847) If a figure can be rotated about a point by a rotation of less than 360° so that the figure coincides with itself, the figure has rotational symmetry. See also *center of rotation*.

rounding (p. 224) Expressing a number to a given place value.

run (p. 1537) The horizontal distance between two points on the graph; change in x.

S

same-side interior angles (p. 630) Interior angles on the same side of a transversal.

sample (pp. 1218, 1222) A subset of the population.

sample space (pp. 1232, 1358) The set of all possible outcomes of an experiment.

sampling with replacement (p. 1359) When a population element can be selected more than one time in an experiment.

sampling without replacement (p. 1360) When a population element can be selected only one time in an experiment.

scalar (p. 1066) A real number used as a multiplier.

scalar multiple of a vector (p. 1078) The vector with magnitude $|a| \cdot \|\mathbf{v}\|$ and the same direction as vector **v** if $a > 0$ and direction opposite to **v** if $a < 0$.

scalar multiplication (p. 1778) The operation of multiplying a real number by every element in a matrix.

scale (p. 372) A ratio between the measurements in a scale drawing and the measurements of a real object.

scale drawing (p. 372) An enlarged or reduced drawing of a real object.

scale factor of a dilation (p. 850) The number that describes the size change in a dilation. See also *dilation*.

scalene triangle (p. 156) A triangle with no congruent sides.

scatter plot (p. 1264) A graph that shows data points on a coordinate grid.

scientific notation (p. 588) A number written as the product of a power of 10 and a number greater than or equal to 1 and less than 10.

secant (p. 754) A line that intersects the circle in two points.

secant ratio See *trigonometric ratios.*

secant segment (p. 758) A segment of a secant that has one endpoint on a circle, one endpoint outside the circle, and intersects the circle in two points.

second (p. 896) One-sixtieth of a minute.

second quartile (p. 1331) The median of the data; the 50th percentile.

second-order differences (pp. 1690, 2042) The differences between the first-order differences in a function or sequence.

sector of a circle (or circle graph) (pp. 194, 732) A part of a circle that looks like a wedge, bounded by two radii and an arc of the circle.

segment (p. 132) Part of a line consisting of two endpoints on the line and all points between the two endpoints. Also called *line segment.*

self-similar figure (p. 808) A figure that can be divided into parts that are similar to the original figure.

semi-regular tessellation (p. 855) A tessellation consisting of more than one type of regular polygon where the arrangement of polygons is the same at each vertex.

semicircle (p. 728) Half a circle.

separation of variables (p. 2302) A technique where certain differential equations are rewritten in the form $f(x)dx = g(y)dy$, which is then solvable by integrating both sides of the equation.

sequence (p. 432) A set of numbers, objects, or shapes arranged in a specific order. See also *pattern.*

sequence (p. 1858) A function whose domain is a set of ordered numbers. See also *arithmetic sequence, geometric sequence, finite sequence, infinite sequence.*

series (p. 1862) Sum of the terms of a sequence.

set (pp. 268, 1290) A collection of items or objects.

set theory (p. 1290) The branch of mathematics that deals with the properties of sets.

similar figures (p. 790) Figures that have the same shape but not necessarily the same size.

similarity ratio (p. 790) The ratio of the lengths of corresponding sides of similar figures.

similarity transformation See *dilation.*

simple interest (pp. 398, 1838) Interest calculated only on the amount originally deposited, called the *principal.*

simple random sample (p. 1227) A sample in which every member of a population has an equal possibility of being selected.

simplest form of a fraction (p. 311) A fraction in which the numerator and denominator have no common factor other than 1.

sine ratio See *trigonometric ratios.*

skew lines (pp. 144, 630) Noncoplanar lines.

slant height See *right cone, regular pyramid.*

slope (pp. 814, 1537) The steepness of a line expressed as a ratio; the slope m of the line containing points (x_1, y_1) and (x_2, y_2) is given by the formula $m = \frac{y_2 - y_1}{x_2 - x_1}$.

slope field (p. 2298) A graph of the slopes determined by a differential equation at multiple points.

solid (p. 166) A three-dimensional geometric figure.

solid of revolution (pp. 716, 2278) The three-dimensional figure that results from revolving a two-dimensional shape about a line, called the *axis of revolution.*

solution of an inequality (p. 1492) The set of all numbers that make the inequality true.

solution set (p. 1492) The set of all solutions of an equation or inequality.

solve an equation (p. 1458) To find the missing value(s) that makes the equation true.

solving literal equations (p. 1840) Solving a formula or equation for one of the variables other than the one that is already isolated.

space (p. 722) The set of all points.

speed (p. 2201) Distance covered per unit of time; the absolute value of velocity.

sphere (pp. 176, 578, 1052) The set of all points in space at a given distance from a given point.

spherical angle (p. 1052) The angle between two intersecting arcs on a sphere.

square (pp. 158, 532, 654) A rectangle with four congruent sides.

square matrix (pp. 1784, 1792) A matrix with an equal number of rows and columns.

square pyramid (p. 172) A pyramid with a square base.

square root (p. 1400) A number that is multiplied by itself, or squared, to form a product.

standard deviation (p. 1325) A numerical value used to indicate how widely data values are spread; the square root of variance.

standard form of a complex number (p. 1896) The form $a + bi$, where both a and b are real numbers.

standard form of a linear equation (p. 1548) $Ax + By = C$, where $A > 0$ and A, B, and C are relatively prime integers.

standard form of a number (p. 44) The form of a number that uses digits.

standard position of an angle (p. 895) An angle with vertex at the origin and initial side on the positive x-axis.

stem-and-leaf plot (p. 1276) A data display that can be used to show how data are distributed.

straight angle (pp. 140, 624, 894) An angle with measure 180°.

stratified sample (p. 1227) A sampling method where the researcher divides the population into separate groups, called *strata.* Then, a sample (often a simple random sample) is drawn from each group.

subset (p. 1290) A set that consists of the items that are common to related sets.

substitution method (p. 1565) A method of solving systems of equations by solving an equation for one variable and then substituting the expression for that variable in the other equation(s).

subtrahend (p. 88) The subtracted number in a difference. In $a - b$, b is the subtrahend.

subtraction (pp. 62, 88) Mathematical operation in which the value of one number is taken away from the value of another number. Subtraction is the inverse of *addition*.

sum (pp. 56, 82) The result of adding two or more addends.

supplementary angles (pp. 148, 625, 894) Two angles whose measures total 180°.

surface area (p. 558) The sum of the areas of all the faces of a geometric solid. See also *cone, cylinder, prism, pyramid, sphere.*

survey (pp. 184, 1222) A way of collecting data from a group of people, called a *population.*

switch factors (p. 71) A way to find the product of two numbers.

switch the order (p. 58) A strategy for finding a sum.

symmetry (p. 846) A figure has symmetry when a transformation maps a figure onto itself.

synthetic division (p. 1678) A shorthand process used to divide a polynomial in standard form by a linear binomial in the form $x - a$ by using only coefficients.

system of linear equations (p. 1564) A set of two or more linear equations with two or more variables.

system of linear inequalities (p. 1582) A set of two or more linear inequalities with two or more variables.

system of trigonometric equations or inequalities (p. 1043) A set of two or more trigonometric equations or inequalities with two or more variables.

systematic sample (p. 1227) A sample where the first element is randomly selected from the first k elements on the population list. Thereafter, every kth element on the list is selected.

T

take apart (p. 71) A strategy to find the product of two numbers.

tally chart (p. 182) A chart that uses tally marks to record the frequency of data.

tangent circles (p. 742) Coplanar circles that intersect in exactly one point.

tangent line approximation (p. 2169) A tangent line is used to approximate a function's value at a point.

tangent ratio See *trigonometric ratios.*

tangent segment (pp. 741, 762) A segment whose endpoints are a point of tangency and another point on the tangent line.

tangent to a circle (p. 740) A line in the plane of a circle that intersects the circle in exactly one point. The point is the *point of tangency.*

term of a pattern (p. 433) Each number, object, or shape in a pattern.

term of a polynomial (pp. 1412, 1600) Each monomial that is added to form a polynomial.

term of a sequence (p. 1858) Each of the numbers in a sequence.

terminal side of an angle See *initial side of an angle.*

terminating decimal (p. 270) A decimal that has a finite number of decimal places.

tessellation (p. 854) An arrangement of shapes that cover the plane with no overlaps and no gaps.

tetrahedron (p. 178) A regular polyhedron with four faces that are congruent equilateral triangles.

theorem (p. 626) A statement that can be proven through deductive reasoning.

theoretical probability (p. 1232) A comparison of the number of favorable outcomes to the number of possible equally likely outcomes.

think addition (p. 64) A strategy for finding the difference of two numbers.

think multiplication (p. 75) A strategy for finding the quotient of two numbers.

third quartile (p. 1331) The median of the data that are greater than the overall median; the 75th percentile.

30°-60°-90° triangle (pp. 686, 900) A special right triangle.

transformation (pp. 834, 1694, 2078) A function that maps each point P in the plane onto a unique point in the plane P', called the *image* of P. The point P is the *pre-image* of P'. See also *translation, reflection, rotation, dilation*.

translation (p. 834) An isometry in which all the points in the plane are moved the same distance in the same direction. A translation can be described with a *vector*.

transversal (pp. 150, 630) A line that intersects two or more coplanar lines.

transverse axis (p. 1932) The segment of length $2a$ whose endpoints are the vertices of a hyperbola.

trapezium (p. 158) A quadrilateral with no parallel sides.

trapezoid (pp. 158, 540, 656) A quadrilateral with exactly one pair of parallel sides. The parallel sides are called the bases.

tree diagram (p. 1240) A diagram that shows all the possible outcomes of one or more events in an organized manner.

trend (p. 1285) A pattern of change in data.

trial (p. 1236) A single observation or one of the repetitions in an experiment.

triangular prism (p. 167) A prism with a triangular base.

triangular pyramid (p. 172) A pyramid with a triangular base.

trigonometric equation (p. 1032) An equation that involves at least one trigonometric function.

trigonometric identity (pp. 904, 996) A trigonometric equation that is true for all acceptable values of the variables in the equation.

trigonometric inequality (p. 1040) An inequality that involves at least one trigonometric function.

trigonometric ratios (pp. 902, 904) In a right triangle with acute angle A, the trigonometric ratios are defined as follows:

$$\textbf{sine} \text{ of } \angle A = \frac{\text{leg opposite } \angle A}{\text{hypotenuse}}$$

$$\textbf{cosecant} \text{ of } \angle A = \frac{\text{hypotenuse}}{\text{leg opposite } \angle A}$$

$$\textbf{cosine} \text{ of } \angle A = \frac{\text{leg adjacent to } \angle A}{\text{hypotenuse}}$$

$$\textbf{secant} \text{ of } \angle A = \frac{\text{hypotenuse}}{\text{leg adjacent to } \angle A}$$

$$\textbf{tangent} \text{ of } \angle A = \frac{\text{leg opposite } \angle A}{\text{leg adjacent to } \angle A}$$

$$\textbf{cotangent} \text{ of } \angle A = \frac{\text{leg adjacent to } \angle A}{\text{leg opposite } \angle A}$$

trigonometry (p. 902) The study of angles and their measures.

trinomial (p. 1600) A polynomial with three terms.

truth value (p. 613) Whether a conditional statement is true or false.

turning points (p. 1626) The places where the direction of a curve changes; also known as points of inflection.

two-column proof (p. 631) A proof organized in two columns—the steps of the proof and the corresponding reasons.

unbounded (p. 1590) A graph is unbounded if it extends infinitely in any direction.

undercoverage (p. 1222) Occurs when some portions of a population are left out of a sample.

union (p. 1291) The elements that are in one or both sets when two sets are combined.

unit circle (p. 944) A circle centered at the origin with the radius equal to one unit.

unit fraction (p. 302) A fraction whose numerator is 1.

unit price (p. 366) A unit rate that gives a cost per unit.

unit rate (p. 366) The rate for one unit of a given quantity.

unit vector (p. 1084) A vector with a magnitude of 1.

universal set (p. 1290) A set containing all elements of a problem under consideration.

unlike fractions (p. 322) Fractions with different denominators.

unlike terms (p. 1412) Terms that differ in either a variable or the power of a variable.

upper extreme (p. 1280) The greatest data value in a set.

upper quartile (p. 1280) The median of the upper half of the data.

use a model (p. 65) A strategy for finding the difference of two numbers.

use tens (p. 64) A strategy for finding the difference of two numbers.

variable (p. 1422) A letter or symbol that represents a quantity that can change.

variance (p. 1324) The sum of the squares of the deviations from the mean, divided by the number of elements in the data set.

vector (pp. 837, 1066) A quantity with magnitude and direction. See also *magnitude of a vector*, *transformation*.

Venn diagram (p. 1288) A graphic display that uses overlapping circles (or squares) to show the relationship between sets and subsets of data.

vertex angle of an isosceles triangle (p. 784) The angle opposite the base.

vertex of a cone See *cone*.

vertex of a parabola (pp. 1688, 1691, 1910) The point on a parabola where it intersects the axis of symmetry; the highest or lowest point on a parabola.

vertex of a polygon (p. 154) A point where two sides intersect.

vertex of a prism (p. 166) A point where two or more edges intersect.

vertex of a pyramid See *pyramid*.

vertex of an angle (pp. 136, 894) The endpoint of the two rays that form an angle.

vertical angles (p. 146) The two opposite angles formed where two lines intersect.

vertical component (p. 1070) The y-coordinate of a point representing a vector $\mathbf{v} = (x, y)$.

vertical translation (p. 1695) A movement of a figure along a vertical line; $f(x) + k$ translates $f(x)$ vertically k units.

vertices (p. 1590) In linear programming, the corner points of the feasible region, where the lines of the equations of two constraints intersect.

vertices (pp. 1930, 1932) In conic sections, the endpoints of the major axis of an ellipse and of the transverse axis of a hyperbola.

volume (p. 570) A measure of the space a three-dimensional figure occupies. See also *cone, cylinder, prism, pyramid, sphere.*

voluntary-response sample (p. 1228) A self-selected sample where members of the population volunteer to be in the sample.

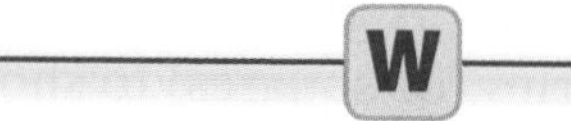

weight (p. 488) The measure of how heavy an object is.

whole numbers (pp. 268, 1402) The set of the natural numbers and zero, $\{0, 1, 2, 3, \ldots\}$.

word form (p. 42) The form of a number that uses words only.

write a number sentence (p. 450) A problem-solving strategy.

***x*-axis** (p. 1442) The horizontal number line on a coordinate plane.

***x*-coordinate** (p. 1436) The x-value in an ordered pair.

***x*-intercept** (p. 1532) The value of x where a graph crosses the x-axis.

***y*-axis** (p. 1442) The vertical number line on a coordinate plane.

***y*-coordinate** (p. 1436) The y-value in an ordered pair.

***y*-intercept** (p. 1532) The value of y where a graph crosses the y-axis.

zero matrix (p. 1778) A matrix where every element is zero.

zero of a function (p. 1626) An input value that has a corresponding output value equal to zero.

***z*-score** (p. 1341) The number of standard deviations between a data value and the mean; the standard score.

Notes

Contributors and Advisors

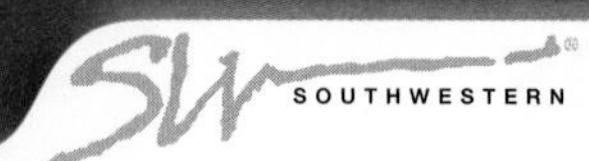

We gratefully acknowledge the invaluable contributions of these educators and writers to the development and production of this book. Their academic and professional awards are testament to their breadth of knowledge and excellence in the classroom, and the accomplishments listed here are merely highlights from their careers.

Jean Armstrong
M.S., Curriculum and Teaching, Teachers College, Columbia University
B.S., Zoology, Memphis State University
Excellence in Publishing Award; Holt, Rinehart & Winston
Teaching Experience:
Montessori pre-K and transitional K to 1
Grade 6, traditional classroom
Grades 2–4, elementary science specialist
Middle school science and math tutor

Jane Books
J.D., Columbia School of Law
B.A., Mathematics, Manhattanville College

Kathy Carter
B.S., Mathematics, Trinity College
President's Club Award at Pearson Prentice Hall (once for innovation, once for best product)
Teaching experience:
High school math, grades 9–12
Alternative education for both adults and youth
High school math tutor

Noralie Cox
M.A.T., Mathematics, Bridgewater State College
A.B., Mathematical Biology, Brown University
Teaching experience:
High school math, grades 9–12

Danielle Potvin Curran
M.A., Applied Mathematics and Curriculum Development, Boston College
Marketing Manager of the Year (Houghton Mifflin)
Strategic Achievement Reward (STAR) (McDougal Littell)
University of Michigan Student Recognition Award
John F. Kennedy Award for Service and Leadership
Teaching experience:
Curriculum specialist, 6–12+
Teacher
Department chair

Concetta M. Duval
Ed.D., Mathematics, Curriculum, and Administration, University of Rochester
Director of Mathematics and Science, Brighton School District, Rochester, New York
Other titles after leaving public education include
Director of Mathematics, Wasatch Education Systems, Jostens Learning Corp.
Senior Software Designer, Riverdeep (now HMH)
Educational Consultant, Duval & Associates

Michael Green
Ph.D., Mathematics, University of Wisconsin
M.A.T., Yale University
B.A., Mathematics, Amherst College
Teaching experience:
High school math
College instructor

Jess E. Hendricks
B.S., Mathematics, Schreiner University

Frances H. Jenkins
B.A., Miami University
Teaching experience:
Middle school math and science
High school chemistry and earth science

Suzanne Langebartels
M.S., College Teaching with emphasis in psychology, Northeastern State University
B.S., Mathematics Education, Northeastern State University
Teaching experience:
High school math, grades 9–12
Math department chair
University professor, Algebra and Statistics
Curriculum writer for secondary and post-secondary courses
Author of university courses, on-ground and online
Senior editor: Grade level/content/lead editor, across multiple grades, multiple companies, multiple projects
Extra Mile Award presented by Oral Roberts University to secondary teachers

Laura J. Osterbrock
M.A., Mathematics, University of Minnesota
B.A., Mathematics, Carleton College
Teaching experience
Math, grades 8–12
Math coach and tutor, grades K, 3, and 6

Blake E. Peterson
Ph.D. and M.S., Pure Mathematics, Washington State University
B.A., Secondary Mathematics Education, Utah State University
Professor of Math Education, Brigham Young University
Other teaching experience:
Project SMART; high school math
Coauthor of, among other books, *Mathematics for Elementary Teachers: A Contemporary Approach, 8th Edition;* author of encyclopedia articles; frequent contributor to such scholarly publications as *Journal for Research in Mathematics Education* and *Journal of Mathematics Teacher Education*

Joseph C. Power
M.A., Mathematics, University of Maryland
Teaching experience:
Junior high school math
High school math
Junior college instructor
University instructor
Author of *Algebra Essentials and Applications*, Holt, Rinehart and Winston

Thaddeus T. Wert
M.Ed., Vanderbilt University
B.S., Engineering, Vanderbilt University
Awarded the Ellen Bowers Hofstead Chair in Mathematics and Science
Teaching experience:
Math grades 9–12
Department chair
Curriculum developer

Glenn Worthman
M.S., Management and Policy, Stony Brook University
B.S., Applied Mathematics and Statistics, Stony Brook University

Photo and Illustration Credits

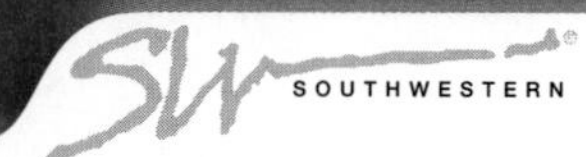

Page	Credit
7	Compassionate Eye Foundation/joSon/Getty Images
8	Photos.com
9	Photos.com
10	Photos.com
13	Photos.com
15	Photos.com
36–37	Photos.com
38	Photos.com
52	Photos.com
108	Photos.com
126	Photos.com
152	Photos.com
164	Photos.com
180	Photos.com
209	Photos.com
212–213	Michael Turek/Corbis
214	Photos.com
266	Photos.com
300	Photos.com
362	Photos.com
378	Photos.com
408	Photos.com
430	Photos.com
446	Photos.com
473	Photos.com
474–475	altrendo images/Getty Images
476	Photos.com
498	Photos.com
522	Photos.com
556	Photos.com
586	Photos.com
604–605	altrendo images/Getty Images
608–609	Fuse/Getty Images
610	Photos.com
636	Photos.com
662	Photos.com
692	Photos.com
726	Photos.com
764	Photos.com
788	Photos.com
812	Photos.com
832	Photos.com
858	Photos.com
884	Fuse/Getty Images
886	Fuse/Getty Images
888	Fuse/Getty Images
890–891	David Gunn/Getty Images
892	Photos.com
926	Photos.com
948	Photos.com
994	Photos.com
1020	Photos.com
1046	Photos.com
1090	Photos.com
1133	Photos.com
1139	Michael Turek/Corbis
1140–1141	altrendo images/Getty Images
1142	altrendo images/Getty Images
1148–1149	Darren Greenwood/Design Pics/Corbis
1150	Darren Greenwood/Design Pics/Corbis
1152–1153	Fuse/Getty Images
1154–1155	Fuse/Getty Images
1156	Fuse/Getty Images
1158–1159	Frank Krahmer/Getty Images
1166–1167	Photos.com
1207	Photos.com
1209	Photos.com
1211	Photos.com
1213	Photos.com
1214–1215	Willoughby Owen/Getty Images
1216	Photos.com
1230	Photos.com
1258	Photos.com
1292	Photos.com
1310	Photos.com
1356	Photos.com
1382–1383	Darren Greenwood/Design Pics/Corbis
1384	Photos.com
1434	Photos.com
1456	Photos.com
1490	Photos.com
1522	Photos.com
1562	Photos.com
1598	Photos.com
1622	Photos.com
1658	Photos.com
1686	Photos.com
1726	Photos.com
1746–1747	Darren Greenwood/Design Pics/Corbis
1748–1749	Darren Greenwood/Design Pics/Corbis
1750–1751	Frank Krahmer/Getty Images
1752	Photos.com
1770	Photos.com
1818	Photos.com
1856	Photos.com
1892	Photos.com
1908	Photos.com
1950	Photos.com
1994	Photos.com
2018	Photos.com
2040	Photos.com
2060	Photos.com
2102–2103	Frank Krahmer/Getty Images
2106	Photos.com
2108	Photos.com
2156	Photos.com
2188	Photos.com
2232	Photos.com
2260	Photos.com
2292	Photos.com
2310	Photos.com
2328	Photos.com
2335	Photos.com
2341	Michael Turek/Corbis
2342–2343	altrendo images/Getty Images
2344–2345	altrendo images/Getty Images
2350–2351	Darren Greenwood/Design Pics/Corbis
2352–2353	Darren Greenwood/Design Pics/Corbis
2354–2355	Fuse/Getty Images
2356–2357	Fuse/Getty Images
2358	Fuse/Getty Images
2360–2361	Frank Krahmer/Getty Images
2368	Photos.com
	all illustrations © The Southwestern Company

SW SOUTHWESTERN
advantage
www.SWadvantage.com

How to Use Math Advantage

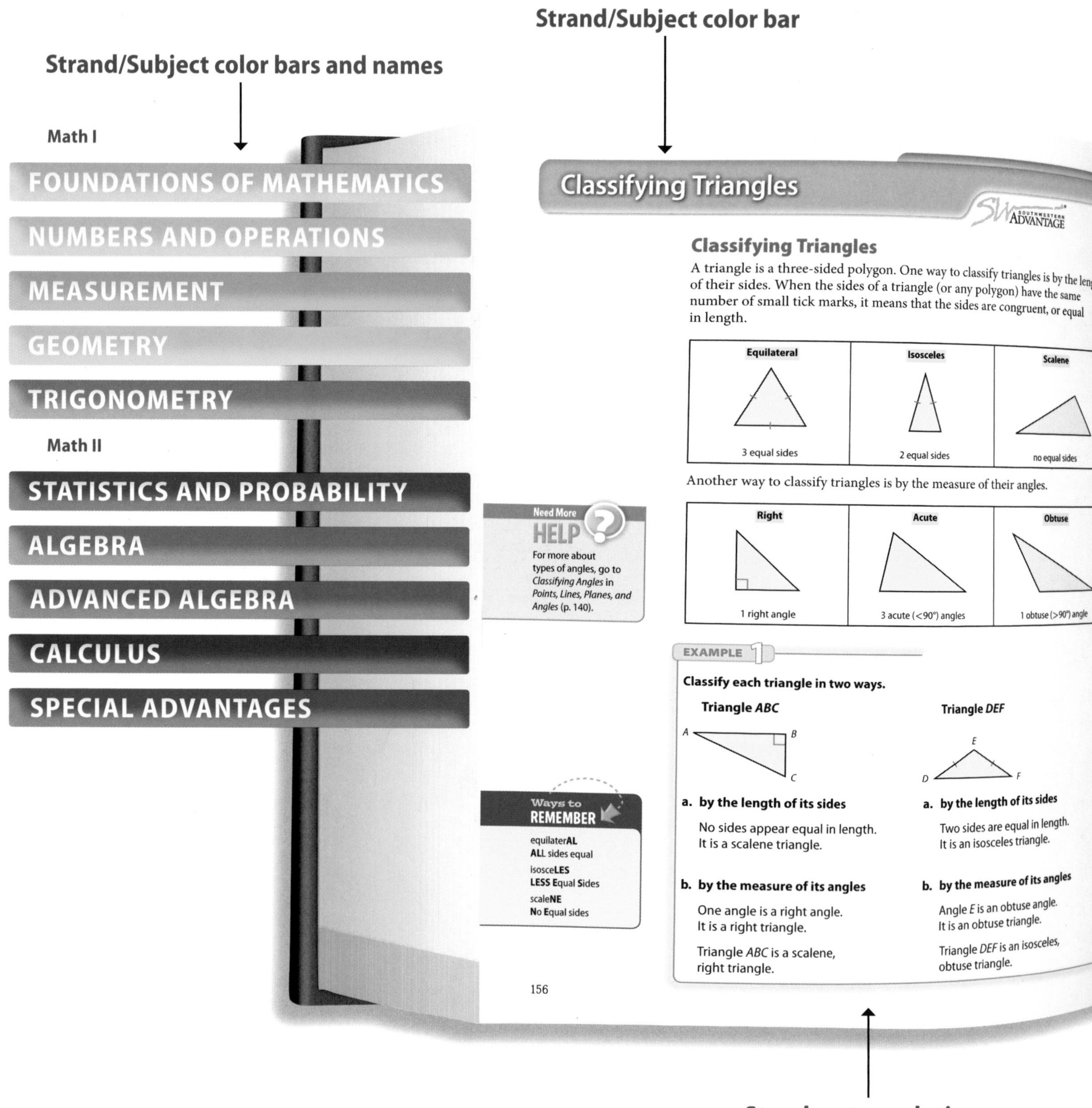

Strand/Subject color bars and names
Strand/Subject color bar
Math I
FOUNDATIONS OF MATHEMATICS
NUMBERS AND OPERATIONS
MEASUREMENT
GEOMETRY
TRIGONOMETRY
Math II
STATISTICS AND PROBABILITY
ALGEBRA
ADVANCED ALGEBRA
CALCULUS
SPECIAL ADVANTAGES
Classifying Triangles
Classifying Triangles
A triangle is a three-sided polygon. One way to classify triangles is by the length of their sides. When the sides of a triangle (or any polygon) have the same number of small tick marks, it means that the sides are congruent, or equal in length.
Equilateral
3 equal sides
Isosceles
2 equal sides
Scalene
no equal sides
Another way to classify triangles is by the measure of their angles.
Right
1 right angle
Acute
3 acute (<90°) angles
Obtuse
1 obtuse (>90°) angle
Need More HELP
For more about types of angles, go to Classifying Angles in Points, Lines, Planes, and Angles (p. 140).
EXAMPLE 1
Classify each triangle in two ways.
Triangle ABC
Triangle DEF
a. by the length of its sides
No sides appear equal in length. It is a scalene triangle.
b. by the measure of its angles
One angle is a right angle. It is a right triangle.
Triangle ABC is a scalene, right triangle.
a. by the length of its sides
Two sides are equal in length. It is an isosceles triangle.
b. by the measure of its angles
Angle E is an obtuse angle. It is an obtuse triangle.
Triangle DEF is an isosceles, obtuse triangle.
Ways to REMEMBER
equilaterAL
ALL sides equal
isosceLES
LESS Equal Sides
scaleNE
No Equal sides
156
Step-by-step solutions